THE ENCYCLOPEDIA OF

BRITISH BIRDS

Made and Printed
in Great Britain
by the
Amalgamated Press Ltd
London

Eric Hosking

GOLDFINCH, *loveliest of our native finches*

Frontispiece   *For text see page 254*

THE ENCYCLOPEDIA OF

BRITISH BIRDS

including
Every Rare Visitor from Overseas

*A Book of Reference on All Matters of Interest
to the Bird Watcher and Bird Lover*

Edited by
LUDWIG KOCH

in collaboration with

R. A. BAYNTON, B.SC.
General Editor

EDGAR STERN-RUBARTH, PH.D.
Associate Editor

RUTH HINGSTON, B.SC.
Assistant Editor

and
50 Eminent Contributors

*Arranged Alphabetically
In 592 pages with 600 black-and-white illustrations and
over 50 Plates and Charts—42 in Full Colour*

LONDON
THE WAVERLEY BOOK COMPANY LIMITED

CONTRIBUTORS

PHILLIS BARCLAY-SMITH — *Secretary, National Committee for Bird Preservation*

ARNOLD BENINGTON, B.SC. — *Director, Copeland Bird Observatory*

R. H. BLAIR — *Chairman, Cornwall Bird Watching and Preservation Society*

P. E. BROWN — *Secretary, Royal Society for Protection of Birds*

ELIOTT L. BURNE, B.A. — *Research Worker and Journalist*

BRUCE CAMPBELL, PH.D. — *Secretary, British Trust for Ornithology; Author and Broadcaster*

JOHN CLEGG — *Curator, Haslemere Educational Museum*

M. G. DAVIES — *Assistant Secretary, Royal Society for Protection of Birds*

JAMES FISHER, M.A., F.L.S., M.B.O.U. — *Ornithologist, Editor, Author and Broadcaster*

R. S. R. FITTER — *Author and Editor*

J. A. GIBB, D.PHIL., M.A. — *On the Staff of the Edward Grey Institute*

DEREK GOODWIN, M.B.O.U. — *Experimental Officer, British Museum of Natural History*

DESMOND HAWKINS — *Features Producer, B.B.C., Bristol*

W. C. OSMAN HILL, M.D., F.L.S., F.R.S.E. — *Prosector, Zoological Society of London*

C. HORTON-SMITH, PH.D. — *Member of Scientific Staff of Animal Health Trust*

ERIC HOSKING, F.R.P.S., M.B.O.U. — *Photographer and Naturalist*

JULIAN HUXLEY, F.R.S., D.SC., M.A. — *Director-General, U.N.E.S.C.O., Biologist, Author and Broadcaster*

DAVID LACK, M.A., SC.D., F.R.S. — *Director, Edward Grey Institute*

DAVID LE ROI, M.A., B.SC. — *Author and Editor*

FRANK W. LANE — *Author and Broadcaster*

FRED LEXSTER — *Chief Swanherd, Abbotsbury Swannery, Dorset*

R. M. LOCKLEY — *Chairman, the West Wales Field Society*

ELIZABETH SCOTT MACHARDY — *Lately of the Royal Society for the Protection of Birds*

JAMES M. MACKELLAR — *Hon. Secretary and Treasurer, Scottish Society for Protection of Wild Birds*

A. J. MARSHALL, D.PHIL. — *The Dept. of Zoology and Comparative Anatomy, St. Bartholomew's Medical College*

G. V. T. MATTHEWS — *Dept. of Zoology, University of Cambridge*

L. HARRISON MATTHEWS, SC.D., F.L.S. — *Director, Zoological Society of London*

SIR LEWIS RITCHIE, K.C.V.O., C.B.E., R.N. — *Author and Naturalist*

COL. H. MORREY SALMON, C.B.E., M.C. — *Author and Ornithologist*

PETER SCOTT, C.B.E. — *Director, The Wildfowl Trust*

ERIC SIMMS, D.F.C., M.A., M.B.O.U. — *B.B.C. Naturalist*

FRED SPEAKMAN — *Secretary, School Nature Study Union*

STUART SMITH, PH.D., M.B.O.U. — *Author and Ornithologist*

W. E. SWINTON, PH.D., B.SC. — *Palaeontologist, Principal Scientific Officer, Reptiles, British Museum of Natural History*

SIR LANDSBOROUGH THOMSON, C.B., O.B.E., D.SC. — *President, Zoological Society of London*

ROSEMARY UPTON, M.B.O.U. — *President, The Essex Bird Watching and Preservation Society*

BRIAN VESEY-FITZGERALD — *Vice-President, Gamekeepers' Association of Great Britain, Author and Broadcaster*

R. WAGSTAFFE, M.B.O.U. — *Keeper of Vertebrate Zoology, Liverpool City Museum*

GEORGE WATERSTON, F.R.S.E., M.B.O.U. — *Hon. Secretary, Scottish Ornithologists' Club*

CECIL S. WEBB — *Superintendent, Royal Zoological Society of Ireland*

RALPH WHITLOCK, F.Z.S., M.B.O.U. — *Author, Editor and Broadcaster*

RALPH WIGHTMAN, B.SC. — *Author and Broadcaster*

KENNETH WILLIAMSON, M.B.O.U. — *Director, Fair Isle Bird Observatory*

E. R. YARHAM, F.R.G.S. — *Author and Journalist*

JOHN YEALLAND — *Bird Curator, Zoological Society of London*

The Editor's Introduction

I WAS DELIGHTED WHEN THE PUBLISHERS asked me to compile this first ENCYCLOPEDIA OF BRITISH BIRDS, for I had long been aware of the need for such a work, which would both help and interest bird watchers of all ages, and indeed, all those who love birds. Although there are books without number dealing with the various species of birds, and with all manner of specialist subjects, few, except the professional ornithologist, are in a position to build up a library of such books or to find time to search through them for the information that they are likely to require. Furthermore, many of them are written in language that is difficult for the amateur bird watcher to understand, and a fascinating subject is thus rendered dull and uninteresting.

Nobody has ever before attempted to produce an Encyclopedia such as the present one, which has condensed into one volume, arranged in alphabetical order, all the subjects on which those interested in bird life—from the amateur bird watcher to the serious student of ornithology—are likely to require information. In fact, it can claim to be *the first of its kind*. Moreover, it is the first book which, in describing birds and their characteristics, gives full consideration to their vocal performances. This subject is neglected in some bird books, while in others it is represented by musical notes or symbolic notations, which I have always considered not only inadequate but entirely misleading. In the present book I have been able to offer information drawn from my own life work.

The number of those interested—actively interested in one form or another—in the life, song, habits and individual characteristics of the most lovable of all living creatures, can be counted by millions in Great Britain alone. Every day one is reminded of this increasing interest in birds and bird life, an interest which is fostered and encouraged not only by the numerous societies and organisations which have come into being, but also by the Talks which have become a regular feature in radio and television programmes. On glancing through the List of Contributors the reader will find the names of most of the outstanding personalities in the bird world, with many of whom he has already become familiar, for these are the people who, through the medium of such programmes, have brought the knowledge and love of birds right into our very homes.

And now a word about the contents of the book, and why I believe it to be unique :

Forming the basis of the book are descriptions under their own individual headings of every known species and subspecies of British bird, not only those which are resident in the British Isles, or visit them regularly, but also all the rare vagrants, some of which have so far paid only one recorded visit here. Also included among the birds described, totalling nearly 500, will be found most of the Continental species as well as many from America, Africa, and Asia. These articles not only cover points of identification, habitat, breeding, eggs, etc., which are, of course, found in most bird books, but they also give lively accounts of the daily life and behaviour of the different species, together with notes of their songs and calls gathered from my own observations over a lifetime.

To assist the reader, there are articles under the Common English Family names describing characteristics of the family in question, including a comparison of its various members, and listing them, so that reference can easily be made to the individual headings. Scientific names or orders, families, genera and species are included, since the reader will doubtless see references to these names in other bird literature, and, unless a trained ornithologist, would be at a loss to know what was being referred to.

Supplementing these articles are special contributions by well-known personalities on such subjects as Behaviour, Bird Nesting, Bird Watching, Courtship, Dances, Eggs, Food and Feeding Habits, Habitat, Oil Pollution, Migration, Navigation, Nests and Nesting, and Speed. There are also my own contributions on Recording and Bird Songs, the latter supplemented by the specially prepared Calendar of Bird Song facing page 518. Special mention must also be made of the article on Flight, accompanied by its beautiful 4-page inset which faces page 224.

The interest of young people has been kept in mind throughout the preparation of this Encyclopedia, as has indeed the interest of all those making a start on this hobby. The work should prove of great assistance to children in their natural history studies at school, particularly those wishing to be among the 10,000 who annually enter the big Essay Competition organised by the Royal Society for the Protection of Birds. For this purpose the articles on Education and School Nature Study Union should be consulted, in addition to the main article which discusses the various organisations existing for the benefit of amateurs as well as that of serious students. Throughout the work the articles have been written in the simplest possible language.

The work can boast a wealth of illustration. There are 42 Plates in full colour, 8 Charts, some in black-and-white and others tinted—all specially prepared. In addition there are over 600 photographs in the text pages. A feature of the book, not found in any other bird books, is that the birds illustrated, both in black-and-white as well as in colour, are, with the exception of extinct species, from photographs taken in natural surroundings by photographers who are themselves bird watchers, and whose work in this field is known to a wide circle. In the case of some of the rarer vagrants, where no photographs were available in this country—probably because observers were not equipped with cameras at the time—no effort has been spared to search the world over for such photographs, and I may say that we met with great success in obtaining them in this way. Line drawings have been used to illustrate certain points or features which would not lend themselves to photography. In this connection attention should be drawn to the specially prepared topographical Chart facing page 1, which shows all the principal parts of a bird. Other characteristics, e.g. beak, ear coverts, tail, wings, are shown in clear diagrammatic form, and a series of drawings show how to recognize a bird by its behaviour on water, in the air, or on the ground.

Another important feature is the combined Dictionary of Bird Names in four languages—English, Latin, French and German. The English names are arranged alphabetically under the Common Family name of the species, and index references are given to the main species headings in the text pages. In the interests of space, however, subspecies of almost identical names have been omitted, although they are described in the main body of the Encyclopedia.

In order to get the maximum benefit and enjoyment from the use of this Encyclopedia, the following points should be borne in mind :

1. In some cases the names of birds, both English and scientific, appearing in this Encyclopedia will be found to differ from those in other popular or authoritative handbooks. This is because we have throughout adhered to the rulings of a competent committee of experts of the British Ornithologists' Union, as embodied in their Check-List of the Birds of Great Britain and Ireland published in 1952.
2. The alphabetical order in which these various species are described depends on the full name of the bird in question as given in the Check-List : thus, the Lesser Spotted Woodpecker will be found under " L " and not " W," the Greater Spotted Woodpecker under " G," and so on. But under the Woodpecker heading will be found references to all the woodpeckers which may be classed as British birds, with indications of their places in the Encyclopedia. Similarly, under " Picidae " and " Dendrocopos," the scientific names of the Woodpecker family and genus.
3. Adjectives such as " common," or " little," are spelt with capital letters only when belonging to the official name of a bird as registered in the Check-List. Thus you will find a Common Gull and a Little Grebe, but a reference to the common Starling, e.g. in comparison with the Rose-coloured one.
4. Capital letters are used only in relation to a particular species and *not* when referring collectively to a group of birds : thus, the Black-capped Petrel, but petrels, because there are many different species of petrels.

It is not possible for me to make detailed reference here to all those who have assisted me in the compilation of this Encyclopedia, but I should like to pay tribute to the many eminent authorities whose names appear in the List of Contributors and elsewhere ; also to the well-known bird photographers, Mr. Eric Hosking, Mr. John Markham, Mr. G. K. Yeates, Mr. R. P. Bagnall-Oakeley, Mr. A. Brook, Mr. R. Thompson, Mr. C. W. Teager, my daughter Erica, and Mr. W. Farnsworth, and others here and overseas ; and to the artists whose work has enlivened our pages, with special reference to the unusual and outstanding series of drawings for the alphabetical letter headings which were prepared by Miss Erna Pinner ; and the excellent anatomical diagrams by Miss Jane Graham.

I also wish to acknowledge my indebtedness to those pioneers of bird study, Gilbert White, W. MacGillivray, T. A. Coward, Alfred Newton, Hans Gadow, and Henry Eeles Dresser, whose early work in the field of ornithology has always been an inspiration to me.

I should also like to acknowledge the assistance obtained from the many existing standard works of reference, such as, for example, Witherby's *Handbook of British Birds* ; Collins' *Field Guide to the Birds of Britain & Europe* ; *Birds of the British Isles*, by Bannerman & Lodge ; *British Birds*, by Kirkman & Jourdain, and the books which have been written by some of our contributors.

In conclusion, a word of thanks is due to my editorial colleagues, without whose assistance this Encyclopedia would never have come into being—Mr. R. A. Baynton, the General Editor, who was responsible for seeing the production through its various stages, Dr. E. Stern-Rubarth, my Associate Editor, Miss R. Hingston, the Assistant Editor, Miss E. S. MacHardy, who rendered invaluable assistance with the entries on the individual species, and Miss W. Harvey, who assisted with some of the editorial work.

LUDWIG KOCH

PLATES

IN FULL COLOUR

CONTINUED ON FOLLOWING PAGE

PLATES IN FULL COLOUR—Continued

CHARTS AND BLACK-AND-WHITE PLATES

DICTIONARY OF BIRD NAMES

IN FOUR LANGUAGES

and

Page Guide to Principal Species

Specially prepared for this Encyclopedia by Edgar Stern-Rubarth, Ph.D.

ENGLISH NAME		SCIENTIFIC NAME	FRENCH NAME	GERMAN NAME
Accentor Alpine	9	Prunella collaris	Fauvette des Alpes	Alpenbraunelle, Fluhvogel
Albatross, Black-browed	6	Diomedea melanophris	Albatros	Albatross
Auk, Little	332	Plautus alle	Guillemot nain	Krabbentaucher
Avocet	36	Recurvirostra avosetta	Avocette	Säbelschnäbler
Bee-Eater	46	Merops apiaster	Guépier vulgaire	Bienenfresser, Spint
Bittern	71	Botaurus stellaris	Grand butor	Grosse Rohrdommel
,, American	10	,, lentiginosus	Butor Américain	Amerikanische ,,
,, Little	333	Ixobrychus minutus	Héron blongios	Zwergrohrdommel
Blackbird	72	Turdus merula	Merle	Amsel, Schwarzdrossel
Blackcap	73	Sylvia atricapilla	Fauvette à tête noire	Mönchsgrasmücke
				Schwarzplättchen
Bluethroat	86	Cyanosylvia suecica	Gorge-bleu ordinaire	Blaukehlchen
Brambling	91	Fringilla montifringilla	Pinson d'Ardennes	Bergfink
Bullfinch	105	Pyrrhula pyrrhula	Bouvreuil ordinaire	Gimpel, Dompfaff
Bunting, Black-headed	77	Emberiza melanocephala	Bruant crocote	Kappenammer
,, Cirl	127	,, cirlus	,, zizi	Zaunammer
,, Corn-	155	,, calandra	,, proyer	Grauammer
,, Lapland	323	Calcarius lapponicus	,, lapon	Spornammer
,, Little	333	Emberiza pusilla	,, nain	Zwergammer
,, Meadow-	351	,, cioides	,, fou	
,, Ortolan	397	,, hortulana	,, ortolan	Ortolan, Gartenammer
,, Pine-	425	,, leucocephalos	,. jaunâtre	Fichtenammer
,, Red-headed	453	,, bruniceps	,, des roseaux, brun	(Rotköpfige Ammer)
,, Reed-	460	,, schoeniclus	,, de roseaux	Rohrammer
,, Rock-	475	,, cia	,, fou des prés	Zippammer
,, Rustic	484	,, rustica	,, rustique	Waldammer
,, Snow-	514	Plectrophenax nivalis	Ortolan des neiges	Schneeammer
,, Yellow-breasted	590	Emberiza aureola	Passerine auréole	Weidenammer
Bustard, Great	258	Otis tarda	Outarde barbue	Trappe
,, Houbara	295	Chlamydotis undulata	,, houbara	Kragentrappe
,, Little	333	Otis tedrax	Canepétière	Zwergtrappe
Buzzard	108	Buteo buteo	Buse	Mäusebussard
,, Honey-	292	Pernis apivorus	Bondrée	Wespenbussard
,, Rough-legged	481	Buteo lagopus	Buse pattue	Rauhfussbussard
Capercaillie	114	Tetrao urogallus	Coq de bruyère	Auerhuhn
Chaffinch	122	Fringilla coelebs	Pinson	Buchfink
Chiffchaff	125	Phylloscopus collybita	Becfin veloce	Zilpzalp, Weidenlaubsäger
Chough	126	Coracia pyrrhocorax	Crave	Steinkräbe
Coot	152	Fulica atra	Foulque	Blesshuhn
Cormorant	153	Phalacrocorax carbo	Grand Comoran	Kormoran
Corncrake	155	Crex crex	Râle des genéts	Wachtelkönig Wiesenralle
Courser, Cream-coloured	160	Cursorius cursor	Courvite	Rennvogel
Crake, Baillon's	39	Porzana pusilla	Râle de Baillon, or	Zwergsumpfhuhn
			Poule d'eau naine	
,, Little	334	,, parva	Poule d'eau poussin	Kleines Sumpfhuhn
				(Motthühnchen)
,, Spotted	528	,, porzana	,, ,, marouette	Tüpfelsumpfhuhn
Crane, Demoiselle	159	Anthropoides virgo	Demoiselle de Numidie	Jungfernkranich
,, Common	159	Megalornis grus	Grue cendrée	Kranich
,, Sarus	159	,, ,, antigone	,, antigone de l'Inde	Sarus-Kranich
Creeper, Tree-	558	Certhia familiaris	Grimpereau	Waldbaumläufer
Crossbill, Parrot-	404	Loxia pityopsittacus	Bec-croisé perroquet	Kiefernkreuzschnabel
,, Scottish	498	,, curvirostra	,, ,, des sapins	Fichtenkreuzschnabel
,, Two-barred	563	,, leucoptera	,, ,, bifascié	Bindenkreuzschnabel
Crow, Carrion	119	Corvus corone	Corneille noire	Rabenkrähe
,, Hooded (Royston)	393	,, cornix	,, mantelée	Nebelkrähe
Cuckoo	163	Cuculus canorus	Coucou	Kuckuck
,, Black-billed	72	Coccyzus erythroph-	Piaye aux yeux rouges	Schwarzschnabelkuckuck
		thalmus		
,, Great spotted	266	Clamator glandarius	Coucou-geai	Häherkuckuck
,, Yellow-billed	589	Coccyzus americanus	,, américain	Gelbschnabelkuckuck
			(Coulicou à bec jaune)	

ENGLISH NAME			SCIENTIFIC NAME		FRENCH NAME		GERMAN NAME
Curlew		166	Numenius arquata		Courlis		Grosser Brachvogel
,,	**Eskimo**	202	,,	borealis	,,	Esquimau	Eskimo- ,,
,,	**Slender-billed**	512	,,	tenuirostris	,,	mince-bec	Dünnschnabliger ,,
,,	**Stone-**	534	Burhinus oedicnemus		Grand Pluvier		Triel
Dipper		173	Cinclus cinclus		Aguassière, Cincle		Wasseramsel
						plongeur	
Diver, Black-throated		33	Colymbus arcticus		Plongeon à gorge noire		Prachttaucher, Polar-
							Seetaucher
,,	**Great Northern**	263	,,	immer	,,	imbrin	Eistaucher
,,	**Red-throated**	458	,,	stellatus	,,	catmarin	Sterntaucher
							Nordseetaucher
,,	**White-billed**	574	,,	adamsii	,,	blancbec	Gelbschnabeltaucher
Dotterel		182	Charadrius morinellus		Pluvier guignard		Mornellregenpfeifer
Dove, Rock-		476	Columba livia		Pigeon biset		Felsentaube
,,	**Stock-**	533	,,	oenas	,,	colombin	Hohltaube
,,	**Turtle-**	562	Streptopelia turtur		Tourterelle des bois		Turteltaube
Duck, Buffel-headed		105	Bucephala albeola		Garrot Américain		Amerikanische Schellente
,,	**Eider-**	199	Somateria mollissima		Eider à duvet		Eiderente
,,	**Harlequin-**	282	Histrionicus histrionicus		Canard histrion,		Kragenente, Harlekin
					Garrot arlequin	
,,	**Long-tailed**	339	Clangula hyemalis		,,	de miclon	Eisente
						(Miquelon)	
,,	**Ruddy Sheld-**	483	Casarca ferruginea		Tadorne casarca (Roux)		Rostgans
	(Brahminy)						
,,	**Sheld-**	503	Tadorna tadorna		,,	de Belon	Brandente
,,	**Tufted**	561	Aythya fuligula		Morillon		Reiherente
Dunlin		185	Calidris alpina		Bécasseau variable		Alpenstrandläufer
Eagle, Golden		250	Aquila chrysaëtos		Aigle d'or, or royal		Goldadler, Steinadler
,,	**Spotted**	528	,,	clanga	,,	criard	Schelladler, Grosser
							Schreiadler
,,	**White-tailed**	575	Haliaëtus albicilla		Pygargue à queue		Seeadler
	(Gray Sea-)				blanche serpentaire	
Egret, Cattle		121	Ardeola ibis		Héron garde-boeuf		Kuhreiher
,,	**Large (White**	325	Egretta alba		,,	aigrette, or crabier	Silberreiher, Edelreiher
	Heron)						
,,	**Little**	334	,,	garzetta	,,	garzette	Seidenreiher
Eider, King-		319	Somateria spectabilis		Eider royale		Prachteiderente
,,	**Steller's**	532	Polysticta stelleri		,,	(Steller's) à duvet	Scheckente
Falcon, Gyr		280	Falco rusticolus		Faucon gerfaut, or		Jagdfalk
					des Perdrix	
,,	**Peregrine**	414	,,	peregrinus	,,	pélerin	Wanderfalk
,,	**Red-footed**	452	,,	vespertinus	,,	Kobez	Rotfussfalk, Abendfalk
Fieldfare		217	Turdus pilaris		Grive litorne		Wacholderdrossel
							Krammetsvogel
Finch, Citril		128	Carduelis citrinella		Venturon alpin		Zitronenzeisig
,,	**Snow-**	515	Montifringilla nivalis		Pinson des neiges		Schneefink
Firecrest		219	Regulus ignicapillus		Roitelet triple bandeau		Sommergoldhähnchen
Flamingo		222	Phoenicopterus ruber		Flamant rose		Flamingo
Flycatcher, Brown		102	Muscicapa latirostris		Gobe-mouche brun		(Brauner Fliegenschnäpper)
,,	**Pied**	422	,,	hypoleuca	,,	,, noir	Trauerfliegenschnäpper
,,	**Red-breasted**	450	,,	parva	,,	,, rougeatre,	Zwergfliegenschnäpper
						or nain	
,,	**Spotted**	528	,,	striata	,,	,, gris	Grauer Fliegenschnäpper
,,	**White-**	574	,,	albicollis	,,	,, à collier	Halsbandfliegenschnäpper
	collared						
Gadwall		239	Anas strepera		Chipeau bruyant		Schnatterente
Gannet		240	Sula bassana		Fou de Bassan		Basstölpel
Garganey		242	Anas querquedula		Sarcelle d'été		Knäkente
Godwit, Bar-tailed		42	Limosa lapponica		Barge rousse		Pfuhlschnepfe,
							Rostrote Limose
,,	**Black-tailed**	81	,,	limosa	,,	à queue noire	Uferschnepfe
Goldcrest		250	Regulus regulus		Roitelet huppé		Wintergoldhähnchen
Golden-Eye		251	Bucephala clangula		Garrot		Schellente
Goldfinch		254	Carduelis carduelis		Chardonneret		Stieglitz, Distelfink
Goosander		255	Mergus merganser		Grande Harle		Gänsesäger
Goose, Barnacle-		40	Branta leucopsis		Bernache nonnette		Nonnengans,
							Weisswangengans
,,	**Bean-**	44	Anser arvensis arvensis		Oie vulgaire, or des		Saatgans
						moissons	
,,	**Brent**	98	Branta bernicla		Cravant		Ringelgans, Rottgans
,,	**Canada**	112	,,	canadensis	Bernache du Canada		Kanadagans
,,	**Grey Lag-**	273	Anser anser		Oie cendrée		Graugans
,,	**Lesser**	329	,,	erythropus	,,	naine	Zwerggans
	White-fronted						
,,	**Pink-footed**	426	,,	arvensis	,,	à bec court	Kurzschnabelgans
				brachyrhynchus			
,,	**Red-breasted**	450	,,	ruficollis	Bernache à cou roux		Rothalsgans
,,	**Snow-**	515	,,	hyperboreus	Oie des neiges		Schneegans
,,	**White-fronted**	574	,,	albifrons	,,	rieuse	Blässgans

ENGLISH NAME			SCIENTIFIC NAME	FRENCH NAME	GERMAN NAME
Goshawk		257	Accipiter gentilis	Autour	Habicht
Grebe, Black-necked		79	Podiceps caspicus	Grèbe à cou noir	Schwarzhalssteissfuss
„	Great Crested	259	„ cristatus	„ huppé	Haubentaucher
„	Little	334	„ ruficollis	Castagneux	Zwergtaucher
„	Red-necked	454	„ grisegena	Grèbe jou-gris	Rothalstaucher
„	Slavonian	511	„ auritus	„ cornu	Ohrentaucher, Horn-taucher
Greenfinch		268	Chloris chloris	Verdier	Grünling, Grünfink
Greenshank		270	Tringa nebularia	Chevalier gris	Heller Wasserläufer, Grünschenkel
Grosbeak, Pine		425	Pinicola enucleator	Dur-bec vulgaire	Hakengimpel
„	Scarlet	493	Carpodacus erythrinus	Roselin cramoisi	Karmingimpel
Grouse, Black		75	Lyrurus tetrix	Coq de bruyère	Birkhuhn
„	Pallas's Sand-	402	Syrrhaptes paradoxus	Syrhapte	Steppenhuhn
„	Red	452	Lagopus scoticus	Lagopède écossaise	Schottisches Moorhuhn
Guillemot		227	Uria aalge	Guillemot troile	Trottellumme
„	Black	76	„ grylle	„ noir, or à miroir	Gryllteiste
„	Brünnich's	102	„ lomvia	„ de Brunnich	Dickschnabellumme
Gull, Black-headed		77	Larus ridibundus	Goëland rieur	Lachmöwe
„	Bonaparte's	89	„ philadelphia	„ Bonaparte	Bonaparte-Möwe
„	Common	140	„ canus	„ cendré	Sturmmöwe
„	Glaucous	248	„ hyperboreus	„ bourgmestre	Eismöwe
„	Great Black-headed	258	„ ichthyaëtus	„ or Mouette ichthyaète	Grosse Lachmöwe
„	Greater Black-backed	260	„ marinus	„ à manteau noir, or marin	Mantelmöwe
„	Herring-	289	„ argentatus	„ argenté	Silbermöwe
„	Iceland	299	„ glaucoides	„ leucoptère	Polarmöwe
„	Ivory	313	Pagophila ebureca	„ sénateur	Elfenbeinmöwe
„	Lesser Black-backed	326	Larus fuscus	„ brun	Heringsmöwe
„	Little	335	„ minutus	Mouette pygmée	Zwergmöwe
„	Mediterranean Black-headed	353	„ melanocephalus	„ mélanocéphale	Schwarzkopfmöwe
„	Ross's	481	Rhodostethia rosea	„ de Ross	Rosenmöwe
„	Sabine's	485	Xema sabini	„ de Sabine	Schwalbenmöwe
Hammer, Yellow		599	Emberiza citrinella	Bruant jaune	Goldammer
Harrier, Hen-		287	Circus cyaneus	Busard St. Martin	Kornweihe
„	Marsh-	347	„ aeruginosus	„ harpaye	Rohrweihe
„	Montagu's	362	„ pygargus	„ cendré	Wiesenweihe
„	Pallid	402	„ macrourus	„ pâle	Steppenweihe
Hawfinch		284	Coccothraustes coccothraustes	Grosbec	Kernbeisser
Hawk, Night-		384	Chordeiles minor	Engoulevent américain	Nachtfalke
„	Sparrow-	523	Accipiter nisus	Epervier	Sperber
Heron		288	Ardea cinerea	Héron huppé	Fischreiher
„	Night	384	Nycticorax nycticorax	Héron bihoreau, or Bihoreau d'Europe	Nachtreiher
„	Purple	439	Ardea purpurea	„ pourpre	Purpurreiher
„	Squacco	530	Ardeola ralliodes	„ crabier	Rallenreiher
Hobby		291	Falco subbuteo	Hobereau	Lerchenfalke
Hoopoe		294	Upupa epops	Huppe	Wiedehopf
Ibis, Glossy		249	Plegadis falcinellus	Ibis falcinelle	Sichler
Jackdaw		314	Corvus monedula	Choucas gris	Dohle
Jay		315	Garrulus glandarius	Geai commun, or glandivore	Eichelhäher
Kestrel		318	Falco tinnunculus	Faucon cresserelle	Turmfalk
„	Lesser	327	„ naumanni	„ cresserine	Rötelfalk
Kingfisher		319	Alcedo atthis	Martin pêcheur	Eisvogel
Kite		320	Milvus milvus	Milan royal	Roter Milan, Gabelweih
„	Black	79	„ migrans	„ noir	Schwarzer (Brauner) Milan
Kittiwake		321	Rissa tridactyla	Mouette tridactyle	Dreizehenmöwe
Knot		322	Calidris canutus	Maubèche	Knutt, Isländischer Strandläufer
Lapwing		324	Vanellus vanellus	Vanneau huppé	Kiebitz
Lark, Black		79	Melanocorypha yeltonensis	Calandre nègre	Mohrenlerche
„	Calandra	109	„ calandra	Calandre	Kalanderlerche
„	Crested	161	Galerida cristata	Cochevis huppé	Haubenlerche
„	Shore-	505	Eremophila alpestris	Alouette de la Sibérie, hausse-col	Ohrenlerche
„	Short-toed	506	Calandrella brachydactyla	„ calandre, or grosse	Kurzzehenlerche
„	White-winged	577	Melanocorypha leucoptera	„ lulu, or Mauviette	Weissflügellerche
„	Wood-	584	Lullula arborea	„ lulu	Heidelerche
Linnet		332	Carduelis cannabina	Linotte	Hänfling, Bluthänfling

xi

ENGLISH NAME		SCIENTIFIC NAME	FRENCH NAME	GERMAN NAME
Magpie	343	Pica pica	Pie ordinaire, or bavarde	Elster
Mallard	344	Anas platyrhynchos	Canard sauvage, or col-vert	Stockente
Martin, House-	295	Delichon urbica	Hirondelle de fenêtre	Mehlschwalbe
„ Sand-	488	Riparia riparia	„ de rivage	Uferschwalbe
Merganser, Hooded	293	Mergus circullatus	Harle (à capote)	Haubensäger
„ Red-breasted	451	„ serrator	„ huppé	Mittelsäger
Merlin	354	Falco columbarius	Faucon émérillon	Merlin, Zwergfalk
Moorhen	363	Gallinula chloropus	Poule d'eau	Teichhuhn
Nightingale	385	Luscinia megarhynchos	Rossignol ordinaire	Nachtigall
„ Thrush-	555	„ luscinia	„ majeur, or progné	Sprosser
Nightjar	386	Caprimulgus europaeus	Engoulevent	Nachtschwalbe, Ziegenmelker
„ Egyptian	198	„ aegyptius	„ d'Egypte	Aegyptischer „
„ Red-necked	9	„ ruficollis	„ à collier roux	Rothals- „
Nutcracker	389 554	Nucifraga caryocatactes	Chasse-noix	Dickschnäbliger Tannenhäher
Nuthatch	389	Sitta europaea	Torchepot	Kleiber, Spechtmeise
Oriole, Golden	252	Oriolus oriolus	Loriot	Pirol
Osprey	397	Pandion haliaëtus	Balbuzard	Fischadler
Ouzel, Ring-	437	Turdus torquatus	Merle à plastron	Ringamsel, Ringdrossel
Owl, Barn-	41	Tyto alba	Chouette effraye	Schleiereule
„ Eagle-	187	Bubo bubo	„ grand duc	Uhu
„ Hawk-	285	Surnia ulula	„ la surnie	Sperbereule
„ Little	336	Athene noctua	„ chevêche	Steinkauz
„ Long-eared	338	Asio otus	Hibou vulgaire	Waldohreule
„ Scops	496	Otus scops	„ petit duc	Zwergohreule
„ Short-eared	505	Asio flammeus	Chouette de marais	Sumpfohreule
„ Snowy	516	Nyctea scandiaca	Harfang des neiges	Schneeeule
„ Tawny	548	Strix aluco	Chat-huant	Waldkauz
„ Tengmalm's	550	Aegolius funereus	Chouette de Tengmalm	Rauhfusskauz
Oystercatcher	399	Haematopus ostralegus	Huitrier-pie	Austernfischer
Partridge	404	Perdix perdix	Perdrix	Rebhuhn
„ Red-legged	454	Alectoris rufa	„ rouge	Rothuhn
Petrel, Black-capped	74	Bulweria hasitata	Pétrel diablotin	Teufels-Sturmschwalbe
„ Bulwer's	106	„ bulwerii	„ de Bulwer	Bulwer-Sturmvogel
„ Frigate- (White-faced)	237	Pelagodroma marina	Thalassidrome à face blanche	Fregatten-Sturmschwalbe
„ Fulmar	238	Fulmarus glacialis	Pétrel glacial	Eissturmvogel
„ Kermadec	317	Bulweria neglecta	„ des iles Kermadec	Kermadek-Sturmschwalbe
„ Leach's	326	Oceanodroma leucorrhoa	„ cul-blanc	Gabelschwänzige „
„ Madeiran	343	„ castro	Oceanodroma de castro	Schwalben-Sturmvogel
„ Storm-	536	Hydrobates pelagicus	Thalassidrome tempête	Sturmschwalbe
„ White-winged	577	Bulweria leucoptera	Pétrel à ailes blanches	Brustband-Sturmschwalbe
„ Wilson's	580	Oceanites oceanicus	Thalassidrome de Wilson, or Pétrel océanite	Buntfüssige- „
Phalarope, Grey (Red)	273	Phalaropus fulicarius	Phalarope gris	Thorshühnchen
„ Red-necked (Northern)	455	„ lobatus	„ cendré	Odinshühnchen
Pheasant	417	Phasianus colchicus	Faisan	Fasan
Pigeon, Wood-	585	Columba palumbus	Pigeon ramier	Ringeltaube
Pintail	427	Anas acuta	Pilet	Spiessente
Pipit, American	11	Anthus spinoletta rubescens	Pipit américain	Amerikanischer Wasserpieper
„ Meadow-	351	„ pratensis	„ des prés, or farlouse	Wiesenpieper
„ Petchora	415	„ gustavi	„ de la Petchora	Petschorapieper
„ Red-throated	459	„ cervinus	„ à gorge rousse	Rotkehlpieper
„ Richard's	468	„ richardi	„ Richard	Spornpieper
„ Rock-	476	„ spinoletta petrosus	„ obscur, or aquatique	Strandpieper
„ Tawny	549	„ campestris	„ rousseline, or Argodrome champêtre	Brachpieper
„ Tree-	559	„ trivialis	„ des arbres	Baumpieper
„ Water-	568	„ spinoletta spinoletta	„ spioncelle	Wasserpieper, Bergpieper
Plover, American Golden	11	Charadrius dominicus	Pluvier doré américain	Amerikan Goldregenpfeifer
„ Caspian	120	„ asiaticus	„ caspien	Kaspischer Regenpfeifer
„ Golden	253	„ apricarius	„ doré	Goldregenpfeifer
„ Grey	274	„ squatarola	Vanneau pluvier	Kiebitzregenpfeifer
„ Kentish	317	„ alexandrinus	Gravelot à collier interrompu	Seeregenpfeifer
„ Killdeer	319	„ vociferus	Pluvier kildir	Keilschwanz-Regenpfeifer
„ Little Ringed	336	„ dubius	Petit Pluvier, or Gravelot à collier	Flussregenpfeifer
„ Ringed	468	„ hiaticula	Pluvier, or Gravelot à collier	Sandregenpfeifer
„ Sociable	517	Chettusia gregaria	Chettusie sociable	Gemeiner Regenpfeifer
Pochard	430	Aythya ferina	Milouin	Tafelente
„ Red-crested	452	Netta rufina	Brante rousseâtre	Kolbenente
„ White-eyed	574	Aythya nyroca	Canard myroca	Moorente

ENGLISH NAME			SCIENTIFIC NAME	FRENCH NAME	GERMAN NAME
Pratincole, Black-		84	Glareola nordmanni	Glaréole melanoptère	Nordmann-Brachschwalbe
	winged				
„	Collared	136	„ pratincola	„ à collier	Brachschwalbe
Ptarmigan		437	Lagopus mutus	Poule de neige	Alpenschneehuhn
Puffin		438	Fratercula arctica	Macareux moine	Papageitaucher
Quail		440	Coturnix coturnix	Caille	Wachtel
Rail, Sora		522	Porzana carolina	Marouette Caroline	Carolina-Sumpfhuhn
„ Water-		568	Rallus aquaticus	Râle d'eau	Wasserralle
Raven		443	Corvus corax	Corbeau, grand, or noir	Rabe
Razorbill		445	Alca torda	Pingouin macroptère	Tordalk
Redpoll		456	Carduelis flammea	Sizerin boréal, or flammé	Birkenzeisig, Lein-Zeisig
„	Arctic	26	„ hornemanni	„ Hornemann, or	Hornemann's Zeisig
				blanchâtre	
.,	Coue's	157	„ hornemanni		(Nordischer) Hänfling
			exilipes		
Redshank		456	Tringa totanus	Chevalier gambette	Rotschenkel, Gambett-
					Wasserläufer
„	Spotted	529	„ erythropus	„ brun	Grosser Rotschenkel,
					Dunkler Wasserläufer
Redstart		458	Phoenicurus phoenicurus	Rouge queue	Gartenrotschwanz
„ Black		80	„ ochruros	„ „ noir	Hausrotschwanz
Redwing		459	Turdus musicus	Mauvis	Rotdrossel
Robin		473	Erithacus rubecula	Rouge-gorge	Rotkehlchen
Roller		477	Coracias garrulus	Rollier	Blauracke, Mandelkrähe
Rook		477	Corvus frugilegus	Corbeau freux	Saatkrähe
Ruff		484	Philomachus pugnax	Chevalier combattant	Kampfläufer
Sanderling		488	Crocethia alba	Sanderling	Sanderling
Sandpiper, Baird's		39	Calidris bairdii	Bécasseau de Baird	Baird's Strandläufer
„	Bartram's	43	Bartramia longicauda	Bartramie à longue queue	Bartram's „
„	Bonaparte's	89	Calidris fuscicollis	„ longicande	Bonaparte's „
„	Broad-billed	102	Limicola falcinellus	Bécasseau platyrhynque	Sumpfläufer
„	Buff-breasted	105	Tryngitis subruficollis	„ rousset	Grasläufer
„	Common	141	Tringa hypoleucos	Chevalier guignette	Uferläufer
„	Curlew-	168	Calidris testacea	Bécasseau cocorli	Sichelstrandläufer
					(Bogenschnäbliger St.)
„	Green	270	Tringa ocrophus	Chevalier cul-blanc	Waldwasserläufer
„	Grey-rumped	275	„ brevipes	„ à pieds courts	Graubürzel-Wasserläufer
„	Marsh-	348	„ stagnatilis	„ stagnatite	Teichwasserläufer
..	American	412	Calidris melanotus	Bécasseau tacheté	Graubruststrandläufer
	Pectoral				
„	Purple	440	„ maritima	„ violet	Klippenstrandläufer
„	Semi-	500	„ pusilla	Maubèche semi-palmée	Sandstrandläufer
	palmated				
„	Siberian	508	„ acuminata	., à queue	Spitzschwänziger
	Pectoral				pointue Strandläufer
„	Solitary	517	Tringa solitaria	Chevalier solitaire	Einsamer Wasserläufer
..	Spotted	529	„ macularia	„ or Actitis perlé,	Amerikanischer
				or grivelé	Uferläufer
„	Terek	551	Xemis cinerea	Bécasseau maubèche	Terekwasserläufer
.,	Wood-	586	Tringa glareola	Chevalier sylvain	Bruchwasserläufer
Scaup		494	Aythya marila	Canard Milouinan	Bergente
Scoter, Common		142	Melanitta nigra	Macreuse noire	Trauerente
„ Surf-		541	„ perspicillata	„ à lunettes	Brillenente
„ Velvet		566	„ fusca	Grande Macreuse brune	Sammetente
Serin		500	Serinus canarius	Serin cini	Girlitz
Shag		501	Phalacrocorax aristotelis	Cormoran huppé	Krähenscharbe
Shearwater, Audubon's		30	Procellaria lhermineri	Puffin de Lherminier	Audubon's Sturmtaucher
„	Great	265	„ gravis	„ majeur, or	Grosser „
				à face blanche	
„	Little	337	„ baroli	„ obscure de Madère	Kleiner „
„	Manx	345	„ puffinus	„ des Anglais	Schwarzschnabel- „
				or manks	
.,	Mediterran-	353	„ diomedea	„ cendré	Gelbschnabel- „
	ean		diomedea		
„	North	388	„ diomedea	„ „ atlantique	Atlantischer Gelbschnabel
	Atlantic		borealis		Sturmtaucher
	Sooty	521	„ grisea	„ fuligineux	Dunkler „
Shoveler		506	Spatula clypeata	Souchet	Löffelente
Shrike, Great Grey		262	Lanius exubitor	pie-grièche grise	Grauwürger, Raubwürger
„ Lesser Grey		327	„ minor	„ „ d'Italie	Kleiner Würger
„ Masked		350	„ nubicus	„ „ masquée	Masken- „
„ Red-backed		449	„ collurio	Ecorcheur	Rotrückiger „ ,
					Neuntöter
„ Woodchat-		583	„ senator	Pie-grèche rousse	Rotkopfwürger
Siskin		508	Carduelis spinus	Tarin	Zeisig
Skua, Arctic		26	Stercorarius parasiticus	Stercoraire or Labbe	Schmarotzer-Raubmöwe
				parasite	

ENGLISH NAME		SCIENTIFIC NAME	FRENCH NAME	GERMAN NAME
Skua, Great	265	Stercorarius skua	Stercoraire or Labbe cataracte	Grosse Raubmöwe
„ Long-tailed	340	„ longicaudus	„ or Labbe longicaude	Kleine or Falken- „
„ Pomatorhine	431	„ pomarinus	„ or Labbe pomarin	Spatel- „
Skylark	510	Alauda arvensis	Alouette des champs	Feldlerche
Smew	513	Mergus albellus	Petit Harle huppé, or piette	Zwergsäger
Snipe, Common	143	Capella gallinago	Bécassine des marais	Gemeine Sumpfschnepfe
„ Great	266	„ media	Grande Bécassine, or B. double	Grosse Doppelschnepfe
„ Jack	315	Lymnocryptes minimus	Bécassine sourde, or petite	Zwergschnepfe
„ Red-breasted	452	Limnodromus griseus	„ rousse	Rotbrust-Schnepfe
Sparrow, Hedge-	285	Prunella modularis	Mouchet	Heckenbraunelle
„ House-	296	Passer domesticus	Moineau	Haussperling
„ Tree-	559	„ montanus	Friquet	Feldsperling
Spoonbill	527	Platalea leucorodia	Spatule blanche	Löffler
Starling	530	Sturnus vulgaris	Etourneau	Star
„ Rose-coloured	481	„ roseus	Martin roselin	Rosenstar
Stilt, Black-winged	84	Himantopus himantopus	Echasse blanche	Stelzenläufer
Stint, Little	337	Calidris minuta	Bécasseau minute	Zwergstrandläufer
„ Temmincks	550	„ temminckii	„ de Temminck	Lerchenstrandläufer
Stonechat	534	Saxicola torquata	Traquet (or Tarier) pâtre	Schwarzkehlchen
Stork, Black	81	Ciconia nigra	Cigogne noire	Schwarzer Storch
„ White	575	„ ciconia	„ (blanche)	Storch
Swallow	541	Hirundo rustica	Hirondelle	Schwalbe, Rauchschwalbe
„ Red-rumped	456	„ daurica	„ rousseline	Rötelschwalbe
Swan, Bewick's	51	Cygnus bewickii	Petit Cygne, or de Bewick	Kleiner Singschwan, Zwergschwan
„ Mute	365	„ olor	Cygne domestique, or muet	Höckerschwan
„ Whooper-	577	„ cygnus	„ sauvage	Singschwan
Swift	544	Apus apus	Martinet noir	Mauersegler
„ Alpine	10	„ melba	„ à ventre blanc	Alpensegler
„ Needle-tailed	374	Chaetura caudacuta	„ épineux	Stachelschwanzsegler
Teal	549	Anas crecca	Sarcelle sarcelline, or d'hiver	Krickente
„ Blue-winged	88	„ discors	„ soucrourette, or à ailes bleues	Blauflügelente
Tern, Arctic	27	Sterna macrura	Hirondelle de mer paradis, or Sterne arctique	Küsten-Seeschwalbe
„ Black	82	Childonias nigra	Guifette noire, or épouvantail	Trauer- „
„ Bridled	98	Sterna anaethetus	Sterne à sourcils blancs	Zügel- „
„ Caspian	120	Hydroprogne caspia	„ caspienne	Raub- „
„ Common	144	Sterna hirundo	Hirondelle de mer Pierre-Garin	Fluss- „
„ Gull-billed	280	Gelochelidon nilotica	Sterne hansel	Lach- „
„ Little	338	Sterna albifrons	„ naine	Zwerg- „
„ Roseate	480	„ dougallii	„ de Dougall	Paradies- „
„ Sandwich	489	„ sandvicensis	Hirondelle de mer cauguek	Brand- „
„ Sooty	522	„ fuscata	Sterne fuligineuse	Russbraune „
„ Whiskered	573	Chlidonias hybrida	Hirondelle de mer moustac	Weissbart- „
„ White-winged Black	577	„ leucopterus	Guifette à ailes blanches	Weissflügel „
Thrush, Black-throated	84	Turdus ruficollis	Grive à gorge noire	Schwarz- or Rotkehl- Drossel
„ Dusky	186	„ eunomus	„ à ailes rousses	Rostflügel- „
„ Golden Mountain-	252	„ dauma	Merle doré	Bunte, Wechsel-, Gold- or Berg-Drossel
„ Mistle-	361	„ viscivorus	Grive draine	Mistel- „
„ Rock-	477	Monticola saxatilis	Merle de roche	Steinrötel or Stein- „
„ Song-	521	Turdus ericetorum	Grive musicienne	Sing- „
Titmouse, Bearded	45	Panurus biarmicus	Mésange barbue	Bart-Meise
„ Blue	86	Parus caeruleus	„ bleue	Blau- „
„ Coal-	135	„ ater	„ noire	Tannen- „
„ Crested	161	„ cristatus	„ huppée	Hauben- „
„ Great	266	„ major	„ charbonnière	Kohl- „
„ Long-tailed	341	Aegithalos caudatus	„ à longue queue	Schwanz- „
„ Marsh-	348	Parus palustris	„ nonnette	Sumpf, or Nonnen-Meise
„ Willow-	580	„ atricapillus	„ boréale	Weiden-Meise
Turnstone	562	Arenaria interpres	Tournepierre	Steinwälzer
Twite	563	Carduelis flavirostris	Linotte	Berghänfling
Vulture, Egyptian	199	Neophron percnopterus	Vautour	Aasgeier
„ Griffon-	276	Gyps fulvus	„ griffon, or fauve	Gänsegeier

xiv

ENGLISH NAME		SCIENTIFIC NAME		FRENCH NAME	GERMAN NAME
Wagtail, Grey		275	Motacilla cinerea	Bergeronnette des ruisseaux	Gebirgs-Stelze
,,	Masked	350	,, alba personata	,, masquée	Maskenbach- ,,
,,	Pied	423	,, ,, yarellii	,, d'Yarrell	Trauerbach- ,,
,,	White	577	,, ,, alba	Lavandière	Bach- ,,
,,	Yellow	590	,, flava	Bergeronnette flavéole	Schaf- or Kuh-Stelze
Warbler, Aquatic		25	Acrocephalus paludicola	Becfin aquatique	Seggensänger, Binsenrohrsänger
,,	Arctic	28	Phylloscopus borealis	Pouillot boréal	Nordischer Laubsänger
,,	Barred	42	Sylvia nisoria	Babillarde épervière	Sperbergrasmücke
,,	Blyth's Reed-	88	Acrocephalus dumetorum	Phragmite des joncs	Buschrohrsänger
,,	Bonelli's	89	Phylloscopus bonelli	Pouillot de Bonelli	Berglaubsänger
,,	Booted	90	Hippolais caligata	Hippolais pygmée	Buschspötter
,,	Cetti's	122	Cettia cetti	Bouscarle de Cetti	Seidenrohrsänger
,,	Dartford	170	Sylvia undata	Pitchou de Provence	Provencegrasmücke
,,	Dusky	186	Phylloscopus fuscatus	Pouillot brun	Dunkler Laubsänger
,,	Garden-	242	Sylvia borin	Fauvette des jardins	Gartengrasmücke
,,	Grasshopper-	257	Locustella naevia	Locustelle tachetée	Feldschwirl, Heuschreckensänger
,,	Great Reed-	265	Acrocephalus arundinaceus	Rousserolle turdoïde	Drosselrohrsänger
,,	Greenish	269	Phylloscopus trochiloides	Pouillot brillant	Grüner Laubsänger
,,	Icterine	300	Hippolais icterina	Fauvette icterine	Gelbspötter, Gartenlaubvogel
,,	Marsh-	349	Acrocephalus palustris	Rousserolle verderolle	Sumpfrohrsänger Getreidesänger
,,	Melodious	354	Hippolais polyglotta	Fauvette lusciniole	Orpheusspötter, Sängerlaubvogel
,,	Olivaceus	396	Hippolais pallida	Hippolaïs pâle	Blasspötter
,,	Orphean	397	Sylvia hortensis	Fauvette orphée	Orpheusgrasmücke
,,	Pallas's	402	Phylloscopus proregulus	Pouillot roitelet	Goldhähnchenlaubsänger
,,	,, Grasshopper	401	Locustella certhiola	Locustelle de Pallas	Streifenschwirl
,,	Radde's Bush-	441	Phylloscopus schwarzi	Pouillot de Schwarz	Bartlaubsänger
,,	Reed-	461	Acrocephalus scirpaceus	Rousserolle effarvatte	Teichrohrsänger
,,	Rufous	484	Agrobates galactotes	Agrobate rubigineux	Heckensänger
,,	Rüppell's	484	Sylvia rüppelli	Fauvette de Rüppell	Maskengrasmücke
,,	Sardinian	492	,, melanocephala	,, melanocéphale	Schwarzkopfgrasmücke Samtköpfchen
,,	Savi's	492	Locustella luscinioides	,, des Saules	Rohrschwirl, Nachtigallrohrsänger
,,	Sedge-	499	Acrocephalus schoenobaenus	Becfin des joncs	Schilf- oder Uferrohrsänger
,,	Subalpine	540	Sylvia cantilans	Fauvette passerinette	Bartgrasmücke
,,	Willow-	580	Phylloscopus trochilus	Pouillot fitis	Fitis
,,	Wood-	586	,, sibilatrix	,, siffleur	Waldlaubsänger, Waldschwirrvogel
,,	Yellow-browed	590	,, inornatus	,, à grands sourcils	Gelbbrauenlaubsänger
Waxwing		569	Bombycilla garrulus	Jaseur de Bohème, or boréal	Seidenschwanz
Wheatear		572	Oenanthe oenanthe	Cul-blanc, Traquet motteux	Steinschmätzer
,,	Black	84	,, leucura	Traquet rieur	Trauer- ,,
,,	Black-eared	74	,, hispanica	Cul-blanc roux, Traquet oreillard	Mittelmeer- ,,
,,	Desert-	173	,, deserti	,, ,, du Désert	Wüsten- ,,
,,	Isabelline	313	,, isabellina	Traquet isabelle, or sauteur	Isabell- ,,
,,	Pied	424	,, leucomela	,, pie	Nonnen- ,,
Whimbrel		572	Numenius phaeopus-	Courlis corlieu	Regenbrachvogel
Whinchat		573	Saxicola rubetra	Tarier des prés	Braunkehlchen
Whitethroat		576	Sylvia communis	Babillarde grisette	Dorngrasmücke
,,	Lesser	329	,, curruca	,, ordinaire	Zaungrasmücke, Müllerchen
Wigeon		578	Anas penelope	Canard siffleur	Pfeifente
,,	American	13	,, americana	,, ,, américain	Amerikanische Pfeifente
Woodcock		583	Scolopax rusticola	Bécasse	Waldschnepfe
Woodpecker, Greater Spotted		261	Dendrocopus major	Pic épeiche	Buntspecht, Rotspecht
,,	Green	271	Picus viridis	,, vert	Grünspecht
,,	Lesser Spotted	328	Dendrocopus minor	,, épeichette, or mar	Kleiner Buntspecht, Zwergspecht
Wren		587	Troglodytes troglodytes	Roitelet	Zaunkönig
Wryneck		588	Jynx torquilla	Torcol fourmilier	Wendehals
Yellowhammer—see Hammer, Yellow					
Yellow-Legs, Greater		262	Tringa melanoleuca	Grand Chevalier à pieds jaunes	Grosser Gelbschenkel
,,	Lesser	330	,, flavipes	Petit Chevalier à pieds jaunes	Kleiner ,,

TOPOGRAPHY–Principal Parts of the Bird

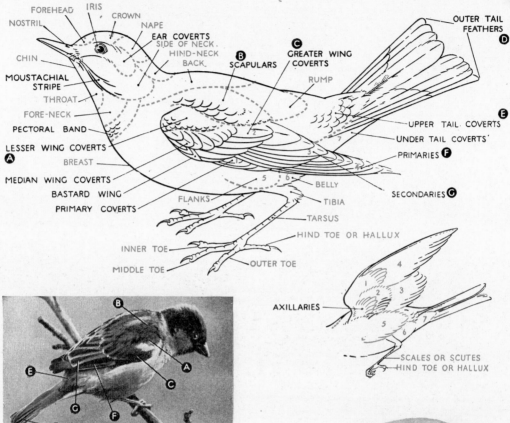

FOREHEAD
IRIS
CROWN
NOSTRIL
NAPE
EAR COVERTS
SIDE OF NECK.
HIND-NECK
BACK
CHIN
MOUSTACHIAL STRIPE
THROAT
FORE-NECK
PECTORAL BAND
LESSER WING COVERTS
A
BREAST
MEDIAN WING COVERTS
BASTARD WING
PRIMARY COVERTS
INNER TOE
MIDDLE TOE
FLANKS
OUTER TOE

B SCAPULARS
C GREATER WING COVERTS
RUMP

OUTER TAIL FEATHERS
D
E
UPPER TAIL COVERTS
UNDER TAIL COVERTS
PRIMARIES **F**
SECONDARIES **G**

BELLY
TIBIA
TARSUS
HIND TOE OR HALLUX

AXILLARIES

SCALES OR SCUTES
HIND TOE OR HALLUX

PERCHING BIRD

NAIL
HIND TOE OR HALLUX
SCALES OR RETICULATIONS
WEB

SWIMMING BIRD

EAR COVERTS
TARSUS

BIRD OF PREY

KEY TO TOP DIAGRAM

Plumage names are *black* ; other features *red*. Area boundaries are shown by broken lines. Red numbers correspond to under-wing features (small diagram), and the circled letters to photographs

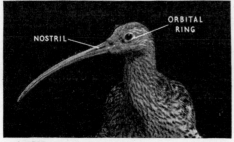

NOSTRIL
ORBITAL RING

WADER

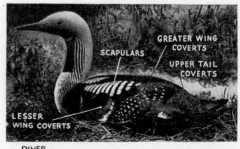

SCAPULARS
GREATER WING COVERTS
UPPER TAIL COVERTS
LESSER WING COVERTS

DIVER

ABBOTSBURY and its Swannery. This village in Dorset, lying about midway between Bridport and Weymouth, is known to all naturalists and bird-lovers as the home of the oldest and largest Swannery in Great Britain, if not in the world. It is set in a valley, girdled by hills, at the western end of the Fleet, a stretch of water about 9 miles long enclosed by the Dorset mainland and the Chesil Beach, which shelters it from the severity of the gales.

The Fleet is almost completely landlocked, being connected to the sea by only a narrow strait which opens into Portland Bay. In its brackish waters, fed by numerous small streams, grow acre upon acre of *Zostera marina*, a long ribbon-like fleshy water-grass, which is the natural food of the Mute Swan, and is undoubtedly one of the main reasons why the swans have chosen to make their home at Abbotsbury, where, for centuries, it has been their habit to return at breeding time to nest among the reeds.

No one knows when the Swannery was started. One old belief was that the swans were brought to Abbotsbury by King Canute (about 900) ; another that they were introduced there by Henry II or his successor, Richard the Lionheart. The view taken by most modern ornithologists is that the swans came to this part of the coast of their own free will, long before man attempted to exercise any control over them. It is quite possible to reconcile these apparently conflicting views. The first record of the pinioning and marking of the swans appears during Richard's reign (1189–1199), so it may be that the Swannery, as such, can be said to have started at that time, even though the swans were present there in Canute's day. or perhaps earlier.

The first mention of a " Keeper of the Swans ", one William Squilor, occurs in the Court Rolls of the Manor of Abbotsbury for 1393. He was the forerunner of a long line of " swanherds", the present swanherd and decoyman being Mr. Fred Lexster, who is the third member of his family to hold this office ; his uncle, whom he

succeeded, having acted in this capacity for no less than 65 years.

The reason why so much interest was taken in the ownership of swans in earlier times was that in the Middle Ages the swan was greatly prized as a table-bird. It was a bird Royal, and no subject could possess a swan without a licence from the Crown. One condition of the granting of such a licence was that every bird in the " game " (the old legal term for swannery) should be marked on the bill. By the reign of Elizabeth I more than 900 marks, or *cygninota*, as they were called, were recognized by the Royal Swanherd, who was responsible for swans throughout England.

Failure to mark all her swans caused Lady Joan Young, an ancestress of Lord Ilchester, the present owner of the Swannery, to lose over 400 of them to Queen Elizabeth. Abbotsbury swans are no longer marked on the bill, but by

Fred Lexster

ABBOTSBURY. Swanherding runs in the Lexster family, and Fred is the third man to hold this post

Fred Lexster

ABBOTSBURY. For hundreds of years swans have come to breed by the Fleet. Here they are drinking from the freshwater stream, undisturbed by the swanherd's presence

a nick in the outer web of the left foot. This is done as soon as they are hatched.

During modern times the greatest number of swans recorded at Abbotsbury has been 1,500 ; in bad times, when the *Zostera marina* grass has failed because of bad weather or disease, the numbers have fallen to as low as 200 or 300. Swans do not take kindly to artificial feeding, and die in their hundreds if they cannot obtain their natural food.

The Swannery is open to visitors on weekdays from the middle of April to the middle of September, and thousands visit it each year. If possible, several visits should be made to Abbotsbury ; the first in May, when the swans are building their nests. They winter at the far end of the Fleet and come down to Abbotsbury to breed. One morning they will be seen marching up in pairs to claim sites for their nests, usually those they had the previous year, and although the nests are within five yards of one another, each cob (the male swan) claims a territory (*q.v.*).

The Swannery is approached through some sub-tropical gardens, and is suddenly revealed to view. Several acres of waterside growth have been cleared so that what appears to be a rough lawn, studded with mown clumps of reeds and sedges, runs down to the water's edge, where, in nesting time, two or three dozen swans can be seen sitting on their nests. There are many more hidden away in the uncut part where the growth is normally high. It is a truly wonderful sight to see the swans on their nests, the

male and female taking it in turns to sit on the eggs. It is possible to pass quite close to some of the nests, which are protected.

I made my first recording of the Mute Swan at Abbotsbury in 1946, setting up my recording studio within a few yards of a swan's nest. Although the swans looked at us with defiance, they did not attempt to interfere with the nest which we were building for ourselves in the muddy water. Only once did a pen (female) block my road to the studio ; and, as I wanted to avoid a struggle, I had to make a detour of almost half an hour. When we come to the description of the so-called " Mute " Swan, I will tell the story of how I recorded the large vocabulary of this species and why I urge everybody to change the misleading name " Mute " into " Silent Swan."

It is interesting to compare the differences at Abbotsbury in April and May, when the reeds are still very low, and in June when animals and men are virtually hidden in the high reeds. This proved to me almost fatal. On an early morning walk in the reeds, about two miles off the Swannery, I found a cygnet in a pitiful state. I went to pick it up and in the same moment I got a heavy stroke in my face, close to my eyes. It was the greatest and most aggressive of the Gull family, the Greater Black-backed Gull, which attacked me for having taken away its prey. Covered with blood, I reached the studio, but my eyes were safe and so was the poor cygnet which some hours later was adopted by a Swan family.—EDITOR.

Usually the swans take very little notice of visitors, for these birds are semi-domesticated in that they are normally indifferent to man ; but they feed exclusively on *Zostera marina* grass, and would fail to understand it if anyone tried to feed them with titbits. In June the visitor can watch the cygnets and study the family life of the swan. He may even be lucky enough to see the mother (pen) with as many as nine cygnets on her back.

Besides the Swannery, there are other things in and around Abbotsbury to interest and attract visitors, and particularly nature lovers. First there is the Decoy Pond, where hundreds of wild fowl are trapped and ringed each year. For years this has been a ringing station for southern Britain, and seventeen kinds of wild fowl have been recorded. Near-by Chesil Beach is a Ternery (*see* Tern), one of the few remaining in Great Britain. The Common Tern, Little Tern, and Sandwich Tern live here almost regularly, and even the rare Roseate Tern has been seen here. The Sooty Tern was a visitor in 1935, and the Arctic Tern has also been recorded on the Beach.

About three miles of the Fleet at the Abbotsbury end of the Beach is kept strictly private to form a natural reserve, where many different species of birds, including occasional rare visitors from the Continent, have been seen.

> In the sub-tropical gardens are to be found many of our more or less common birds, regular Winter and Summer visitors, mostly song birds ; and in the reeds and marshes, the Redshank is predominant, but you are almost certain to see and hear the Reed-, Sedge-, and the less common Marsh-Warbler.—EDITOR.

Not only is Abbotsbury fine country for warblers and waders, but the Osprey comes here most seasons. The village itself has often been described as part of Old England. On approaching it the first thing one sees is the stone-built chapel of St. Catherine, perched on one of the surrounding hills, and built by the monks when there was still an Abbey at Abbotsbury. The Abbey, from which the village derives its name, is now in ruins, but some of the out-buildings, notably the famous old Tithe Barn, still stand.

The estate has been in the possession of the family of the Earl of Ilchester for many generations, and the present Earl, takes great personal interest in the upkeep of this wonderful colony.

ABERDEVINE FINCH. Bird fanciers' name for the Siskin (*q.v.*).

ABERLADY BAY. A local Nature Reserve (*q.v.*) acquired by the East Lothian County Council in 1952. This Reserve is a coastal strip which stretches from the mouth of the Peffer Burn to Hummel Rocks. It consists of a small area of saltmarsh, dune, and a raised beach on the southern shore of the Firth of Forth ; and is a fine wintering place for waders and other wild fowl.

ACCENTOR. Familiar name of the family *Prunellidae* (*q.v.*), of which two species are known in Britain: these are the Hedge-Sparrow (*q.v.*), also called the Hedge-Accentor or Dunnock, and the Alpine Accentor (*q.v.*). It is difficult to find an entirely satisfactory reason why the name Accentor was applied

ACCENTOR. Anxious foster-mother feeding her changeling offspring is a Hedge-Sparrow. Unafraid of her huge ward she works frantically to keep the hungry cuckoo fed

John Markham

to members of this family. It was probably given by an early observer who was charmed by their singing and compared them to an accenter, the leading singer in a choir—a well-deserved compliment even though these are not the most outstanding songsters in the bird world.

ACCIDENTAL. Definition adopted by ornithological scientists for a species of birds that has been recorded in a region a limited number of times, the maximum authentic recordings being about 20.

As opposed to residents (birds remaining all the year round), partial migrants (species of which a certain number leave in Winter), and summer visitors (birds which stay in Summer but regularly winter outside Europe), there is no kind of rule or possible explanation for the occasional presence of accidentals. They may be carried off-course by strong winds during migration (q.v.) ; this is the most likely explanation of the arrival of rare trans-oceanic visitors as stragglers on the coasts or islands of Great Britain.

The list of accidentals although carefully maintained is never complete, and nearly every year one species or another is added to it, e.g. the Frigate Bird (q.v.) of 1953. Up to 100 species described in this Encyclopedia are usually registered as accidentals, among them birds from Asia, Africa, and even from as far away as America.

ACCIPITER (Latin, "hawk"). Genus of the family Falconidae of the order Falconiformes containing altogether a hundred species. The only British resident of this genus is the Sparrow-Hawk (q.v.) ; while the Goshawk (q.v.) and American Goshawk (q.v.), though on the British list, are rarely seen here. Hawks are characterised by short, strongly curved bills ; comparatively short, but broad, rounded wings ; and longish tails. Their nostrils are round or oval, with a thin covering of bristles or bristle-like feathers (Sparrow-Hawk). The tarsus is long and thin, and the claws sharp and strongly curved. The females are larger than the males.

ACROCEPHALUS (Greek, "pointed head"). Genus of the family Sylviidae of the order Passeriformes. The common British members are the Reed-Warbler, Marsh-Warbler, and Sedge-Warbler ; more rarely encountered are the Great Reed-Warbler, Blyth's Reed-Warbler, and Aquatic Warbler ; while the Paddy-field Warbler has been recorded only once in this country (these species are described under their own names). In some species the bill is narrow and slender, while in others it is broader and depressed. The tarsus is long, and in youngish birds is divided into long scutes

(horny scales) ; in old birds the scutes are absent except at the base.

AEGITHALOS (Latin, " titmouse "). Genus of the family Paridae of the order Passeriformes. There is only one resident British member of this genus, the Long-tailed Tit (q.v.), although the White-headed Tit (q.v.) has been recorded as a vagrant from Europe on one or two occasions. The Great Tit, Blue Tit, etc., belong to the genus Parus, whilst the Bearded Tit is the only Tit belonging to Genus Panurus. See also Tit and the individual species under their own names.

AEGOLIUS (Latin, " a kind of screech owl "). Genus of the family Strigidae of the order Strigiformes. There are only two species in this genus, both restricted to the northern part of the Northern Hemisphere, but there are several sub-species. The only species on the British list, Tengmalm's Owl (q.v.), is a very occasional visitor from Europe, but the English translation of Aegolius is misleading, as Tengmalm's Owl is far from being a screech owl.

AEGYPIIDAE (Latin, " Egyptian "). Family of carnivorous, scavenging birds of the order Falconiformes, comprising the genera Neophron and Gyps. The only members of this family on the British list are the Egyptian Vulture (q.v.) and the Griffon-Vulture (q.v.), both of which have been recorded a few times as stragglers from Europe.

AFTERSHAFT (hyporhachis). A subsidiary plume, or its shaft, which is connected to the axis of a contour feather where the main shaft passes into the quill, i.e. at the superior umbilicus. See also Feather.

AGE OF BIRDS. Because of the difficulties involved in collecting the necessary information, very little is known about the age to which various species of birds may be expected to live, and few ornithologists will commit themselves on this point.

Until the comparatively recent introduction of systematic ringing (q.v.) it was not possible to obtain any information on wild birds, and most of the particulars available relate to observations made on birds kept in captivity. These particulars may be misleading for several reasons, one being that they mainly concern in-dividual birds and therefore are not necessarily typical of the species as a whole ; furthermore, there are indications that a given species of bird may live much longer in captivity than in the wild state. There is also the added difficulty that the owner of a bird may not know its exact age when it comes into his possession.

Among captive birds parrots achieve the greatest age. The record is probably held by one who lived to be 140, but quite a number have been reported as having lived well beyond a century, including one of 125. Cockatoos also enjoy a long life, several having been known to reach their nineties without loss of perkiness ; with advancing age, however, they tend to become bald and to suffer from loss of memory.

Although it has been suggested that ravens may live to 200, this is probably regarded as being either very exceptional or a gross exaggeration ; however, as a species they do enjoy a long life, and there is a reliable record of one living to the age of 69. The Eagle also probably attains 100 years, taking 10 years to reach maturity. An eagle shot in France in 1845 was found to be wearing a metal collar with a Latin inscription indicating that the bird had been used for falconry in the Caucasus in 1750, over 90 years before.

Mr. W. P. Pycraft, in his book *A History of Birds*, quotes the case of an Eagle-Owl belonging to Mr. E. G. B. Mead Waldo which lived 90 years in captivity, and first started to lay eggs when it was fifty ; thereafter rearing a family annually until within a few years of its death. The Mute Swan, according to Mr. Fred Lexster, of the Abbotsbury Swannery, may also live to about 100, and if the conditions are unfavourable, it may, like the Eagle-Owl mentioned above, not start a family until fairly late in life. In support of Mr. Lexster's contention may be quoted the case of a Mute Swan shot in Derbyshire in 1887, which bore a ring dated 1711 or 1717, indicating that it was at least 170 years old at the time of its death.

Captive geese live much longer than their wild brethren ; one was 44 years old when it died, and records of 33 and 37 years have been verified. Not all birds, however, have such good ex-pectation of life ; and really old age amongst truly wild birds is difficult to prove. A Magpie at 30, an Arctic Skua at 25, a Chaffinch at 17 and several ducks at 14 are all probably at or near the maximum age for their species.

It seems likely that the average expectation of life of a Magpie in captivity is about 20 years, and for the smaller passerine birds it is not more than 15 or 16 years. Indeed, to reach 10 is a feat for most small birds, and larger birds of 20 (despite the exceptions mentioned above) are uncommon.

Sparrows are believed to reach a maximum age of about 3 to 5 years in the wild state, but about 12 to 15 years in captivity.

AGGREGATION, NOUNS OF. Names given to groups or collections of the same species. Like groups of animals and insects—such as a herd of cattle, swarm of bees, shoal of fish, school of whales—flocks of birds have their own special names, varying according to their kind. Thus we speak of :

a Siege of Bittern	a Muster of Peacocks
a Covert of Coots	a Nid of Pheasants
a Herd of Cranes	a Congregation of
a Herd of Curlews	Plovers
a Trip of Dotterels	a Bevy of Quails
a Flight of Doves	a Building of Rooks
a Pudding of Ducks	a Dopping of Shel-
a Gaggle of Geese	drakes
a Charm of Goldfinches	a Walk or Wisp of
a Brood of Grouse	Snipe
a Cast of Hawks	a Host of Sparrows
a Brood of Hens	a Murmuration of Star-
a Siege of Herons	lings
a Desert of Lapwings	a Flight of Swallows
an Exaltation of Larks	a Herd of Swans
a Suite of Mallards	a Spring of Teal
a Watch of Nightin-	a Skein of Wild Geese
gales	(in flight)
a Covey of Partridges	a Fall of Woodcock

AGGREGATION, NOUNS OF. *Ducklings seem far too pretty to be called a "Pudding" ; but, maybe, this description is reserved for their more stodgy elders*

John E. M. Sumner

AGROBATES (Greek, " feeding in fields "). Genus of warblers of the family *Sylviidae* of the order *Passeriformes*. It includes two birds on the British list, the Rufous Warbler (*q.v.*) and the Brown-backed Warbler (*q.v.*), both of which have been recorded in this country fewer than half-a-dozen times as stragglers from Europe. They may be distinguished from members of the genus *Sylvia* (which includes the garden-warblers, blackcaps, whitethroats) by their long rounded tails, cinnamon-red in colour, with the outer feathers tipped with white ; these are sometimes spread out fanwise.

AIR ROADS. *See* Migration ; Navigation.

AIR-SAC. Thin-walled membraneous chamber which forms part of a bird's respiratory system. There are two distinct systems of air-sacs. In the main one, the pulmonary system, ten air-sacs, arranged in pairs along each side of the body from the neck to the stern, are connected by air passages to the lungs. The chambers are relatively large, and some of them pass into bones, including those of the wings. Other air-sacs have small side branches which run up the neck and into cavities in the bird's head.

In many birds this elaborate system is further complicated by an extensive system of pneumatic cells which penetrate between the muscles and between the muscles and the skin, so that the bird is virtually enclosed in an " air-jacket ".

When a bird breathes in these air-sacs are filled with air, which has first passed through one of the lungs, and they are emptied through the lungs when the bird breathes out. The air-sacs thus greatly increase a bird's " lung-power " ; more fresh air is taken in with each breath, providing the blood with the comparatively large amount of oxygen which a bird's intense activity demands. Carbon dioxide, the waste gas, is also eliminated more rapidly than would otherwise be possible. Since a bird's lungs are fixed to its ribs, the movement of the latter in flight assists the process of drawing in and expelling air, and the movement of the wings also helps to operate a form of " air-pump ". Thus, in contrast to the effect of strong activity on other forms of vertebrates which " get out of breath ", a bird's exertion in flying actually helps its breathing.

The air stored in these reservoirs also helps to regulate the bodily temperature of the bird, and in this way compensates for the lack of sweat glands.

In the other system (the " tympanic " or " naso-pharyngeal "), the air-sacs are connected not to the lungs but to openings in the throat or nasal cavity. In most birds this is merely for supplying air to the bones of the skull, but in some it gives rise to extraordinary air pouches. Thus the Adjutant Stork has a remarkable pouch, running down the front of the neck as far as its middle, which can be inflated and deflated at will. The only bird on the British list having this peculiarity is the Great Bustard (*q.v.*), which formerly bred in England and Scotland, but is now only an irregular visitor to this country. The male of this species has a relatively enormous cavity, with extremely thin walls, immediately under the skin of the neck and opening under the tongue. During courtship this pouch is inflated to impress the female.

ALAR BAR (L. *ala*, " wing "). A bar (white, black, etc.) across the wing.

ALARM NOTE. *See* Call Note.

ALAUDA (Latin, " lark "). Genus of the family *Alaudidae* of the order *Passeriformes*, The members are distributed over Europe, North Africa, and much of Asia, the only species on the British list being the Skylark (*q.v.*), which is resident and abundant, and the Eastern Skylark (*q.v.*), which strays here only very rarely. These birds may be distinguished from those belonging to the genus *Lullula* (Woodlark) by their stronger bills and longer tails, and their very distinctive voices.

ALAUDIDAE (Latin, " lark "). Family of the order *Passeriformes ;* includes the following genera : *Alauda*, *Calandrella*, *Eremophila*, *Galerida*, *Lullula*, and *Melanocorypha*. The larks form one of the most clearly defined families in their order, although there is much variation in structure between the individual members. In some members of the family the bill is thickish, while in others it is rather slender and pointed. The sides of the tarsus are covered with scutes (horny scales), and not with an unbroken thin plate, or " lamina " ; the hind claw is straight or very nearly so, sharp, and frequently very long. Except in the case of the Black Lark (*q.v.*), the plumage is brown or sandy-coloured, streaked with dark brown or black, and in most cases the outer tail feathers are whitish. The sexes are very much alike (again with the exception of the Black Lark), but in most cases the juveniles are well spotted. Larks run on the ground, i.e. they do not hop.

ALBATROSS. This " pious bird of good omen " of Coleridge's *The Ancient Mariner* is called the " Mollyhawk " by sailors, who believe that it brings good luck when it follows their ship. The only albatross recorded in Britain was a Black-browed Albatross which was picked up in an exhausted condition in Cambridgeshire in 1897. There is a record of one living among some gannets in the Faroe Islands; it was shot, and is now in a museum in Copenhagen.

The Albatross, of which there are several forms, belongs to the Petrel family and is also a member of the " Tubenoses ". The largest sea-going bird, it has enormous wings with a span of about 10 ft.; but they are narrow for their size—a hindrance when the bird is rising from the sea, except in a gale. The bird's huge wing span enables it to put up a wonderful gliding performance in the air.

Outside the nesting season, these birds spend their lives far out at sea, and revel in stormy weather. They will follow in the wake of vessels, keeping pace with even the fastest, and seem to have little fear of man.

The Black-browed species (*Diomedea melanophris*) is the commonest. Its predominating plumage is white, with dark wings and tail tip. Its large, fierce-looking bill is yellow, with the upper part curved and hooked over the lower. The Albatross has a length of about 29 in., and its tarsus is over 3 in. Its weight is 17 lb. It is normally a silent bird, but during the mating season both male and female make grunting and croaking sounds; in addition to these noises the male bird emits a loud bray, especially during display. The young chicks like to imitate their parents, but their sound is more like a falsetto.

The Albatross breeds in large colonies in the Falklands and other islands of the South Pacific, nesting on steep cliffs. The nest is built with mud mixed with water, which is dug out of the ground round the nest, thus forming a sort of trench. Some nests rise to a height of 3 ft. or more and the same nests are used year after year. One egg, about the size of a swan's,

ALBATROSS. It is hard to reconcile the airy acrobat (above) with the stolid creature (centre), or with the courting dancer (below); but this bird is a creature of contrasts, often regarded with awe

Paul Popper

Ronald Thompson

ALBINISM. A "white Blackbird" seems a contradiction in terms but actually this type of albino "sport" is seen reasonably often

is laid each season (this covers the month of October and, in some islands, a longer period). Hatching takes about 60 days ; the hen never leaves the nest while sitting, and is fed by her mate. The Albatross gets its food—chiefly fish—at sea, but when following a vessel it devours the refuse thrown overboard.

An attempt once made by King Edward VII to acclimatise the Albatross in Britain failed completely Although a special expedition of experts was despatched, and the greatest care taken, all the captive birds fell ill on board ship, refused food, and died before arriving.

ALBINISM. An abnormality found in some plants, animals (including Man), and birds. Except in plants, where it is caused by lack of chlorophyll, albinism (from the Latin *albus*, " white ") is due to the absence of natural pigment in skin, hair, feathers or other outer covering, so that these appear white or abnormally pale. In true albinos the eyes are peculiarly affected : the iris is a pale rose colour and the pupil bright red, owing to the absence of *pigmentum nigrum*, the colouring matter of the eye membrane.

Albinism is congenital (i.e. the victims are born with it), and should not be confused with the seasonal changes which cause a number of animals and birds to adopt a white coat, fur or plumage as a camouflage or protective coloration during the season of snow and ice, and to assume their normal colouring when the Winter ends. An example of this seasonal change is found in the Ptarmigan (*q.v.*), which is predominantly brown in Summer and white in Winter.

In birds, most of the so-called albinos are not really true albinos, because the normal pigment is retained in the eyes, beaks and feet—and only the feathers are deficient in pigment. In some species white " sports " of normally coloured-plumaged birds are relatively common, whereas in others they are exceedingly rare. " White black-birds" may be seen quite frequently, and " white " sparrows, swallows and wheatears are not uncommon. Although these sports are often called " white " varieties, they are not, of course, separate species.

In general, " white " varieties are most likely to be discovered among black- and grey-plumaged birds. Those with green or red plumage seldom show this variation ; although most green birds, but not all, have yellow varieties. Red appears to be the most difficult to change, and white bullfinches, for example, retain their red under-surface.

Between absolutely white and albino varieties, and those with normal plumage, every gradation of shade may be found, indicating that the lack of colour is due to failure to produce sufficient pigment. Isabelline (pale or straw-coloured) varieties found, for example, among rooks and starlings, are due to the " watering down " of the natural black (melanin) pigments. Sometimes only a few of the feathers are affected, resulting in a pied bird—in which white feathers are mixed with the normal plumage.

So far no satisfactory explanation has been found to account for these variations, or for the failure of some birds to produce the normal amount of pigment.

Occasionally white varieties regain their normal plumage at the next moult ; usually, however, this abnormality is congenital, and may even appear in the offspring of normally coloured birds through successive generations, some of the young of each brood being white while the others have normal plumage.

It has not been found possible to produce white varieties artificially by feeding them on a special diet, although it has been possible to induce the converse of albinism (*see* Melanism) by this method.

Bullfinches, as is well known, become black if fed on a diet of hemp seed. There are also instances of abnormal red varieties being induced in a similar way (*see* Erythrism).

Eric Hosking

ALCIDAE, the Puffin's Latin name, "little friar", derives from its clasping its feet, as if praying, on taking wing

For text see pages 9 and 438

To face page 8

ALCA (Latin, " auk "). Genus of the family *Alcidae* of the order *Charadriiformes* The only existing British species in this genus is the Razorbill, the Great Auk having been extinct since 1844. The bills of these marine birds are laterally compressed and deep, and are transversely grooved. They are slightly hooked at the tip, and the basal part is feathered for almost half its length. The middle toe with its claw is longer than the tarsus, for, like other members of their family, these birds have very short legs, set far back. Their wings are small and narrow, and the tails short. The wing-beats are very rapid, and these birds never glide or soar. *See also* Auk ; Extinct Birds.

ALCEDINIDAE (Latin, " kingfisher "). Family of fish-eating birds of the order *Coraciiformes*. Its genera are widely distributed, but the majority are confined to the Tropics. Only one of them, *Alcedo* (*q.v.*), is on the British list of birds, and the only British species in that genus is the Kingfisher (*q.v.*).

ALCEDO (Latin, " kingfisher "). Genus of the family *Alcedinidae* of the order *Coraciiformes*. It comprises some twelve species of which only one, the Kingfisher (*q.v.*), occurs in the British Isles.

ALCIDAE (Latin, " auk "). Family of marine birds of the order *Charadriiformes*, comprising about twelve genera, all confined to the northern areas of the Northern Hemisphere. There are only four genera on the British list : *Alca, Fratercula, Plautus,* and *Uria.* The members of this family, which includes the puffins, auks, and guillemots, are stout, small to medium-sized birds. They have short necks, and small narrow wings with 11 primary feathers. Their tails, which have between 12 and 18 feathers, are very short. They have short legs, set very far back. There are only three toes, all at the front and all fully webbed. The bills are variable in shape, but short and strong, and laterally compressed. The flight is swift, low, and direct, with very rapid wing-beats. Most of these birds patter over the water when taking off.

ALECTORIS (Greek, " domestic fowl "). Genus of the family *Phasianidae* of the order *Galliformes*. It contains four species, of which only one, the Red-legged Partridge (*q.v.*), is on the British list.

ALGERIAN RED-NECKED NIGHTJAR—Caprimulgus ruficollis desertorum. This bird breeds in Algeria and Tunisia, and only one recorded example has wandered to this country. Larger than the British Nightjar, it has a much redder appearance, with a prominent white patch on the throat. In display this species makes the typical wing-clapping sound of our Nightjar (*q.v.*), but its song and call notes have nothing in common with those of the British bird. Its general habits and characteristics are the same, but it frequents more open country. The length is 12 in.

ALLIED SHEARWATER. American name for Little Shearwater (*q.v.*).

ALPINE ACCENTOR—Prunella collaris. A breeding bird of the mountains of South and Central Europe, Africa and Asia, this is a rare visitor to Britain, and has been authoritatively identified twenty-nine times, chiefly between the months of August and January.

In appearance it is not unlike a large Hedge-Sparrow (*q.v.*), but its chestnut plumage, white-tipped wings and speckled throat make it a much more colourful bird. It is 7 in. long and has a wing span of about 9 in. ; the tarsus is 1 in. Its voice, especially during the courtship flight, is much superior to the Hedge-Sparrow's, and has been likened to the song of the Lark.

The nesting sites of the Alpine Accentor are found on rocky ground, high up and very well hidden. There are four pale-blue eggs, and two broods a season. Both parents take part in bringing up their young. The bird's food consists chiefly of insects, but in Winter it has to feed on Alpine plants and berries.

The Alpine Accentor is less gregarious than the Hedge-Sparrow, but, outside the nesting season, it sometimes congregates in large flocks.

Eric Hosking

ALCIDAE. *Razorbills, or razorbilled auks, are the most typical members of the Alcidae family extant*

ALPINE CHOUGH—Coracia gracula. The Alpine Chough is confined to the mountainous districts of the Continent and is not included in the British list of birds. The ordinary bird watcher would think it no different from our own Chough (*q.v.*) Its appearance is practically the same, though it is a slightly smaller bird with a curved but yellow beak (contrary to the ordinary Chough's red one). Its call, however, differs and its song reminds one of the Blackbird's call, though it is much stronger. When alarmed, the Alpine Chough clearly shows its relation to the crow family.

ALPINE RING-OUZEL—Turdus torquatus alpestris. A bird of the mountains, the Alpine Ring-Ouzel breeds in such countries as Spain, France, Italy, the Balkans, Austria and Germany, and winters in North Africa and the Mediterranean Islands. Two or three authentic appearances in England have been recorded in comparatively recent years.

The much paler plumage of the Alpine species distinguishes both male and female from the typical Ring-Ouzel (*q.v.*). Their behaviour and habits are similar, but the Alpine bird shows a tendency to frequent wooded areas rather than moorlands, and to nest in trees, especially conifers, rather than among rocks. Its clear and resonant song is more powerful than that of our lowland Ring-Ouzel.

The breeding season is from May until July, according to the country frequented. Four or five eggs are laid in the single brood of the season, and both parents rear and feed the young. The food consists chiefly of insects, but some vegetable matter is taken.

ALPINE SWIFT—Apus melba. This is a rare vagrant to the British Isles, its home being usually in the mountains of the Pyrenees, south of France, Switzerland, Austria and Yugoslavia. It is larger than the common Swift (*q.v.*), and is also a much paler brown ; it has a white belly (conspicuous as it turns and wheels in the air), its chin is white, and there is a brown patch separating this from the white of its underparts. It has a forked tail. The length is about 8 in. and the tarsus 0·5 in. Its wing span is nearly 1½ ft.

The Alpine Swift is one of the most aerial of birds. Its behaviour and nesting habits are similar to those of the rest of its family. It nests in colonies under the eaves of buildings, and in holes in cliffs and crags. In the breeding season the noisy alpine swifts set up a loud and persistent, though rather musical, chattering, which differs from that of the common Swift. The whole colony will suddenly take to flight and join together, chasing one another in the air with many turns and twists while uttering

their unique cry. At other seasons it is a silent bird.

The breeding season is towards the end of May and June. Both birds help to build the solid nest, which is in the shape of a round cup, often 5 in. in diameter, and is composed of material such as grasses, straw and leaves, picked up in flight and welded together with saliva. The nest is so compact and strong that the birds can use it year after year. The normal number of the dull white eggs is three, and there is only one brood in a season. Both male and female share in the hatching of the eggs and the rearing of the chicks, which takes about six weeks. The food consists of insects of the larger size, all taken on the wing ; as many as a hundred insects have been found in the throat pouch of one Alpine Swift.

ALULA. Bastard wing, or *ala spuria*, which acts as an anti-stalling or safety device when the bird flies very slowly. It is situated half-way along the leading edge of the wing, and usually consists of one main feather overlaid for strength and thickness by several smaller feathers, borne on the first digit, or " thumbbone " of the wing. It is controlled by three muscles and can be moved up, down, or forward. Not all birds have it, and in those species that do, its structure varies with the habit of flight.

During normal flight the alula lies flat against the wing proper, but it is brought into use to prevent stalling when the flying speed is dangerously low, such as at take-off, on landing, and when climbing steeply. It then traps part of the air-stream which passes over the wing, and causes it to flow over the upper surface and smooths out any eddies that may tend to form there and cause the bird to lose control. If the alula is removed from the wings of some birds they cannot take off or land without crashing. The slotted wing for aeroplanes, invented by Sir Frederick Handley Page, and the alula operate on the same principle.

The alula is usually of the same colour as the primaries, and if these differ markedly from their coverts, as in the Gannet, may form a conspicuous area at the angle of the wing. *See* Flight ; Wing.

AMERICAN BITTERN—Botaurus lentiginosus. A breeding bird of north America, this Bittern has wandered to Great Britain only on very rare occasions ; no more than 20 birds have been recorded, all observed in the Winter.

A somewhat smaller bird than the common Bittern (*q.v.*), it has paler brown and black plumage and lacks the barred effect of the British bird. Its length is 24 in. and its wing span is about 2½ ft. In general habits it is similar to the common Bittern, but it is said to be less secretive and is seen more often in the open. It has a deep, resonant boom, with two different sounds—one likened to the noise of an old-fashioned pump, and the other to the sound of a stake being driven into the ground.

The breeding period in the northern states of the U.S.A. is from May until June, in the south from the end of April until June, and there is one brood a season. The American Bittern's food consists of fish, and animals such as voles, mice, lizards, and snakes ; it has been known to feed to its young a snake as long as 16 in.

AMERICAN GOLDEN PLOVER—Charadrius dominicus. This member of the large family of plovers is confined only to America, breeding in Arctic North America and wintering in South America. It rarely wanders to Britain, but two or three have been recorded, the last in 1916. In the main its behaviour and habits resemble those of the Golden Plover (*q.v.*) of Europe, but it is a smaller bird, and, when observed at close quarters, is seen to have smoke-grey instead of white axillaries ; it is consequently not unlike the Grey Plover (*q.v.*), especially in Winter. Its length is a little over 9 in. Its song has great variety, and it is recorded that in its vast vocabulary it has many notes resembling those of our Golden Plover.

The American Golden Plover breeds in pasture lands, prairies and heathlands, its unprotected nest being merely a slight hollow in the ground. Insects are its principal food. The breeding season is from the beginning of June until the middle of July, and four eggs are laid. As far as is known, one brood is reared in a season. The Asiatic Golden Plover (*q.v.*) is closely related and almost identical to the American bird.

AMERICAN GOSHAWK—Accipiter gentilis atricapillus. An infrequent visitor to the British Isles, the American Goshawk has the typical build and long rounded tail of the European Goshawk, but a much lighter appearance. Its mantle is slate-grey, with paler grey underparts, but it has a black crown. In breeding habits, behaviour and voice it resembles the European Goshawk, but it is a bolder and fiercer bird, and during the breeding season the female will attack any intruder venturing near the nest.

The American Goshawk lives and breeds in many parts of the American Continent, and in some years the U.S.A. sees large invasions of these birds. The male is about 19 in. in length, and the female is considerably larger ; this difference in size between the sexes is also characteristic of European goshawks. *See also* Goshawk.

A. A. Allen
AMERICAN GOLDEN PLOVER. This inhabitant of Arctic wastes has visited Britain but rarely

AMERICAN HAWK-OWL—Surnia ulula caparoch. A species which breeds in North American and winters in the South. One or two have been known to wander to Britain at very long intervals. The bird differs slightly from the European Hawk-Owl (also a very rare visitor to Britain) by having broader bars on its under-plumage ; otherwise, the two birds are virtually the same. *See also* Hawk-Owl.

AMERICAN NIGHTJAR. Name sometimes applied to the Night-Hawk (*q.v.*), a straggler from North America, only once recorded in this country.

AMERICAN PECTORAL SANDPIPER. *See* Pectoral Sandpiper.

AMERICAN PIPIT — Anthus spinoletta rubescens. A member of the same genus as all European pipits, this is a bird of the Arctic Zone, frequenting barren tracts and often breeding on the steep slopes of towering sea-cliffs and high mountains in such countries as Siberia, Alaska, Greenland and Newfoundland. One or two have been recorded in Scotland, but it is a very rare visitor to Britain. In song and behaviour it resembles our Rock-Pipit (*q.v.*), but it is slimmer and more colourful. Its movements show a similarity to those of the Wagtail.

AMERICAN RED-NECKED GREBE— Podiceps grisegena holböllii. Except for its larger size, the American Red-necked Grebe—sometimes called Holböll's Grebe—is practically identical in habits and characteristics to the Red-necked Grebe (*q.v.*), which comes to Great Britain as a winter visitor. One only has been recorded—in Scotland. It breeds in North America and north-east Asia.

A. A. Allen

AMERICAN RING-NECKED DUCK. *Ornamental waterfowl often escape from private ponds ; among them was probably the only duck of this kind ever seen in this country*

AMERICAN RING-NECKED DUCK—Anas collaris. This is a breeding bird of North America, wintering in the south. Its only recorded appearance in Britain was when a single specimen, said to have been killed in Lincolnshire, was found among the birds sent to Leadenhall Market.

AMERICAN SNIPE—Capella gallinago delicata. Sometimes called Wilson's Snipe, this bird so closely resembles the Common Snipe (*q.v.*) in every way that only an expert can distinguish it. The only one officially recorded as having visited Great Britain was seen on South Uist in the Outer Hebrides in 1920 ; previous records have not been admitted to the British list.

The bird breeds in North America and migrates to the south. Its principal food is earthworms, though some vegetable matter is also taken. The nest, which is always in marshes and swampy ground, is merely a depression in the moss, lined with grass. The normal number of eggs is four, laid in May or June, but sometimes in other months according to the country frequented.

AMERICAN STINT—Calidris minutilla. Sometimes called the Least Sandpiper, this bird visits England, usually in the south, on rare occasions. It breeds in N.W. Alaska, British Columbia, Labrador and Newfoundland, and winters in Brazil. It bears a close resemblance to the Little Stint (*q.v.*), but is smaller, and the summer plumage of both the adult birds and the young of the American species is much

darker and less colourful ; their winter dress, however, is much the same. The bird's length is 5 in. and its tarsus less than 1 in. ; its wing span is about 8 in.

The general behaviour of the American Stint follows the pattern of its family. It is a quiet and tame bird, goes about in flocks and associates with other waders. American stints keep together on the wing and perform some wonderful aerobatics, while uttering their short, sweet, high-pitched trill. The call, which has many variations, is also heard on the ground.

June and July are the breeding months, and the American Stint makes its nest in sphagnum moss bogs, near pools of water. The nest is merely a hollow, lined with grasses and leaves. Four eggs, varying in colour from pale olive to yellowish buff, are laid, and the male usually hatches them out. Very little information is available concerning breeding, but so far as is known, only one brood is reared in a season. Insects and some vegetable matter make up the diet of the American Stint.

AMERICAN WHITE-WINGED CROSSBILL—Loxia leucoptera. It is extremely doubtful whether this beautiful and colourful Crossbill has ever visited, or is ever likely to visit, Great Britain in the wild state, but there is a record of one being shot in Shetland in 1859. It takes its name from the brilliant white wing feathers, so distinctive in this branch of the family. It has a smaller, finer bill than the Two-barred Crossbill (*q.v.*), and the brown on its upper parts is much darker.

AMERICAN WIGEON—Anas americana.

Sometimes called the Baldpate, this North American bird breeds in Alaska, British Columbia, etc., and winters in central America. It rarely visits this country, but is often kept as an ornamental waterfowl in private collections ; it is therefore difficult to say whether or not those specimens which have been recorded were genuine visitors or had escaped from captivity.

The drake is a more colourful bird than our Wigeon (*q.v.*), and can be recognized at once by its white forehead and the broad green stripes running from its eyes down each side of its head. The darker mantle also shows up more vividly the white of the tail coverts ; the breast is light brown, shading to light buff underparts.

The duck, however, cannot easily be distinguished from the typical Wigeon duck. The length is 18 in. and the tarsus 1·5 in. The female is recorded as having the same whistling note as the male, but the voice of both possesses less volume than that of our Wigeon.

The American Wigeon breeds on islands in lakes and ponds, especially if they are treeless, sometimes at a considerable distance from the water. The nest is a sheltered hollow in the ground, made with grass and weeds, and well lined with down and feathers. Nine to eleven eggs, exactly like the typical Wigeon's, are laid in June. The hatching, which takes about three weeks, is done by the duck alone, who also tends the young. One brood is reared in a season. The food of the American Wigeon consists chiefly of vegetable matter, though some animal food is also taken.

AMNION. Membranous sac containing fluid which encloses the embryo in birds, reptiles and mammals. In growth it unites with other structures and forms the " bag of waters." *See* Egg ; Embryo ; Reproduction.

ANAS (Latin, " duck "). Genus of the family *Anatidae* of the order *Anseriformes*. It includes all the British surface-feeding ducks, with the exception of the Shoveler, which belongs to the genus *Spatula*.

The British species included in the genus *Anas* are the American Wigeon and the Blue-winged Teal (both very rare), the Gadwall, Garganey, Mallard, Pintail, Teal, and Wigeon. These species are all fully described under their own headings.

ANATIDAE (Latin, " duck "). Family of web-footed birds, comprising the ducks, geese and swans ; it is one of the two families belonging to the order *Anseriformes*. It contains a large number of genera, of which the following 16 are included in the British list : *Anas, Anser,*

Aythya, Branta, Bucephala, Casarca, Clangula, Cygnus, Histrionicus, Melanitta, Mergus, Netta, Polysticta, Somateria, Spatula and *Tadorna*.

All the members of this family are aquatic birds, large or medium-sized, with small heads and long or very long necks. They have heavy bodies, large and rather pointed wings, and short tails. The wings have eleven primaries, of which the first is reduced, and there are between 14 and 24 rectrices (tail quills). There is a covering of down under the feathers. The short but stout legs are set far back. In the ducks there is a row of scutes (horny scales) along the front of the tarsus.

The three front toes of members of this family are united by webs, and the small hind toe is elevated. The bill is generally rather long, broad and flattened in most ducks, but thin in the mergansers (" sawbills "), and conical and rather shorter in the geese. The bills of the swans closely resemble those of most ducks in shape. The bills of all these birds are covered with a soft and sensitive membrane, and at the tip of the upper mandible is a horny plate shaped like a finger nail and called the " nail ". In most cases the edges of the mandibles are set with transverse rows of horny ridges, or lamellae, which act as strainers, enabling the birds to sift their food from mud and water, and to bite off plant and grass stems. The birds of the genus *Mergus* (" sawbills "), however, have a series of saw-like " teeth ", which point backwards and enable them to hold on to slippery fish. *See also* Duck ; Goose ; Merganser Swan.

Erica

AMERICAN WIGEON (right), swimming happily on the Severn among a group of overseas visitors

WHAT LIES BEHIND THE FEATHERS

A. J. MARSHALL, D. Phil. (Oxon)

Under Ancestry we show how, over many millions of years, birds developed a specialised structure and conquered the air. Below Dr. Marshall describes the anatomy of modern birds and how it differs from that of any other animal. See also Feather ; Wing ; etc

ANATOMY. Birds are often called " glorified reptiles," and it is undeniable that however great the differences between a crocodile (to use an apparently extreme example) and a robin, both have many internal features in common which show evidence of a common origin (*see* Ancestry).

External Features. All birds—and only birds—possess feathers (*q.v.*). Even the most beautiful plume of a bird-of-paradise is essentially a modified reptilian scale and, in its beginnings, developed in the same way. The scales of fishes, on the other hand, are entirely different in origin. In birds horny, reptile-like scales are still retained on the legs and sometimes, as in reptiles, modified as claws. The bills of birds are of similar origin.

It is probable that feathers were first developed not for flying, but as a part of a heat-regulation mechanism. Feathered birds and furred mammals, although derived from different reptilian stocks, are the only groups which have become *homiothermous* (having a constant temperature, or " warm-blooded "). This characteristic, a great advance on the *poikilothermous* (" cold-blooded ") condition of reptiles, amphibians and fishes, has arisen alongside enhanced efficiency in respiration, circulation, and the development of perfect powers of flight. It has largely freed birds from the dictates of the environment, so that, for instance, birds can exist in the high Arctic where " cold-blooded " non-marine animals would freeze stiff in Winter.

Unlike mammals, birds lack sweat-glands and must regulate their temperature primarily by panting. The only skin gland they possess is the *uropygial* or *preen gland*, which is situated above the base of the tail and provides oil for waterproofing and cleaning the plumage.

Skeleton. The adaptation of birds to aerial life has left its permanent imprint on almost every part of the internal skeleton. The vertebral column, skull, sternum (breast-bone), ribs, pectoral (shoulder) and pelvic (hip) girdles (Fig. 1) and the limbs (Figures 2 and 3) are all extremely specialised, and, with the exception of a few elements in the toes and lower part of the spinal column, there is scarcely a bone in the avian body that could be confused with its counterpart in any other vertebrate. This is true also of the flightless birds of the Southern Hemisphere, which are descended from early flying birds. The development of flight has led to the extensive fusion of many skeletal components and has, in particular, resulted in the development of two wide and rigid girders (*sternum* and *synsacrum*) (Fig. 1), so that the whole weight of a bird can be carried efficiently on either the paired wings or the hind limbs (*see* Locomotion). Again, the axis of a bird is relatively much shorter (and therefore well adapted to flight) than that of other vertebrates except frogs and toads (which are adapted to leaping through the air).

The avian *skull* is basically similar to that of the archosaurian reptiles (*see* Ancestry), but can be immediately recognized by its rounded brainbox

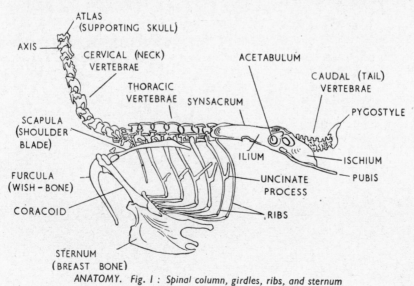

ATLAS (SUPPORTING SKULL)
AXIS
CERVICAL (NECK) VERTEBRAE
THORACIC VERTEBRAE
SYNSACRUM
ACETABULUM
CAUDAL (TAIL) VERTEBRAE
PYGOSTYLE
SCAPULA (SHOULDER BLADE)
ILIUM
ISCHIUM
FURCULA (WISH-BONE)
UNCINATE PROCESS
PUBIS
CORACOID
RIBS
STERNUM (BREAST BONE)

ANATOMY. *Fig. 1 : Spinal column, girdles, ribs, and sternum* the large orbits and the elongated, forwardly directed premaxilla bone (of upper jaw), and dentary bone (of the lower), to which the horny beak is attached. The unusually large eyes, the extremely small (in most birds) olfactory (smell) organs, and the development of bills of various weights, shapes and functions have led to modifications of adjacent bony structures.

Thus the *foramen magnum* (the aperture in the skull through which the spinal cord passes from the cranium) opens not only downwards but also backwards. Most of the cranial bones are fused in the adult bird.

Some of the components of the *vertebral column* (Fig. 1) show certain similarities to those of reptiles, but the complete structure in any kind of bird can be instantly recognized as avian. The spinal cord passes first through two vertebrae, an *atlas* and *axis*, into the *cervical* or neck region proper, which is relatively long and mobile. To its hind vertebrae are attached short *cervical ribs* which do not unite with the sternum or breast-bone. The cervical region merges with little alteration into the *thoracic* or chest region. To the vertebrae of this region are attached the *thoracic ribs* which unite with the sternum and which, with their *uncinates* (Fig. 1), form the lateral boundaries of the rigid box which houses and protects the lungs.

Three of the thoracic vertebrae are always fused into a simple structure which give rigidity and stress-resistance to the body in flight.

The next vertebral region is the *synsacrum*—a second solid mass of about a dozen fused vertebrae. To the first of these is attached the final pair of ribs ; it is therefore probably a thoracic vertebra despite its union with the others. The following five or six fused vertebrae have no ribs ; these are *lumbar* vertebrae. Fused also into this general synsacrum are two true *sacral* vertebrae, and finally several *caudal* (" tail ") vertebrae. This compound synsacrum supports the massive pelvic girdle, with which the hind-limbs articulate.

Behind the fused caudal vertebrae are several free caudal vertebrae. The vertebral column as a whole terminates with the upturned *pygostyle* or " ploughshare bone " (Fig. 1), which is itself composed of several fused caudal vertebrae. In addition to the characteristically avian pattern of fused sections of vertebral column, most of the free vertebrae have a complicated interlocking structure which ensures unusually efficient articulation during the twists and turns of flight.

Sternum, Pectoral Girdles and Wings (Figs. 1 and 2). In flying birds, the sternum is a big, keeled, plate-like structure to which the princi-pal flying (pectoral) muscles of the wing are attached. The keel not only gives a greater area for attachment, but also strengthens the structure as a whole. The sternum supports much of the weight of the bird in flight. To it the paired pectoral girdles are articulated by their paired *coracoid* bones ; these are stout, pillar-like struts which, in conjunction with the slender *furcula* or " wish-bone " (which represents fused clavicles and interclavicle), serve to brace the mobile wing out from the sternum. The flimsy *scapula* (shoulder blade) holds the wing up away from the ribs. At the union of coracoid and scapula is a round

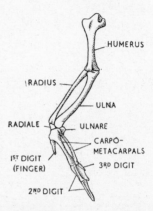

ANATOMY. *Fig. 2 : Forelimb*

glenoid cavity, a socket into which articulates the long stout *humerus*, the top bone of the forelimb (wing). The humerus is prominently ridged and otherwise shaped for the attachment of the pectoral muscles of flight. The humerus, and the two succeeding wing-bones, *radius* and *ulna* (Fig. 2), are arranged in much the same way as in Man and other vertebrate animals, but from the " wrist " onwards fascinating modifications occur. Two brief, but substantial, free wrist bones, the *radiale* and *ulnare*, provide articular surfaces for two long *carpometacarpals* of unequal bulk which are fused at both ends. These four are all altered wrist-bones.

Attached near the more substantial carpometacarpal is the first *phalange* (equivalent to the thumb), which is often jointed and capable of independent movement. It supports the small *alula* (q.v.) or bastard-wing. At their far ends the long carpometacarpals articulate with the second and third phalanges. The fourth and fifth " fingers " do not exist in birds.

Pelvic Girdles and Hind Limbs (Fig. 3). Each side of the pelvic girdle, which resembles that of no other living animal, is composed of an elongated *ilium* which, in the adult, is fused to the synsacrum mentioned above. The girdle is continued backwards as an *ischium* and a spindly curved *pubis*. No part of the girdle unites to form a pubic symphysis such as occurs in Man. In the standing bird the centre of gravity is postero-ventral and the above arrangement of bones provides a rigid basis for the transference of weight to the legs. Each leg articulates with the pelvic girdle by means of a short *femur* (thigh-bone), the head of which fits into a socket, the *acetabulum*. The other end of the femur articulates with a long *tibio-tarsus* at a point corresponding to the knee-joint, where there is also a *patella* (knee-cap). A slight, tapering, spine-like *fibula*, unattached at its far end, runs parallel. At a point corresponding to the ankle joint there articulates a *tarso-metatarsus* which is made up of several fused tarsal bones. With this composite bone articulate the four *digits* or toes which, ending in claws, are arranged in different ways in different species (*see* Foot).

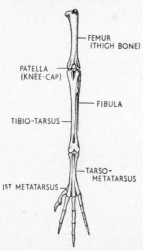

FEMUR (THIGH BONE)

PATELLA (KNEE-CAP)

FIBULA

TIBIO-TARSUS

TARSO-METATARSUS

1ST METATARSUS

ANATOMY.   *Fig. 3 : Hindlimb*

In general the bones of birds are unusually light ; both in flying and flightless birds many bones are hollow, and are connected with airsacs (*q.v.*) and thus, ultimately, with the lungs. Tubular bones no doubt increase buoyancy, and some of them, in notable flyers, are internally strutted (Fig. 4) ; the same principle is today used in aircraft wings. The skull-bones, too, are pneumatic, and this is the chief reason why so many cage-birds die of cerebral haemorrhage when they are frightened and strike their heads on the cage wire.

Digestive System.   There are no teeth in modern birds. The tongue exhibits numerous adaptations related to diet ; it may be short and horny in grain-eaters, soft, sticky and protrusible in insectivorous birds, or even tube- or brush-tipped in birds that live on nectar. In the mouth the food is mixed with saliva which, in seed-eating species, is believed to contain a starch-splitting enzyme or digestive juice. The food passes down the gullet (Fig. 5) to a storage *crop*, or in many insectivorous and carnivorous species (in which the crop may be very small or absent) straight to the stomach. In certain fish-eating and vegetarian species the crop is relatively huge. Here food is macerated before being passed on to the stomach. In pigeons of both sexes the lining of the crop contains glands producing a proteinous " crop-milk " which is regurgitated to feed the nestlings.

The form of the stomach varies widely according to species and diet. In most birds it consists of an anterior thin-walled *proventriculus* and a muscular *gizzard*. The glandular walls of the proventriculus secrete digestive enzymes. The gizzard, with the help of a horny lining, of swallowed grit, or even of large stones grinds up the food. This facilitates the action of the digestive juices.

The partly digested food then passes to the *duodenum* (the first part of the small intestine), into which run one or more *bile-ducts* carrying bile or gall from the near-by liver, and a *pancreatic duct* or ducts carrying additional digestive enzymes from the *pancreas* gland, which lies in a loop of the intestine.

From the walls of the small intestine arises a capillary system of blood-vessels into which digested foodstuffs are absorbed. These are then carried in the blood to the liver. The *ileum* (the hinder part of the small intestine) leads to the *rectum*. Where they join are paired *caeca*, blind pouches of uncertain function. The rectum leads into a *cloaca* of three, sometimes ill-defined, communicating chambers—the *coprodaeum*, the *urodaeum* (which receives the urinary and genital ducts), and the *proctodaeum* —through the walls of which water is reabsorbed into the blood-stream.

A blind pouch, the *bursa Fabricii*, opens into the hind wall of the proctodaeum. This con-

Fig. 4 : Hollow, internally strutted bone

tains lymphoid tissue, and produces lymphocytes which probably guard against local infection. The proctodaeum opens to the exterior at the cloacal aperture or anus (Fig. 5).

Heart and Circulation.   A bird's heart is large and shows a great advance in that it has both streams of blood—arterial and venous—completely separated. Thus, although certain features betray its reptilian origins, the heart has independently come to resemble that of mammals.

Used or " impure " blood comes from the right and left *precaval veins* and the *postcaval* directly into the right *auricle*. Four big *pulmonary veins* carry oxygenated (" pure ") blood from the lungs into the left *auricle*. From the auricles the blood flows into corresponding right and left *ventricles*, and as the heart contracts completely, separate streams of blood are squeezed out.

The left (oxygenated) ventricular blood goes into the right *aortic arch*, as in the Crocodilia, and thence into the *dorsal aorta* and to the arterial system in general. (The left aortic arch is absent in the adult.) The deoxygenated or " impure " contents of the right ventricle are pumped into the *pulmonary artery*, one branch of which conveys the blood to each lung for aeration. Some small flying birds have a heart-rate of almost 500 contractions per minute. This arrangement allows for a high arterial pressure and the rapid carriage of oxygen and other essential substances to the tissues.

There is no elaborate renal portal system. Each kidney receives a renal portal vein (from the *caudal* vein) but, instead of breaking up into a large capillary system, each portal vein gives off only minor tributaries to supply the organ and then continues forwards to join first the *femoral vein*, and next the *iliac*. This unites with the iliac vein of the other side to form the large postcaval vein which enters the right auricle. Thus, all blood (except that carried to the liver) passes through only one capillary network in its journey from and back to the heart. The right and left *innominate* arteries which supply each pectoral muscle mass are relatively enormous. The red cells are nucleated as in reptiles, frogs and fishes.

Respiration and Voice. The *trachea* runs beneath the gullet, but may be displaced to the left for a short distance by the crop. As it enters the thorax it forks into right and left *bronchi* leading to the *lungs*. The respiratory organs are unique in their structure and mode of operation. Through the relatively small and inelastic primary lung-sacs run the primary bronchiae which give off bronchial branches ; these take inspired air beyond the lungs into capacious air-sacs which extend in several directions and even into the hollow bones (Fig. 4). The bulk of indrawn air passes more or less unchanged into the smooth-walled air-sacs and from there, still unchanged, it is driven back across the highly vascular respiratory surface of the lung proper. Thus, there is no " dead space air " as in mammals ; but there is a true and constant circulation of a relatively enormous amount of air, controlled by rib movement when the bird is at rest, and by the movement of the pectoral muscles during flight.

The vocal organ, the *syrinx*, is found in no other animal. An expansion of the lower part of the trachea near the bronchial junction, it is made up of a system of membranes, two of which, the *semi-lunar membranes*, produce the voice when vibrated by air. Specialised syringeal muscles alter the pitch. The apparatus shows much variation from species to species.

Nervous and Endocrine Systems. Apart from mammals, birds have relatively the largest brain. The component organs differ from group to group, and comparatively little is known of their functioning. The *fore-brain* is very big, but unconvoluted. The unusually advanced development of the *cerebellum* is no doubt connected

with the unique regulation of balance in relation to movement in flight. The *corpus striatum* is immense and strikingly differentiated : it is possibly concerned with the control of many of the reflex activities that mark birds' behaviour. The *thalamus* is large and complex. The small *hypothalamus* is connected with the *anterior pituitary gland* (*see below*). The *olfactory lobes* are generally reduced except, notably, in certain pungent-smelling sea-birds. The *medulla oblongata* exhibits a ventral flexure similar to that of certain reptiles.

For particulars about a bird's various sense organs *see also* Bill ; " Ear " ; Eye ; Nostril.

The *pituitary gland* (hypophysis) can be crudely differentiated into anterior and posterior lobes, but little is known of the latter's functions in birds. *Gonadotrophic* secretions from the anterior pituitary undoubtedly regulate the sex organs and indirectly the breeding seasons and migration, and also exert other important influences. A pituitary secretion, *prolactin*, stimulates the production of proteinous "milk" from the crops of pigeons of both sexes during the breeding season. It is also partly responsible for the onset of broodiness. This secretion appears to be very like the lactogenic hormone of mammals. Paired *thyroid glands* occur at the base of the neck. They appear to have essentially the same functions as in mammals. They undergo considerable changes during the moult, but the part played by their secretion, *thyroxin*, is not clear. The *thymus*, of doubtful function, occurs as a paired body in the neck region. The *adrenals* (Fig. 6) are paired, irregular, yellowish masses just in front of the kidneys and gonads. The two components are united (unlike the condition found in

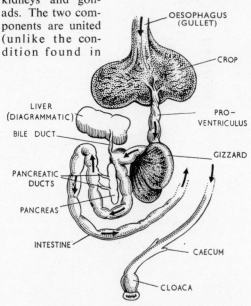

ANATOMY. *Fig. 5 : Alimentary canal*

fishes), but the counterparts of the mammalian *cortex* and *medulla* interdigitate in birds as in amphibians and reptiles. *Islets of Langerhans* are present in the pancreas (Fig. 5). The primary sex organs, the *testes* and *ovaries* (Figs. 6 and 7), produce male and female sex hormones, which have profound effects on behaviour as well as in the development of secondary sexual characters and the accessory organs.

Reproductive and Urinary Systems. (Figs. 6 and 7.) The paired *testes* are oval and vary greatly in size and productivity under the seasonal influence of pituitary gonadotrophic hormones.

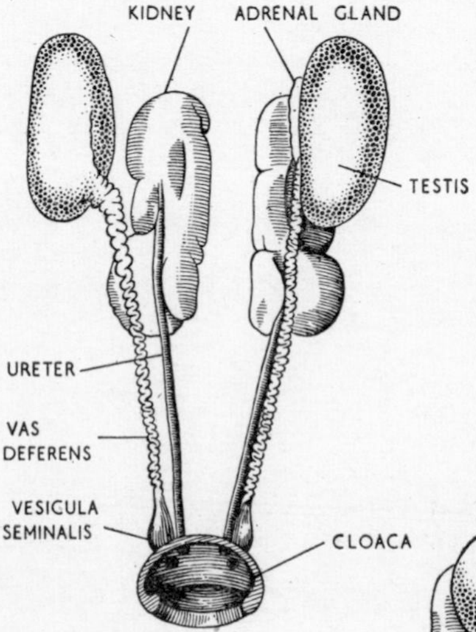

KIDNEY   ADRENAL GLAND

TESTIS

URETER

VAS DEFERENS

VESICULA SEMINALIS

CLOACA

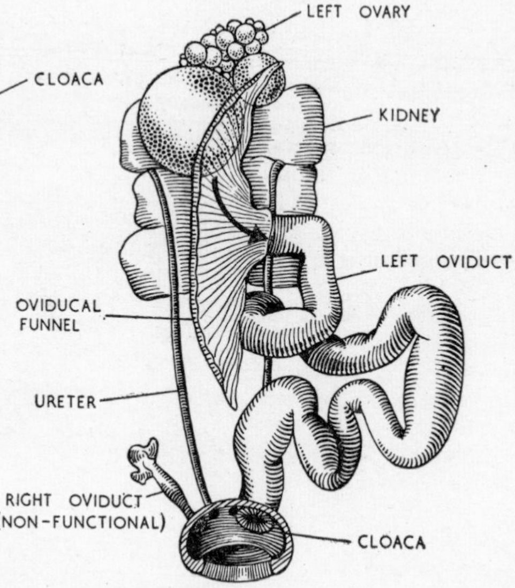

ANATOMY
Fig. 6 (above) shows the reproductive system of the male; Fig. 7 (right), the reproductive system of the female

★

Figures 2, 3, 6 and 7 have been drawn after Parker and Haswell; Fig. 4 after Prochnow

LEFT OVARY

KIDNEY

LEFT OVIDUCT

OVIDUCAL FUNNEL

URETER

RIGHT OVIDUCT (NON-FUNCTIONAL)

CLOACA

tube, the *vas deferens*, which is dilated behind to form a *seminal vesicle* for the storage of semen (Fig. 6). The sexual products are discharged through minute papillae into the urodaeum. Ducks and large flightless birds have a penis.

Only one *ovary* (Fig. 7) is normally present : the organ on the right side fails to develop in most groups. The female sex hormones, as well as influencing the secondary sexual characters, the accessory organs and behaviour, have the effect, unique to birds, of stimulating the seasonal appearance of special bone material within the long bones. At the time of egg-laying this osseous material is given up to the blood, from which it is taken to be utilised in · the egg-shells. The surface of the ovary is studded with *oocytes*, a few of which become mature and heavily yolked and then break through the surface into the body cavity, where they pass into an *oviducal funnel* and thence down the single, muscular, internally ciliated *oviduct* (Fig. 7) towards the urodaeum. Ducks and large flightless birds have a clitoris.

During copulation, the proctodaeum of each bird is everted and brought into contact, so that the male spermatozoa are discharged into the female urodaeum, and pass up the oviduct where impregnation occurs. As the heavily yolked, now fertilised egg passes down the oviduct, it is invested with products from the glandular lining. Layers of albumen ("white") surround it, followed by *shell-membrane* and the calcarious *shell*. In coloured eggs, the ground-colour is deposited during the formation of the shell and the secondary pattern further down. A mucous secretion is finally produced ; this facilitates egg-deposition.

Each *kidney* (Figs. 6 and 7) is a large lobed, flattened organ sunk into depressions in the hinder body wall. Waste nitrogenous substances are excreted, largely in the form of uric acid, and pass down paired *ureters* which open into the urodaeum, the middle chamber of the cloaca. In the cloaca reabsorbtion of fluid occurs, and the urinary products are then discharged with the faeces.

In some species they may increase one thousand-fold in size each Spring. They are of the typical vertebrate pattern—an extensive system of convoluted seminiferous tubules in which are produced the male germ-cells (*spermatozoa*) and, between the tubules, massed *Leydig* or *interstitial cells* which produce the male sex hormone mentioned above. The testes are anchored near the forward end of the kidneys. Each discharges its spermatozoa down a convoluted

Consult : Textbook of Zoology, Vol. II: Vertebrates, Parker and Haswell, 1954 ; The Life of Vertebrates, J. Z. Young, 1950.

FROM EARLY REPTILES TO BIRDS

W. E. SWINTON, Ph.D., B.Sc.

Here Dr. Swinton, one of our greatest living authorities, follows up the few clues, separated by millions of years, which prove that modern birds are descended from lizard-like creatures of the primeval swamps. See also Evolution, written by the same author

ANCESTRY. The origin and history of most groups of animals can be traced in the records of the rocks. The evidence consists of fossils—parts or complete specimens of the life of former times, many of them remote in antiquity and far beyond the experience of Man. The word fossil means " dug up," for these pieces of evidence are collected from the soil or rock in which they had become buried.

The preservation and discovery of such remains is to a certain degree accidental, and the story unfolded by them cannot be complete. But the remains can be seriously studied by naturalists and anatomists, and the life of these remote animals reconstituted by analogy. The methods of comparative anatomy are largely used by modern students of fossils, or palaeontologists as they are called.

Of all the vertebrate groups—fishes, amphibians, reptiles, birds and mammals—the birds have by far the least satisfactorily preserved record. But the course of their evolution is fairly clear. If we go back in time to the geological period known as the Trias, approximately 200 million years ago, we find a number of specially interesting reptiles. At that time there were no higher animals ; birds and mammals had not yet come into existence ; and the whole world appears to have enjoyed a climate more equable than that of to-day's temperate regions. The red colour of the rocks of this age in many parts of Europe and North America, and the occurrence of salt deposits among them, testify that aridity and desert conditions were not uncommon. Some of these rocks can be seen in Cheshire.

Warm conditions tend to make reptiles more active ; desert conditions act as a stimulant to movement, since the scarce vegetation has to be sought, and the more active vegetarian animals

ANCESTRY. Much excitement was caused by the discovery of this fossil—the first remains of a feathered animal ever to be found. See also illustration in page 25

British Museum (Natural History)

demand more active carnivorous pursuers. Fossils bearing witness to these developments have been discovered in New Mexico and Arizona in the United States, the Karroo in South Africa, in Germany, and, to come nearer home, in north-east Scotland.

False Crocodiles. One of the groups of reptiles of great importance in the history of modern forms is that called the *Thecodontia*, which had their teeth arranged along the jaws in sockets, as the name indicates. One sub-order of this group is the *Pseudosuchia*, or false crocodiles. A typical example of this kind (below) is *Ornithosuchus*, a small reptile, fossils of which have been discovered in the Trias of Morayshire. This little animal was about 3 ft. in total length, but about half of this was taken up by the tail. It looked like a largish lizard, but its front legs were only about half the length of its hind ones, and it is clear that the animal walked semi-erect on its feet. Its head was narrowly triangular, rather pointed in front at the nostrils and broadening out to the level of the back of the eye sockets. The jaws had sharp pointed teeth in sockets, and from their character it can be inferred that the animal was carnivorous. Its eyes, like those of most of its contemporaries, were fortified by a small ring of overlapping plates. The arm bones were short and the fingers small, but the leg bones were long and the toes both long and raised as in a semi-running creature. The skin is not preserved, but there were undoubtedly rows of small bony scutes, resembling the plates on a crocodile's back, as shown in the illustration.

Ornithosuchus was probably very

ANCESTRY. Climbing up the evolutionary ladder from early reptile to modern bird took millions of years. Some of the strange forerunners are shown here, from left to right : Ornithosuchus, Archaeornis, Hesperornis, Ichthyornis and Dinornis

nearly related to the ancestor of four important groups of animals —the crocodiles, the flying reptiles or pterodactyls, the large, land-living reptiles known as the dinosaurs, and the birds.

A gap of at least 50 million years separates the fossils of *Ornithosuchus* and the oldest fossil birds so far discovered. These have all come from limestones near Solenhofen, in Bavaria, South Germany. The geological age of this deposit is Kimmeridgian or Upper Jurassic (about 100 to 140 million years old).

The limestones are very fine-grained and must have been gently accumulated in the quiet waters of a deepish lake or inland sea. Animals that died or were swept into its waters would ultimately sink into the fine limy mud on the bottom, and, little disturbed by ripples, become entombed under fresh deposits until, in the course of the centuries, they were fossilized in the hardened limestone.

The fine grain, size and high degree of purity of the Bavarian limestone caused it to be greatly prized for the printing process known as lithography, and the demand for it in the mid-19th century ensured that the deposits were worked with great care and discrimination. It

EMU

MAGPIE

CRANE

SHAG

ANCESTRY. *These modern birds show a surprising, if spurious, resemblance to their prehistoric ancestors illustrated on the opposite page*

happened that in the Soienhofen area the district medical officer, Dr. Häberlein, was particularly interested in the remains uncovered by the quarrymen, and amassed a great collection of them. It was the fineness and softness of this limestone that led in 1862 to a great discovery—the imprint of a tail feather, clearly and distinctly marked on both sides of a slab when it was cracked open. The importance of this relic was at once recognized, and von Meyer described it in a German periodical. Shortly afterwards, the remains of a small bird-like skeleton were discovered when a block of the limestone was split. Like the feather, this was named by von Meyer *Archaeopteryx* (Greek, " ancient wing ").

One half of the imprint of the first feather went to Munich and the other half to the Berlin Natural History Museum, but ultimately the whole of the skeleton, both slab and counter-slab, was purchased for the British Museum, and the specimen is publicly exhibited in the Geological Department of the Natural History Museum, South Kensington, London. A few years later another, more complete, specimen was discovered in another quarry, and this is now in the Berlin Natural History Museum.

Archaeopteryx. The two skeletons have been the subject of much study. Despite disagreements on points, there is no doubt whatsoever that they are the remains of birds, and the well-marked impression of wings indicates that they had real feathers for flight. Many characteristics of modern birds, however, are missing.

The living *Archaeopteryx* was about the size of the domestic fowl. Its head was similar to that of the *Ornithosuchus*, but the eyes were larger. Like that reptile, the jaws of this bird bore sharp pointed teeth in sockets. The bones of the skeleton were much like those of modern birds in appearance and the wings at the side of the body had feathers arranged similarly to those of modern birds. But the tail arrangements were quite different, for *Archaeopteryx* had a reptilian tail with 20 vertebrae, and to each vertebra a pair of feathers was attached.

The reptilian characters of *Archaeopteryx* are the socketed teeth, the flat-ended surfaces of the

vertebrae of the neck and trunk series, the persistence and completeness of three clawed fingers in the wing, the long tail, and the fact that the bones of the skeleton are solid (modern bird's bones are hollow and pneumatic—*see* Anatomy). The principal bird characters are the feathers, the imprint of wings in which 7 primary and 10 secondary remiges and their coverts can be made out, and the indications of contour feathers on the neck and along the lower limbs. Further, the skull has the shape and the fused bones of a modern bird's. Finally among the mass of isolated bones a typical wishbone or " merrythought " (furcula) can be seen (but also an untypical sternum). The differences between the London and Berlin specimens of this ancient survival are relatively slight, and there is no basis for the suggestion that running birds are descended from one and flying birds from the other.

No Missing Link. So far, no link of any kind has been found between the reptile *Ornithosuchus* and the undoubted bird *Archaeopteryx*. The chief mystery is how bird's feathers could have evolved from reptilian scales, and to this there is not the slightest clue.

Several suggestions have been made to bridge the gap. The Pseudosuchians, like *Ornithosuchus*, went on two legs and were perhaps capable of a good turn of speed. The theory of Baron Nopcsa of Vienna was that, as their activity—and their speed—increased, there was a tendency for the scales of the hinder edge of the forearms and the thighs to lengthen, and that from this there was ultimately developed almost a fringe of scales, which might be useful to the animals. In the course of time these frayed fringe scales gradually became the beginnings of feathers.

An elaboration of this theory suggests that the main change took place in tree-living creatures whose modified scales assisted them to glide from high branches to lower, in much the same way as some modern mammals (e.g. flying fox), can " fly " by extensions of their skin. For the hypothetical animal that would have played this part in the evolutionary sequence the name *Proavis* has been invented, but so far

ANCESTRY. *This Moa, a giant of 10 ft., haunted the New Zealand swamps in the not-so-distant past*

there is not the slightest evidence of its existence.

The story of the evolution of birds can, however, be guessed at with some accuracy. An examination of the *Archaeopteryx* wing feathers suggests that they were used for flight in the modern sense of the word, but a study of the shoulder girdle suggests that this flight was not so powerful as that of modern birds (the evidence of the solid limb bones and the absence of pneumatic cavities confirms this suggestion). Yet the excellent state of preservation of the specimens shows that they had not been carried far by water, for the skeletons are almost unruffled. This supports the theory that these specimens had been able to fly out some distance over the Solenhofen Sea before death overtook them.

The wings are less well developed and the breast-bone simpler than those of modern birds, and the length of the tail must have made the flight of the *Archaeopteryx* unstable. This would impose a greater strain on the vertebral column in course of time and also demand a constant visual and balancing sense, with the result that, in the further stages of evolution, the vertebral column developed a better series of joints, the eye and other reception centres of the brain became greatly improved and enlarged, and the tail became shorter and flight more

stable. Further, with the development of longer and more muscular flight, the sternum became keeled, and the skeletal bones lighter in adaptation to the higher rate of activity and metabolism. All these suppositions are borne out.

First Swimming Birds. The geological record goes on for many millions of years before there is further evidence of flight. The next information comes from England, where scattered remains of a type of sea-bird have been found in the Cambridge Greensand. This bird has been given the name *Enaliornis*. In the chalk deposits of Kansas, U.S.A., there have been found remains of two toothed birds ; the first and largest, named *Hesperornis regalis*, must have been nearly 4 ft. long and appears to have been a precursor of such modern swimming birds as the divers or loons. The teeth were in a groove in the jaw, and the forward half of the upper jaw was without teeth and presumably covered with a horny beak. *Hesperornis* had a flat breast-bone, and was thus flightless. This may be an indication that quite early in their evolution some birds abandoned flight and returned to the ancestral levels of the ground or the waters.

The second bird of the Kansas chalk, a smaller swimming bird, has been given the name *Ichthyornis victor*. It had teeth in sockets, but again the anterior half of the upper jaw was toothless. The sternum had a large keel, yet some of the vertebrae were biconcave, as were those of its distant ancestor *Archaeopteryx*. This swimming bird can have been only 8 in. long, but appears to have been a real flying bird.

With the opening of the Tertiary Era some seventy million years ago, the pattern of modern development in birds and mammals was well under way. At that time Britain, like many other now temperate areas, was a tropical region : a rich tropical fauna is evidenced by remains in the London Clay, especially that exposed in the Isle of Sheppey. Here have been found jaws of a gannet-like bird called *Odontopteryx toliapicus* which had no teeth but had developed in both upper and lower jaws a series of denticles used for the capture of fish. Later remains, often very fragmentary, are all of modern types of birds.

Development of Flightless Birds. The southern hemisphere has yielded remains of large—sometimes almost gigantic—birds, which had abandoned flight and taken to a running habit. It seems almost a complete reversal of the evolution sequence. In Australia and New Zealand, especially, there are series of comparatively recent—in the geological sense—flightless birds, such as *Dinornis* which was over 11 feet high. These moas must have been varied and numerous, and much is known about them. They had flat breast-bones, and this suggests to some that they may have developed from *Archae-opteryx* without ever achieving a flying stage.

Yet it seems to the writer that their typical bird development and short tail could only have come about by descent from a flying ancestor which was on the way to flight stability. It is likely that flight was developed in the beginning as a result of fierce competition on the ground. First the development of the running habit, then an arboreal phase that led to lengthening of the forearms and the acquisition of grasping feet, brought about the conquest of the new element, the air. But among birds, as among all vertebrates, there would be some forms that would revert to the habits of the past when conditions permitted. And conditions did permit this in Australasia. The isolation of the continent has fostered the survival there of many kinds of animals long extinct elsewhere ; and birds, having less need for flight there, might well revert to the running habit. Even under more competitive conditions, flightless birds can hold their own as is shown by the Ostrich.

Much of the evolutionary history of birds is inevitably lost because of their very nature. How seldom today do we see the body of a sparrow ! Nature's scavengers see to that. Moreover, the fossilisation of birds' wings and feathers demands conditions of exceptionally gentle deposition of material, which rarely occurred in geological history. None the less, the few existing fossils are highly significant, and their value as signposts to directions of development is out of all proportion to their numbers. *See also* Classification ; Evolution ; Fossils.

ANGLE. 1. Projection (*see* gonys) on the under part of the lower beak (mandible) of certain species ; *e.g.*, the larger gulls. 2. Angle (of commisure), corner of the beak.

ANNET. Unofficial bird sanctuary in the Scilly Isles. This small uninhabited islet off the coast of St. Agnes, is known locally as the " island of birds ". Permission to land on it must be obtained from the owner, Major Dorrien-Smith. Its local name is well founded, for as one approaches its rocky shores it appears to be literally " alive " with sea-birds that have adopted it as their home. Shags and cormorants are to be seen swimming low in the inshore waters, and many whole colonies of guillemots and razorbills crowd the rocky ledges of the precipitous cliffs ; innumerable gulls wheel overhead, including both the Greater Black-backed Gull, with its huge wing span, and the Lesser Black-backed Gull. The Rock-Pipit nests in crevices in the rocks, and a colony of storm-petrels is hidden away in the clefts between the massive boulders. Terns, including the Arctic Tern and Roseate Tern, add to the throng.

The islet is capped by a flattish plateau covered with short, springy turf treacherously honeycombed with rabbit holes and the deep burrows of the Manx Shearwater. In the space of a few yards there may be as many as ten burrows with a bird at the bottom of each. Puffins often nest in burrows abandoned by the shearwaters.

So closely packed is the island with bird life, that at certain times of the year it is almost

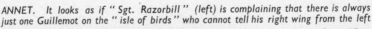

ANNET. *It looks as if " Sgt. Razorbill " (left) is complaining that there is always just one Guillemot on the " isle of birds " who cannot tell his right wing from the left*

James Gibson

A. R. Thompson

ANSERIFORMES. Geese need not be fat and waddling, as is shown by these Canada
Geese, who share something of the swan's grace and the drake's bright plumage

impossible to walk over it without treading on a nest or catching one's foot in an inhabited burrow. At times, also, there are bodies of many dead birds, victims of the Atlantic gales.

It was on Annet that the Editor, after many disappointments, secured his unique record of the fantastic symphony of the nocturnal flight of the manx shearwaters.

ANSER (Latin, " goose "). Genus of the family *Anatidae* of the order *Anseriformes*, containing about 13 species altogether. The five species which occur in the British Isles—the Bean-Goose, Grey Lag-Goose, Lesser White-fronted Goose, Snow-Goose, and White-fronted Goose—are described under their own headings; so is the Pink-footed Goose, belonging to the same species as the Bean-Goose.

The members of this genus are known collectively as grey geese, as distinct from the black geese of the genus *Branta*. The bill of the *Anser* geese is about as long as the head, and is high at the base. From the side it appears almost triangular, and it has strong tooth-like serrations, visible from outside, which enable the birds to bite off plant and grass stems with ease. The inverted shield-shaped horny plate known as the " nail " occupies the whole of the tip of the upper mandible. The longitudinal-shaped nostrils are located slightly behind the middle point of the bill. The wings are long and pointed, and the tail is short and rounded. The legs are short and set rather far back ; the three front toes are united by webs, and the small hind toe is elevated. The general colour of the plumage is grey-brown, with lighter edges to the body feathers. The tail quill-feathers, or rectrices, are tipped with white, and the tail coverts are white ; as the latter overlap the rectrices, the grey geese in flight appear to have white tails with broad, dark-coloured sub-terminal bands. *See also* Anatidae ; Goose.

ANSERIFORMES (Latin, " goose-like "). Order of web-footed birds. It is divided into two families, *Anatidae* and *Anhimidae*. The former includes the ducks, geese, and swans of the Old World, while the *Anhimidae* family comprises the South American screamers. *See also* Anatidae ; Duck ; Goose ; Swan.

ANTHUS (Latin, " a small bird "). Genus of pipits of the family *Motacillidae* of the order *Passeriformes*. These birds are found in almost all parts of the globe, except the Pacific islands, and there are seven species on the British list. These are : Meadow-Pipit, Rock-Pipit, Tree-Pipit, Petchora Pipit, Red-throated Pipit, Richard's Pipit, Tawny Pipit. Only the first three are at all common in the British Isles, the others being found here only rarely or very rarely. Also on the British list, although each of them has only been found in this country once, are the American Pipit and Water-Pipit, which belong to the same species as the Rock-Pipit. A detailed description of each bird will be found under its own heading.

ANVIL BIRD. Name given in some districts of England and of the lowlands of Scotland to the Song-Thrush (*q.v.*). This bird is very fond of snails and, when it catches one, often carries it to a large stone where, holding the snail in its beak, it beats it against the stone until the shell breaks. The shell is beaten from side to side on the stone, much as a blacksmith hammers iron upon his anvil ; hence the name. In a garden or other regular hunting ground, a thrush will always use the same " anvil " for breaking snail-shells, even though there may be many other stones lying about. In some places, the " anvil ", which is usually flat on top, is called the " song-thrush breakfast table ".

The term " anvil bird " is also sometimes inadvertently given to certain waders and other swimming birds which drop shellfish from a height to break the shells.

APEX. The tip or far end (distal) of a feather, beak, toe, etc.

APODIDAE (Latin, " the black martin "). Family of swifts of the order *Apodiformes*. It is represented in almost all parts of the globe, and includes a considerable number of species. Two of the genera belonging to it are on the British list, *Apus* (*q.v.*) and *Chaetura* (*q.v.*).

These, the most aerial of all birds, are small, with very long, thin, scimitar-shaped wings. There are ten primary feathers, the first of which is generally the longest, although the second is the longest in the genus *Apus*. The secondaries are very short. The tail, which is forked, has ten rectrices (quill feathers). The skin is very strong, and the plumage hard and smooth. The skull is flattish, and the bill is short, slightly curved and triangular in shape.

A marked feature is the enormous gape, which enables these birds to capture large numbers of insects while in flight. The salivary glands are well developed, and are particularly active during the nesting season, for these birds use the glutinous secretion of the salivary glands to cement together the nesting materials.

The legs are short and often feathered ; the feet have four toes, all of which are directed forwards in the genus *Apus*, and three forwards and one inwards in the genus *Chaetura*. These birds cannot run or hop on the ground because of their small legs and feet, but are adepts at clinging to rough surfaces.

APODIFORMES (Latin, " the black martin "). Order of small or very small birds, which includes the swifts and the humming-birds. It contains three families, of which only one, *Apodidae* (*q.v.*), includes species which occur in the British list. *See also* Swift.

APUS (Latin, " the black martin "). Genus of swifts of the family *Apodidae* of the order *Apodiformes*. It contains many species in Europe, Africa, and much of Asia ; but there are only two species on the British list, the common Swift (*q.v.*), and the much rarer Alpine Swift (*q.v.*).

AQUATIC WARBLER — *Acrocephalus paludicola*. A rare visitor to Britain, this warbler has its breeding home in Holland, Denmark, Germany and many other parts of the Continent. Only an expert ornithologist could distinguish it from the Sedge-Warbler (*q.v.*), its distinctive marks being a light buff streak down the centre of its forehead and darker markings on its back. In summer plumage it has also a lighter appearance when flying. Its length—about 5 in.—is much the same as that of the Sedge-Warbler ; it nests near rivers and marshes ; but once its brood is fledged, it will resort to reed-beds in company with sedge-warblers. Its breeding season is in May and June. Its general habits seem to resemble those of the Sedge-Warbler, and it is thought to be single-brooded.

Unlike the song of reed- and sedge-warblers, its high-pitched calls are continually repeated without variation.

AQUILA (Latin, " eagle "). Genus of the family *Falconidae* of the order *Falconiformes*. This genus includes the true eagles, of which there are only two species on the British list, the resident Golden Eagle (*q.v.*) and the Spotted Eagle (*q.v.*), which occasionally wanders here from the Continent.

These majestic-looking birds of prey possess strong, hooked bills, which have sharp cutting edges ; there is a conspicuous patch of fleshy skin (the " cere ") at the base of the upper mandible where the large nostrils are situated. The wings are large and broad, and somewhat rounded. The fourth and fifth primary feathers are the longest, while the first visible primary is shorter than the second. The tarsus is feathered as far as the toes ; these number four, three of them directed forwards and one behind, all with sharp, curved claws. The females are larger than the males.

ARCHAEOPTERYX (Greek, " ancient wing "). Group name applied to the oldest known fossil birds. Remains of two of these birds were discovered nearly a century ago in Bavaria, preserved in the lithographic stone of Solenhofen, which is a limestone of Jurassic age. The first specimen, discovered in 1862,

British Museum (Natural History)

ARCHAEOPTERYX. *Scientific reconstruction of the first bird from the fossil shown in page 19*

ARCTIC SKUA. *Magnificent in flight, this graceful bird is a pirate, feared by terns and gulls whom it robs of their prey, devouring its ill-gotten gains in mid-air*

was given to the British Museum. The second skeleton, in a much more perfect state of preservation, was discovered 16 years later, and is in the Berlin Museum.

These primitive birds, which lived about 120 million years ago and were about the size of a fowl, possessed several distinctly reptilian characters, and they may be regarded as a very important evolutionary link between reptiles and birds. *See also* Ancestry ; Evolution.

ARCTIC REDPOLL—Carduelis hornemanni. This rare vagrant, of which there are several varieties, is very similar to the mealy and lesser redpolls, but its rump and underparts are unstreaked. For more detailed information *see* Coues's Redpoll ; Hornemann's Redpoll.

ARCTIC RINGED PLOVER—Charadrius hiaticula tundrae. A bird of the Far North, breeding in such places as Spitsbergen, Iceland, Bear Island, north Siberia and north Scandinavia, this is an occasional winter visitor to Britain, several having been identified in Scotland and on the coasts of England. Whether it is also a passage migrant has not been established. Its habits are believed to resemble closely those of the Ringed Plover (*q.v.*).

ARCTIC SKUA—Stercorarius parasiticus. The skuas belong to a small family of brown and white sea birds which, at first sight, appear gull-like. Four species can be seen in the British Isles—either as summer residents in the north of Scotland or as passage migrants round our coasts. The commonest, the Arctic Skua, or Richardson's Skua, which is smaller than the Great Skua (*q.v.*), is both a summer resident and a passage migrant. It breeds freely in the Orkney and Shetland Islands, the

Outer Hebrides and some of the northern counties of Scotland. It is also found in many parts of Europe, America and Asia.

Arctic skuas appear in two distinct plumages —one dark brown and the other much lighter— and as the two types interbreed freely, a third of mixed colouring often emerges. The darker birds are in the majority in Scotland ; they are almost completely dark brown, the underparts being of a slightly lighter shade. The paler bird has a brown-and-white appearance, for, although its mantle is dark brown, its neck, breast and underparts are a dirty white, and it has a dark cap on its head. The almost swift-like tail has two long central feathers which stream out behind. The slightly hooked beak, legs and feet are black. The length of the Arctic Skua is 17-18 in., of which at least 3 in. is due to its long tail-feathers. Its tarsus is 1 in. Its weight is 11 oz., and its wing span approximately $2\frac{1}{2}$ ft.

Although it attacks intruders less fiercely than the Great Skua, the Arctic Skua is also a bird to be reckoned with when it is defending its nest and young during the breeding season ; it will swoop down upon dogs, sheep, and even human beings who venture near. The *Handbook of British Birds* records that " a skua will cling with its feet to the wool on the neck of a sheep, while beating it about the head with its wings, and dogs will be scratched with its claws." An Arctic Skua colony is organized in almost a military way. Two or three watchers are appointed—changing guard from time to time—and these immediately give the alarm signal at the approach of any intruder.

The Arctic Skua carries " injury-feigning " to a fine art, and while one parent is putting on a convincing pretence of broken wings, broken legs or seriously injured body, the other leads the young well away from danger under cover of the heather. The same tactics are carried out to protect the nest and eggs, and many an egg collector has had to come away without having obtained the slightest clue regarding the position of the nest.

Pirate of the Air. The Arctic Skua has an awkward, waddling walk, but it is a good swimmer, and breeding birds are fond of bathing in fresh water. It is magnificent in flight, the buoyant epitome of grace, and there is something hawk-like in its regular wing-beats as it glides along. It is feared by its fellows, for it is a pirate by nature and a great deal of its food is procured by robbing others of their prey. Terns, kittiwakes and gulls are its chief victims, but almost any bird will be attacked, irrespective of size. The pursuit is relentless, the victim turning and twisting in a vain attempt to escape and the pursuer following every movement, until at last the fish is dropped; the skua catches it in the air and usually devours it at once.

The Arctic Skua has a special display flight, of which, however, little has been recorded. On the whole its courtship resembles that of the gulls. Its voice, heard in the breeding season, is a wailing, mewing cry, but when the bird is pursuing a victim or driving off an intruder, it has a harsh and piercing note. Otherwise it is a silent bird.

The Arctic skuas return to their breeding haunts in April and nest in small colonies; September sees the last of them depart for their warmer winter quarters, where they spend most of their time at sea. They breed on barren moorland and shingle, and the nest is only a hollow in the grass or heather. Usually two eggs are laid at the end of May or early June, but sometimes only one; they are smaller than the Great Skua's, and may be olive, green or brown. Both male and female assist in the hatching, which takes about 24 days. The young are reared and fed by both parents, but soon become independent. One brood is reared in a season.

The Arctic Skua's food is very varied; a good deal of it is fish stolen from other birds, but it also kills and eats adult and young birds, and it has been known to kill lambs. It will even feed on dead animals and birds, and some vegetable food is also devoured when available.

Besides Richardson's Skua, the Arctic Skua goes by the names of Boatswain (or Bosun), Shooi and Alan. "Skua" is a Norwegian word, meaning a brown bird. In North America the bird is called Parasitic Jaeger. *See also* Skua; Stercorarius.

ARCTIC TERN—Sterna macrura. One of six attractive and beautiful terns which come as summer residents to the British Isles, the Arctic Tern breeds freely in the extreme north of Scotland, less commonly in the south, and is a common passage migrant both inland and around our coasts. Abroad it lives and breeds in the northern and Arctic countries of both Europe and America.

A typical species of the Tern (*q.v.*) family, it is a medium-sized bird, with a long, forked and swallow-like tail and a long, tapering bill. Its face, breast and underparts are white, and its wings silvery-grey. A black cap completes its dress in the summer plumage. The resemblance to the Common Tern (*q.v.*) is so complete that it is usually mistaken for that bird, unless seen at close quarters. The only distinguishing mark is the black tip of the Common Tern's bill; the Arctic Tern's bill, like its feet and legs, is deep, blood red. This difference is most in evidence in the breeding season; outside that it is difficult even for experts to distinguish between the two birds. The length of the Arctic Tern is 15 in., and its tarsus 0·8 in. Its weight is about 7 oz., and it has a wing span of approximately 2½ ft.

The Arctic Tern's habits and behaviour follow closely those of the family, especially those of the Common Tern, but it is perhaps more of a sea-going bird than the other terns. It is very vicious in defence of its nest and young, and will always attack an intruder, whether man, animal

Eric Hosking

ARCTIC TERN. Only a hollow in the ground marks this nest, fiercely defended against all or bird. Saxby's *Birds of Shetland* gives an account of a flock of Arctic terns relentlessly following a Hooded Crow which had dared to intrude, until the much-pecked bird was forced into the water, where it was drowned.

> My own experience is that any approach, even from a distance of 100 yards by boat or on foot, towards the breeding site provokes a fierce mass attack by these birds. When I was in Iceland filming these birds at their breeding site, I was so viciously pecked that I had to have medical treatment. On that occasion I noticed that the birds did not fall silent after our party had moved 200 yards away.—EDITOR.

Arctic terns have the typical graceful flight of all terns, and it is a pleasure to watch them on the wing. At their terneries the birds can create a tremendous clamour. It is recorded that in the midst of this there comes a sudden silence, followed by an equally sudden rising of the whole flock ; after wheeling and turning for a short time, they return to their nests and resume their din.

> I have studied the behaviour of Arctic terns for many years without ever witnessing this habit. I conclude that this is yet another warning never to generalise about the behaviour of any bird.—EDITOR.

The call of the Arctic Tern cannot be confused with that of the Common Tern. Their cries of defence and attack in the breeding season are very varied and quite individual.

The Arctic terns return to the same site year after year, and nest in colonies. The breeding season is during May and June, and the nest is only a hollow in the sand of dunes or banks, or a depression in the rock or moss of rocky islets ; often it is not even lined, and the eggs lie on the bare ground. The normal number of eggs is two, but three are often laid ; they vary greatly in colour from ground-colour to pale and dark blue and brown, blotched and spotted with dark brown. Hatching takes about three weeks ; both male and female take part, but the female has the major share, especially during the night. The young, which are fed and reared by both parents, leave their nests after three days and are able to fly in about three weeks, but are fed for a short while after this. Terns are single-brooded.

Small fish are the chief item in the diet of Arctic terns ; the birds fly low over the surface of the sea with head lowered in search of their prey. They seem to know instinctively the depth of the water. Where it is deep, they will suddenly dive down to snatch their fish, sometimes completely submerging themselves ; but in shallow water they are much more cautious. An appropriate popular name for the Arctic Tern (and other terns) is Sea-Swallow.

ARCTIC WARBLER—Phylloscopus borealis. The Arctic Warbler, also called Eversmann's Warbler, breeds in Scandinavia, Finland, Siberia and occasionally wanders to the British Isles. It is similar to other leaf warblers, especially the Willow-Warbler (*q.v.*), although it is distinctly larger and has a dark green mantle. These factors also distinguish it from all other warblers. The length of the Arctic Warbler is 4¾ in. Its behaviour and habits are like those of other leaf warblers, flitting in and out of the trees in quest of insects. Its song, which has many variations, is delivered from among the branches and is uttered through

ARCTIC TERN. It is hard to imagine that this peaceful-looking creature was among those who attacked the Editor so viciously that he had to call in a doctor

John Markham

a rapidly moving bill. In North Finland, this song is best heard from mid-June to mid-July.

The Arctic Warbler's nest is dome-shaped and is found among the ground vegetation. Five to seven eggs are laid ; but little authentic information is available about their hatching or about the rearing of the young.

Insects, including many mosquitoes, are the Arctic Warbler's favourite diet.

See also Phylloscopus ; Warbler.

ARDEA (Latin, " heron "). Genus of large herons of the family *Ardeidae* of the order *Ardeiformes*. It contains some eleven species, two of which occur in the British Isles, the common Heron (*q.v.*), and the Purple Heron (*q.v.*)—an irregular visitor.

ARDEIDAE (Latin, " heron "). Family of the order *Ardeiformes*, which includes six genera on the British list : *Ardea, Ardeola, Botaurus, Egretta, Ixobrychus* and *Nycticorax* (*see* under these names). The herons, egrets and bitterns are members of this family.

These birds are characterised by a long, pointed bill (sometimes slightly curved), rounded above, and laterally compressed ; the tip of the upper mandible is often serrated. The lores (spaces between the eyes and the bill) are bare. The body appears much larger than it really is, owing to the great amount of soft, loose feathers covering it. There are long featherless tracts at the sides of the neck. The neck has a " kink " in the middle, which is caused by the unequal length of the vertebrae, the sixth of which is particularly long. The wings are broad and rounded, and have eleven primary feathers, ten of which are functional, the first being rudimentary. The tail is short and rounded, and generally has twelve rectrices (quill-feathers), but occasionally less. The legs are long, and the front of the tarsus has long scutes (horny scales). The toes are long, and the claw of the middle front toe is serrated.

ARDEIFORMES (Latin, " heron "). Order of birds, including the storks, herons, bitterns, ibises and the spoonbills. There are three families of this order on the British list : *Ardeidae, Ciconiidae* and *Plataleidae* (*qq. v.*). The members of this order are marsh and wading birds, mostly large-sized, with long bills and long legs. The neck also is generally long. The wings are broad and rounded, and the tail usually short and rounded. The lower jaw is truncated at the back, except in the *Plataleidae*.

ARDEOLA (Latin, " heron "). Genus of herons of the family *Ardeidae* of the order *Ardeiformes*. It contains five species altogether, and these are mostly restricted to southern Europe, Africa and Asia. Two species occasionally occur in the British Isles, the Squacco

Eric Hosking

ARDEA. *This common Heron (Ardea cinerea) looks uncommonly wise standing guard over its offspring*

Heron (*q.v.*), which is a very irregular summer visitor, and the Cattle Egret (*q.v.*), also known as the Buff-backed Heron, which occurs only rarely as a straggler from Europe.

These birds are smaller in size than the members of the genera *Ardea* and *Egretta* ; otherwise they are not markedly different in structure from the birds in the genus *Ardea*. However, they have more white on their plumage, and their wings are almost entirely white. This applies particularly to the Cattle Egret (also known as Buff-backed Heron).

ARENARIA (Latin, " of the sea-shore "). Genus of wading birds of the family *Charadriidae* of the order *Charadriiformes*. It contains only two species, one of which, the Turnstone (*q.v.*), occurs in the British Isles.

ASHY-HEADED WAGTAIL—Motacilla flava cinereocapilla. Records show only one authentic visit to England of this bird, which breeds in the Camargue in France, in Italy, Sicily and Algeria, and migrates to tropical Africa. It closely resembles all other wagtails in appearance, behaviour and nesting habits, but frequents salt marshes more than its relatives. Its food consists entirely of insects. *See also* Wagtail ; Yellow Wagtail.

ASIATIC GOLDEN PLOVER—Charadrius dominicus fulvus. Except for its breeding ground this bird, which is sometimes called the Pacific Golden Plover, is almost identical with the

American Golden Plover (*q.v.*). It breeds in North Siberia and winters in India, where huge flocks are seen ; in its migration it travels over 2,000 miles without a landmark.

Some 15 of these birds have wandered to Britain, but they are difficult to identify. At close quarters they are seen to be slightly smaller and more colourful than the American golden plovers ; otherwise, in general behaviour and breeding habits the Asiatic Golden Plover follows the pattern of its family. Its song and call notes are also typical of the Golden Plover (*q.v.*) family. It is about 9 in. in length.

ASIO (Latin, " a horned owl "). Genus of the family *Strigidae* of the order *Strigiformes*. It contains about fifteen species in many parts or the world, except Australia, New Zealand and certain Pacific Islands. There are only two British species, the Long-eared Owl (*q.v.*) and the Short-eared Owl (*q.v.*). These are medium-sized owls, characterised respectively by long and prominent, or very short and hardly visible, ear-tufts. The ear-openings are very large.

The wings are comparatively long and, when folded, extend to the end of the tail, or further. In the British species the third and fourth primary feathers are usually the longest, while the first primary is very small and hidden by the coverts. There are eleven primaries altogether, and ten tail-feathers. The short, but well-hooked, beak is set in a flattened facial disc. The legs are feathered to the toes.

ATHENE. Genus of the family *Strigidae* of the order *Strigiformes*. It contains two or three species, with several sub-species, in Europe, North Africa and much of continental Asia. There is only one British species, the Little Owl (*q.v.*).

ATLANTIC MURRE, or Common Murre, or Murre. American names for Guillemot (*q.v.*).

AUDUBON'S SHEARWATER—Procellaria lherminieri. Audubon's Shearwater lives and breeds in the tropical zones of the Indian, Atlantic and Pacific Oceans. Only one has been officially recorded as reaching the British Isles ; it was found alive on the Sussex coast in 1936. The bird closely resembles the Little shearwaters (*q.v.*) in behaviour and appearance, except that it has darker undertail coverts and flesh-coloured legs. It is 1 ft. in length.

Audubon's Shearwater breeds in colonies, and nests in holes and crevices of rocks. Little or no material is used for its nest, and one white egg is laid ; the breeding season varies according to the region frequented, but it is usually at the end of March or beginning of April. There is only one brood. Both birds take part in hatching the egg, but when the chick appears it

is not brooded for a day or two, the parents seeming content to sit beside it during that time ; later, it is left all day and fed at night. The food of this shearwater consists chiefly of fish, cleverly caught in the open sea. Its voice is very different from that of the Manx Shearwater (*q.v.*). The Audubon has a plaintive, sometimes cat-like call.

AUGUR (from Latin *avis*, " bird "). A member of a college of priests in ancient Rome, who predicted the course of future events by observing and interpreting omens. Originally these related solely to the behaviour of birds, hence the name, but later the range was greatly extended, and any unusual happening, from a thunderstorm to a violent sneeze, would cause the superstitious to rush to an augur.

The college, originally of four members and, in late Republican times, 15, had great religious and political power, and no enterprise of any consequence could be undertaken without the approval of its members—whether it was the election of an important officer of state, a declaration of war, the taking of a wife in marriage, or the disposal of a plot of land.

The oldest, and at all times the most important, methods of augury were based on either the cries and calls of birds, or on their flight— the direction and height, the number of birds involved, and their grouping. Observations based on flight were known as Auspices (*q.v.*), from the Latin *avis*, " a bird " ; *spicere*, " to see." Auspices were thus a particular branch of augury, the taking of which was not confined to augurs but could also be practised by the Chief Magistrate of Rome, and by the Commander-in-Chief of an army in the field.

Only a few birds were regarded as the special messengers of the many gods. Generally those consulted were the eagle, vulture, crow, raven, owl and hen, the first two revealing the will of the gods by their flight, and the others by their voices. The taking of auguries from the way in which chickens fed was a later innovation. At a still later period auguries were eclipsed by a technique exercised by the Etruscans, but developed under the Caesars by the *Haruspices* (*see* Haruspex), which provided for the killing of certain birds and the inspection of their entrails for particular indications.

While it can be assumed that in ancient times the augurs believed implicitly in their gifts and teaching, they seem later to have become mere magicians and charlatans, whence the phrase, used even today in some languages, " winking like two augurs".

Although not graced by the name, augury is to be found in the folklore of every people, and in Britain to this day there are superstitions relating to crows, magpies and owls.

James Gibson, W. Farnsworth, British Museum (Natural History), S. Crook

AUK. The Great Auk (centre) has been extinct for over a hundred years ; · but his close relatives, shown here, bear a marked family likeness to him. They are, top : Puffin (left) and Guillemot (right) ; bottom : Razorbill (left) and Little Auk (right)

AUK. Bird belonging to the family *Alcidae*, of the order *Charadriiformes*. In addition to the Great Auk or Garefowl, extinct since 1844, and Little Auk, this family includes the razor-billed auks, or razorbills (*q.v.*) which are the most typical resident members of the family, the guillemots (*q.v.*) and the puffins (*q.v.*). They are highly specialised derivatives of the plover tribe, their origin being indicated by the name of the order to which they belong.

All the members of this family are medium-sized, black and white (sometimes brown and white), rather duck-like, salt-water diving birds with elongated bodies and stubby necks and very short tails. Their feet, which have only three toes, are webbed and relatively large. The legs are placed far back, near the base of the tail, and this both increases the power of their stroke when swimming, and accounts for their upright stance, and their walk with an almost nautical roll. In this and other ways they rather resemble the penguins, although they are not in any way related to them. They have short, narrow wings, and their flight, though strong and rapid, is apt to be a little laboured and seldom of long duration or for long on a straight course. They are very buoyant and float high in the water, submerging quickly but flurriedly, with a kick of their legs and a flick of their partly opened wings. They swim well under water—faster, indeed, than on the surface—driving themselves along with their wings and steering with their feet. Their bills are strong and pointed, sometimes flattened laterally, and are suited for catching fish which, with crustacea and marine worms, form their staple diet. The food is caught under water and eaten by the birds before they emerge.

They are typically open-sea birds, and their breeding places are usually on cliffs and steep shores. There is usually only a single egg (sometimes two or three), which is laid on a rocky ledge (Razorbill, Guillemot) or in a burrow (Puffin).

AURICULARS. The feathers overlying the ear. *See* Anatomy ; Ear.

AUSPICES (or *Auspica*, from Latin *avis*, " bird " ; *spicere*, " to see "). In ancient Rome, observations of the way in which the sacred chickens (*pulli*) were taking food, given to them by the augurs (*q.v.*), and interpreted as omens. It was considered a fortunate omen for an enterprise, e.g. a Senate meeting, an election or a war, if the food was taken greedily, so that the grain was spilled or dropped from the bills ; and an unfavourable omen if the birds hesitated to feed. *See also* Haruspex.

AUTUMN MOULT. The complete moult, which occurs annually, shortly after the end of the breeding seasons, when *all* birds discard all their old feathers and replace them with new. Typically it takes place between August and October, but there are wide variations between species and individuals, and the moult may begin as early as June and may remain incomplete until the end of the year. It may also be abnormally delayed if the bird has not mated.

Some birds moult two, or even three, times a year, but others (usually, but not invariably, those with the most brilliantly coloured plumage) moult only once a year—always in autumn. It is only during the autumn moult that the old quills are discarded. Ducks, rails and grebes shed these almost *en masse* and may be grounded for several weeks. In most families, however, so that the power of flight shall not be lost, the remiges (*q.v.*) and retrices (*q.v.*) are renewed in pairs over a long period, e.g. about six months for pigeons, and nearly a whole year for birds of prey.

The feathers are renewed in a definite order, which varies slightly in different species. In general, the rectrices are moulted from without inwards ; the primaries outwards ; and the secondaries inwards from the wrist. In larger birds it is often possible to see the resultant irregularities in the outline of the wing in flight, indicating that a moult is in progress. The change of the body feathers usually begins on the head, so that in late Summer one may see birds in partial or complete winter dress.

See also Feather ; Wing.

AVES (Latin, " birds "). Scientific name given to birds as one of the two highest classes of backboned animals, the other class comprising the mammals.

The most important of the many characteristics which distinguish birds from other kinds of animals is the transformation of the forelimbs into feathered wings (*q.v.*). This remains the governing characteristic of birds, even in those which have lost the power of flight, such

Alfred Saunders
AUTUMN MOULT. *Bedraggled and pitiful—a moulting Penguin*

as the Penguin and the Ostrich. In the former the wings have become specialised for swimming, while in the Ostrich they are only rudimentary (*see* Ancestry).

Feathers (*q.v.*) form another distinctive feature of the *Aves* which is not to be encountered anywhere outside this particular class of animals. Feathers may be regarded as a kind of specialised scales, for they are curious outgrowths of the skin. They serve not only as wing and tail surfaces for flying, but also as a light and efficient body covering.

The jaws of birds possess no teeth, and are covered by a horny sheath, forming a bill or beak which is used for such purposes as picking up or dividing the food and transferring it to the gullet, preening, nest-building, fighting, and so on. In fact, the bill has to perform many of the functions of a hand.

Birds are bipedal (two-footed), and they possess not more than four toes, three anterior, one posterior ; but the latter is often lacking, and the African Ostrich is unusual in possessing two toes only on each of its feet. The feet and legs of a bird serve for perching, swimming, and climbing, as well as for walking.

Most of the bones of a bird's skeleton are hollow, but a few are filled with marrow. Some of them contain air-prolongations of the air-sacs of the lung. The bones provide another example of adaptation for the purpose of flight, for, generally speaking, they are much lighter than mammalian bones of a similar size.

Members of the class *Aves* are, of course, warm-blooded animals, but their body temperature is maintained at a constant level which is from 2° F. to 14° F. above that of mammals. The blood is richer in red corpuscles than that of mammals, and its circulation is maintained by extremely rapid heart-beats. The breathing of birds is also very rapid, and the lungs are small indistensible bags prolonged into numerous cavities called air-sacs (*q.v.*). These serve to increase the capacity of the lungs and to render the body buoyant.

Birds eat a proportionately larger amount of food than Man, because of their much higher bodily temperature. Their digestive processes are extremely rapid, and nearly all the food is absorbed. *See also* Anatomy ; Flight, etc.

AUK FAMILY, *razorbills bear the closest resemblance to the now extinct head of the family, the Great Auk*

Eric Hosking

To face page 32

For text see pages 31 and over

LOOKING AFTER CAPTIVE BIRDS

DAVID LE ROI, M.A., B.Sc.

Although the Editor disapproves of keeping birds in captivity, it is generally agreed that, as long as birds are kept thus, they should receive the greatest care. This practical article will help both in building an aviary and in looking after its occupants

AVIARY. An aviary is a cage or other enclosure for keeping birds in captivity, and varies from the large public aviary, such as that of a Zoo, to the aviary kept by an individual or by a bird-breeder or bird-fancier. Here we are concerned with the latter kind of aviary, which can be of the indoor or outdoor type. The size of either must be governed by the species and number of birds to be housed. The style depends upon the fancy of the builder, but it must be remembered that the plainer the lines on which an aviary is built the more satisfactory it will prove in service ; ornate housing of birds should be avoided, as a lavishly decorated aviary is difficult to keep clean and provides a breeding ground for parasites.

If space is available, an outdoor aviary is always preferable, for if it is properly built and equipped the birds housed in it are living as close as possible to nature—assuming, of course, that the inhabitants are such as can endure the British climate. Although budgerigars and certain of the hardier breeds of canaries thrive in outdoor aviaries, it would be fatal to keep outdoors in Britain tropical birds or British birds which do not winter in this country, unless they have been acclimatised by generations of breeding, or the aviary has some system of artificial heating.

British wild birds are in general the most successful stock for an outdoor aviary. But it should be borne in mind that the Protection of Birds Act prohibits the trapping or catching of any British wild bird for sale. The only native wild birds which may legally be offered for sale are those which have been bred in captivity and wear a closed leg-ring in proof thereof. The ring is slipped over the leg when the chick is a few days old ; *any bird offered for sale that is wearing a ring that can be slipped off should be rejected, as it is probably an adult bird caught wild and then rung.* Regulations forbidding the taking of wild birds from their natural haunts do not apply to the collecting of wild birds for Zoo and similar public aviaries, but persons making such collections must be licensed by the appropriate government department.

British wild birds that do best in outdoor aviaries are : blackbirds, blackcap warblers, bullfinches, buntings, chaffinches, doves, greenfinches, goldfinches, jays, larks, linnets, magpies, nightingales, redpolls, siskins, starlings, thrushes, tits, wagtails, and warblers. Bullfinches, chaffinches, jays, magpies, and tits are seldom " good mixers ", either with one another or with other species, and are best housed on their own, as they are inclined to fight. When any new variety is introduced into a stocked aviary its behaviour should be carefully watched, and if it seems at all quarrelsome it should be removed before it has an opportunity of bullying the others.

Dietetically, wild birds are divided into seed-eaters and insect-eaters ; correct feeding of either is not difficult, as packet foods can be bought suitable to any wild-bird taste. Seed-eaters are content with much the same diet as canaries. Insect-eaters will pick up a fair amount of food from the bushes in the aviary, and this can be supplemented by meaty bones, suet and coconut ; there are also patent insectile foods—high-grade for the smaller varieties, and a coarser grade for bigger birds, such as the thrushes.

About 20 wild birds selected from those already listed can be comfortably accommodated in an outdoor aviary 12 ft. long, 6 ft. wide and

Cage Birds

AVIARY. *Well protected against wind and weather, these birds are taking the air in their magnificent flight. On the left is their shelter shed*

D

7 ft. high. The best situation is one facing the south and open to the sun, neither heavily screened by trees nor overshadowed by buildings. At the same time, the birds must be adequately protected from the hot sun in Summer, and from northerly and easterly winds in Winter. Wherever possible, the aviary should be built against a wall or fence to give its inmates additional protection.

Building the Aviary. Approximately a quarter of the overall length of the aviary should be built up from matchboarding to provide a shelter shed, the roof of which should be carried 2 or 3 ft. along the top of the aviary to form a covered run. This run should be separated from the shelter shed by a wooden partition, in which there should be an opening about 15 in. square to permit the birds to pass from the run into the shelter shed. The remainder of the length of the aviary is enclosed with ⅜-in. wire mesh to form the flight. At the end of the flight is the door, which must open inwards into a kind of wire "lock" to prevent birds escaping when anyone enters.

Shelter shed and covered run are best made of wood covered with tarred felting to render it waterproof. It is advisable to board up the wired portions of the aviary to a height of 2 ft. All woodwork should be creosoted, not only to preserve the timber, but also as a preventive of bird-lice and mites. On no account should creosote be applied to painted wood. It is advisable to coat the netting with a hard japan paint, which besides preventing rust has the curious property of making the birds more easily seen.

Concrete is the best material for the floor. It is vermin-proof and easily kept clean, and prevents rats and other rodents from burrowing their way in. Failing concrete, hard, beaten-down earth—but not a damp, sticky clay soil—makes a satisfactory floor, provided that it is periodically raked over and renewed. Whatever the floor, it must be covered with peat litter or fine gravel. Alternatively, the floor can consist of growing grass, which always looks attractive in a larger aviary, but in a small one is apt to lose its freshness. If it is impracticable to have an all-grass floor, large boxes of grass can be used, but they should be given regular spells outside the aviary to recuperate. Small growing trees and shrubs or boxes improve the appearance of the flight, and are much appreciated by the birds.

The shelter shed needs a good selection of perches, but care must be taken that no perch is fixed directly above another ; otherwise the bottom ones will be fouled by birds roosting on upper perches. Indeed, it is always preferable to have all perches at a uniform height from the ground ; otherwise the birds are apt to fight for the highest. Nesting places can be small boxes, baskets, and coconut shells. Hay, small twigs, moss and cow hair are among the best nesting materials. Unless there are more nesting places in the aviary than there are pairs there will be a constant squabbling and a succession of wrecked homes. Food and water dishes should be kept off the ground, and they should not be too large, or their contents will be fouled.

Twigs and branches, which look natural and are easily renewed, make the best perches in the flight. Perches placed too near the roof or sides of the flight will encourage cats to become interested in the aviary's occupants. If cats do become a potential menace, a second layer of netting along the roof and some 3 or 4 in. above it, will be found extremely effective.

Indoor Aviaries. These can range in size from a large all-wire cage with a rounded top, to a converted attic. The maximum convenient

Fox

AVIARY. *One of many aviaries at London Zoo. Bird-fanciers, of necessity, are forced to make do with a much less ambitious type of structure*

dimensions of a cage are 4 ft. long, 3 ft. high, and 3 ft. wide. The internal fittings are on the lines of those of an outdoor aviary. The cage must not be crowded with birds, and should stand in a well-lit corner of a living room, or before a window ; but whatever its situation, it must be away from draughts.

When it is possible to convert an attic into an indoor aviary, many more birds can be accommodated, and more ambitious nesting and perching facilities arranged. The attic floor should be covered with heavy linoleum or zinc, carried up the wall a distance of 1 ft., to prevent mice from entering. The door to the attic should have a wire " lock," and there should be large windows or skylights to admit the maximum amount of light and sun. If there is a fireplace in the attic, the flue should be blocked to prevent the escape of birds.

Pine sawdust is best for floor covering, and this must be renewed regularly. Absolute cleanliness is essential if an indoor aviary is not to become an offence instead of a pleasure. To ensure a fresh atmosphere in an attic aviary, windows or skylights should be covered with fine wire mesh, so that they can be opened to admit fresh air. But when windows are open the doors must be kept shut, to prevent the draughts which are so often fatal to birds.

AVICULTURE. The breeding of birds in captivity. Birds breed readily in cages or aviaries, and, provided a few fundamental rules are observed, no troubles should attend the mating, the laying of the eggs, and the rearing of the chicks. The golden rule is not to interfere with the birds' parental activities; after all, it is their business to bring up their families, and they do not need any outside help other than the provision of facilities for making their nests and a plentiful supply of the right kind of food.

Whether the birds are to breed indoors in cages or outdoors in an aviary (*q.v.*), they must be given nesting boxes (*q.v.*). There are many varieties of nesting boxes and pans, and all claiming to give the birds or their breeder some special advantage; but in general the most

Lionel E. Day

AVIARY.   *If a whole room cannot be spared for an indoor aviary, the clever use of a corner for cages and flight (shown) makes a good substitute*

satisfactory is the old-fashioned, square, wooden nest box. The wood must be absolutely smooth and free of crevices, otherwise it will become infested with red mite. Another, and very efficient, type of nesting box is made of tin and has a perforated zinc bottom ; the latter stops the hen sweating her young.

When the hen is sitting on a clutch of eggs it is important that the temperature of the nesting box be kept constant. This is a simple matter when the nesting box is in an indoor cage, but may be difficult when it is in an outdoor aviary. In the latter instance the nesting boxes are placed in the shelter shed (*see* Aviary).

With some species of birds artificial heating may have to be provided for the outdoor aviary during the breeding season. This is most efficiently done with steam piping similar to that used for a greenhouse, but the pipes must be covered with netting to stop the birds roosting on them. In large aviaries, the modern trend is to heat with infra-red lamps. These give a moderate warmth and their mellow light is much appreciated by the hen and her fledglings.

Where steam heating or infra-red lamps are impracticable, an oil stove can be used, but must on no account be kept inside the shelter shed as the fumes may suffocate the birds. The stove is best placed near the outer side of the shelter shed and enclosed in a wooden box so that it warms the side of the shed.

Many amateur breeders make the mistake of building nests in the breeding boxes. This is fatal to success, as the birds will refuse to use them. The most that should be done is to place within the cage or aviary the type of nesting material favoured by the particular kind of bird and leave this for the birds to make their own nests. The birds know much more about nest-building than do their owners.

Another common fault is to examine periodically eggs or fledglings. This only worries the hen and she will probably desert the nest. Never be inquisitive about breeding birds and do not disturb them.

Rules for Breeders. As a general rule, not more than one pair of a particular species should be put up for breeding in an aviary. Some species are amiable enough at ordinary times, but become savage when breeding. In a large aviary of mixed birds, careful watch must be kept at the breeding season, and any bird found interfering with sitting hens or their attendant cocks should be immediately removed.

Bullfinches, and, to a lesser extent, chaffinches, are best kept in separate pairs when breeding, as the cocks are liable to fight each other. Keeping more than one pair of bullfinches even in a large aviary is sure to end in disaster. It is a safe rule not to attempt to breed large species and small species in the same aviary, as large birds will always bully small ones.

On the other hand, many species of birds readily mate with each other. Greenfinches and goldfinches produce hybrids when mated with canaries, redpolls, linnets, siskins and certain foreign birds. Linnets readily cross with canaries and redpolls. Canaries will hybridise with many British and foreign seed-eaters, the best results being obtained from hen canaries.

When buying birds for breeding it is essential to choose those which have themselves been bred in large aviaries, otherwise they will prove to be failures as far as breeding is concerned. Either the cocks will prove sterile, or if they do breed, the fledglings soon die off. In-breeding and breeding in aviaries that are too small have resulted in many inferior birds being offered for sale as breeding stock. These birds are usually cheap and so tempt the beginner, but they only lead to disappointment.

Breeding and sitting birds present no particular feeding problems. Provided plenty of their normal food is available, parents and chicks will thrive. One point to remember, however, is to supply plenty of cuttle-bone, particularly for the hens, as it helps to form the shell of the eggs.

Occasionally a hen deserts her chicks soon after hatching, but this does not necessarily mean the loss of the nestlings. If the youngsters are kept warm, by placing them on flannel over a hot-water bottle, they can be fed artificially.

Eric Hosking

AVOCET. *Father is ready to take a turn in brooding the eggs, but mother is reluctant to leave the nest*

There are several patent foods that can be given to them from a fountain-pen filler, and as the chicks grow stronger they will take ordinary solids provided the food is slightly softened. Shredded meat is an ideal diet for insect-eating fledglings that have been deserted.

AVOCET—Recurvirostra avosetta. The return of the Avocet to its old breeding grounds in the marshlands of East Anglia in 1947 was perhaps the most important event in the recorded history of British ornithology ; and its establishment there was one of the greatest achievements of organized bird-watching, especially by the Royal Society for the Protection of Birds (*see* under that name).

This beautiful wader, a member of the Plover family, had hardly been seen in the British Isles for over a century. Formerly a breeding bird of the whole east coast from the Humber to Kent and south-east Sussex, it disappeared from Norfolk about 1824, from Lincolnshire about 1837, and from Kent about 1843. The reason for its departure is uncertain ; it may have been due partly to the drainage of marsh-land for agriculture, partly to the depredations of egg-collectors, and partly to the shooting of the bird for the pot, but there was probably some other more important factor that remains unknown. The Avocet continued to breed in Holland, but was not recorded, even as a wanderer or passage migrant, in the British Isles until 1938, when two pairs nested in Ireland.

During the Second World War the eastern coastal area of England was put " out of bounds " to casual visitors, and parts of it were flooded as a defence measure. The recurrence of their natural breeding conditions, and the unwonted absence of human visitors, combined to attract the Avocet back to East Anglia. In 1944 it was first suspected that the bird was breeding again in Essex ; in 1946 a pair attempted to breed in Norfolk ; and in 1947 four pairs re-appeared at Minsmere, and four or five on Havergate Island, in Suffolk. These last eight or nine pairs reared 16 young, and it was upon the Suffolk breeding-grounds that protective activity was concentrated. Local ornithologists had devotedly watched and guarded the Minsmere colony in 1947, and the R.S.P.B. organized parties to perform the same service there and at Havergate in 1948. In that year, however, the Minsmere nesting site was abandoned by the birds, and the Havergate site was so seriously raided by rats that only 13 young avocets were reared.

The Society, determined to protect the birds at all costs in following years, purchased Havergate Island, dis-infested it of rats, and repaired the breaches in the sea wall caused by high tides in early 1949. As a result, 17 pairs of avocets nested on the island that year, and 31 young were reared. In 1950 the numbers still further increased, to 21 pairs and 40 chicks ; in 1951 the figures were 24 pairs and 40 chicks ; in 1952, 40 pairs and 100 chicks ; in 1953, 45 pairs and about 65 chicks, inclement weather having killed off many of the young. It seemed certain that the re-establishment of the Avocet as a British breeding species was complete— thanks to the efforts of local bird-lovers and the R.S.P.B. with its nation-wide membership.

Appearance and Nesting Habits. The black and white plumage of the graceful Avocet is unique among British waders. Another distinguishing feature is its long, slightly upturned, black bill, with which it delves into shallow pools for its food, using a curious side-to-side movement of its head. It walks upright on its long grey-blue legs. The length is 17 in., the bill being 3¼ in. ; the tarsus is 3 in. The wing span is approximately 2 ft. ; and the weight 8 oz. It is impossible to distinguish between the sexes.

I have had an opportunity of watching and recording the song of the avocets on their breeding ground among myriads of gulls which, especially after dusk, try to steal their eggs. It was amazing how fiercely most avocets defended their nests, uttering a very loud and long-sustained call, which could be heard above the din of the gulls. Shortly afterwards, the avocets attacked the gulls, calling still louder, but this time with a more musical intonation. This manoeuvre on the part of the avocets caused the gulls to retire, though they could still be heard in the background. Later they became silent for the rest of the night.

On another night, I moved my microphone to another position, as I remembered from my Continental observation that masses of avocets have a very pleasant sound uttered in flight. After 4 o'clock that morning several of the birds flew over the microphone calling, and this song was recorded. When alarmed, the Avocet has a loud, harsh, yelping cry.—EDITOR.

The birds arrive at their breeding sites in April or early May. They usually come in pairs, and their nesting activities, which begin almost at once, are characterised by the most

AVOCET. *Thanks to the efforts of bird-watchers, this beautiful wader now breeds again on the Suffolk marshes. Here he is in his favourite stance waiting for fish*

Eric Hosking

elegant movements. The Avocet has a fairly fast flight, with neck and legs extended and regular wing beats ; before landing there is a graceful gliding movement.

The Avocet is gregarious at all times, including the nesting season. The nests are carelessly placed on the ground and not even lined, but sometimes dead vegetation or refuse from the tides is placed round the eggs ; these number four, and are light buff in colour, with spots and blotches varying from grey to dark brown. The parents share the duties of sitting on the eggs, which lasts about 23 days. The young birds take to the water at once, and it is delightful to see them bobbing about on the surface. They are very independent little creatures ; but the parents brood them for about a week, and any Redshank, Ringed Plover or other bird that dares to intrude is driven off at once with loud and angry cries.

As soon as the young are able to fend for themselves, families tend to flock together and go off to feed on the muddy estuaries. The breeding places are gradually deserted and the birds drift up and down the coasts, making ready for their departure to winter quarters in Africa and Asia (it has been recorded that of late some birds have spent the winter in south-west England).

The Avocet's food mostly consists of water insects of all kinds, and fish spawn.

Much remains to be investigated about the habits of these lovely birds. Avocets are as a rule peaceful creatures, but it is recorded that excited communal displays take place continually ; the birds will suddenly rise, flying towards each other, calling loudly, and to all appearances quarrelling. This activity ends as suddenly as it began, and no explanation of it has yet been forthcoming.

Local names applied to the Avocet are Awl-bird, Cobbler's Awl, Clinker, Barker, and Yelper, the last derived no doubt from its angry call when driving off intruders.

AWLBIRD. Local name for Avocet (*q.v.*).

AXILLARIES (L. *axilla*, " armpit "). Small bunch of distinct shortish feathers in a fanwise arrangement under the wing (*q.v.*), at a position corresponding to the armpit.

AXIS. The central " stem " of a feather. This is often popularly referred to as the quill, but this is not always correct, because in some feathers (e.g. flight and tail feathers) the axis is divided into two main parts : the quill and the shaft. The quill forms the lower half, the cylindrical portion whose base is embedded in the bird's skin, and passes at its upper end into a more solid portion, the shaft, which carries the vane of the feather. In down feathers, on the other hand, the shaft may be absent, and then the quill forms the whole of the axis. *See also* Feather.

AYTHYA. Genus of diving ducks of the family *Anatidae* of the order *Anseriformes*. It contains about twelve species, which are distributed over much of the globe. Four species occur in the British Isles : the common Pochard, the Scaup, the Tufted Duck, and the White-eyed Pochard (also known as Ferruginous Duck). The Pochard and Tufted Duck include resident birds and winter visitors ; the Scaup is a winter visitor and a passage migrant ; while the white-eyed Pochard is a comparatively rare visitor to this country. They are described fully under their own headings.

The bill of members of this genus is about the same length as the head. Towards the tip the bill is at least as wide as it is at the base, but the " nail " at the tip of the upper mandible is less than half the width of the bill. The nostrils are situated near the base of the bill. *See also* Anatidae ; Anseriformes ; Ducks.

Erica

AYTHYA. Four members of this genus are among the ducks here. They are (back) from the left : female Scaup, Pochard, Scaup (drake), and Tufted Duck

BAER'S DUCK—Aythya nyroca baeri. The two examples of Baer's Duck which have been recorded in England—one in 1901 at Tring, Hertfordshire, and the other on the Trent in Nottinghamshire—may have been escapes from the many which are kept as semi-domestic waterfowl on private estates. Since it was not considered certain that these two were wild ducks, the records were not admitted to the British List.

Baer's Duck breeds in East Siberia, and winters in China, Japan, and occasionally India.

BAILLON'S CRAKE—Porzana pusilla. A passage vagrant from time to time during the Spring and Autumn, chiefly to Norfolk and Cambridgeshire, Baillon's Crake has also been known to breed in the British Isles. Like all crakes, it is very shy and secretive and might well breed unknown even to expert ornithologists. Central and south Europe and many parts of Africa are its chief breeding homes. Difficulty may be experienced in distinguishing it from the Little Crake (q.v.), but Baillon's Crake is a smaller bird, and, although it is similar in plumage to the male Little Crake, its flanks are clearly barred in black and white, and white streaks also appear on the back and wings. Both male and female are alike. The length is 7 in., the tarsus 1 in., and the wing span about 8½ in.

Nesting site, behaviour, habits and even voice are all similar to those of the smaller crakes. Insects are its chief food.

BAIRD'S SANDPIPER—Calidris bairdii. A bird of the Far North, breeding in such parts of the world as West Alaska, Baffin Island, and wintering in South America, Baird's Sandpiper has been recorded as visiting the British Isles occasionally in Autumn. It is one of the most difficult birds of the genus *Calidris* to identify—even for an expert. It is about the size of the Dunlin and resembles in some measure the Pectoral Sandpiper, the American Stint and Bonaparte's Sandpiper (qq.v.). The general plumage is dark ; it has a brown streaked mantle, with light buff underparts, and a dark brown tail with dark, pointed, central feathers. Its length is about 7 in. Reports regarding its calls and songs vary, but one characteristic sound of several Baird's sandpipers together is said to resemble that of a swarm of little frogs.

BALD COOT. Popular name for the Coot (q.v.), given to the bird because of its conspicuous white frontal shield which greatly resembles a bald pate.

BALDPATE. American name for the American Wigeon (q.v.).

BALEARIC SHEARWATER — Procellaria puffinus mauretanicus. Since it has been established that this bird lives and breeds only on the Balearic Islands, its name has been changed from Western Mediterranean Shearwater to Balearic Shearwater. Several have visited the west of Great Britain, but at

John Markham

BALD COOT. *The frontal shield of this bird has given rise to the saying " as bald as a coot "*

long intervals. The bird frequents the same type of country as the Manx Shearwater (q.v.), and breeds in colonies on islets, nesting among rocks at the foot of steep cliffs. Although its habits and behaviour are to all intents and purposes the same as those of the Manx Shearwater, its appearance is quite distinct ; a much paler-looking bird, it has a brown instead of a black mantle, and this shades into a much lighter colour on the underparts. It has the typical Shearwater beak, legs and feet, and its voice closely resembles that of the Manx Shearwater. One egg is hatched a season.

BALEARICIDAE. Family of the order *Ralliformes* ; it contains four genera, with over twelve species, distributed over a large part of the globe, excepting South America. The only genus on the British list is *Megalornis* (q.v.).

BARB. One of a series of closely planted thin narrow plates (or *rami*), which branch out diagonally from the axis of a feather (*see* Fig. 1c on page 215) and form the main part of the structure of the vane (web, or vexillum).

In a typical contour feather (tail and flight feathers come in this class) the barbs spring from the shaft (*rhachis*) or upper part of the axis, and in turn carry on each side a smaller series of flattened plates, known as *radii* or barbules (q.v.). A barb with its barbules somewhat resembles a miniature feather.

Except in certain foreign species (e.g. some members of the ostrich tribe), the barbules of

John Markham

BARNACLE-GOOSE. *This winter visitor from cold lands is evidently pleased with us and itself*

the contour feathers interlock to form a continuous web which is resistant to the passage of air—an essential requirement in flight feathers.

Down feathers differ from contour feathers in that the barbs of the former, which are usually of great length and slenderness, often arise from one common base—the top of the quill—instead of being ranged along each side of a long shaft.

In the " filo-plume " (q.v.) the barbs are short and weak, and usually spring from the end of a simple, solid axis. *See further* under Feather ; *also* Barbicel.

BARBICEL. One of the very small, simple (not recurved) processes fringing the lower edges of the barbule of a feather. *See also* Barb ; Barbule ; Feather.

BARBULE. One of a series of narrow flattened plates which spring from the barb (q.v.) of a feather (*see* Fig. 1d in page 215). The structure varies with the type of feather

A typical flight feather has two distinct types of barbule. Those facing towards the tip of the feather (anterior barbules) end in a series of small hooks or *lamuli ;* and those facing towards the rear (posterior barbules) are shaped like scrolls with a deeply curved upper edge. The anterior and posterior barbules of adjoining barbs cross one another diagonally and, when the feather is unruffled, interlock—the hooks on one barbule each catching on to a separate scroll. Similarly, each scroll is caught by hooks from several different barbules. This interlocking causes the web to form almost a solid surface.

If the feather is ruffled the barbules disengage, but when it is smoothed out again they lock together. The action is somewhat like that of a zip fastener.

In down feathers the barbules are mere threads or swellings, and do not interlock. *See also* Feather.

BARKER. Popular name for the Bar-tailed Godwit (q.v.), given to the bird probably because of its shrill alarm note.

BARNACLE-GOOSE—Branta leucopsis. A regular winter visitor to the Hebrides and Solway Firth, and also to some places in Ireland, the Barnacle-Goose is seldom seen in its wild state in England. Of late its visits have declined even in Scotland and Ireland. Abroad, as far as is known, it breeds only in north-east Greenland, Spitsbergen and Russia

It is a large handsome bird, with black, grey and white plumage. The crown, neck and breast are glossy black, the underparts a very pale grey and white, the face and forehead creamy-white, and the bill and legs black.

BARN-OWL, *returning after a successful foray*

To face page 40   *For text see page 41*

Eric Hosking

The total length is 25 in., the body being 18 in. The tarsus is 2·2 in. The weight is 5 lb., and the wing span about 3 ft.

Much observation of the Barnacle-Goose has been carried out on captive birds. In general habits and behaviour it follows the pattern of other geese, although it is perhaps more friendly to Man. Its voice is a mere bark, not unlike that of a terrier. Its powerful flight carries it to great heights, and it can run swiftly. A highly gregarious bird, it will consort with other geese; it breeds in colonies, though these are sometimes quite small. Its food consists of twigs, leaves, catkins, and the seeds of plants and grasses.

Its nest, placed in niches and crevices in rocks and cliffs, may be used year after year. Three to five greyish eggs are laid at the end of May or the beginning of June. The hen brings out the chicks alone, with her mate keeping watch near by; hatching lasts a little over a month. One brood is reared in a season, the young being looked after by both parents for about seven weeks.

BARN-OWL—Tyto alba. Also known as the Screech-Owl, White-breasted Barn-Owl, and White Owl, this is perhaps the best known of all British resident owls. It has the distinction of being the most widely spread land bird in the world, for varieties are found everywhere, except in the Polar regions, New Zealand and some of the Pacific islands. It is never seen in the Shetland Islands, and, indeed, is counted a rare bird throughout the north of Scotland.

It likes to be near human habitation, and many a village barn, church tower, or derelict building houses a pair of barn-owls; they are even found nesting in the suburbs of large

BARN-OWL. *Mother Owl has picked up a tasty bit of food (top), while her young huddle together (below) and wonder who will be the lucky one to get the first bite*

John Markham

Ludwig Koch

BARRED WARBLER. *It took the Editor a long time to succeed in photographing this shy songster*

towns. Like other birds of prey, the Barn-Owl suffered some persecution in the past, but it is now recognized as one of Man's most valuable allies in the war against mice, rats and other destructive rodents. A solitary and nocturnal bird, it roosts during the day in ruins, church towers, holes in trees, and suchlike, and only in the Winter, when hard pressed for food, is it seen hunting by day.

Its appearance by day is quite beautiful. The golden-brown satin coat is flecked with grey, and contrasts with the white breast and underparts. These last give the bird its weird and ghostly shape by night, and explain one of its local names—the White Owl. (This name should not lead to confusion with the Snowy Owl, which is quite a different bird.) The typical owl-face of the Barn-Owl is covered with white feathers, and encircled with an orange-coloured ring. Its powerful feet have strong talons with which it grasps its prey. The length is 14 in., and the tarsus 2 in. ; the wing span is about 2 ft., and the weight 11½ oz.

As it goes out by night on its hunting forays, its flight is noiseless and buoyant. Its white breast makes it most conspicuous, and some watchers have declared that it has a luminous appearance in the dark.

The Barn-Owl does not "hoot", but utters an eerie, blood-curdling and prolonged shriek, as it flits past in the night: a truly startling sound to hear on an evening stroll. It also has a curious "hiss", and a distinct " snore " which often gives away its presence to other birds when it is sleeping during the day. The courtship display includes the bringing of food to the nesting place even before the eggs are laid,

and this may result in an unsavoury accumulation of decaying carcases.

Like other owls, the Barn-Owl cannot digest the fur and bones of the animals on which it feeds, and it ejects them in the form of "pellets", sometimes 1 or 2 in. long. As it builds no nest, these are used as a foundation on which to lay its four to six white eggs. The usual breeding season is from April to early May, but occasionally eggs have been laid in late February or March. The duration of hatching is very variable, but is usually about a month ; the hen accomplishes it alone, but her mate brings her food. For three months or more, both parents look after the quaint little young birds which are clad in thick white down. In many cases, two broods are reared in a season.

The Barn-Owl lives almost entirely on small animals, including, it must be admitted, small birds which also find their way into its crop.

BARRED WARBLER—Sylvia nisoria. A regular passage migrant in small numbers to Britain, chiefly seen in the Autumn in the northern islands, the Barred Warbler breeds in many parts of Europe—in Denmark, Germany, Sweden, Poland and Central Russia—and winters in south Arabia and north-east Africa.

Its appearance is that of a large, bulky-looking and long-tailed warbler. The mantle of the adult male is brownish-grey, with rather browner wings ; and its underparts are dark grey and very distinctly barred—whence its name. The female has much the same colouring, but is, if anything, browner and less distinctly barred. The length is 6 in. and the tarsus 1 in. ; the wing span is approximately 8 in.

The Barred Warbler is shy and skulking, moving restlessly among the bushes and thickets where it breeds, and is seldom seen in the open. Its flight is variable and rapid. In common with the rest of the *Sylvia* genus, the Barred Warbler has a continuous harsh and jarring alarm note. Its song is variable and includes many individual calls, loud and soft, but in the main it is typically warbler-like.

The nest, placed in a hedge, is built of bents and grasses and lined with hair. Five is the normal number of eggs laid in late May or early June ; both birds take a share in hatching and rearing the one brood. Insects form the chief item in its diet. *See also* Warbler.

BARREL. Another name for the quill, or *calamus* of a feather (*q.v.*).

BAR-TAILED GODWIT—Limosa lapponica. Two godwits, the Bar-tailed and Black-tailed (the latter at one time a breeding species), come to the British Isles as passage migrants and winter visitors ; they arrive on the east coast from August until November and leave again in the Spring. These are wading birds and belong to the family *Scolopacidae*, which contains the Snipe, Woodcock, curlews, whimbrels, godwits, sandpipers and similar birds.

The Bar-tailed Godwit can be seen in hundreds on the coast, but rarely wanders inland. It breeds in Norway, Sweden, Iceland, Finland, Russia and other northerly regions. Between a Redshank and a Curlew in size, it can be recognized at once in Summer, for it is then adorned with beautiful plumage in various shades of chestnut-red. In winter, when it is likely to be seen in Britain, it is much duller, for it loses its reddish hue and is a paler fawn on breast and underparts. The hen is a duller bird.

The long, almost straight bill is used for finding food in the tidal mud and sand-banks on the shore. The long legs are greenish-black at all times. The bird's length is about 15 in., including the bill, which is usually about $3\frac{2}{3}$ to $3\frac{3}{4}$ in. long ; the tarsus is 2 in. ; the weight about 12 oz. ; and the wing span about 18 in.

The Bar-tailed Godwit both walks and runs on the ground, and wades in the water. Its flight is fast and direct. In common with the rest of its family, it is a very gregarious bird, and is always seen in company with such other waders as knots, oystercatchers, redshanks and others, sometimes indulging in astonishing aerobatics. When the tide is up these birds congregate in huge numbers along the edge of the water. The calls of the Bar-tailed Godwit have all the typical flute-like timbre of the waders. The song is a composition of the various notes of the Black-tailed Godwit.

The Bar-tailed Godwit breeds in the ooze and mosses of marshy plains, estuaries and swamps, the nest being only a hollow in the ground, lined with dry leaves and grasses. Four glossy greenish eggs are the normal number, laid in late May or early June, and both birds assist in the hatching, which, as far as is known, takes some three weeks. One brood is reared in a season.

Bar-tailed godwits live on insects of all kinds and water larvae. They are interesting birds to watch, especially when feeding, and they have a curious way of moving their heads up and down in order to get the food down their long bills. *See also* Black-tailed Godwit.

BARTRAMIA. Genus of wading birds of the family *Scolopacidae* of the order *Charadriiformes*. It contains one species only, Bartram's Sandpiper (*q.v.*), which very occasionally strays to the British Isles on migration.

BARTRAM'S SANDPIPER—Bartramia longicauda. While Bartram's Sandpiper has the appearance of a sandpiper, its behaviour resembles that of the plovers—indeed, in the American Ornithological Union's check list it goes by the name of Upland Plover. It sometimes wanders to the British Isles from its breeding places in the far north of North America, and 13 altogether have from time to time been seen in different parts of the country. It is about the size of a Reeve (the female of a Ruff), and the general colour of its plumage is brown, with the typical mottled brown mantle and white underparts of sandpipers. The tail is long and wedge-shaped, the bill slightly decurved, and the legs long and yellowish. Its length is 10 to 11 in.

The bird carries itself in the same way as the Plover, and has the typical Plover run, advancing

BAR-TAILED GODWIT. It is rare to see a Godwit on his own but, maybe, this one was too busy admiring his own reflection to note the departure of all his friends

Eric Hosking

W. Farnsworth

BASS ROCK. Thousands of gannets have made their home on this rock, impregnable from all sides except for the south, where boats can land—if the sea is dead calm

for a short distance, stopping apparently to peck food and then running on again. It has a rich vocabulary of song notes, amongst them a bubbling call reminiscent of the Curlew.

Bartram's Sandpiper seldom associates with other species. In its breeding season, which is usually in April and May, it frequents the open meadows and prairies of the far north. Its nest is a mere hollow among the brushwood, lined with some dry grass. Four is the normal number of eggs. Both parents take their share in the three weeks' sitting, and both tend the young for about a month. Presumably only one brood is reared in a season, for these birds migrate in small flocks as early as mid-July. Insects are their chief food.

BASS ROCK. A remarkable island rock near the mouth of the Firth of Forth, about 3¼ miles out from North Berwick, which serves as a bird sanctuary. It is about a mile in circumference, almost round, and 350 ft. high.

It is inaccessible on all sides, except the south, where it shelves down to the water. Here landing is difficult, and almost impossible when there is any swell. Elsewhere the cliffs rise sheer out of the sea. The island is specially famous for its great numbers of gannets, of which over 4,000 breeding pairs were noted at the last count in 1939. Fulmar petrels and other sea-birds also inhabit Bass Rock, so much so that the cliffs look white from a distance.

BASTARD WING. See Alula; Flight; Wing.

BEAK. See Bill.

BEAN-GOOSE—Anser arvensis. This is a winter visitor to the British Isles, arriving usually in September and October, and leaving again in the Spring for its breeding places in

Scandinavia, Finland and Russia. The Bean-Goose is chiefly observed in Northumberland, Norfolk and Suffolk. But it also appears as a visiting migrant on several Scottish rivers, lochs and estuaries, and the Editor has seen thousands in the Solway district.

The Bean-Goose is the brownest of the grey geese ; its appearance is so dark that it looks almost black in some lights. The bill is black at tip and base, with a deep orange band at each side, and the legs are orange. The total length is about 30 in., the body being about 19 in. ; the tarsus is about 3 in. With a weight of 6½ lb., this goose has a wing span of approximately 3½ ft.

In general habits the Bean-Goose does not differ materially from other wild grey geese, but it has perhaps most in common with the Grey Lag-Goose (*q.v.*,) with which it is often confused. Its voice is also likened to the Grey Lag ; although recorded as the least vocal of British grey geese, it produces a very deep nasal, but almost musical, sound. It belongs to the same species as the Pink-footed Goose (*q.v.*).

The nest, which is only a scrape on the ground, always near water and sometimes sheltered by growth, is composed of grasses, dead leaves and mosses, and is made by the hen. The four or five eggs are white and are laid in June in Scandinavia and in July farther north. Hatching, which takes about a month, is done by the hen alone, but the cock is never far away from the nest. One brood only is reared in a season.

The Bean-Goose feeds on grasses and water plants, but on migration will eat clover, grass, and even grain. As far as is known it has no preference for beans—as its name might imply.

BEARDED TIT, *the male sports a black moustache*

For text see page 45

BEARDED TIT—Panurus biarmicus. Also called Reedling and Reed-Pheasant. The severe winter weather in early 1947 was disastrous for the small-bird population of Great Britain. Among the greatest sufferers were the Bearded and Long-tailed tits, both of which were almost put out of existence. Thanks to strict and watchful protection, however, both have recovered their former numbers. The Bearded Tit was already on the decline ; whereas at one time it bred in the reed beds of many English counties, it is now restricted to Norfolk and Suffolk, and is only a rare vagrant to its former haunts in the south.

Erica

BEAN-GOOSE. *As far as is known, the name of this goose has nothing to do with the vegetable*

Eric Hosking

BEARDED TIT. *Rarely settling on the ground, this dainty Tit flits in and out among the reeds*

being 3 in. long ; the tarsus is $\frac{3}{4}$ in. The weight is about $\frac{1}{8}$ oz., and the wing span about 5 in.

The Bearded Tit is one of the few small birds which does not appear to have any real song ; its voice is only a repetition of its metallic call notes. But when going about in small flocks— as they do in the reed-beds and waterways outside the breeding season—these birds announce their presence by a kind of continuous twitter.

The Bearded Tit rarely settles on the ground. But its flight is far from strong, and it merely

An attempt to introduce it into Yorkshire was a failure. This attractive little tit is the only reed bird that has a long tail. It is not likely to be confused with the Long-Tailed Tit (*q.v.*), which is a bird of the woodland and is not seen in reed beds. The Bearded Tit is distinguished by its unique moustaches, which issue from a black stripe of glossy feathers between its eye and cheek. Its colouring mingles with those of the surrounding reeds ; its mantle is predominantly tawny-brown and its head bluish-grey ; its breast and underparts are a much paler brown, and the long tail is edged with white. The hen is less colourful and has no moustaches. The length of the Bearded Tit is 6½ in., the tail

John Markham

BEARDED TIT. *Small wonder Father Tit looks worried, for he takes his duties very seriously*

flies over the tops of the reeds, flitting from stem to stem. These tits are confiding little birds and roost side by side, the cock often sheltering the hen with his wing.

The nest, which is built among the sedges and reeds, is made on a layer of decaying stems, raised some inches above the water ; it is composed of dead sedge and reed leaves, and is cosily lined with reed flowers and some feathers. The five to seven eggs are white, with streaks of liver-brown. The hatching takes about 12 to 13 days ; both cock and hen take turns at it. The young are fed by bill for about the same period. At least two broods—sometimes three—are reared in a season ; young birds have been seen in a Bearded Tit's nest even in September.

A good deal of its food, especially in Winter, consists of reed seeds, but insects are also taken, the young being fed entirely on these.

BECCAFICO (Italian, " fig-pecker "). Name applied to a number of small birds, sometimes called " Pettychaps ", prized as table delicacies in Italy. The name was first given to *Sylvia hortensis* (Orphean Warbler) and later extended to other members of the same family and to the Bluethroat.

BEE-EATER—Merops apiaster. A member of a family of brightly coloured birds which breed in south Europe and north Africa. A wanderer by nature, this bird visits Britain occasionally in Spring and Autumn. With its brilliant tropical colourings of orange, yellow, green, blue and chestnut, and its long, slightly curved beak, it is indeed a startling sight in this country. The brilliant blue Kingfisher flashing along the riverbank is the only British bird that can bear comparison.

The Bee-Eater normally breeds in southern Europe (e.g. Spain, Italy, Yugoslavia, Greece), western Asia and Africa, but it has also been known to breed occasionally in Denmark, and southern Germany.

It has a friendly disposition, and is neither shy nor secretive. It might even remain in Britain to breed if it were allowed to do so, and it is recorded that one pair actually attempted to raise a family in Scotland.

Like sand-martins, bee-eaters nest in colonies in holes in sand-pits, river banks, etc., and the eggs are the typical white of birds nesting in holes. The length of the Bee-Eater is about 11 in. and its tarsus 0.4 in. Its wing span is approximately 1½ ft. Its very graceful flight is not unlike that of the Swallow. It has an unmistakable throaty call, and its musical song is uttered several times in short phrases.

It lives chiefly on insects and, as its name implies, has a great liking for bees. In countries where bee-eaters abound they can do much damage to apiaries.

The Blue-cheeked Bee-Eater (*q.v.*), a tropical bird, has paid at least one visit to this country— in 1951, when it was observed for the first time in Cornwall by the Editor.

BEE-EATER. Startlingly beautiful in their bright plumage, bee-eaters are but rare visitors to this country. and only one pair has ever attempted to breed here

G. K. Yeates

INSTINCT OR INTELLIGENCE?

L. HARRISON MATTHEWS, Sc.D., F.L.S.

One of our leading authorities on the subject here discusses the ways in which birds react to various circumstances, and whether their behaviour is the result of instinct or intelligence—a question to which there is, as yet, no really satisfactory answer

BEHAVIOUR. The study of behaviour (ethology) aims to give an objective account of the observed actions of birds, and to discover their causes and their biological significance.

Birds are often said to be governed in all their actions by instinct rather than by intelligence, which is held to be an attribute more characteristic of mammals. Some students of bird behaviour have even suggested that birds are the slaves of set patterns of behaviour from which they cannot deviate—that if a stereotyped train of actions is interrupted they cannot continue them after the interruption, but have to go back to the beginning again. Like all generalisations this statement contains much truth, and much error.

There is no precise definition of instinct : it has been designated as "action without fore-knowledge of the end in view," and as an inherited pattern of behaviour performed by an animal which does not know why or for what end it performs it. Instinctive behaviour differs from reflex actions in that the whole of the animal is involved, and in that it is made up of many co-ordinated actions. Instinctive actions are called forth by environment, but they are not wholly dependent upon it, for they may be profoundly altered by the internal condition of the animal.

The behaviour of birds has been the subject of considerable research of late years, and among the work done in Europe that of Howard, Lack, Lorenz and Tinbergen is prominent. These workers have established that instinctive actions are performed in response to specific signals, sign stimuli or "releasers", that act as triggers to set off the appropriate innate reactions. Lack, for example, has shown that the aggressive behaviour of the Robin is elicited by the presence of a strange bird trespassing on its territory. He experimented by setting up a stuffed robin as a trespasser on the territory of an established bird, and found that the rightful owner approached, threatened, and

James Gibson

BEHAVIOUR. *Something must have annoyed the Cormorant, for here he is in a fighting mood*

finally attacked it. In one trial the owner attacked so violently that the head of the stuffed victim was knocked off, but the owner continued the attacks after this, although robins are not in the habit of meeting headless trespassers on their home ground in nature. Further parts of the dummy were removed until it was found that a bunch of red feathers from a Robin's breast, perched on a twig with a piece of wire for feet, was quite as effective as a complete bird in calling forth aggressive behaviour. When Lack set up an undamaged stuffed Robin with the breast painted brown, the territory-owner made no response.

Elliot Howard was the first to show that territory plays a great part in bird behaviour, particularly in the breeding season—though in some species it is of equal importance all the year round. In the breeding season almost every bird is necessarily confined to the neighbourhood of its nest ; each pair occupies a territory, " private property " from which all intruders of the same species are excluded. Even in the social species that congregate in thousands in limited areas and build their nests in close proximity, each pair has its own jealously guarded territory, however small.

It has been suggested that among the small song-birds the territory is primarily a feeding ground, on which a pair has the exclusive right to forage while rearing the young ; but this view is not shared by all experts. In birds that nest on the ground in colonies, such as the terns and some gulls, one effect of holding individual territories is to spread the nests over a large area, and thus to minimise the risk of molestation by predators such as foxes. On the other hand, nesting in close proximity, as in some kinds of penguins, gives mutual protection from such egg stealers as skua gulls. In the King and Emperor penguins the territory is reduced to a minimum, for an incubating bird carries its egg about on its feet ; even so, although the birds sit packed close in their rookeries, each preserves a narrow zone of territory around it, and keeps trespassers away by rapid pecks and blows with the flippers.

Singing—and Imitating. Birds are among the noisiest of animals, and their comparatively loud voices enter largely into their characteristic behaviour patterns. The far-carrying alarm calls of some species not only put other individuals of the same species on the alert, but warn every bird within hearing of the approach of danger.

Similarly the quieter calls of the mother to her chicks elicit characteristic responses from them. In some species the song that is so highly elaborated in many small perching birds is innate or inherited, for it is still produced by birds that have been hand-reared from the egg in isolation from others of their own kind. In other species the song must be learned by listening to that of the adult, for birds of these species, if hand-reared in isolation, learn the song of any species in whose company they are kept. It is, naturally enough, those birds that do not inherit their songs which are successful mimics and can be taught to utter sounds similar to human speech. In yet other species some basic notes or a basic pattern are inherited, but the full song is not developed unless the opportunity for listening to the adult is presented.

Birds do not sing because they are happy, in the human sense of the word: the song serves two main functions, both part of the breeding cycle. In the first place song is important in maintaining a bird's territory; it advertises that a territory is occupied and warns trespassers away. Secondly, during the early part of the breeding season, in some species, the song of the cock gives notice to the hens that he has established himself in a territory and is ready for a mate.

Song is largely confined to the breeding season, and is elicited by both external and internal conditions. The seasonal increase in activity of the sex glands causes an increase in the amount of certain hormones in the blood, and these substances produce the singing behaviour as one of their effects; the artificial administration of such hormones during the " off season " can bring a bird back into full song. Similarly, the recrudescence that occurs in the glands of some species in the Autumn leads to a partial return to breeding behaviour and the resumption of singing.

Display—or Showing Off. Much study has been devoted to the display behaviour of birds—the showing-off of conspicuous parts of the plumage, and the sequence of actions that may amount almost to a set ritual. The

aggressive display of the Robin, for example, not only informs a rival that he is confronted with another bird of the same species, but warns him to leave an already occupied territory. Such warnings are usually promptly taken by the intruder, who at once departs; this behaviour pattern is therefore an advantage to the species as a whole, in that it prevents fighting and injury. But recognition behaviour is not necessarily bound up with aggressive displays; in many species the sexes are alike in appearance, and it is only by their behaviour that they are able to recognize each other. The male Penguin, for example, recognizes the female by her reactions when he places a small stone as an offering at her feet.

The most spectacular displays, however, are those performed during the breeding season. Song is one form of sexual display, but posturings and rituals are of equal importance. Whatever its form, one of the most important effects of display is to create in a pair of birds an emotional bond that keeps them together throughout the breeding season. In some species the display chiefly consists of the cock feeding the hen, but in others it is much more elaborate. Everyone is familiar with the display of the Peacock, whose elongated tail coverts are erected into a magnificent fan of brightly coloured plumes; and pheasants make similar displays of the brightly coloured parts of their plumage. In the birds of paradise the display is even more spectacular; the various tufts, crests and developments of the tail and wings are shown off to the greatest advantage, to the accompaniment of ritualised steps and dances. In at least one species the display culminates with the male erecting his plumes and hanging head downwards from his perch. In many other species the " courtship " display is an elaborate ritual of stereotyped actions, from the Penguin's formal bowing to the Albatross's dance (*q.v.*) which finishes with an exhibition of the huge wing span.

It is generally agreed that the most important effect of the display of birds is a stimulation of the reproductive system through the reaction of the pituitary gland. The hormones produced by the pituitary have a profound effect upon the sex glands, and through them on sexual behaviour. The hens of many species fail to lay if the ritual display has not taken place, and isolated hens of some species (for instance, pigeons) can be induced to lay if they are provided with a mirror, so that they can produce the necessary stimulation by display to, and by, their own images.

In a special type of display occurring among such birds as the Ruff and the Blackcock, the cocks assemble in certain areas and go through

Eric Hosking

BEHAVIOUR. From left to right, starting at the top: Nightingale in a peaceful and aggressive mood; Oystercatchers performing their strange piping ceremony; Trouble in the Rookery, for the hen in the top nest tried to flirt with the cock from below, only to be attacked—unsuccessfully—by the rightful spouse; Ringed Plover displaying to itself in a mirror. Hawfinch and Mistle-Thrush fighting over their territory; Gannets nesting together peacefully, as long as no bird attempts to trespass

a complicated tournament of posturing and mock fights, before they pair off with the hens. One of the most elaborate forms of display is shown by the bower birds, which construct, as a " stage " on which to perform, an arbour of twigs decorated with brightly coloured objects—pebbles, berries, leaves, feathers and so on ; in one species it is even painted with plant juices. In all species in which it has been investigated, display has been shown to depend upon the activity of hormones.

In some birds, courtship displays stop as soon as the eggs are laid, but in others the displays continue throughout the period during which the young are reared. This behaviour usually takes the form of courtship feeding, and has been interpreted as strengthening an emotional bond between the pair, which is biologically important where the foraging of two birds is necessary to the rearing of a brood. *See also* Courtship ; Display.

Central Press

BEHAVIOUR. *Albatross displaying wing span*

Nestbuilding and Nestlings. Nestbuilding appears to be an inherited pattern of behaviour in all species of birds, not an action learned by observation of other individuals or from impressions gained as a nestling. Behaviour at the nest is also governed by a set pattern, for if a nest is moved a short distance from its proper position, the parents return to the original place with their loads of food for the young and make no attempt to feed their starving brood a few feet away. Tinbergen has shown that instinctive brooding behaviour is not always biologically the most advantageous to the species ; for he found that if an Oyster-catcher is offered the choice between a normal egg and one many sizes too large, or between a normal clutch of eggs and one containing far too many, the bird chooses the abnormal in preference to the normal.

It has long been known that among gregarious birds an order of precedence, or "peck order", is established whereby each member of the flock dominates the individuals below it in rank and is dominated by those above. This phenomenon has been studied particularly in the domestic hen, but it is known to occur in other gregarious birds. A peculiar form is the triangle relationship in which A dominates B, which dominates C, although C dominates A.

A special form of aggressive behaviour is shown by the small birds which are impelled to chase or mob predatory species such as hawks and owls. This behaviour is elicited by the visual image of the silhouette of a flying Hawk ; if the silhouette is made to move backwards, when it resembles that of a Duck, no response is produced.

Such behaviour is an innate or inherited response. So, too, is the gaping reaction in nestling birds. Tinbergen found that in nestling blackbirds and thrushes, before the eyes are open, any jarring of the nest causes the gaping reaction (opening the beak wide to receive food), and that after the eyes are open the same reaction is caused by any moving object near the nest provided it appears above the horizontal. When the nestlings are slightly older the gaping is directed towards any lump projecting from the object, because normally it is directed towards the parent's head. Objects or circumstances that produce such innate responses are known as specific releasers, the response awaiting only the releaser to " trigger it off ".

Follow-my-Leader ? We have seen that birds communicate by voice and behaviour, but the question how birds that perform " aerobatics " in flocks communicate is not yet settled. Birds in migrating flocks keep in touch at night or in fog by voice, as anyone can verify during an autumn evening ; but the voice does not control those wonderful evolutions shown particularly by the great flocks of wading birds. Many hundreds of birds turn and wheel about as if each individual were simultaneously given some signal—as if, indeed, a single mind were in control. It is probable that the action which seems simultaneous to the human observer is really consecutive, and that each bird is actually following the one in front. The reactions of birds are extremely quick—a Sparrow perching on a twig from full flight might be likened to a jet aeroplane landing on a house-roof within seconds of flying at several hundred miles an hour. Thus, a turn which appears simultaneous to the observer of a flock may be no more than " follow-my-neighbour " to the birds within it.

If a bird is presented with a situation in which two antagonistic releasers act at the same time, or in which the train of external releasers is not complete, the innate response may be replaced by behaviour known as a displacement activity. This is usually expressed by preening the feathers, but may also be shown by the unnecessary gathering of nest material or food, or by the actions of doing so although the material or food may not be present.

Although it is for the most part entirely innate, bird behaviour is very largely dependent upon the internal physiological state, for this fundamentally determines whether or not releasers call forth responses. Moreover, behaviour can be to some extent modified by learning, which is itself part of the behaviour pattern. Further, like any other specific character, behaviour has undergone and is still undergoing the process of evolution. What is certain is that all innate behaviour gives a biological advantage of one sort or another—whether it be the avoidance of fighting and competition between individuals of the same species, the strengthening of the bond between a pair engaged in rearing a brood, or the maintenance of a species by preventing hybridisation with " strangers " whose behaviour does not release the appropriate response.

BEINN EIGHE. First National Nature Reserve to be established in Great Britain by the Nature Conservancy (*q.v.*). It is situated at the south-east corner of Loch Maree in Western Ross, Ross and Cromarty, and comprises 10,450 acres. It is about 50 to 60 miles from Inverness, and was formerly part of the great Kinlochewe Deer Forest. The mountain from which it derives its name is not at present part of the property, but lies outside the western boundary. Most of the Reserve is rugged mountain country, moorland unsuitable for agriculture or sheep grazing and, in parts, devoid of trees. But covering about a square mile of it are the remains of the old Caledonian Forest, running along the slopes above Loch Maree.

The Golden Eagle may be seen over the Reserve on most days. The bird sometimes nests on the property and sometimes outside it. This alternation is usual, for only very large properties hold their eagles as nesters all the time—about 10,000 acres of territory are normal for one pair of eagles. Buzzards are numerous over the loch side, and merlins are to be found on the moor in Summer. Ptarmigan are fairly common on the high barren mountain slopes. There are a few Red Grouse, and the Black Grouse, though on the decline, may still be seen in small numbers. With the exception of the Goosander, which is increasing in the Highlands, there are very few water-fowl in the Reserve. Greenshanks breed regularly on the wet moors, and the Black-throated Diver is also an occasional, welcome breeding visitor.

BEWICK'S SWAN—Cygnus bewickii. The three swans of the British Isles—Bewick's, the Whooper and the Mute—all belong to the order *Anseriformes*, which comprises swans, geese and ducks. Bewick's Swan is the smallest of the three, and the yellow patch on its bill covers a smaller area than in the other swans, and finishes short of the nostril. Otherwise, it resembles the other two, but is said to be less aggressive than the Mute Swan (the species most commonly seen on our lakes and rivers).

Bewick's Swan breeds in Russia and Siberia, and is only a winter visitor to the British Isles. The number arriving in Britain seems to depend on the weather, for during severe Winters, such as those of 1938 and early 1947, more than usual came to England and Wales. It is, however, a more common visitor to the north of Scotland, especially the Shetland Isles, and during severe Winters many have been known to visit Ireland. It is a very gregarious bird.

Bewick's Swan is about 50 in. in length, and its tarsus 3 in. Its wing span is about 4½ ft., and its weight about 9 lb.

Its general habits, nesting, movements and food closely resemble those of the Whooper Swan. Its voice in migration is a loud, barking "honk", uttered while swimming as well as in flight. The male, especially by night, has a most extraordinary song which seems to slide along a whole scale of notes from top to bottom.

The large nest is built in the shape of a cone hollowed out to house the eggs. These are fewer than those of the Whooper, which hatches from five to ten, but have the same greenish-white colour. Hatching and rearing the chicks follows the same pattern as found in other swans. *See also* Mute Swan ; Whooper Swan.

H.M.S.O. Geological Survey

BEINN EIGHE. Just beyond the western boundary of the first Nature Reserve to be established lies the mountain from which it takes its name

USEFUL SUBSTITUTE FOR A HAND

ELIOTT L. BURNE, B.A.

The bill is one of several specialised features that distinguish birds from other animals. It has many important uses, and serves largely as a hand for picking up food, preening, nestbuilding, fighting and so on. See also Food and Feeding Habits ; Tongue

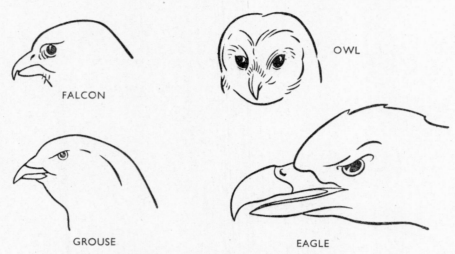

FALCON

OWL

GROUSE

EAGLE

BILL. Selection showing birds in whom the upper mandible is longer than the lower one

BILL. The words " bill " and " beak " are generally regarded as synonymous by ornithologists, although some take " beak " to include the jaws as well as the bill. In common parlance, " beak " is often used of such birds as hawks and parrots, in which the upper mandible curves down over the lower, while " bill " is restricted to the broad flat ones of ducks and the long curved ones of wading birds.

One of the most distinctive features of bird anatomy, the bill is an elongation of the frontal bones of the skull and the under jaw, covered with a horny sheath. The sheath is to some extent moulded to the shape of the supporting bones, and in structure resembles the other horny parts of the bird's anatomy, such as the claws. The upper and lower parts of the bill are generally equal, but in birds of prey the upper portion is longer than the lower.

The horny sheath may consist of several distinct pieces, or it may be undivided. In the Albatross and the Puffin, for example, it is made up of several distinct horny plates, but in the majority of birds these are fused to form one undivided sheath. The Puffin sheds the colourful outermost layers of its bill in the Autumn, as well as the horny excrescences above the eyes and at the gape of the mouth. All these are not replaced until the breeding-season.

The Puffin also has its nostrils placed well forward on the beak, whereas in the majority of birds they are situated near the base. Generally, birds' nostrils are simple apertures, but they are sometimes prolonged into a tube, as is the case with the Nightjar and petrels. Sometimes the external nostrils are only rudimentary, as in the Cormorant, or absent altogether, as in the Gannet.

The sense of taste, which is only slightly developed in birds, is conveyed by the nerve endings of the tongue, and by the "cere", a soft area of skin at the base of the bill. The bill itself is not sensitive in most birds, but in ducks and waders, which feel for their food in the mud, a large part of the bill is soft and well equipped with nerve endings, particularly at the tip ; this is also true of the Snipe and Woodcock. Woodpeckers' bills are unusually sensitive, too.

Lamellae and Egg-Teeth. Although many, if not all, birds possessed teeth up to about the beginning of the Tertiary Period (fifty million years ago), no living birds have them. But sometimes the edges of the bill exhibit saw-like notches not unlike teeth. For instance, in certain of the ducks, such as the fish-eating " saw-billed " goosanders and mergansers, these serrations assist the birds in gripping their prey. In those Anserine birds which seek their food in the soft mud under water, the serrations take the form of horny ridges (*lamellae*) which, with the aid of the thick, fleshy tongue, provide an efficient sifting apparatus. This horny

" sieve " attains its maximum development in the Shoveler, whose spoon-like bill possesses *lamellae* of great length. In the embryo stage, birds develop a calcareous protuberance on the upper surface of the bill, known as the " egg-tooth", the only function of which is to help the young bird to " batter " its way through the egg-shell ; it is shed soon after.

Though the bill is formed in the embryo stage, some time may elapse before a young bird develops the specialised type of its species. But in the majority of birds bill-specialisation is not carried to extreme lengths, and the bills of the young of many species undergo little change as they grow into adult birds. The bills of newly-hatched thrushes, for example, have much the same shape and relative length as those of the adult birds. But in such birds as the Avocet and the Curlew, the young possess comparatively short and straight bills, which only gradually develop into the long, curved " instruments " of the adults.

Sometimes the shape of the bill differs in the two sexes, but usually this only happens in the case of birds with peculiarly shaped bills ; thus both cock and hen of the New Zealand Huia (which became extinct in 1907) possessed bills adapted for capturing wood-boring insects, but while the male bird had a strong, slightly curved beak of medium length, the female's was comparatively slender, much longer, and considerably more curved.

There are many variations in the structure of the tongue, which in some birds is used as an organ of manipulation. In most species it is small, while in birds such as the Cormorant, which would find even a small tongue a serious obstruction, it is virtually non-existent. Sometimes, as with the woodpeckers, it is protrusible, and is used as an accessory to the bill.

The bill has to serve to a large extent as a hand in such varied activities as picking up food, preening, nest-building and fighting. The food factor has the greatest influence upon its shape and size, and there are innumerable adaptations for every kind of food and mode of feeding. Such adaptations have probably evolved very gradually : the original impetus may have been the overcrowding of a feeding area, favouring those birds whose bills were so shaped that they gave their owners an advantage over other birds in the search for a new diet, or in fighting for possession of the most nourishing food.

Adapted to Feeding Habits. Where the diet is very mixed, there is comparatively little bill-specialisation. Thus, such birds as the thrushes, which live on a varied diet of worms, snails, berries and so on, possess a generalised type of bill with no very remarkable adaptations. Among the waders, however, the picture is very different: the Lapwing, with its mixed diet, not unnaturally possesses a short and unexceptional type of bill; the " pickaxe " bill of the Turnstone, on the other hand, has greater density, and is much more pointed, so that it is admirably suited to the task of levering up and over-turning stones along the shore, and seizing the small crustaceans which lurk underneath. The

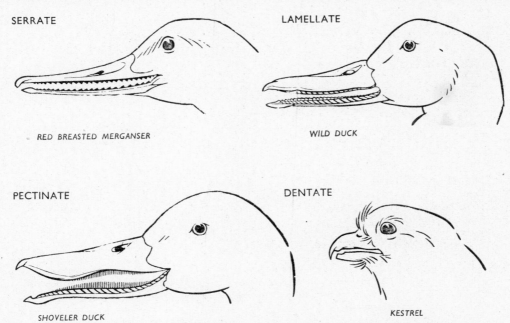

SERRATE

LAMELLATE

RED BREASTED MERGANSER

WILD DUCK

PECTINATE

DENTATE

SHOVELER DUCK

KESTREL

BILL. *Modern birds have no teeth, but some bills are specially adapted to do duty for them*

STARLING BULLFINCH SPARROW

BLACKBIRD TREE CREEPER CROSSBILL

WOODPECKER SKYLARK NIGHTJAR

WREN GODWIT

AVOCET CURLEW

SNIPE KINGFISHER

BILL. *Birds living off an unmixed diet have bills adapted to cope with their particular food*

Oystercatcher's bill is longer and even denser, and can be used for opening the shells of mussels and other molluscs, and for knocking limpets from their holds. The long bill of the Common Snipe is so flexible that it can be opened at the tip only, like a pair of forceps, to grasp worms deep down in the mud; this bill is well supplied with nerves ending in small pits at the tip, which enable the bird to feel for its food in the mud.

Some waders have remarkably curved bills. The curlews, for example, have long, narrow,

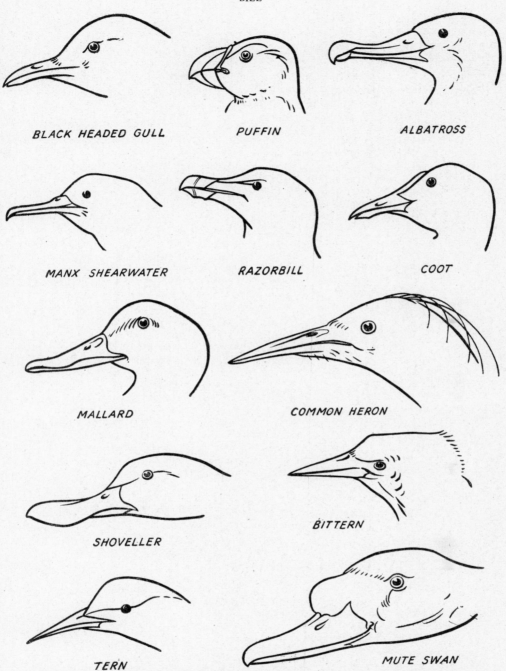

BLACK HEADED GULL   PUFFIN   ALBATROSS

MANX SHEARWATER   RAZORBILL   COOT

MALLARD   COMMON HERON

SHOVELLER   BITTERN

TERN   MUTE SWAN

BILL. *Among waders and waterfowl, bill specialisation has been carried to its highest point*

downwardly curved bills, with which they can either pick up food on the surface of shallow stretches of water, or probe deeply into the mud for it. The Avocet has a long, upcurved bill, with which it feeds in shallow water or in mud, skimming its food from the surface with a side-to-side swinging movement. The Wry-billed Plover of New Zealand is unique in having a bill curved laterally to the right.

The sieve-like bills of the mud-grubbing ducks, such as the Shoveler, have already been noted, as have the saw-like bills of the fish-eating goosanders and mergansers. Another type of bill common among fish-eaters is the strong, straight " spear ", as seen in such birds as the Kingfisher, Heron, and Gannet. The Pelican's bill can be used either for spearing fish or for scooping them up, and it also serves as a pouch for storing them.

Tearing and Crushing Apparatus. Predatory birds like owls and hawks possess sharp, hooked beaks to help them in striking down their prey and tearing it to pieces. The beaks of many gulls are also hooked, though to a lesser extent, for some of these birds also tear flesh when feeding ; this is also true of the shrikes. Although parrots have the hard, hooked beak typical of birds of prey, they are vegetarian birds, their bills being well adapted for gnawing and grinding nuts and hard seeds.

Most seed-eaters possess cone-shaped beaks, short and strong. The finches come into this group, and the bills of some of them provide particularly remarkable examples of adaptation to feeding habits. The typical Finch bill may be seen in the Bullfinch, Greenfinch and House-Sparrow, and a very exaggerated version of this type of bill is seen in the Hawfinch. For its size this bird possesses a truly massive conical beak, internally strengthened by horny " pads " which provide an efficient crushing apparatus. Though it gathers berries and soft fruits, such as the cherry, it rejects the fruit pulp and uses its strong beak to crack open the stones to get at the kernel. An even more remarkable example of adaptation occurs in the Crossbill, the tips of the upper and lower portions of whose bill are crossed, enabling the bird to extract the oily seeds of pine cones.

The insect-eaters generally have small, delicate bills, an exception being the Woodpecker, which possesses a hard, chisel-like bill, with which it can get at insects under the bark of trees and in dead wood, and which it can also use for boring nest holes in tree-trunks. More typical of the insectivorous birds are the soft, pointed bills of the warblers and wrens, which are

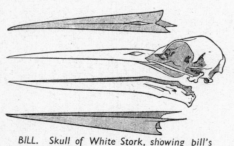

BILL. Skull of White Stork, showing bill's bony foundation (centre) and its horny sheath

suited for feeding on caterpillars and soft insects. Birds such as the Swallow, Swift and Nightjar, which catch insects in flight, possess short, weak beaks, with an exceptionally wide gape to enable them to engulf their prey.

BIRD-BAITING. Catching of birds with clap-nets (*q.v.*).

BIRD-CALL. This may be either an instrument used for decoying birds by imitating their notes, or a bird's note in calling (*see* Call Note).

BIRD-DUFFER. Dealer who artificially changes the colour of living birds or who cheats in the preparation of stuffed specimens.

BIRD-GLUE. *See* Birdlime.

BIRD-HAWK. Local name for Shrike (*q.v.*) family, given to these birds because of their sweeping, undulating flight and their way of hovering after prey.

BIRD HOSPITAL. Phyllis and Dorothy Yglesias, who live in a house on the hill above the Cornish fishing village of Mousehole, have known little peace since 1928. In that year they nursed back to health their first patient— a badly wounded Jackdaw brought by a boy who begged them to save it. Their reputation as bird nurses quickly grew locally, and in time spread so that their hospital is now world-famous and has some hundred patients, about half being chronics and long-stay cases. Forty to fifty are cured each year and released, and rather more than this die or are put to sleep.

A ship's bell on the steep garden path is the means of summoning the Misses Yglesias at any hour of the day or night to take in a new patient —often a large sea-bird bravely carried by a local child. Many gulls are cared for in a large paddock ; some have mated, nested and laid eggs while in hospital. Oiled sea-birds, mostly guillemots and razorbills, are cared for here with a good percentage of recoveries.

Rare and lovely birds such as the Great Shearwater, Great Northern Diver, Red-throated Diver, Leach's Fork-tailed Petrel, Peregrine, Woodpecker and Kingfisher, have been admitted and nursed back to health, as well as sparrows, tits, starlings, black-birds and thrushes. Francesca, a Greater Black-backed Gull, has been fifteen years in hospital, while a brood of mallards, deserted by their mother, were less than a week old at the time the writer visited the hospital.

The wonderful work done at this bird hospital has brought recognition and help from the Royal Society for the Prevention of Cruelty to Animals, and from countless admiring friends throughout the world.

BIRDING, or Fowling. The capturing or killing of birds for sport or for food by the use, respectively, of traps, nets and snares, or of smooth-bore shotguns.

BIRD ROOM, *this arcade at London's Natural History Museum is a good example of the modern approach*

For text see page 58

To face page 56

BIRDLIME. Sticky substance used for capturing small wild birds. It is applied to baited screens, trunks, planks, etc., and when the birds alight on these they are held fast. In Great Britain the use of birdlime is strictly forbidden by law, but it is still used in several southern countries.

There are various methods of making birdlime ; and it was made formerly from the middle bark of the holly tree, the distaff thistle, the Canary Island houseleek, mistletoe berries, and suchlike. It can also be produced from ordinary wheat-flour by pressing out the starch and leaving the viscous *gluten*.

BIRD-LOUSE. Popular name given to a member of one of several species of insects belonging to the family *Mallophaga* (Latin, " wool-eaters "), which live on birds. Common species are : *Trichodectes canis*, *Philopterus versicolor*, *Philopterus leontodon*, *Liotheum anseris* and *Menopon pallidum*.

Lice are permanent parasites, that is, they complete their life cycle on the same host, and, unlike bird-ticks (*q.v.*) do not leave to lay eggs or moult. There are two distinct kinds of lice ; those which feed on feathers and debris from the skin and have strong biting jaws, and those provided with a hollow sheath through which the body fluids are abstracted.

Feather lice may also be sub-divided into two main classes. One type is long and thin and is usually found on the web of the flight and tail feathers. They are said to be beneficial because they live on the downy parts of the feather, and during hot weather afford relief to the birds, as long as they do not become too numerous. The other kind is flat and round, or slightly oval in shape, and usually inhabits the plumage of the hackle, rump and thighs.

BIRD-LOUSE

Canaries are not much troubled by lice, but many other small birds are, as are also parrots, poultry and pigeons. Cage-birds usually keep free of these parasites if they are kept clean and allowed free access to the bath (water or dust as the case may be). If they should become infested, dust with a good insecticide ; one composed of equal parts of refined fuller's earth and sodium fluoride is about the best. This should be placed under the wings, about the neck, the rump, and the root of the tail.

There is also a form of louse which infests the base of the beak, destroying the small feathers round the nostrils. In this case, the powder must be used carefully to prevent any from entering the nostrils. *See also* Parasite.

BIRD-MITE. Minute parasitic creature belonging to the acaridan *Arachnida*. Many species of bird are liable to infestation, and there are several types of mite.

Red mite (*Dermanyssus gallinae*) which infests poultry, pigeons, and other small birds— particularly those kept in captivity—is the most common. During the day, this parasite inhabits the ends of perches and cracks and crevices in house, cage, and the like, emerging only at night to crawl on any birds in the vicinity to suck their blood. Red mite flourishes in dark and badly ventilated places and breeds prolifically during the summer months. It

BIRD-MITE

can remain dormant in an unused house or cage for several months.

The only way to deal with this pest is to remove the bird from the affected dwelling and wash out the cage or aviary with hot water and strong disinfectant, taking particular care to disinfect all corners, woodwork and ends of perches. Red mite never attack their host during the day, and therefore any cleansing of the bird alone, without cleaning out the cage, will be of no avail in the long run.

Other types of mites, the *Epidermoptidae*, live on the skin of birds and cause bare patches on the head and neck—the so-called " depluming scabies ". These patches sometimes thicken due to the attack of the fungus *Acorion schoenleini*. " Scaly-leg " is caused by the tiny *Knemidocoptes gallinae* mites.

Some feather-mites, usually of a dull grey colour so as to be more effectively camouflaged, live inside the bird's quills on pith (the *Syringobia* species) ; and many that as adults live on the feathers, feeding on scurf, lay their eggs in the quills. The *Harpyrhynchus* species live in the feather follicles of Passerine birds and cause small tumours.

Several species never leave their host during their life-cycle but migrate internally, or pass their nymphal stage encysted in the connective tissue round the bird's trachea.

The blood-sucking mites not only cause loss of condition and emaciation due to loss of blood, but are also vectors of relapsing fever. They should, therefore, be dealt with at once. A safe and sure cure against all mites is to dust affected birds with a powder composed of equal parts of fuller's earth and sodium fluoride. Pigeons and canaries, and other small birds, may also be dipped carefully in warm water containing a little Jeyes' Fluid.

BIRD OBSERVATORY. *See* Observatory.

BIRD ROOM AND BIRD GALLERY

W. E. SWINTON, Ph.D., B.Sc.

*Visitors to a modern bird gallery are no longer faced with dry-as-dust collections, but
find exhibits arranged to arouse and maintain interest. To achieve this, much work
is done behind the scenes in the bird room, whose functions are described below*

BIRD ROOM and Bird Gallery. Both of these have important uses and are only to be found in museums. The Gallery is the place for display to the public, whereas the Bird Room may be likened to a private study where an enormous amount of scientific research is carried out.

Nearly every museum of any size in Britain has a good Bird Gallery, and some of those listed below have superb collections. But only the largest of natural history museums or some of the zoological departments of universities possess what may truly pass for a Bird Room.

Spectacular kinds of birds, the demonstration of the methods of flight, the history of flight among vertebrates, and the origin of bird flight itself may all be found in the Bird Gallery. Colour patterns, male and female colour differences, nest forms and locations, shape and colour of eggs are all displayed there, together with ample collections. Their purpose is to make visitors aware of the wonders of Nature as displayed by birds ; so that they may be encouraged to go into the fields and seek for themselves, and then return to the museum to identify their finds and confirm their observations.

But these displays for public education and entertainment have to be made laboriously and are often the result of years of patient study and observation, carried out in the museum's Bird Room. The general public is not admitted there as a matter of course, though the student and enquirer may frequently find himself in this room.

Collections that are made or presented will first come to the Bird Room. Each of the many birds—sometimes thousands—will have to be identified. This may itself entail a great deal of comparison and even research before a name can be applied. Thus a very large number of specimens must be kept, but the matter is simplified by not having these birds mounted in a natural way, as they are in the exhibition cases of the Gallery. Instead, nearly all of them are represented by skins which have to be very carefully preserved and labelled, with every possible detail of their locality and the circumstances under which they were found.

To explain the Bird Room it is therefore necessary to start sometimes far away from the museum. The specimens in the field may be shot or trapped ; they are then carefully wrapped up on the spot, though sometimes they may be skinned by the experienced collector ; and the full details of the place where they were found—of their nest or other circumstances, the time of year, and so on—have to be noted in the field note book. Often these details may be supplemented by photographs of similar birds in flight.

The specimens are despatched to the museum where they are unpacked so that no

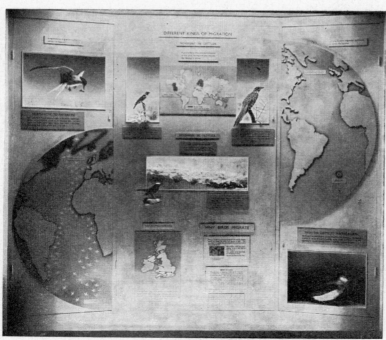

British Museum (Natural History)

*BIRD ROOM. It is a far cry from the stereotyped exhibit on a dusty shelf
to this chart, telling the visitor at a glance all about bird migration*

damage is done and no detail of any kind or field note lost. This is tremendously important. The specimen may then be skinned and the skin and feathers cured and cleaned. They must then be stored in cabinets, together with their appropriate materials, away from the sun whose ultra-violet light might make the colours fade. (Indeed, care often must be taken that the ultra-violet light from fluorescent lamps does not shine too long and unscreened on them.) Thus hundreds of smallish specimens can be housed in a comparatively small space.

If the skin is to be mounted, the specimen

British Museum (Natural History)

BIRD ROOM. You have to look twice before realizing that these ducks were not surprised by a photographer in their usual haunts, but in a museum

goes to the taxidermist who " stuffs " it with great skill and models the whole, with legs and beaks, so that the complete specimen is to all intents as good for the student or the artist as the original was ; and will last for years if due care is taken (*see* Taxidermy).

Should the skeleton be required there is a modern method whereby the bones can be rapidly and easily cleaned. Small beetles, known as dermestids, avidly consume flesh of all kinds, and most large museums now keep a colony of these in a room that looks like a large refrigerator, but is kept at a temperature that best suits the little beetles. The skinned bird is put on shelves in this sealed room and left to the dermestids. In a few days they will have completely removed the flesh and only the very delicate bones remain, clean and undamaged. These are then degreased and wired together, and the bird skeleton is ready for the osteological collection.

Although most museums and universities have some skeletons of birds, the amount of work done upon the bird skeleton is much smaller than that spent in the study and comparison of skins.

Most birds are identified on their general appearance, in which beaks and feet, colour and size, play important parts. When a new collection of birds appears in the museum, each is examined in minute detail and if it can be identified in this way, it is carefully labelled and is then ready to take its place in further

research or in the cabinet series. If it is not identifiable, after comparison with the collections in the museum and the various forms recorded in the great literature on birds, the bird may be new to science. It must then be given a scientific name by giving a detailed description of it and an analysis of those characters in which it appears to differ from the nearest known birds (i.e. nearest in structure, colouring and appearance and so on) and publishing these facts and the new name in a scientific journal. The place of publication is important, for it should be a journal or scientific magazine likely to be available to other workers. It follows, therefore, that the Bird Room must have not only lots of birds but very many ornithological books and journals.

All bird work is not, however, done on the skins. The carefully prepared skeletons must also be labelled and stored. Cabinets of eggs, too, are kept for identification purposes.

Many museums also have numbers of nests (*q.v.*), for birds vary widely in the types of nest they build. Many of the most attractive bird exhibits deal with nesting arrangements.

The typical Bird Room must therefore have facilities for the storage and ready reference of birds mounted as in life ; cabinets of skins preserved as far as possible in dust- and light-proof cases. There should also be a collection of skeletons, illustrating the main groups ; series of nests ; and as many eggs as can be conveniently dealt with. All of these, with the relevant data preserved in museum catalogues and card indexes must be supplemented by a good specialist ornithological library.

Thus equipped, the collection can be used to identify new arrivals ; artists and authors will get the information they require for their books ; students will receive sound instruction; and the public will have a stimulus to study birds and to interest themselves in bird preservation.

This work is necessary not only because of the intrinsic interest of birds themselves and as part of nature and zoological study, but because birds play an important part in the economy of life and in the balance of nature. They are not often the carriers of disease but they are frequently the enemies of insect vectors ; they have their food value ; some are helpful to the farmer, others destructive, and the ramifications of their world can only be studied in a well-furnished Bird Room.

The most famous Bird Rooms are those of the largest museums and certain university departments or specialist museums. These major institutions are :

British Museum (Natural History), London, S.W.7;
Tring Museum, Tring, Herts, a subsidiary of the preceding ;
Royal Scottish Museum, Chambers Street, Edinburgh, 1 ;
National Museum of Wales, Cathays Park, Cardiff.

Important British University centres are :

University Museum of Zoology, Cambridge ;
University Museum, Oxford.

The following museums have collections of note and are listed alphabetically and not in order of importance, to encourage readers to discover the treasures of their local museum :

Barnsley Museum ;
Birmingham Natural History Museum ;
Bolton Museum, Lancashire ;
Brighton, The Booth Bird Museum ,
Bristol, City Museum ;
Burton-on-Trent Museum ;
Canterbury Museum ;
Chelmsford Museum ;
Doncaster Museum ;
Exeter, Royal Albert Memorial Museum ;
Glasgow Corporation Museum ;
Haslemere Educational Museum ;
Huddersfield, Tolson Memorial Museum ;
Ipswich Museum ;
Leicester Museum ;
Liverpool, Free Public Museum ;
Horniman Museum, London, S.E.23 ;
Maidstone Museum ;
Manchester, University Museum ;
Newcastle-on-Tyne, Hancock Museum ;
Norwich, Castle Museum ;
Nottingham, Natural History Museum, Wollaton Hall ;
Oldham, Werneth Museum ;
Paisley Museum ;
Preston, Harris Museum ;
Reading Museum ;
Hanley, Pall Mall Museum ;
Worthing Museum ;
York, The Yorkshire Museum.

Children in the Museum. As an example of the encouragement given by museums to the young naturalist, the Natural History Museum, London, may well be cited. Here a Children's Centre and Junior Naturalists' Club were started in 1948. The Centre caters for children between the ages of seven and fifteen ; and utilizes the child's natural desire to draw to train him in observation.

The Junior Naturalists' Club is a more serious affair. Its members, varying in age from 11 to 15½, are recruited from the Centre and must produce some original field work to show their interest in Natural History. The Club provides a library, workroom and occasional help from Museum experts. There is also the Country Club for children of 12 to 17 years of age who, living outside London. need help with their field work.

Apart from these, the Museum provides special facilities for schools, by encouraging visits from school parties and by arranging talks for school-children, often in conjunction with the B.B.C.'s school-broadcasting programme. *See also* Education.

BIRD SANCTUARY. *See* Sanctuary ; *also* Conservation ; Nature Reserve.

BIRD-SEED. Canary or other seed, like hemp, rape and millet, used to feed cage-birds.

British Museum (Natural History)

BIRD ROOM. *This more conventional exhibit seems so true to life, one expects the birds to fly away*

LOOKING FOR—AND FINDING—NESTS

Birdsnesting is not the same as egg-collecting, but is done for information. Below practical hints are given on how to find nests, a difficult art which can be learnt only by experience in the field but which should be mastered by all serious bird-watchers

BIRDSNESTING. To modern ornithologists this term means " the art of finding nests, not for the sake of collecting eggs but for the purpose of collecting facts and information." It is used in this sense in the present article and throughout this work.

It is necessary that the meaning of this term should be clearly understood, because until about thirty or forty years ago birdsnesting was synonymous with egg-collecting, and there may be some who still consider it to be the same thing. Egg collecting, other than for *truly* scientific purposes, and then only when carefully controlled, has always been regarded with abhorrence by true bird-lovers, who now are backed by public opinion and the Law.

The taking of eggs by thoughtless children is luckily now on the decrease, and in any case the nests which they despoil are usually those of the more common species, and the consequences are not generally serious. But when egg collecting is undertaken by adults in search of the rarer varieties, there is a very real danger.

If only one or two eggs are taken from a nest, the parent bird has correspondingly fewer chances of rearing its young. On the other hand, if a whole clutch is removed the bird will lay another one (the Golden Eagle and some large sea-birds excepted), but if the repeat clutch fails to develop it will probably, by then, be too late for the bird to rear a brood successfully that season. Thus when there are only a few pairs of a species of birds in the country, the survival of the species is endangered.

The activities of those prepared to make piratical raids on birds' nests, have been curtailed by the passing of the Protection of Birds Act, 1953 (*q.v.*), which makes it an offence, punishable by fine, or in some cases by imprisonment, to take (or destroy) the eggs of certain species except under licence, or, in certain circumstances, of any species, except a relatively small number regarded as " noxious ". Further, the Act makes it an offence to take, damage or destroy the nest of any wild bird while that nest is in use.

Thus, detached from its evil associations, birdsnesting is now defined as the finding of nests for the purpose of collecting information, and this gathering of information may take several forms. Some may wish to find nests to photograph them ; others, to prepare a case-history of the breeding-cycle from the time the building of the nest commences until fledging. Others again may wish to ring young birds before they leave the nest, so that thereafter their age may be accurately known—an essential item in obtaining certain vital information. Yet others may wish to make a detailed study of the behaviour of birds with their young.

BIRDSNESTING. Tap branch lightly to flush bird, and thus reveal where its nest is hidden

Nest Records Schemes. Although such investigations may give a great deal of pleasure when carried out merely to satisfy personal curiosity, they are much more valuable when the results are recorded, and information collected is collated by some central body. With this in mind, Professor Julian Huxley and James Fisher started, in 1939, the Hatching and Fledging Enquiry, subsequently called the Nest Record Inquiry Scheme, and operated by the British Trust for Ornithology (*q.v.*). The Trust has produced two types of Nest Record Card : the standard card for visits to a single nest, and the colonial card (for a single colony).

Completed cards are sent to the Trust, which collates and analyses them. Information that was collected thus is helping to fill gaps in our knowledge of birds; but there is still much to be learned about even some of the commoner species. Probably the most fruitful type of investigation is that carried out on a single nest to which repeated visits are made starting as early as possible in the breeding-cycle. If the standard card designed for this purpose is fully completed, it gives information on habitat nesting site, nesting materials and construction of nest ; on the date, and even the time, when building commenced, laying, hatching and fledging : on the clutch and brood size, the length of incubation and breeding success. The colonial card relates, of course, to a single species, but is more general, covering locality, habitat and site, description of nests, number of birds in the colony (accurate or estimated count), occupied nests and pairs of birds, and the contents of each nest (eggs and/or young).

SEARCHING FOR NESTS

Since the breeding cycle is the annual focal point in the life of the adult bird, every serious student of bird-life should know how to search for nests. Nest-finding is an art which can only be acquired by experience ; from books it is possible to learn only the guiding principles and general directions on where to look and when, but the finer points of the art can only be mastered after long practice in the field. Every nest discovered should, theoretically, at least, make it easier to find another nest.

WHERE ?

In narrowing down the field of search, one must select first the right *locality*, then the correct *habitat*, next a probable *nesting site*, leading finally to the discovery of the nest.

Locality. If the search has to be restricted to an area within easy reach of one's home, or where one is spending a holiday, it is necessary to know what species are likely to breed in the neighbourhood and to select one of these for investigation. On the other hand, a keen student not limited by distance or time, may select his species first, and will then want to know the localities where it is to be found.

About 50 of the common species (*see* Bird-Watching), some of whose nests are difficult to find, breed in every inhabited part of the British Isles. The more local distribution of all species is given under their individual headings. For those who require it, more detailed information will be found in Witherby's *Handbook of British Birds*. As some species change their localities from time to time, or may be driven away from a favoured spot by other birds, an enthusiast requiring up-to-date information on breeding localities of some of the rarer birds should obtain this through one of the ornithological societies, or by reference to current literature.

Habitat. Information on the habitat (*q.v.*) of the species of one's choice will be found in this Encyclopedia, in the *Handbook* and, in fact, in nearly all books dealing with individual species, including the excellent *Field Guide to Birds of Britain and Europe* (Collins, 1954). But probably the most practical source of information, for beginner and advanced student alike, is *Finding Nests* (Collins, 1953), written from a fund of first-hand knowledge and a lifetime of experience by Bruce Campbell.

Nesting Sites. The last-mentioned book also gives sound, practical information on nesting sites. The importance of having this knowledge at hand cannot be too heavily stressed. Habitat is a subject on which the birdsnester must be well informed, but it is only a general guide ; it is knowledge of the likely sites for each species that produces success in nest-finding. Without this knowledge, although in the right spot, one might not know whether to look in a bush, under a rock, up a tree, in a

BIRDSNESTING. *Field-glasses are often useful, particularly when observing cliffs from a distance*

hole in a tree, in which particular type of tree, or at what height.

For example, the habitat of the Green Wood-pecker, which is generally distributed throughout England and Wales as far as Yorkshire and Lancashire, where it becomes local, is described as " wooded country rather than woodland ; parks, orchards, and large gardens, timbered hedgerows, copses, roadside and riparian trees, heaths and commons, generally avoiding conifers ". This wide choice is narrowed down by additional information about the nesting-site which is a hole in a tree, generally a tree that is externally sound but has a rotten centre, sometimes a perfectly dead tree ; the hole is usually in the trunk, but sometimes in a large sloping bough ; apart from conifers, tree species are unimportant, although the ash, oak, elm and apple are popular, and in certain regions birch, alder, and both sweet and horse-chestnuts.

WHEN?

When a nest has been found one has to verify that it is indeed the type sought ; this is done by recognition of the occupants, or of the eggs, or of the construction of the nest—initially by comparison with a printed description, later by personal experience.

The breeding seasons of selected species are given in pages 96-97 ; additional information

John Markham

BIRDSNESTING. Once you know the locality and type of country a bird is likely to frequent, you can narrow down your search until you come to the actual nesting site. Thus the Sedge-Warbler always builds his nest among sedges near streams (top) and (below) is the actual site of his nest

will also be found in the *Handbook*, in *Finding Nests*, and in most reference books relating to individual species. Wherever possible it is best to carry out systematic and periodic searches before nest-building begins in the hope of being present on the day it actually starts. This may involve many fruitless visits, and probably should not be attempted by a novice.

HOW?

The two chief ways of finding a nest are: (*a*) by straightforward searching, and (*b*) by " watching back "—that is to say, getting the bird to lead one to its nest. The former method may be sub-divided into " cold " searching (finding the nest by solid plodding) and " hot " searching (by flushing the bird off its nest).

Finding by searching is considered by the experienced birdsnester to be rather crude compared with finding by watching, and to require less knowledge and less patience. When it is desired to study all the nests of all species in a given area, however, cold searching is the most useful method, particularly if time is limited ; scientific skill is not necessary, and the reward goes to those who spend the longest time in the largest number of places. This

BIRDSNESTING. Clapping the hands is specially useful when trying to flush birds off cliff-tops

method is likely to be most successful early in the season, before the foliage is out and the grass too high and thick.

Useful Hints on "Cold" Searching.

1. It is generally advisable to have the sun and wind behind you, as in bird-watching, but when searching bushes or along hedges it is better to have the sun on the far side, so that the nest can be seen in silhouette.

2. When examining hedges or bushes it is advisable to carry a stout stick, to part the canopy of leaves so that one can peer round inside. Four feet is about the right length, unless it is desired to attach a mirror to the end, in which case it should be considerably longer and, preferably, telescopic. Having found the nest, mark its position in some way ; otherwise it may be difficult to find it again.

3. It is usually better to look upwards rather than downwards when searching bushes, trees, or hedgerows.

4. When searching cliffs it is also advisable to look upwards, and to be as far away as possible from the cliff in order to obtain a wide angle of view. This improves the chances of spotting indications of nest sites, such as detached material, tracks and approaches to holes and burrows. Field glasses are often essential, and always helpful, for this.

Flushing. There are several ways of flushing a bird off the nest :

1. When searching bushes, etc., the bird may sometimes be flushed by tapping the bush or branch with a stick. For the best results tap lightly to avoid frightening the bird. Then stand still and listen. A sitting bird may not show itself, but may give away its position by rustling among the twigs.

2. Clapping the hands may produce useful results, particularly for flushing birds from cliffs, when one has a wide view. It is best to cup the hands, with the palm and fingers almost at right angles.

3. In surveying heathland a drag-rope is sometimes used. The rope may be worked by a single observer if one end is pegged down and the other moved in the arc of a circle. But it is better to have someone at each end of the rope to drag it in the arc of a circle, with a third person walking behind at about the middle of the arc. To help in fixing the nest site, the rope may be marked at intervals with pieces of white cloth, so that, when the bird rises and the rope is stopped, all observers can concentrate on the mark nearest to it.

Watching Back. Finding nests by watching birds back to them is considered by experienced ornithologists to be altogether on a higher plane than either of the two slogging methods

BIRDSNESTING. *Drag-ropes worked by one, two, or three people are used in open country. Neither of the pictures on this page is drawn to scale*

Curlew. The watcher must take advantage of every possible hide, such as provided by a rock tree, or even car.

In watching back one must not be between the bird and its nest. But, generally speaking, it is impossible to know whether or not one is on the line of approach. If the bird fails to return to its nest after five or ten minutes, it is advisable to move to a fresh position. When at last it has returned to its nest the *apparent* position should be marked by reference to surrounding objects—stones, rocks, trees, flowers, etc. When searching for the nest, allowance must be made for the fact that some species land at a distance from their nests, and only reach them after many devious movements. Further, if field-glasses (*q.v.*), which are almost indispensable, have been used in locating the spot, allowance must be made for foreshortening.

After finding the approximate position of the nest, it may sometimes be necessary to flush the bird off it in order to discover its exact location (*see also* above, in page 64).

EXAMINING THE NEST

When the nest has been found the art of examining it comes into play. Nests on cliffs or water, or in trees overlooked by cliffs or high ground, may be examined from above through field-glasses—but if a nest has

of search already described. This is a matter of opinion, but "watching back" certainly has the advantage that it provides a better opportunity to study the habits of the birds, combined with the thrill of outwitting those species that try all manner of tricks to prevent the discovery of their nests. Except when many birds are building in a small area, or when a pair have young and, like some of the Passerine species, give themselves away by call notes as they move towards their nest, watching back requires a great deal of time and patience.

This is particularly true of many important groups of ground-nesting birds, such as ducks, gulls and game-birds, who do not, strictly speaking, "build" nests and whose young leave the nest almost immediately after hatching. Waders and gulls are easier, but here success usually depends on finding a suitable "hide". It is comparatively simple, after making contact with ringed plovers by walking along the beach, to lie up in the sand dunes and wait for them to return to their nests, or to watch for an Oystercatcher or Tern from behind cover. But on open moorland the problem is much more difficult: if the watcher lies well hidden he cannot see the bird, while if he stands up the bird can see him. This explains the difficulty of tracking down the Golden Plover and the

If watching back leads you nowhere, try again, for you may have been on the bird's path to its nest

a deep cup, some of the eggs or young may be hidden from view by its near side.

Where possible it is best to make observations at close quarters. With nests high up in trees or on a cliff face this involves climbing up or being lowered down—an operation often requiring special apparatus and training, a description of which is outside the scope of this article. Practical instructions are given in Bruce Campbell's *Finding Nests*.

To examine nests in bushes, etc., a stick is useful for parting the foliage, and a mirror fixed to its end facilitates the examination of the contents of nests which are difficult to reach directly. The mirror is also useful for investigating nests in comparatively low branches.

A torch is a great help when investigating nests in hedgerows and holes, but if a hole is very deep it is better to have a bulb connected to a battery by a long piece of flex on which it can be dangled in the hole.

Birdsnesting is a fascinating pastime which can be made the hobby of a lifetime. There is always something fresh to learn, and as an observer gains experience he will discover for himself fresh tips to add to the necessarily brief list of hints given in this Encyclopedia.

Nests in deep holes can be investigated properly only with a torch or an electric bulb on a flex

BIRDS OF PREY. *See* Prey, Birds of.

BIRD-TICK. Minute, blood-sucking parasite, member of the acaridan *Arachnida*. They attach themselves to the skin of their host and suck its blood. They are extremely troublesome and, as among most *Arachnida*, the female is the larger and more active. Ticks may not only cause anaemia in their host due to loss of blood, which may in extreme cases lead to death, but may also act as vectors in the transmission of disease. Unlike the louse, these parasites seldom remain in once place for long and usually leave their host at some stage during their life-cycle.

Pigeons and poultry are often seriously affected by ticks. The only cure is to keep the birds scrupulously clean and isolated from healthy birds; and cages or roosting places must be disinfected frequently. As some ticks pass the larval stage on the ground before they climb up their host or are taken in food, special care must be taken to keep chicken-runs, shelter sheds, aviaries, cages, etc. clean.

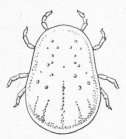

BIRD-TICK

See also Aviary ; Disease ; Parasite.

BIRDSNESTING. A stick is handy to search bushes for nests and to examine them at close range

INTRODUCTION TO BIRD WATCHING

There are over a million bird watchers in this country—members of both sexes, young and old—drawn from all walks of life. This article explains what is meant by bird watching and offers guidance to those who would like to take up this fascinating hobby

BIRD WATCHING. The study of birds has always attracted more people than has any other branch of natural history, but during the past fifteen to twenty years it has become increasingly popular, particularly in western Europe and north America, and nowhere more so than in Great Britain.

Although it is impossible to assess accurately the number of bird watchers in Great Britain, because some belong to no recognized organization, whereas others belong to several, it has been estimated that there are over a million active bird watchers in this country, compared with a few hundred thousands before 1939.

There is enough diversity in bird watching to interest everybody, and it is a hobby that can be pursued all the year round, outdoors or indoors. It may be begun at any age, but, as with many other things, it is best to make as early a start as possible. Many schools have a nature study club ; if not, young enthusiasts would do well to press for one to be started. Also there are a number of organizations and societies whose object is to promote and encourage a lively interest in birds. These include the Royal Society for the Protection of Birds (*q.v.*) and the British Trust for Ornithology (*q.v.*). They and others are dealt with under their own headings, but full particulars of the main organizations and societies are also to be found under the heading Study, Facilities for.

Identification. One of the first things a beginner has to learn is *how* to identify birds. Some people can recognize them in the field from coloured illustrations which they have seen. Those who lack this ability (except in the simplest cases) must adopt the systematic method described in the article on Identification.

The initial target should be an ability to recognize at sight the resident birds, of which there are about 50 species. This in itself may seem difficult, but most people without any specialised training will find that they can tell about 25 birds at a glance.

The following is a list of the resident birds (i.e. species in which at least some members are present all the year round) which, with the exception of those marked, are to be found throughout the country :

Heron	Jay
Mallard	Great Tit
Mute Swan	Blue Tit
Sparrow-Hawk	Coal-Tit
Kestrel	Marsh-Tit * †
Partridge	Long-tailed Tit
Pheasant	Nuthatch * †
Moorhen	Tree-Creeper
Coot	Wren
Lapwing	Mistle-Thrush
Common Snipe	Song-Thrush
Herring-Gull	Blackbird
Black-headed Gull	Robin
Wood-Pigeon	Goldcrest
Barn-Owl	Hedge-Sparrow
Little Owl †	Meadow-Pipit
Tawny Owl †	Pied Wagtail
Kingfisher	Grey Wagtail
Green Woodpecker	Starling
Greater Spotted Wood-pecker	Greenfinch
	Goldfinch
Skylark	Linnet
Carrion-Crow †	Bullfinch
Rook	Chaffinch
Jackdaw	Yellow Hammer
Magpie	House-Sparrow

Overleaf is given a list of the common summer visitors which, with a few notable exceptions,

Eric Hosking

BIRD WATCHING. *Only experienced bird watchers should attempt to ring birds. Here a group of enthusiasts is shown how to perform this operation*

are not so well known as the winter residents—probably because they do not arrive until the trees are in leaf :

Corncrake	Nightingale * †
Common Sandpiper	Sedge-Warbler
Lesser Black-Back	Blackcap
Turtle-Dove * †	Garden-Warbler
Cuckoo	Whitethroat
Nightjar	Lesser Whitethroat †
Swift	Willow-Warbler
Swallow	Chiffchaff
House-Martin	Wood-Warbler †
Sand-Martin	Spotted Flycatcher
Wheatear	Tree-Pipit †
Whinchat	Yellow Wagtail †
Redstart †	Red-Backed Shrike * †

Sea and Sea-Shore Birds (common in some localities).

Gannet	Redshank
Cormorant	Dunlin
Shag	Greater Black-Back
Wigeon	Kittiwake
Sheld-Duck	Common Tern
Oystercatcher	Razorbill
Ringed Plover	Guillemot
Turnstone	Puffin
Curlew	

Note : * Not found in Scotland.
† Not found in Ireland.

In Ireland and much of the north of Scotland the Hooded Crow replaces the Carrion-Crow.

To these lists may be added the winter visitors : Fieldfare, Redwing, Pochard, Tufted Duck and Common Gull.

In learning how to identify birds, the beginner will also become acquainted with the names of the principal parts of a typical bird (*see* Plate *f.p.*1). He should also acquire a working knowledge of the way in which birds are classified or grouped into orders, families, and species (*see* Classification), and gradually familiarise himself with their scientific names (*q.v.*). He will also find it helpful to learn something about the elementary biology of birds (*see* Anatomy ; Breeding Season ; Moulting ; Reproduction) and of their habits (*see* Behaviour ; Display ; Flight ; Food ; Nesting ; Roosting ; Song ; Territory).

PROBLEMS FOR STUDY

Some people are content merely to spot birds, rather like small boys collecting the numbers of trains. Greater value is usually obtained from a more detailed study of some specific problem or problems. So when the beginner has learnt to recognize about a hundred of the commoner birds, he is advised to undertake some simple field problem, either alone, or with the assistance of friends.

Although everyone is entitled to watch birds to obtain the greatest personal enjoyment, and although nobody should be dogmatic about how others spend their leisure time, it is generally felt that after an initial apprenticeship has been spent in learning how to identify birds, and learning also about their biology and habits, the bird watcher should conduct his observations scientifically.

A scientific approach to a problem is an attitude of mind, not a matter of academic degrees. Above all, it means having a definite purpose and a burning enthusiasm to discover the truth. It also means approaching each problem with an open and receptive mind, recording systematically and methodically one's observations, however unimportant the details may seem, and, finally, drawing from the information thus collected conclusions that can honestly be substantiated.

Most of the problems that may be studied fall under one of the following headings :

Distribution and Population. These two are closely related. The former is largely qualitative—where a particular species is to be found, what type of country it favours (i.e. locality and habitat), and how widely it is distributed. The latter involves a census of the birds in a particular area—either all the birds in the area may be counted or only selected species.

A favourite problem is to take a census of the rookeries in a given neighbourhood. This has been done many times by natural history societies and schools, and in 1945 a nation-wide census was carried out under the supervision of the B.T.O., which collated the information thus obtained. Counting rookeries, however, is not the simplest problem for a beginner. A simpler one is to take a census of the blackbirds and song-thrushes in one's home area. It has been established that the proportion of thrushes to blackbirds has changed considerably in recent years, and it would be of interest to determine if any definite trend exists.

Food. There is as yet no good textbook on the foods birds eat at different seasons and in different places, and much remains to be learnt about feeding habits of even the commoner varieties. The tables under Food are a sound guide to the general food preferences of the various species found in Britain.

Migration. This is hardly a problem for a beginner, but it attracts many who have passed their novitiate. The main work is the catching and ringing of migrant birds using an observatory as a stopping place on their travels. Most observatories have one or more large permanent traps into which the birds are enticed or driven, and from which they can be extracted at leisure through the catching box at the end, and ringed. The use of numbered aluminium rings of the National Scheme is restricted to those who have been vouched for by the Ringing Committee of the B.T.O. There is no restriction on the use of coloured celluloid rings, but nobody should attempt any

FALCON FAMILY, *female Kestrel returning with a tasty morsel for its fluffy, snow-white young*

For text see page 209

ringing without first receiving tuition from an experienced ringer.

Bird Behaviour and History. This covers the everyday habits of birds—their pairing, display and courtship, and their breeding cycle. Much is to be learnt not only about feeding, but such daily routines as sleeping, preening and bathing. Moreover, little is known about what birds do with their " spare time ", i.e. when they are not engaged in some purposeful activity.

Although some kudos is attached to visiting inaccessible places to observe birds, it is a mistake to think that these out-of-the-way visits are essential ; equally, if not more, valuable work can be accomplished in one's own garden, as Hartley sensibly points out in his article on Back Garden Ornithology (*Bird Study*, March 1954), in which he also describes some simple experiments that can be carried out to increase our knowledge of common birds.

Finally, the B.T.O. and local natural history societies are always ready to assist those who find it difficult to decide for themselves what kinds of problem to tackle.

PERMANENT RECORDS

In bird watching, observation and note-taking in the field is backed up by study and research in home, library and museum ; by the production of permanent records based on field observations ; and by attending meetings of naturalist societies.

Note-taking and Recording. Every serious bird watcher should keep a record of his observations. There are many systems of record keeping, but all depend initially on the *Field Note-Book* (*see* Identification), in which, as its name implies, notes are kept of observations made in the field, and—this is very important—at the time they are made and *not from memory*.

Every Field Note-Book should be given a serial number, marked on the cover, and each trip should be started on a fresh page which should be numbered and dated. Similarly, every paragraph should be numbered. The time of day when a particular observation is made should also be entered. A note should be included on the weather and the force and direction of winds. Notes on the type of locality and habitat are also very important. For certain purposes it is useful to give the exact position in the form of a six-figure map reference (not forgetting to state the reference number of the map). It may also help to give the name of the vice-county (recognized sub-division of a county).

If a bird cannot be positively identified in the field, it should be drawn in the note-book, together with a record of any distinguishing

Kenneth Rittener

BIRD WATCHING. *Trying to find nests can be a strenuous performance, as is shown by these two*

marks and details that might help to identify it (*see* Identification). An identification or any other statement about which some doubt exists should never be recorded without including the reasons as to why it is doubtful.

The results of one's field work should be converted into a permanent record at the *earliest possible moment*. There are several different systems for keeping permanent records, each with its particular advantages. The *loose-leaf* system is widely used ; some people preferring to keep a separate note-book for each species. Every note-book is divided into sections, each of which deals with a separate subject, such as description (plumage, weight, size, etc.), food, display, nesting, eggs, incubation, migration—to quote just a few.

An alternative is the *year book*. This is merely a strongly-bound note-book, kept in the form of a diary, with the entries written on one side of the paper only, and wide margins left for further notes. Blank pages provide an opportunity for pasting in photographs, Press cuttings and so on. A subject index giving page references is compiled at the end, or kept on separate cards. There is one obvious objection to this method : after recording one's observations for some years, the entries on a particular subject will, naturally, be scattered through several volumes.

Many professional ornithologists favour a triple *card index* system, but this is hardly recommended to amateur bird watchers, not only because of the high cost but also because of the complications involved to keep the index up-to-date. *Geographical Tally-Lists*—lists of birds known to be in a definite geographical area—can be of great use. A skeleton list of this type is published by the British Trust for Ornithology. A similar list is Sir Hugh S. Gladstone's *An Ornithologist's Field Note-Book* (Truslove and Hanson). Small pocket tally forms are also published by the London Natural History Society and the Birmingham Bird Club.

FIELD EQUIPMENT

One of the advantages of bird watching is that one need not spend a lot of money before making a start. The beginner needs only his own unaided eyes, note-books and pencils, a light stick to part foliage and suchlike in the nesting season, and a few reference books, including a good one on identification (*see* Library). To this simple list may be added an Ordnance Survey Map —a scale of one inch to the mile is suitable for most general purposes.

But the more experienced bird watcher will not remain content with this simple equipment. One of his first wants is a good pair of field-glasses (*q.v.*) or a telescope. The latter is cheaper than field-glasses of comparable quality, but awkward and tiring to use without a stand, unsuited for watching birds other than in open country, and hopeless for watching birds in flight. The enthusiast may also want a camera for obtaining permanent records, and most find a compass invaluable.

For specialised work the bird watcher may want traps (*q.v.*), rings (*see* Ringing), stuffed and dummy birds (*q.v.*), nestboxes (*q.v.*) and bird tables, dummy eggs, mirrors and periscopes, drag and climbing ropes, climbing irons, camouflage material and hides. For further descriptions of some of these special implements *see also* Birdsnesting ; Photography.

Every bird watcher is advised to form at least a small library of reference books—in fact he will find it absolutely essential. This Encyclopedia supplies a fund of information on the varied aspects of bird watching, and will form the nucleus of any such library, but, as in any encyclopedia, space is unfortunately limited. The enthusiast is recommended to include in his library several basic books, a selection of which is given under Library.

Personal Camouflage. This may be of considerable assistance in preventing a bird from being frightened away by an observer. Bright colours such as reds and yellows should be avoided, as should " unnatural " shades like navy-blue and the bluish-greens. Instead, the watcher should choose colours that will blend with the type of country to be worked—a faded mackintosh that is difficult to see against a background of bents or water reeds, will contrast sharply with a fir wood or with snow.

It is important to break up the outline : one simple method is to have a strong contrast in tone between the principal garments, e.g. to wear a dark coat with light-toned slacks, or vice versa. A contrast in tone is more important than a colour contrast. In general, a symmetrical object tends to be more conspicuous than an asymmetrical one, so the outline should be broken up by, say, wearing a scarf draped down one side.

Paul Popper

BIRD WATCHING. *These volunteers are taking part in a nation-wide survey into the waking-times of birds*

Finally, as the head and shoulders are the outlines most characteristic of Man, the more this outline can be disguised the less the birds are likely to be alarmed. A coat over the head is effective but clumsy ; a scarf round the head may also help, but far better is a specially made " camouflage shawl ", consisting of a 4-ft. square piece of brown or green material to which small scraps of pale green, black and khaki are sewn. Worn over the head like an Arab's headdress, this breaks up the outline.

BIRD-WAVE. Sudden migratory wave of exceptional proportions, indicating a previous check in the ordinary flow of migration (*q.v.*).

BITTERN—Botaurus stellaris. Like the Avocet, the Bittern was once common in all suitable marshes in England, Scotland, and Ireland, where its curious " boom " was a familiar sound. Its disappearance about 1830 was due partly to the draining of the fens and partly to its destruction by sportsmen and egg collectors. The Bittern was once a favourite dish, and it has been said that people seldom sat down to their Sunday meal without a roast Bittern on the table.

The Bittern therefore gradually lapsed into the category of rare visitor. As time went on, however, people became more alive to the beauty and interest of birds, and when, in 1911, a pair of bitterns returned to breed on the Norfolk Broads, the nest was carefully guarded. Today the " Butterbump ", as the country folk call it, breeds freely in both Norfolk and Suffolk and even seems to be extending its range to some other counties.

A member of the Heron family, the Bittern is one of the most mysterious as well as most interesting of birds, and there is still much to be learned about its secretive habits. Very little is known, for instance, of its courtship display, and its recognition of the sex of another Bittern at a distance is still a mystery. A solitary bird, it is rarely seen with other species, and is never found far from its cover of reeds. It is so perfectly camouflaged that it can identify itself completely with its surroundings. A sitting Bittern can look so like the stump of an old tree that a watcher can approach within a few yards and still fail to distinguish it from its surroundings. *See also* Camouflage ; Protective Coloration and Camouflage.

In appearance the Bittern is quite different from all other birds, except its two relatives—the Little and the American Bittern (*qq.v.*). It has the form and long beak of the Heron, but its plumage is a warm brown pencilled in streaks of black, and it has an elongated neck which it can push out and draw in at will. Its yellow eyes have a decided squint. The bird has a " powder puff " which it can use in its cleaning processes. The length of the Bittern is 30 in., and its tarsus 3 in. Its wing span is approximately 2 ft., and its weight 3½ lb. Both sexes are alike.

On the ground, the bird has a slow and deliberate walk, but it can move quickly enough when necessary. It has the typical slow and direct flight of its family, with neck and feet both outstretched ; it moves faster than a Heron. but rarely flies very high.

The most curious thing about this queer bird is its " boom ", uttered during the Spring. It has been likened to various sounds—including a distant foghorn and the far-away " moo " of a cow—and has extraordinary carrying power,

John Markham

BITTERN. A lucky shot—for the nest of this shy bird is very difficult to find among the reeds

for it can be heard with ease over two miles away. But very few people have heard it at close quarters ; even the Editor managed only once, after much patient waiting and watching, to approach near enough to procure a satisfactory recording of the Bittern's " boom ". The sound is delivered at all hours of the day and night, but is most frequent after sunset and before dawn, from the middle of February until well into June. Those fortunate enough to hear the Bittern at close range will notice, before the " booming ", the bird making an intake of breath followed by four clicks, but this sound does not carry more than 10 yards at the most.

It is almost impossible to discover the nest of the Bittern, for it is extraordinarily well hidden among the reeds of the marshes. Resting on matted roots, well above the water, it is built of bits of reeds and sedge. Four to six eggs (matching the olive-brown colour of the reeds) are laid in April and May. Hatching is done by the hen alone, for about 26 days, and the young birds are also fed by their mother, who brings the food in her crop and disgorges it into the nest. The young are able to leave the nest after two or three weeks, but cannot fend for themselves for about eight weeks. One brood is usually reared in a season.

The food of the Bittern consists of such animals as water-voles, shrews, mice and young birds, some of which it can swallow whole ; fish and insects are also eaten.

BLACK-BACKED GULL. *See* Greater Black-backed Gull ; Lesser Black-backed Gull.

BLACK-BELLIED PLOVER. American name for the Grey Plover (*q.v.*).

BLACK-BILLED CUCKOO — **Coccyzus erythrophthalmus.** A bird of North America, the Black-billed Cuckoo has occasionally wandered to the British Isles, but only two visits have been recorded. It lacks the reddish-brown on the wings of its yellow-billed relative, and has no black on the tail and very little white. The mantle is brown and the underparts greyish-white ; the bill is black and round, and the eye is a red ring. The length is 11½ in., and the tarsus 0·95 in. The wing span is 11½ in.

A graceful, long-tailed bird, it frequents woods, thickets, orchards and gardens, moving furtively among the trees, for its habits are secretive. The song is entirely different from that of the British Cuckoo, but not unlike that of the Yellow-billed Cuckoo, though softer and not so harsh. It is frequently heard during the night.

Although it is known to show parasitic tendencies, it generally builds its own nest and rears its young. The nest, placed among the branches of a tree, is made of twigs and roots and lined with wool and moss. In late May, June, or even July, two to seven greenish-blue eggs are laid ; both male and female share the hatching and rearing of the young. The food consists entirely of harmful insects.

BLACKBIRD—**Turdus merula.** Were a general vote taken to choose the favourite song bird in the British Isles, there is little doubt that the Blackbird would top the poll. A member of the Thrush family, it stays to charm us at every season of the year, not only in the countryside, but in all the gardens, shrubberies, parks, squares and open spaces of our cities and towns. Some local migration takes place from the north to the south in the Autumn and even over the English Channel. The Autumn also brings an influx of Continental birds to spend the Winter in Great Britain. Abroad, the Blackbird is found all over Europe, in many parts of Asia and in North Africa.

It is with the liquid beauty of its song that the Blackbird delights the human race, and in this it has no rival among British birds. To begin with the call notes : the Blackbird has a large vocabulary of these ; and to describe them, I must confess, is merely guess-work, although I have watched blackbirds for many years. I have come to some conclusion, however, as to what the different calls *may* mean. I have studied four different call notes :

(1) A very soft call which can be heard only at very close range. I believe this is an alarm call inspired by danger from the air—from an enemy bird of prey or a Jay, but I have heard the same call when vermin were near the nest.

(2) A quiet call, a little sentimental, heard especially when the chicks are in the nest.

(3) The well-known alarm call, heard the whole year round. This is a warning to its own species, and also to other birds, that an enemy, probably a cat or a dangerous human, is near. I have also heard this continuous alarm note when blackbirds were mobbing an Owl or other bird of prey.

(4) A note of extreme alarm, uttered on the wing. This took me eight years to record, as it is impossible to know when and where the bird will make this particular call which lasts only a fraction of a second.

As to the song, I must say it has no peer among British songsters. No instrument or bird imitator can reproduce its flute-like timbre. Long experience has proved to me that every song bird has its own version of the song of its species ; this is noticeable among blackbirds, and it is possible to recognize by its song one individual Blackbird that has returned to territory that it occupied earlier. Even off-spring, returning to the place where their parents reared them, can be recognized by the same " family " song. The Blackbird is perhaps heard at its best in its evening song, uttered from some high place just before going to roost. It is also a good mimic, and I have recorded a very fine imitation of the Song-Thrush, with the Blackbird's characteristic timbre.—EDITOR.

From March to mid-June is the best song period of the Blackbird, but individual birds sometimes sing an incomplete song in Winter. Listeners are, however, often deceived by that master mimic, the Starling; imitating the Blackbird's song.

The jet-black glossy plumage, bright orange bill and marked ring round the eye make the male Blackbird distinctive, but the female's dark brown mantle, wing and tail, lighter and rather rufous-brown underparts and more or less distinct mottled markings on the breast

W. Farnsworth

BLACKBIRD. *Three hungry youngsters are asking Father to hurry up and decide whom to feed first*

BITTERN, *past master of protective coloration*

For text see pages 71 *and* 406

often cause her to be confused with the Song-Thrush. The young blackbirds are browner and more mottled than the hen, and have blackish bills. Albinism (*q.v.*) is not uncommon in this species. The length of the Blackbird is 10 in., and the tarsus 1·4 in. The wing span is up to 14 in., and the weight 4 oz.

The Blackbird is not really gregarious, except on migration and in Winter, when it will consort and roost with other thrushes. An " early " bird, it is one of the first to be seen and heard after daybreak. Its progress on the ground is distinctive and characteristic : it hops along, breaks into a run and then stops as if to listen—probably for worms, one of its favourite foods. The movements are not unlike those of the Song-Thrush, but there is more action of the tail and, indeed, the Blackbird is in every way a much livelier bird. The flight is quick, direct and undulating but, as a rule, for no great distance, except on migration. Alighting with ease and grace, the Blackbird has a curious habit of airily flirting its tail constantly up and down. It is perhaps more timid than others of its family, and, especially during the breeding season, is never very far from the shelter of bushes and undergrowth.

The Blackbird is said to mate for life. The varied courtship display and posturing begins early in Spring. No definite procedure seems to be followed, but the male shows his excitement by his fanned tail and spread feathers as he pursues the female. In one recorded instance the male circled round the hen, singing softly. " Injury-feigning " appears to be rarely indulged in.

The Blackbird's breeding season begins in March, but is not in full swing until April, and it can continue until July, for two, three, and sometimes four broods are reared in a season, often from the same nest. Bushes, hedges, wall ivy, gardens, parks and even buildings provide the favourite sites for blackbirds' nests. As a rule, the nest is not far from the ground, although the Editor has found one 30 ft. above ground in a tree. Normally the hen alone builds the nest, which is fashioned with moss and grass, held together with mud and lined with dried grass. The eggs, varying in number from three to five—but as many as nine have been recorded—are bluish-green, boldly speckled and blotched in reddish-brown. The hen takes on the greater part of the brooding, which begins on the completion of the clutch and lasts for about a fortnight. The young are reared and tended by both parents for about the same period.

Worms, beetles, spiders and other insects, often obtained by turning over dead leaves.

Eric Hosking

BLACKBIRD. *One of the favourite pastimes of this bird is to listen for worms early in the mornings*

form the chief food of blackbirds. There is no denying, however, that they are most destructive to fruit, especially during a drought, but this can often be prevented in a small garden by placing bowls of water within their reach. During a hard Winter the Blackbird is almost wholly dependent on human charity.

BLACK-BROWED ALBATROSS. *See* Albatross.

BLACKCAP—Sylvia atricapilla. One of the Warbler family, the Blackcap is among the finest of our songsters. It is to be seen in most parts of England, but is scarce in Scotland and Ireland. A migratory bird, it is a summer visitor, arriving some time during March and April from its winter home in the south and leaving again in the Autumn. Blackcaps have been known to remain in Britain for the Winter, but this is very rare.

Only the male bird has the black " cap ", the rest of his plumage being different shades of brown and grey, much darker towards the tail and lighter underneath. The " cap " and plumage of the female are chestnut brown, with light grey underneath. The young birds resemble the female. The length of the male bird is 5½ in., and the tarsus 0·85 in. The wing span is about 7 in., and the weight ½ oz.

The bird's flitting flight and movements resemble those of the Garden-Warbler (*q.v.*),

Eric Hosking

BLACKCAP. *Shyly flitting from branch to branch, this fine songster produces wonderfully rich notes*

but the distinctive " cap " prevents confusion between them. Blackcaps and garden-warblers are seen hopping about the same areas of dense vegetation together ; they favour bushes, hedgerows, brambles and briars, and some have a fondness for rhododendrons. Later, when nesting duties are over, they often frequent gardens and orchards.

A shy bird, the Blackcap slips in and out among these growths, and only its sweet and charming song attracts attention. The volume of the rich notes which comes from this little bird is amazing, but only a minority can produce the perfect song. The finest of them begin their performance with a prelude cleverly brought to a crescendo that has no equal among British song birds. Apart from this well-known song, the Blackcap has many other notes, among them a wonderful continuous warbling which it utters while well hidden in the undergrowth. This sound is not so familiar, but the Editor heard it once and was able to get a very good record. The Blackcap's song is heard throughout April and continues into July. Like all warblers, it has a very harsh alarm note.

The nest, which is built in thick growth, brambles, bushes, etc., looks a fragile affair, but is as strong as it needs to be. It is constructed of hay, grass and roots, and cosily lined with hair. The eggs are laid late in May ; they number four or five and vary considerably in colour, but as a rule are whitish-brown with

dark blotches, similar to the Garden-Warbler's. Both birds assist in hatching, and the male has been known to sing on the nest. Blackcap chicks are quite naked when hatched—another similarity to the warbler family. One clutch, sometimes two, are laid in a season.

The Blackcap feeds on various insects, but is not welcome in orchards, where it consumes berries and fruit.

BLACK-CAPPED PETREL—Bulweria hasitata. This bird is now believed to be more or less extinct, and the only reason for its inclusion here is that many years ago one was caught on a heath in Norfolk. This petrel is described as larger than the Manx Shearwater (*q.v.*), which it otherwise resembled except that it possessed a distinct black " cap " and more white on its tail ; its white nape made a very distinct band between the black " cap " and the mantle. It was 16 in. long, with a wing span of about 2½ ft.

The Black-capped Petrel used to breed in burrows among the roots of trees in mountainous districts of the West Indies, but very few reliable details exist concerning its habits and behaviour.

BLACKCOCK. *See* Black Grouse ; the male of which is known as Blackcock, the female as Greyhen.

BLACK CORMORANT. Common name for the Cormorant (*q.v.*) because of its all-black appearance from a distance. Actually, the bird has a blue-black head, neck and underparts, with bronze-green wings and tail, with a white patch on the face and, in Summer, also on the thigh.

BLACK CURLEW. Common name for the Glossy Ibis (*q.v.*). This bird closely resembles a Curlew in shape, and its plumage seems almost black, although at close range it is seen to be shot with purple, bronze and green.

BLACK DUCK. *See* Common Scoter. The male is the only duck with a completely black plumage, relieved only by the bright orange patch on the otherwise black bill.

BLACK-EARED WHEATEAR—Oenanthe hispanica. There are two types of this bird—the Western Black-eared Wheatear (*Oenanthe hispanica hispanica*) and the Eastern Black-eared Wheatear (*Oenanthe hispanica melanoleuca*) both breeding in Mediterranean countries, and both rare visitors to the British Isles. The names Western and Eastern refer to the region of the Mediterranean where they breed.

Unlike their relatives, the males of both types have two distinct contrasts in their plumage—one a blacked-eared phase and the other a black-throated phase.

In the Western bird, the male plumage is pale sandy buff, often pure white on the head.

The underparts are white and the wings black. In the blacked-eared phase, only the ear coverts and the line through the eye are black ; in the black-throated phase, the whole throat is black. The female has much the same appearance as the common Wheatear (*q.v.*).

In the Eastern bird, the whole plumage is whiter than in the Western. The black-eared phase has the area of black round the ear coverts extended across the forehead ; in the black-throated phase, the black on the throat extends much lower down. The female is generally darker than the Western.

The song of both wheatears follows the usual pattern ; the " alarm " note near the nest is recorded as a rasping sound.

Apart from differences in appearance, the country frequented, behaviour and breeding habits do not differ materially from those of the common Wheatear. Insects form the main food.

BLACK GROUSE—Lyrurus tetrix. As a British resident this handsome game bird decreases in numbers year by year, probably because it is so good to eat. The efforts of bird protectionists and bird lovers to educate the public to preserve wild life, which have been attended by so much success in general, have not availed to save the Black Grouse. This bird is more likely to be seen in Scotland than in England or Wales. It does not breed in the Orkney or Shetland Islands, and is unknown in Ireland ; attempts to re-introduce it to its former haunts in England have so far been in vain.

The appearance of the male, which goes by the name of Blackcock, is unmistakable. He has a beautiful black plumage with a glossy sheen ; his under-tail coverts are pure white,

as is also his wing bar. Over his eye there is a red wattle, and his legs are feathered. But his most outstanding feature is his magnificent and unique lyre-shaped tail. The female—called the Greyhen—is a smaller and much less spectacular bird, with barred brown and black plumage and broad white wing bar ; her tail is distinctly forked. The length of the Blackcock is 22 in., and his tarsus $2\frac{1}{4}$ in. ; his wing span is $2\frac{1}{2}$ ft., and he weighs approximately 4 lb. The Greyhen is 17 in. in length, with a tarsus of 2 in. ; her wing span is 2 ft., and she weighs $2\frac{1}{2}$ lb.

The Blackcock has the typical game-bird flight, low when rising from the moor but fast and high if necessary, and he has a slow, majestic walk on the ground. He usually roosts on the ground.

The most extraordinary characteristic of the Blackcock is the great display exhibition in the Spring. The cocks gather in open moorland places called " leks ", where they indulge in competition for the favours of the greyhens standing around like an admiring audience. Each cock selects his own territory, and there dances, jumps in the air, fights with his competitors, and generally shows off the many and varied contortions of his body with his graceful tail widespread and elevated in order to show his white expanse of back feathers. This display is not intended for any one particular Greyhen, for the Blackcock is polygamous and, strange to relate, these displays sometimes occur in Autumn, so that they are not always a special characteristic of mating time.

The Editor writes that in this country the Blackcock is heard but rarely, but on the Continent he has listened to as many as 300

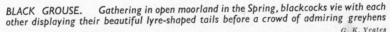

BLACK GROUSE. *Gathering in open moorland in the Spring, blackcocks vie with each other displaying their beautiful lyre-shaped tails before a crowd of admiring greyhens*

G. K. Yeates

John Markham

BLACK GUILLEMOT. *Being an unsociable creature, each Black Guillemot tries his hardest not to look his fellow in the face, pretending he is the only bird on the beach*

calling after midnight. Their actual note is a "rookcooing", a sound best described as very excited and high-pitched. Otherwise the Black Grouse's call is not unlike the Pheasant's, and there is a special high-pitched call to bring their chicks to them.

Black Grouse breed in moorland, heaths, the outskirts of woods containing larch and pine trees, mountainous districts, and occasionally even cultivated land. The breeding season is usually in May. The nest is only a hollow in the ground, sheltered by the growth around ; its position is selected by the Greyhen, which lays 6 to 10 yellowish-looking eggs with reddish-brown markings. One egg is laid every 36 hours, the nest being covered over in the interval. The hen alone carries out the hatching ; sometimes as many as 16 eggs have been found under one hen, the result, of course, of more than one "marriage". The chicks appear in about three weeks' time, and the Greyhen looks after them alone for another three weeks. One brood is reared a season.

The food of the Black Grouse is mainly vegetable and includes the buds of pine and larch trees, bilberries, bog myrtle and other wild plants. Some insects are also eaten, the diet varying according to the kind of country frequented. Black Grouse can do a good deal of harm to ripe corn.

The Blackcock will sometimes mate with a female Capercaillie or Pheasant, and hybrids of such unions are not infrequently seen.

BLACK GUILLEMOT—Uria grylle. This is the least known of the three guillemots, members of the Auk family, which are resident in the British Isles. Yet it is a most attractive bird, and one of the most interesting marine species to watch. Its members have been on the decline of recent years, and it is now more or less confined to the north, especially the islands of Scotland. It is a common bird in Orkney and Shetland (where it is called the "Tystie"), and also breeds freely round all the coasts of Ireland. Abroad its home is in Northern Europe. Other local names for it are "Dovekie" or "Scout".

The Black Guillemot has two distinct seasonal plumage changes. In the Summer, in its beautiful dress of glossy black, with a large white patch on its wings, no bird is more easily recognized. In Winter, its head and underparts are nearly all white, its back being barred black and white ; the white patches on the wings remain, but are not so conspicuous. Between seasons, while it is changing its plumage, the bird presents a very bedraggled appearance. Its feet are red. The inside of its mouth is also red, so that when the bird gapes its bill has a red appearance, although it is actually black. The Black Guillemot is about 13½ in. long, and its tarsus 1¼ in. ; its wing span is about 2½ ft., and its weight 13 oz.

In common with its near relatives, it has a curious way of standing on its toes and walking upright. An expert swimmer, it moves fast and keeps close to the water, propelling itself with wings and feet ; some of its dives have been known to last for as long as 45 seconds. It has the whirring flight of the auks and seems to take off from water with some difficulty.

In contrast to those of the Northern and Southern Guillemot, the Black Guillemot's call and song are so high pitched that they are inaudible to most people. The human ear detects sounds of a frequency of between 6,408 and 8,000 vibrations per second, and the frequency range of the Black Guillemot's song is from 5,000 to 16,000.

Unlike the rest of its family, it is not at all sociable. It is usually seen alone, or in small parties of three or four. Nor does it nest in colonies, though several nests may be seen together or not far from one another. The birds spend the Winter at sea, not far from the shore and their breeding sites, and are seldom, if ever, seen inland. They will return year after year to the same nesting places.

Black guillemots begin to arrive on the coasts and islands about the end of February, but they seldom take up their positions at their nesting sites until late April or early May. No attempt is made to construct a nest, and the eggs are merely deposited in a crevice of a cliff at no great height, or placed under the stones or boulders at the foot of a crag. Two eggs—or sometimes only one—are laid at the end of May or in early June. Smaller than the eggs of the common Guillemot, they are white or pale green, blotched over with reddish-brown or grey. Both birds assist in the hatching, which takes about three weeks. The chicks are fed by both parents, and it is a month before they can leave the nest and look after themselves. One brood is reared in a season. Black guillemots begin to leave their nesting sites at the end of July, and most of them have departed by the end of September.

Their food consists entirely of small fish, shrimps, rock-eels and prawns. *See also* Auk ; Guillemot.

BLACK-HEADED BUNTING — Emberiza melanocephala. A rare visitor to Great Britain, this bird has nevertheless been observed more frequently than some other rare visiting buntings. It has appeared in England and Scotland seven or eight times, but no visit has been recorded in recent years. Its natural breeding places are in south-eastern Europe and Asia. Great flocks of these birds winter in India.

It is very similar in appearance to the Yellow Bunting (*q.v.*), but can be distinguished by its larger size, the black head of the male, and the absence of the white in the tail which is characteristic of all other buntings except the Red-headed. The female is brown with dark streaks, and has yellow underparts. It is said that the Black-headed Bunting flies, like the Corn Bunting (*q.v.*), with its legs dangling behind. Its length is about 6 in. and its tarsus 0·8 in. ; its wing span is 9 in.

From all accounts its song, which is delivered from a bush, telegraph wire or tree, is more musical than that of most buntings.

The breeding season is from the middle of May until the end of June. The Black-headed Bunting nests in thick bushes, brambles, vineyards, olive groves and gardens. Its nest is not placed on the ground (like those of so many other buntings), but at least 2 ft. above it. It is loosely built of thistle leaves, dead plants and grass, and lined with hair and fine grass. Four or five eggs are laid, and the hatching is done by the hen alone for a fortnight.

In Summer the bird's food is chiefly seeds and insects, and in Autumn it lives on fruit and grain. *See also* Bunting.

BLACK-HEADED GULL—Larus ridibundus. This is the commonest seagull of town and country ; and has the distinction of being one of the most numerous of British birds. There is some evidence of a continual increase, especially inland ; and so many thousands of these gulls live and breed inland that, were it not for its name, many people would not associate the bird with the seaside. Although it is, of course, still very much a bird of the shore, it is probable that the number of those that breed near the coasts is today no larger than the number breeding in inland country where there is water of any kind.

Outside the nesting season, it is commonly seen in many places where it does not breed,

W. Farnsworth

BLACK-HEADED GULL. *Thousands of these gulls breed inland wherever there is water of any kind*

Eric Hosking

BLACK-HEADED GULL. These gulls are lazy builders and may place their nests anywhere

notably in large cities on a river ; for instance, hundreds collect on the Thames Embankment in London. The Black-headed Gull has even become a garden bird in the Winter, and relies on the food provided by householders. There is nothing more thrilling than to watch the graceful plunging and diving of the gulls as they catch tit-bits thrown into the air.

The Black-headed Gull is one of the smallest of the Gull family. Slim in build, it is the only gull with a red bill and red legs. Its seasonal changes of appearance sometimes cause it to be confused with the Common Gull (*q.v.*)—which is a much less common bird, despite its name. Both in Summer and Winter, the main plumage of the Black-headed Gull is white with a silver-grey mantle, but in the breeding season the head becomes dark brown—*not* black, in spite of its name—with a white circle round the eye. In Winter the dark brown disappears, leaving only a few dark markings. Both sexes have the dark head. The bird is about 15 in. long, and its tarsus 1¾ in. Its wing span is slightly under 3 ft. ; its weight 10 oz.

An extremely sociable bird, the Black-headed Gull consorts not only with its own kind, but also with various wading birds—and, when inland, with such birds as lapwings, starlings, rooks and golden plovers. Gulleries containing huge numbers are found on the edges of lakes, estuaries, islands, tussocks in large pools, and moors. At Ravenglass Gullery (*q.v.*), in Cumberland, one of the best known sites, the gulls nest in hundreds on the sand-dunes near the shore. In Yorkshire, they are known to breed at a height of 2,000 ft. on the moors.

The flight of the Black-headed Gull is graceful and buoyant, and it can cover long distances.

It is often seen perching on posts, walls of embankments and harbours, but rarely on trees. It is fond of swimming.

British gulls have a large vocabulary, but most people hear only the shrill feeding note of the Black-headed Gull, which has given it its other name of " Peewit Gull ". There is also a softer note, which is a kind of communication between the two or three birds who are acting as look-outs and the rest of the flock, to warn the latter of approaching danger. The look-outs do not feed with the flock. Whenever they hear this special call the whole flock instantly rise in flight and does not return to feed until quite sure that all danger is past.

Black-headed gulls have many different calls, used in courting, attack, defence, etc., a very characteristic sound, not often heard, is the open laughing call from which it takes its Latin name *ridibundus* (" full of laughter ").

When the gulls arrive at their nesting sites about the middle of April, they are, as a rule, already in pairs. The nest is an indifferent affair, composed of any available vegetable matter and placed almost anywhere—on the ground at the edges of pools, in shallow water, near lochs or sandhills, or on a moor. Normally the number of eggs is three, but as many as five or six have been known. Their ground colour is very variable—sometimes bluish, sometimes greenish, sometimes buff or brown—but all have blotches of grey, brown and black. Both cock and hen take part in hatching, which lasts about three weeks, and in feeding the chicks. These are at first covered with soft brown down ; they soon take to the water, and are able to look after themselves in about a couple of months. One brood is reared in a season.

A cloud of gulls following the plough in company with other birds is a familiar country sight, for their food consists mainly of worms and many kinds of insects ; but almost anything edible is taken—small fish, birds and their eggs, seeds, plants and garbage.

The gulls begin to desert their nesting sites about the middle of July, and they have all gone by the end of August. Some migrate, but most of them move only to other parts of the country seeking marshes, reservoirs, or sewage farms. and entering the river cities in great numbers.

Gulls' eggs have long been a table delicacy and still appear in shops and restaurants. Many so-called plovers' eggs (which are protected by law) in the shops and on the menu are actually eggs of the Black-headed Gull.

BLACK-HEADED GULL, GREAT, *See* Great Black-headed Gull.

BLACK-HEADED GULL, MEDITER-RANEAN. *See* Mediterranean Black-headed Gull.

BLACK-HEADED WAGTAIL—Motacilla flava feldegg. A very rare visitor to the British Isles—only four have been recorded in England and one in Scotland—the Black-headed Wagtail breeds in the Balkan Peninsula, Greece and Asia Minor. The male, with his black head and yellow throat, is very distinctive, and is quite unlike any of our wagtails. The female also has a dark head, but this is less conspicuous. The song of the Black-headed Wagtail is not so sweet as those of other members of the Yellow species (*see* Yellow Wagtail). The bird has a length of 6 in. and its tarsus is 1 in. Its wing span is approximately 9 in.

It resembles other wagtails in behaviour and habits, but some authorities report that, outside its breeding season in May and June, it is more of a woodland bird. In the breeding season, it frequents sea and salt marshes. Its nest, which is placed on the ground, is built of grass and stalks, and lined with hair and feathers. Four to six eggs are laid; both parents assist in the hatching and rearing of the young. Insects form their chief food.

BLACK KITE—Milvus migrans. Three visits at least have been paid to the British Isles by the Black Kite from its breeding haunts in north Africa and central and southern Europe. It is smaller, and has darker plumage and a much less deeply forked tail, than the common Kite (*q.v.*). The length is 23 in. and the tarsus 2 in. The wing span is 3–4 ft., and the weight 2½ lb.

The Black Kite seems to have fared better than the British species, which is now one of our rare birds. This is partly due to the more plentiful food supply where the Black Kite breeds, for it feeds chiefly on carrion, dead and dying fish, and the floating refuse found in estuaries and inland waters. It also haunts refuse and garbage dumps in large towns.

The behaviour and habits of the Black Kite mostly resemble those of the common species, but it is said to be much noisier. It is a social breeder, and many nests are found close together in trees and on the sides of cliffs. The nest, a conglomeration of sticks, refuse, earth, paper and moss, is built by both male and female. The eggs are white and number two or three; they are laid in April or May in the Mediterranean region, and somewhat later in countries farther north. Both male and female share the hatching of the eggs and the rearing. One brood is brought out in a season.

BLACK LARK—Melanocorypha yeltoniensis. A rare visitor to the British Isles—its last recorded appearance was in 1915—the Black Lark is a wanderer from its home in the steppes of south Russia and Siberia. In many ways it resembles another rare visitor, the Calandra Lark (*q.v.*), and may be confused with it, even by the expert, except at close quarters. In its summer plumage, the Black Lark justifies its name, but in Winter the black changes to a brownish tinge. The bird is about 7½ in. long.

Its voice is said to resemble our Skylark's (*q.v.*), but is described as less melodious. In the breeding season, which is in May, the Black Lark nests near salt marshes. The nest is placed in a hollow in the ground and lined with dead leaves; four or five greyish-white eggs are laid. Insects are the chief item in its diet.

BLACK-NECKED GREBE—Podiceps caspicus. This is one of the rare summer visitors to the British Isles, and only a few breed here and there on lakes and lochs. It is also a winter visitor to the east and south coasts, and a passage migrant, usually inland. It breeds in a number of European countries, and in North America is known as the Eared Grebe. In many ways it resembles the Slavonian Grebe (*q.v.*), but its slightly curved bill serves to distinguish it.

In breeding plumage the Black-necked Grebe has a glossy black mantle, with flanks of a rich copper colour; its head and neck are black. From behind its pink eyes a sheaf of silky bronze feathers (its " ears ") flows downwards. It has a white wing bar and its underparts are pure white; its legs are grey. In Winter it loses its colour and becomes a mere black-and-white water bird. Its total length is 12 in., the body being 7 in.; its tarsus is 1 in. It weighs

Arthur Christiansen

BLACK KITE. *Strange to think that this noble-looking creature, seen about three times in Britain, feeds chiefly on dead matter*

approximately 7 oz., and its wing span measures about 12 in.

The Black-necked Grebe nests in colonies on lakes and ponds, reservoirs and meres. It is shy during the day and never ventures far from cover of the reeds, but becomes more courageous as dusk approaches. Outside the breeding season it mingles freely with the Slavonian Grebe. It is not much given to flying, and when swimming carries itself very erectly, fluffing out its side feathers to produce a very broad, squat appearance from behind. When danger is near, it will sometimes submerge completely.

Its voice has varied notes, but is mainly a soft, whistling whinny ; some of its calls closely resemble those of other grebes.

The floating nest is similar in structure to that of the Little Grebe (q.v.), and is placed among the vegetation of rivers, ponds, lakes and marshes. Sometimes very large, it is a collection of decaying matter and water weeds, gathered together by both male and female. The breeding months in Britain are May and June. Both birds take their share in the three weeks' hatching of the three or four white eggs—often stained dark brown from vegetation in the nest —and both tend and feed their young, carrying them on their backs, as grebes often do.

In contrast to its relatives' diet of fish, the Black-necked Grebe's food consists mainly of insects, although the young sometimes eat fish.

Eric Hosking

BLACK REDSTART. This is the only rare bird to have paid a special visit to Broadcasting House

BLACK REDSTART—Phoenicurus ochruros.
In the past this was only an interesting passage migrant and winter visitor to the British Isles, breeding occasionally in the south and east of England. But in recent years it has shown a considerable increase in its numbers and breeding haunts in England ; in Scotland it has recently been recorded as a passage migrant in small numbers in Spring and Autumn ; and in Ireland it appears as a regular autumn visitor and less frequently in Spring. Since the Second World War, it has even become one of London's breeding birds, much to the joy and interest of the City's ornithologists and bird-watchers.

Ages ago the Black Redstart must have nested on lonely rocks, a preference it seems never to have lost, for it still chooses such places as ruins, building sites and waste ground ; London's bomb sites therefore offer it an ideal home. It also breeds on cliffs, both beside the sea and inland, and mountains in the south of Europe, where it is regularly found at 6,000 ft. and it has even been recorded at 11,000 ft. Winter finds it alone in much the same places, but at other times it is seen in small flocks.

> My recording of the voice of the Black Redstart made bird history. On my return to London one day from an 800-mile recording trip, a colleague in Broadcasting House, whose office was on the sixth floor, drew my attention to a bird which, he believed, was " no sparrow ". Half-an-hour's watch on the balcony brought not only the call note of the Black Redstart, but also its warbling, and a close-up recording was made.
>
> I should like to mention specially the curious pebble-like note which the bird frequently interposes between his two different tunes. I watched carefully, and came to the conclusion that this sound is produced by the mandible of the bill, similar to the note preceding the call of the Wheatear.
>
> The bird was so close to the microphone that its voice could be heard even above the roar of West End traffic, with Big Ben striking in the background. This was the first time that a rare bird had paid a visit to Broadcasting House itself.—EDITOR.

The Black Redstart's song is usually delivered from a perch on a building, sometimes at a good height ; it lasts about four seconds and is repeated several times a minute. The best time to hear it is in the early morning, from April until June.

It has the rust-coloured tail of its relative, the common Redstart (q.v.), but much darker plumage—almost black, in fact—and the absence of orange colour on its underparts is a difference visible at all ages. The male is greyer, and its white wing patch is much in evidence. The less dark female is more a smoky-grey colour, but she, too, has the reddish tail. Both bills and legs are black. The length of the Black Redstart is 5½ in. and its tarsus

0·9 in. Its wing span is about 8 in., and its weight ½ oz.

The two species of redstart have much in common in their movements ; both show the same flitting flight from branch to branch or from perch to perch, and a curious flicking of the tail and body. The Black Redstart has a more rapid running hop on the ground and is more in evidence, usually perching openly on rocks, buildings, trees and walls.

The nest of the Black Redstart is built inside farm sheds, under eaves and in crevices and holes in rocks and cliffs. In towns, any hole or crevice in buildings will suffice. It is generally constructed of moss and grasses and lined with hair and feathers, most of the work being done by the hen. Four to six glossy white eggs are laid early in April (later in mountainous districts). The hen does all the hatching, which takes about a fortnight, but both parents feed the chicks for a little over two weeks. Two broods—but occasionally three—are brought out in a season.

The Black Redstart feeds chiefly on insects which, with graceful aerobatics, it catches on the wing. Some berries are also eaten.

BLACK SHEARWATER. Common name for Sooty Shearwater (*q.v.*) because the bird looks all-black from a distance. On closer inspection, it is seen to have an uniform sooty plumage, with a paler area on the under-surfaces of its wings, mostly in the form of an indistinct whitish stripe along the centre.

BLACK STORK—Ciconia nigra. A rare visitor to the British Isles, the Black Stork breeds throughout Europe, Africa and in northern Asia. The plumage is black with a beautiful rich bronze-green sheen, except for the breast, underparts and under-tail coverts which are white. The legs and beak are red. The length is 38 in., the body being 20 in.; the tarsus 7 in. The wing span is from 4 to 5 ft.

The behaviour of the Black Stork differs greatly from that of the White Stork (*q.v.*), for it is seldom seen near human habitation and single pairs breed in deep forests. The Black species also has a very individual guttural voice, with many well-developed notes.

The nest, which is built in a tree, some 30–70 ft. from the ground, is made with sticks, earth and moss, and lined with bits of soft green moss. The same nests are used year after year, with usually some small addition so that in time they become very bulky structures. Both male and female share the work. The breeding season in Europe is in late April or early May, and the eggs, oval and white, number three to five, one being laid every two days. Both birds hatch the eggs, though the

Eric Hosking

BLACK-TAILED GODWIT. *Driven away by the egg-collectors, this wader is breeding here again*

hen takes the greater share, the period being well over a month. The young are fed by regurgitation, the food being emptied on to the nest. The Black Stork feeds entirely on animal matter, chiefly fish.

BLACK-TAILED GODWIT—Limosa limosa. Like several other waterside birds once common in Britain, the Black-tailed Godwit had, by about 1850, been almost exterminated by changes in the agricultural scene, coupled with the facts that it was hunted as food and, as a consequence of its scarcity, became a prey to egg-collectors. It continued to be a passage migrant and winter visitor, however, and has recently shown a tendency to return as a breeding bird. Of the increasing numbers which arrive every year, some stay to breed on the east and south coasts of England. Abroad, it breeds in Holland, Sweden, Denmark, France, Poland and the Baltic States.

When seen on the ground the Black-tailed Godwit is so similar to its near relative the Bar-tailed Godwit (*q.v.*) that they are often and easily confused.

But when the black-tailed species takes to the air, its noticeable tail immediately distinguishes it. This is black, with one broad and very conspicuous white bar at the top, the white tips of which show at the end of the tail. Although at first glance its summer plumage seems similar to that of the bar-tailed bird, it is actually much lighter on its breast and underparts—also conspicuous in flight. At close range its bill is seen to be straighter. Its long greyish legs are held well behind its tail when it flies. The size varies, but the average length is about 16 in., the bill being from $3\frac{3}{4}$–$4\frac{3}{4}$ in. long; the tarsus is about 3 in., and the wing span about $1\frac{1}{2}$ ft. The average weight is 12 oz.

The Black-tailed Godwit has a different display flight from the Bar-tailed Godwit's, and seems to indulge in fewer aerobatics. It has a loud and clear call when in flight, with harsher notes when the birds are chasing each other on the ground. A rather musical display flight is heard at the start of the breeding season.

A very gregarious bird, it is seen in company with many other kinds of waders on the shore. Its breeding, general habits and food do not differ from those of the Bar-tailed Godwit.

BLACK TERN—Chlidonias niger. This tern belongs to the genus of marsh terns (*see* Chlidonias) which are different from the sea-going terns. It disappeared from the British scene as a breeding species about the middle of the 19th century. Until then, this graceful and elegant bird was quite abundant in the Fen country; but the draining of the marshes

for agriculture, the lack of adequate protection and the depredations of the egg-collector—ever on the watch for a rare bird—took their toll, and the " great clamour " of the Black Terns was silenced at their haunts on the Norfolk Broads and in Lincolnshire.

Today it is only a passage migrant in the Spring, between Kent and Norfolk, although in recent years there have been signs that, with encouragement, it might return to breed in Britain; indeed it did so in the early years of the Second World War, when a marsh in Essex was flooded in case of invasion. Southern Scotland and Ireland occasionally see it as a passage migrant.

The Black Tern is quite different from all its relatives in appearance. No other tern has its summer dress of dark slate-grey, shading to black on its head and underparts; only its under tail coverts are white. On its migratory passage, when it is most likely to be seen, it is white, with a dark grey patch on its head; the wings are slate-grey, as also is the tail, which is less forked than that of other terns. Its feet also are distinctive, for the webs are deeply indented between the toes. Its bill is blackish, and its legs are reddish-brown. The Black Tern has a length of $9\frac{1}{2}$ in., and its tarsus 0·6 in. Its weight is $2\frac{1}{2}$ oz. and its wing span about 2 ft.

The Black Tern frequents wet marshes, lagoons and swamps; but its habits and behaviour are in the main similar to those of its family. In its buoyant and graceful flight it wheels high

BLACK TERN. This Marsh Tern is quite unlike any other Tern. It is shown here both in its autumn dress (left) and its summer plumage (below). It is but a poor swimmer but a wonderful acrobat in its flight

Eric Hosking

BLACK-THROATED DIVER. Almost helpless on dry ground, this bird is, as its name
implies, an expert diver and has been known to stay as long as two minutes under water

Eric Hosking

in the air and stoops low over the water. It goes about in small flocks in Winter, often in company with sea terns. It seldom swims, but walks with short tripping steps and perches on stones and posts in the water. On migration it is a silent bird, and even at its breeding place it has only a short, shrill note. Not a great deal is known about its voice.

It breeds in colonies on marshes and lagoons. Its floating nest is made of water reeds and plants and lined with finer grasses and leaves ; both male and female take part in building it. The eggs, usually three, are brown or green, with blotches of blackish-brown. The breeding season is in May, but varies with the country ; it is later in northern Europe. Both male and female share in hatching and also in the rearing of the young of their one brood. The young leave the nest in a fortnight, and are on the wing in about a month. The food of the Black Tern consists mainly of water insects, many being caught on the wing. *See also* Tern.

BLACK-THROATED DIVER—Colymbus arcticus. Three divers, the Great Northern, the Black-throated and the Red-throated, may be seen in the Highlands and islands of Scotland, all described in detail under their own headings. The Great Northern does not breed in this country—at least there is as yet no proof that it does—but is quite common as a winter visitor from October to June. Both the Black-throated and the Red-throated breed in Britain, as well as visit in Winter. All are powerful divers

with strong bills, and differ only in size and the colour of their plumage.

The Black-throated Diver breeds on the large lakes and lochs of the Highlands, Orkneys and Outer Hebrides. Some non-breeding birds stay there all Summer. It is rarely seen in the Shetlands, and seldom visits England, Wales or Ireland. Abroad it breeds in northern Europe and North America. Another name for it is the Pacific Loon.

The general behaviour and habits of the Black-throated Diver scarcely differ from those of the Great Northern Diver. Its manner of diving is identical, and its longest recorded dive lasted for nearly two minutes, in which time it travelled under water for a quarter of a mile. It has the typical wailing shriek of the divers, often uttered in flight. Considering its size and weight, its wings are feeble-looking, but can carry it along with power and speed.

In Summer the head and the back of the neck are slaty-grey and, as its name implies, the throat is black. Down the sides of the longish neck, there are even streaks of black and white. Above, the bird is black with streaks and spots of white, and underneath it is pure white. Its straight and pointed bill, which looks less powerful than the Great Northern Diver's, is black, and its legs are black and grey. In Winter its plumage changes to dark brown above, but remains white below. The male and the female are alike. Its total length of 25 in. includes a 15 in. body ; its wing span is roughly

G. K. Yeates

BLACK-WINGED STILT. The Stilt uses his legs not only for wading, but also as a rudder when flying

3 ft. and its tarsus 3 in. long. The bird weighs 3 lb.

These birds can walk on the ground only with the greatest difficulty ; the nest is therefore always placed near water—usually on an islet just above the water, or on the edge of the shore. It is merely a hollow or depression in the ground, and little or no nesting material is used. Two eggs, dark brown or olive with spots of black and brown, are laid. The nesting season is during May, and both birds take their share in hatching the eggs, the process lasting about a month. The chicks are looked after by both parents for as long as 60 days. One brood is reared in a season.

Most of the Black-throated Diver's food is animal ; it catches sea fish of many kinds under the water, swimming at great speed. Rivers are also visited for freshwater fish.

BLACK-THROATED THRUSH — Turdus ruficollis atrogularis. This is a very infrequent wanderer to the British Isles, the last available record being dated 1911. An Oriental bird, it breeds in Russia and China, and winters in Iraq and northern India. The black throat and breast of the male distinguish it from other thrushes. The mantle is greyish-brown and the underparts white ; the long tail has some reddish feathers. The female is lighter in colour ; her throat and chin are whitish, speckled with black, which gives her the look of the Song-Thrush. The length of the Black-throated Thrush is about 9½ in., and its wing span 11 in. ; the tarsus is 1 in., and it weighs about 2½ oz. In the Eastern form (*Turdus*

ruficollis ruficollis) the black throat is replaced by brick-red.

Its habits are said to resemble those of the fieldfare. Its song is composed of whistling notes resembling those of the Song-Thrush, but without the characteristic repetition. Some notes in the song of the Black-throated Thrush are reminiscent of those of the Blackbird.

It nests in coniferous forests, usually building in the fork of a tree. The nest, which is very like that of the Blackbird, is composed of coarse grass and lined with mud, with an inner lining of grass. The four to six eggs, laid in May, also resemble those of the Blackbird. Worms, insects and berries constitute the food of the Black-throated Thrush.

BLACK WHEATEAR — Oenanthe leucura. A breeding bird of Spain, Portugal and the south of France, the Black Wheatear has been recorded only twice in the British Isles. A larger bird than the Wheatear (*q.v.*), it has all-black glossy plumage and a white rump. The tail is typical of its species, but the under-tail coverts are white, the central feathers black, and the whole tail has a black border. Male and female are alike, but the female is slightly duller in colouring. The length is about 7 in., the tarsus 1 in. ; the wing span about 9 in.

The Black Wheatear has the habits and behaviour of its family. Its song is a soft warbling, beginning and ending with a chirring note. The bird frequents cliffs and gorges, chiefly in mountainous districts, sometimes at an altitude of 6,000 ft. It nests in crevices and holes in rocks, walls and caves, and has the unique habit of hiding its nest behind a façade of stones which it builds itself. The nest is made of grasses and plants, and lined with feathers, wool and hair. In April and May, four to six bluish-white eggs, with reddish spots, are laid : hatching and rearing of the young are done chiefly by the hen. Insects form the greater part of the diet.

BLACK-WINGED PRATINCOLE —Glareola nordmanii. This unusual type of wader very occasionally visits the British Isles when it wanders from its breeding haunts in south-east Europe, south Russia and south-west Asia. It winters in Africa. Its appearance, behaviour and breeding habits closely resemble those of the Collared Pratincole (*q.v.*). The only difference is that its under-wing coverts are black instead of chestnut. The length is 10 in., and the tarsus 1 in. The wing span is about 1½ ft.

BLACK-WINGED STILT — Himantopus himantopus. Always an irregular and rare spring and autumn vagrant to the British Isles, this striking black and white bird has, in recent years, visited Britain more often.

The numbers arriving in 1945 were unusually large, and the fact that at least two pairs bred and brought off young on a sewage farm in the Midlands caused a sensation among ornithologists. It naturally breeds in southern Europe, Africa and southern Asia.

Recognition of the Black-winged Stilt is immediate, for it has disproportionately long pink legs, nearly half the length of its body ; the only other bird with comparable legs is the Flamingo. In the male, the mantle and underparts are white and the wings and tail black ; in Summer, the crown and head are also black. The female is like the male in Winter, but with a browner mantle. Both have long, slender and straight bills, and narrow pointed wings. The young are clad in pale buff with brown streaks, and the underparts are white. The length, including the 2½-in. bill, is 15 in. ; the tarsus is 4 in., and the wing span approximately 2 ft.

The movements of the Black-winged Stilt are not unlike those of the Avocet (q.v.), a bird with which it has some relationship. The walk is graceful and dignified, now and then breaking into a run, and the bird delights in wading out into shallow water. The flight is direct, with quickly beating wings, and the fantastically long legs, kept close together and stretched straight out behind, act as a rudder.

In the dancing and posturing characteristic of the Spring display the male and female career round each other. " Injury-feigning " occurs should an intruder approach the nest. A sharply repeated single note is the bird's ordinary voice, but it has several variations in the breeding season. Sociable in habit, the black-winged stilts go about in small flocks, and frequent flooded areas, especially lagoons, grasslands, and shallow lakes. They are rarely seen on the seashore.

They breed in large and small colonies, building their nests in shallow water or on tussocks of vegetation moored in the water. April and May are the normal breeding months, but the date varies according to the country frequented. Built of twigs and mud, the nest is sometimes quite a substantial structure, but often a mere apology for one. The three or four eggs of the single brood take about 25 days to hatch, both male and female bearing their share. Soon out of the nest, the chicks are reared by both parents.

Specially adapted for seeking its food, the long legs of the Stilt wade deeply into the water in search of insects and floating edible matter. Tadpoles and fish spawn are eaten.

BLEATER or Heather-Bleater. Local name for Common Snipe (q.v.), bleating being another word for the bird's " drumming " in flight.

BLUE-CHEEKED BEE-EATER — Merops superciliosus. This tropical bird has been observed once in Great Britain ; this was in Cornwall, in 1951, when Dr. Koch was fortunate enough to see it on its first appearance :

> I happened to be on a sound-recording expedition in the Scilly Isles, and was staying in St. Agnes with Miss Hilda Quick, the Secretary of the Cornwall Bird Watching and Preservation Society. One morning the news reached us that a strange and wonderful bird had been seen in the district; it turned out to be a Blue-cheeked Bee-Eater.
>
> This bird is about the size of a Cuckoo, is clad in most beautiful iridescent green plumage, and has the long tail and curved bill characteristic of bee-eaters. I was able to watch it for a long time as it sat on a telegraph wire. It dived down at intervals, obviously to catch insects.
>
> The Blue-cheeked Bee-Eater is never likely to breed in Britain, but it was a very interesting and welcome visitor.—EDITOR.

BLUE-HEADED WAGTAIL—Motacilla flava flava. This rare Wagtail breeds in small numbers in some parts of the British Isles, principally in Sussex and Kent. It is the European counterpart of the Yellow Wagtail (q.v.) and is usually found in company with that bird. Except at very close quarters, it is difficult to distinguish the two. The chief differences are in colouring, the Blue-headed Wagtail having a bluish-grey head and ear coverts, and white, instead of yellow, eye stripes and chin, the white extending back beyond its ear coverts. Its mantle is olive-green and its underparts a bright yellow. Its length is 6½ in. and its tarsus 1 in.; its wing span is nearly 9 in.

In flight, voice, nesting and other habits the Blue-headed Wagtail closely resembles the

Eric Hosking

BLUE-HEADED WAGTAIL. The bird was too quick for the fly, and now the hunter settles down to eat

Yellow Wagtail. It is gregarious outside the nesting season. At breeding time, it frequents the thick vegetation of low-lying meadows; the nest, well hidden in the growth, is built by the hen of bents and roots, and lined with hair. The five or six eggs are laid in May or June, sometimes even in July, and the greater share of the hatching and rearing of the young is taken by the hen. Insects are the principal item in the bird's diet.

BLUE ROCK. This is a variety of London Pigeon (*q.v.*), indistinguishable in plumage and behaviour from the true Rock-Dove (*q.v.*), a wild bird. The Blue Rock and Rock-Dove, whose plumage closely resembles that of the Stock-Dove (*q.v.*), another wild species, have blue-grey upper parts with glossy green and lilac sides to the neck, whitish rump, two broad black bands across the secondaries (but, unlike the Stock-Dove, no black wing-tips), and a terminal black band to its tail.

Even experts find it impossible to distinguish between the Blue Rock and Rock-Dove, although the locality where the bird has been observed is usually a good pointer. The London Pigeon and its Blue Rock form occurs practically always in and near cities or on cliffs or in quarries, though it may be found occasionally in extremely mixed flocks elsewhere.

Country-people often refer to the Stock-Dove as Blue Rock although, strictly speaking, this is not the correct name of the bird.

Fischer-Wahrenholz

BLUETHROAT. This bird is only rarely seen here though it breeds fairly commonly in Central Europe

BLUE-TAILED BEE-EATER—Merops philippinus. This bird has been recorded only once in Great Britain—and that was as far back as 1862. A tropical bird, it nests and breeds in southern Europe and Africa. Its plumage is in brilliant greens, yellows and browns, with blue predominating in the long tail which distinguishes it from the Bee-Eater (*Merops apiaster*) more often seen in Britain. Its other characteristics, size, nesting habits and food resemble those of that bird. *See also* Bee-Eater.

BLUETHROAT—Cyanosylvia svecica. Beautiful and melodious little bird, similar in form and actions to the Robin, the Bluethroat derives its name from the bright blue throat patch sported by the male in Spring. There are two closely related forms, distinguished from each other by the colour of the spot in the centre of the blue throat patch—the Red-spotted Bluethroat having a chestnut spot, and the White-spotted Bluethroat a white one. These are described under their own headings.

In Autumn the male loses its distinctive blue patch, and the throat usually becomes whitish, with some blue and black bordering, and a dark breast band. Females and immatures of both forms are indistinguishable in the field, and are less colourful than the males. They closely resemble females and immature young of the Robin (*q.v.*).

The Bluethroat is closely related to the Nightingale, belonging to a different genus of the same family (*Turdidae*), and its musical and varied song in part faintly resembles those of both the Nightingale and the Woodlark, although it is weaker and less rich. From its power of imitating the notes of other birds, the Laplanders give the Bluethroat a name signifying " bird of a hundred tongues ". It was also at one time called *Luscinia svecica*, or Swedish Nightingale.

The bird is one of those known as Becfin or Beccafico (*q.v.*), and unfortunately appeals to epicures in certain parts of the world.

BLUE TIT—Parus caeruleus obscurus. Of the eight different kinds of Tit which are to be seen in the British Isles, the Blue Tit is the most popular. A charming, lovable and friendly little creature, it seems to have little fear of Man; indeed, some people think it is almost too friendly and cheeky when they catch the little thief cleverly removing the metal cap from a milk bottle and enjoying the " top of the milk ", or when the note left for the milkman is later found torn to pieces on the doorstep ! (Incidentally, the Blue Tit is not the only Tit to behave in this fashion.) Blue tits are favourites of the town bird-watcher; they are the first occupants of any nesting box put out for their

Eric Hosking

BLUETHROAT. *Laplanders call this gay little relative of the Nightingale and the Robin " the bird of a hundred tongues "; and indeed, his song is exceptionally beautiful*

convenience, and will come back to it year after year; and there is no more fascinating pastime than watching their acrobatics round a swinging piece of fat or coconut.

The Blue Tit delights us with its presence all the year round, in woods, copses, gardens, city parks and squares. Although so small, it is one of our most colourful birds : its plump little body is decorated with cap, wings and tail of azure blue, a yellowish-green mantle, and yellow breast and underparts. Its white face is encircled with a dark blue stripe, the line passing through the eye. The Blue Tit is $4\frac{1}{2}$ in. long, and its tarsus $\frac{3}{4}$ in. Its wing span is about 6 in., and it weighs $\frac{1}{3}$ oz.

Much of the Blue Tit's general behaviour and habits are identical with those of the Great Tit (*q.v.*), its nearest relative ; especially its weak, flitting and undulating flight. It hops on the ground, and will sometimes creep up a tree like a tree-creeper. As far as is known, the pairs keep together all the Winter. Though rather pugnacious and quarrelsome, it is nonetheless inclined to be social and, when its domestic duties are over, it will be found in the company of other tits and also with other small birds such as goldcrests and warblers.

The Blue Tit's song is well-known, but many different varieties of notes are heard from individual birds. The song is at its best from January to June. It generally stops during the greatest part of July and August ; then the bird starts calling again, but it does not resume its song until December.

Any hole that takes its fancy will do for the Blue Tit to rear its young—even a letter-box— and it loves to have a nesting box put out for it early in the New Year. The nest, which is

built by both birds, has a foundation of moss and grass, and is cosily lined with wool, hair and feathers. From 8 to 11, but sometimes as many as 14, white eggs are laid towards the end of April, or a little later in the north. Hatching is done by the hen alone, and she will begin sitting before all the eggs are laid ; the cock feeds her while she is brooding—which is for about a fortnight. The pretty little chicks are fed by both parents for about three weeks ; after that they are able to find their own food. The little parents are most valiant in defence of

John Markham

BLUE TIT. *Any hole that takes its fancy will do as a nesting-place for this colourful little bird*

John Markham

BLUE TIT. There are times—this is one of them—when the Blue Tit behaves like a tree-creeper

their nest and young, but despite their courage many a tragedy takes place. One brood is usually reared in a season.

There is no doubt that the Blue Tit sometimes works havoc among autumn fruit and spring buds, but this damage is offset by the good work it does in devouring many injurious insects.

The Blue Tit is well distributed throughout the British Isles, but is not as common as might be believed ; for instance, it is quite scarce in some parts of the north, and is unknown in the Outer Hebrides. "Tom Tit", "Pick-cheese" and "Billy-biter" are the commonest of its many local names.

Continental Blue Tit. *Parus caeruleus caeruleus.* This close relative of the British species breeds all over Europe and comes to Great Britain as an irregular autumn migrant. Little different in plumage from our Blue Tit, it can be seen at close quarters to have a darker and more bluish-green mantle, with brighter blue wings ; also much of the yellow has been lost through cross-breeding in the Continental bird. Its song contains various notes not in our Blue Tit's range, but heard in the Coal-Tit's song. This is particularly noticeable at the height of the season when the song is enriched by a bell-like note that is a real sign of Spring.

The general behaviour, characteristics and habits of the Continental Blue Tit are those of its family. Its breeding season varies according to its country ; in north Europe it is mid-May, and in the south it is at the end of April. Two broods are normally reared in a season.

BLUE-WINGED TEAL—Anas discors. A rare vagrant to the British Isles, the Blue-winged Teal has occasionally been recorded, but it is thought that some of these birds may have been escapes from private collections of ornamental waterfowl. The white crescent in front of the eye on the drake's dark head, and the vivid blue of the shoulder wing of both drake and duck distinguish it from all other ducks. The rest of the plumage is reddish-brown, streaked with black and buff markings, the duck's colouring being less vivid than the drake's. The length is 15 in., with a body of 10½ in. ; and the tarsus 1 in. The wing span is 12 to 14 in.

The habits, behaviour and breeding of the Blue-winged Teal have much in common with those of the Garganey (*q.v.*), a close relative. It is normally a silent bird, and it swims and flies in flocks. During the breeding season, ponds, lakes and pools in almost any type of country are frequented ; the nest is well concealed among the vegetation of a hollow in the ground, and lined with grass and down. Eggs, numbering 10-12, and dull white in colour, are laid in May in the United States, and in June in north Canada. The duck hatches the eggs alone, and rears the young with great devotion ; the drake takes no part in looking after the one brood which is brought out in a season.

The Blue-winged Teal feeds on both animal and vegetable matter. In Winter, when it flies south to the Bahamas, West Indies, Brazil and Chile, it is said to feed in the rice-fields.

BLYTH'S REED-WARBLER—Acrocephalus dumetorum. Only nine or ten birds of this species are recorded as having visited the British Isles, but they are so similar to our marsh- and reed-warblers that even the expert ornithologist finds it difficult to identify them in the field.

Blyth's Reed-Warbler breeds in Russia and Siberia, and winters as far south as India and Ceylon. Its general behaviour, nesting habits and richly melodious song are said to be similar to those of the Marsh-Warbler (*q.v.*). The length is 5 in. and the tarsus 0·9 in. The wing span is about 7 in.

BOATSWAIN (Bosun). Local name for Arctic Skua (*q.v.*) ; probably because of the bird's alarm note, said to be as shrill as a bosun's pipe, and possibly because of this Skua's habit of appointing a watch or guards, changed at regular intervals, to its nesting-colony.

BOHEMIAN CHATTERER or Waxwing. This is the name by which the Waxwing (*q.v.*) is known in North America. The Latin name of this bird is *Bombycilla garrulus*, the latter word meaning "chattering" or "gossiping".

Eric Hosking

BLUE-HEADED WAGTAIL, *rare visitor from the Continent*

To face page 88   *For text see page 85*

BOMBYCILLA (Latin, " silken "). Genus of the family *Bombycillidae* of the order *Passeriformes*. There is only one species on the British list, the Waxwing (*q.v.*), which is an irregular winter visitor to the British Isles.

BOMBYCILLIDAE (Latin, " silken "). Family of the order *Passeriformes*, containing the genus *Bombycilla*. There are three species, which breed in sub-Arctic regions and move south for the Winter. One species, the Waxwing (*q.v.*), occurs in the British Isles as an irregular winter visitor.

BONAPARTE'S GULL—Larus philadelphia. Only one or two Bonaparte's gulls have been observed in Britain, for they breed in the Arctic regions of North America and winter on the Pacific coast. The head, like that of the Black-headed Gull, is slaty-black in Summer and white in Winter ; but this gull is a smaller bird, of a size between that of the Black-headed and the Little Gull. The bill is black, and the legs are red. The flight is tern-like, and the length is about 12½ in.

A very gregarious bird, Bonaparte's Gull nests in wooded districts in the Arctic Circle. Its breeding season is in June, and the normal number of eggs is three ; these are oval and have a ground colour varying from brownish-yellow to olive-buff, spotted and blotched with brown. Both birds take part in building the nest. One clutch is laid in a season. Insects form most of the food on the breeding grounds, but in Winter on the coast small fish are eaten.

BONAPARTE'S SANDPIPER — Calidris fuscicollis. An infrequent visitor to the British Isles, usually during October and November, Bonaparte's Sandpiper breeds on the Arctic coast and islands of North America and Canada, wintering in the south. It is about the size of the Dunlin (*q.v.*) and has the typical appearance of the sandpipers, except that at close range a conspicuous and distinguishing patch of white across the dark tail can be seen. The mantle is streaked brown, and the underparts pale grey or dull white. It is 7 in. in length, with a wing span of some 12 in.

Its behaviour and habits resemble those of the Dunlin. It is more or less a silent bird, and its voice, when it is heard, is said to be like the squeak of a mouse. It flies high with rapidly beating wings, and sometimes hovers. During June and July, it nests in the grassy hillocks and ridges of wet marsh or tundra, and feeds on the animal and vegetable matter there.

In the American Ornithological Union's check-list this bird is called the White-rumped Sandpiper. *See also* Sandpiper.

BONELLI'S WARBLER—Phylloscopus bonelli. The Yorkshire Natural History Museum now houses the body of the only Bonelli's Warbler which, as far as is known, has ever wandered to the British Isles. It was identified at Skokholm, Pembrokeshire, in August 1948. Bonelli's Warbler breeds in central and southern Europe, west Asia and north-west Africa, and winters in tropical Africa. It looks rather

BLUE TIT. Although he is inclined to be quarrelsome—or, maybe, because of it —the Blue Tit is a sociable little bird, delighting in the company of his fellows

Eric Hosking

like a slightly smaller Wood-Warbler (q.v.), but with a yellowish patch on the rump and a pale eye stripe. It is about 4½ in. long.

Woods and parkland are its favourite haunts, and its behaviour and habits are the same as those of other members of the *Phylloscopus* genus. *See also* Warbler.

BONXIE. In the Shetland Isles, the Great Skua (q.v.) is always referred to thus ; in North America it is merely called Skua.

BOOBY. Scottish name for the Gannet (q.v.) or Solan Goose, possibly deriving from the bird's ungainly movements on land and its heavy, flapping take-off from water.

BOOKS. *See* Library ; Study, Facilities for ; *also* bibliographies of specialist articles.

BOOMER. Common name for the Bittern (q.v.) because of its " booming " note in Spring, described variously as " a cross between a lowing cow and a foghorn ". It is interesting to note that its Latin name *Botaurus* signifies " bellowing of a bull ".

BOOTED WARBLER—Hippolais caligata. Only one Booted Warbler is recorded as having wandered to Great Britain from its home in Russia and Siberia ; this was in 1936, when it was seen on Fair Isle, in the Shetlands. The smallest of its genus, it has greyish-brown plumage and white underparts ; its outside tail feathers are nearly all white. Its length is 4½ in. and its wing span is about 4¾ in. to 5 in.

It is an extremely secretive bird and nests in bushes, cornfields and coppice growth, on both marshy and dry ground. Its sweet and powerful song, which is heard both by night and by day, has much in common with that of its near relative, the Icterine Warbler (q.v.). It is the typical song of the *Hippolais* genus, and includes a rather unexpected clicking sound, which changes from loud to soft.

BOTAURUS (Latin, *boatum tauri*, " bellowing of a bull "). Genus of the family *Ardeidae* of the order *Ardeiformes*. It contains two species which are on the British list, the Bittern (q.v.), which is a rather scarce resident as well as an irregular visitor from Europe, and the American Bittern (q.v.), which is only an irregular winter visitor.

These birds have a fairly long, strong, pointed bill, laterally compressed and finely serrated near the tip. The legs are long, and the front of the tarsus is covered with scutes (horny scales). There are four toes, three directed forward and one behind. Each toe has a long, slightly curved claw, the one belonging to the middle front toe being serrated. The broad, rounded wings have eleven primaries, and the short, rounded tail has ten rectrices (tail quills).

BRAHMINY DUCK. Indian name for Ruddy Sheld-Duck (q.v.). The etymology of this name is dubious, although it may possibly derive from the similarity in colour between the duck's orange-chestnut plumage and the orange-yellow robes of certain priests or *Brahmins*.

BRAIN. All bird behaviour and body activity is controlled by the central nervous system which consists of the spinal cord and its forward continuation into the head, i.e. the brain. The control is carried out through the intermediacy of nerves, which deliver messages to and from the central nervous axis.

Most bird behaviour is of an instinctive type (*see* Behaviour), hence the birds' brain differs considerably from that of mammals where lower centres come under the domination of a surface layer of grey matter, termed *cortex*. This is poorly developed in birds, but in compensation there is a very elaborate development of basal grey centres (the basal ganglia) which renders the fore-brain of the birds a very large structure, which is nevertheless smooth, lacking the foldings (convolutions) characteristic of mammalian brains. Associated with this arrangement, the central cavity (ventricle) of the birds' brain is reduced to a mere slit.

There is little development of smell in birds so that the olfactory lobes, so prominent in mammalian brains, are comparatively small. Sight, on the contrary, is dominant, and is reflected in the brain by the development of huge optic lobes. The hind-brain of birds much resembles that of lower vertebrates, the cerebellum being very large and folded. This is necessary as a centre for stability and

G. K. Yeates

BOTAURUS. The Bittern's boom gave rise to its generic name which means " bellowing of a bull "

Eric Hosking

BRAMBLING. The white rump, shown clearly in flight, serves to distinguish the Brambling from other finches. He is, perhaps, most easily confused with the Chaffinch

equilibration especially in connection with flying. The central part of the cerebellum is dominant, the lateral lobes (prominent in aquatic vertebrates) being small.

Differences in brain structure occur between the families of birds in proportion to their differences in behaviour and habitat, e.g. between swimming, diving, walking, hopping or other modes of progression or in relation to other types of behaviour.

The relative proportion of the fore-brain over the rest of the organ is greatest in passerines, parrots and owls, and least in gallinaceous birds and pigeons, where the fore-brain weighs less than all the rest of the brain, compared with three times the weight of the remainder of the brain in passerines.

See also Anatomy ; Ancestry ; Behaviour ; Flight ; Hearing.

BRAMBLE-FINCH. As the Brambling (*q.v.*) is a typical member of the Finch (*q.v.*) family, it is often, particularly among country-folk, referred to by this name.

BRAMBLING — Fringilla montifringilla. Large numbers of bramblings or bramblefinches come to Britain as winter visitors and birds of passage from northern Europe, arriving on our north and east coasts in September and October, and returning home some time in March and April.

The Brambling is closely related to the Chaffinch, and can be seen with chaffinches in the vicinity of beech trees, beech mast being one of the principal foods of both birds. They also rid the land of many injurious insect pests.

The Brambling differs from the Chaffinch in its darker plumage and more striking colours ; its beak, head and neck are a glossy black, its throat and breast a light orange, and it has a white rump very noticeable in flight. Its flight and movements are similar to those of the Chaffinch, and, like that bird, it prefers beech woods and plantations as nesting sites. Its length is 5 in. and its tarsus 0·7 inches. Its wing span is about 7 in. and it weighs approximately 1 oz.

Since the Brambling does not breed in Britain, its song is not heard here. It seems to be a poor songster and, even in the breeding season, has very little to distinguish it.

Some of its notes have been likened to the drowsy, long-drawn-out note of the Greenfinch. But after one has observed this bird for many years, the Editor writes, one may be fortunate enough to hear its rare, sweet song, resembling that of some of the Arctic members of the Thrush family.

BRANTA. Genus of geese of the family *Anatidae* of the order *Anseriformes*. It includes four species which are on the British list : the Brent Goose and the Barnacle-Goose, both of which are regular winter visitors to our coasts ; the Red-breasted Goose, which has been recorded only a few times ; and the Canada Goose, which was introduced in the 17th century. These birds are separately described under their own names.

The members of this genus, known collectively as the black geese, do not differ very

Erica

BRANTA. *Red-breasted Geese are among the smallest and prettiest of all geese. They belong to the so-called black geese of the genus Branta, and are only rarely seen here*

markedly in structure from the grey geese of the genus *Anser*, except that they have no visible tooth-like serrations on the cutting edge of the upper mandible.

BREATHING. *See* Air-Sac ; Anatomy.

BREEDING, CROSS-. *See* Cross Breeding ; Hybridisation ; Reproduction.

BREEDING CYCLE. This term has two distinct meanings, depending on whether it is used by a biologist or a bird-watcher. The former applies it to the complete cycle of physiological changes which occur annually in adult birds and stimulate the mating instinct, and make it possible for mating and reproduction to take place—normally under conditions likely to favour the survival of the young (*see* Breeding Season).

To bird-watchers, breeding cycle refers to the sequence of events occurring each breeding season which are the *outward* expression of the internal changes ; i.e. courtship, selection of nesting sites, nest-building, laying of eggs, and rearing of young. *See also* Behaviour ; Breeding Tables ; Pairing ; Reproduction.

BREEDING DRESS. Name sometimes given to the brighter plumage worn during the period of sexual display and the beginning of the breeding season ; an alternative term is *nuptial dress.* Normally it is merely the full *summer plumage* in fresh condition, but there are certain exceptions. Some species, following a spring moult (*q.v.*), start the season with elaborate plumes or patches, which wear down or are shed long before the autumn moult (*q.v.*). In these species the general appearance at the

start of the breeding season is very different from that at the end. By contrast, ducks of both sexes assume a dull plumage at the autumn moult, but a few weeks later the male gets a brighter dress, which does not appear to undergo any heightening of colour as the critical period of courtship begins in the early Summer.

Although the vast majority of birds which take on a nuptial dress do so through the agency of moulting (mostly through a partial moult in the Spring), there are a number of species in which the brightening of the plumage is due to other causes. For example, in certain birds, such as the Linnet, Chaffinch, Brambling, House-Sparrow and Snow-Bunting, which have only a single, post-nuptial moult, the brightening of plumage that occurs just before the breeding season is brought about by the shedding of the *tips* of the feathers and the *outer surface* of the barbs and barbules. After the autumn moult, feathers of these birds have long brown or grey tips but, as the breeding season approaches, these sombre-coloured tips, which have served as a dust-cloak to protect the gay spring dress, are shed to reveal the beauties beneath.

It is also claimed by some ornithologists that certain other species assume the breeding dress through the infusion of pigment into feathers previously uncoloured. According to Gatke‘ the brown hood of the Black-headed Gull is acquired in this way, the pigment appears first at the edges of the feathers, gradually extending inwards until the whole feathers are darkened.

BREEDING GROUND. *See* Colonial Nesting ; *also* Behaviour ; Territory.

BREEDING SEASONS—Causes and Effects

A. J. MARSHALL, D.Phil. (Oxon)

Here Dr. Marshall discusses the factors controlling the breeding time of birds—one of the most fascinating and baffling problems. Information about the length of the breeding seasons of nearly 100 birds can be found under Breeding Tables, pages 96 to 97

BREEDING SEASONS. These have been evolved by natural selection in both birds and other animals. Individuals which bred at times propitious for the survival of their young (and, therefore, of the race) successfully reproduced their kind ; and stock with tendencies to breed at inappropriate seasons failed to rear their young and so suffered natural elimination.

Each successful species gradually evolved the capacity to respond seasonally to specific and appropriate external stimuli which, operating via the eyes, ears, temperature receptors, etc. (Figs. 1 and 2), set in train certain nervous activities in the brain ; these ultimately stimulate the near-by anterior pituitary gland to increase its secretion of the hormones (gonadotrophic hormones) which affect the sexual glands. Thus the testes in the male and the single ovary of the female become seasonally active.

In the male testes, the interstitial cells (Fig. 1) produce male sex hormone, which is carried by the blood-stream to the accessory sex organs, causing their development and making mating possible. In addition, male sex hormone flows to the brain, and acts there on specialised centres which stimulate the expression of the behaviour patterns (e.g. display and song) concerned with reproduction. In the female (Fig. 2) the ovary produces a female sex hormone which in much the same way brings about appropriate changes in the accessory sex organs and behaviour. Meanwhile, under the influence of one of the pituitary hormones (Fig. 1) the seminiferous tubules in the testes of the male are producing spermatozoa, and the ovary of the female (Fig. 2) is ripening its eggs. Finally, individuals mate, build nests and lay eggs.

The determination of the precise factors that control the breeding time of any species is one of the most fascinating and baffling problems challenging naturalists today. We still do not know exactly what regulates reproduction in even a pair of London sparrows.

Utility of Spring. Most temperate zone birds breed in Spring. It is particularly necessary for them to do so in countries subjected to severe Winters (such as Britain), since otherwise the naked, newly-hatched young would freeze or possibly starve to death. The nestlings of many birds eat the equivalent of more than half their weight per day. Very young, small birds must perish if not kept almost constantly warm and well-fed, for they are inevitably at the mercy

of their size. The surface of an object increases as the square of its diameter, and its volume as its cube. Thus the smaller the bird, the greater its surface in relation to its bulk. Like Man, birds are " warm-blooded " (they have a constant temperature), but this advantage is offset in the newly-hatched young because they are generally naked and always lack the insulating subcutaneous fat deposits that they later acquire. Therefore, although the nest-lining (when present), the proximity of their fellows, and the warmth of the parent (when present) make for heat-conservation, the relatively huge surface of a tiny chick means that the production of heat is a tremendous factor in its chance of survival, because loss of heat is proportional to the surface of an object from which it escapes. Heat is obtained from the oxidation of food. Therefore, to offset their relatively great heat-loss, small nestlings must consume enormous amounts of food—even without taking into consideration the requirements of growth—merely to keep warm and stay alive. Excluding pigeons and doves, in which the adults produce " crop-milk " (*q.v.*), the young of birds are dependent upon the day-to-day supply of food gathered by their parents.

Secondly, the provision of amino-acids essential to animal development must be considered. Many of the comparatively few birds

John Markham

BREEDING SEASONS. Nestlings eat huge amounts partly to prevent them from freezing to death

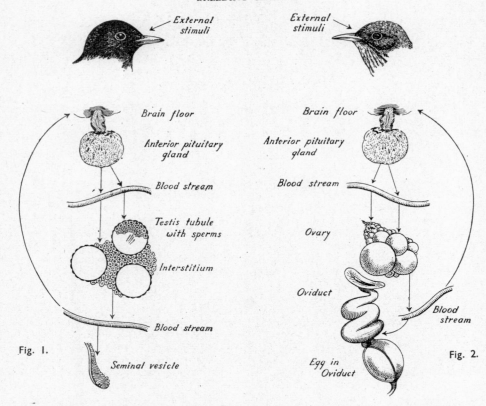

BREEDING SEASONS. Mechanism (in part) of reproduction in male birds (Fig. 1) and female birds (Fig. 2). See also text in previous page. External stimuli (from the environment) influence the brain and cause the pituitary gland in each sex to secrete hormones which flow in the blood to the testes of the male and the ovary of the female. The testes (Fig. 1) produce sperms and also the male sex hormone which, in turn, flows in the blood to the accessory sexual organs, which now enlarge. These include the seminal vesicles which receive the sperms and store them in readiness for reproduction. The male hormone flows also to the brain, where it calls into play the operation of reproductive behaviour. In the female (Fig. 2), comparable events take place, and so both sexes are made ready to breed

that are largely vegetarian appear compelled to switch, at least partially and sometimes almost wholly, to a diet richer in protein for their developing young, because protein is the only source of amino-acids. For instance, domestic fowls, which at first sight appear to subsist largely on vegetarian food, do in fact scratch up a considerable amount of animal food ; and artificially reared chicks must be given a diet enriched by protein foods such as skim-milk, meat- or fish-meal, or soya bean.

Thus the young of most birds must, if they are to survive, hatch at a time of year when it is relatively warm, when there is plenty of appropriate food readily available, when the days are long enough to enable adequate quantities of food to be gathered, and when nights are sufficiently short for the tiny young to survive without food from the last meal of one day until the first meal of the next. So much for the " utility " of the breeding season. Now, what starts it off? What stops it in any pair of birds ? It is con-

venient to deal first with the latter. After the number of hatchings traditional to the species, the testes of the male collapse. The interstitial cells are exhausted, and the seminiferous tubules no longer contain living spermatozoa but instead are loaded with a special fatty material of unknown function. However appropriate for reproduction the environment may be, breeding cannot now occur, because the primary breeding apparatus of the male has gone into a "refractory" phase. In most British birds this generally lasts until August, and sometimes right through the Winter.

During this phase the interstitial cells are regenerated and the tubules slowly rehabilitated. Then, if the environment presents appropriate stimuli, the seasonal cycle can begin once more. This renewed functioning is responsible for the autumnal song of the Robin, the September and October nest-building and other sexual behaviour of rooks, and the post-moult chasing and display of many other familiar species. Thus, autumn song and sexual activity are not late but *early* behaviour.

A few birds, notably rooks, robins, sparrows and starlings, breed each Autumn, but their young seem rarely to survive the Winter. This is an example of natural selection at work. The renewed autumnal activity is damped down by environmental conditions—cold, wet, food scarcity, lack of nesting cover and, possibly, lessened day length. Thus, not only are stimuli appropriate to reproduction absent, but actual deterrents to breeding are present. Most birds must now more or less mark time through Winter until the reappearance of these stimuli.

The recrudescence of sexual activity begins late in Winter in some species and early in Spring in others. In the Robin it sometimes begins late in December, but generally about the first week in January. In the Rook it begins about one month later. The most generally held theory is that the " spring " resurgence is stimulated by increasing day length ; certainly in the laboratory numerous birds (and other animals) can be stimulated to premature sexual activity by an additional ration of ordinary white light. It has also been generally held that temperature plays little or no part in the regulation of the sexual cycle. This is erroneous. While there is no evidence that increasing temperature in itself starts sperm-production, warm days and increasing sunshine (apart from mere day length) undoubtedly hasten the cycle.

From its inception the sexual cycle of any given pair or colony of birds is under the influence of week-to-week events in the environment, including behaviour interactions between members of the pair or flock. An " early Spring " causes an early breeding season, a " late Winter " a delayed one. In all species examined the male cycle far outstrips that of the female—the testes quickly become packed with spermatozoa, while the ovary remains relatively undeveloped. The female is awaiting the seasonal combination of external stimuli, to which she will respond by accepting the male, nest-building and laying.

Such stimuli differ from species to species. One seemingly obvious one is the seasonal appearance of quantities of some special protein food, but there is no experimental evidence that such is the case. All we know for certain is that the vast majority of young birds are hatched at about the time that large quantities of the traditional food of such young appear. Another specific factor is the seasonal appearance of a safe nesting site ; species which build low in hedges (e.g. the Hedge-Sparrow) as a rule nest slightly before those that build in the overhanging foliage which does not provide adequate concealment until a little later (e.g. the Chaffinch).

An interesting example of interaction between external stimuli and internal reproductive processes is provided by the parasitic Cuckoo. The female Cuckoo watches her intended victim building its nest, and it would seem that the latter's activities operate as a stimulating factor to help synchronise the Cuckoo's reproductive mechanism with that of its victim. Although larger than their victims, cuckoos in general seem to have evolved an unusually short incubation period, so that the young parasite hatches in ample time to oust from the nest its competitors for the vital food.

The ultimate " timing " of the breeding cycle in most species is probably primarily controlled not by overall factors such as day length, but by regional conditions that permit of successful nest-building and rearing of the young. Temperature is probably very important in controlling the nesting date of many species. This is most obvious in Arctic countries, where extreme fluctuations in their environment often prevent birds from breeding when they are physiologically ready to do so.

See also Behaviour ; Display and Courtship ; Nestling ; Young, Care of.

Consult : Evolution of Breeding Seasons, J. R. Baker (*Evolution*, ed. G. R. de Beer, Oxford), 1938 ; Bower Birds : their Display and Sexual Cycles (Chapters 2 and 3), A. J. Marshall (Oxford), 1954.

John Markham

BREEDING SEASONS. *The logical outcome of external and internal breeding stimuli : a pair of gulls standing guard over their eggs and nestling*

BREEDING TABLES FOR SELECTED SPECIES

These tables should be read in conjunction with the following notes:

Laying Period: The first column under this heading gives the normal limits of the season (including, where applicable, all broods and repeat clutches) during which the various species lay their eggs. The second column gives the peak period, during which the search for eggs is likely to be most fruitful.

The times given can, however, only be approximate because they are affected by many factors. For example, when a breeding species is distributed throughout the British Isles, the laying season usually begins and finishes later in the north than in the south—the variation between the two extremes being as much as a month or more.

Similarly, for birds nesting at high altitudes the season is usually later than for those breeding nearer sea-level. Laying may also be delayed by severe weather in early Spring, or if conditions are otherwise unfavourable (*see* Breeding Seasons). There may also be freak layings outside the normal seasons.

E, L, or M before the name of a month mean early, late, or middle part of that month.

Clutch: Normal clutches are shown without brackets, abnormal ones (reported more than once) in brackets. " Repeat " clutches are those laid after the failure of a nest. " Second " and " third " clutches are those laid after one brood (or more) has been successfully fledged; i.e. they indicate true double-broodedness.

(D) after the name of a species in the following table shows that more than one brood is usual; (d) that it occurs occasionally.

Compare also with table under Nest and Nesting.

Species	Laying Period		Clutch	Incubation Period (days)	Age Fledgling leaves nest (days)	Fledging Period (days)
	Duration	Peak				
Avocet	L. Apl.–July	——	(3) 4 (7)	23–25	2 hours	42
Blackbird (D)	M. Mar.–June	April–May	3–5 (6–9)	12–14	13–15	13–15
Blackcap (d)	L. Apl.–June	May	(3) 4–5 (6)	11–13	10–13	10–13
Bullfinch (D)	L. Apl.–Aug.	May	4–5 (6)	13–15	15–17	15–17
Bunting, Cirl (D)	E. May–Aug.	May–June	(2) 3–4 (5)	12–14	11–13	11–13
„ Reed- (D)	L. Apl.–E. July	May–June	4–5 (6)	12–14	11–13	11–13
Chaffinch (D)	M. Apl.–June	May	4–5 (6)	11–13	12–14	12–14
Chiffchaff (d)	L. Apl.–June	May	5–6 (7)	13–15	14–15	14–15
Chough	L. Mar.–E. May	L. April	4–6	17–18	38–40	38–40
Coot (D)	M. Mar.–July	Apl.–June	6–9 (10–13)	21–23	3–4	56
Cormorant	L. Mar.–July	Apl.–May	3–4	28	30+	30+
Corncrake (d)	M. May–Aug.	L. May–E. June	8–12 (13–17)	14–19	34	49–56
Crow, Carrion-	L. Mar.–May	April	4–5	18–20	30–35	30–35
Cuckoo	E. May–E. July	L. May–June	2–3	12–13	18–23	18–23
Curlew	M. Apl.–June	L. Apl.–E. May	3–4 (5)	27–30	1–2	35–42
„ Stone- (d)	E. Apl.–M. Aug.	L. Apl.–E. May	2 (3)	25–27	1–2	40–45
Dove, Rock- (D)	All year round	Apl.–July	2	17–19	30–37	35–37
„ Turtle- (D)	E. May–July	L. May–June	2 (3)	13–15	18–20	20–21
Duck, Sheld-	L. Apl.–June	May	8–15	28–29	1–2	55–60
„ Tufted	E. May–July	M. May–E. June	6–14	24–28	1–2	40–45
Eagle, Golden	L. Mar.–E. Apl.	E. Apl.	1 (3)	40–45	77–84	77–84
Fulmar	M. May–M. July	June	1	45–60	50–60	50–60
Gannet	L. Mar–June	Apl.–May	1	43–45	80–85	80–85
Goldfinch (D)	L. Apl.–Aug.	May	(3) 4–5 (6)	12–13	13–15	13–15
Goose, Grey-Lag	Apl.	L. Apl.	4–6	27–29	1–2	55–60
Greenfinch (D)	L. Apl.–Aug.	E. May–June	(3) 4–5 (7)	12–14	13–16	13–16
Greenshank	L. Apl.–L. May	May	(3) 4 (5)	24–25	1–2	25–30
Grouse, Red	April–June	L. Apl.	6–11	20–24	1–2	14–21
Guillemot	M. May–E. June	M. May–E. June	1	28–30	13–15	no data
Gull, Common	L. Apl.–June	May–M. June	(2) 3 (4)	21–24	3–5	30–35
„ Herring-	L. Apl.–E. June	May	(2) 3 (4)	25–27	3–5	50–55
Hawfinch (d)	L. Apl.–July	L. May–M. June	(3) 4–5 (6)	10–13	10–11	10–11
Heron (d)	Feb.–June	Mar.–Apl.	3–5 (7)	23–28	50–55	50–55
Jackdaw	E. Apl.–May	L. Apl.–May	4–6	16–18	30–35	30–35
Jay	L. Apl.–M. May	E. May	4–6 (8)	16–17	20	20
Kestrel	M. Apl.–L. May	E. –May	4–5 (6)	27–29	28–32	28–32
Kingfisher (d)	L. Mar.–Aug.	L. Apl.	(4) 7	19–21	23–29	23–29
Kittiwake	E. May–July	L. May–June	2	22–26	30–35	30–35

Species	Laying Period		Clutch	Incubation Period (days)	Age Fledgling leaves nest (days)	Fledging Period (days)
	Duration	Peak				
Lapwing	M. Mar.–June	L. Mar.–May	(3) 4 (5)	24–28	1–2	33
Lark, Sky (D)	M. Apl.–July	May–June	3–4 (6)	10–12	9–10	20
Linnet (D)	M. Apl.–Aug.	May–June	4–6 (7)	12–13	12–14	12–14
Magpie	L. Mar.–May	L. Apl.–M. May	(3) 5–7 (10)	17–18	22–27	22–27
Mallard	Mar.–July	April	10–12	27–29	1–2	50–55
Martin, House- (D)	E. May–Aug.	L. May–July	4–5 (6)	14–16	20–25	20–25
Moorhen (D)	E. Mar.–Aug.	April–June	5–10 (11–16)	20–22	2–3	42–49
Nightingale	E. May–June	M. May–E. June	4–5 (6)	12–14	10–12	11–12
Nightjar (D)	M. May–Aug.	L. May–June	2 (3)	17–19	10–14	16–18
Nuthatch (d)	M. Apl.–E. May	L. Apl.–E. May	5–8 (9–13)	13–17	23–27	23–27
Owl, Barn- (d)	Apl.–July Some freaks	L. Apl.–May	4–6 (7–11)	31–34	64–68	64–68
„ Tawny	L. Feb.–Apl.	L. Mar–E. Apl.	2–4 (6–8)	28–30	32–37	32–37
Oystercatcher	L. Apl.–July	May–M. June	2–3 (5)	21–28	1–2	28–35
Partridge	E. Apl.–June	L. Apl.–May	8	23–25	1–2 hrs.	16
Petrel, Storm-	L. May–July	June–E. July	1	38–40	54–64	54–64
Pigeon, Wood- (D)	Jan.–Nov.	Mar.–July	2 (3)	16–18	20–25	20–25
Pipit, Meadow- (D)	M. Apl.–July	May	4–5 (6–7)	12–14	12–14	12–14
„ Rock- (D)	M. Apl.–June	L. Apl.–June	4–5 (6)	13–15	15–16	15–16
Plover, Golden	M. Apl.–May	M. Apl.–May	(3) 4 (5)	27–28	1–2	25–30
„ Ringed (D)	Mar.–Aug.	May–June	(3) 4 (5)	22–25	1–2	22–25
Puffin	May–June	M. May	1	36–43	47–51	50–55
Quail (d)	L. May–onwards	June onwards	7–12 (13–18)	16–20	2–3 hrs.	19
Raven	Feb.–Mar.	Feb.–Mar.	(1) 4–5 (6)	19–21	35–42	35–42
Razorbill	May–June	May	1	25–30	12–18	no data
Redshank (d)	E. Apl.–June	M. Apl.–May	4	23–25	1–2	26–30
Robin (D)	L. Mar.–June	M. April	(3) 5–6 (7–10)	13–14	12–15	12–15
Rook	M. Mar. onwards	L. March	3–5 (6)	16–18	29–30	29–30
Sandpiper, Common	M. May–L. June	M. May–M. June	(3) 4	21–23	1–2	35 (?)
Snipe (d)	L. Mar.–M. July	E. Apl.–May	(3) 4 (5)	19–20	1–2	14+
Sparrow, Hedge-	L. Mar.–July	Apl.–May	4–5	11–13	11–13	11–13
„ House- (D)	L. Apl.–E. Aug. Some freaks	May–July	3–5 (6–8)	12–14	12–16	12–16
Starling (d)	L. Mar.–June	L. Apl.–May	4–6 (7–8)	11–13	20–22	20–22
Stonechat (D)	L. Mar.–July	L. Mar.–May	(3–4) 5–6 (7)	12–15	12–14	12–14
Swallow (D)	L. Apl.–Sept.	M. May–June	(2–3) 4–5 (6–8)	14–15	19–22	19–22
Swan, Mute	L. Mar.–May	M. Apl.–M. May	4–5 (6–7)	35–40	1–2	120–130
Swift	M. May–June	L. May–E. June	2–3 (4)	18–21	38–46	38–46
Tern, Common	M. May–July	May–June	(2) 3 (4)	21–23	3	28–30
Thrush, Mistle- (D)	Feb.–June	L. Mar.–May	4 (5–6)	13–15	14–16	14–16
„ Song- (D)	E. Mar.–Aug.	Apl.–May	3–5 (6)	12–14	13–14	13–14
Tit(mouse), Blue (d)	M. Apl.–May	L. Apl.–E. May	8–11 (18)	13–14	18–21	18–21
Wagtail, Grey (D)	L. Mar.–June	L. Apl.	(3–4) 5–6 (7)	12–14	12–13	12–13
„ Pied (D)	L. Apl.–July	L. Apl.–May	5–6 (7–8)	12–14	14–16	14–16
Warbler, Garden-	M. May–L. June	L. May–E. June	(3) 4–5 (6)	12–13	9–12	9–12
„ Reed (D)	L.. May–Aug.	June	4 (5)	12–13	11–13	11–13
„ Willow- (d)	L. Apl.–July	M. May	5–7 (8–9)	13–14	13–15	13–15
Wheatear	L. Apl.–June	E. May	(4) 5–6 (7)	13–15	15	15
Whimbrel	L. May–M. June	L. May–E. June	4	24 (?)	1–2	30 (?)
Whinchat (D)	M. May–L. July	L. May–E. June	(4) 5–6 (7–8)	12–13	13–15	13–15
Woodcock (D)	M. Mar.–July	M. Mar.–June	(3) 4 (6–8)	20–22	1–2	no data
Woodpecker, Great Spotted	L. Apl.–June	M. May	(3) 5–6 (7–8)	11–14	20–25	20–25
„ Green	L. Apl.–June	E. May	(4) 5–6 (7–8)	14–16	27–28	27–28
„ Lesser Spotted	L. Apl.–June	May	4–6 (7–8)	11–14	21–28	21–28
Wren (D)	M. Apl.–Aug.	L. Apl.–May	(4) 5–6 (7–16)	14–17	16–18	16–18
Yellow Hammer (D)	L. Apl.–Aug.	May–June	3–4 (5)	12–14	12–13	12–13

H

BRENT GOOSE—Branta bernicla. The smallest of the goose family of birds, called the Brant in the north of England. There are two varieties of Brent Goose—the dark-breasted (*Branta bernicla bernicla*) and the pale-breasted (*Branta bernicla hrota*). Both are winter visitors to the British Isles, arriving from September onwards and leaving in March. Except for this difference in colour, the two birds appear the same. Outside the breeding season, the Brent Goose is rarely seen inland.

Like the Barnacle-Goose (*q.v.*), the Brent Goose is a black rather than grey bird, especially about the neck and head ; but there are small white patches on the neck and the rear under-feathers are white and conspicuous in flight. Its mantle is a slaty-grey, with some white edging to the feathers. In the dark-breasted bird, the breast is a lighter shade of the grey mantle ; in the pale-breasted bird, it is a still lighter shade of grey, with the white more conspicuous. The bill and legs of both birds are black. The total length is about 24 in., with a body of about 17 in. The tarsus is 2 in., the wing span about 2½ ft. ; the weight about 2 lb.

The Brent Goose is very gregarious. It flies with speed and grace and often performs wonderful aerobatics at no great height. It is a fine swimmer. The sound of a gaggle of brent geese is higher pitched than that of other geese. Brent geese breed in the mouths and valleys of Arctic rivers, but never far away from the sea. A hollow between the rocks, lined with down feathers, forms the nest. The three or four eggs, laid about June, are hatched by the hen alone, with her mate on guard. One brood is reared in a season.

The chief food of brent geese in Winter is a sea-grass called *Zostera marina*. In countries where this failed, the geese had to change their feeding grounds. Long lines of the birds can be seen at low tide digging up their food, their white sterns alone visible. A little animal food is also taken.

BRIDLED TERN—Sterna aneathetus. The Bridled Tern found dead near Dungeness, Kent, in 1931, was apparently the only specimen of its kind ever to have been recorded in the British Isles. This is a bird of tropical seas, but it is so like the Sooty Tern (*q.v.*) that identification (except by the expert) is difficult. When the two birds are seen in company, however, it can be observed that the Bridled Tern is smaller, and has a light collar dividing its neck from its mantle, and a bigger patch of white on its forehead. Its length is 13 or 14 in.

BRITISH ORNITHOLOGISTS' CLUB. This club recruits its members from the British Ornithologists' Union (*q.v.*). It meets in London nearly every month ; its *Bulletin*, published monthly except July-September, contains articles relating to subjects discussed at the meetings, and descriptions of new species and races (or subspecies) of birds.

BRITISH ORNITHOLOGISTS' UNION. This organization, founded in 1859, is the senior society in Great Britain for the advancement of the science of ornithology. Its interests are not restricted to Great Britain, but are world-wide. Anyone interested in ornithology is eligible to join, but must be proposed by one member and seconded by two others. The annual subscription is £3 (£2 under the age of 25). There is no entrance fee.

The B.O.U. issues an important quarterly journal, the *Ibis*, and, as from 1883, has compiled and published at intervals lists of British birds, and in 1952 issued the latest *Check-List of the Birds of Great Britain and Ireland* (*see* Check-List ; Classification) in which the system of classification was brought into line with modern practice. The system of classification adopted throughout the *Encyclopedia of British Birds* is in conformity with this authoritative work.

The B.O.U. arranges scientific meetings and takes a leading part in all international ornithological affairs. Address : c/o The Bird Room, British Museum (Natural History), Kensington, London.

Eric Hosking

BRENT GOOSE. This winter visitor from Arctic lands delights many with its duck-like antics—turning up its white stern—when diving for food

BRITISH TRUST for ORNITHOLOGY

BRUCE CAMPBELL, Ph.D.

Despite this somewhat formal name, the main object of the British Trust is to encourage research by amateur bird-watchers, any of whom may join on paying a small subscription. Here the present secretary discusses the important work the Trust is doing

BRITISH TRUST FOR ORNITHOLOGY. This organization was a new departure when it was founded in 1932, and remains unique in its field today—a body composed mainly of amateur bird-watchers, concerned with the promotion and encouragement of research into the lives, habits and numbers of British birds. The Trust was incorporated in 1939, and is recognized as a charity. It is governed by a Council, at present of eleven members, who include the chairman, two vice-chairmen, the honorary secretary and honorary treasurer (at present these two offices are combined). The Council has set up permanent committees to look after the more important aspects of the Trust's work; these are the Scientific Advisory Committee, the Bird Ringing Committee and the Bird Observatories Committee. There is an executive staff of five—three at the registered office, 2 King Edward Street, Oxford, and two at the Bird Room of the British Museum (Natural History), which is the headquarters of the national Ringing Scheme. There are also nearly 70 honorary regional representatives.

Growth and Membership. The Trust was founded on the idea of large-scale co-operative field work. We can trace the germ of the co-operative method in the circles of correspondents of the early naturalists, more clearly in the studies of bird migration promoted by the British Association and the British Ornithologists' Club early in the 20th century, and fully developed in the national census of heronries organized in 1928 for the magazine *British Birds* by E. M. Nicholson, who became the first honorary secretary of the Trust.

It was the application to birds of the ecological concepts already applied to botany that triggered off the explosive enthusiasm of Nicholson, B. W. Tucker and their colleagues, and resulted in the formation not only of the Trust but also of the " Edward Grey Institute of Field Ornithology " at Oxford University. The " E.G.I.", the Trust's first offspring, was established in 1938 and incorporated in the Department of Zoological Field Studies at Oxford in 1947.

The Second World War, far from harming the Trust, gave it an enormous access of strength and vigour, partly because people turned to nature, and to birds in particular, as a release and a recreation for their snatched leisure, and partly because for the first time Government money was available for large-scale investigations into the life-histories and populations of birds with economic importance.

The new surge of interest in birds was harnessed to the nation-wide organization needed by the Wood-Pigeon and Rook Investigations, and the Trust emerged from the war a thousand strong and growing rapidly. Many new members were attracted through the tear-off slip at the end of James Fisher's book *Watching Birds*, perhaps the most widely read of all guides to bird-watching; Fisher, then Hon. Secretary of the Trust and organizer of the Rook Investigation, made bird-watchers think on new, ecological lines in keeping with the objects and aims of the Trust.

But development brought its problems and obligations; the Edward Grey Institute was no longer dependent on the Trust, and new fields for the latter's energies had to be found. Important steps taken in 1948 were the doubling of the annual subscription for those over 21, and the setting up of a permanent office organization in Oxford. By 1950 the new orientation of the Trust was clear : to encourage research by the vast company of leisure-time bird-watchers, individually, in groups or

John E. M. Sumner

BRITISH TRUST. *Bird-ringing is not just an art but an honour, conferred only on reliable watchers*

on a national basis. The members seemed to endorse the policy, for in 1951 their total reached the 2,000 mark for the first time.

The membership of the Trust was over 2,250 at the end of 1953. This was made up of about 150 life members, 1,900 ordinary subscribers, and 200 subscribers between 17 (the lower age-limit) and 21. Included in the first two categories were over a hundred corporate members—institutions of all kinds, but mainly local natural history or ornithological societies and schools. Both corporate and individual members pay £1 a year; individuals under 21, 10s. Distribution of the Trust's members is roughly related to the great centres of human population —London and the Home Counties, the West Riding of Yorkshire and south Lancashire, and the west Midlands—but the first of these areas is by far the most important, for over a third of the Trust's individual members live within easy travelling distance of London.

There is a regional representative for almost every English county (four in Yorkshire), and one for groups of counties in Scotland, Ireland and Wales; the Isle of Man, Isle of Wight and Channel Islands are also represented. The representatives' task in the more populous areas is to keep in touch with members, advise them on local problems, act as regional organizers for the Trust's field studies, and help with meetings. In the remoter parts their chief task is to advise visiting members how to make the best of their time without disturbing any very rare birds. Regional representatives, who meet annually for discussion, form an essential part of the Trust's organization and maintain the vital link with the local society and the local member.

Outside England membership has increased considerably in the past five years; there are over 200 members in Scotland, nearly 100 in Wales, 35 in Northern Ireland, 30 in Eire and over 20 in the Channel Islands, where the ornithological interest is very well organized. About 70 members have overseas addresses, and many more are working or serving abroad but are registered at home. Through its corporate members the Trust is linked to about 5,000 more bird-watchers, many of them still at school.

Activities of the Trust. The Trust's main work is to promote and carry on field investigations. Three of these are so important that they are organized directly by the Trust. Pre-eminent is the national Ringing Scheme, under which about 100,000 birds are marked each year with numbered aluminium rings round the leg. A special Committee looks after this scheme, which is operated by a full-time organizer, an appointment made possible (on the retirement of the honorary secretary, Miss

Leach, who had guided the scheme devotedly for over 20 years) by a grant from the Nature Conservancy. But ringing is a privilege : new ringers must be thoroughly vouched for and must have received definite training in putting on rings ; even when admitted, they have to buy their rings and recording schedules. Ringing began as a field method for the study of migration, but it has now been found to have many other uses, particularly in making estimates of population and in telling us how long birds live and what are the causes of their deaths. *See also* Ringing of Birds.

A somewhat similar but much newer scheme is the collection of nest records. These are " case histories " of individual nests noted on *pro forma* cards (visits to large colonies are recorded on special cards), and from them an accurate picture of the breeding cycle of each kind of bird can be built up : when it lays, how many eggs it lays, how long they take to hatch, how long to fledge and leave the nest—and the reasons why nests come to grief. If there are sufficient cards for a species, we can compare its breeding season (*q.v.*) in different parts of the British Isles or in different seasons. Ultimately these cards may help to explain some of the mysterious changes that are always taking place in the numbers of birds.

The census of heronries has already been mentioned ; this has been maintained on a sample basis ever since 1928, and is now the longest population study of any fairly common bird on a national basis. The annual " index " has shown how herons (*q.v.*) die off in a very severe Winter, and how their numbers gradually recover to reach a sort of invisible " ceiling ". What sets this limit is still unknown, but a full national census in England and Wales was organized in 1954 to provide the basis for new calculations.

Apart from these permanent studies, the Trust sponsors a number of investigations proposed and organized by its members. These may last only for a year or run over several years, and usually deal with problems of distribution, habitat or population. But some are concerned with questions of behaviour and habits ; two inquiries into the opening of milk-bottles and the tearing of paper by birds attracted world-wide attention, and were examples of co-operation between bird-watchers and the general public, for housewives, milkmen, railway porters and many others had better opportunities to see the birds at work than had the ornithologists.

As well as these officially sponsored studies the Trust is always, through its publications, asking for information on all manner of problems on which individual members or small groups are working. The office also copes with all kinds of requests by correspondence, and a large part of its work may be said to consist of " putting chaps in touch with other chaps "—an essential service if research is to go forward with the proper exchange of ideas and without overlapping.

The Scientific Advisory Committee, which controls this side of the Trust's work, examines all proposed investigations and passes all reports on them before they are offered for publication to scientific journals.

The Bird Observatories Committee, on the other hand, is purely advisory. It was formed to link the British Observatories for discussion of their common scientific problems. Twelve of these stations are now recognized by the Committee and send representatives to it, while the Saltee Observatory in Eire maintains close touch; other observatories are projected. The annual meeting and conference of the Committee is now one of the year's biggest events.

In the field of recorded sound, the Trust is responsible for a permanent panel which advises the B.B.C. on the scientific use of the mass of material now at its disposal, founded on the great collection made by Ludwig Koch. In return the B.B.C. has supplied the Trust with three complete sets of its recordings for research purposes, and selections from these are now played at meetings organized by the Trust. *See also* Radio, Birds on; Recording.

The organization of meetings is now one of the Trust's main activities. They are held at the rate of almost one a week during the Winter months, and are nearly always arranged in conjunction with a local bird or natural history society. At large meetings it is usual to have a symposium of speakers to deal with different aspects of the same subject; at all meetings discussion is encouraged, and the Trust believes no meeting is complete without a cup of tea afterwards to promote the flow of informal argument and give its officers and staff the

Fox

BRITISH TRUST. This cheeky fellow stealing the milk was the subject of a serious inquiry

chance to meet members personally. Since 1948, when the present emphasis was first laid on meetings, they have been held in over 30 English counties, and in all parts of the British Isles from Inverness to Jersey, from Lowestoft to Armagh.

The Trust is concerned with several other activities bearing on its main purposes : it organizes courses in Bird Biology (the application of proper scientific method to observations); it keeps a register of all those who mark birds with coloured rings for special purposes ; it operates a scheme for the examination of freshly dead birds at laboratories ; it can arrange visits by members to weather ships and lightships ; it supplies evidence to Government committees ; most important, it can give small grants to help its members carry out special research, or lend them the necessary equipment.

Members of the Trust may use the Alexander Library of the Edward Grey Institute at Oxford. This is the finest reference collection of modern bird books, journals and papers in Europe, perhaps in the world. Those who cannot get to Oxford can borrow from the Lending Library, which contains about 600 books, series of about 200 journals and thousands of separate papers. It is growing rapidly and has recently received the magnificent addition (not included in the total above) of the entire ornithological library of the late Bernard Tucker, one of the founders of the Trust, presented by Mrs. Tucker. Members in the British Isles may borrow from the library for the cost of postage both ways. For the serious bird-watcher this is undoubtedly the most useful service offered by the Trust.

The Trust publishes its own quarterly journal, *Bird Study*, edited by H. N. Southern. This is intended to carry mainly reports on the Trust's own investigations, but independent contributions are welcomed. *Bird Study* and a short Annual Report are sent free to all members. In addition the Trust publishes a series of Field

Guides on methods—for example, on trapping methods for those who ring birds, on how to choose and use field-glasses, and on the design and maintenance of nestboxes. The Trust was the first body to publish a pocket field list of British birds in the Wetmore classification. By a special arrangement the Trust is able to offer its members free that section of the *Ibis*, the journal of the British Ornithologists' Union (*q.v.*), which contains summaries of all important bird books and papers published anywhere in the world.

It should be remembered, however, that the Trust is not concerned with bird identification, which is done by local societies through their beginners' meetings and by the museums ; nor with records of rare birds, which are dealt with by county bird recorders and the magazine *British Birds* ; nor with protection and education, which are the functions of the Royal Society for the Protection of Birds (*q.v.*). Nor is the office anxious to arrange " bird holidays " for its members unless they have a definite research aspect or a relatively unworked area to be visited. This applies to other countries, in which the Trust now has several contacts, as well as to Britain, where its work primarily lies.

BROAD-BILLED SANDPIPER—Limicola falcinellus. Only some twenty specimens of this rare passage migrant to the British Isles have been recorded, usually in the Autumn. It breeds in Norway, Sweden, Denmark and Finland. Its blackish bill, as its name implies, places this Sandpiper in a category by itself ; broad and flat, it is slightly curved downwards. The

W. Farnsworth

BROWN OWL. *True wisdom seems to lead to an infinite sadness—at any rate in the case of owls*

Broad-billed Sandpiper has something of the Dunlin in its build, and is rather like the Common Snipe in its summer plumage, especially as regards the mantle, the feathers of which are black, edged with buff. Its head and breast are mottled dark brown, the breast feathers shading into its white underparts. Its length is 6½ inches, and its wing span about 12 in.

Like its relatives, it flies low over the water, and its flight is never very long sustained. Its voice is high-pitched, and its song has a very musical and pleasant sound, sometimes changing to a harsher call. It frequents, and nests in, bogs and morasses, sometimes at an altitude of 3,000–4,000 ft. Its nest is placed on a tussock of cotton-grass among the oozy mud of the marsh, and lined with grasses. Four or five eggs are laid in June, and both parents take part in the hatching and rearing of the young. Insects of many kinds form the main diet. *See also* Sandpiper.

BROOD. All the young of a bird hatched at one time. As a verb, the word means to sit upon eggs to incubate or hatch them, also to cover the young with the wings as a protection. *See also* Egg ; Hatching ; Nestling.

BROWN-BACKED WARBLER—Agrobates galactotes syriaca. This bird has only been recorded as a visitor to the British Isles four times. It breeds in Yugoslavia, Albania and Greece, and winters in Somaliland and Kenya. Except that its plumage is browner and its underparts somewhat greyer, it is indistinguishable from that other rare visitor, the Rufous Warbler (*q.v.*). Its song is usually uttered from a high perch and has many variations, changing from soft to loud. The bird is about 6 in. long.

BROWN FLYCATCHER—Muscicapa latirostris. The only Brown Flycatcher recorded in Great Britain visited Kent in May 1909. Its breeding home is in south Siberia, Japan and Manchuria, and it winters in India and Ceylon. It is a small bird with some resemblance to the Spotted Flycatcher (*q.v.*), but without the streaks in the plumage. Its song, sweet and very musical, is usually uttered from a high position. The bird's length is about 4½ in.

BROWN OWL. One of the various names by which the Tawny Owl (*q.v.*) is often known in this country. Another popular name for it is Wood Owl.

BRÜNNICH'S GUILLEMOT—Uria lomvia. This bird visits Great Britain only occasionally, for it is the most Arctic of its kind, and lives and breeds in the countries of the far north. There is very little difference in its habits and behaviour from those of other guillemots, but its greatest likeness is to the common Guillemot (*q.v.*). It has a rather darker mantle and a

Herbert W. Newey

BUDGERIGAR. Once again the photographer has been lucky, for it is only rarely
that the camera manages to catch such a magnificent shot of a Budgerigar in full flight

distinctly shorter and thicker bill, and the adult
birds have a thin white line going from nostril
to gape"; but these differences are not always
visible, except at a very short distance. Its
legs and feet are yellow, the bands of the joints
being black. In winter plumage, its throat,
breast and underparts are white, but this is
common to all the Auk (q.v.) family at that
season. Its normal voice resembles that of the
common Guillemot, but there are records of
individual variations ; even a sheep-like note
has been reported. The length of the bird is
16½ in., and the tarsus 1 in. ; the wing span is
about 1½ ft.

Brünnich's guillemots breed about June in
huge crowded colonies on the ledges of Arctic
sea cliffs. Only one egg is laid in a season, and
this is deposited on the bare rock. Both male
and female assist in the hatching, and tend the
young chick. Fish is the chief food of both
parents and young. In North America this
bird is known as Brünnich's Murre.

BUBO (Latin, " long-horned owl "). Genus
of owls of the family *Strigidae* of the order
Strigiformes. It contains about twelve species
altogether, as well as a number of subspecies.
They are distributed over a wide area of the
globe, but do not occur in Australia or New
Zealand. There is only one species on the
British list, the Eagle-Owl (q.v.), which occasionally wanders to Britain from the Continent.

BUCEPHALA. Genus of diving-ducks of
the family *Anatidae* of the order *Anseriformes*.
There are three species altogether, two of
which are on the British list : the Golden-Eye
(q.v.), which is mainly a winter visitor and

passage migrant, and the Buffel-headed Duck,
(q.v.) which wanders here only occasionally.

One of the most striking features of these
birds is the " buffel-shaped " appearance of
their heads (" buffel " being a contraction for
" buffalo ") ; the elongated feathers of the
crown and nape stand out, and make their
heads appear larger and more triangular in
shape than those of most other ducks. Apart
from this, the main difference is that the bill is
shorter than the head, and narrower near the tip
than at the base. Also, the " nail " is generally
wider than in the genus *Aythya*, and the nostrils
are nearer to the tip of the bill. The pointed
wings have the same 11 primaries as other members of the *Anatidae*, but the rounded tail has 16
stiffish rectrices (tail quills). *See also* Duck.

BUDGERIGAR—Melopsittacus undulatus.
This is not, of course, a British bird in the sense
in which this term is used by ornithological
science and in this Encyclopedia. For the
home of the Budgerigar is Australia, where it
exists in huge numbers and is called the Warbling
Grass-Parrot ; it is found all over the Continent, changing its haunts according to the
supply of the seeds of wild grasses on which it
feeds. But it is included in this work as one of
the favourite cage-birds of the British Isles, and
because of experiments undertaken to establish
it as a British wild bird.

The breeding of budgerigars for exhibition
purposes and for competitions has become an
extremely popular and attractive hobby, and is
fostered by numerous societies.

As far as can be ascertained, budgerigars
were introduced into Britain by Gould, a

naturalist of repute, in 1840. At first only a light green variety was seen here, but by cross-breeding some 20 or 30 different types of colours have been developed.

Yellows were raised in 1870, and since then breeders have produced the White-winged Cobalt, which has a white head, wings and tail and a beautiful light blue body ; mauve and olive varieties ; and a great variety of mixed colours based upon the original green.

Experiments intended to turn the Budgerigar into a truly British bird have been made in recent years. The late Duke of Bedford, after designing a special aviary at Woburn, began in 1950 to set free the birds he had bred. He maintained that reliable birds always returned home and brought young ones with the same characteristics. Other bird fanciers have followed his example ; consequently more birds will probably be seen at large, as a few of them will inevitably fail to return home. Such " wild " budgerigars have implicitly been given an added protection by the Bird Protection Act, and while others still live in specially designed aviaries, they may well be seen more frequently flying and feeding with sparrows and other seed-eating birds. For budgerigars this may be a doubtful blessing, for it is possible that many of them will not survive the Winter, owing to the absence of seeding grasses, and because they will lack the resistance of their more robust Australian ancestors. It will not be difficult for the bird watcher to recognize them, for their exotic colourings of yellows, greens and blues, the characteristic markings on their backs and wings, and, in most cases, the regular dark spots on a light ground which they show on their throats, distinguish them from all other British birds.

In flight, budgerigars are not unlike swallows. but they indulge in steep dives with closed wings.

C. & F. McKean

BUDGERIGAR. These youngsters know what is good for them and are getting down to raw carrot

On the wing they are generally silent unless alarmed, but at rest in trees they make a noisy chatter which stops and starts suddenly as if at a command.

Contrary to the belief attested by their (incorrect) description as "love birds", budgerigars are rather promiscuous breeders. If one of a pair dies it is soon replaced ; but if such a loss occurs after the chicks have hatched, the survivor continues to feed them alone. It is not unusual for a cock or hen to have two mates. Six to eight eggs are laid, which are incubated by the hen alone from the laying of the first egg, while the cock feeds her. It is about seven weeks from the time of laying before the chick flies, and it soon fends for itself.

In the wild state the Budgerigar consumes the roots of small plants, occasionally small leaves, bark from twigs and trunks, and, contrary to widespread belief, water—although if deprived of water it will survive longer than almost any other bird.

There is very ample literature on the keeping and breeding of budgerigars, the proper construction of their aviaries and nesting boxes, and the particular demands of prize-winning contests. Usually dry canary seed and millet are recommended as their staple food, but it is desirable to supplement this by a supply of live grass seeds, green food and earth. In the wild, birds peck at twigs and the trunks of trees, and pick off leaves but apparently very seldom trouble to eat them.

The nesting boxes should be designed on the lines of the nests of wild budgerigars, which consist of holes in trees and tree trunks, in easily excavated rotting stumps and so forth. A characteristic feature is that the entrance hole is never exactly opposite that part of the nest in which the eggs are to be laid and hatched.

This may be a means of defence, for this graceful little bird has many enemies. In this country it would mainly have to fear the Sparrow-Hawk and the Tawny Owl, the former singling it out because of its lively colours, and the latter finding it at night resting in trees.

Even so, the pursuit of experiments with budgerigars set free and left to their own devices should prove extremely interesting, for it may well enrich our bird life with a pretty, amusing and lively species.

Consult : All about Budgerigars, F. W. Pratley (Cage Birds), 1953 ; Budgerigar Matings and Color Expectations, F. S. Elliott & E. W. Brooks (Cage Birds), 1949 ; Budgerigars, Parrots, and Parrakeets, R. Mannering (Cassell), 1953 ; The Cult of the Budgerigar, W. Watmough (Cage Birds), 1952 ; Homing Budgerigars, Duke of Bedford (Poultry World), 1953 ; Inbreeding Budgerigars, M. D. S. Armour (Cage Birds), 1949, 1952 ; Talking Budgerigars and How to Train Them, A. Wilson (Cage Birds), 1949, 1951.

BUFF-BACKED HERON. *See* Cattle Egret. Many British ornithological works refer to this bird as Buff-backed Heron, but, as it has only been seen in the wild state twice in this country, this work follows the British list in adopting the name Cattle Egret, commonly used in South Africa, one of the countries in which this bird breeds.

BUFF-BREASTED SANDPIPER—Tryngites subruficollis. An occasional wanderer to the British Isles—some twenty have been reported from different parts of the country—the Buff-breasted Sandpiper breeds on the Arctic coasts of North America and winters in South America.

It is easily recognized. In Summer and Winter the main colouring is buff ; only the head and streaked mantle are of a darker shade, and the outer tail feathers are barred. It has the build of the Common Sandpiper (*q.v.*). Its bill is short and slender. The length is 7 or 8 in., and the wing span approximately 13 or 14 in. ; the female is considerably smaller than the male. It is as a rule a silent bird, except for the breeding season.

Buff-breasted sandpipers begin to assemble at their nesting sites about mid-June or July. The nest is merely a shallow depression in the peaty soil, lined with moss and grass. Four eggs are laid ; information regarding hatching and rearing of the young is still scanty.

BUFFEL-HEADED DUCK—Bucephala albeola. American relative of the Golden-Eye (*q.v.*) but a much less frequent visitor, the Buffel-headed Duck has been recorded in the British Isles at the most half-a-dozen times. The name "buffel" is a contraction of "buffalo", the shape of the head of both this bird and the Golden-Eye resembling that of the American bison. It is a considerably smaller bird than the Golden-Eye and, although its black and white dress is very similar, it can be distinguished easily by the broad white band behind its eye, running up to its crest. Both duck and drake have the white patch, but in the drake it covers a bigger area. The bill is bluish, with a yellow tip. The bird's length is about 15 in., the body being 10 in.

The behaviour, flight and nesting habits of the Buffel-headed Duck are the same as those of the Golden-Eye, but it is an even more silent bird. It is a fine diver and can remain 6–12 ft. below the surface for about 23 seconds.

It breeds in the forests of North America and Canada, and winters in the south. Wherever there are pools and lakes it will choose a hole for its nest, for which practically no material is used except perhaps some down and feathers. There are usually 8–12 eggs, laid in late May or June. The duck hatches

John Markham
BULLFINCH. *This mimic has no song of his own, but makes up for this by picking up popular tunes*

them alone, and she also looks after the chicks. One brood is reared in a season. Both animal and vegetable matter are eaten.

BUFFON'S SKUA. *See* Long-tailed Skua.

BULLFINCH—Pyrrhula pyrrhula. Of the Bullfinch sub-group of the Finch family only the British Bullfinch lives and breeds in Great Britain, although other members occasionally visit England from their homes in Central Europe. The British bird is found all over the country, but less commonly in Scotland and Ireland. Unlike many other resident British birds, the Bullfinch seldom leaves the country.

A great favourite with bird fanciers, the Bullfinch does well in aviaries and is much used in breeding with other cage birds. In years gone by, many families, especially on the Continent, had bullfinches as pets. They are clever mimics and can even be taught to whistle popular tunes (musical boxes have often been used to teach them).

The fat round body of the Bullfinch is unmistakable, and it is the only small British bird which has both a black cap and rose-pink underparts ; the back is grey, and the white rump is very noticeable in flight. The female is not so grey, nor are her pink underparts so bright. The young birds have no black on the head. The Bullfinch has the heavy beak common to its kind. Its flight is undulating, and it has a very awkward hop on the ground ; but it is seldom seen on the ground and much prefers to perch on trees or bushes. Its length is about 6 in. and its tarsus 0·7 in. Its wing span is about 8 in., and the weight about 1 oz.

The Bullfinch has no pretensions to be a singer, for its only sound is like someone

Eric Hosking

BULLFINCH. Maybe the Bullfinch is afraid that his colourful eggs would be an easy prey to thieving birds and other foes, for he takes great pains to hide his nest

blowing across a key. The call note, a soft and plaintive crooning sound, is uttered as part of the cock's display in the courtship season, as he sways from side to side, puffing out his pink breast feathers. He is a very attentive and affectionate mate, and it appears more or less certain that these birds pair for life, for, as Winter approaches, they are always seen together in pairs and do not appear to associate much with other birds.

A true woodland bird, the Bullfinch builds its nest in any suitable place—trees, gardens, or thick hedges—so long as it is well hidden. Shaped like a shallow cup, the nest is an interwoven affair of thin sticks, lined with roots and hair. The eggs, numbering four to six, are greenish blue, spotted with red and purple ; they are laid in April and May. The hatching is done chiefly by the female, taking about 14 days, and both birds feed the young. There are at least two broods a season.

Some weed seeds and berries are eaten, but the bird's natural food is unfortunately chiefly the buds of fruit trees and flowering plants ; these are not always eaten, and the ground may be strewn with destroyed buds. Small wonder then that no bird is less welcome in orchards.

See also Northern Bullfinch.

BULWERIA. Genus of the family *Procellariidae* of the order *Procellariiformes*. It contains four species which are on the British list, all of them occasional wanderers : the Black-capped Petrel, Bulwer's Petrel, Kermadec Petrel, and White-winged Petrel. *See* under those names ; *also* Procellariidae ; Procellariiformes.

BULWER'S PETREL—Bulweria bulwerii. Birds of the ocean, breeding on Atlantic and Pacific Islands, Bulwer's petrels have been occasionally blown to our shores during storms. This bird is apt to be confused with other petrels, but it is smaller and has a uniform dark colour. Its rather long wedge-shaped tail also distinguishes it from other petrels seen here. It has a length of $10\frac{1}{2}$ in. and its tarsus 1 in. Its wing span is approximately 2 ft.

Its behaviour and habits are in the main typical of the tube-nosed family, but it is almost completely nocturnal in its habits. Its voice, with its many varied notes, reminds one of the croaking of frogs. It nests under rocks and boulders and in crevices at the foot of sea cliffs. Only one egg is laid in a season, and the chick, which has its eyes open when hatched, is more active than the young of some other members of the petrel family. *See also* Procellariidae.

BUNTING. Common group name applied to several species of small, seed-eating, strong-billed birds related to the finches, crossbills and linnets, the most popular in this country being the Yellow Bunting, better known as the Yellow Hammer (*q.v.*).

All in this group belong to the order *Fringillidae*, and, with the exception of the Lapland Bunting and the Snow Bunting, to the genus *Emberiza*. Of the seventeen varieties included in the British list, the only residents are the Cirl Bunting, Corn-Bunting, Reed-Bunting and Yellow Hammer. The Snow-Bunting is a winter visitor which has bred in small numbers in Scotland, the Shetlands and St. Kildare ; the

Little Bunting is an irregular visitor, chiefly to Scotland, and the Ortolan Bunting normally a passage migrant and only an occasional visitor. The rest are stragglers which have visited this country only a few times; and these include the Black-headed Bunting, East Siberian Meadow-Bunting, Green-headed Bunting, Pine-Bunting, Red-headed Bunting, Reed-Bunting, Eastern Large-billed Reed-Bunting, Rock-Bunting, Rustic Bunting, and Western Large-billed Reed-Bunting. *See also* articles under these names.

In silhouette buntings somewhat resemble the House-Sparrow, but, with the exception of the Little Bunting, they are rather larger ; the Corn-Bunting is the largest (7 in. long compared with 5¾ in. for the Sparrow). Apart from the Corn-Bunting, the males—particularly after the spring moult—are handsome little birds, with distinctive markings, usually on the head, throat and rump. Female and juvenile buntings are generally less showy than the males.

The distinguishing features which all species have in common are a short, straight, conical bill, a curved form of gape, and a hard, rounded knob on the palate or inner surface of the upper jaw, particularly marked in the Corn-Bunting. This knob probably assists in crushing the seeds which form their principal food. The diet is supplemented with small insects and larvae, which also form the sole food of the young.

BURHINIDAE. Family of the order *Charadriiformes*. It comprises several tropical genera and one genus, *Burhinus*, on the British list. This contains the Stone-Curlew (*q.v.*). The members of this family are medium-sized terrestrial birds ; they have a shortish, stout bill, large head, very large eyes and a long neck and legs. The wings are long and pointed, and the tail is rounded or wedge-shaped.

BURHINUS. Genus of wading birds of the family *Burhinidae* of the order *Charadriiformes*. It contains about seven species, as well as several sub-species ; they are distributed over Europe, north Africa (tropical Africa in the breeding season), Asia, and Central and South America. One species only, the Stone-Curlew (*q.v.*), is on the British list.

BUSTARD. Member of the family *Otididae* of the order *Ralliformes*, which also comprises such birds as the cranes, crakes and rails. Bustards are bulky birds with a stout body, long neck and lank, naked legs. They have a slow and stately walk, and are not well adapted for flight. Their wings are broad and rather rounded, and their bills are of moderate length, straight or nearly so, with a wide gape, in form not unlike that of a hen.

They are mostly inhabitants of dry open plains, grassy steppes or cultivated fields. They are shy but cunning, and live gregariously, feeding on the green parts of plants, seeds, insects, worms and so forth.

Only three species are to be found on the British list : the Great Bustard (*Otis tarda*) ; the Little Bustard (*Otis tetrax*) ; and a sub-species of the Houbara Bustard (*Chlamydotis undulata*), which are described in detail under their own headings. Non-British species are the Black-headed Bustard (India) ; Kori Bustard (South Africa) ; and the Australian Bustard, or Wild Turkey.

The Great Bustard was at one time plentiful in England and was also an inhabitant of south-east Scotland. But extending cultivation and the persecution to which it was subjected, because its flesh was prized for the table, ultimately banished it from these isles ; the last record of its nesting in England was in 1836 at Great Massingham, Norfolk. Now it is only an irregular visitor.

The Little Bustard, common in the south of Europe, western Asia and north Africa, is only an accidental visitor to Great Britain. The Houbara Bustard, sometimes called the Collared or Macqueen's Bustard, belongs to a separate genus and has visited Great Britain on a few occasions only.

BUTCHER-BIRD. Name for various members of the Shrike family (*Laniidae*). The name refers to their habit of impaling on the thorns of a hedge or bush the insects, mice and small birds they catch, the medley of small corpses resembling a butcher's shop ; and it is applied particularly to the Red-backed Shrike (*q.v.*).

BUTEO (Latin, " a kind of hawk "). Genus of the family *Falconidae* of the order *Falconiformes*. It contains many species, distributed over a wide area of the globe ; only two occur in the British Isles, the common Buzzard (*q.v.*),

Paul Popper

BUSTARD. An interesting profile—some might even go as far as to call the Bustard handsome!

which is resident in a few areas, and the Rough-legged Buzzard (*q.v.*), which is an irregular winter visitor.

The members of this genus are closely related to those of the genus *Aquila*, but they are smaller and weaker, and the curve of the bill is sharper and shorter. The wings are large, broad and rounded, and the tail is relatively short. The tarsus is bare in the common Buzzard, but in the Rough-legged Buzzard is feathered in front. There are four toes, all with sharp, curved claws.

BUZZARD—Buteo buteo. Of the three species of Buzzard to be seen in Britain—the common, Honey and Rough-legged (*qq.v.*)—the common Buzzard is the only resident. Of late it has increased in many districts, including Devon, Dorset, and other parts of the West Country. In Ireland, it is a rare breeding bird and an occasional spring and autumn visitor. It breeds all over Europe in suitable country.

To the ordinary observer the principal difference between the three buzzards is in the tail ; the common Buzzard's tail has narrow dark and light bars. On the wing this bird is often taken for an eagle, but at close range it is seen to be much smaller and more stoutly built, with a shorter tail and a much less fierce-looking or powerful head and beak. Its plumage varies considerably, but the mantle is usually dark streaked brown, with much lighter underparts. The legs are yellow. The female resembles her mate in colouring, but is larger. The length of the male is 21 in. and

his wing span 4½ ft. ; the length of the female is 23 in. and her wing span 4¾ ft. The tarsus is 3 in., and the weight about 2½ lb.

The common Buzzard has a plaintive mewing call and it has also various call notes, especially when feeding the young. It has an awkward walk on the ground, but possesses the wonderful flight of all its family. The bird moves with a graceful and effortless motion of its great wings, soaring to great heights, and appearing motionless in the air for hours on end.

The common Buzzard is naturally a woodland bird, and builds its nest in a tree ; in the mountains it builds on a broad ledge among steep crags. The nest is a substantial and bulky affair, the framework being composed of sticks and branches of trees to which sometimes even bones are added. The hen artistically lines it with freshly plucked leaves of many kinds of mountain trees, regularly renewing the decoration even after the eggs are laid.

The eggs usually number two, but often three, while older birds lay only one ; they are dirty white with a bluish tinge, marked with red, brown and purplish blotches. The breeding season starts at about the end of April or beginning of May, and the eggs are laid at intervals of some days. The cock assists in sitting, but the hen does the greater part. The hatching of each egg takes about 28 days. The young are reared by both parents, and it is at least six weeks before the chicks are able to fend for themselves. Only one brood is usually reared in a season.

BUZZARD. *At first sight this bird of prey appears far gentler than its close relative, the Eagle. This seems particularly true in the case of the fluffy nestling (inset)*

Eric Hosking ; John Markham

CAGE BIRDS. *See* Captive Birds ; *also* Aviary ; Aviculture ; First Aid.

CALAMUS (Greek *kalamos*, " reed "). The quill or hollow lower portion of the axis (*q.v.*) of a feather whose base is inserted into the skin and whose upper end passes into the rhachis (*q.v.*) or shaft. Tubular in shape and semi-transparent, it encloses a series of hollow, oblong cells containing, during growth, the nutrient matter out of which the feather is built up.

CALANDRA LARK—Melanocorypha calandra. A native of the Mediterranean region, this bird seldom visits the British Isles, but some years ago, a party of five did wander here. Its stout and heavy bill, and a large black patch on the sides of its throat, conspicuous against the surrounding white, are features which distinguish it from other larks ; its wings and tail are also tipped with white. It is 7½ in. long, and has a wing span of about 12 in.

This lark frequents waste lands, as well as cultivated districts. Its habits and behaviour show much resemblance to those of the Skylark (*q.v.*), though it does not appear to soar to the same extent. Its song is Skylark-like, but has greater volume and a more varied vocabulary ; it is very imitative. The Calandra Lark sings more on the ground, in a manner very similar to that of the Crested Lark (*q.v.*), and has a number of highly musical notes. In Spain and other countries where it breeds, its song has made it a favourite cage-bird.

CALANDRELLA. Genus of the family *Alaudidae* of the order *Passeriformes*. Its members occur in Southern and Central Europe, palearctic Asia and N.W. Africa ; in the non-breeding season also in the Sahara, Sudan and N.W. India. There is only one species on the British list, the Short-toed Lark (*q.v.*), which has visited this country about 13 times. The Eastern Short-toed Lark (*q.v.*), a geographical variant, has also been recorded here about 13 times. Members of this genus are distinguished from all other larks by their smaller size and pipit-like behaviour on the ground. Their

short straight hind claw is about the same length as the hind toe, and a little curved ; and the bill is short and almost conical. *See also* Lark.

CALCARIUS. Genus of the family *Fringillidae* of the order *Passeriformes*. Its members occur throughout the Arctic and sub-arctic regions of the northern hemisphere, as well as in temperate regions outside the breeding-season. There is only one species on the British list, the Lapland Bunting (*q.v.*), which occurs as a passage migrant in the Autumn and as an irregular visitor. at other times. The members of this genus are closely related to those of the genus *Emberiza* (*q.v.*) but they have longer and somewhat more pointed wings.

CALIDRIS. Genus of wading birds of the family *Scolopacidae* of the order *Charadriiformes*. The many species of this very large genus are distributed over most of the globe. The twelve species on the British list are described under their own headings : the Curlew-Sandpiper,

G. K. Yeates

CALIDRIS. *The Purple Sandpiper (C. maritima) has the long bill and long legs typical of this genus*

Dunlin, Knot, Little Stint, Purple Sandpiper, and Temminck's Stint ; and much rarer, the American Stint, Baird's Sandpiper, Bonaparte's Sandpiper, Pectoral Sandpiper, Semi-palmated Sandpiper, and Siberian Pectoral Sandpiper.

The members of this genus vary in size, and show marked differences in length of bill, legs and feet. Generally speaking, the bill is slender, straight or only slightly curved, rather soft and flexible, with the skin before the frontal feathering somewhat wrinkled. Both the upper and lower mandibles have a narrow groove. The female birds often have longer bills than the males. The legs are generally rather long. There is either no web, or only a very small one between the outer and middle toes, but in the case of the Semi-palmated Sandpiper the front toes are webbed to about the first joint. There is a hind toe. The wings are rather pointed. The tail is squarish, often with a notched edge.

CALL NOTE. Call notes can be popularly described as the language in which birds carry on their everyday conversation. No hard and fast line can be drawn between call notes and true song; but, in general, only certain birds, mostly (but not solely) passerines, burst into song—to proclaim their territory and defend it against possible intruders and, during the breeding season, to attract and serenade a mate —whereas call notes may be heard all the year round. A further difference is that call notes are inborn and instinctive whereas songs usually have to be learnt by the young birds.

Every species of bird has a distinctive series of call notes to meet every type of contingency. Birds have no light conversation, every call has a purpose—to help in the battle for survival.

Birds use call notes to give an alarm or warning : when they are frightened or distressed; to show that they are hungry, or, alternatively, that they have found food; to

claim a tree or other territory as their own and to warn off intruders; to chatter and scream excitedly at their rivals; to keep a flock together by day or by night and wherever they may be ; in fact, for almost anything that is essential for their day-to-day existence.

At present the study of call notes is only in its infancy, and it is still only possible to hazard a guess at what a particular call note may mean. A great deal of work will have to be done before one can be at all certain or dogmatic; particularly as there are strong indications that sometimes the same call may mean more than one thing, although there may be some subtle difference that cannot be detected by the human ear. For example, many people know the alarm note uttered by a Blackbird when it senses danger on the ground, perhaps from a human being, prowling cat, or other enemy; and the majority when they hear this sound are convinced that it inevitably means that the bird is expressing vocally its fear of some threat in the offing, or giving a warning to other members of its species.

But the Editor once heard the same call used by a number of blackbirds, when, together with thrushes and other birds, they were mobbing a Little Owl. In this case the particular sound usually employed as an alarm note was used as a war cry—and sustained for more than a quarter of an hour—while the blackbirds were attacking their foe.

When a Blackbird suspects danger from the air, such as a bird of prey, its alarm note is comparatively soft, and quite distinct from that it emits when the danger is on the ground, but the Editor has heard the same soft call uttered when vermin was approaching close to a Blackbird's nest.

Another distinctive alarm note heard only when the bird is on the wing took the Editor eight years to record ! This may seem a long time; but is understandable, for if one is to have any chance of recording this fleeting sound one must be on the spot at the right moment, with the microphone close to the bird, and the recording machine already running.

As already mentioned, the alarm note varies with each bird; it usually consists of two or three notes, short and sharp, which may be repeated. In many species, during the nesting season, the cock-bird stations itself at some vantage point in the neighbourhood of the nest to act as sentinel. If he is a singing bird he will be in full song during this season, and he will sing to his mate while she is sitting on the nest. If he hears someone, or something, approaching, he will stop singing and listen, and then probably utter a fairly low, soft alarm note, which may be answered even more quietly by

Eric Hosking

CAMOUFLAGE. *Stripes matching the surrounding vegetation help to protect the Snipe from enemies*

the hen. If the cock actually spots someone moving in his direction, his notes will be much louder and more agitated; they will also be thus if he is close to his sitting hen and knows that she is covering a clutch or there are fledglings present. This is a useful indication for birdsnesters, and is a better way to find nests than by beating or flushing (*see* Birdsnesting).

Some observers state that the Nightingale and certain other birds sing when badly frightened, or when quarrelsomely chasing one another. The Editor has never witnessed such a dramatic scene ; instead he has heard the usual sweet call note change to a harsh croaking and unpleasant grating sound, as if the birds would go into the attack at any moment.

Certain species have developed the ability to communicate with one another by, what may be termed, mechanical means. For example, the White Stork produces a form of percussion music by throwing its head back until the point of its beak almost touches its back, the jaws are then set rapidly in motion, clashing one against the other, producing a rattling sound.

Pigeons and nightjars when on the wing can produce a curious snapping sound by bringing the wings together sharply over the back. The " bleating " of various species of snipe during the courting season by diving from a great height at prodigious speed is well known.

The study of bird-calls can be of absorbing interest, and a start can be made by listening and trying to interpret the call notes of ten common birds living in your neighbourhood. Not only will this add to the enjoyment of a ramble but you will hear unexpected sounds, such as the ticking alarm note of the Robin, or the rattling of a Chaffinch.

CAMOUFLAGE. Two world wars have familiarised people with this word, originally derived from French slang for a " puff of smoke in the face ". As now used, it may be defined as the art of concealment by which anything is made to appear inconspicuous in its surroundings, and thus more difficult to see and *recognize* by a potential enemy or quarry. The term is also applied to any means employed to achieve this end.

Camouflage may be effected by the object being so disguised that it merges into its background, or by making it resemble some feature that is unlikely to arouse any attention, even if it is seen. Birds who practise the art of camouflage to protect themselves, their young and their nests appear to realize this instinctively, but it is a lesson that has to be learnt, together with many others, by bird watchers who wish to observe birds at close range.

The use of camouflage by bird watchers is discussed more fully in the article Bird-Watching.

Eric Hosking

CAMOUFLAGE. *Stretching its neck and sitting motionless, the Bittern imitates a clump of reeds*

One usual misconception regarding camouflage is that it can be achieved almost entirely by the use of colour and pattern. These frequently play an essential part, but the nature of the coloured surface, the position and posture of the person or creature attempting concealment, change of outline, and the elimination or breaking up of strong shadows, are, in some circumstances, equally, if not more, important.

Examples of the various ways in which the coloured and patterned plumage of certain birds helps to hide them from their potential enemies are given in the article on Protective Coloration, which also deals with the protection of nests, eggs and nestlings. This article explains that there are two main classes of coloration—that which matches the owner's usual background and merges with it, and that which conceals by breaking up the outline ; sometimes the two forms are found combined in one bird.

One of the finest examples of combination of coloration with posturing is provided by the common Bittern, which haunts reed beds. The black streaks on this bird simulate the dark spaces between the reeds, which themselves are represented by the buff ground colour of the plumage. On alarm the bird straightens itself out so that head, neck and spine are almost in one vertical line pointing skyward. Thus posed it remains absolutely still until the danger is past. An observer can approach quite closely to it without spotting it. Many birds, when

G. K. Yeates

CAMOUFLAGE. *The Eider duck is a dull-looking bird against the gorgeous drake, but her plumage merging into the grasses protects her while she sits brooding her eggs*

threatened with danger, flatten themselves out and lie quite prone on the ground, remaining motionless for considerable periods: e.g. Norfolk Plover and Courser, hen Pheasant and Partridge, Snipe and Woodcock, and even the brightly coloured Hoopoe.

Instances of the use of camouflage by birds to track down a quarry are more difficult to find. The best, and perhaps only clear case, is that of the Snow Owl, which, from its white plumage, is able to creep up unawares on its prey which is also commonly coloured white, such as hares, Ptarmigan and Willow Grouse.

See also ; Bird Watching ; Pattern and Colour ; Protective Coloration.

CANADA GOOSE—Branta canadensis. It is almost three hundred years since the Canada Goose was introduced into the British Isles in the collections of ducks on the private lakes of large estates. It is first mentioned in 1678 as one of the King's wildfowl in St. James's Park, London. From time to time some of these birds escape from their domestic surroundings, and from them have descended the Canada geese of today which are resident in many parts of England and Wales, Scotland and Ireland. Abroad it breeds freely in Canada, Alaska and the northern U.S.A.

Being a very large grey-brown bird, the Canada Goose is often mistaken for the Barnacle-Goose, although their breeding haunts are very different—the Barnacle is seldom seen inland and the Canada is rarely seen near the sea. At close quarters the Canada Goose is seen to be a larger bird than the Barnacle species, with browner all-over barred plumage ; it has a black neck and head and a large white stripe extending from the top of one cheek down and under the chin to the top of the other cheek. Its breast is a pale brown, and it has a dark tail with very conspicuous white feathers underneath. The total length of the Canada Goose is about 40 in., the body being about 22 in., its tarsus is 3 in. Its wing span of about $3\frac{1}{2}$ ft. supports a weight of about 7 lb.

A gregarious bird, the Canada Goose is often seen in Winter in company with other water fowl. In many of its general characteristics and habits it resembles the grey rather than the black geese, especially in its high-speed flight. Its voice is a loud resounding trumpet, but in the breeding season there are remarkable differences in the calls of the male and female, especially after the chicks are hatched. The voice of the Canada Goose is more musical than that of most other geese.

The Canada Goose still breeds on many private lakes, but will also be found on inland pools, meres and marshes. A very hard Winter may drive it far from its breeding place in search of food. It has been known to nest on rocky ledges far from water and to occupy the old nest of some bird of prey. But usually the nest is placed on the ground in some sheltered spot near water ; it is lined with grasses, leaves, down and feathers. The normal number of eggs, laid in April, is four or six, but as many as 11 have been recorded ; they are a creamy-white without any gloss. They are brought out by the goose, with the gander never very far away, in about a month. The chicks are fully grown after six weeks and are looked after until then by both parents.

The Canada Goose feeds on grasses of various kinds, water plants and weeds ; animal food is eaten when vegetable matter is not available.

CAMOUFLAGE, *hen Partridge taking concealing action*

For text see pages 111 and 406

CANARY. Although not a native of Britain, the Canary has been domesticated in this country for so long that any book on British ornithology would be incomplete without some reference to this ubiquitous cage bird. It is not intended to treat the Canary here from the point of view of the fancier, nor to give hints on breeding. Housing presents no special problems and the article Aviary covers that aspect of the bird.

There are over a dozen principal breeds of Canary, besides several hybrids or crosses with other birds, but all are descended from the wild canary, *Serinus canaries*, a member of the Finch family native to the Azores, Madeira and the Canary Islands. An indifferent songster, the wild Canary is yellowish brown or green, with ashy sides streaked with black, and having a yellow forehead and underparts. The uniform yellow of some cage varieties is the result of artificial selection in breeding.

Seldom exceeding five inches from beak to tail-tip, the wild Canary nests in shrubs in its native mountains. The female lays three clutches of her blue eggs every year and does all the nest building, but the male is responsible for feeding the chicks.

Introduced into Italy from the Canary Islands in 1510, the bird immediately became popular because of its song, and the latter was greatly improved in power and variety by selective breeding. The Italians became expert Canary breeders and evolved a number of varieties which found a ready market throughout Europe. The birds were first domesticated in Britain as cage pets towards the close of the 16th century.

Since then the Canary has been bred and interbred and in the process of development has changed in colour, shape and markings to produce the different breeds, now known principally by the geographical names of the districts in which they were first bred. In this way have evolved the Belgian, Border Fancy, Crested Norwich, Dutch Frills, German or Roller, Gloucester Fancy, Lancashire, Liverpool Green, London Fancy, Norwich, Scots Fancy and Yorkshire. A few breeds, such as the Cayenne, Cinnamon and Lizard, have been named after their colour and marking. Food has an important bearing upon plumage ; the brilliant red of the Cayenne Canary's plumage is due to feeding with red peppers, i.e. it is a case of erythrism. (*q.v.*)

Canaries are bred for both song and colour, but the songsters are generally buff or yellow, seldom having the striking plumage of the Cayenne, Liverpool Green or Lizard. White canaries are comparatively new breeds, conspicuous for their pure white plumage ; blue canaries are bred from white and green parents.

Some breeds of Canary, notably the Norwich and Yorkshire, are deep orange or peach, due to their having been fed on a sweet red pepper imported chiefly from Spain. If this diet is discontinued, the birds revert to their

CANADA GOOSE. *This waterfowl was first introduced to London in 1678. Its effortless grace when swimming comes as a shock to those who have met only the farmyard goose*

John Markham

CANARY. *The beautifully marked Lizard Canary is renowned for its looks—but not for its singing*

Cage Birds

natural buff or yellow after the first moult. The striking green plumage of the Liverpool Green, and the variegated, scale-like plumage of the Lizard (hence the name) are inherited, but their unique plumage lasts for only one year and has almost disappeared after the first or second moult.

Canaries with variegated plumage are often incorrectly referred to as " mules ". A Canary having a " splash " of dark colour is correctly termed variegated, no matter where the colour is found, provided it is larger than a sixpenny piece. Birds completely variegated are termed " self " while those with just one light marking, such as a single feather, are called " foul ".

Most singing canaries in Britain are descended from the German or Roller canaries, which were originally bred in the Harz Mountains. Until their importation was stopped by the First World War, the only pure-bred Rollers came from Germany, and the males were used to improve the strain of British-bred singing varieties. In Germany, the young birds were carefully guarded from hearing the song of any untrained bird, and were kept in the dark, where they listened for hours to the notes of a bird organ until they learned to imitate it faultlessly.

After the First World War British fanciers bred a strain of pure Rollers from imported German birds, but did not adopt the elaborate German training methods, relying on the bird's imitation of each other. The quality and range of the British and German Roller's song is lost when the bird is taken from the seclusion in which it lives with its fellows. Its song then reverts in large measure to that of the ordinary singing Canary.

CAPERCAILLIE — Tetrao urogallus. The largest of the Grouse family, and, like most or all of that family, a game bird, the Capercaillie disappeared about two centuries ago from the Scottish scene for some reason never explained, but probably connected with changes in agriculture and the shooting of the bird for food. Several attempts were made to reintroduce it, but these were not successful until 1837, when some birds brought from Sweden flourished and spread. Today this handsome bird is once again resident in the pine and fir forests of Scotland. Abroad, it breeds in the coniferous forests of northern and central Europe, the Balkans, Russia and Siberia.

Its great size—it is almost as big as a hen turkey—easily distinguishes it from all other game birds. In general, it presents a dark-grey appearance, but at close quarters it is seen to have various colourings of grey, brown, bluish-green, and white. Its eyes are surrounded by bright red skin ; it has a pale coloured bill, feathered legs and a rounded tail. The hen, rather smaller than the cock, is dressed in a mottled and barred plumage of light-brown, grey and black. The cock is about 30 to 35 in. in length ; his tarsus is 3 in., and his wing span about 4 ft. 4 in. The hen is about 22 to 25 in. long, her tarsus being 2 in. ; her wing span is 3½ ft. The weight of the male, usually about 13 lb., sometimes reaches 17 or 18 lb.

The Capercaillie has a heavy walk on the ground. It roosts, and is very fond of perching, on the low branches of trees, where it makes a great fluttering if disturbed. Once on its way, its flight is rapid, and it can cover several miles. Its voice produces various raucous and unmusical noises which have been likened to the drawing of a cork followed by the sound of liquid pouring out of a bottle.

The spring courtship of the Capercaillie is most striking. The cocks indulge in extravagant displays and tremendous fights for their mates, sometimes becoming so excited that they are literally deaf and blind to the consequences of their battles. The hens give every evidence of treating the scene as an entertainment, and the victor is much admired as he struts about. It is believed that the Capercaillie is polygamous. The females are said to breed occasionally with blackcocks.

The Caper, as sportsmen call it, frequents woods of larch, pine and fir, nesting among the vegetation. The nest is only a hollow scraped in the ground by the hen, and lined with pine needles and moss while the eggs are being laid. The breeding season is from April into May. Normally five to eight eggs, pale yellow with blotches of yellow and reddish-brown, are laid; when as many as 15 or 18 are found, it means that two hens are laying in the same nest ! Hatching, which takes 26 days, is done by the hen alone when all the eggs are laid. The young are also reared by the hen, and begin to get active in about three weeks or so. One brood is brought out in a season.

Shoots and buds of various trees form the food of the Capercaillie from October to April. In the Summer plenty of other food is available—grass, clover leaves, bracken shoots, heather, and the seed pods of many wild flowers and berries of various kinds. Some insects are also eaten.

The name Capercaillie is also spelt occasionally Capercailye or Capercaizie. A Celtic word, it means horse, bird, goat, or old man, of the wood.

CAPE SEA-PIGEON—Procellaria capensis. Sometimes called the Cape Pigeon or Pintado Petrel, this bird breeds in south Atlantic and south Pacific countries. It is not included in the British list, although it has been recorded once or twice. It is doubtful, however, whether these arrivals were genuine stragglers or birds captured at sea, brought to the Channel, and then released.

The Cape Sea-Pigeon has boldly chequered upper-parts, two large, round white patches on the upper surface of each wing, a dark head, and white under-parts. Its length is 14 in, the same as that of the much better-known Manx Shearwater, a distant relative. One single white oval egg is laid.

CAPE VERDE LITTLE SHEARWATER—Procellaria baroli boydi. The Cape Verde Islands in the North Atlantic are the home of this Little Shearwater but two specimens have been picked up on the Sussex Coast. The bird is similar in every way to the Madeiran Little Shearwater (*q.v.*), except for its dark under tail-coverts (Madeiran's are white). It is indistinguishable in the field from Audubon's Shearwater (*q.v.*), except by experts.

CAPPED PETREL. Alternative name for Black-capped Petrel (*q.v.*).

CAPRIMULGIDAE. Family of insectivorous nightbirds, the nightjars (*q.v.*), of the order *Caprimulgiformes*. This family is widely distributed over the globe, but only two of its genera, *Caprimulgus* and *Chordeiles*, occur on the British list. Members of this family are distinguished by their long wings, ample tails, large eyes and gapes, and very small feet. Their plumage is usually soft and beautifully camouflaged to enable them to pass the day unnoticed perched lengthways along a branch or on the ground.

CAPRIMULGIFORMES. An order of medium or large-sized night birds, consisting of the nightjars, frogmouths, and the aberrant South American Oil-Bird. Of its four families only *Caprimulgidae* includes British species.

CAPRIMULGUS (Latin, " goatsucker "). Genus of the family *Caprimulgidae* (*q.v.*) of the order *Caprimulgiformes*. It contains more than fifty species, distributed over much of the globe except New Zealand and some other islands, and the Arctic and Antarctic regions. There are three species on the British list: the Nightjar (*q.v.*), which is a common summer visitor, and the Red-necked Nightjar (*q.v.*) and Egyptian Nightjar (*q.v.*), neither of which has been recorded more than once in Britain.

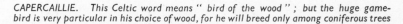

CAPERCAILLIE. This Celtic word means " bird of the wood " ; but the huge game-bird is very particular in his choice of wood, for he will breed only among coniferous trees

Eric Hosking

ACCUSTOMING BIRDS TO CAGE LIFE

CECIL S. WEBB, C.M.Z.S.

This interesting and unusual article by the Superintendent of the Royal Zoologica!
Society of Ireland describes techniques used to tame wild birds and acclimatise them
to a life in captivity.   A section is included on the transportation of exotic species

CAPTIVE BIRDS. The vogue of keeping birds in captivity is spreading rapidly in Great Britain.   Cage-bird societies are springing up everywhere, and it is doubtful if there is a single large town that does not have its annual cage-bird show.   These shows are an indication of Man's progressive success in the domestication of certain species of birds and the establishing of new varieties by the process of careful selective breeding.

In the past Man devoted much time to the domestication of birds of a utilitarian value, such as fowls, ducks, geese, turkeys and pheasants.   Then came the vogue for songsters, and today this has spread to any small bird that will breed in captivity.   To judge by the exhibits at our national and other large bird shows, there must be thousands of people deeply engrossed in the hobby of breeding species and varieties up to a required standard.

The pleasure and satisfying knowledge gained in such a pursuit cannot be overstressed ; for, if anyone is to succeed in this hobby, he must develop certain qualities, such as the power of observation, patience, kindness to animals, etc., and in his unstinted efforts to keep his delicate charges in perfect condition and to induce them to breed, he is unwittingly making a finer person of himself.

Perhaps the oldest domesticated cage-bird is the Canary (*q.v.*), and this still remains the most popular, although fashions change regarding the different varieties.   Its chief rival nowadays is the Budgerigar (*q.v.*), which until not many years ago was known only by the typical species—mainly green in colour—imported from its natural habitat in Australia. From these have been evolved so many varieties of greens, yellows, whites and blues, that it would be difficult to enumerate them all.   So intricate is the mating of the various strains to bring about some desired colour scheme that to be a successful Budgerigar fancier today one must be something of a geneticist.   Something of the bird's popularity may be gauged from the fact that in 1953 the membership of the Budgerigar Society was about 15,000.

Strangely enough, our own British birds have never been bred in captivity to the same extent as certain foreigners, except perhaps for crossing with canaries.   This may be because in the past stock was easily replaced by catching wild birds, and also because, on the whole, they do not breed very readily in close confinement.   Whereas canaries, budgerigars and certain foreign finches will reproduce freely in cages, the best results with British finches are obtained when they are kept in aviaries in small flights (*see* Aviary).

Nevertheless, of recent years a tremendous advance has been made in the technique of rearing and breeding British birds, and more and more uncommon varieties of our own native birds are now appearing at the big shows.

In the grim struggle for survival most wild birds have become distrustful of Man.   This is a strong natural instinct that has to be

By courtesy of Magdalen Girdlestone

CAPTIVE BIRDS.   Not only rare birds are kept in captivity, for here a baby Sparrow, who had fallen from his nest, finds a new home in a pudding basin

Paul Popper

CAPTIVE BIRDS. Even a large bird, like the Bateleur Eagle with his red and mahogany plumage, set off by black, is quite happy as long as he has room to " spread himself "

overcome before newly captured specimens can settle down to a contented existence. Fear is the survival instinct that impels birds to flee for safety when necessary, and if they find themselves in a situation, such as an uncovered cage, in which they are frightened but unable to seek cover they are being subjected to unnecessary suffering. The faculty of adaptation to changed conditions varies with the individual, the species and the age of the bird. In general it will take considerable time and patience to bring about the change-over to the desired state in which a bird has lost practically all fear of Man—or at least of its owner.

Taming Wild Birds. No doubt different people have evolved different methods, but the principles are the same, if one is guided by recognized standards of humane treatment. The Chinese employ some methods which may seem cruel to us, but are extraordinarily successful in taming birds completely in a short space of time. Moreover, the Chinese are very devoted to their pets and seem to have a complete understanding of their requirements. Who, for instance, in England would think of taking a daily walk with a caged bird in order to let it see and hear other birds and look at fresh surroundings ; and how many birds, for that matter, would be tame enough to appreciate such treatment ?

One Chinese technique for taming is to attach about two feet of string to the leg of a newly caught bird and fasten the other end to a vertical stand. On top of this is a small wooden platform on which the bird is placed by an attendant, usually a small boy, whose duty it is to catch and replace the bird every time it takes off, fluttering violently and finishing up by dangling down on the string. This process goes on and on until the bird is exhausted and

has no will to try to escape. Once the bird's wild spirit has been broken, it becomes completely changed in character, and is the tamest creature imaginable.

My own method of dealing with newly captured birds was to put them into strong wooden boxes—caging insectivorous and nectar-feeding birds singly, and seed-eating birds a few, but not too many, together. The boxes were of standard size, and stacked easily and neatly in rows. They were, in fact, the wooden containers, so easily obtained throughout the tropics, for two four-gallon cans of petrol or paraffin. Placed on its side one of these boxes was of ideal dimensions for small seed-eating birds ; 20 in. across, 17 in. deep and 10 in. high.

Across the lower part of the front was nailed a board 6 in. wide, at one end of which was a door. The space above the board was covered with galvanized cage-front with vertical bars, but no cross-bars (except at the top and bottom). Perches were put in by drilling holes in the front and back of the box, only 2 in. above the floor and about 4 in. apart, leaving the space opposite the door clear.

Tacked to the top of the front was a curtain of thin hessian which allowed air and a certain amount of light to pass through, but prevented the inmates from seeing out. A small water-tin was put in the corner opposite the door.

This arrangement has the following advantages : the occupants cannot foul one another as the perches are too low for any birds to get under them ; the food and water keep fresh and clean since they are not placed under the perches ; if the birds are frightened when being fed they will fly against the front and will thus avoid falling in the water-pot and getting miserably wet ; there is ample flying space above the perches ; the board along the front

W. S. Berridge

CAPTIVE BIRDS. This tiny Humming-Bird makes a
pretty but difficult pet, for it eats only nectar

affords protection when the birds are perched ;
the porous curtain allowing light and air to
pass through ensures that the birds will behave
almost as confidently as if they were still at
liberty ; and the birds are protected against
heat and cold.

I had tiny peep-holes in the tops of my boxes,
and it gave me great satisfaction to look through
and see newly caught birds quietly cracking
seeds in their screened quarters. They gradually
became used to my visiting them, so that I was
able to raise the curtain, slightly at first and
more and more as the birds got tamer, until it
could be left up permanently.

Considerable patience is necessary to get birds
tame enough for the show bench. Generally
speaking, insect-eating birds are the least
difficult in this respect, for they will soon learn
to take a mealworm or gentle from one's fingers.

In any case the birds need to be caged singly,
and with seed-eating birds it is an advantage
to have two exhibition cages with a trap door
leading from one to the other. The bird can
be induced to enter the second cage by gently
using a stick. It should then be sprayed, using
slightly warmed water, with a fine bird spray.
It will soon look forward to the daily bath,
becoming tamer in the process. After the bath
it should be transferred back to its dry cage.

Transport of Exotic Species. The problems
of transport do not arise to the same extent
with British birds as with exotic species, and
even with the latter great changes have come
about since the Second World War, owing to
the ever-increasing use of aircraft. Birds sent
by air need no longer be subjected to all the
changeable moods of the elements encountered

on a long sea voyage, with alternate risks of
being baked by the sun, battered by storms and
chilled by icy-cold winds.

One of the greatest sins in transporting birds
is overcrowding, usually with the idea of saving
freight. In the end it is false economy, because
heavy losses are inevitable, and many birds
will remain sick and miserable for months
afterwards. The temptation to pack as many
creatures as possible into a given space is even
greater when sending them by air, as it is
supposed that they will stand any conditions
on a comparatively short journey.

As a rule, sufficient food is put in the cages
to last the whole trip, and the only thing left
for the air-host or hostess is to see that birds are
supplied with water. This may work out well
if every precaution has been taken beforehand
for the birds' comfort. The water-tin should be
of the kind that will not spill, otherwise the cage
may get water-logged and the food ruined.

Insectivorous birds will need a good insectile
mixture that will not go sour on the voyage.
Such foods are sold under proprietary names,
but they can be made up with a mixture of
granulated sweet biscuit or ordinary biscuit meal,
melted fat, honey, dried flies, " ants' eggs " and
dried yolk of egg.

Care must be taken when transporting exotic
birds by air to ensure that the box, if thin or of
plywood, is not liable to be left on some tropical
airfield exposed to the full heat of the sun. In
such cases, the heat passing through the wooden
top of even a well-ventilated box is sufficient to
kill the small birds inside. This is especially so
if the perches are high, and the birds are thus
near the roof.

When dealing with nectar-feeding birds, which
require liquid food only, it is more than ever
necessary to employ non-spilling containers, such
as the drip suction type of bottle with a lip near
the bottom and a cork at the top, so that even
if the cage is tipped upside down when being
handled the liquid food remains intact. A few
hours without this special sweetened liquid is
sufficient to kill a whole consignment of sunbirds
or humming-birds.

Acclimatising Foreign Birds. There are no
hard and fast rules about acclimatising birds in
captivity. Many foreign birds will not stand
the English climate in Winter, but that may be
partly due to the fact that they are living under
artificial conditions and are not a hundred
per cent. fit. Because the normal habitat of a
particular bird is in a temperate zone it does not
follow that it will stand prolonged cold conditions in captivity ; on the other hand a bird
from the tropics may soon be in distress if
exposed to hot sunshine when in a cage. Generally speaking, birds appreciate warmth, but the

hardier species will thrive in unheated outhouses, etc., that are free from frost. The more delicate tropical birds will require artificial heat, preferably not falling below 50° F., but again fitness will largely be the determining factor.

Reverse seasons are apt to upset natural cycles when birds are introduced from one hemisphere to the other. Winter in the south means Summer in the north, so that if, for instance, some whydahs were introduced into England from South Africa in the English Summer, the males would be in their eclipse, (q.v.) or non-breeding plumage, and a hot Autumn might induce them to change into their breeding plumage just as Winter was approaching.
This would be all wrong, for whydahs in South Africa are always in their dull " sparrowy " plumage during the cold weather. It is more likely that the natural breeding cycle of such birds would be delayed for a season, so as to conform to the reverse seasons in England. This applies to all birds with seasonal plumage change, and likewise affects these and any others as regards breeding in a different hemisphere. In the latter case it may take a couple of years before the bird's natural cycle adjusts itself.

The breeding of wild-caught birds in captivity is not merely a matter of season. They must be brought into breeding condition by correct feeding over a period of time, and in many cases nesting-sites must be provided, as well as nesting material. Finally, many birds prefer privacy both from other birds and from humans, before they will nest successfully. *See also* Aviary; Aviculture ; Budgerigar ; Canary.

CARDUELIS (Latin, " thistle-finch " or " gold-finch "). Genus of the family *Fringillidae* of the order *Passeriformes*. Its species are distributed over a wide area of the globe, including Europe, north Africa, much of Asia including China and Japan, and north and south America. The seven species on the British list are described under their own names : the Goldfinch, Siskin, Linnet, Twite, Redpoll and the much scarcer Arctic Redpoll and Citril Finch.

These birds have hard, almost conical, bills, very thick at the base. The upper mandible is straight or only very slightly curved. The nostrils are very close to the feathers and concealed by them. The wings, which have nine primaries, are long and rather pointed, with the first, second and third primaries forming the tip of the wing. The medium-long tail has 12 feathers; the tarsus is short and strong.

CAROLINA CRAKE. English name for a rare migrant from North America, the Sora Rail (q.v.). As this bird has been authoritatively recorded in this country only five times, it is described fully only under its American name.

CARPODACUS. Genus of the family *Fringillidae* of the order *Passeriformes*. Its members are distributed over eastern Europe and much of northern Asia, and, outside the breeding-season, in south-eastern Europe and southern Asia. Only one member of this genus, the Scarlet Grosbeak (q.v.), occurs in the British Isles.

CARRIER PIGEON. Type of homing pigeon used to carry messages. It belongs to one of the four principal groups of domestic pigeon (*see* Pigeon). Carrier pigeons were used extensively by all contestants in both World Wars. They are mentioned as early as *Genesis*, when Noah sent out a dove which returned with an olive branch to show that the waters of the flood were beginning to subside.

CARRION-CROW—Corvus corone. One of our commonest but certainly not one of our best-loved birds. A resident in Great Britain, it frequents practically all parts of the country and is also very much at home in towns. It is quite common even in London, and many of the city squares, including those in close proximity to noisy thoroughfares, have at least one pair of carrion-crows bringing up a family in the Spring and residing all Winter as well.

Since the carrion- and hooded crows come from common stock they interbreed fairly freely, especially in Scotland where both are resident. In Ireland the Carrion-Crow appears only as a rare vagrant. In September and November, carrion-crows arrive from central Europe in company with rooks, hooded

CARRIER PIGEON. *Life and death may depend upon the message that is fastened to the pigeon's leg*

crows and jackdaws, returning to the Continent in the Spring.

A smaller bird than the Raven (*q.v.*), it is often confused with the Rook (*q.v.*). But its plumage is, if anything, less black than the Rook's and has a greenish gloss, while the distinctive difference in the beaks of the two birds is unmistakable. The Carrion-Crow's beak is more curved and is at all seasons covered with bristle-like feathers, while that of the Rook is completely bare. The length of the Carrion-Crow is 20 in., and its tarsus 2 in. It has a wing span of 2½ ft., and a weight of 1 lb. 3 oz.

Like the other birds of this family, the Carrion-Crow feeds on the ground, its movements closely resembling those of the Raven. Although it walks in a clumsy and ungainly way, often with a curious sidling action, its flight is direct and straight, with regular wing beats—rather slower than the Rook's and rarely as high as the Raven's. This crow is seldom seen to soar.

In the courtship display of the Carrion-Crow, the cock bows to the hen with quick movements, head lowered, tail fanned and wings outspread. This may take place either on the ground or in a tree. The bird is believed to mate for life. It is a solitary bird, and pairs are usually seen going about alone ; but in Winter they do occupy roosts with other crows and even with rooks.

The distinctive voice of the Carrion-Crow is quite different from that of the Raven, Rook and Jackdaw. It is a repeated harsh croak, but with many independent variations different from the common call note. The Editor has recorded calls of the Carrion-Crow which only a very few field ornithologists have ever heard. In early Spring there is a courtship note reminding one of the sound of a motor horn.

The nest, which is very similar to that of the Hooded Crow (*q.v.*), is usually built in the fork

Eric Hosking

CARRION-CROW. Though neither her name nor her voice is lovely, this Crow makes a devoted mother

of a high tree, but in hilly districts will often be found among bushes ; on the coast, it may be built in a rocky crevice. Both birds take part in the construction, using sticks, twigs, earth and moss, and lining it very cleverly with hair and wool. The number of eggs is usually four or five —sometimes as many as six—and they are blue-green in varying shades, with spots of brown. They are laid in April, occasionally earlier. The three weeks' hatching is done by the hen alone, but she is fed by the male. The young birds, which are fed by the hen with food procured by the cock, are usually on the wing in 30-35 days. One brood is reared in a season.

Food consists mostly of carrion, but the Carrion-Crow will kill and eat any small beast it can find. It does great damage in game-bird preserves, but its ravages are not confined to game birds and many a small bird's nest is robbed of both eggs and young.

A good deal of vegetable food is also devoured, and the Carrion-Crow has a well-known habit of breaking hard articles of food, such as walnuts, crabs, and so on, by dropping them from a height. It will bury surplus food.

CASARCA. Genus of ducks of the family *Anatidae* of the order *Anseriformes*. It contains four species, of which one occurs in Australia, and one in New Zealand. The only species on the British lists is the Ruddy Sheld-Duck (*q.v.*), which occurs here as an occasional visitor only.

CASPIAN PLOVER—Charadrius asiaticus. Rare visitor to the British Isles, only four or five authentic arrivals having been recorded, the Caspian Plover breeds in south-east Russia and Siberia. In appearance it shows some likeness to the Dotterel, and, as far as is known, its behaviour and habits resemble those of the Golden Plover (*q.v.*). It is brown above, with white neck, face and underparts ; across its breast is a broad band of chestnut, bordered with black. Its length is 7½ in.

The Caspian Plover nests on arid steppes and lonely desert tracts, within reach of water; but in Winter, when it wanders in flocks, it is often found far from water and at high altitudes. Its nest is only a depression on the ground, and three oval eggs are laid in May. This species of plover is single-brooded ; as far as reliable information goes, both parents take part in hatching the eggs and rearing the chicks. Insects form the chief item in its diet.

CASPIAN TERN—Hydroprogne caspia. Largest of the terns, the Caspian Tern comes to the British Isles only as a rare vagrant. It breeds on the Scandinavian coasts, but during its migration it is extremely widespread, appearing in many countries of both the Old and

CASPIAN TERN. It is easy to see that this Tern is the least sociable of gulls and terns, though perhaps the bird on the right had trespassed on the territory of the others

the New World. About the size of the Common Gull, it is easily recognized by its conspicuous red bill. It has a typical tern-like body and colouring, with a silver-grey mantle and white underparts ; its head is black. Its tail is forked, but not quite so much as that of its relatives, and its black legs are longer than theirs. Its length is 19 or 20 in., and its wing span 3 or 4 ft.

The behaviour and habits of the Caspian Tern are more or less typical of its family (see Tern) but its flight is less light and graceful and rather resembles the Gull's. Although it nests in colonies, it is less social than gulls or other terns. The nest is a mere hollow made in the sand. The Caspian Tern is single-brooded ; the normal number of eggs is two or three, laid in May or June according to the latitude. The hatching and rearing of the chicks are shared by both parents. Fish forms its main food.

CATTLE EGRET—Ardeola ibis. An uncommon visitor to the British Isles, the Cattle Egret, also called Buff-backed Heron, was last recorded in Norfolk in 1917. It breeds in tropical Africa and in southern Spain and Portugal. It is often confused with the Little Egret (q.v.) as it is similar to it in practically all respects, including size, flight, walk and breeding. It has, however, one characteristic habit ; it is nearly always seen walking in the fields with cattle, whence its name.

Although it has in the main the pure white plumage of the Little Egret, a tuft of long pinkish-buff feathers, runs down its head and back and some of these also appear on its breast. From a distance this colouring is evident only in Summer—hence the confusion of this bird with other egrets. It is some 20 in. long, its body being 11 in.

The song of the Cattle Egret is a series of guttural notes, usually heard in the nesting season. The bird breeds in colonies, which are often very large, together with little egrets, Glossy Ibis, and others. Its breeding season differs according to the country frequented, and its nesting procedure follows the pattern of its species.

CENTRAL EUROPEAN CRESTED TIT— Parus cristatus mitratus. Only one bird of this species has been recorded in Great Britain. In appearance, song and habits, the bird resembles the Crested Tit (q.v.), which lives and breeds in the Scottish Highlands. It frequents country with coniferous trees, nesting in the holes of stumps—but it will also occasionally make use of the old nests of other birds (especially birds of prey), the borings of woodpeckers and the burrows of kingfishers. It is said to have two broods in a season. Both parents take part in hatching and rearing the five to eight chicks. The length is 4½ in.

Another form, the Northern Crested Tit (Parus cristatus cristatus), breeds in Scandinavia and other northern European countries ; a few have from time to time been seen in England. It is identified by a slight difference in plumage from the Central European Crested Tit.

CERE. Waxlike skin on the base of the upper mandible. See also Bill.

CERTHIA. Genus of creepers of the family Certhiidae of the order Passeriformes. It contains five species and a number of sub-species. These non-migratory birds are distributed over Europe and much of North America and Asia. The Tree-Creeper (q.v.) is the only member of this genus which occurs in the British Isles as a common resident. Small, brownish and streaked, these birds are often seen climbing up tree trunks. They are the only small land birds with curved bills, which are laterally compressed, long and scimitar-shaped.

CERTHIIDAE. Family of the order *Passeriformes*. It contains the creepers, and is divided into five genera, its members being distributed over Europe, much of Asia, Africa and North America. *Certhia* (*q.v.*) is the only genus on the British list.

CETTIA. Genus of warblers of the family *Sylviidae* of the order *Passeriformes*. The only species recorded in the British Isles is Cetti's Warbler (*q.v.*), and this has been observed only three times, as it is usually confined to southern Europe, western Asia and north-west Africa.

CETTI'S WARBLER—Cettia cetti. Species of Warbler breeding in many parts of the Continent, including the Iberian peninsula, France, Italy and Corsica, and in parts of Africa. Only three have been recorded in the British Isles.

Cetti's Warbler is quite different from all other warblers, and is characterized by the fact that the lateral feathers of its ten-feathered and well-rounded tail are much shorter than the middle pair ; the under tail-coverts cover more than half the tail. The rounded wings are of medium length, and the first primary is about half the length of the second. The latter is only a little longer than the secondaries. The plumage is long and soft. The bill is thin, narrow and pointed. *See also* Sylviidae.

A very shy and skulking bird, Cetti's Warbler is difficult to identify ; but at close range is seen to be decidedly reddish-looking, with brown mantle, light grey underparts and reddish tail. It also has a conspicuous white stripe above its eyes. Male and female are alike. The length is 5½ in. The most distinguishing characteristic

CHAFFINCH. *This pretty songster, found almost everywhere, is quick to imitate the songs of others*

\John Markham

of this warbler is its marvellous song : a sudden outpouring of varied, rich and melodious notes uttered from its hiding-place in the undergrowth. In Italy this is heard at its best from March until June.

Cetti's Warbler frequents thickets, bushes and vegetation near water, marshy places and reed beds. Its nest, made of grasses and leaves, is in the form of a deep cup, lined with fine grasses and hair. Three or four brick-red eggs are laid in April or May. The chicks are reared by both parents, two broods being sometimes brought out in a season. The diet consists mainly of insects.

CHAETURA. Genus of swifts of the family *Apodidae* (*q.v.*) of the order *Apodiformes*. Several species occur in Asia, Africa and America, but only one, the Needle-tailed Swift (*q.v.*), in Europe. This has been recorded only twice in the British Isles. Members of this genus can be distinguished from those of the genus *Apus* (*q.v.*) by the tail, in which the shafts of the feathers are longer than the webs and protrude like spines.

CHAFFINCH—Fringilla coelebs gengleri. This is the commonest land bird of the British Isles, with a population of about 10 million ; its nearest rival is the Blackbird, with about 6 million. The attractive and friendly Chaffinch is found in every part of the country, and at all seasons ; although outside the nesting season chaffinches move about from county to county, there is no evidence that they ever cross the Channel. The Chaffinch has much in common with the Brambling; and in Winter, when the latter arrives in Britain, the two are constantly seen feeding in company, together with greenfinches, sparrows, and yellow hammers. The Chaffinch is a gregarious bird, and roosts with others in hedges and shrubberies. A familiar bird in its trim and dainty plumage, the male has a slate-grey head, pink breast and chestnut mantle, and his wings are dark with brilliant white patches (which are very evident in both sexes in flight).

The female is less colourful, the pink on her breast being a much paler shade, and her mantle and head being yellowish brown. The young birds resemble her. The length of the Chaffinch is 6 in. and its tarsus 0·7 in. Its wing span is 8 in., and its weight varies from ½ to 1 oz.

Its movement on the ground is neither a walk nor a hop, but a mingling of both, and it has the graceful undulating flight of the Finch (*q.v.*) family. It is a delightful sight when a flock of these birds rises in a flurry to settle on the branches of a near-by tree. Their courtship and display follow the pattern of the Finch family with the rapid chase of the male after his mate, his wings quivering and tail fanned as he repeats all the while his mating song.

One could almost write a book about the voice of the Chaffinch. During the past 30 years, I have made a special study of many individual chaffinches in many different parts of the country as well as abroad. The call notes, which are so familiar to everyone, can be heard all the year round. The song starts about the middle of February and can still be heard in July. During the breeding season the male sings without interruption—with the help of Oscar Heinroth, I once counted the record number of 824 songs within two hours !

There are geographical variations in the song of the Chaffinch. What I consider the perfect song lasts for 2½ seconds, but in the highlands of Scotland the Chaffinch's song lasts only 1½ seconds. The song heard in Kent has the popular translation of " Go quick, fetch me a bottle of ginger beer", while the Continental Chaffinch ends its song with a sound like the German word " Würzgebühr ". Indeed, the chief variation from county to county and country to country, is in the last syllables of the song.

Yet it is not possible to assign a bird to its home county or country by analysing its song, for chaffinches are great mimics and British birds often pick up the typical phrases of Continental migrants. I have often heard the Continental bird's typical "Würzgebühr" phrases in Essex, and in Kew Gardens I have heard the typical song of a Belgian Chaffinch, ending with its high note phrase. It is impossible to say whether these two birds were migrants from the Continent, or British birds which had heard the variations long enough to imitate them.

Over a dozen songs of chaffinches, each one recorded in a different place, show remarkable variations. These differences are not inborn : they may be produced by the bird's own musical taste, or what is more likely, through mimicry. In this connection, it is interesting that in 1952, after the great Continental Robin invasion, I heard at close quarters a Chaffinch marvellously imitating the song of the Robin.—EDITOR.

The Chaffinch will nest almost anywhere where there are bushes—in gardens, woods, copses and parks. Its nest is placed in a hedge or the fork of a tree ; a fine and beautiful piece of construction, it is built of moss, lichens, wool or anything soft, and lined with wool, hair and down. The hen does most of the building work, but her mate brings some of the material. The four to six eggs are laid in May ; they vary in colour but the majority are green-blue with streaks of dark purple and brown. The hatching is also done almost entirely by the hen, for 12 days, and the young birds are fed by both parents for about the same period. Only one clutch of eggs is laid in a season.

The Chaffinch should be welcomed everywhere, for it is one of those birds of which it can confidently be said that it does more good than harm to agriculture. Some fruit and corn may be taken, but injurious insects form the largest part of its diet, and it devours the seeds of many weeds. *See also* Continental Chaffinch.

W. Farnsworth

CHARADRIIDAE. The Lapwing, or Green Plover is a member of the Plover family, or Charadriidae

CHALAZA. One of two spirally twisted albuminous threads attached to the lining membrane of an egg at each end to keep the yolk in position and to act as a pad to reduce shock. The interior of the cords resembles a series of white knots, hence the name which is the Greek word for " hailstones". The germinal portion of the egg is not kept at the top by the chalazae, but by its lower density. *See also* Egg ; Embryo ; Reproduction.

CHARADRIIDAE. Family of wading birds of the order *Charadriiformes*. It includes four genera on the British list : *Arenaria*, *Charadrius*, *Chettusia* and *Vanellus*. Its members vary from 6 in. to 12 in. in length ; they are usually squat and compactly built, with thick necks and stout shortish bills and large eyes, made more conspicuous in most species by bold eye-stripes. Most birds of this family have a boldly patterned summer plumage, with a band or patch of darker colour across the breast and a dark tail-band, which gives way to a more sober-hued winter dress. The *Charadriidae* are widely distributed, frequenting rivers and estuaries, mud-flats and coastal districts.

There are 12 species on the British list, described fully under their own headings. Of these the Dotterel, Golden Plover, Lapwing, Little Ringed Plover and the Ringed Plover breed in this country, although the Dotterel is only a scarce and local bird ; the Grey Plover, Kentish Plover and Turnstone are non-breeding but regular visitors ; and the American Golden Plover, Caspian Plover, Killdeer Plover and Sociable Plover occur as occasional stragglers.

The Arctic Ringed Plover, closely related to the Ringed Plover, occurs as a passage migrant ; and the Asiatic Golden Plover, which is practically indistinguishable from the American variety, has been recorded 13 times in this country.

Eric Hosking

CHAT. Only two chats occur in Britain, the Whin-chat and the Stonechat (above), both very similar

CHARADRIIFORMES. Very large order of birds, including the waders, coursers and pratincoles, terns, gulls, skuas, and the auks. The majority of its members are aquatic or frequent the vicinity of water. The order is divided into a number of families, the following ten of which contain species occurring in the British Isles : *Alcidae, Burhinidae, Charadriidae, Glareolidae, Haematopodidae, Laridae, Phalaropodidae, Recurvirostridae, Scolopacidae* and *Stercorariidae*. For British members of the order, *see* under the family names.

CHARADRIUS. Genus of the family *Charadriidae* of the order *Charadriiformes*. The nine species on the British list are described under their own names : the Ringed Plover, Little Ringed Plover, Kentish Plover, Grey Plover, Golden Plover and Dotterel ; and the much rarer Killdeer Plover, Caspian Plover and American Golden Plover.

The bills of these birds are thick, strong and comparatively short ; they are hard at the tip and soft at the base. In many species they are deeper at the base than at the terminal part, and they are sometimes parti-coloured, darker towards the tip than at the base. The wings are long and pointed, with the inner secondaries elongated but not quite reaching the tips of the primaries. The tail is rounded or wedge-shaped, and about half the length of the wing. The head is somewhat flattened on top, with steep forehead. The legs, medium in length or rather long, are, like the feet, stout and strong. The tarsus is reticulated (i.e. covered with small variable-shaped plates). The hind toe, when present, is small, but is absent in most species.

CHAT. Name sometimes familiarly applied to members of the genus *Saxicola*, belonging to the Thrush family (*Turdidae*). The genus contains the Stonechat and Whinchat (*qq.v.*).

Male stonechats are colourful little birds with red breasts, black heads and throats, a broad white half-collar and a whitish patch on the chestnut underparts. Females and juveniles are duller : their upperparts are brown with black streaks and they lack the white on the rump. They are very similar to the male Whinchat, except that the latter boasts a prominent white eye-stripe and white patches at the base of the tail. Female whinchats are paler, with a less pronounced buff eye-stripe.

Stonechats are to be found throughout Europe, Asia and South Africa. They are among the most common resident birds of the Thrush family to be found in Britain, though they are local and somewhat erratic in their distribution. An Eastern variant has also been recorded as a rare straggler. Whinchats are common breeding visitors to the British Isles from Africa.

CHECK-LIST. Unless otherwise stated, *Check-List* and *British List* are used interchangeably in this work for the 1952 edition of the *Check-List of the Birds of Great Britain and Ireland*, published by the British Ornithologists' Union.

This is the standard list of all species of wild birds and recognizable races found *naturally* in the geographical area of Great Britain and Ireland, together with the status (i.e. resident, breeding visitor, straggler and so forth) of each in that area.

The List gives the correct scientific name of each genus, species and race ; the most generally accepted English name of each species and, where this is different, the corresponding American name ; and it classifies the various species into genera, families and orders.

Check-Lists were published by the B.O.U. in 1883, 1915 and 1923. At the time of writing, the 1952 List is the most up-to-date one, intended to supersede previous Lists. It is based on the 1923 List, but the general method of classification has been changed materially to bring it into line with modern practice.

As a result, some species have been transferred from one genus to another. Thus the American Golden Plover, previously known as *Pluvialis dominica*, has joined the genus *Charadrius*—the most typical genus of the Plover family (*Charadriidae*)—and has become *Charadrius domenicus*. Similarly, the Caspian Plover, formerly *Eropa asiatica*, is now *Charadrius asiaticus*.

The system of classification of the 1952 List has been followed in this Encyclopedia. This accounts for any difference in nomenclature

CHIFFCHAFF, *one of the cheerful harbingers of Spring*

To face page 124   *For text see page 125*

between it and works published before 1952 and a few published later, as some ornithologists refuse to accept the new classification. It must also be remembered that, although at the time of going to press (1955), the 1952 List can be regarded as the final word, there are bound to be modifications as fresh information comes to hand. Pending any further edition of the List, these are published in the *Ibis*, the quarterly journal of the B.O.U.

CHEEPER. Onomatopoeic name for young Grouse or Partridge (*qq.v.*), given especially to the Red Grouse (*q.v.*) because of its shrill note.

CHETTUSIA. Genus of the family *Charadriidae* of the order *Charadriiformes*. It contains two species only, distributed over eastern Europe and northern Asia, and occurring outside the breeding season in north-east Africa and northern India. One species, the Sociable Plover (*q.v.*), occurs occasionally in the British Isles, a straggler from the Continent.

CHIFFCHAFF—Phylloscopus collybita. Belonging to the *Sylviidae*, one of the largest bird families, which includes all the warblers, the Chiffchaff is a leaf-warbler. It has the distinction of being one of the earliest of our summer visitors, if not actually the first. Its early appearance may in some cases be attributed to the fact that the birds did not leave the country at all during the winter months. Most chiffchaffs arrive from the south of Europe. not later than mid-March.

In appearance the Chiffchaff is very similar to its near relative, the Willow-Warbler (*q.v.*), and even an expert may find it very difficult to distinguish between the two. Their voices, however, are unmistakably different, and their choice of nesting site and feeding habits also differ. Both are small birds, the Chiffchaff being, if anything, the smaller. It has olive-green plumage, a paler colour underneath, and its dark legs form another point of difference from its close relative. The Chiffchaff's length is 4 in., and its tarsus 0·8 in. Its wing span is 6 in., and its weight is less than ½ oz.

> The song of the Chiffchaff is one of the real harbingers of Spring in Great Britain. I always call it the " conductor " of our song birds because the rhythm on which its two-syllabled song is based has within its range so many varieties. It uses one of its sweet call notes to produce an unusual song which is beyond comparison even with the Willow-Warbler's. The song can be heard at its best from the end of March to early July ; then there is a decline, but in September you hear it again, rather weaker and not so beautiful as in April and May. The interspersed churring notes are characteristic of the *Sylvidae* family, and are shared with the reed-, sedge- and garden-warblers, the Blackcap and others.—EDITOR.

The Chiffchaff hops when on the ground, but it is a very restless bird and has a flitting flight

among the branches of the trees where it finds most of its food.

The courtship of these little birds is very charming to watch : the male pursues his mate on the wing, singing his spring song with his feathers fluffed out and tail fanned. The nest is well concealed among brambles and low bushes ; it has a domelike shape with a foundation of dead leaves, and is built of moss and twigs and cosily lined with feathers. The eggs, usually six in number, are white, with spots of purple and brown, and are laid early in May. The hatching, which takes about a fortnight, is done by the hen alone and she also feeds the young for another fortnight almost entirely by herself. There is normally one brood in a season but two have been recorded.

Chiffchaffs feed entirely on grubs and insects, many of which are cleverly caught on the wing. There is no evidence that fruit is taken from gardens, which it rarely visits.

Besides being a common summer visitor to England, Wales and Ireland, the Chiffchaff is a passage migrant. In Scotland it is scarcer and confined to specific areas. It leaves for its long journey to its winter quarters in the south about the middle of October. The Scandinavian Chiffchaff and Siberian Chiffchaff (*qq.v.*), two geographical varieties, are indistinguishable from each other in the field, but differ from the common Chiffchaff by greyer upper-parts and whiter under-parts. The Siberian Chiffchaff has a sad, single note. Both these varieties occur as passage migrants, the Siberian bird leaving this country only as late as the month December.

John Markham

CHIFFCHAFF. *This little leaf-warbler is careful to hide his dome-shaped nest well among the bushes*

Paul Popper

CHOUGH. Not only egg-collectors, but his cousin, the Jackdaw, ousted the Chough from his haunts

CHLAMYDOTIS. Genus of the family *Otididae* of the order *Ralliformes.* It contains only one species, the Houbara Bustard (*q.v.*), which is distributed over south-east Europe, south-west Asia and northern Africa ; individual birds have been recorded in the British Isles fewer than half-a-dozen times.

CHLIDONIAS. Genus of the family *Laridae* of the order *Charadriiformes*, containing the marsh-terns. For the only three species on the British list *see* Black Tern ; Whiskered Tern ; and White-winged Black Tern.

These birds differ from all other terns in that they frequent inland waters, breeding in shallow marshes or lagoons, and are found at the coast only during migration. Their bills are straight and rather slender, their necks short. The wings are long, but the tail is less than half the length of the wing, and, unlike the tails of other terns, is only slightly forked, with the lateral rectrices (tail quills) not elongated. The tarsus is covered in front with scutes (horny scales). The legs and feet are small, and the webs between the three front toes are deeply incised. The marsh-terns can also be distinguished by their darker colour and small size (the only other tern which is about the same length—9 in.—is the Little Tern, whose plumage is whitish).

All the marsh-terns are more or less irregular visitors to this country, and, with the exception of the Black Tern which bred in this country in 1941 and 1942, do not breed here.

CHLORIS. Genus of the family *Fringillidae* of the order *Passeriformes*. Its members occur in most parts of Europe, northern Asia, China and Japan, and north-west Africa. One species, the Greenfinch (*q.v.*) is a common resident bird throughout the British Isles.

CHORDEILES. Genus of the family *Caprimulgidae* of the order *Caprimulgiformes*. It contains about five species, mainly confined to the temperate regions of North and South America, the Bahamas and Great Antilles. There is only one, the Night-Hawk (*q.v.*), that has been recorded here, and then only once.

CHOUGH—Coracia pyrrhocorax. Member of the Crow family, the Chough was at one time a comparatively common bird in Great Britain, but it has in recent years become a rare bird. As a resident it is confined to some districts of north Cornwall (hence its alternative name of Cornish Chough), and parts of north and central Wales. It is rare in Scotland and Ireland.

The Chough has the same glossy black plumage as most of the Crow family, but is distinguished by its long, curved, red bill and its red legs. Male and female are alike, but the young bird has an orange bill. The Chough is a walking bird, but it sometimes breaks into a hop or a run. Its flight is beautiful to watch—it is strong and leisurely, with outspread wings. The length of the Chough is 16 in., and its tarsus 2 in. Its wing span is 2 ft., but smaller in the female, and its weight 13 oz.

The Chough's aerial displays, especially round the cliffs and shores, are a fine sight—particularly during the nesting season in April or May—the birds tumble and twist, soar with outspread wings, and, like the Raven, often turn completely upside down.

The calls of both male and female are an unmistakable reminder that the Chough is a member of the Crow family. Yet they differ from those of all its relatives, especially in courtship, when the Chough has long conversational notes which on the whole are more musical than those of crows or rooks. One of its calls has given the Chough its name.

Choughs are gentle and sociable, and, so far as is known, pair for the year. The very bulky nests are placed in inaccessible spots in sea-caves and holes around the cliffs; they are made of roots and heather stalks, and lined with hair and wool. The three to six eggs (unlike those of other crows), white with grey and brown spots, are laid in April and May. The cock does not take part in the hatching, which lasts about 17 days, but he feeds the hen while she is sitting. Both parents feed the young birds for about 38 days. Only one brood is hatched in the year.

Insects and small animals form the chief part of the Chough's food, but it also takes some corn, and it has been known occasionally to attack new-born lambs. Apart from Cornish Chough, the Chough is also known colloquially as Red-Legged Daw and Sea-Crow.

For its close relative which, however, never frequents sea-coasts, *see* Alpine Chough.

CICONIA (Latin, " stork "). Genus of the family *Ciconiidae* of the order *Ardeiformes*. Its members occur in many parts of Europe and Asia, north-west Africa, and in South Africa outside the breeding-season. There are two species on the British list : the White Stork (*q.v.*), which is an irregular visitor during the Summer on passage migration ; and the Black Stork (*q.v.*), which occurs here even more rarely.

These very large birds have long, straight, and stout bills. The nostrils are reduced to short horizontal slits. Part of the chin is bare, and likewise part of the lores (spaces between the eyes and the bill). The wings are very large, and the tail is short and slightly rounded. The lower feathers of the neck are elongated. In flight these birds may be distinguished from the herons by the fact that they fly with the neck outstretched and the legs trailing slightly downwards.

CICONIIDAE. Family of the order *Ardeiformes*. Its members, the storks and their allies, are distributed over most of the warmer parts of the world. One genus, *Ciconia* (*q.v.*), is on the British list.

CINCLIDAE. Family of the order *Passeriformes*. It contains only one genus, *Cinclus*, which is on the British list. The members of this family are known as the dippers. They are aquatic in habit, and frequent streams and rivers, mainly in mountainous or hilly areas of Europe, much of northern Asia as well as China and Formosa, north-west Africa, north America, and the Andes region to Tucuman in Argentina.

CINCLUS. Genus of the family *Cinclidae* of the order *Passeriformes*. It includes the dippers (*q.v.*), of which three subspecies occur in the British Isles : the British Dipper, which is resident in England, Wales and eastern Scotland ; the Irish Dipper which is resident in western Scotland, the Isle of Man and Ireland ; and the Black-bellied Dipper, which occasionally wanders here from the Continent during the Winter.

These birds have none of the structural peculiarities typical of aquatic birds. They are medium-sized, but otherwise strongly resemble the wrens, having the same short (if more pointed) wings, short tail, and copious plumage, the same short, but well-developed first primary feather, and the same peculiar musty smell. The dippers have a straight but slender bill, slightly depressed above the nostrils, which are reduced to narrow slits and are overhung by a membrane.

The body is plump, the legs rather long. The tarsus is covered with an unbroken lamina, except at the base where it is divided into two scutes (horny scales). There are four toes, three directed forwards and one behind, each furnished with a stout claw.

CIRCUMNOCULAR (Latin, " surrounding the eye "). *See* Orbital Ring.

CIRCUS. Genus of the family *Falconidae* of the order *Falconiformes*. It includes four species on the British list : the Hen-Harrier, Marsh-Harrier, Montagu's Harrier and Pallid Harrier, described under their own names.

These birds have a short, strongly curved bill. Their nostrils are longitudinal, and have a thin covering of upward directed loral bristles. The wings are long and pointed ; the secondaries are considerably shorter than the primary feathers. The tail is rather long. The tarsus is long and thin, the upper part of it often overhung with feathers. The feet have four toes, three front and one hind, all with sharp and strongly curved claws.

CIRL BUNTING—Emberiza cirlus. This British resident is chiefly confined to the counties south of the Thames, although it also breeds in some districts of the south Midlands and in parts of Wales. The narrow distribution makes it the most " local " of the buntings, if not of all British birds. Abroad it breeds in central and southern Europe.

Both the male and female have the shape of the Yellow Hammer (*q.v.*), but the Cirl Bunting is distinguished by his black throat and grey crown, the yellowish band followed by one of sage green below the black throat, and by its

Eric Hosking

CIRL BUNTING. *The little hen has to do all the work to feed her hungry offspring, for it is only rarely that the cock deigns to play devoted father*

G. K. Yeates

CLANGULA. The Long-tailed Duck (C. hyemalis)
is a visitor from the north, but has bred in Britain

olive-brown rump. It also has conspicuous yellow streaks above and below the eye and a decided black streak through it. The underparts are yellow, with chestnut colouring at the sides. The band of white feathers in the tail (also seen in the Yellow Hammer) is very conspicuous in the Cirl Bunting's flight, which is similar to, but perhaps faster than, the Yellow Hammer's. The female and young birds can be recognized only by their brown rump. The length of the Cirl Bunting is 6 in., and its tarsus 0·7 in. Its wing span is about 7½ in., and its weight less than ½ oz.

This bird is so undemonstrative in courtship that no display has ever been recorded. Most observers find the Cirl Bunting's song difficult to recognize. It is not unlike the " little bit of bread and no cheese " of the Yellow Hammer, but omits the drawling end note of " cheese ", it also has another variant somewhat like the rattle of the Lesser Whitethroat. The song is continuous from February until October.

The Cirl Bunting frequents country rather different from that favoured by the Yellow Hammer and is found in wooded districts, especially where there are elms. Unlike other resident buntings, it usually builds its nest a few feet from the ground in high bushes, brambles or trees. The nest is made by the hen from bents, roots and a good deal of moss, and lined with grasses and horse hair. The breeding season begins in the middle of May and continues until August, sometimes even into September. The eggs number three or four, and are very similar to those of the Yellow Hammer, though with fewer of the peculiar scribble-markings. Hatching takes about a fortnight ; the hen sits alone, but her mate feeds her. She is usually responsible for rearing the young chicks also, for only exceptionally has the cock been seen to take part. At least two broods —and sometimes three—are reared.

The Cirl Bunting's food consists mainly of corn, seeds of grasses and weeds, but many insects are also eaten, and the young are wholly fed on them.

In Autumn and Winter, cirl buntings wander in small parties in company with yellow hammers, and other species, and probably roost in hedges ; but little information seems to be available about their habits at that time.

CITRIL FINCH—Carduelis citrinella. In recent years only one specimen of this bird has wandered to Britain. Its home is beside the conifer forests of the mountain ranges of central and southern Europe, and it is rarely found below 5,000 ft., except in Winter.

Its plumage—olive-green shading into ashy-grey—is not unlike that of the Siskin (q.v.). Its rump and under parts are greenish-yellow. The hen has similar but duller colouring. The length of the Citril Finch is 4½ in., and its tarsus 0·6 in. Its weight is about 1 oz., and it has a wing span of 7 in. In song, flight and general behaviour the Citril Finch is similar to both the Goldfinch (q.v.) and the Siskin. It is a sociable little bird, and in Winter goes about in small parties of its own kind.

The nest is built in a coniferous tree, usually by the hen only, and is constructed of grasses, roots and lichens, and lined with thistle-down. Its outside is covered with hair, down and feathers, and decorated with cocoons. Four or five eggs, similar in colour and appearance to those of the Siskin, are laid about the end of April. Information regarding hatching is scanty. One or two broods are reared in a season.

CLAMATOR. Genus of the family *Cuculidae* of the order *Cuculiformes*. It contains eight species, which are distributed over southern Europe, western Asia and Africa. The only species on the British list is the Great Spotted Cuckoo (q.v.), which has been recorded only a few times. The members of this genus differ from those of the genus *Cuculus* (the common Cuckoo) mainly in having a long crest and longitudinal, slit-like nostrils.

CLANGULA. Genus of maritime ducks of the family *Anatidae* of the order *Anseriformes*. It contains only one species, which frequents mainly the Arctic regions of the northern hemisphere. This species, the Long-tailed Duck (q.v.), occurs in the British Isles as a non-breeding visitor between September and May.

CLAP-NET. Net so hinged that it may be made to close quickly over its prey by pulling a string. It is used for bird-baiting (see Trap).

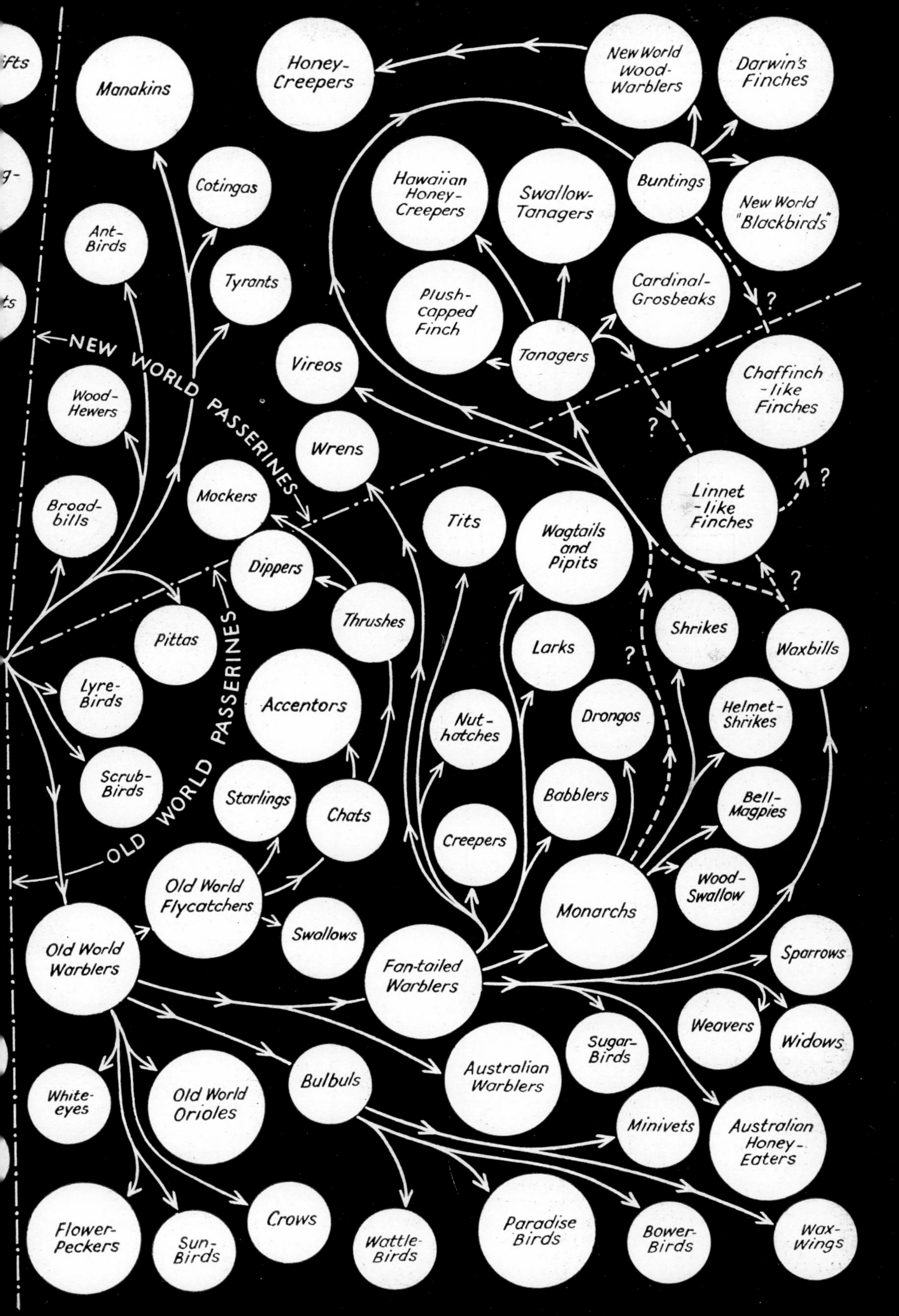

ifts
g-
ts
Manakins
Honey-Creepers
New World Wood-Warblers
Darwin's Finches
Cotingas
Ant-Birds
Tyrants
Hawaiian Honey-Creepers
Swallow-Tanagers
Buntings
New World "Blackbirds"
Plush-capped Finch
Cardinal-Grosbeaks
Tanagers
?
NEW WORLD PASSERINES
Vireos
Chaffinch-like Finches
Wood-Hewers
Wrens
?
Linnet-like Finches
?
Broad-bills
Mockers
Tits
Wagtails and Pipits
Dippers
?
Pittas
Thrushes
Larks
Shrikes
Waxbills
?
OLD WORLD PASSERINES
Lyre-Birds
Accentors
Nut-hatches
Drongos
Helmet-Shrikes
Scrub-Birds
Starlings
Chats
Babblers
Bell-Magpies
Creepers
Old World Flycatchers
Monarchs
Wood-Swallow
Swallows
Old World Warblers
Fan-tailed Warblers
Sparrows
Sugar-Birds
Weavers
Widows
Australian Warblers
White-eyes
Old World Orioles
Bulbuls
Minivets
Australian Honey-Eaters
Crows
Flower-Peckers
Sun-Birds
Wattle-Birds
Paradise Birds
Bower-Birds
Wax-Wings

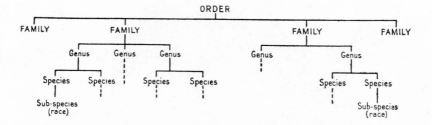

SUBDIVISIONS OF AN ORDER—with (below) an actual example

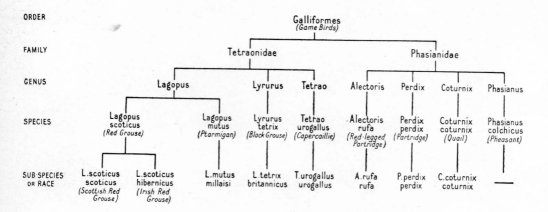

SCIENTIFIC SYSTEM OF NAMING

The class *Aves*, which includes all the birds, is subdivided into orders, which are further subdivided as shown :

ORDER. Single word spelt with initial capital—ending in " *iformes* " ; e.g. *Passeriformes*.

FAMILY. Single word spelt with initial capital—ending " *idae* " ; e.g. *Corvidae* (Crow family).

GENUS. Single name, spelt with initial. When standing alone may be followed by name of author, with or without reference to publication. Every genus must have type species, which is only one that cannot be removed if species placed in one genus are transferred to other genera ; e.g. *Corvus*, Linnaeus.

SPECIES. Binomial (two-word) combination of which first term is generic name and second specific name. May be followed by author of specific name with or without reference to publication ; if species was named in different genus from that shown, the author's name is placed within brackets ; e.g. *Corvus* monedula Linnaeus (Jackdaw).
Repetition of the generic name (e.g. Ciconia ciconia) indicates a nominate, or type, species. This is not necessarily the most important. The present method of determining a type species is for the author to designate one of the included species as a type ; where, as with some of the older generic names, the author failed to do this, certain other methods are adopted. If species placed in a Genus are transferred to other genera, the only one that cannot be removed is the type species.

SUB-SPECIES (or RACE). Trinomial combination of which first two terms are the generic and specific names, and *third* is racial name. Author quoted is author of third or racial name, and rule for brackets is same as for species :

> *Corvus monedula spermologus* Vielliot
> *Corvus monedula monedula* Linnaeus

The repetition of the specific name in the second example indicates that it is the nominate race. This has no pre-eminence over other races, but is nominate because the first to be described.

CLASSIFICATION OF BRITISH BIRDS

JAMES FISHER, M.A., F.L.S.

This article deals with a difficult and complicated subject, but one which must be mastered by serious students of ornithology. Although discussing the wider aspects and implications, it is particularly concerned with the classification of British birds

CLASSIFICATION. This word means the arrangement of different sorts. For living things, this involves, first, a precise system of naming the sorts and a method, as precise as can be devised, for recognizing and defining them ; and, secondly, the grouping of related sorts in a definite sequence within categories, and of those categories within higher ones.

While the study of birds is as far advanced as that of any branch of the animal kingdom, our knowledge is at present inadequate for the task of making a final and true classification of the class *Aves* (*q.v.*). Neverthless, there is now a large measure of agreement on the nature and naming of bird species, on the major categories (particularly families and orders) and on the pattern and sequence of the ideal world list of living and extinct birds.

Theory and Practice. The purpose of bird classification is both practical and theoretical. The practical objective is to arrange birds in a sequence suitable for their display and study in museums, text books and scientific journals— a sequence which shall be both generally accepted and realistic. The system must be easy to memorise, generally inflexible (for sudden changes produce international confusion), yet flexible enough to admit the new species of birds that are still being discovered at the rate of three or four a year, and the very large number of newly described subspecies or " geographical races" of existing species. The science of practical classification, which always has and still must involve the application of artificial " rule of thumb " methods, is known as *systematics*, and its exponents and administrators are systematists. Nearly all systematists work in museums.

The theoretical object of classification is to arrange birds in an order representing their " natural " relationship. That there was such a thing as a natural, or ideal, relationship was recognized by the very earliest classifiers, although it was not until the publication of Darwin's *Origin of Species* in 1859 that the true meaning of natural relationship emerged. Even then it was some years before the theory of evolution was fully accepted by the theoretical classifiers and incorporated in their system. The science of theoretical " evolutionary " classification is known as *taxonomy*, and its exponents and administrators are taxonomists. Most, but not all, taxonomists work in museums.

It is impossible sometimes to detect whether the early classifiers were inspired by tidy-mindedness or by a real wonder at the mysteries of natural relationship. Some were inspired by mere superstition ; with a few exceptions there was scarcely any scientific ornithology between the end of the Graeco-Roman civilization and the Renaissance. The Greeks and Romans were taxonomists, for there was little need for Aristotle (384–322 B.C.) to apply systematics to the 170 species of birds he believed he knew (only about 126 of his descriptions of birds are recognizable). His taxonomy placed them in a natural system of eight groups ; Pliny (A.D. 23–79)—probably a better ornithologist— placed them in three.

Linnaeus and Darwin. The ornithologists of the Renaissance were mainly taxonomists— notably Gesner (1516–65) and the fine anatomists Belon (1517-64) and Coiter (1534–90). The father of British natural history, John Ray (1627–1705), was perhaps more systematist than taxonomist, concerned as he was more with elucidating differences between species than with the natural relationships of groups, which he was content to base on a study of their beaks and feet. It is certain that the great figure of the succeeding century, Carl Linné (1707–78), better known as Linnaeus, was not much more of a taxonomist than Ray. But as systematist he was supreme, and he was, indeed, the father of modern systematics. The first edition of his *System of Nature* was published in 1735, and the tenth—the book upon which the world's present system of naming all living things is based—in 1758.

For a century after the publication of Linnaeus's great tenth edition the bias of ornithologists was towards systematics. So rapidly did material pour in to the museums of the world from newly-explored continents and islands that there was little opportunity for taxonomy, and a very great need for systematics. Nevertheless, during that century the basis for the great advance in taxonomic thought of the last hundred years was being laid down by, among others, the great bird anatomists— Cuvier (1798), E. G. Sainte-Hilaire (1807–33), Tiedemann (1810-14), Nitzsch (1811–40), Merrem (1812–19), l'Herminier (1827–28), Gloger (1833–34), MacGillivray (1837), Strickland (1840–48), J. P. Müller (1845–47) and Cabanis (1847). (The dates represent the periods in which these scientists published their more important works.)

After the publication of the *Origin of Species*, the spate of accessions to the world's great museums and private collections of birds became even more rapid—it has scarcely abated to this day. However, the evolutionary view met with long opposition from many important systematists, so that taxonomy and systematics did not finally converge until the 1920s. Only then was there sufficient agreement among taxonomists about the natural relationship and membership of the principal families and orders of birds for it to be of *practical* convenience for the systematists to follow them.

20th Century. All modern attempts at the classification of birds aim at suiting both evolutionary (taxonomic) truth and systematic convenience. Nevertheless, taxonomic finality is by no means with us, for the relationships of many of the most "difficult" families in the *Passeriformes*, the largest order of birds, are still very imperfectly understood, notwithstanding many excellent new anatomical studies, such as those of Beecher (1953) in America. Systematic finality, on the other hand, is at last both possible and desirable, and, largely as the result of the International Ornithological Congresses of 1950 and 1954, *the museums and the text-book editors of the world have generally agreed to use the classifi-*

SYSTEMATIC LIST OF THE ORDERS OF LIVING BIRDS (Based on Wetmore's classification, with the approximate numbers of species in each order after Mayr & Amadon)	
SPHENISCIFORMES	Penguins (16)
STRUTHIONIFORMES	Ostrich (1)
RHEIFORMES	Rheas (2)
CASUARIIFORMES	Cassowaries, emus (5)
APTERYGIFORMES	Kiwis (3)
TINAMIFORMES	Tinamous (33)
GAVIIFORMES	Divers, or loons (4, all on British List)
COLYMBIFORMES	Grebes (20, including 5 on British List)
PROCELLARIIFORMES	Albatrosses, petrels, etc. (90, including 17 on British List)
PELECANIFORMES	Cormorants, gannets, pelicans, etc. (54, including 3 on British List)
CICONIIFORMES	Herons, storks, etc. (105, including 14 on British List)
Phoenicopteriformes *	Flamingoes (6, only 1 on British List)
ANSERIFORMES	Geese, ducks, screamers (148, including 42 on British List)
FALCONIFORMES	Diurnal birds of prey (271, including 24 on British List)
GALLIFORMES	Game-birds, etc. (241, including 8 on British List)
GRUIFORMES	Cranes, rails, cariamas, etc. (199, including 12 on British List)
CHARADRIIFORMES	Waders, gulls, auks, etc. (308, including 100 on British List)
COLUMBIFORMES	Sand-grouse, pigeons (308, including 6 on British List)
PSITTACIFORMES	Parrots (316)
CUCULIFORMES	Turacos, cuckoos (147, including 4 on British List)
STRIGIFORMES	Owls (134, including 10 on British List)
CAPRIMULGIFORMES	Nightjars, etc. (97, including 4 on British List)
APODIFORMES	Swifts, hummingbirds (398, including 3 on British List)
COLIIFORMES	Mouse-birds (6)
TROGONIFORMES	Trogons (35)
CORACIIFORMES	Rollers, kingfishers, bee-eaters, hoopoes, hornbills, etc. (194, including 4 on British List)
PICIFORMES	Puffbirds, barbets, woodpeckers, toucans, etc. (381, including 4 on British List)
PASSERIFORMES	Perching and singing birds (**5072**, including **161** on British List)

cation that originated in the United States and is particularly associated with Wetmore.

Up to this time the chief difficulty in reaching agreement on the sequence of a world classification lay in the European practice, associated particularly with the work of Hartert and Stresemann, of starting with what were held to be the "highest" families of birds (e.g. the *Corvidae* [crows] in the order *Passeriformes*) and ending with the "lowest", or most primitive, such as the Ostrich (order *Struthioniformes*). The system in use in America was practically the reverse of this. Both systems, of course, are equally truthful and scientific. But the use of both created systematic confusion. Hence the change agreed on in 1950, which has caused difficulties in Europe.

This agreement has not, of course, made final the sequence of every country's list of birds, nor could it do so. But it has resulted in lists of which the arrangement down to family level coincides absolutely or very nearly with that of Wetmore; that is, in *predictable* arrangements. (The recent *Birds of the Soviet Union* is an exception, for though it accepts the "low-to-high" principle of Wetmore in the arrangement of orders, it differs very radically in the actual sequence of orders and families.) In general, differences of opinion and the variations in national lists which result from them are now usually only minor, and quite easy to

* The **Phoenicopteriformes** are placed by Wetmore as a *suborder* of the **CICONIIFORMES**.

follow. The "official" list for Britain, the *Check-List* of the British Ornithologists' Union, arranges the orders according to the Wetmore pattern, but uses different names for a few orders (*see* this page) and differs from Wetmore's list on the status of some families.

Wetmore's classification, promulgated in 1934, with revised versions in 1940 and 1951, classifies the birds of the world (fossil and living) into 34 orders and 213 families, of which 27 orders and 172 families are living, or were recently living. Another contemporary classification, that of Mayr and Amadon (1951), classifies the living, or recently living, birds into 28 orders and 134 families. Wetmore and Mayr and Amadon differ in their choice of orders only regarding the flamingoes, which Wetmore places in a suborder of the *Ciconiiformes*, the Heron-Stork order, while Mayr and Amadon place them in a separate order, the *Phoenicopteriformes*, between this order and the *Anseriformes* (geese and ducks) ; there would be some justification, in fact, for making the flamingoes a suborder of the *Anseriformes*.

It must be stressed that the higher categories of classification —class, subclass, superorder, order, suborder, superfamily, family, subfamily, tribe and genus—are made by man for his convenience, to describe trunk, bough, branch, twig, stem, leaf and so forth of the family tree. No *definition* of any of these terms, or way of distinguishing between one and another, is possible, save that of *use* by

generations of systematists. They are *systematic*, not taxonomic terms. Long use has hallowed them—in particular the categories order and family, so that there is a large and universal measure of agreement as to what constitutes an order, and a fair measure of agreement on what constitutes a family. But the next unit down the scale below the genus — the species — has (now) biological reality.

Species. The species is the fundamental unit of classification, and the great contribution of Linnaeus is his recognition of this fact, and his system of naming species in an unequivocal and standardised way.

The Linnaean name of a species consists of two words, usually derived from Greek or Latin. For example the Common Gull is *Larus canus*. The first word, *Larus*, is a systematic term, indicating the genus ; and there may be several other species belonging to this, e.g. *Larus ridibundus*, the Black-headed Gull, and *Larus argentatus*, the Herring-Gull.

The second word (*canus*) is *not* the specific name, but an adjective describing the first ; the *two words together* constitute the scientific and specific name of the species. In text books, scientific names are often followed by a human name and date, for example *Larus canus* Linnaeus, 1758. This records the first describer of the species, and the year in which he first published his description. If the describer first described a species in a genus other than that in which it is now placed, his

COMPARISON BETWEEN WETMORE AND BRITISH CHECK-LIST	
(It must be remembered that whereas Wetmore classifies ALL living birds, the Check-List deals only with those officially recorded in the British Isles. *See also* Systematic List in opposite page)	
Wetmore	**British Check-List**
SPHENISCIFORMES (penguins)	*No British birds*
STRUTHIONIFORMES (ostrich)	*No British birds*
RHEIFORMES (rheas)	*No British birds*
CASUARIIFORMES (cassowaries, emus)	*No British birds*
APTERYGIFORMES (kiwis)	*No British birds*
TINAMIFORMES (tinamous)	*No British birds*
GAVIIFORMES (divers)	COLYMBIFORMES (divers)
COLYMBIFORMES (grebes)	PODICIPIDI-FORMES (grebes)
PROCELLARIIFORMES (petrels, etc.)	PROCELLARII-FORMES (petrels etc.)
PELECANIFORMES (cormorants, etc.)	PELECANI-FORMES (cormorants, etc.)
CICONIIFORMES (herons, storks, flamingoes)	ARDEIFORMES (herons, storks) PHOENICOPTERI-FORMES (flamingoes)
ANSERIFORMES (geese, ducks, etc.)	ANSERIFORMES (geese, ducks, etc.)
FALCONIFORMES (diurnal birds of prey)	FALCONIFORMES (diurnal birds of prey)
GALLIFORMES (game-birds, etc.)	GALLIFORMES (game-birds, etc.)
GRUIFORMES (cranes, rails, etc.)	RALLIFORMES (cranes, rails, etc.)
CHARADRIIFORMES (waders, gulls, etc.)	CHARADRII-FORMES (waders, gulls, etc.)
COLUMBIFORMES (sand-grouse, pigeons)	COLUMBIFORMES (sand-grouse, pigeons)
PSITTACIFORMES (parrots)	*No British birds*
CUCULIFORMES (cuckoos)	CUCULIFORMES (cuckoos)
STRIGIFORMES (owls)	STRIGIFORMES (owls)
CAPRIMULGIFORMES (nightjars)	CAPRIMULGI-FORMES (nightjars)
APODIFORMES (swifts)	APODIFORMES (swifts)
COLIIFORMES (mouse-birds)	*No British birds*
TROGONIFORMES (trogons)	*No British birds*
CORACIIFORMES (rollers, hoopoes, etc.)	CORACIIFORMES (rollers, hoopoes, etc.)
PICIFORMES (woodpeckers, etc.)	PICIFORMES (woodpeckers, etc.)
PASSERIFORMES (perching and singing birds)	PASSERIFORMES (perching and singing birds)

name is usually (but not in some modern works) placed in brackets, for example the Pomarine Skua is now *Stercorarius pomarinus* (Temminck, 1815).

All the naming of living things is now, by universal international agreement, done on the Linnaean system. The genus remains a systematic term, without a definition, save that it is used by systematists to group together species which have obvious similarity and close relationship. There is now, however, close agreement between systematists on what constitutes a genus ; this agreement is based entirely on the sharing of opinions after practical experience. Linnaeus, whose approach was purely systematic, no doubt regarded the species also as a systematic category, and for many years—long after the theory of evolution had begun to influence classification—it bore a purely practical definition. As late as 1926 Tate Regan wrote : " A species is a community, or a number of related communities, whose distinctive morphological characters are, in the opinion of a competent systematist, sufficiently definite to entitle it, or them, to a specific name ".

This indeed put the species back in museum drawers and text-book lists, and, by the standards of Regan's time, fairly so—for there were then, as now, many competent systematists. Nevertheless (and no doubt Regan knew it), the species was something better than that ; it was, and is, a taxonomic, a biological unit, not simply a unit of systematic convenience.

The latest, and perhaps the best, definition of a species, which stresses its biological reality, is that of Mayr who, in 1951, described it as " *an aggregate of interbreeding natural populations which are not only reproductively isolated from other such aggregates but also ecologically specialised sufficiently so as not to compete with other such species* ". Some of the older definitions of species, such as " if two animals can breed together and produce fertile offspring, then they are of the same species ", have had to go (there are many examples now known of fertile wild hybrids of different " good " species). To define a species nowadays—real though a species is—it is almost necessary to write a book. This Mayr has done (*Systematics and the Origin of Species*, New York, 1942) and the reader is warmly recommended to this important work, some of the essence of which is summarised by Fisher (*A History of Birds*, London, 1954). Mayr's contribution to our understanding of species goes far beyond definition, for he has shown conclusively that new species are derived, in the course of evolution, by the geographical isolation of populations of their parent-species : in fact from what are now universally known

as subspecies, " geographical races " which differ significantly from each other in form (and often also in behaviour).

Although species arise from subspecies, the difference between them is real, and the subspecies remains a systematic category, to be admitted into the practice of museum and text book under practical and man-made rules, not rules of nature. Before the nature of speciation and subspeciation was understood, they were long confused. The famous 27-volume *Catalogue of the Birds in the British Museum*, edited by R. Bowdler Sharpe, was completed in 1909, with a 5-volume *Hand-List* which listed no less than 18,937 species belonging to 2,810 genera. In fact, as Mayr showed in 1946, only 8,200 of Sharpe's great list of species are acceptable by modern standards.

Since then the list of known bird species has increased to about 8,600,* with a little under 30,000 subspecies, and—so well have collectors now explored the world—new species are now discovered at an average rate of only about three a year. It seems doubtful whether more than a hundred remain to be discovered, though others must be always emerging (at a slow rate) in the course of evolution.

Rules of Nomenclature. Every student of ornithological text books will find that the scientific names of the birds are changed from time to time—more often (at least in countries like Britain) than their vernacular names. There are two reasons for this : First, scientific descriptions may be dug up in obscure publications with Linnaean names which, under the rules of nomenclature, must be applied to the species if published earlier than any other name. This priority rule causes a lot of interesting, but rather valueless, research, and the International Commission of Zoological Nomenclature has the power to overrule priority and, in the interests of stability, " freeze " a Linnaean name in general use for years, even if a prior name has been found. Fortunately a diminishing number of such names is now unearthed.

Secondly, there may be a change in opinion whether two sorts of birds are of the same species, or of the same genus, or even of the same higher category. Our increasing understanding of the nature of species, and the methodical application of this understanding to neglected groups, must inevitably produce further changes, even in the names of some familiar birds on the British list.

Example of Classification. Let us take a kind of bird and see how it is fitted into the present hierarchy of bird classification. Supposing we take our own Willow-Warbler. The " geographical race " or subspecies of this

---

* In 1951. Mayr and Amadon's census of world species gave 8,595, when 426 were on the British List.

breeding in Britain is : *Phylloscopus trochilus trochilus* (Linnaeus, 1758). This is the breeding Willow-Warbler of Britain and most of Europe. Another subspecies, *Phylloscopus trochilus acredula* (Linnaeus, 1758) breeds in northern Europe and most of Russia. (When Linnaeus first described this he thought it a different species.) The third subspecies is *Phylloscopus trochilus yakutensis*, Ticehurst, 1935, of eastern Siberia.

A modern practice in defining a population of birds as a subspecies is known as the "three-quarters rule". If a particular character (e.g. wing-length, or coloration of a part) in 75 per cent of one population differs significantly from 98 per cent of that from another region, the two populations can be regarded as of different subspecies.

Phylloscopus trochilus, the Willow-Warbler species, belongs to the same genus, *Phylloscopus*, as 29 other species, according to the monographer of the genus, C. B. Ticehurst. Those on the British List are *P. collybita* (Chiffchaff), *P. sibilatrix* (Wood-Warbler) and seven other species which are highly irregular passage-migrants to our shores. The close similarity in form and habits of the members of the genus, which has caused them to be called the "leaf-warblers", has long confused ornithologists.

Phylloscopus is one of about 25 genera belonging to the family *Sylviidae*, of which seven other genera have members on the British List. Many authorities include in this family also the gnatcatchers (*Polioptila*) and two other genera of the New World, some making the two groups separate tribes, the *Sylviinae* and the *Polioptilinae*. (The gnatcatchers evidently represent an old colonisation of north America by ancient sylviid stock.) The goldcrests (*Regulus*) are placed in the *Sylviidae* by some and in a separate family, the *Regulidae*, by others, including Wetmore and the British list.

Mayr and Amadon, on the other hand, keep subfamily status for sylviids, goldcrests and gnatcatchers together, making them members (the *Sylviinae*) of a huge (1,460 species) family, the *Muscicapidae*, of which other subfamilies are the *Muscicapinae* (Old World flycatchers), *Timaliinae* (babblers), *Malurinae* (Australian warblers), *Turdinae* (thrushes), *Miminae* (mockers and thrushes), *Troglodytinae* (wrens) and *Cinclinae* (dippers).

Wetmore simply classes the *Sylviidae* as one of 40 families in the suborder *Passeres*, or singing birds, which, by his classification, make up the *Passeriformes* or perching birds with three other suborders, the broadbills (*Eurylaimi*), the tyrants (*Tyranni*) and the lyrebirds (*Menurae*). But Mayr and Amadon use the name *Oscines* for the singing-bird suborder and *Passeres* for the whole order. They maintain only 36 families in the *Oscines*, and make much use of subfamilies and tribes within it ; Wetmore uses none of these.

In other suborders of the *Passeriformes* (or *Passeres* of Mayr and Amadon) both Wetmore and Mayr and Amadon use a category, the superfamily, between suborder and family.

All this has taken us rather far from the Willow-Warbler, but it is intended to show how

BIRD FAMILIES OF BRITAIN

(The 19 orders enumerated in the Check-List—*see* Table of Comparison in page 131 — embrace 59 families, each of which contains at least one British species. The scientific name of each family is shown below, together with the English name of the family, derived from its most typical bird, or group of birds.)

English Name	Latin Name
Accentor Family	*Prunellidae*
Albatross Family	*Diomedeidae*
Auk Family	*Alcidae*
Avocet Family	*Recurvirostridae*
Bee-Eater Family	*Meropidae*
Bustard Family	*Otididae*
Cormorant Family	*Phalacrocoracidae*
Crane Family	*Balearicidae*
Creeper Family	*Certhiidae*
Crow Family	*Corvidae*
Cuckoo Family	*Cuculidae*
Dipper Family	*Cinclidae*
Diver Family	*Colymbidae*
Dove Family	*Columbidae*
Duck Family	*Anatidae*
Falcon Family	*Falconidae*
Finch Family	*Fringillidae*
Flamingo Family	*Phoenicopteridae*
Flycatcher Family	*Muscicapidae*
Gannet Family	*Sulidae*
Grebe Family	*Podicipidae*
Grouse Family	*Tetraonidae*
Gull Family	*Laridae*
Heron Family	*Ardeidae*
Hoopoe Family	*Upupidae*
Kingfisher Family	*Alcedinidae*
Kinglet Family	*Regulidae*
Lark Family	*Alaudidae*
Nightjar Family	*Caprimulgidae*
Nuthatch Family	*Sittidae*
Oriole Family	*Oriolidae*
Owl Family	*Strigidae*
Oystercatcher Family	*Haematopodidae*
Phalarope Family	*Phalaropodidae*
Pheasant Family	*Phasianidae*
Plover Family	*Charadriidae*
Pratincole Family	*Glareolidae*
Rail Family	*Rallidae*
Roller Family	*Coraciidae*
Sand-Grouse Family	*Pteroclidae*
Sandpiper Family	*Scolopacidae*
Shearwater Family	*Procellariidae*
Shrike Family	*Laniidae*
Skua Family	*Stercorariidae*
Sparrow Family	*Passeridae*
Spoonbill Family	*Plataleidae*
Starling Family	*Sturnidae*
Stone-Curlew Family	*Burhinidae*
Stork Family	*Ciconiidae*
Swallow Family	*Hirundinidae*
Swift Family	*Apodidae*
Thrush Family	*Turdidae*
Tit Family	*Paridae*
Vulture Family	*Aegypiidae*
Wagtail Family	*Motacillidae*
Warbler Family	*Sylviidae*
Waxwing Family	*Bombycillidae*
Woodpecker Family	*Picidae*
Wren Family	*Troglodytidae*

classification, at least between species and order, is very much a matter of opinion, and that no two authorities are likely to agree. Only continual systematic practice and further taxonomic research will produce agreement—and agreement is never likely to be final. Meanwhile, the practical ornithologist, who is by no means always concerned with classification, needs a reliable system. This Encyclopedia follows throughout the system of classification adopted in the *1952 Check-List of the Birds of Great Britain and Ireland* published by the British Ornithologists' Union.

The diagram, *facing* page 128, represents a taxonomic family tree of birds, compiled from many sources, some of which are mentioned in the following reading list of important post-Darwinian works on bird classification.

Consult : History of North American Birds, Baird, Brewer & Ridgway (Boston), 1874 ; Hand-List of the Genera and Species of Birds in the British Museum, R. B. Sharpe (London, B.M.), 1899–1909 ; Die Vögel der paläarktischen Fauna, E. Hartert (Berlin & London), 1903–38 ; Check-List of Birds of the World (unfinished), J. L. Peters (Harvard U.P.), 1931 onwards ; Systematics and the Origin of Species, E. Mayr (Columbia U.P.), 1942 ; Birds as Animals : I. A History of Birds, J. Fisher (Hutchinson), 1954.

CLIMATIC INFLUENCE. Climate is the most important of all external factors influencing bird-life ; particularly when one considers its influence on the relative disposition of land and sea masses, terrain, vegetation, availability of food supplies, and on human communities.

The effects of climate may be the gradual and inevitable result of causes acting over thousands, and sometimes millions, of years : cyclic changes —major ones such as those which brought about the ice-ages, or minor ones in which there are relatively small, but still noticeable, fluctuations in the *average* climatic level, taking place over shorter periods (various periods have been suggested, ranging from a few years up to $35\frac{1}{2}$ years) ; seasonal changes ; and, finally, sporadic outbreaks of inclement weather.

Climate controls the geographical distribution and evolutionary developments of the various species, largely because, over a long period, it serves to eliminate all but the most perfectly developed individuals, and those well adjusted to their environment. It also plays an important, if somewhat baffling, part in the annual migratory movement of birds, when the instinctive memory of past conditions seems to exert at least as great an influence as present seasonal changes (*see* Migration).

Certain other inherited characteristics are influenced by the seasons, notably, amongst others, the physiological changes underlying the breeding cycle and seasonal transformations in plumage—a particularly striking example of

which is the white " winter dress " adopted by the Ptarmigan.

Although there have been several major changes in climatic conditions during the past history of the world, the period taken for these to be effective is so great that one is not conscious of them. The *average* annual climatic level appears thus to be constant, although superimposed on it are minor cyclic changes of a relatively short period which, while causing only small fluctuations in the average temperature, have an effect out of all proportion to the actual variation. Thus, the increase of a few degrees in the average temperature of the seas around the British Isles has caused a drift northwards of shoals of fish ; this again may account for a similar movement by the fish-eating birds.

Sporadic outbreaks of inclement weather have such varied and numerous effects on bird-life that it is only possible to mention a few below. Birds are recorded as having been blown many hundreds of miles off their normal course during migration, and this accounts for the arrival of some rare stragglers on these shores. During heavy gales many sea-birds, such as razorbills, puffins, guillemots, little auks and similar birds, succumb either to the buffeting of wind and waves or because they cannot reach their usual food supplies ; and are found dead on the shores or floating out at sea.

Hard Winters may be equally disastrous to certain species of land birds. Song-thrushes are very susceptible to severe cold and in some areas, as a result of the eight weeks of continuous frost in 1947, the number of breeding pairs was reduced to less than 5 per cent of that of the previous season. Similarly, the cold Winter of 1939-40 was almost as fatal to the Stonechat. Great numbers of starlings cross from Great Britain to Ireland each year. In severe Winters the numbers of these migrants are increased, and they move further westward, fleeing before the cold weather. Sometimes they fail to stop on reaching the coast and, continuing on their path, perish miserably in the Atlantic.

CLINE. A term with several related, but distinct, meanings. In the field of biology alone it may be interpreted in the following ways, depending on context :

(1) any pronounced variation or tendency to differ from hitherto observed characteristics or standard form ;

(2) a decline or falling off from a developed characteristic ;

(3) a temporary change, or one that shows itself in certain species of the same genera ;

(4) a spatial gradation in the characteristics of certain species.

The last definition may best be explained by example. Thus, puffins may be arranged in order of size according to the latitude in which they are found ; they increase in size from south to north. A puffin from, say, Spitzbergen, is so much larger than one from Brittany that it appears to belong to a different species, but this is not so. At the most, those found in different latitudes can be said to be different geographical races, but it is preferable to say that they are members of the same species, and that there is a *cline* from south to north.

Similarly, with the Bridled Guillemot, a variant of the common Guillemot : among the breeding stocks of guillemots in Britain, the proportion of bridled birds increases from $\frac{1}{4}$ per cent of the total in the south of England to 15 per cent in Scotland, and 26 per cent in Shetland. Once again there is a gradation or cline from south to north, although of a different type from that in the previous example.

CLINKER. Local name for Avocet (*q.v.*), probably because of its main call note, which sounds somewhat like the clinking of glasses.

CLUTCH. Set of eggs brooded together. Their number may vary from one, as is the case with the Albatross (*q.v.*), to as many as twenty, as may happen with Black Grouse (*q.v.*). Clutch is also sometimes applied to a brood of chickens or other nestlings.

COAL-TIT—Parus ater britannicus. The smallest of our resident tits, the Coal-Tit (or Cole-Tit) is found all over England, Wales and Scotland, with the exception of the Orkney and Shetland Islands.

Primarily a forest bird, it is especially plentiful wherever there are deep coniferous woods, but it does not wholly neglect gardens ; and if, by chance, it should choose to settle near human habitation, it will become quite friendly and visit the bird table and occupy a nesting box.

Although confusion with the Marsh-Tit (*q.v.*) might arise, the Coal-Tit can be identified beyond question by the large white patch on the nape of its neck, which no other Tit has. For the rest, it has the usual white cheeks of its family, and its head, throat and the front of its neck are black. Its plumage is not unlike that of the Great Tit (*q.v.*)—it has the same smoky-grey mantle—but underneath it is more buff-coloured than yellow, and its wings have double white bars. Cock and hen are alike. The Coal-Tit has a length of about $4\frac{1}{2}$ in., and its tarsus is 0·6 in. Its wing span is about 6 in., and its weight is $\frac{1}{8}$ oz.

In general behaviour and habits the Coal-Tit resembles other tits. It indulges in the same fascinating acrobatics, but it seems to have an even greater liking for creeping up trees. It displays a special preference for the company of goldcrests and tree-creepers, as well as its own

Eric Hosking

COAL-TIT. Any deep hole will serve as nesting site—even an ancient petrol tin as in this case

kind, as they gather in flocks seeking food among the trees and bracken.

The spring call of the British Coal-Tit resembles the so-called "teacher" note of the Great Tit, but is sweeter and more musical, and includes a wider range of notes. The call, which is usually delivered from a high tree, is best heard from the beginning of February until the middle of June. Some people claim to have heard the Coal-Tit in almost every month of the year.

The nest is placed in any deep hole in old tree stumps, crevices in walls, or burrows in the ground or in banks. Both cock and hen assist in building the cosy nest with moss, wool, hair and feathers. The eggs, ranging in number from seven to eleven, are white with reddish-brown spots ; they are laid in April or, in the north, in May. Hatching is done almost entirely by the hen, but her mate brings her food during the fortnight or so while she is sitting. The chicks are tinged with yellow where they will later become white, and are tended for nearly three weeks by both devoted parents, whose efforts to satisfy their hungry offspring are unwearying.

The natural food of the Coal-Tit consists of insects of many kinds, nuts, kernels and seeds, but it will accept bits of meat and fat if feeding at a bird table or nesting box.

Two other species of Coal-Tit, one breeding entirely in Ireland and the other on the Continent, are occasionally recorded in England. Neither differs to any great extent from the British bird. The Continental Coal-Tit (*Parus ater ater*) has slate-grey upperparts with very few or no greenish tints and is slightly larger than the British variety. Its voice has a still wider range and is generally sweeter. The Irish

Eric Hosking

COCCOTHRAUSTES. The heavy-billed Hawfinch is the only member of this genus found in Britain

Coal-Tit (*Parus ater hibernicus*) is darker than the British bird, with its white parts deeply tinged yellow and its rump, flanks and the tail coverts cinnamon-coloured instead of buff.

COBB, or Sea-Cobb. Local names for Common Gull (*q.v.*).

COCCOTHRAUSTES. Genus of the family *Fringillidae* of the order *Passeriformes*. It contains only one species, the Hawfinch (*q.v.*) which occurs in four forms in Europe, northern Asia and north-west Africa. The Hawfinch occurs in the British Isles as a resident bird, but it is rather scarce in Wales and Scotland, and very scarce in Ireland. These birds can easily be recognized by their large head with its massive bill.

COCCYZUS (Latin, " cuckoo "). Genus of the family *Cuculidae* of the order *Cuculiformes*. It contains seven species, which are distributed over north and south America, including the West Indies and Galapagos Islands ; a few individuals occasionally wander to Greenland and Europe. There are two species on the British list, the Yellow-billed Cuckoo (*q.v.*) and the Black-billed Cuckoo (*q.v.*), but neither has been recorded here more than a few times.

The members of this genus have no crest, but, unlike the common Cuckoo's, their nostrils are longitudinal ; the bill is more compressed than in the genera *Cuculus* and *Clamator*. These birds also differ from the common Cuckoo in having less copious rump-feathers, and their underparts are not barred. The wings have ten primary feathers, of which the third and the fourth are the longest. The tarsus is completely bare. The Yellow-billed Cuckoo builds a nest and incubates its eggs.

COCK OF THE WOODS. Colloquial name for Capercaillie (*q.v.*), a game bird that is found mostly in coniferous, hilly woodlands.

COCK'S NEST. This term does not designate nests built only by cock birds, but is used to describe " false " nests never used for breeding. Such nests are sometimes made by cocks, presumably as part of their courtship ritual ; others might have been constructed for breeding but were abandoned for unknown reasons. One theory holds they are built to draw enemies away from the genuine breeding nests.

Although many species indulge in this somewhat mysterious practice, the two British birds particularly prone to producing cock's nests are the Redshank and the Wren.

COLLARED FLYCATCHER. *See* White-collared Flycatcher.

COLLARED PETREL. *See* White-winged Petrel, a very rare vagrant to Britain.

COLLARED PRATINCOLE — Glareola pratincola. This rare wanderer from southern Europe, Asia and Africa has been recorded several times in this country, mostly in May and June. It is an unusual-looking wader, for the wings are long and narrow and the tail deeply forked, giving the bird a swallow-like appearance, enhanced by its quick movements in flight.

The Collared Pratincole is brown above, paler on the breast, with white underparts ; the tips of the wings and the base of the tail are also white. The male, in its summer plumage, has a narrow black band or collar (hence the name) running in a curve from the chin down to the throat. The bill is dark brown, red at the base. The bird's length is 10 in., with a tarsus of 1·4 in. The wing span is 14 or 15 in.

Its flight is rapid and buoyant, reminiscent of the Swallow's, as the Pratincole dashes after insects on the wing. The bird runs swiftly, with something of a Plover's action ; it does not perch and will sometimes wade in shallow water. Although by no means a nocturnal bird, it is often on the move towards evening. Its voice is harsh and angry, and the noise of pratincoles calling at their breeding colonies is tremendous and not unlike that heard at a ternery.

Pratincoles frequent open and barren land—stretches of sun-dried marshes, river deltas, borders of lakes and lagoons, and suchlike. A scrape hollowed in the ground, with little or no nesting material added, serves as nest. In the south of Spain and north Africa, three eggs are laid in May or June. Both male and female incubate for 17 to 18 days, and both parents feed the chicks, which are able to fly in about four weeks. As far as is known, only one brood is reared in a season.

Insects caught on the wing—locusts, grasshoppers, crickets and many others—are the main diet of the Collared Pratincole.

NESTING ALONE OR IN COMPANY

R. A. BAYNTON, T.D., B.Sc.

Like humans, some birds prefer to build their homes in splendid isolation, whereas others like to crowd as closely together as summer visitors on a seaside beach. Some of the reasons behind their choice are discussed here. See also *Nesting; Territory*

COLONIAL NESTING. Such expressions as "solitary", "gregarious", "social" and "colonial" occur whenever the nesting habits of birds are discussed. At first sight these terms appear to be self-explanatory, but actually it is difficult, if not impossible, to give any one of them a short, all-embracing and exact definition; for this would have to be so much qualified that it would prove lengthy, cumbersome and, probably, difficult to follow.

The term "solitary" is primarily associated with non-social, so-called territory-holding, or territorial, birds—i.e. those who claim a comparatively large area (about half an acre in this country) and defend it against all members of the *same* species, other than their chosen mates. Solitary habits are said to be not due to a morose disposition, but to stern necessity, for an area supplying abundant food for one family may cause a flock to starve miserably. Often, however, not lack of food, but competition for available nesting sites is responsible for this fierce defence of a territory. Hence, it is the instinct of self-preservation that begets pugnacity.

In distinct contrast to the solitary birds are those who spend most of their lives in flocks. Between these two extremes there is every possible degree of association. Some species associate only during migration and disperse immediately on arrival at their destination; there are others, like the Heron, who may nest in colonies and live a very solitary existence outside the breeding season.

Solitary Birds. In general, provided they can recognize them as such, territorial birds will not attempt to drive out birds of species other than their own, and will willingly share the same breeding ground with others, even though these may be, to some extent, competing for the same food supplies.

Some territorial birds, however, display to, and even attack, members of other species likely to compete for nesting-sites, and will even attempt to drive off mammals, including Man, if there is a possibility of nest, eggs or nestlings being endangered. Thus, nuthatches will attack tits and starlings; ringed plovers will attack skylarks and linnets; and the Little Ringed Plover will even try to chase sheep.

Thus a solitary bird or pair is not solitary in the sense that it is entirely segregated from all other birds, but only in that it lives apart from other members of its kind—and this, possibly,

only before and during the breeding season. Some birds prefer this type of existence throughout the year, notably the male Robin, who sometimes maintains a territory in Winter, even though the female may migrate.

Gregarious Birds. Usually birds of gregarious habits associate in small parties. But some species, e.g. flamingoes and starlings, may go about in huge flocks which are, however, never so large as those gathering together at breeding time. With some species, such as albatrosses, penguins and terns, flocks at breeding time may number millions of birds.

The Starling is the most gregarious of all British Passerines. Even in the nesting season, flocks of unmated starlings are seen in the fields and, as soon as their young are grown up, family parties join them to scour the country for food. Both in and out of the breeding season, magpies will roost communally—200 to 250 settling together are not uncommon.

Gregarious species usually fare better in the struggle for existence; this is most noticeable where the development of social instinct is highest. Such species are also generally stronger numerically; swifts are more numerous than nightjars, plovers and rails; and tits more common than the solitary nuthatch.

Large assemblages of the same species are only possible where there is an abundant food

Eric Hosking

COLONIAL NESTING. *Sand-martins live in holes bored in sand or gravel pits, river banks or cliffs*

supply, and the gregariousness of some birds is said to be due to this fact alone (e.g. gannets and guillemots) and not because they are bound by ties of mutual protection—although there is no doubt that communities of these species will act in concert to attack a suspected aggressor, including Man.

Social Birds. Some species, which were first drawn together by a bountiful food supply, may later develop more social instincts. Rooks find security against surprise while feeding by appointing one or more guards. Long-tailed tits foraging for food utter a distinctive call note to advise others that their search has been successful. Common partridges, which live in small companies, or coveys, and only scatter while feeding, depart later in the day to some spot where they " jug ", i.e. nestle close together in a ring with tails together and heads outwards.

The Jackdaw is a good example of a social bird, and although every bird is jealous of his own position in the colony and often bickers with his direct subordinates, is distinctly tolerant of those far below him in the social order. He does not object to sharing his territory with a well-known citizen of the colony, but if a strange daw comes near a *nesting* colony during the breeding season, the intruder is driven away by the whole community.

COLONIAL NESTING

Most British sea-birds breed in colonies, probably mainly because, in comparison with their numbers, suitable nesting sites are limited. Frequently, but not always, the same geographical area is used by several species. However, colonial nesting is not, as will have been seen already, restricted to sea-birds. Land-birds that prefer to breed in communities include rooks, crows, ravens, starlings, jackdaws, sparrows, house-martins, sand-martins, ospreys, herons, and broad-billed sandpipers. Swifts form scattered colonies.

Even with species whose nesting habits are normally colonial, or social to colonial, it is not uncommon to find a few individual pairs nesting alone ; e.g. the Greater Black-backed Gull and the House-Sparrow. Some types of colony have, by common usage, been given a specific name ; thus we have gannetry, ternery, gullery, swannery and rookery.

Size of Colonies. This varies from a few pairs to tens of thousands or even millions. In general, the largest colonies occur with sea-birds ; but in 1876, Brewster, while exploring, found a colony of passenger-pigeons, a land-bird not seen in this country. The colony was 28 miles long and 3 to 4 miles wide—every tree having one or more nests. But, as will be seen, an assemblage of birds does not have to be large to be described as a colony. This description is generally associated with a certain way of life, and not with numbers.

Frequently, in colonies, the nests—sometimes no more than scrapes—are so close together that when they are constructed on the ground, as many of them are, it is almost impossible to step between them without causing damage. For example, with gannets, cormorants and guillemots, the nests are extremely close together, but nevertheless so sited that each sitting bird is out of pecking range of its neighbours, each of whom jealously guards his territory, small though it be.

In other cases the nests may be more widely separated ; for example, shags sometimes build their nests close together, but generally their colonies are more scattered than those of the cormorants and guillemots. Similarly, some rooks' nests may be placed relatively far apart. Perhaps the most clear-cut example of colonial nesting is afforded by the Gannet. This bird breeds in well-defined and established colonies, of which the exact location of each is known. In 1939, there were 22 gannet colonies in the world, in 1954 there were 29, of which 13 were in Great Britain, the largest being at St. Kilda, where about 17,000 breeding pairs were counted at the last census. This contrasts with the fresh colony started at Bempton Cliffs, Yorkshire, in

John Markham

COLONIAL NESTING. *Guillemots build no nests, but merely deposit their eggs on a ledge or clifftop, where many thousands of birds may live together*

1939, which originally contained only four pairs of breeding birds.

With sea-birds at least, the members of a given species tend to use the same breeding haunts year after year, unless they are forced out of any of them by adverse circumstances or predatory birds or mammals—as, for example, at Dungeness, where terns and gulls were driven away by foxes. Consequently, the number and location of the various colonies do not, in general, vary much from one season to the next; though from time to time established sites are discarded and fresh colonies started elsewhere. Moreover, a few British species are tending to increase and spread, and others to decrease and disappear from their previous haunts.

A good example of the former is provided by the spectacular spread of the Fulmar in recent years. In 1878 a single colony was established on Foula, one of the Shetland Isles. In 1939 there were 208 different stations where birds were definitely known to be breeding, and 61 where they were known to be present during the breeding season. By 1949 there were 365 known breeding colonies and 61 prospecting stations in the British Isles, extending from the Shetlands to south Devon. Most of the colonies, except those in the far north, are still small, so the establishment of new colonies does not appear to be the result of overcrowding.

COLORATION. *See* Pattern and Colour.

COLUMBA (Latin, " pigeon "). Genus of the family *Columbidae* of the order *Columbiformes*. It contains more than fifty species, distributed over all the continents of the world. The three species on the British list are: the Rock-Dove, Stock-Dove and Wood-Pigeon; these are described under their own names.

These birds are large pigeons, with long, broad, but somewhat pointed wings, with eleven primary feathers. The tail is square or wedge-shaped, and has twelve feathers. The head is relatively small. The bill is shortish, its basal portion covered with soft skin. The tarsus is rather shorter than the middle toe with claw. Its upper part is overhung with feathers. There are four toes, three in front and one behind.

COLUMBIDAE (Latin, " pigeon "). Family of the order *Columbiformes*. It contains several hundred species, and its members are distributed throughout almost the whole world, except the Arctic and subarctic regions. A very large proportion occur in the islands of the Malay Archipelago and the south Pacific. There are two genera on the British list: *Columba* and *Streptopelia*, each containing several species.

The pigeons and doves of this family are almost all at least partly arboreal, but a few are

Eric Hosking

COLONIAL NESTING. *Unlike guillemots (opposite) rooks leave ample space between individual nests*

terrestrial or are mainly confined to rocky habitats. They vary considerably in size, but have the following features in common: The head is relatively small, and the bill short with its basal portion covered with rather soft and swollen skin which envelopes the generally slit-like nostrils. The terminal part of the bill is comparatively hard and somewhat enlarged. The neck is rather thick, and has fourteen or fifteen vertebrae. The wings are rather broad and long, and have eleven primary feathers, the outermost considerably reduced. The tail is generally rather long, and is wedge-shaped or slightly rounded; it usually has between twelve and fourteen feathers, but occasionally there are between sixteen and twenty. The feathers are soft and plentiful, and they are of characteristic structure, the shaft being broad and flattish, narrowing sharply some distance from the tip; there is an extensive area of down. Generally, the sexes do not differ markedly in plumage. The oil-gland is naked or absent. The tarsus is rather short, and its upper part is generally feathered. The crop is bi-lobed and well-developed, and the gizzard is usually very strong.

The members of this family feed mainly on seeds, berries, and fruits. Unlike other birds, they do not sip when drinking, but immerse their bills and take long draughts.

COLUMBIFORMES (Latin, " pigeon-like "). Order of birds comprising the pigeons and the sand-grouse. It is divided into three families, two of which, *Pteroclidae* and *Columbidae*, include British species. The members of this order are distributed over all continents of the globe. They are arboreal and terrestrial, and are mostly medium-sized. The wings have eleven primary feathers. The legs are generally feathered. There is a well-developed crop and very strong gizzard. The plumage is thick and close, and the feathers are set loosely in the skin. The oil-gland is naked or absent.

COLYMBIDAE. Family (the only one) of the order *Colymbiformes*. It consists of large aquatic birds (the divers), and its members are mainly confined to the northern parts of the northern hemisphere. The family contains the single genus, *Colymbus*, which is on the British list.

COLYMBIFORMES. Order of large aquatic birds (the divers). It contains only one family, *Colymbidae*, and one genus, *Colymbus* (*see* below), all the species of which are on the British list.

COLYMBUS. Genus (the only one) of the family *Colymbidae* of the order *Colymbiformes*. It comprises the four species of divers, all of which are on the British list. They are : the Black-throated Diver, Great Northern Diver, Red-throated Diver, and White-billed Diver. Descriptions of these birds are given under their individual names. In North America divers are called " loons ".

These are foot-propelled diving birds. The bill is strong, compressed and pointed. The head is large, and the neck is of medium length and thick-set ; it has fourteen or fifteen vertebrae. The wings are set rather far back and are short, narrow and pointed ; they have eleven primary feathers, the outermost very small. The tail is very short, with between sixteen and twenty small but distinct rectrices (tail quills). The legs are short, and are set very far back ; and the tarsus is laterally compressed. The tibial segment of the leg is enclosed in the body tissues, so that these birds stand and walk with some difficulty. The three front toes are connected by webs, and there is a small, elevated hind toe.

COMMISSURE. Joint, junction, or point of union between two parts or organs. In a bird it denotes either the line of closure of the mandibles (i.e. of the two halves of the beak) or the point where the two halves actually join. To avoid ambiguity, this latter junction is sometimes referred to as the angle of the commissure or, more briefly, the angle. *See also* Anatomy ; Bill.

COMMON BUNTING. Alternative local name for the Corn-Bunting (*q.v.*).

COMMON GULL—Larus canus. Of the six resident gulls of the British Isles, the Common Gull is, in spite of its name, the least common south of the Border and only occasionally breeds in England. The Black-headed Gull (*q.v.*) is the real " common " gull in England and Wales, but confusion frequently arises during the winter months between common gulls arriving from the Continent and black-headed gulls which by then have lost their dark heads. In Scotland, however, especially in the north and the islands, the Common Gull lives up to its name and is very abundant and, by all accounts, on the increase. It is also quite common in Ireland.

The Common Gull has pure white plumage, except for its pearl-grey mantle. The tips of its wings are black, and dotted or " mirrored " with white spots ; both bill and legs are a yellowish-green. It is smaller, more slender and, on the whole, more attractive in appearance than the Herring-Gull (*q.v.*), with which it is sometimes confused. In its winter plumage its head is often darker and streaked with brown. It is 16 in. long, with a tarsus of 2 in., its wing span is about $3\frac{1}{2}$ ft., its weight $1\frac{1}{2}$ lb.

In habits and behaviour, the Common Gull closely follows the pattern of its species. Its flight is strong and buoyant, with regular wing beats, and it often glides in a leisurely manner. It walks quite happily on the ground, and likes to perch on walls, stumps and fences. It is an excellent swimmer and diver, often completely submerging. *See also* Gull.

The Common Gull has the most musical of all our gulls' voices. I have been able to record it ; but a good record was only possible under Arctic conditions, and during a lull in the middle of a great gale.

It has a very characteristic alarm note if an intruder ventures near a nest containing young ; and the chicks, while in the nest, have a very individual chirping note.—EDITOR.

G. K. Yeates

COMMON GULL. *South of the border, this is the least common of the six gulls breeding in Britain*

The Common Gull is gregarious, and is rarely seen far from land. Outside the breeding

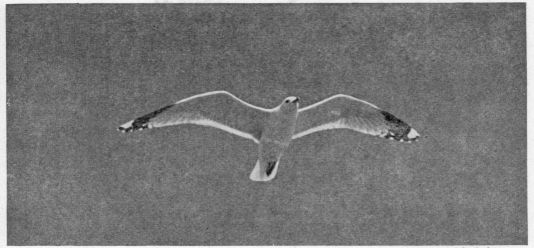

John Barlee

COMMON GULL. Gliding effortlessly on its strong wings, this Gull looks anything but a common sight, etched against the sky, with the sun outlining its wings and body

season it sometimes penetrates far inland to agricultural districts where it follows the plough ; it also visits lakes, ponds and reservoirs. It nests in large colonies on low rocks and islands in lochs, sometimes at a considerable distance from the coast and sometimes at high altitudes. Its nest, a bulky affair, is substantially built of grass, heather, moss and seaweed. The number of eggs is usually three— sometimes only two—and they vary in colour from dark to light olive, with various dark streaks and blotches. They are laid in late May or early June, and both parents share in the hatching, which takes some three weeks. The chicks, which are attended by both parents, are able to fly in about three weeks. One brood is reared in a season.

The food eaten by common gulls is often very varied. They are great scavengers and nothing seems to come amiss to them ; worms and slugs of all kinds are devoured (a good service to the farmer), but these gulls are also habitual egg-thieves and will even raid the nests of their own family. Yet they are clannish birds, and will courageously come to the rescue of their fellows, should trouble arise from, say, a Sparrow-Hawk or an Arctic Skua.

Common gulls usually leave their nesting sites in July, when our breeding birds spread themselves round the Scottish and Irish coasts and into England before the winter visitors from Europe arrive in huge numbers in Autumn.

Other names for the Common Gull are Mew-Gull, Cobb, and Sea-Cobb or Sea-Mew. In north America the bird is called Short-billed Gull. " Gull " is derived from an old Celtic word meaning " wailer ", and no doubt derives from the plaintive call note of these birds.

COMMON MURRE. One of the names by which the Guillemot (*q.v.*) is known in north America. Others are Murre or Atlantic Murre.

COMMON SANDPIPER—Tringa hypoleucos. This attractive wader, often called the " Summer Snipe ", breeds in many parts of the British Isles, when it arrives from its winter quarters in April. It is also an abundant passage migrant, some birds staying throughout the Winter. This is the Sandpiper of the hills, rejoicing in the clear rocky streams, where it has the company of the Dipper and the Grey Wagtail, and sometimes nesting at an altitude of 2,500 ft. in the central highlands. It is also found breeding wherever there is suitable water. It breeds all over Europe and beyond, as far as the Himalayas ; in Winter it flies south, sometimes as far as Australia and Tasmania.

A small bird, the Common Sandpiper is wholly brown above and pure white beneath, and has a conspicuous white wing bar. It has a long slender bill, a short tail, and greenish-grey legs. Male and female are alike. The length is 8 in., and the tarsus 0·8 in. The wing span is approximately 12 in., and the bird weighs 2 oz.

It is a simple matter to identify this bird, for it has a characteristic (and attractive) habit of standing or running about with its short tail constantly bobbing up and down ; its flight is different from those of the other waders, for it flies low over the water with a curious and regular flickering of its wings, while uttering its cheerful whistle. When travelling greater distances, however, its flight resembles that of the other members of its family.

The Common Sandpiper both walks and runs, likes to perch on posts, railings and boulders in mid-stream ; it wades in shallow waters, where much of its food is delved out with its long bill.

Before the breeding season, there are short but musical call notes to be heard. During mating time, the male chooses a favourite spot, usually on a sandy shore or shingle bed, where he delivers a most attractive song, sometimes lasting four or five minutes, or even longer. At this time the bird is very shy, and, should any intruder appear, it will at once break off its performance and fly away, not returning for many hours. The song is heard during May.

Common sandpipers nest on the banks of streams and at the edges of lochs and tarns. The nest is a mere sheltered hollow, lined with grass and leaves. At any time in May or early June, depending on the altitude, four cream-coloured eggs, with brown and grey spots, are laid. Hatching, which does not begin until all the eggs are laid, is shared by both male and female for a period of three weeks. The delightful little chicks are tended by both watchful and devoted parents for about four weeks ; one brood is reared in a season.

Saxby in his *Birds of the Shetlands* mentions the curious behaviour of common sandpipers during a thunderstorm, when they seem to show every evidence of terror ; on one occasion, he says, a number of these birds cowered against rocks, where he easily captured one with his hat.

The Common Sandpiper is not very gregarious ; outside the breeding season it is often seen alone or, sometimes, in small parties.

COMMON SCOTER—Melanitta nigra. One of the most common of the sea-ducks, the Common Scoter—also called Black Duck—breeds in the British Isles in only a few northern counties of Scotland and on one lake, Lough Erne, in Ireland. It is, however, one of our most abundant winter visitors, arriving in thousands on all the coasts except the south coast of

Ireland. Abroad, the Common Scoter breeds in the northern areas of Europe, Asia and America.

There is no difficulty in recognizing this bird, for it is the only sea-duck whose drake is entirely black, the sole touch of colour being the conspicuous reddish patch in the centre of the upper mandible of his black bill, which has a large knob at the base. His plumage is little different during the eclipse. The duck and young are dark brown, the only distinctive mark being a pale whitish patch on the side of the head and breast. The tail is short and pointed, the legs blackish-brown. The length is 19 in. and the tarsus 1·75 in. ; the wing span is from 1½ to 2 ft. and the weight 2 lb. 9 oz.

Gregarious and often in the company of his close relation, the Velvet Scoter (*q.v.*)—both sexes of the latter can be told from the Common Scoter by the white wing patch, apart from the fact that they are larger birds—the Common Scoter swims easily and buoyantly with its tail elevated and bill held high.

Outside the breeding season, it is seldom seen inland. On the ground its walk is awkward and ungainly. Essentially a marine duck, most of its time is spent far out at sea in deep water. The Common Scoter can dive to a great depth, where it propels itself along with its wing and feet. It sometimes remains under water for as long as one minute, though normally for only half that time. The flight of the Common Scoter, though low over the water, is swift and direct, its rapid wing beats emitting a whistling sound. During their courtship, male and female chase each other along the water, playing follow-my-leader and engaging in bowing ceremonies.

The drake has a low, musical, piping call, usually uttered in the Spring and late Autumn and often on the wing ; the duck has a hoarse croak similar to that of other diving ducks.

Unfortunately the Common Scoter must be added to the roll of the victims of oil pollution (*q.v.*) caused by the discharge from ships.

Lochs on moorlands and tundras, sometimes at quite high altitudes, are the favourite breeding haunts of the Common Scoter. A sheltered hollow among the peat or heather, lined with grass, moss and down, provides the nest for the five to ten buff eggs laid in early June in Scotland. On completion of the clutch, the duck hatches them alone for 27 to 28 days. The chicks are clad in dusky brown and are looked after by only the duck for six to seven weeks, when they are ready to fly and become independent. One brood is reared in a season.

Molluscs of all kinds, chiefly mussels, form a great part of the food of the Common Scoter ; but fish, insects, worms and marine plants are also eaten. *See also* Anatidae ; Duck.

Eric Hosking

COMMON SANDPIPER. *This little wader and his mother nest in a mere hollow, lined with grasses*

COMMON SCOTER. *This, the most common of the sea-ducks, is found here mostly as a winter visitor*

Eric Hosking

COMMON SNIPE—Capella gallinago. Both an autumn passage migrant and a winter visitor, the Common Snipe is one of the most distinctive and easily recognized of our breeding waders. Its colouring, however, provides excellent camouflage, and, in common with such birds as the Bittern, Pheasant and Nightjar, it can completely merge itself into its background, especially when on the nest. It has a dark brown mantle, intricately patterned in black and brown, with buff-coloured stripes, and its wings are barred with buff, brown and black. Its unmistakable bill—long, slender and straight—is about $2\frac{1}{2}$ in. in length. The Common Snipe weighs 4 oz. and has a wing span of about 18 in; it is 11 in. long, and its tarsus is 1 in.

Much has been written about the remarkable and well-known " drumming " or " bleating " flight of the Common Snipe during its aerial display. At one time it was thought that only the male bird produced the sound ; now it is known that both birds " drum ", although the male does so more frequently. When the birds are " flushed ", they rise with sharp, repeated and raucous calls and circle high in the air, with rapidly beating wings, and outspread tail ; when they swoop suddenly down at an angle of 45°, this extraordinary and resounding " drumming " is heard.

Much controversy has arisen among ornithologists about the purpose of the noise and how it is made, but it seems certain that the sound is caused by the vibration of the air passing through the wings and tail on the downward swoop. The manoeuvre is repeated again and again, and " drumming " can be heard during the night as well as by day. It is not always confined to the breeding season, but in that season is said to be heard more often in wet or misty weather.

This is not the Common Snipe's only accomplishment in the air, for in the intervals between

" drummings " it will turn completely on to its back and glide along with wings outspread for some distance. Its well-known normal zigzag flight makes aiming difficult for the sportsman.

Besides the " song " uttered during its aerial display, the Common Snipe has another call quite as individual, but not so well-known. It is a quick double-rhythm, piston-like note, which is uttered both from some vantage point and also on the wing. Both calls are heard at their best from the latter end of March until the middle of June.—EDITOR.

The bird rests during the day in some well-concealed spot, protected by its wonderful camouflage. It is not particularly gregarious, but a " wisp " (as a flock of snipe is called) will often be observed flying together.

It can be seen throughout the British Isles in suitable country ; preferring to breed in marshes, swamps, bogs and peat mosses. Its cup-shaped nest, which is never very far from water, is placed in a well-concealed hollow among herbage or heather, or in a clump of rushes, and is lined with fine grasses. The four eggs, normally laid in April, have an extraordinary variety of colour and occur in many shades of cream, blue, brown, olive-green and olive-brown, with varying markings and blotchings ; but all the eggs in one clutch are the same. The hen broods them, leaving the nest only for food, for about three weeks. Both parents tend and rear the pretty grey and chestnut chicks, which are less independent than the young of many other waders and have to be fed for a time. One brood is usually reared in a season, but two are not unknown.

The Common Snipe is found in most parts of the Old World, and is very abundant in India, especially in the flooded rice-fields, where it affords excellent sport. It is generally known by the name of " Fantail Snipe " in that country.

G. K. Yeates

COMMON SNIPE. *The long bill and intricately patterned plumage render the Snipe unmistakable*

COMMON TERN—Sterna hirundo. Of the five species of tern which come to the British Isles to breed, the Common Tern is probably the most abundant ; it can be seen all round the English coasts from April until August, when it leaves for its warmer winter quarters, travelling sometimes as far south as the Cape of Good Hope and Madagascar. It is also a passage migrant in the Autumn. In Scotland and Ireland it is often outnumbered by the Arctic Tern (*q.v.*), and in the Orkney and Shetland Islands the Common Tern is almost a rare species.

The common and Arctic terns are so alike that the ordinary observer has great difficulty in distinguishing between them. At close range, the most evident point of difference is in their bills ; that of the Common Tern in breeding plumage is vermilion-red. Again, although the feet and legs of both birds are red, the legs of the Common Tern are longer. The Common Tern is a graceful bird, attractive in its pearl-grey mantle, with dark wing tips and pale grey underparts. Its tail, which earns it the name of " Sea-Swallow " — applied to all terns—is white and forked, and it has a black head and nape, though much of this colour disappears in its winter dress. Its length depends on its tail " streamers ", but is usually about 14 in. Its tarsus is a little less than 1 in. Its wing span is $3\frac{1}{4}$ ft., and it weighs 7 oz.

All terns have a graceful and buoyant flight, and the Common Tern is no exception ; it is a pleasure, during a summer visit to the coast, to watch its carefree abandon in the air. The Common Tern is not a good swimmer and rarely alights on the water for any length of time. It has an awkward walk on the ground, in contrast to the beauty of its flight.

> Terns are noisy birds, and I have found that once common terns start calling in the Spring, about 4 a.m., there is no hope of recording any other bird. The breeding note of the Common Tern is softer than that of the Arctic Tern, although the latter's many variations include some softer calls. Although the similarity in appearance of the two birds may lead to confusion, their calls are unmistakable.—EDITOR.

The Common Tern is gregarious and will nest in company with others of its family. In the breeding season the terneries resound with the clamour of their bickering and quarrelling. The courtship display flights of the Common Tern have always held much interest for the ornithologist, but so far no explanation has been offered to explain the birds' curious " dread " flights and the strange silences which occur when a whole colony will suddenly sweep across the sea, returning after a few minutes to their domestic duties. During the mating season, common terns have a most attractive and charming habit of feeding one another with fish and afterwards bowing to one another. Sometimes they will go through this performance with other species of their family ; and mating with other species has been recorded.

John E. M. Sumner
COMMON TERN. *Even when alighting, something of the aerial grace of this bird is seen*

Usually the Common Tern will return year after year to the same colony, situated on some rocky island, shingle bank or sand dune. Its nest is only a hollow scraped in the ground or in the shingle, and is sometimes not even lined. The eggs, three as a rule, but often only two, are laid in May and June ; they vary in colour from whitish to olive-green, buff or grey, and are much blotched and streaked. The nest and eggs are so very exposed that they are in constant danger of being trodden on by a careless walker. Both cock and hen take their share in the hatching, which begins with the first egg laid, but the hen seems to do the major part. The attractive little chicks remain in the nest for a few days, while the hen broods them and the male feeds them, and they are ready to fly in about a month. One brood is generally reared in a season. Though less aggressive during the breeding season than the Arctic Tern, the Common species is fierce enough, and these birds have been known to swoop down on both humans and animals, often with fatal results to the latter. The average length of life of the Common Tern is said to be about ten years, and some live even longer.

The name " Tern " or " Tarn " is of Scandinavian origin (Danish " Terne " ; Swedish " Terna " ; and Old Norse " Therua "). In several languages the bird is known as the " Sea-Swallow ".

CONSERVANCY. *See* Conservation ; Nature Conservancy ; *also* Nature Reserve.

PRESERVING BIRD LIFE IN BRITAIN

P. E. BROWN, M.B.O.U.

Here the Secretary of the R.S.P.B., after grouping British birds according to their rarity, discusses the reasons for fluctuations in their numbers and what is being done to protect the rarer birds. See also *Nature Conservancy; Nature Reserve; Sanctuary*

CONSERVATION. The aim of bird conservation is to promote the richest and most varied bird life possible by nurturing rare species and helping to establish new breeding species. The task is particularly difficult in a relatively small country, highly developed industrially and agriculturally, and with a large and mobile population.

It is beyond doubt that the most careful conservation of bird life is worth while. The aesthetic value of birds is beyond dispute, and they bring pleasure to the hearts of men and women everywhere, forming an integral part of the pattern of Britain and its people. Birds have also great scientific interest ; one need only look at the pages of the *Ibis*, *Bird Study*, or *British Birds* to realize the amount of scientific study which is being devoted to them. Finally, birds have an economic value. It is true that this is a field in which we have lately discovered our own ignorance. Dogmatic statements about the economic value of most species are impossible. None the less, birds are so numerous that they must play a vital part in the general stability or " balance " of nature.

The Black Ages. Probably the worst period for British birds occurred during the 18th and 19th centuries. The four dominant factors in this period of serious decline were (1) the reclamation of the fens and marshes ; (2) the industrial revolution, leading to a great increase in the population and, through railways and better roads, to the opening up of hitherto almost inaccessible areas ; (3) the gradual perfection of the gun ; and (4) an almost slavish devotion to the preservation of game. Minor factors included the extreme poverty of the agricultural labourer, which made it well worth his while to hunt for Plover's or Lapwing's eggs at less than a farthing per clutch in order to satisfy the gourmets of the cities. It would not be unjust to say that the outlook of the majority of people interested in birds 100 years ago was usually bounded by their vanity or their stomachs.

Another product of the Victorian age was the egg-collector. It may seem curious today that so much trouble and money were spent in acquiring a few ounces of calcium carbonate. So far as the common birds' eggs were concerned, collecting may not have had very serious effects. But collectors always pride themselves on their rarities, and by the middle of the 19th century the hunt was on. Egg-collectors, skin-collectors,

bird-trappers with net and with quicklime taking goldfinches, linnets and other small birds to fill cages large and small, and the incessant persecution of harriers, falcons, hawks and owls : these and other things make it remarkable that even more damage was not done to bird life.

BIRD POPULATION

At the present time the surprisingly large number of 184 species of birds breed regularly in the British Isles. It is possible to divide these into three groups : common ; uncommon or local ; and rare. These are rough-and-ready divisions, and border-line cases can well be put into one or the other.

Common Species. Of the 184 breeding species, the following 117 may be described as common, though some are rare or absent in many localities, others are purely coastal species :

Great Crested Grebe ; Little Grebe ; Fulmar ; Cormorant ; Shag ; Mallard ; Teal ; Shoveler; Tufted Duck ; Eider ; Red-breasted Merganser; Sheld-Duck ; Mute Swan ; Buzzard ; Sparrow-Hawk ; Kestrel ; Red Grouse ; Black Grouse ; Red-legged Partridge ; Partridge ; Pheasant ; Moorhen ; Coot ; Oystercatcher ; Lapwing ; Ringed Plover ; Golden Plover ; Snipe ; Curlew ; Common Sandpiper ; Redshank ; Dunlin ; Arctic Skua ; Greater Black-backed Gull ; Lesser Black-backed Gull ; Herring-Gull ; Common Gull ; Black-headed Gull ; Kittiwake ; Common Tern ; Arctic Tern ; Little Tern ; Razorbill ; Guillemot ; Black Guillemot ; Puffin ; Stock-Dove ; Wood-Pigeon ; Turtle-Dove ; Cuckoo ; Little Owl ; Tawny Owl ; Nightjar ; Swift ; Green Woodpecker ; Greater Spotted Woodpecker ; Skylark ; Swallow ; House-Martin ; Sand-Martin ; Raven ; Carrion-Crow ; Hooded Crow ; Rook; Jackdaw ; Magpie ; Jay ; Great Tit ; Blue Tit ; Coal-Tit ; Marsh-Tit ; Willow-Tit ; Long-tailed Tit ; Nuthatch ; Tree-Creeper ; Wren ; Dipper ; Mistle-Thrush ; Song-Thrush; Ring-Ouzel ; Blackbird ; Wheatear ; Whinchat; Nightingale ; Robin ; Reed-Warbler ; Sedge-Warbler ; Blackcap ; Garden-Warbler ; Whitethroat ; Lesser Whitethroat ; Willow-Warbler ; Chiffchaff ; Wood-Warbler ; Goldcrest ; Spotted Flycatcher ; Hedge-Sparrow ; Meadow-Pipit ; Tree-Pipit ; Rock-Pipit ; Pied Wagtail ; Grey Wagtail ; Yellow Wagtail ; Starling ; Greenfinch ; Goldfinch ; Siskin ; Linnet ; Twite ; Redpoll ; Bullfinch ; Chaffinch ; Yellow Hammer ; Corn-Bunting ; Reed-Bunting ; House-Sparrow ; Tree-Sparrow.

These species cause the conservationist least anxiety unless it be that one or two of them may be too numerous locally. Thus the Carrion-Crow can cause considerable damage to a marshland bird reserve, where the interests of breeding

S. C. Porter

CONSERVATION. Hides are specially constructed to facilitate observation without alarming birds

duck are of vital importance, while herring-gulls may affect adjacent tern colonies.

Bird numbers are constantly undergoing changes, often from causes at present unknown or only very vaguely understood. Thus in the above list of common breeding birds, the following species have increased in the last 25 years :

Great Crested Grebe ; Fulmar ; Tufted Duck ; Eider ; Sheld-Duck ; Mute Swan ; Buzzard ; Coot ; Oystercatcher ; Greater Black-backed Gull ; Lesser Black-backed Gull ; Herring-Gull ; Stock-Dove ; Wood-Pigeon ; Raven ; Carrion-Crow ; Hooded Crow ; Rook ; Jackdaw ; Magpie ; Starling.

In the same period the following are among those which have decreased : Lapwing ; Common Snipe ; Nightjar ; Ring-Ouzel.

Uncommon or Local Species. In the list of uncommon or local breeding species there are the following 35 species :

Red-throated Diver ; Storm-Petrel ; Manx Shearwater ; Gannet ; Heron ; Wigeon ; Pintail ; Pochard ; Goosander ; Canada Goose ; Merlin ; Ptarmigan ; Capercaillie ; Water-Rail ; Corncrake ; Woodcock ; Stone-Curlew ; Great Skua ; Roseate Tern ; Sandwich Tern ; Rock-Dove ; Barn-Owl ; Long-eared Owl ; Short-eared Owl ; Kingfisher ; Lesser Spotted Woodpecker ; Woodlark ; Stonechat ; Redstart ; Grasshopper-Warbler ; Pied Flycatcher ; Red-backed Shrike ; Hawfinch ; Crossbill ; Cirl Bunting.

These species, although not necessarily a matter for immediate conservational action, need to be watched.

If the Red-throated Diver, Gannet, Wigeon, Pintail, Woodlark and Pied Flycatcher are certainly increasing in numbers, the Corncrake, Stone-Curlew, Long-eared Owl, Stonechat, Redstart and Red-backed Shrike have declined. The Corncrake was undoubtedly a common bird throughout the British Isles less than a century ago. Its decline, especially since the First World War, can almost certainly be ascribed to improved agricultural methods, especially to the mechanical mower and the generally earlier cutting of grass for haymaking. The Corncrake has almost vanished from England and Wales, but in the western isles of Scotland, in Orkney and Shetland and in much of western Ireland it is probably as numerous as ever.

The Stone-Curlew, like many other birds, enjoys a fairly specialised habitat, nesting only on chalk, large areas of permanent coastal shingle and, above all, sandy grasslands and stony heaths. It has for long been confined to the area east and south of a line drawn from Teesmouth to Exmouth, but its numbers are steadily declining even in this area. It is not difficult to point to some of the causes : the extensive ploughing or afforestation of East Anglian heaths and " brecks " ; ploughing up of downlands in the south ; and disturbance by Man, especially by bird-watchers whose enthusiasm is unmatched by experience.

The decline of the Redstart and the Red-backed Shrike is more puzzling. Eggs laid by the latter bird are very varied in colour and, in spite of legal protection, have for long been a quarry of the collector. But egg-collecting seems unlikely to have been the chief cause of the bird's decline and climatic factors may well have been involved with both the Redstart and the Red-backed Shrike.

Certainly it is climate which has so seriously reduced the Stonechat. This attractive small insectivorous resident is extremely susceptible to very cold Winters. Between the two World Wars. Winters were generally unusually mild, and the species was fairly common and widely distributed in 1939. But the severe Winters of 1939-40 and the two succeeding years were almost disastrous in their effects. The bird maintained something like its old numbers only in the relatively milder climate of the maritime west and south, and vanished completely from many inland areas where it had previously been common. Just as it was showing signs of revival, the severe spell of weather early in 1947 again decimated the species. Although it had shown signs of recovery by 1954, a long succession of reasonably mild Winters will be necessary if it is to regain its former status.

Rare Species. The last and, from the point of view of protection, the most important list of British breeding birds comprises the following 32 rare species :

Black-throated Diver ; Slavonian Grebe ; Black-necked Grebe ; Leach's Petrel ; Bittern ; Garganey ; Gadwall ; Common Scoter ; Grey Lag-Goose ; Golden Eagle ; Kite ; Marsh-Harrier ; Hen-Harrier ; Montagu's Harrier ; Hobby ; Peregrine ; Quail ; Spotted Crake ; Little Ringed Plover ; Dotterel ; Whimbrel ; Greenshank ; Avocet ; Red-necked Phalarope ; Wryneck ; Chough ; Crested Tit ; Bearded Tit ; Black Redstart ; Marsh-Warbler ; Dartford Warbler ; Snow-Bunting.

It is probable that there are not more than a thousand breeding pairs of any of these species, and in the majority the figure is probably well below 500. In an average year, it would be safe to say that there are less than 100 pairs breeding in the whole of Britain in the case of the following :

Bittern ; Kite ; Marsh-Harrier ; Spotted Crake; Little Ringed Plover ; Dotterel ; Whimbrel ; Avocet ; Bearded Tit ; Black Redstart ; Snow-Bunting.

Half-a-dozen other species, such as Montagu's Harrier and the Red-necked Phalarope, must be regarded as borderline cases. The Bittern, Little Ringed Plover and Avocet are increasing; but some of these rare birds have only a precarious foothold. The average number of breeding pairs of kites, marsh-harriers and snow-buntings is below ten in each species.

A further nine species once nested regularly in this country but do so no longer :

Black Tern ; Kentish Plover ; Ruff ; Black-tailed Godwit ; Whooper-Swan ; Spoonbill ; Osprey ; Honey-Buzzard ; White-tailed Eagle.

Finally, 18 other species have bred sporadically in Britain ;

Gull-billed Tern ; Great Bustard ; Black-winged Stilt ; Temminck's Stint ; Wood-Sandpiper ; Green Sandpiper ; Scaup ; Golden-Eye ; Long-tailed Duck ; Goshawk ; Hoopoe ; Bee-Eater ; Redwing ; Moustached Warbler; Icterine Warbler ; Tawny Pipit ; Brambling ; Golden Oriole.

The total number of species, therefore, which breed or have bred in our Islands is 211.

The objectives of bird conservation are to promote a numerically strong *and* richly diversified avifauna; and we must not lose sight of the second objective in an excess of zeal. It would be a dull country for the bird-lover that had twice as many birds as now, but comprising only avocets and house-sparrows.

DECLINE IN POPULATION

An animal population must have an upper limit to its numbers. In birds this " saturation point " is probably fixed by food supply, but availability of nesting sites and other factors are involved. The *potential* increase in a species is often very great. A pair of blackbirds may rear six or more young birds in a breeding season. If this *potential* rate of increase went unchecked for 10 years, one would have difficulty in putting a foot down without treading on a Blackbird. If every egg laid by a hen Blackbird were hatched out and fledged successfully, the potential increase of a pair would be raised from 6 to nearer 13 young per season.

In fact, many Blackbird's eggs are taken by squirrels, mice, crows and small boys, while early clutches are sometimes deserted if the wintry weather returns. Inclement weather at any time during the breeding season may cause all or some of the chicks in a nest to die of starvation (for female birds do not in any way compare with mammals in their maternal devotion). Allowing for this failure of a high proportion of eggs and nestlings, we know that blackbirds have a high potential rate of increase ; yet, common as they are, they do not increase. The answer is almost certainly that this species is at a " saturation point " set by food supply in Winter, when the amount of food available is little and the daylight hours, during which it can be gleaned, are short.

In discussing bird protection, it is important to realize that there are these limits to numbers imposed by Nature. We must also take into account the *resilience* of a species, i.e. the ability to recover fairly quickly from a sharp setback. The Song-Thrush, a bird susceptible to severe cold, was seriously affected by the eight weeks of continuous frost early in 1947. No exact figures are available, but in some areas the number of breeding pairs in 1947 was less than one-twentieth of that in the previous year. But a

Arthur Brook

CONSERVATION. *The Golden Eagle, one of our rare birds, is finally protected by special legislation*

lower population means more food for the survivors during the following Winter, and therefore more birds survive (that is, the potential increase goes unchecked or only partially checked), so that the numbers are soon back to normal.

As far as the more common birds are concerned, numbers are permanently reduced, generally speaking, only by alteration of *habitat*. A habitat (*q.v.*) may be simply described as a place which supplies a particular creature with its wants. If the present policy of destroying hedgerows and replacing them by wire fences continues, we must expect a decline in the numbers of hedge-nesting birds such as the Blackbird, Chaffinch and Greenfinch. The protectionist obviously cannot buy up all the hedges. All he can do in this case is to mitigate the danger through influencing public opinion.

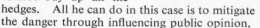

A. W. P. Robertson

CONSERVATION. *This baby Avocet would not have hatched here, were it not for the R.S.P.B.*

Small Boys—and Cats. In urban and suburban areas, where nesting sites for most species are few, small boys and cats are a serious factor. Perhaps not much can be done to prevent the keeping of cats, but education of children, of the practical type carried out by the Royal Society for the Protection of Birds, can certainly pay rich dividends (*see* Education). Far fewer schoolboys pillage nests or take eggs than in the past, but their activities are still sometimes very harmful. It is often stated (truthfully) that this boyish sport cannot have any serious effect upon the numbers of a common species. But it must be remembered that boys take any eggs they come across, and the fact that they may only occasionally come across a rarity does not make for complacency.

In 1954, for instance, a party of small boys, aged 8–12 years, took a clutch of Avocet's eggs in East Anglia. It was an isolated nest, and the children had no idea to what species the eggs belonged. The eggs were on the point of hatching and quite useless. If the boys had been taught not to take eggs, this tragedy would never have occurred. A clutch of Marsh-Warbler's eggs was also taken by boys in 1954, probably in the belief that they were Whitethroat's.

Further, a great deal of serious ornithological field-study is now going on in this country. Much of this work is being conducted on nests. In an unfavourable area, as the writer knows from bitter experience, a whole season's work can be completely negatived by local boys.

It should be emphasised that the education of the young in a proper appreciation of Nature,

though undramatic, is probably the most important field for the bird-conservationist. Children must be taught to see more interest in the exquisite artistry of a Chaffinch's nest than in four or five shells of slightly-pigmented calcium-carbonate abstracted from it. Moreover, a person who is interested in a common bird, such as a Chaffinch or Robin or Blackbird, will not be less interested if he comes across a rarer bird, such as an Avocet or, perhaps, a Golden Eagle.

Education in its broadest sense is the best method of fostering interest in birds, among adults as well as children. None the less, in the final resort, a strong and uncomplicated law is necessary to protect birds from those who will learn in no other way. Until recently legislation for the protection of wild birds was virtually useless. It was based upon an inadequate Act of 1880, with the confusing addition of various amending Acts. Protection varied from county to county, so that a bird which flew across an arbitrary line might lose or gain protection ; and if a prosecution were obtained, the penalties were wholly inadequate to act as a deterrent.

Protection of Birds Act. Northern Ireland first paved the way to better things, with an Act passed in 1931 ; this was based on the principle of protection for all birds, their eggs and nests, but sporting birds were given an " open " season when they could be shot, and certain harmful or allegedly harmful species were not protected. In 1953 Lady Tweedsmuir sponsored a Bill which passed on to the Statute Book in the next year as the Protection of Birds Act, 1954 (*q.v.*). For the first time the law gives some real protection to rare species, for with them the maximum penalty is stiff enough to be unwelcome—£25 *per egg or bird* and/or a month's imprisonment (three months for a second offence).

It is to be hoped that this legislation may help birds of prey, of which 12 species and their eggs are specially protected :

Honey-Buzzard ; Golden Eagle ; White-tailed Eagle ; Goshawk ; Hen-Harrier ; Hobby ; Kite ; Marsh-Harrier ; Merlin ; Montagu's Harrier ; Osprey and Peregrine.

Landowners and owners of sporting rights vary greatly in their attitude to the birds. Many have done a great deal for their protection, particularly in the case of the Golden Eagle. Others have flouted both the law and public opinion. The old idea of the damage done by birds with a hooked beak dies hard with many gamekeepers. Golden eagles are still shot or trapped in far from negligible numbers ; and the Hen-Harrier, perhaps the most graceful of our birds of prey, is still ruthlessly shot (yet if it were not for keepers it would have been safely established on the Scottish mainland years ago). It is known that three ospreys were shot in Scotland in 1951–54 and this is a bird, lost as a breeding species 40 years ago, which we are hoping to re-establish.

Much good work has been done by the Royal Society for the Protection of Birds by giving " bounties " for the successful breeding of the Golden Eagle and certain other birds of prey ; and also by enlisting the interest and sympathy of landowners—which, more often than not, has been readily forthcoming. But for the selfish individual who is quite unmoved either by public sentiment or by a reasonable approach, strong legislation, such as the Protection of Birds Act, may well prove the only answer.

Nature Reserves. In recent years much headway has been made in the promotion of bird reserves (*see* Nature Reserve). Broadly speaking, the object of a bird reserve is to encourage bird life in general, but especially those species whose habitats are endangered by other developments. That birds will come to suitable areas, provided that they are reasonably free from disturbance and that steps are taken to maintain ideal conditions, is proved beyond doubt. Havergate Island (*q.v.*), a reserve owned by the Royal Society for the Protection of Birds, may be cited as an example. This island of some 250 acres near the mouth of the River Alde was grazing land before the Second World War. During the agricultural slump of the 1930s it became derelict, an area of coarse herbage very little patronised by birds except pipits, wagtails and a few breeding duck During the war it was taken over by the military, and in 1946 a sluice draining a small part of the island ceased to work, so that sea-water seeped in, killing the vegetation and forming shallow lagoons. In 1947 four or five pairs of avocets, a species which had not bred regularly in Britain since 1842, nested successfully. Later, when the R.S.P.B. purchased the island, the whole area was flooded and the water maintained at an ideal level. Today over 50 pairs of Avocets breed there, as well as a large Sandwich Tern colony, common terns, black-headed gulls, oystercatchers, redshanks and duck.

The R.S.P.B., as befits the national body for bird protection in Britain (it was founded in 1889 and incorporated under Royal Charter in 1904), has taken a leading part, not only in education but also in the formation and maintenance of bird reserves. It owns or leases over a dozen, ranging from quite small ones like the 23-acre island of Grassholm, off the Pembrokeshire coast, famous for its colony of some 8,000 breeding gannets, to the 1,500-acre reserve at Minsmere and Westleton, in Suffolk.

The object of a bird reserve is to preserve birds. For this reason access to the Society's reserves is restricted. Some cannot be visited at all except by special arrangement ; others can be visited by permit, but the number of permits issued is limited. In some cases, such as Minsmere and Havergate Island, special observation hides have been put up for visitors.

Other organizations that have done fine work in promoting reserves include the Society for

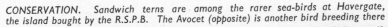

CONSERVATION. *Sandwich terns are among the rarer sea-birds at Havergate, the island bought by the R.S.P.B. The Avocet (opposite) is another bird breeding there*

W. Farnsworth

the Promotion of Nature Reserves, the Norfolk Naturalist's Trust, and many other societies.

The formation of the Nature Conservancy (*q.v.*) in 1949 has undoubtedly helped materially in the protection of birds, and will do so still more in future. This recognition by the State of the importance of Nature conservation is one of the most vital events in the history of conservation in Great Britain.

How the Individual Can Help. In the last resort it is the individual, mindful of the beauty and importance of our natural heritage, who must be the mainstay of conservation.

What can the *individual* do ? He can give his support to his national and local organizations. He can tackle his local schools and try to foster interest amongst the younger generation. He can make himself familiar with the law relating to wild birds and, if necessary, inform the police or the R.S.P.B. of any breaches of it. He can enlist the co-operation of local landowners and farmers, get his local council to put up nesting-boxes in the parks, and put them up in his own garden. In pursuing these and other activities he will find a life hobby which is not only worth while, but also great fun.

CONTINENTAL CHAFFINCH—Fringilla coelebs. Although the British Chaffinch is not known to cross the Channel, large flocks of the Continental species arrive on the east coast of Great Britain from the third week in September until the middle of November. The majority of these migrants remain, but some have been known to reach Ireland. In March and April they return to the Continent to breed.

In appearance this Chaffinch is virtually identical with the British bird, but it has more white on its wings and its breast is a deeper pink. *See also* Chaffinch.

The variations in the song of the Continental Chaffinch are on the whole similar to those of the British bird, but are much more extensive. Every Continental country seems to have its own recognizable Chaffinch song, but these birds are such skilful mimics that it is impossible to " place " a Chaffinch in its native land by its song alone. For instance, there is the story of a Belgian Chaffinch trained by its owner to " star " in a world competition of cage-birds in Vienna. There the cages were all put in the same room for two nights and a day. Alas ! the famous Belgian " star " had adopted so many inferior songs from its neighbours during that short time, that he had to be " scratched ".—EDITOR.

CONTINENTAL COAL-TIT—Parus ater. The differences between this and the British variety, *Parus ater britannicus*, are so slight that even expert ornithologists often mistake the one for the other. Both birds are therefore described under Coal-Tit.

CONTINENTAL GOLDCREST — Regulus regulus. The Continental Goldcrest is a passage migrant in the British Isles arriving in September and staying until the end of November. It differs slightly from the British Goldcrest in that the black border surrounding the red crest is broader and the bill is longer. Its song, behaviour and nesting habits are similar to those of the British variety, but it is said to choose spruce rather than pine trees for nesting. *See also* Goldcrest.

CONTINENTAL GOLDFINCH—Carduelis carduelis. This bird regularly visits the east coast of England, arriving in September and leaving in November. It breeds all over Europe, but is specially abundant in the south.

It differs slightly in appearance from the British bird, and is easily recognized by an experienced watcher by the lighter shades of colouring in its plumage and the more brilliant red of its crest.

A very talkative bird, it can be heard until the middle of August in the countries where it breeds, its characteristic call note of two syllables being easily recognizable. The song usually starts with a series of pearl-like notes interspersed with the call note, but there is always one harsh note recalling that of the

Oscar Moberg

CONTINENTAL CHAFFINCH. *Every country seems to produce a Chaffinch with a distinct song—but these birds also quickly learn each other's tunes*

Siskin. This Goldfinch is one of the pleasantest songsters coming here from the Continent. The habits, behaviour and breeding of the Continental Goldfinch are similar to those of the British species. *See also* Goldfinch.

CONTINENTAL GREAT TIT — Parus major. This very irregular visitor to Great Britain arrives in the Autumn and Winter. It breeds in many parts of Europe—Norway, Sweden, Finland, and south to the Mediterranean—being replaced by allied forms in Portugal, Spain, Africa, the Balearic Islands and other Mediterranean islands. In Asia, it breeds in Palestine, Persia, Japan and China.

Similar to the British Great Tit in size and coloration, it can be distinguished only by its more slender bill. The song is sweeter and the calls more varied than the British bird's. Its length is 5½ in., and its tarsus 0·8 in. Its wing span is 7 in., and weight 1 oz.

A wilder bird than the British Great Tit, it breeds in woodlands, but Autumn and Winter find it haunting bird tables in gardens and parks. Nest, habits and food are similar to those of its relatives. *See also* Great Tit.

CONTINENTAL JAY — Garrulus glandarius. This bird is a migrant to Britain, arriving on the east coast of England in the Autumn. In appearance, voice, nesting habits and courtship it resembles the British species, and it is difficult to distinguish except by its slightly larger measurements.

The Continental Jay finds its food in the Spring among the eggs and young of other smaller birds, but supplements these with insects, worms and garden produce. In the Autumn and Winter it exists on acorns, nuts, grain and potatoes. *See also* Jay.

CONTINENTAL REDSHANK — Tringa totanus. Passage migrant and winter visitor. Since this bird arrives with its Iceland relative, and since both are almost identical in appearance, only an expert could hope to recognize it. In fact, one bird only of this species has been authentically identified—at Tring Reservoir, Herts, in 1934. Its appearance is similar to that of the British Redshank, though in Summer its mantle is a darker brown and more distinctly barred. Its behaviour, song habits and breeding are similar to those of its relatives. *See also* Redshank.

CONTINENTAL ROBIN — Erithacus rubecula. Passage migrant and winter visitor, this Robin breeds in the western palaearctic region, and winters mainly in Africa. It is much wilder than the British Robin, and is found frequenting rural woodlands rather than gardens or parks near human habitations.

Gösta Håkansson

CONTINENTAL SONG-THRUSH. *Even experts may fail to distinguish this from the British bird*

Its alternative name " Redbreast " is rather misleading, for, despite its red throat, it is a relative of the Bluethroat (*q.v.*).

The Continental Robin is of the same size as the British ; the only difference in its appearance is the colour of its breast, which is rather more orange.

In the Winter of 1951–52, about 100,000 Continental robins invaded England for some unknown reason, causing bewilderment among bird-watchers. Some of these birds remained to breed. I watched some hundred of them in Surrey, and noted how they always kept together and did not mingle with the British species.

This Robin's song, when heard at its best on the Continent, is very like that of the British Robin, but is even sweeter in tone. It can often be heard in Britain as well for it sings all the year round, except in July and August. It has an unusual, harsh alarm note.—EDITOR.

The nest of the Continental species, unlike that of the British Robin, which is usually near human habitation, is often hidden in the undergrowth of woods and copses. The breeding season varies according to its native country—April in the south and May or June in the north. The eggs, usually six in number, are the same as our Robin's eggs, and the hatching and rearing of the young are similar. Two broods are regularly brought out in a season. The food is very varied ; insects of all kinds are eaten, and more fruit and berries are taken, probably because more are available on the Continent. *See also* Robin.

CONTINENTAL SONG-THRUSH — Turdus ericetorum philomelus. Autumn migrant and winter visitor to the British Isles, this bird is almost impossible to distinguish from the native species, with which it is virtually identical in every respect. It is, however, said to be less inclined to breed near human habitation, and often confines itself to mountainous districts, venturing down to the plains only in Winter. Its voice resembles that of our Song-Thrush, but specialised observers have established that the British species has a more varied and sweeter song. No song is heard from the Continental bird when wintering in north Africa. It will eat grapes and olives in countries where they grow abundantly.

COOT — **Fulica atra.** This is the most easily recognizable bird of our ponds and lakes, and can be identified by the vivid and conspicuous white patch on its head joining on to its white bill. Its comical bald look has given it the name of " Bald Coot ", and explains the common phrase " as bald as a coot ". Its plumage is completely black, and it can be distinguished from all ducks by its rounder body. Both cock and hen are alike.

The Coot, which is not a duck but a member of the Rail family, can be seen all the year round, usually in company with its near relative, the Moorhen (q.v.). It breeds everywhere in the British Isles, except in the Shetland Isles, and even there it sometimes appears after a storm. Abroad, it can be found in most countries, even in the heat of India. In the Autumn, coots collect in their thousands on the shores ; in the Camargue, at the mouth of the Rhône, in France, they are so numerous as to appear to move in a solid mass. The Coot is 15 in. long, its wing span about $1\frac{1}{2}$ ft. and its tarsus $1\frac{3}{4}$ in. Its weight is $1\frac{1}{2}$ lb.

Anyone who has watched coots and moorhens on a pond will have noticed that the Coot is the more quarrelsome of them ; it always seems to be having a set-to with its neighbours. In spite of this (or perhaps because of it), it hates to be alone, and will always be found in company with other water birds, especially in the Winter.

The Coot is an excellent swimmer and diver and it is amusing to watch it constantly disappearing from view, tail uppermost, for some seconds, reappearing with food which it has found among the weeds at the bottom. It will sometimes come ashore, but it is not so much at home on the ground as the Moorhen.

The Coot has a peculiar way of rising from the water : it flutters along the surface before taking off, as if it had difficulty in doing so.

Once airborne, however, it flies in much the same way as the Moorhen, with neck extended and feet stretched out behind.

The chief call note of the Coot, which can be heard by night and by day, varies in pitch. The high-pitched notes are rather musical. The conversational note, with which the Coot communicates, is high and shriller than that of the Moorhen. There is also a harsher call when it is alarmed or danger is near.

The Coots' courtship and mating begin early in Spring—about March or, sometimes, even earlier. The male birds rush through the water with a great display of their wings, and fight fiercely among themselves for their mates.

A Coot's nest is a feat of construction. Placed among the reeds on the margins of lakes and large ponds, well above water level, it is made of reeds, sedge, flags and dead leaves. Should the water rise, fresh material is brought by the bird to build it higher, sometimes to a height of a foot.

COOT. *Apart from his conspicuous white frontal shield, the Coot has disproportionally large feet to enable him to walk over marshy ground without sinking into the mud*

Eric Hosking

Eric Hosking

CORMORANTS, *nesting colony of these fish-eaters, the presence of which is often announced by its stench*

For text see page 153

Both parents play their part in building the nest, the cock fetching the material. Even " sleeping berths " and platforms for the chicks are provided ! The eggs, numbering six to nine, are stone-coloured, with spots and speckles of dark brown. They are laid at 24-hour intervals, apparently only in the morning, and both cock and hen take turns in sitting on them for about three weeks.

The chicks are almost entirely black. They leave the nest in a day or two, and are able to swim from the start, but they return to the nest at night. In about a month, however, they begin to dive and look for their own food, and they are soon quite independent. Two broods, and sometimes three, are reared. It is amusing and interesting to watch the chicks of the first family bringing food for the second brood. Young coots, before assuming the final adult plumage, are dark above and pale underneath and have no frontal shield.

Coots find their food among the weeds and insects at the bottom of ponds. Whatever they fancy is brought to the surface, and there sorted out and eaten.

CORACIA. Genus of the family *Corvidae* of the order *Passeriformes*. Its members are distributed over western and southern Europe, northern Asia and north-west Africa ; and include the Chough (*q.v.*) and Alpine Chough (*q.v.*).

CORACIAS. Genus of the family *Coraciidae* of the order *Coraciiformes*. It contains 15 species, which are distributed over Europe (one species only), Asia south to Celebes, north-west Africa and south Africa outside the breeding-season. The European species is on the British list ; it is the Roller (*q.v.*), which occurs as an irregular visitor during the summer months.

CORACIIDAE. Family of the order *Coraciiformes*. Its members are distributed over a wide area of the Old World. The only genus on the British list is *Coracias*, which contains but one species (the Roller):

CORACIIFORMES. Very large order of bright-plumaged birds divided into nine families and including the bee-eaters, rollers, hoopoes, kingfishers, and the purely neotropical todies and motmots. Four of the families are on the British list. These are the *Alcedinidae* (kingfishers), the *Coraciidae* (rollers), the *Meropidae* (bee-eaters) and the *Upupidae* (hoopoes).

The most obvious structural feature common to the members of this order is the tendency for the three forward-directed toes to be connected together ; this is particularly true of the kingfishers and bee-eaters, in which the second and third toes are united for most of their length. There is generally a fourth (hind) toe. The

Jan P. Strijbos

CORMORANT. *The young are waiting for Mother to regurgitate the fish she has caught to feed them*

flexor tendons of the toes are arranged like those of the swifts and nightjars, except in the hoopoes, where they take the normal " passerine " form. The young of hoopoes are hatched with a covering of down, but the young of other members of the order are hatched blind and naked.

CORBIE. Scottish name for crows, including the Hooded Crow and Carrion-Crow, and the Raven. (*See also* separate entries under these names.) It occurs in old poems and ballads, where its meaning is clear from the context. The name seems to be a corrupted form of the Latin *corvus*, meaning " crow " or " raven ".

CORMORANT—Phalacrocorax carbo. Member of the Pelican order of sea birds, the Cormorant is related to the shags, darters and frigate birds. Although essentially a marine bird, it also breeds in fresh waters, where its numbers have to be kept in check because of its depredations among game fish. The Cormorant has a huge appetite and daily devours its own weight in fish.

A resident British bird, it breeds on all our coasts; no one who has spent much time at the seaside can have failed to notice this curious-looking but rather handsome bird standing upright, with its long neck bent double, like a figure in a heraldic design. In the distance it appears entirely black—hence it is often called " Black Cormorant "—but at close quarters the white throat and cheeks are quite distinct, and in the breeding season there are also conspicuous

James Gibson

CORMORANT. With its wing span of over 4 ft., the Cormorant is, indeed, a magnificent sight. This bird prepares to leave his nest, which is merely an untidy, flat structure

white patches on its thighs, very noticeable in flight. It has a slightly curved, horn-coloured beak covered with bright yellow skin at the base. The Cormorant is often confused with its close relative, the Shag, but the latter is smaller and has no white on throat or cheeks. Young cormorants are a brownish colour above, with pure white underparts. The Cormorant is 36 in. in length, and has a body of 22 in. Its tarsus is about 2 in. Its wing span is over 4 ft., and its weight is 5–7 lb.

An expert diver and fisher, the Cormorant can remain under water for as long as a minute or more. Propelling itself by its feet, it easily out-swims its prey which it brings to the surface in its hooked beak and devours whole. When fully fed, it likes to stand semi-erect on the rocks, with its neck drawn back, yawning from time to time, as if bored or dozing. The bird has an awkward gait on the ground and takes off clumsily from the water, but it is surprisingly agile in the air and soars to a great height when crossing land. Its flight over water is straight and direct, with regular wing beats and neck outstretched.

The Cormorant is a silent bird, and it is only in the Spring that its voice, consisting of some harsh guttural notes, is heard and, even then, never far from its nest. I have witnessed an attack by a huge flock of herring-gulls on a Cormorant's nest and, although the defence was clever, accompanied by loud calls, two chicks were taken by the gulls. The young cormorants have two different calls. One, a rather musical and sentimental note, can be heard if a chick is taken away for a few minutes.—EDITOR.

In courtship, the male selects his mate by offering her sticks for the nest, but after that, it is said, the female makes most of the advances. The nest, placed on a steep ledge facing the sea, is a very large, flat construction, made of sticks and any other materials available. It soon becomes filthy with decayed vegetation, and gives off a horrible stench. Both birds assist in building the nest, and in hatching the three or four elongated whitish eggs, laid in the latter part of April or early May, according to the district. Hatching takes about 28 days. The young are fed with half-digested food, plunging their heads as far as possible into their parents' mouths in order to reach it. One brood is reared in a season.

The food of the Cormorant consists almost entirely of fish. In the Far East these birds have been bred and trained in captivity for centuries to catch fish ; a cord is tied round the bird's neck to prevent it from swallowing the fish caught for its master.

Like other birds of the seashore, cormorants suffered severely from the oil discharged from vessels at sea which clogs their feathers and thus kills them. For details of this tragic loss of sea birds, and of the steps taken to reduce it, *see also* Oil Pollution.

The Scottish name for the Cormorant is Scart or Scarf. It is also called the Sea-Raven, Black Pelican, Black-throated Goose, and Great Cormorant. The Southern Cormorant (*q.v.*), which is closely related and practically identical to the common Cormorant, occurs as a rare migrant in Britain.

CORN-BILL. Colloquial name for Corn-Bunting (described in the opposite page).

CORN-BUNTING—Emberiza calandra.

CORN-BUNTING—**Emberiza calandra.** This resident British bird, found all over the British Isles, is more local than the Yellow Hammer (or Yellow Bunting), but is quite common in those areas which it favours. As its name implies, it is to be found mostly in open arable land, but it also likes coastal areas ; in common with the rest of the buntings, it is rarely seen near human habitation.

Perhaps the dullest and least interesting of its family, the Corn-Bunting has nothing distinctive about its appearance. A large bird compared with other buntings, it has the stout bill of the finches with a palatal knob. The general hue of its plumage is sandy-brown, the upper parts streaked with a dusky brown and the under parts buffish white, streaked with brown on throat, breast and flanks. It is yellower in Autumn and Winter. Unlike the Yellow Hammer (*q.v.*) it has no white on wings or tails. The sexes are similar. The juveniles lack the dark " bib ". Its length is 7 in. and its tarsus 1 in. ; its wing span is about 7 in., and its weight 2 oz.

The Corn-Bunting hops on the ground, and its flight is very similar to the Sparrow's. At close range, however, it can be seen that its yellowish legs are dangling behind, and it is the only small bird which flies in this way. The courtship and spring flight are normal for its kind. The male bird's rapid chase after his mate ends with both birds fluttering from branch to branch of a tree.

The Corn-Bunting's penetrating song carries for about a quarter of a mile. It is a monotonous, wheezing and jangling sound, likened by W. H. Hudson to " several sounds emitted simultaneously, as of a note broken up into splinters, or issuing from a bundle of minute windpipes instead out of one of a larger size ". It is usually delivered on the road from a telegraph wire, dead tree or bush, a habit which has earned the bird the title of " Songster of the Road ". The song continues practically throughout the year, but is at its fullest from February to August.

The Corn-Bunting's nest is so well concealed that it is difficult to discover, even though the male bird is often wheezing away in a near-by tree. One of the favourite nesting-sites is among long grass, brambles, dense weeds or thistles, but the nest may be placed in bushes, some height from the ground. The rather untidy nest built by the hen alone, is of grass, straw and moss, and lined with hair. The four to six eggs are a dirty white, with purplish and reddish marks of varying design. The Corn-Bunting is a late breeder ; the eggs are usually laid by late May, but sometimes not until well into June, and there are records of clutches even in August and September. The hatching is done by the hen but she leaves the nest to feed with her mate ; brooding lasts about 13 days. The young are reared by the hen ; she sometimes has the assistance of the cock, but since he may have as many as seven mates at one time, he can devote only a little attention to each. Two broods are mostly reared in a season, but three have been observed.

The food of the Corn-Bunting consists mainly of vegetable matter—wild fruit, the seeds of various weeds and some corn—but insects are also devoured.

Many of the breeding birds leave in the Autumn for the Continent. Those which remain flock together and move about with other buntings and finches, roosting on the ground among stubble and furrows.

CORNCRAKE—Crex crex.

CORNCRAKE—**Crex crex.** Perhaps no bird has suffered so severely from the changing methods of agriculture as the Corncrake or Land-Rail. Time was when its familiar and far from musical voice was almost irritatingly common during Spring and Summer in practically every part of the British Isles ; today it is never heard in many of its former haunts. The disappearance of the Corncrake was investigated for the British Trust for Ornithology (*q.v.*) by some 2,000 observers. Their report showed beyond question that the modern mowing machine was in great part responsible for he destruction of many corncrakes and their young. Earlier grass cutting was also mentioned as a contributory cause of the decline.

The Corncrake is a summer resident, breeding regularly in northern England and Wales and throughout Scotland and Ireland. In 1952,

Eric Hosking

CORN-BUNTING. A late breeder, the female takes her duties seriously—but not so the male bird

155

it bred on the outskirts of Gloucester. It is also a passage migrant in the Spring. Some corncrakes winter occasionally in England and Ireland. Abroad, they breed in central and northern Europe, and winter in Africa.

This is one of the most secretive of birds, and, although its rasping voice indicates its whereabouts, it is rarely seen in the open. Most of its time is spent hidden in the grass of the fields where it nests. In some parts, notably in Ireland, a single Corncrake may be seen on the road or perching on a wall, and then the beauty of the bird can be appreciated. In form it is rather like a Partridge, but smaller. Its brown dress is speckled in darker shades, and there is bright chestnut on its wings and grey on its throat and above its eyes ; underneath it is a paler speckled brown.

Male and female are alike, and the young are pretty little black birds, very similar to the young of the Moorhen. The length of the Corncrake is about 10 in., and its tarsus about 1 in. Its weight is $5\frac{1}{2}$ oz., and its wing span about 1 ft.

The Corncrake both walks and runs on the ground. Although a member of the Rail family, it is not a water bird, but it likes to swim and bathe itself. Its flight is weak, except when travelling on migration ; its legs dangle behind it in flight.

The Corncrake's Latin name *Crex crex* is an almost exact imitation of its call ; running one's nail over the teeth of a comb is a way of reproducing the sound. It is generally held that the call goes on without ceasing both day and night, from May sometimes well into July. But the Editor recalls watching corncrakes in June for 18 hours on end, and they called together only for one hour during the night. On the same occasion he saw a Corncrake fly straight into the face of a farmer without doing any harm either to the man or to itself.

In the breeding season, the Corncrake frequents grasslands, cornfields and low-lying meadows. Its nest, composed of grass, weeds and nettles, and lined with softer vegetation, is said to be built by the hen alone. A large number of eggs is laid in May ; from 6 to 14 is usual, but even 18 and 19 have been recorded. The colour varies from greenish-grey to buff, with spots and blotches of red-brown and grey. Hatching takes about a fortnight, and the young are able to fend for themselves in approximately a month.

One of our most useful birds, the Corncrake lives chiefly on insects injurious to the farmer.

CORNISH CHOUGH. Local name for Chough (*q.v.*), a very local bird, one of whose favourite breeding-areas is south-west England. The Chough is also variously called Red-legged Daw and Sea-Crow.

CORSICAN WOODCHAT-SHRIKE—Lanius senator badius. Only one authentic visit to the British Isles has been made by this bird, which breeds in Corsica and winters on the Gold Coast. Its behaviour and habits are similar to those of the species breeding in France, Holland, Belgium and Germany, and the only difference in its appearance is the absence of the conspicuous white wing bar. *See also* Woodchat-Shrike.

CORVIDAE (Latin, " raven-like birds "). Family of the order *Passeriformes*. It includes five genera on the British list : *Coracia, Corvus, Garrulus, Nucifraga* and *Pica*. Members of this family occur in practically all parts of the globe. The largest birds of the *Passeriformes*, they are omnivorous, and are among the most intelligent of birds. For a description of their characteristic features *see* Corvus (below) ; also the other four genera listed.

CORVUS (Latin, " raven " or " crow "). Genus of the family *Corvidae* of the order *Passeriformes*. It contains the ravens, crows, rooks and jackdaws. Its members are distributed over a wide area of the globe, but do not occur in New Zealand, Madagascar, South America or the Lesser Antilles. There are five species on the British list : the Raven, the Carrion-Crow and Hooded Crow, Rook and Jackdaw (*see* under these names).

These large perching birds have longish and powerful bills, and nostrils covered by bristles

John Markham

CORNCRAKE. The plump, chicken-like body and large feet, typical of all crakes, are easily seen here

which are directed forwards. The wings have ten primary feathers, the first of which is only about half as long as the second ; the third and fourth are the longest. The primary feathers are considerably longer than the longest secondaries. The tail is shorter than the wing, and is slightly graduated or rounded. All the British members of this genus have black, or black and grey, plumage, but the black often has a violet, purple or bluish gloss.

CORY'S SHEARWATER. The North Atlantic Shearwater (*q.v.*) was formerly always called thus, after the man who spent much time studying its habits. Its full scientific name is *Procellaria diomedea borealis* (Cory).

COTURNIX (Latin, " quail "). Genus of the family *Phasianidae* of the order *Galliformes*. It contains five species in Europe, Asia, Africa and Australia. There is one species on the British list, the Quail (*q.v.*).

COUES'S REDPOLL—Carduelis hornemanni exilipes. Very rare vagrant to the British Isles. This bird breeds in Lapland, Russia and the northern parts of Asia and America. Named Hoary Redpoll in the American ornithological check list, it differs little in appearance from Hornemann's Redpoll (*q.v.*), but is said to be smaller, with the white parts greyer in colour. Both these redpolls are varieties of the Arctic Redpoll species.

The behaviour and habits of Coues's Redpoll are the same as those of other redpolls, but its voice is described as sharper. A social bird, it breeds in birch woods and scrub lands, and lays four to six greenish-blue eggs. In Lapland its breeding season is in June, and one brood is reared in a season.

COULTERNEB. Local name for the Puffin (*q.v.*), given to the bird because of its unique, massive beak. The word comes from *coulter*, meaning " cutting edge of plough, ploughshare " ; and *neb*, meaning " nose, beak ".

COUNCIL, FIELD STUDIES, for the Promotion of. A non-profit-making organisation, receiving grants-in-aid from the Ministry of Education, the universities and other educational and cultural bodies. It was founded in 1943 by Mr. F. H. C. Butler, M.A., M.Sc., with the object of providing educational facilities for the study of various branches of natural science *in the field*.

At the time of writing (1954) it maintains and administers four Field Centres :

> **Dale Fort Field Centre, Haverfordwest, Pem.** (*with Skokholm Bird Observatory*) ;
> **Flatford Mill Field Centre, East Bergholt, near Colchester, Essex** ;
> **Juniper Hall Field Centre, near Dorking, Surrey** ;
> **Malham Tarn Field Centre, near Settle, Yorks.**

At each Centre, which is in charge of a

W. Farnsworth

COULTERNEB. " With a nose like a plough " is the real translation of this local name for the Puffin

warden, there is accommodation for up to 50 visiting students, and laboratories, workrooms and basic equipment for field work.

Set one-week courses, under resident tutors, are run at each of the Centres from early March to late October. Each Centre has a different programme covering a wide range of subjects —including many of special interest to bird-lovers and ornithologists. Thus, the 1954 programme for Skokholm includes work on :

> *Migration:* trapping, ringing, observation.
> *Cliff and Maritime Heathland Bird Population:* finding nests, nest records, breeding behaviour.
> *Birds Feeding at Sea:* Kittiwakes, shearwaters and similar sea-birds.

Some courses are specially reserved for school and university students; others are open to all who are interested.

In general, wardens will consider additional courses to suit students' special requirements, and individuals or parties can also attend with their own tutors. Moreover, those wishing to work independently, or less formally than suggested by the word " course ", are welcome at any time, whether or not any special subject of study is listed for that particular week.

The Council has at present a membership of 2,000 and all who wish to make use of the Centres, for which a moderate fee is charged, are encouraged to become members (minimum subscription 5s.). Programmes may be obtained from the wardens of the respective Centres.

The registered office of the Council is Balfour House, 119–125, Finsbury Pavement, London, E.C.2, from which further information about the Council's activities can be obtained.

COURTSHIP. There is a certain similarity between the courtship of birds and of human beings, but, generally speaking, the type of behaviour and sequence of events is very different. The term courtship has been applied to three different phases of bird behaviour :

(1) the " advertisement display " of a cock bird for a hen, leading to pair formation;
(2) the phase immediately before coition, when there may, or may not, be any very evident display;
(3) the so-called " bond-forming display ", occurring after mating to cement the bond between a pair.

It must, however, be remembered that there are individuals in every species whose behaviour differs from that generally regarded as typical of their kind.

Pair Formation. Some species form pairs *long* before nesting and courtship proper; with others, only a few days elapse between pairing and mating. Among the former are the Blackbird, which apparently pairs in late Autumn; the Starling, which pairs in late Autumn or early Spring; the Robin, which pairs from December to mid-February; and the Chaffinch, Yellow Hammer, Reed-Bunting and most resident song birds, which pair in February and March.

Migrant song birds, who arrive at their breeding grounds shortly before the females, do not form pairs until April or May, a few days before nesting starts. It is more difficult to obtain exact information about gregarious and colonial birds on the time pairing occurs.

Lack has made a careful study of the courtship behaviour of the Robin, which may be considered a typical territorial bird. Here, as in most birds studied so far, it is the female who selects her mate. At first the cock bird sings lustily in his territory (*q.v.*), probably partly to ward off intruders and partly to advertise his presence and the fact that he is seeking a mate. When a female arrives, she may not like his look and may fly away again. If she decides to stay, a fight ensues (usually aggressive posturing), that may last a few days.

At first the cock does not recognize the female and displays to her as he would to an intruding male. But after she has repeatedly refused to be driven away, he accepts her, and (except for a few inconstant individuals) will recognize her as his chosen mate—at least until the brood has been brought out. Not only the cock sings during this phase, but sometimes the hen also.

After a period of excited singing, and sometimes posturing, the cock begins to follow the hen closely, and the pair is formed. Then comes a quieter period of about three days when the hen takes short flights about the territory, followed by the cock singing very quietly; then a long engagement period, sometimes lasting several months, during which the two birds ignore each other—the hen being retiring and the cock singing moderately loudly.

Similar behaviour has been noted in the Heron and other " territorial " birds, in whom the " advertisement display " leading to pair formation cannot be regarded as true courtship, despite the views of some experts. It must be noted, too, that the cock bird sings, during this phase at least, because he fails to recognize his future mate as a female—not to serenade her nor to impress a possible rival.

The males of some species, however, posture aggressively to one another and even stage mock or real tournaments to attract females. Blackcocks, for instance, arrive before the greyhens at their " leks " or tourney grounds (*see* Black Grouse), where combatants indulge in mock skirmishes or even bloody fighting until a hen alights, when the cock bird nearest to her will fight any male disputing his possession. On arrival, each hen causes intense excitement until claimed by a cock. This is repeated until the " harem " is filled—one cock having at a time as many as six or seven hens.

Mating Display. This is the sexually stimulating display leading to coition, and occurs usually about the time the nest is being constructed. For various postures of different species *see* Display. Some species show little excitement at this time, and display is relatively unimportant. Thus the female Robin remains still, lowers her head, somewhat humping her body, and the cock mounts. If the cock fails to respond, the hen may adopt a more exaggerated humped attitude and sway her body—but there is still no elaborate display.

Display performs a more important part with some species, being sufficient to cause a hen to lay an infertile egg. Thus a female dove will

Alfred Saunders

COURTSHIP. Albatrosses form pairs only just before mating. Here the female awaits the male

lay an egg if she can display to herself in a mirror, the displaying image providing her with sufficient stimulus.

In many song birds the courtship period is characterised by violent chasing of the female by the male, followed by elaborate displays by both sexes on the ground. Rooks also indulge in chases and general " play ", and pairs of hooded crows perform aerial displays, taking " corkscrew " and " figure-of-eight " flights to great heights.

Bond-Forming Displays. In some species, courtship ceases immediately the eggs have been laid, in others it continues long after the need for coition has ceased. This post-nuptial courtship was first observed by Julian Huxley with the Great Crested Grebe, where it takes the same form as pre-mating courtship, the cock even mounting the hen, although, of course, no eggs follow.

In other species it takes the form of courtship feeding, i.e. the cock feeding the hen (*see* Display). Courtship feeding does not lead up to any other form of courtship; the birds apparently derive much excitement from it, sometimes more than from pre-nuptial display.

Among species indulging in courtship feeding are robins, ravens, jackdaws, many of the finches, doves and pigeons, tree-creepers, the Ibis, nuthatches, gulls and terns, budgerigars and parrots and many birds of prey. It is absent in most game birds and ducks. Usually the male feeds the female, but with the Button Quail it is the reverse, as with most of its sexual behaviour. In doves, courtship feeding is reduced to billing; no food actually passes, and thus the display action has become a formalised ceremony, like so much of the display behaviour of birds. *See also* Behaviour.

CRAKE. These are compact little birds, shaped somewhat like chickens, with large feet—similar in build to, though not so large in proportion to their size as those of the closely related Coot and Moorhen (*qq.v.*). The body is plump and the wings short and rounded. The tail, also, is short, and so is the bill. The upperparts are generally streaked or spotted, and the flanks and/or under tail-coverts barred.

Crakes are shy and secretive, and are more often heard than seen. Their voices are harsh and they indulge in repetitive calls. They walk and run on the ground, swim and dive on water, but are slow to take to the air and fly with their legs dangling.

Apart from the Corncrake who prefers meadows and fields (hence its name), crakes like marshy ground, full of dense vegetation.

None of the crakes are seen often in the British Isles, though the Corncrake—by far the largest of them—is a breeding visitor and passage

Paul Popper
CRANE. This African lady, known as the Demoiselle Crane, wears her skull cap with feathers drooping

migrant, and the Spotted Crake a rare breeding visitor. Baillon's Crake and the Little Crake are irregular visitors, and the Carolina Crake, called Sora Rail (*q.v.*) in north America, where it is found breeding, has been recorded here only five times. All the crakes are described under their own names.

CRANE—Megalornis grus. No one seems to know when this large and noble-looking game bird ceased to grace the British countryside. It is known to have bred in Great Britain up to the 16th century, and both the bird and its eggs were protected even in those days by an Act of Parliament. The Orkneys and Shetlands seem to have been its last stronghold, for there are various records of its appearance there in small numbers between 1831 and 1848. Gradually it became only a winter visitor, and today it is no longer seen in the wild state in the British Isles. The Crane thrives in captivity and will live for many years (one bred in the London Zoo was there for some 40 years).

Its disappearance was due in part to " sportsmen ", but, as with most of our lost birds of the marshlands and swamps, the reclamation of such areas for agriculture was undoubtedly the greatest contributory factor. The Crane, a shy and wary bird, breeds in many northern parts of the Old World—Scandinavia, Germany, Finland, Poland and Russia. In Japan this graceful bird is held in high esteem, and it is often depicted on Japanese cloth, pictures and screens.

The long neck and legs of the Crane often caused it to be mistaken for the Heron. Its predominant colour is lead-grey, and its most striking feature is its graceful tail, with its loosely hanging plumes of dark feathers. Its long neck is dark grey in front with a lighter streak down

W. S. Berridge

CRANE. *The most striking feature of this bird is its graceful tail of loosely hanging feathers*

the sides, and the top of its head is crowned with a red patch. The female is much duller in colour, and has no red patch.

The Crane is one of the largest birds. Its length is 3 ft. 8 in., with a body of 2 ft., its tarsus is 9 in., and its wing span 6 ft. 7 in. As for its weight, it is on record that one man alone was unable to carry a Crane which had been killed.

On the ground the Crane walks, and when preparing for flight it takes a running start; on the wing it has a slow and powerful flight with both legs and neck stretched out. A flock travels in V-formation. The voice, heard as often in the air as on the ground, is a loud guttural and harsh trumpeting, uttered both day and night. The spring " dance " of the Crane is one of the most interesting bird " ceremonies ". The breeding season varies from April to June according to the country. Marshes or swamps near or adjoining woods are generally frequented. The nest is built on the ground with all kinds of vegetable matter, twigs making a solid foundation. The usual number of eggs is two, and one brood is reared in a season, with both parents taking their share. The young birds are able to fly in about ten weeks.

CRAVAT GOOSE. Alternative name for the Canada Goose (*q.v.*) which was very possibly given to the bird because of its white throat patch extending up the cheeks behind the eyes.

CREAM-COLOURED COURSER—Cursorius cursor. It seems extraordinary that this bird, essentially an inhabitant of the desert regions, should ever wander to Britain; but it has been recorded many times in England, Wales and Scotland, mostly in the Autumn. It belongs to the Pratincole family, a special type of wader, and normally inhabits the deserts of north Africa and Asia.

It is easy to identify: a small bird about the size of a Starling, with movements similar to those of a Plover, it is an excellent runner. Its general colour is a light buff, with contrasting black in its tail, noticeable in flight. It has a black and white band behind its eye and round its head, and a curved beak. Its long legs are very light in colour. Its length is 8 in., and its tarsus 2 in. Its wing span is about 14 in.

The Courser has a rapid run and a strong, swift flight. Its call, which is rarely heard, is a short, harsh bark. Breeding in or near the desert, from April to July in north Africa, it builds no nest, but lays its eggs—usually two which are spotted and streaked with brown—on the bare ground. Both parents tend the young, and probably two broods are reared in a season.

Its food consists chiefly of insects, but it also takes lizards and snails.

CREEPER. These are lively little birds, continually on the move; with long, slender, downward-curved bills resembling in general shape those of the Curlew family. The Wall-Creeper and the Tree-Creeper, the only creepers on the British list, are fully described under their own names.

Apart from their characteristic bills, these birds are distinguished by their movement. The Tree-Creeper, which is a little smaller than a Sparrow, uses his stiff tail to brace himself against the bark as he climbs in jerky spirals up a tree. The Wall-Creeper, a larger bird, whose tail is stumpier and resembles that of the Nuthatch (*q.v.*), flicks his very broad wings almost continually, while his flight is spasmodic and butterfly-like.

The word " creeper " is also sometimes applied to nuthatches, woodpeckers, wrynecks and other birds that " creep " up tree-trunks.

CREST. Cluster of feathers on the crown of a bird's head. It may be of the same colour as the rest of its plumage, as in the young Purple Heron, the Spoonbill, and many ducks—e.g. Tufted, female Mandarin, Pochard, Merganser and Goosander—and the Woodpecker, Sandwich Tern, Hoopoe, Lapwing, Waxwing, Skylark, Rosy Starling, Woodlark and Crested Tit. In other cases, the crest may be distinguished by special colouring, as in the Heron, adult Purple Heron and Night-Heron;

the Crested Grebe, Smew, male Mandarin Duck, Goldcrest and Firecrest. *See also* separate entries for these birds.

CRESTED LARK—Galerida cristata. This member of the Lark family is a rare wanderer to the southern shores of Great Britain from its home in northern and central Europe, where it is quite common. Identification is made easy by its conspicuous crest (it is the only lark to have this bunch of head feathers), and it is heavier in build than the Skylark (*q.v.*), with a longer and heavier bill and a shorter tail, which shows no white. Its length is about 7 in., and its wing span 9 in.

The Crested Lark is agile on the ground and is commonly seen perching on walls, bushes by the roadside, and on buildings. Its flight somewhat resembles that of the Wood-Lark (*q.v.*). Its sweet and melodious song has a lark-like quality, but in contrast to the Skylark it ascends only a short distance, starting its shorter song at a height of about 60 ft. It does not remain very long in the air, and soon returns to its ground perch, where it continues its lovely song for hours on end.

The Crested Lark breeds everywhere—on plains, in mountainous districts, in thickly populated country, and even in great cities. It has been known to rest inside a factory where it shows a special liking for garbage bins. Its nest, usually placed on the ground, is built by both male and female of grasses and plants, lined with hair. In April, three to five yellowish-brown eggs are laid. The hen does most of the hatching, but both parents tend and rear the chicks. Two broods, and sometimes even three, are reared in a season. The food is chiefly grain and the seeds of various wild plants, but insects are also eaten sometimes.

Eric Hosking

CRESTED TIT. *This is the only small bird, found breeding in Britain, to have an erect, pointed crest*

CRESTED TIT—Parus cristatus scoticus. Scotland may well be proud of this lovely little Tit, for the pine forests of the Spey valley in the Highlands are the only place in the British Isles where it resides. But for rigorous protection by legislation and careful and devoted watching, the Crested Tit might well have joined the gallery of vanished British wild birds ; instead, it now appears to have even increased its range of breeding and is no longer in danger of extinction.

Its erect and pointed crest makes this bird easily identifiable and prevents confusion with any other small bird. Its cheeks are white, bordered with a black collar, and there is a black line running from behind its eye and curving round behind its ear coverts. The colour of its mantle, its tail and its wings, which have no bar, is brown ; its underparts are light buff. The length of the Crested Tit is $4\frac{1}{2}$ in., and its tarsus $\frac{3}{4}$ in. It weighs about $\frac{1}{8}$ oz., and its wing span is approximately $7\frac{1}{2}$ in. In movement, flight and breeding behaviour it closely resembles other tits, especially the Coal-Tit (*q.v.*), in whose company it is usually found. But it feeds like a creeper, on the trunks of conifer trees. Its song is quite individual and unlike

P. O. Swanberg

CRESTED LARK. *Compared with the little Tit (above), this is quite a large bird. It occasionally wanders to this country from its haunts in Europe*

John Markham

CROSSBILL. *Even the bills of the young show signs of the " crossed over " effect peculiar to the adult*

any other among the tits ; it is described as a persistent loud, short trill, mingled with the high-pitched notes characteristic of other tits.

The breeding season of the Crested Tit is late April or early May. It builds its nest in a hole or crevice of a decayed pine tree or stump, but sometimes uses other places, even the old nest of another bird. The gathering of the material—dead moss with a lining of hair from deer or hare—as well as the building is almost all done by the little hen, and she also hatches the five or six small, white, red-spotted eggs. This takes a fortnight during which the male brings her food. The chicks are fed and reared by both parents. One brood is brought out in a season.

The Crested Tit feeds on insects and their larvae, and the seeds of pine cones.

CREX. Genus of the family *Rallidae* of the order *Ralliformes*. It contains only one species, the Corncrake (*q.v.*), which is distributed over Europe and the western part of northern Asia ; outside the breeding-season it occurs in Africa. Individuals also wander from time to time to America, Greenland and Australasia.

CROCETHIA. Genus of wading birds of the family *Scolopacidae* of the order *Charadriiformes*. It contains only one species, the Sanderling (*q.v.*), which is distributed mainly over Arctic America and Greenland, northern Siberia and Spitzbergen ; and outside the breeding-season over parts of Africa, Australia, south America, and some islands of the Indian and Pacific Oceans.

CROSSBILL—Loxia curvirostra. This bird provides an excellent example of the part played by afforestation in increasing the number of breeding birds in a country. It was not until the beginning of the 18th century that pine and other coniferous trees were planted to any appreciable extent in Great Britain, and it was then that crossbills were first noted by the famous naturalist Gilbert White of Selborne. It seems certain that they were attracted by the cones, the seeds of which form their favourite food. From then on the Crossbill has bred regularly in at least six or seven counties, although it is still principally a winter visitor.

The Crossbill is a member of the Finch family. At irregular intervals large invasions of these birds from northern Europe take place, and it is, of course, from these that our breeding stock has come ; the years 1927 and 1953 saw the largest recent influxes. It has been suggested that such arrivals are due to the failure of the cone crop in the birds' natural homes, but no proof of this has been brought forward yet.

A country walk in August or September, especially in the neighbourhood of pine or larch trees, may well produce the sight of a party of these remarkable and attractive little birds. Recognition offers no difficulty, for the Crossbill has a very distinctive stout Finch beak, crossed at the end like a pair of scissors, as its name suggests. This beak—and its long red tongue—are adapted for prising open fir cones and extracting the seeds.

The Crossbill is about the same size as a Starling, and there is something rather parrot-like in its appearance as it moves among the trees. Its head and body are completely red, only its wings and tail showing dark brown. The much duller hen is dressed in soft green instead of red. The Crossbill varies somewhat in its size, but its average length is about 6 in., and its tarsus 0·65 in. Its wing span is approximately 10 in. It hops along on the ground, and has a bounding flight. It is possible to get a good view of crossbills especially when they are feeding, for they are very tame.

> I include the Crossbill among the birds which have a poor quality of song—more, indeed, what I call a " sub-song." The note of the Crossbill reminds one of the " zip, zip " of the Greenfinch in its monotonous and murmuring recurrence. It is usually delivered from the top of a pine or larch tree, and is heard at irregular intervals well into the Autumn. The Crossbill often calls when flying.—EDITOR.

The Crossbill's cup-shaped nest, built in a pine or larch at varying heights, has a strong foundation of twigs and consists of grass, moss and wool ; the hen builds it alone, but her mate brings the material. This bird is an early and erratic nester, and the eggs, four in number and very like those of the Greenfinch, are laid as early as January, and sometimes as late as July. Hatching, performed by the hen alone, takes about 13 days. The young are fed by both parents, and it is usually longer than three weeks before they can fly. One brood is normally reared in a season, but a late brood might be from a second laying.

Apart from the seeds of pine and larch cones, the Crossbill also devours insects.

The Crossbill may have been the bird of which there is a curious record from a survey of Cornwall in 1602, which states that a flock with their " bills thwarted crosswise at the end " cut apples in two with one snap and ate only the seeds.

In America the Crossbill is called Red Crossbill. For other crossbills visiting this country, *see also* American White-winged Crossbill, Parrot-Crossbill and Two-Barred Crossbill. The Scottish Crossbill (*q.v.*), which is closely related to the common Crossbill, breeds regularly in Scotland but nowhere else.

CROSS-BREEDING. There are two distinct meanings to this term :

(1) the accidental crossing or " marriage " between closely allied species in the wild, e.g. the Carrion-Crow and Hooded Crow, which breed freely together where their geographical ranges overlap ;

(2) the deliberate crossing by bird-fanciers or breeders of *either* different species (e.g. canary and finch) *or* of selected individuals of the same species to perpetuate certain characteristics (e.g. canaries specially bred for singing—the Rollers ; specially bred for their plumage—Lizard canaries).

The term interbreed is often used synonymously with cross-breed, although then, strictly speaking, it really applies to (1) above. *See also* Aviculture ; Hybrid.

CROW. Only two crows proper—the Carrion-Crow and the Hooded Crow (*qq.v.*)—are found in the British Isles. The Carrion-Crow breeds throughout England and in some parts of Ireland and Scotland, though not in the north ; whereas the Hooded Crow is the breeding crow of Scotland, the Isle of Man and Ireland. The Hooded Crow is also a non-breeding visitor to England and is occasionally found in Wales.

Both these crows interbreed freely where their ranges overlap ; they are so closely allied that it is not surprising that some ornithologists regard them as different phases of the same species. Apart from these two true crows, the name " crow " is often applied colloquially to the *Corvidae* (*q.v.*) family which also includes the Raven, Rook, Jackdaw, Magpie, Nutcracker, Jay and Chough. All these are described fully under their own names.

All members of the Crow family have longish, powerful bills and their nostrils are covered with forward-pointing bristles.

The *Corvidae*, or Crow family, are the largest and most intelligent of perching birds (*Passeriformes*). It may be because of this intelligence, or because of their sober colouring or unattractive voices, that they have often been regarded with superstitious awe as harbingers of death and misfortune.

CROWN. Top of a bird's head. It ends in the nape and is normally covered with small feathers, or bears a crest.

CUCKOO—Cuculus canorus. The 13th-century poet and musician who composed the famous old round " Summer is icumen in, Lhude sing cuccu ! " shared the general feeling of joy at Summer's coming, symbolised through the ages by the Cuckoo's call. Along with the popular Robin, the Cuckoo is the one bird that everyone knows—as is shown by the spate of letters to the Press that heralds its arrival in April. But its popularity depends almost entirely on its call, for its nature is disagreeable in the extreme. This is the only completely parasitic bird in this country ; all it does towards its survival as a species is merely to provide eggs.

The Cuckoo's unique and extraordinary habit of laying its eggs in other birds' nests has

Eric Hosking

CUCKOO. *This popular bird heralds the coming of Summer with its cheerful call. Its other habits, however, are far from agreeable*

interested ornithologists everywhere from very early times, and a great deal of investigation has been made into it.

One question that long puzzled observers was how the Cuckoo inserted its egg into another bird's nest ; whether it laid or whether it carried it there. Many a Cuckoo has been seen carrying an egg in its feet or bill, and it was thought that this was its own egg ; but lifelong investigation by Edgar Chance, the acknowledged world authority on the Cuckoo, has established that this egg must be one taken from a nest after the bird had laid its own egg there.

The appearance of the Cuckoo somewhat resembles that of the Sparrow-Hawk (q.v.), which may account for the fact that it is often shot by gamekeepers, and is also mobbed by small birds. The male and female birds are alike and, at first glance, seem completely grey, but there are grey and white bars underneath, and there is no mistaking the white spots on the long, graduated tail. The structure of the Cuckoo's feet distinguishes it from all other British birds—of its four slender toes, the second and third, which are the longest, point forwards, and the first and fourth backwards. The bill is horn-coloured, and the legs, eyes and eyelids are yellow. The young chicks are either grey or red-brown, and barred all over. There is also a rare " hepatic " form of the female—a red-brown of a brighter hue than that of the young. The length of the Cuckoo is 13 in., and its tarsus 1 in. Its weight is 5 oz. and its wing span approximately 1½ ft.

The flight of the Cuckoo is direct, but its movements in alighting and on the ground, where it hops, are somewhat awkward. Its call is so well known that no description is necessary. It is less well known, however, that the call, which may be made from a perch on a tree or on the wing, is sometimes uttered through a closed bill. Every Cuckoo's call has its own pitch and its own tone, as is most evident in the breeding season. When excited the bird utters a guttural, hoarse, low note and a very audible stammering note, especially if there is an intruder or rival in his territory. The hen does not " cuckoo ", but produces a bubbling trill. The juvenile has a persistent cheep, resembling a fledgling song-bird, with which it attracts other birds to feed it. The popular idea that the Cuckoo " changes its tune " is a fallacy. Its song is heard at its height from April to June.

The Cuckoo breeds in woodlands and thickets all over the British Isles, except the Shetland Isles, but even there it has occurred occasionally. In Scotland and Ireland it is called the " Gowk ". By the middle of May the hen Cuckoo has taken up a territory ; in many cases she returns to the same spot year after year, and even chooses the same birds' nests in which to deposit her eggs. One theory is that she chooses nests of the species of bird by which she herself was reared.

Lady of Easy Virtue. It is believed that cuckoos do not pair in the way generally prevalent among birds, and there is much evidence to support the view that cuckoos are polyandrous. Certainly, there appear to be considerably more male cuckoos than females, and there are many recorded instances of a hen consorting with two or more males during the breeding season. This somewhat coquettish behaviour of the female Cuckoo is responsible for a quaint old country superstition that the presence of a young Cuckoo will bring bad luck in the form of conjugal infidelity to the person on whose land or property the bird is discovered !

After mating, the hen Cuckoo takes up her position in a tree, where she will sit quietly for hours watching a pair of birds going about their nest-building activities. When she is ready to lay her egg and opportunity offers, down she swoops, uttering her bubbling cry, and neatly lays her egg, at the same time removing one, and sometimes two eggs, to make room for her own. When next she alights, she proceeds to swallow her victim's egg, and continues, until as many as a dozen eggs have been left with unsuspecting foster-parents. There is a record of 25 eggs being deposited by one Cuckoo, but the usual number is 12. Eggs are generally laid in the afternoon or evening, directly into the nest.

The Cuckoo's eggs resemble in shape, colour and size those already in the chosen nest. The commonest foster-parents are probably the Meadow-Pipit, Hedge-Sparrow, and Reed- and Sedge-Warbler ; but the nests of tits, pied wagtails, redstarts, whitethroats, skylarks, reed-buntings and yellow hammers, blackbirds, wrens and many others are also used. The hen Cuckoo usually stays near the nests where she has laid her eggs, and often feeds her chicks after they have left the nest in about three weeks' time. She sometimes continues to lay her eggs in the same district for about ten years, but her most prolific years are the third, fourth and fifth.

As soon as the Cuckoo chick is hatched it makes room for itself by deftly and effectively pushing out other eggs or chicks until it remains the only occupant. From then onwards, the harassed foster-parents spend their time foraging for food for this large changeling.

The adult Cuckoo's food consists almost entirely of harmful insects and their larvae ; the larvae of craneflies and sawflies, the ermine,

Eric Hosking; John Markham

CUCKOO. *Nature has endowed the young Cuckoo with a very sensitive back, so that for about a day after hatching he will instinctively throw any eggs—or young—with whom his back comes into contact out of the nest by contracting his whole body*

magpie and winter moths, beetles and grubs of various kinds, slugs, woodlice, spiders, butterflies, and occasionally worm-eggs and seeds, all form part of the Cuckoo's diet. However, it is also an egg thief, and often raids the nests of species not used as foster-parents.

The common Cuckoo is the only member of its family known to breed in this country. Others, however, are occasional visitors from time to time ; among them the Black-billed Cuckoo, Great Spotted Cuckoo, and Yellow-billed Cuckoo, described under their names.

CUCKOO'S MATE. Local name for the Wryneck (*q.v.*), a bird formerly regarded with superstitious awe.

CUCULIDAE (Latin, " cuckoo "). Family of cuckoos of the order *Cuculiformes.* Its members are distributed over a wide area of the globe, though the majority are confined to tropical regions. It includes three genera on the British list: *Cuculus, Clamator* and *Coccyzus.*

These are arboreal or terrestrial birds, small or medium-sized. Some of them build simple nests and incubate their eggs, but the majority of Old World species deposit their eggs in the nests of other birds, and leave the hatching and the rearing of the young to foster-parents.

The bill of members of this family is compressed and slightly curved. The wings have ten primary feathers, and there are usually nine or ten secondaries. The long tail is rounded or wedge-shaped, and there are generally ten rectrices (tail quills), though in some cases there are only eight. The skin is thin and tender ; there is down on the featherless tracts only. The oil-gland is naked. The feet have four toes, and the outer toe is reversible.

CUCULIFORMES (Latin, " cuckoo-like "). Order of small or medium-sized birds, varying considerably in appearance and habits. The majority are arboreal, but some are terrestrial. The order includes the cuckoos, and is divided into two families, one of which, *Cuculidae* (*q.v.*), contains species occurring in the British Isles. Members of this order are distributed over a very wide area of the globe, though the majority are found in tropical or sub-tropical regions.

CUCULUS (Latin, " cuckoo "). Genus of the family *Cuculidae* of the order *Cuculiformes*. It contains many species, which occur in almost all parts of the world, but only one is found in Europe—the common Cuckoo (*q.v.*). Members of this genus differ from those of the genus *Clamator* in having no crest, and from both *Clamator* and *Coccyzus* in having round not longitudinal, nostrils.

CULMEN. Ridge, or central longitudinal line, of the upper mandible of the bill (*q.v.*).

CURLEW—Numenius arquata. Largest and most familiar of wading birds, the Curlew, called Whaup in Scotland, is found in most countries of the Old World. It resembles other birds of the same genus, like the much rarer Whimbrel (*q.v.*), only in appearance; and its song and call could never be confused with those of any other wader. Apart from being a resident bird, the Curlew is a summer resident, a passage migrant and a winter visitor. Records show that there has been a welcome increase in its numbers during recent years. It now breeds in almost every suitable district in England,

Wales, Scotland and Ireland. In Spring and Autumn, vast numbers can be seen congregating on the shores and estuaries on migration, in company with other birds.

A rather drab bird, the Curlew is clothed in uniform streaky brown, much lighter on its head, breast and underparts ; it has a white rump and its tail is barred with dark and light brown. It has a long, slender, curved bill varying in length from 5 to 7 in., the female's being the longer. The Curlew varies greatly in size, but the average length is 23 in., and the tarsus 3 in. Its wing span is $2\frac{1}{2}$ ft., and its weight about 2 lb.

Though shy and wary towards humans, the Curlew likes the company of other birds, especially when breeding on the shore. It walks on the ground and wades into the water, where much of its food is delved out with its remarkable beak. Its flight is direct and swift, with some resemblance to that of the Gull, and curlews may sometimes be seen flying in V-formation.

The courtship display and posturing of the Curlew has always held much interest for the bird watcher. Early in Spring the winter flocks begin to disperse. The birds pair and set off for the moors in preparation for breeding. Here the male indulges in some wonderful aerial

CURLEW. These three little balls of fluff with short, straight beaks are the progeny of the Curlew standing by them, whose slightly curved bill measures a good 7 inches

Eric Hosking

G. K. Yeates

CURLEW. *Some might call this wader a rather drab bird, but there is nothing drab about this beautiful creature standing on its lonely rock in a vast expanse of sea*

manoeuvres, flying low over the ground, then rising suddenly with wildly beating wings to hang poised, his wings quivering, before planing down again ; all the while uttering his mating call. Often he will fly in circles without alighting.

Apart from its familiar song the Curlew has various other notes, and I place it among birds having a voice of great quality. Numerous call notes have been recorded. One, which is very musical, has the rhythm of the war-time " V " signal of the B.B.C., resembling the first notes of Beethoven's Fifth Symphony. Another most attractive and musical sound is a long, liquid bubbling call, always heard during the breeding season, but by no means confined to that time and which can be heard all the year round on shore and moor.—EDITOR.

The Curlew has a wide range of nesting sites and is equally at home on the lonely moor and on the sea shore ; it nests in rough pastures, moorlands, meadows, marshes and sand dunes, and has even been found breeding at an altitude of some 2,000 ft. The nest is merely a hollow in the ground lined with grass, but is usually sheltered by vegetation. The breeding season is in April or early May, when four eggs of varying shape and colour are laid at intervals of from one to four days. The hatching, which is done by both birds, takes about a month. The chicks are little balls of dark-streaked, buff-coloured down, and have short straight beaks

entirely different from the adult's. They are tended by both parents, and are able to fend for themselves in about six weeks. One brood is reared in a season.

The food of the Curlew varies according to its habitat. On the coast it will devour small crabs, shrimps and fish of various kinds, and some vegetable matter ; on the moors it eats insects, berries and sometimes grain.

No doubt it is its eerie nightly call that has given the " Whaup " the reputation of an " uncanny " bird, especially in the Highlands of Scotland. No one seems to know whether or not it is good to eat ; there is a story in the Shetland Isles that a visitor once had the temerity to try, and was ever afterwards referred to " as the man that ate the Whaup ".

Apart from the common Curlew, only the Stone-Curlew—a bird belonging to a completely different family—breeds in this country ; while the Eskimo Curlew and Slender-billed Curlew (*qq.v.*) are rare visitors. But the name " curlew " is incorrectly applied locally to a variety of birds, chiefly for some resemblance, real or imaginary, to the Curlew. Thus Jack-, or Half-Curlew, is the Whimbrel (*q.v.*), a close relative of the common Curlew ; Black Curlew is the Glossy Ibis (*q.v.*) ; and Pigmy-Curlew the Curlew-Sandpiper (*see* page 168).

CURLEW-SANDPIPER — Calidris testacea.
This bird of the Far North, breeding in Siberia, Arctic Asia and Bering Island, the Curlew-Sandpiper (or " Pigmy-Curlew ") comes to the British Isles as a regular passage migrant. When seen in Great Britain, it is wearing its drab winter plumage of grey-brown above and white underneath. It has a very individual bill—longer, slenderer and more down-curved than the Dunlin's (*q.v.*)—whom it much resembles—and the white rump and white on its wing distinguish it from other waders. It also has longer legs, and a conspicuous white eye stripe. In its more colourful summer dress it has a beautiful chestnut breast, a black streaked mantle and wings tipped with black. It is 8 in. in length, with a tarsus of 1 in. Its wing span is about 12 in. and it weighs 1½ oz.

There is very little difference in behaviour, habits and breeding between the Curlew-Sandpiper and the Dunlin. The flight of the former is described as being more undulating ; but if the two birds are flying in flocks outside the breeding season, it is impossible to separate them. The Curlew-Sandpiper's voice at its Arctic nesting site contains a surprising variety of sweet calls, often interspersed with curlew-like trills. A pleasant twittering accompanies the birds' feeding.

In the British Isles this bird haunts the salt marshes and flats in company with other waders. It breeds in the Arctic tundra, and chooses for its nesting-site a depression in the grass, where it lays four beautifully marked, olive-green or buff eggs in June or July. Both male and female take part in hatching the eggs and rearing the young, and there is one brood in a season.

Curlew-sandpipers seek their roost late in the evening and are usually the first on the shore in the morning. They are comparatively tame. Marine plants and insects of every kind form their chief diet.

CURSORIUS. Genus of the family *Glareolidae* of the order *Charadriiformes*. It contains three species, which are mainly distributed over parts of Africa and Asia. One occurs in Europe as an irregular and casual straggler— the Cream-coloured Courser (*q.v.*), which has been recorded in Britain about thirty times.

CUSHAT, or Cushie Doo. Local name for Wood-Pigeon (*q.v.*), probably onomatopoeic.

CYANOSYLVIA. Genus of the family *Turdidae* of the order *Passeriformes*. Its members, known as the bluethroats, are distributed over much of Europe and northern Asia, and occur in northern Africa outside the breeding season. Two races of bluethroats (*q.v.*) occur in the British Isles : the Red-spotted Bluethroat (*q.v.*), which is a fairly common passage migrant in Spring and Autumn along the east coast of England and Scotland ; and the White-spotted Bluethroat (*q.v.*), which has been recorded in the British Isles little more than a dozen times.

In appearance and action, and in some of their habits, the members of this genus strongly resemble the Robin (genus *Erithacus*). They are also very closely related to the redstarts (genus *Phoenicurus*) and the Nightingale (genus *Luscinia*). But the bristles surrounding the bill are less developed, the tail is shorter, and the plumage is harder than in most members of *Phoenicurus*. The sexes are unlike.

CYGNUS (Latin, " swan "). Genus of the family *Anatidae* of the order *Anseriformes*. It contains the swans. There are six species, distributed over a large area of the globe, three of which are on the British list : the Mute Swan, Whooper-Swan and Bewick's Swan (*see* under these names).

These are large, rather heavily built birds. Two very distinctive features are the white colour, and the very long neck which is at least equal to the body in length. The bill is generally of medium length ; the nail does not occupy the whole of the tip of the upper mandible. The wings are shortish in relation to the bird's large size, but broad. The tail is very short and rounded. The short tarsus is reticulated (i.e. covered with small irregular

W. Farnsworth

CYGNUS. *The Mute Swan, though not completely voiceless, is the least vocal member of this genus*

plates). The three front toes are fully webbed, and the small elevated hind toe is not lobed. The sexes are similar in appearance.

DIPPER

D

DABCHICK. Smallest of all freshwater birds, the Little Grebe (*q.v.*) is often called thus.

DANCE. Members of certain species from time to time indulge in a series of stylised movements, rhythmical steps, leaps, gyrations or gestures, which may best be described as dancing. With some species only the males perform, using the dance as a method of displaying to the female and of gaining her attention and approbation (*see* Display) ; but in others, both sexes may take part, singly, in pairs or in large groups. Although dancing may form part of the ceremonial of courtship (*q.v.*), it is not restricted to the breeding season or period of pair formation, and as long as there is sufficient stimulus or excitement—for example, such as engendered by the big gatherings which collect before migration—it may take place at most seasons of the year.

It would seem, then, that dancing is an expression of general liveliness and excitement which need not necessarily have a sexual basis. It has been stated that it can easily be induced in some tame birds by human beings performing dance-like movements in their presence.

The dances of British birds are usually less intricate and exotic than those of tropical or sub-tropical species, one of which has been named by natives *El bailidor*, the dancer. Sometimes, however, the movements are quite elaborate. Below some of the various dances of birds found in this country are described.

Terns. These have several little dances. In one, a pair " parade " together, wandering apparently aimlessly side by side, every now and again stopping to display to each other. In another dance, one bird, usually the male, walks round the other with its body slightly tilted so that the wrist joint or the primaries trace a circle or part of one in the sand ; meanwhile, the partner turns to keep facing the circling bird. Sometimes the two birds merely circle round one another.

Stone-Curlews. In the Autumn the stone-curlews indulge in remarkable communal displays or " dances ", in which they behave in a most excited and frenzied manner. Running

forward with wings extended and slightly raised, a bird will suddenly fling them high in the air and then pitch forward while continuing to wave and toss its wings about ; then, in succession, it will stop short, turn, pitch forward again, leap in the air, descend again and continue staggering forward until it brings the sequence to an end by leaping into the air and then finishing off with a short eccentric flight low over the ground, coming down in a sharp curve. The whole performance is repeated, each violent run or plunge ending with a sudden pitching forward of the body, and with the wings, which are often pointed forward on to the head, straggling about in an uncouth, dislocated kind of way.

Oystercatchers. Any form of excitement, other than fear, will stimulate these birds to perform their celebrated " piping ceremony " which, except when used as an aggressive display, appears to be for the entertainment of their fellows. Sometimes a single bird will give a solo performance, piping away with wide open beak, while standing erect on some small eminence. Usually, however, two or three

John Barlee

DANCE. *A critical and by no means impressed audience watches the Gannet's dance movements*

169

James Gibson

DANCE. Like a ballerina waiting in the wings for her cue to whirl on the stage is this Gull

birds, occasionally as many as ten or twelve, take part in the ceremony. Trios are common, probably a pair and an intruding male. For an illustration, *see* Behaviour, page 49.

When the " piping ceremony " takes place on the ground, the participants usually run forward with short quick steps, with neck thrust out and bills pointed downwards for the piping trill. Often they weave a serpentine course, turning occasionally through a half circle, completing the performance by bobbing up and down— particularly in hostile situations. With suitable modifications a similar exhibition of this ceremony may be given in the air.

Albatross. The majestic Albatross is not too proud to dance when overwrought with excitement. Then a pair will begin by standing face to face, nodding and bowing vigorously to one another and rubbing bills together with a whistling cry. They will then shake their heads and snap their bills rapidly ; occasionally they will lift one wing, straighten themselves and blow out their breasts. Then they put the bill under a wing or toss it in the air with a groaning scream, finishing up by walking round each other. The whole performance may take fifteen minutes or more (*see* illustrations, p. 180–181).

Crane. The stately and beautiful dance of this bird, which once bred in the wild in this country and is now found only in captivity, has several variations. It may be performed by single birds, pairs or groups, but the basic movements are similar in each instance.

In one solo sequence the bird, with its wings extended, walks with quick steps in a circle, ellipse or figure of eight. It then springs into the air, and on returning to earth, bends down

and picks up small objects from the ground, throws them in the air, catches them, and finally stops with a jerk, holding itself erect.

Intruding Male. The final example is the dance of a non-British species—the Cayenne Lapwing—included because it illustrates the unusual case of an " intruding male " who has a part to play in the ceremony which is quite distinct from that of the pair he joins. A male of this species will " visit a pair " in an adjoining territory, who will advance to meet him. Placing themselves behind him, they will march rapidly up and down, keeping in step, and uttering drumming notes in time with their movements, while the " visitor " utters single notes at regular intervals. Finally, the march ceases and the leader stands erect and motionless with wings raised, still uttering single notes, while the other two, with puffed-out plumage and standing exactly abreast, stoop forward and downward until the tips of their beaks touch the ground. Sinking their rhythmical voices to a low murmur they keep this posture for some time. Finally, the visitor departs to rejoin his mate, and to wait with her for the arrival of a visitor. Particulars of other dances will be found under the headings of individual species. *See also* Behaviour ; Courtship ; Display (including further illustrations).

DARK-BREASTED BARN OWL—Tyto alba guttata. This infrequent vagrant or passage migrant to the British Isles differs from the resident Barn-Owl (*q.v.*) only in its darker plumage ; its upper parts are much greyer and it has spotted buff underparts. The two birds are otherwise so alike that it is not easy to distinguish them. The Dark-breasted Barn-Owl breeds in many European countries.

DARK-BREASTED BRENT GOOSE. *See* Brent Goose. The dark-breasted race is more frequent in south-east Scotland, east and south England than the pale-breasted variety.

DARTFORD WARBLER—Sylvia undata dartfordiensis. This is the only warbler which does not migrate but braves the British climate throughout the year. Consequently it has often been in danger of extermination ; in the rigorous Winter of early 1947, for instance, it was all but lost as a British species. Since then, however, it has more than recovered its former status and, by all accounts, is increasing both its numbers and its breeding areas. It also occurs in western Europe and north-west Africa.

An extremely local bird it confines itself at present to a few counties in south and south-east England, principally Hampshire and Surrey. It also bred at one time in Cornwall and Devon. It delights in country where gorse or furze bushes are plentiful—so much so that its other name is the " Furze-Wren ". It flits in and out of the bushes and is so shy and secretive that it is rarely seen.

After the breeding season the Dartford Warbler wanders about in company with others on heaths and commons. Its distinctive appearance prevents confusion with any other warbler. It is dark brown above, shading to slate-grey on its head ; its underparts are pinkish-chestnut ; and it has a long, fan-shaped tail with white tips, which is usually cocked and is flicked constantly. The slender bill is black, and the legs yellow. Its length is 5 in., and its tarsus ¾ in., its wing span is approximately 7 in., and its weight about ⅙ oz.

The Dartford Warbler has the typical warbler flight, and has much in common, both in voice and mating display, with the Whitethroat (q.v.), another leaf relative ; the display takes the form of a kind of dance, the male raising its body several feet in the air and gradually descending while delivering its mating song.

G. K. Yeates

DARTFORD WARBLER. *A fine day may entice this bird into the open to sun itself atop a gorse bush*

I regard the song of the Dartford Warbler as of poor quality, and monotonous compared with other songsters. Apart from the breeding song, it has various other notes, one in particular comparable to that of the Black Redstart. Its song is heard best from the middle of March until the end of May, with a marked recurrence in late September and October.—EDITOR.

The breeding season of the Dartford Warbler is in April, and its nest is built in its favourite gorse and furze bushes. Ling, grasses, wool, paper and moss are among the materials used, with grasses, feathers and hair for the lining. Sometimes the nest is placed among the heather. The Dartford Warbler keeps less strictly to territory boundaries than some other warblers.

The nest is built in the main by the hen, the male making a pretence of building what are called " cocks' nests " (q.v.). The normal number of eggs is three or four ; they are pale green or dirty white in ground colour and speckled grey and brown. The hatching is done chiefly by the hen, although the male is recorded as taking some small part ; the period is about 12 days. The young are tended by both parents and two broods are regularly reared.

The Dartford Warbler's food consists mainly of insects of all kinds and spiders ; but it will also eat berries and wild fruit.

DECOY. In the widest sense a decoy is anything that lures or tempts a wild bird into a net, snare, gunshot range, or within the reach of someone who can capture it. The term is also applied to a trained, controlled, or counterfeit bird used to lure wild ones ; and, finally, to the enclosed space into which wild birds are attracted and trapped.

Originally a decoy-man was one who decoyed wild fowl or game, either for the table or for collections, but of the few that now remain, some exercise their art for ringing (q.v.) birds.

Any trap that is baited is in fact a decoy, although it may not be called by that name ; from the simple sieve, baited with corn and supported with a stick

J. Wentworth Day

DECOY. *This picture of the Orwell Park, Suffolk, decoy shows one of the tunnels radiating from the central pond, where wild ducks are trapped*

Eric Hosking

DENDROCOPOS. The Greater Spotted Woodpecker is a member of the genus Dendrocopos

The wild ducks are inveigled into the decoy partly by the blandishments of semi-tame wild ducks, kept on the pond specially for that purpose, and partly by the gambolling of a small red dog, which the wild birds mistake for a fox, their hereditary enemy.

The general procedure is for the decoy-man to approach the mouth of the pipe *towards which the wind is blowing*, give a low feeding whistle to attract the decoy ducks, and throw some grain into the mouth of the tunnel. The wildfowl follow the decoy ducks, and when they are peacefully feeding, the dog is released. On noticing him the wildfowl start in pursuit, leaving behind the tame ducks who are used to the dog. The latter disappears for an instant by leaping over a dog-jump, only to re-appear slightly further down the tunnel.

This hide-and-seek act, with the birds in hot, but vain pursuit, is continued until the decoy-man finally steps out and panics the ducks into the net, which is then detached. In a commercial decoy the victims are taken out and their necks broken one by one. At a ringing station, they are treated more humanely, and frightened as little as possible.

Since the passing of the Protection of Birds Act, in 1954, the only decoys permitted for the wholesale slaughter of birds are those which existed before the Act was passed, but the establishment of decoys for ringing and marking, or for purposes authorised under the Cruelty to Animals Act, are allowed. It is also illegal to use as a decoy any live bird which is tethered, secured by braces, blind or maimed, or any baited board, birdlime, or similar substance.

operated by a draw string, to the more elaborate clap-net and Heligoland Trap (*qq.v.*). Usually, however, when the term decoy is used, it refers to the so-called duck-decoys, which, once fairly common in this country, have now almost vanished.

A century and a half ago there were 214 decoy ponds in England and Ireland ; now there are about half-a-dozen. Of these, three are commercial ponds where wild fowl are trapped and killed for the table—Orwell Park, Suffolk ; Borough Fen, Northants ; and one at Grange, Essex, near Dead Man's Creek, on the Blackwater. The decoy at Fritton Lake, Suffolk, supplies ducks and other wild fowl for parks, zoos and private collections: and those at Abbotsbury, Dorset ; Orielton, Pembrokeshire ; and that at Slimbridge, Gloucestershire, which belongs to the Wildfowl Trust, are used for ringing and other scientific purposes.

A typical decoy pond consists of a central pond with three or more radiating curved tunnels formed by netting mounted on hooped supports. Each tunnel has a wide mouth, about 15 ft. across, and gradually narrows down, so that at the far end, where a detachable trammel net, like a giant stocking, is fitted, it is only two to three feet wide. The tunnels are walled by a series of screens, made of reed, about 5 ft. high, which overlap like scales.

DELICHON. Genus of the family *Hirundinidae* of the order *Passeriformes*. Its members are distributed over Europe, Asia, northern Africa and north America ; outside the breeding season they occur in south Africa, southern Asia and south America. The only genus on the British list is the House-Martin (*q.v.*).

DENDROCOPOS. Genus of woodpeckers of the family *Picidae* of the order *Piciformes*. It comprises all the spotted four-toed woodpeckers in Europe. The genus contains several species, distributed over Europe, much of northern Asia and north-west Africa. Only two species are on the British list : the Greater Spotted (or Pied) Woodpecker, and the smaller Lesser Spotted (or Barred) Woodpecker (*qq.v.*), which are both resident in this country.

The members of the genus *Dendrocopos* differ from those of the genus *Picus* (Green Woodpecker) mainly in size (and, of course, in plumage), and in their much thinner necks. They have four toes, two front and two hind ; the outer hind-toe is longer than the outer front toe. Only the upper part of the tarsus is feathered.

DESERT-WHEATEAR — Oenanthe deserti.
One or two of these birds from the desert
wastes of north Africa and central Asia have
wandered to Scotland from time to time. The
Desert-Wheatear is most clearly distinguished
from other wheatears by its tail, which is
completely black. Another difference, noticeable in the male only, is the black throat ; the
female's is white. The upperparts are buff,
with some black on the wings, and the upper
tail coverts are white. The length of the
Desert-Wheatear is 6 in. Its general behaviour
and habits resemble those of other wheatears.

DEVIL-BIRD, or Devil-Screamer. There
are many local variations on this name for the
Swift (*q.v.*), all associated with the harsh screams
uttered by these birds as they chase each other
round the roof-tops.

DIGESTIVE SYSTEM. *See* Anatomy,
including full illustration of Alimentary Canal.

DIOMEDEA. Genus of oceanic birds of
the family *Diomedeidae* of the order *Procellariiformes.* Its members occur mainly in oceanic
regions of the southern hemisphere, though
some also occur in the North Atlantic region.
The only species on the British list is the Black-
browed Albatross. *See also* Albatross.

DIOMEDEIDAE. Family of large oceanic
birds of the order *Procellariiformes.* It contains
only one genus on the British list, *Diomedea.*

DIPPER—Cinclus cinclus gularis. This
unique little bird, often called Water-Ouzel,
may be seen on a boulder in the middle of
any fast rocky river in hill-country, bobbing
and curtseying in the way that has given it
its name. A British resident, it flourishes only
in such counties as afford the necessary surroundings—a stony stream, usually but not
always among the hills, with preferably an
old bridge passing over it. The little bird is
remarkably well-endowed for its life on rushing
streams, for it can swim both on and under
the water, and can even walk along the river
bottom, propelling itself with its wings and
digging up its food as it goes. It has still not
been established for certain how such a small
bird can keep its balance in the swiftly flowing
water. The Dipper enters the water either by
diving from a rock or from the air, or by
walking into it until it is submerged. Its flight
is direct and rapid, with quickly whirring wings.
It is a plump, brown bird, built not unlike a
Wren but, of course, bigger. It has dark brown
plumage above, on its sides and belly, with a
transverse band of warm rust colour, and its
throat and chest are pure white. Its tail is
short, and its bill and legs are dark brown.
The length of the Dipper is 7 in., and its tarsus

about 1 in. Its wing span is about 9 in. ; and
its weight is 2½ oz.

The friendly little Dipper is a sweet songster.
It is always difficult to hear its song amid the
sounds of rushing water, but there are few
pleasanter sounds on a summer day than the
two together. The song is a short musical
warble, usually uttered from some rock, stone,
or bank, with something of the exuberance
associated with the Wren. The Dipper sometimes sings while flying, but it is never far from
the stream. The song is heard most of the
year, but is sweetest in the Spring.—EDITOR.

The nest, found always near water—on a
cliff, under a waterfall, or in a hole in a bank,
or under a bridge—is a clever dome-like construction of moss and grass, lined with leaves
and partly concealed by over-hanging moss.
Five pure white eggs are laid in March or sometimes earlier, and are hatched out by the hen
in about 16 days ; both parents feed the young
for roughly three weeks. Two broods are
generally reared in a season, sometimes three.
The Dipper's food consists entirely of insects
cleverly dug out from the bottom of the stream.
This bird is confined to the British Isles, but
two other types are known as visitors. The
Black-bellied Dipper (*Cinclus cinclus cinclus*),
which breeds in northern Europe, occasionally
wanders to Great Britain ; it differs from the
British bird, as its name implies, only in the
colour of its underparts which are black instead
of rust-coloured ; its habits and breeding are
similar. The other type is the Irish Dipper
(*Cinclus cinclus hibernicus*), which breeds in
Ireland in the same surroundings as the British
bird ; it is very similar to our Dipper, somewhat darker in appearance. This bird is a
frequent visitor to Scotland, especially to the
Outer Hebrides and other islands of the north.
Local names for the Dipper include Water
Blackbird, Water Crow, and Water Pyet.

Eric Hosking

DIPPER. *This amazing bird not only swims but
walks at the bottom of rivers hunting after food*

CAUSES OF ILLNESS IN WILD BIRDS

W. C. OSMAN HILL, M.D., F.R.S.E.

Much remains to be learned about the illnesses of wild birds, although a great deal can be gathered by examining sick captive birds. Here one of our foremost experts discusses the more common diseases, their causes and transmissibility to other animals

DISEASE. Most of our knowledge of the pathology of birds is based upon post-mortems carried out on specimens dying in captivity. Valuable as this information is, it can provide no more than a distorted picture of the prevalence of abnormal conditions in the wild, for the reasons that captivity

(1) introduces many artificial conditions leading to diseases not, or rarely, occurring in wild birds ;

(2) prolongs the life of individuals by eliminating many factors in the struggle for existence, so that they become liable to affections characteristic of senility and chronic abnormal metabolism, from which in the wild they would escape by early death ;

(3) affords protection to the acutely ill bird, which by careful nursing and appropriate treatment is enabled to recover, whereas in the wild it would die of starvation or from the attacks of its companions, who soon recognize illness in their fellows and take the speediest course to eliminate the ailing or infirm in the interests of the social unit as a whole.

On the other hand, captivity leads to much loss of life from injury inflicted by cage companions, particularly in nuptial combats between rival males, or by the undue attentions of aggressive males to non-receptive females. Injuries are also produced by contact with foreign objects such as aviary wire, when birds fly off their perches in fright. Such flight in wild birds is usually unimpeded.

Much, therefore, remains to be learned of the diseases to which *wild* birds are subject. The importance of adding to our knowledge of the pathology of wild birds cannot be over-stressed, for apart from its intrinsic interest, there is the economic aspect, as for instance with regard to game-birds, and also the question of transmission of disease to domestic stock either directly or by wild birds acting as carriers of parasites. Also to be taken into consideration is the possibility of wild birds acting as carriers of disease (e.g. tuberculosis) to Man.

Until recently it was tacitly assumed that wild creatures were singularly free from disease. The sick have such a small chance of survival that only the healthy are normally encountered ; consequently our knowledge is largely culled from the small number of birds picked up dead in sufficiently fresh condition to allow for a post-mortem examination. Such circumstances are few and far between, except during violent epidemics, such as that which affected grouse some years ago.

That such epidemics are almost a normal occurrence at intervals is now well known— at least among mammals, for it is fully established that there are periodic fluctuations in the numbers of many species. During times of plenty, numbers increase rapidly until congestion occurs. This in itself serves as a background for disease, just as in human societies slum conditions notoriously induce such pathological states as malnutrition, imperfect growth of the young, epidemics of bacterial or virus origin, and so on. This is Nature's way of reducing the population to its average level.

Fluctuations in the populations of such mammals as rodents in turn affects the number of birds of prey, e.g. owls and crows.

In the wild, the hazards of existence are so multitudinous that few, if any, individual birds die of mere old age. Conditions causing mortality in wild birds may be specified under the following headings :

INJURY OR ACCIDENT

Few wild birds escape minor injury during their lives, but injuries involving fracture of bones are commonly fatal. Death is usually from shock, with or without haemorrhage, for the ability of birds to withstand surgical shock is virtually nil.

Today marine birds suffer considerable mortality from oil-pollution (*q.v.*). This waste product of shipping damages the plumage and

A. C. Moore

DISEASE. Fowl suffering from lack of manganese which causes rough and unpigmented feathers thereby upsets the heat-regulating mechanism. The result is almost always chilling, with subsequent death from pneumonia ; but in many cases there is inanition as well as local gastro-enteritis, from ingestion of oil-polluted water.

ACUTE INFECTIONS

These diseases, due to viruses and bacteria, are easily determined by simple laboratory methods.

Fowl Pox, probably the most common filterable virus contagion, occurs in partridges, pheasants, grouse, quails, pigeons and canaries, as well as in domestic fowl and ducks. It is characterised by a pustular eruption on the skin and its appendages (wattles, etc.), and by membraneous deposits.

Roup, caused by the same virus, produces in poultry a greyish-yellow exudate in the respiratory passages ; it is sometimes called avian diphtheria or " swelled head ".

Fowl Pest or Fowl Plague, another virus infection, affects domestic fowl, and occasionally geese, but its mode of infection is unknown. The incubation period of three to five days is shown by apathy, darkening of the comb and wattles, and inflammation of the mouth. It lasts two to four days and is commonly fatal. Post-mortem appearances include haemorrhages in the respiratory tract and in the heart muscle. A similar, possibly identical, disease affects birds of the Thrush family (Valenti, 1903). Pigeons are immune.

Psittacosis, a virus infection originally found in newly imported parrots, was formerly thought to be confined to them. It has since been found in wild passerines (finches) and other birds (e.g. pigeons in Dublin), and is now more correctly termed *ornithosis*. Lesions occur in the spleen, intestines and lungs. Clinically there are no specific symptoms, but merely general signs of illness. The importance of the disease lies in its transmissibility to Man ; apparently healthy birds can act as carriers.

Fowl Cholera is bacteriologically a " pasteurellosis ", associated with a member of the haemorrhagic septicaemia group (*Bacillus aviseptica*), and its pathology is similar to that of mammalian infections of the same type. Enteritis is a prominent symptom, and pneumonia supervenes with usually a fatal termination.

Fowl Typhoid, like human typhoid, is due to a *Salmonella*. One form (*S. pullorum*) causes " white diarrhoea " in chicks, and is highly fatal. Another (*S. gallinarum*) affects adult birds, causing severe anaemia as well as febrile symptoms.

Wild birds, usually in the nestling stage, have been found in America infected with the virus of equine encephalitis, a disease normally affecting horses in the Mid-West. The birds concerned are the Red-winged Blackbird (*Agelaius phoeniceus*) and a Magpie (*Pica p. hudsonia*) (Sooter *et al.* 1951). The birds apparently show no symptoms, but merely act as carriers. It is noteworthy that, among the more common disease bacteria of mammals, the *Pneumococcus* (pneumonia-causing organism) is resisted by birds, which are practically immune to it, probably because their own high body temperature is above the optimum conditions for this organism.

CHRONIC INFECTIONS

These include especially tuberculosis and fungus affections.

Tuberculosis is not particularly common in wild birds, but it has been found in town-dwelling sparrows and pigeons, and has been reported in lapwings (Shattock), kestrels, partridges and blackbirds. The avian strain of the tubercle bacillus differs from the human and bovine strains, and is almost specific for birds, which are, with the exception of parrots, immune to the other two strains. The only mammals ordinarily susceptible to avian tuberculosis are the pig and calf (Hamerton, 1933).

Lesions are almost invariably of the nodular type, and may be large and cheesy in consistence. They affect principally the liver, spleen and intestines, but sometimes the disease is confined to the respiratory system (lungs

DISEASE. *Coccidiosis is one of the most virulent affections of birds, caused by a protozoan parasite. Pheasants, grouse and domestic fowl are particularly prone to it*

R. F. Gordon

DISEASE. A close-up of lice-eggs at the base of the feathers. See also Bird-Louse. Affected birds may, in extreme cases, lose condition generally

and air-sacs), in which event it is not easy to distinguish from mycosis ; indeed, the two diseases are sometimes co-existent, though Hamerton admits never having found the two together at one and the same time.

Fungus Affections (*Mycosis*) are common in birds ; they cause encrustations round the mouth, eyes and naked areas of skin. More serious are the air-borne moulds which enter the respiratory passages, causing inflammation of the lungs and air-sacs. This has been found in wild crows, wood-pigeons and gulls.

ANIMAL PARASITES

Almost all wild birds carry both external and internal parasites. These pertain chiefly to three zoological groups—the protozoa, worms and arthropods (mites, insects, and so forth). *See also* Parasite.

Protozoa. Coccidiosis, the most serious protozoal affection, causes lesions in gut and liver in wild birds, especially in grouse and pheasants (Fantham, 1910, 1911). The causal agent is a microscopic protozoon which invades the bile passages from the intestine.

Black-head (*Histomoniasis*) is also due to a protozoon invading the liver, where it produces characteristic ring-like lesions. A serious scourge in domestic turkeys, it also occurs in wild partridges, which act as reservoir for the causal organism.

Parasitic Worms. These are of many kinds—tapeworms, round-worms, hair-worms, and so on. Host specificity is usually restricted, but the round-worm *Heterakis* is widespread, affecting primarily intestinal caeca (blind gut) causing ulceration, sometimes leading to perforation. Perforation of the gut wall, with subsequent fatal peritonitis, has been found in infected pelicans. The Ostrich harbours a peculiar tapeworm of its own (*Houttuynia*).

Filariasis is a blood-disease characterised by anaemia and fits, and caused by the minute larvae of a worm (*Filaria*) circulating in the blood. It is common in wild passerines, e.g. finches and crows.

Gapes is due to a nematode worm (*Syngamus trachaelis*) which infests the upper airways, causing obstruction. It occurs in the Rook, in which it rarely produces symptoms, but may be passed on to domestic poultry.

Flukes (*Renicola*), related to the liver fluke of sheep, occur in the kidneys of many wild birds, particularly marine birds (divers, gulls, etc.), which acquire them from fish in whose skins the larval stage of the worm develops. When present in large numbers, flukes cause death from renal (kidney) failure.

Arthropods. Mites (*see* Bird-Mite) are the most frequent arthropod parasites of birds. Most species are ectoparasites (surface parasites) affecting the feathers, scales of the feet, and naked parts of the face, where they set up inflammation causing anaemia. Other mites burrow beneath the skin and subsist on the subcutaneous fat (e.g. in storks), or attack the respiratory passages causing lung abscesses (*pulmonary acariasis*), especially in pheasants ; still another mite inhabits the air-sacs.

BLOOD and KIDNEY DISEASES

Apart from anaemia, leukaemia is frequently fatal to wild birds. Characterised by an enormous increase in the white blood-cells and a decrease in red corpuscles, the disease leads to death from internal asphyxia.

Birds of all kinds, but particularly aquatic birds, are very prone to various forms of nephritis, resulting in defective elimination by a sort of "renal constipation", the urinary tubules being blocked with semi-solid secretion. This occurs especially in the metabolic disorder known to veterinarians as "visceral gout", where chalky deposits are found on the serous membranes and nodules develop in the joints—a common occurrence in aged parrots and also in budgerigars.

Both benign and malignant tumours are known in birds, but they are rare, except in captive or domesticated examples.

DISHWASHER. Local name for both the Pied and White Wagtail (*qq.v.*), two birds which are very similar in their appearance and which both show a preference for water—hence also their other name, Water Wagtail.

DISPLAY—A BIRD'S SIGN LANGUAGE

DEREK GOODWIN

Display is an important means of communication, indicating whether danger threatens, a bird is ready to breed, and so forth. It also cements the bond between a pair by such actions as courtship feeding and billing. See also *Behaviour ; Courtship ; Dance*

DISPLAY. This term, as generally used by students of bird behaviour, is applied to various postures or movements whose function is to elicit a particular response in some other creature—usually a fellow-member of the species. Display is often reinforced by calls which form an essential part of the performance.

The bird is not, of course, conscious of the purpose of its display, but in a certain mood it cannot help posturing in a certain way. These movements are instinctively recognized by its fellows—that is to say, they give them

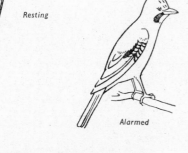

Resting

Alarmed

DISPLAY. This Jay's different postures show clearly how display might very nearly be called a language

information about the displaying bird's condition and probably future actions, and stimulate them to give an appropriate response. This response varies according to circumstances: the same display by a male bird might elicit an aggressive response from a territory-holding male, fear and flight from a trespassing male, or sexual advances from an unpaired female.

The displays of birds in breeding condition (or near it) towards others of the same species may be definitely aggressive or sexual in character, or of a kind that may develop into either. These last might be better termed self-assertive displays, since it is the response of the bird at which the display is directed that chiefly determines whether the display will develop into attack or courtship. Among British birds these three types of display can

be exemplified by the presentation of its red breast by the Robin (aggressive), the formalised preening behind the wing of pigeons and doves (sexual), and the bowing and cooing display of the latter (self-assertive). Even where the sexual and aggressive display are distinct in their " pure " forms, the bird may waver in feeling between the two moods and show consequent intermediate forms of display.

Some displays seem to be intended to demonstrate submissiveness or inferiority and thus inhibit aggressiveness in their " superiors ". Such displays are usually the " opposite " of threatening or self assertive displays. For example, when aggressive, the Red-legged Partridge holds itself erect, presenting the bright contrasting markings of its head, throat and flanks ; but when feeling inferior, it adopts a crouching posture with lowered head. Male rooks and jays show " inferiority " by the same display as that with which the females of their species invite coition—partial spreading of the wings and quivering of the tail.

Colour—and its Social Uses. Bright or contrasting colours in birds almost always have a social function, serving as signals to others of the same species. In display they are often emphasised by special movements, as with the red breast of the Robin or the black and silver markings on the neck of the Turtle-Dove. They may, however, be shown automatically. Thus many birds, e.g. Bullfinch,

Self-Assertive Display

Quivering Display

Turtle-Dove and Chaffinch, have a white area on the rump or outer tail feathers which is conspicuous in flight and flashes into view when the bird takes wing ; in appropriate circumstances this serves to attract the eyes of their companions and induce them to follow.

A bird's eye is normally conspicuous, and the head markings are often designed to conceal it (*see* Camouflage ; Protective Coloration). On the other hand some birds' eyes are backed or surrounded by contrastingly coloured skin or feathers, the purpose of which seems to be to increase its conspicuousness ; e.g. the white feathers around the eye of the Black-headed Gull. In birds which have a brightly-coloured iris, its effect is often enhanced by contraction of the pupil during display. The Wood-Pigeon's pale silvery-yellow eyes look as if they are about to burst out of its head as it bows in self-assertive display before its mate or rival.

The bill is so obviously an organ of aggression and attack that it is not surprising to find it often emphasised by bright colour or contrasting adjacent feathers. Bright or contrasting colours on the bill itself may, however, be connected with parental feeding of the young, and have no aggressive purpose.

Display Flights. These are indulged in by very many species, particularly, but by no means exclusively, those living on the ground in open country. They most commonly serve to advertise the presence of a bird (usually a territory-holding male) in breeding condition.

They vary greatly in form—from, for instance, the crazy-seeming acrobatics of the Lapwing to the alternate wing-clapping and gliding of the common Pigeon or the soaring song-flight of the Skylark—but they almost always have three things in common. They differ in form from the normal " everyday " flight ; they make the bird extremely conspicuous ; and they are reinforced by sound, either vocal (song of Tree-Pipit, piping of Golden Plover) or mechanical (wing clapping of pigeons, the well-known and characteristic " bleating " or " drumming " of Snipe).

Distraction Displays. Aggressive displays directed towards fellow members of the species may be the same as those shown towards other enemies ; they are usually so, indeed, if no parental or sexual impulses are involved. But one class of display is directed exclusively towards other species that the bird fears to attack. These are what are now generally called distraction displays, and are used by many species when an enemy approaches the eggs or young, particularly if it comes upon them suddenly while they are hatching or brooding small young.

The function of a distraction display is to divert the enemy from the eggs or young by causing it to pursue—or at least focus its attention upon—the displaying parent. The bird may flutter or hobble about in an awkward manner as if crippled (the so-called *injury-feigning*), recovering, if pursued, as it leaves the danger zone until it finally flies away unimpeded. The bird may run in a crouching manner suggestive of a small mammal, stand or lie with slowly flapping wings, or make various other conspicuous movements.

Such behaviour merely reveals the presence of a near-by nest to a knowledgeable human, but it is highly effective with other predatory mammals. The writer has seen a dog, jumping from the top of a high bank almost on top of a Mallard and her brood, eagerly pursuing the duck as she floundered across the water, ignoring the scattering ducklings and not even returning to look for them after their mother had taken wing.

Intention Movements. There is much evidence about the probable origin of bird display. When a bird has a rather weak impulse to indulge in some particular activity, it will show movements indicating this, even if it does nothing more. Thus a bird may show incipient movements of leaping and flying away—flexing its legs, flicking its wings and tail, and so forth—without actually doing so. It may then quieten down, or it may perform these movements many times until it finally " works itself up " to a point of actually departing—human guests often show similar behaviour. Such incipient movements, called intention movements, tell the experienced watcher by which particular impulse a bird was moved originally—to fly off, to disgorge food, to fight, to mate—even though it does not actually engage in the activity.

Displacement and Redirected Activities. Like other animals, including Man, birds often practise apparently irrelevant behaviour activities. They may, for example, make preening or feeding movements in the intervals of fighting or courting. These are termed displacement activities, and appear to be shown when a bird is unable to perform the act appropriate to the impulse or *drive* that is exciting it, and finds relief for its tension by an inappropriate action.

If a bird's aggressive feelings are strongly aroused but it is unable (or does not dare) to attack the creature responsible, it may vent its feelings by attacking some other creature or by attacking the ground, branches of trees or other inanimate objects. This behaviour, termed redirected aggression, is, of course, common in human beings also. Redirected activities differ from displacement activities in that the behaviour shown is appropriate to the impulse activating the bird, and only the object on which it is performed is " wrong ".

Such bird displays as have been carefully analysed have been found to consist of intention movements and displacement or redirected activities in various combinations. This discovery provides a clue to their origin. When we find that the aggressive displays of, for instance, the Herring-Gull and the Red-legged

Eric Hosking, W. Farnsworth, G. K. Yeates, James Gibson

DISPLAY. (1) Cock Slavonian Grebe displaying to hen who affects not to take any notice until (2) the cock pretends to turn away; (3) Crossbill feeding the brooding hen; (4) Male Spotted Flycatcher has brought some food for his young, but the hen decides that she needs some attention instead; (5) Little Tern feeding his mate with fish; (6) Heron in an aggressive mood; (7) Avocet family, picture of domestic bliss; (8) Greater Black-backed Gull displaying its wings; (9) Dotterel, injury-feigning; (10) Herons in courtship display, the hen bowing before the cock; (11) Ruffs in communal display

Partridge are "built up" of the combined intention movements of both attacking and fleeing, we have good reason to suppose that the bird is impelled simultaneously by both anger and fear. Like many a human, it is "willing to wound but afraid to strike".

Most, if not all, displays appear to be shown in, or to owe their origin to, conflict situations of this sort. Often in the course of their evolution, the movements have become ritualised and almost unrecognizably differentiated from their original form, or have developed into symbolic movements of a formalised, incomplete or exaggerated character which serve to emphasise the special display plumage that has presumably co-evolved with them.

In some cases, particularly in the more elaborate sexual displays, the whole display seems to have been separated altogether from the conflict situation in which we presume it to have had its origin, and to be shown whenever the bird is in a state of specific excitement.

COURTSHIP

This term, as applied to birds, is used in a rather wide sense. It might be defined as "all those patterns of behaviour which are directed at an individual of the opposite sex with the purpose of initiating or preserving a sexual bond between them". Such a definition will include both those activities which lead directly to coition or nest-building, and those which are *self-exhausting* and do not lead at once to any overt reproductive behaviour.

Courtship starts when the prospective mates have come together. Commonly this will have been effected though the attraction of the female by the calls and display of a territory-holding male. Birds in breeding condition are usually in a predominantly aggressive mood.

The first response of the male is usually to display in a threatening or self-assertive manner, and the female must respond in such a way as to elicit sexual rather than aggressive behaviour from him.

To do this she will often show some form of appeasing or submissive display. This may be a symbolic invitation to mate (as in many corvine birds) or food-begging (as in the gulls). But such behaviour will often be prefaced or interspersed with self-assertive or even threatening display on her part. Such display may have special appeasing gestures added to it, as in paired or pairing Black-headed Gulls, which greet each other by thrusting forward their lowered heads (aggressive display) but then immediately stretch up their necks and turn their dark faces away from each other. With some other species—such as the Jay—self-assertive display between paired birds often seems to express no hostility *towards each other* but rather to be in the nature of mutual "back-slapping". A human parallel might be found in the fact that we tolerate or even welcome behaviour from our friends which we would resent from other people.

Courtship-Feeding of the female by the male (or, more rarely, vice versa) is common in a great many species. The Rook, domestic fowl and Canary might be instanced as familiar birds in which the habit is strongly developed. The method of feeding the female is usually the same as that used in feeding the young. She often begs for food with the same calls and wing-flutterings as are used by the fledged young bird ; but her response varies according to mood or degree of hunger, or the stage she has reached in the reproductive cycle.

Thus female rooks and jays beg in a juvenile manner when they have eggs, are about to lay, or are exceptionally hungry. At other times they are more likely to respond with the tail-quivering appeasing display, or to accept the food without any demonstration. In species in which only the female incubates, courtship-feeding is often carried on into the incubation period, the male regularly bringing supplies to the sitting female.

In some birds courtship-feeding has been reduced to (or has never developed further than) a purely symbolic

Lewis Wayne Walker

DISPLAY. *Mating Dance of the Albatross (1): Cock and hen face each other at the beginning of the dance, often rubbing bills with whistling cries*

act in which no food normally passes ; the pre-copulatory "billing" of the Barbary-Dove and domestic Pigeon is a typical example.

In species which practise courtship-feeding the male may show some reluctance to hand over the food ; this is particularly noticeable in the early stages of the breeding cycle, when his urge to feed his mate is still rather weak. This phase, which is temporary or intermittent in most species, has in others been developed and elaborated to form an important part of the courtship. The *fish flight* of the Common

Lewis Wayne Walker

DISPLAY. *Mating Dance of the Albatross (2) : cock at the end of the dance puts his bill under the wing, after which he will utter a loud, groaning cry*

Tern is an example. One bird (early in the season it may be of either sex, but later it is normally a male) catches a fish and flies round calling loudly until it is joined by a second bird which flies in front of it. The fish is not usually given away—although the second bird may snatch it—and the chief function of the fish-flight appears to be to enable prospective mates to get acquainted. Once the birds have paired normal courtship-feeding is regular.

The male bird usually takes the initiative in finding a suitable nesting site, and he may have special displays to call his mate's attention to it. The cock Lapwing, for example, alternately raises and lowers his tail so that his chestnut undertail coverts catch the hen's eye and entice her to the " scrape " he is making. Appeasing displays, actual or symbolic presentation of food or nesting material, and other affectionate behaviour between the pair commonly take place at the selected site.

Group Displays. In some birds, such as the Black Grouse and the Ruff, there is no paired life apart from mating and general association outside the breeding season. The males gather to display in some traditional place (termed a " lek ") where each acquires a small territory within the main gathering. The females visit these display grounds, and each chooses one of several males which eagerly display to her.

Pair-formation in most ducks takes place in a somewhat similar way (although these birds do live a paired life for months and in some cases permanently). A group of males gathers together to display, usually in the vicinity of a female who has given signs that she is ready to pair. She finally chooses a male, keeping close to him and showing hostility towards others. In some species she herself attacks any " rejected " suitor who approaches her ; in others she incites the drake of her choice to do so. The most common way in which the female Mallard displays attachment for her mate is by making the very calls and movements of threatening another drake (although none is present)—an example of a functional display ritualised into a stereotyped action which has acquired a new meaning.

Tenderness—and the Young. A striking fact about the courtship behaviour of birds (and other animals) is that all the behaviour-patterns and calls that appear to express affection between the partners—that is to say, all that are not *directly* concerned with intimidation, appeasement, nesting or copulation (and some that are)—are the same as those shown towards the young. This suggests that such behaviour and the subjective feelings of tenderness or affection presumably associated with it have their origin in parental care and have only secondarily become incorporated in the sexual behaviour of these animals.

Consult : King Solomon's Ring (New Light on Animal Ways), K. Z. Lorenz (Methuen & Co.), 1950 ; Social Behaviour in Animals, N. Tinbergen (Methuen & Co.), 1953.

DISTRIBUTION. *See* Geographical Distribution ; *further see* Population.

DIVER. Only four species of this large aquatic bird have been observed in the British Isles : the Black-throated Diver, Great Northern Diver, White-billed Diver (recorded only four times) and Red-throated Diver. They are described under their own names.

Divers are seen usually on the coast or on near-by lochs. They are unsociable, and one breeding pair may claim a whole loch as its territory (*q.v.*). Normally they will come to land only for breeding, spending most of their time on the water. They walk with difficulty, for their tibiae are enclosed in the body's skin.

Their bodies are heavy and powerful, their wings small and pointed and set fairly far back, though the birds fly well with quick, regular wing beats. Their flight silhouette is unmistakable—rather humpbacked—for the neck is stretched forward from a plane below the shoulders, while the short legs are stretched beyond the tiny tail. When alighting, divers strike the water with their breasts.

The birds float low in the water, paddling with alternate feet. When diving, they may use their wings to increase their underwater speed, though they usually rely only on their legs. They move faster below than on the surface of water.

As their name implies, these birds are expert divers, feeding under the water—mainly on fish—unless their prey is too large to be swallowed whole. When alarmed, they will submerge rather than take to the air.

DOTTEREL—Charadrius morinellus. This lovely little wader, a member of the Plover family, was once quite a common sight in Great Britain, but was brought to the verge of extinction by a combination of factors. It was friendly and tame—almost stupidly so—and it was good to eat (as far back as 1512, a household book of the Dukes of Northumberland contains the entry " Dotterels to be bought for my Lord ") ; its feathers made excellent dressing flies for anglers ; and when it threatened to become extinct, egg collectors reduced its numbers still further.

Today, thanks to vigorous protection, the Dotterel breeds sparingly in the solitary mountain fastnesses of Scotland, England and Wales. It arrives at its breeding sites in April and May, and leaves again in August or September. It is also a rare passage migrant to England and the south of Scotland ; abroad it is native to north Europe and north Asia.

The Dotterel is difficult to spot, for it is well camouflaged and merges into its surroundings. It has a grey-brown mantle and breast, with a broad white line separating its breast, and rich chestnut coloured underparts, which shade into a black belly. The top of its head is dark brown, and it has a broad white line over each eye, the two meeting in a V at its nape. Its cheeks are white, and the feathers beneath its dark tail are also white. Its bill is black and

G. K. Yeates

DIVER. *The Red-throated Diver is the one most likely to be seen in Britain, usually in the north*

its legs yellowish. The plumage is duller in Winter. Male and female are alike. The length of the Dotterel is 8 or 9 in., its tarsus is 1·4 in. Its wing span is a little over 1 ft., and its weight 3 oz.

Once it has been spotted, the Dotterel's tameness makes it easy to watch at close quarters. It has its family's typical walk ; it runs for a short distance, stops, tilts forward, and perhaps picks up some food. It also has a habit of stretching one or both wings, sometimes in readiness for flight. On the wing the Dotterel is graceful, swift and buoyant, with fast-beating wings.

Its voice is a sweet twittering whistle ; the alarm note is harsher, and there is a special soft and subdued note when the chicks are in the nest.

The Dotterel always nests at high altitudes—usually 3,000 to 4,000 ft. above sea-level, and never lower than 2,000 ft.—on bare mountain fells. The breeding season is in late May or early June, and the nest is merely a depression among the heather, tussocky ground or grasses. The eggs (three is the normal number) are ground-coloured, heavily blotched and spotted in brownish-black. In contrast to the procedure of most birds, the cock seems to do most of the hatching, the period being about three weeks, or shorter if the weather is unusually warm. He also has the major share in looking after and rearing the chicks, although the hen sometimes takes part. The young are in the nest for only about 24 hours, and are fully fledged in a month. One brood is normally reared in a season.

The Dotterel's food consists mainly of insects with some vegetable matter. In the breeding season most of its feeding is done during the night, when it sometimes travels many miles from its nesting ground. The collective term for a party of dotterels is a "trip".

DOUBLE SNIPE. Though certainly not twice the size of the Common Snipe, the Great Snipe (*q.v.*) is often called thus. It is very similar to the Common variety, although it appears heavier and darker. Its flight is slower and heavier, and it is a less vocal bird than the Common Snipe. There is only a difference of ½ in. or so in the size of the two.

DOVE. This term is used almost synonymously with *Pigeon* (*q.v.*), although *Dove* is applied more frequently to the smaller, more slender species, such as the turtle-doves, stock-doves and rock-doves ; whereas *Pigeon* is the name given more often to the larger species, with fuller rounded or squared tails. A typical example of these is the Wood-Pigeon. *See further* under the individual names; *also* Columbidae.

DOVEKIE. Name by which the Little Auk (*q.v.*) is known in north America. In this country the Black Guillemot (*q.v.*), a fairly close relative, is sometimes called thus, particularly in the north.

DOWITCHER. Alternative name for Red-breasted Snipe (*q.v.*), a rare visitor to this country from North America.

DOWN FEATHER. Soft feather hidden below the outer feathers (unless these are absent, as in vultures). Nestling birds have two kinds of down feathers ; those which later make way for the contour feathers, and a very soft sort of down—the *pre-plumulae*—later replaced by the adult down feathers. *See also* Feather.

G. K. Yeates

DOTTEREL. *This beautiful member of the Plover family has become almost extinct in this country*

DRAKE. Male duck. The word is derived from one of the Teutonic languages, though its etymology is somewhat dubious.

DUCK. This, at first sight, is such a well-known bird that it hardly seems to warrant a description. It will, however, come as a surprise to those who associate it only with the village pond, park or poulterer's shop to learn that there are 30 species of duck on the British list.

The Duck family—or *Anatidae*—is one of the two families of the order *Anseriformes*, the other being the *Anhimidae*, comprising the South American screamers. The *Anatidae*, apart from ducks, include the geese, swans and mergansers (*qq.v.*), and total 46 species on the British list. Compared with swans and geese, ducks form a less concise natural unit, and it is usual to divide them into surface-feeding ducks (those inhabiting marshes and ponds) and diving ducks (those found in open waters and the sea).

Sheld-ducks, although surface-feeders, are sea-ducks and are best considered in a separate group ; particularly as they are more goose-like in appearance and behaviour than other ducks, and may, therefore, almost be considered as a link between geese and the more typical ducks. Some ornithologists include the mergansers or sawbills among ducks, but for the purposes of this article they will be considered as a separate group, described under their own heading.

Surface-Feeding Ducks. These feed by dabbling or "up-ending" rather than by diving and, in taking wing, spring clear of the water. The sexes differ, the males (drakes) being brightly coloured, while the females are generally a dull, mottled brown. Both sexes have a bright patch on the secondaries, the *speculum*, which, apart from the drake's distinctive plumage, serves to distinguish the different species.

Drakes moult (or go into eclipse) in Summer or early Autumn, their eclipse plumage resembling that of the female and of juveniles, except for the wings, which retain their characteristic markings. Females acquire their eclipse plumage a little later, though this scarcely alters their usual drab appearance. As the wing-quills and tail-quills are shed almost simultaneously, ducks generally pass through a flightless period, lasting a few weeks, each year. Full plumage is resumed between September and December.

Surface-feeding ducks include the Mallard (from which all British domestic duck are descended), Pintail, Gadwall, Wigeon and American Wigeon, Shoveler, Teal and Blue-winged Teal, and Garganey. All these are described under their own names and, except for the Shoveler (*Spatula clypeata*), belong to

Eric Hosking

DUCK. *Mallards, the wild duck from which all our domestic stock is descended. The picture shows the different plumages of males and females*

the genus *Anas*. Garganeys, gadwalls and wigeons feed by day, while mallards, pintails and teals prefer to feed during the night.

These ducks will rest on land as well as on water, often assuming a characteristic one-legged stance. They fly with slower wing beats than the diving ducks, in tight packs on short flights, but in Indian file for longer distances.

Diving Ducks. These are shorter and more stocky than the surface-feeders and their legs are set further back on the body, so that they walk less easily and more upright. They rarely come to land, except for breeding, and dive for their food, scarcely ever up-ending like surface-feeders. They take off by pattering along the surface of water but, once airborne, they fly with more rapid wing beats. If alarmed when near the shore, they will often swim further out rather than take to the air.

Although the females have a duller plumage than the males, their appearance (apart from the various female eider-ducks) is far more colourful than that of the surface-feeders. There is usually no speculum in either sex, though some species boast a white wing-bar. The eclipse, too, is usually less clearly visible.

There are 15 diving-ducks on the British list, all described under their own names. They are : Red-crested Pochard, Scaup, Tufted Duck, Pochard, White-eyed Pochard (or Ferruginous Duck), Buffel-headed Duck, Golden-Eye, Long-tailed Duck, Velvet Scoter, Surf-Scoter, Common Scoter, Harlequin-Duck, Steller's Eider, Eider-Duck, King-Eider.

Eiders and scoters are essentially birds of the sea and, together with the Harlequin and Long-tailed Duck, are rarely seen inland. All eiders

are distinguished by their longish heads with sloping foreheads and their high-based bills. They are large and heavy-built, and walk with a distinct nautical roll. Scoters, too, are rather heavy-built, but buoyant swimmers. The males of those on the British list are almost entirely black, the females dark brown.

Sheld-Ducks. These are far more goose-like in appearance and behaviour than all other ducks—even to the extent of flying in V-formation, in the manner of geese, on long journeys. Sheld-ducks are sea-ducks which *do not dive* for their food but wade into shallow water for marine molluscs, small fish and such-like, which have been left behind by the receding tide.

Sheld-ducks will submerge their heads and necks, and even *up-end* like the typical surface-feeding ducks of ponds and marshes. Between tides, sheld-ducks usually stay on shore. Unlike the males of the more typical ducks, sheld-drakes assist in the rearing of the young.

There are only two sheld-ducks on the British list—the common Sheld-Duck and the Ruddy Sheld-Duck (*qq.v.*), which is known in India as Brahminy Duck.

DUCK ADOPTION SCHEME. By this scheme, formed under the auspices of the International Committee for Bird Preservation, a gift of 6s. sent to the Duck Adoption Scheme, I.C.B.P., c/o The Natural History Museum, London, S.W.7, brings to the donor as a Christmas card a form for adopting and naming a ringed duck or goose.

The bird will remain in communication with its sponsor, who will be informed of its every appearance as soon as recorded, and will be able to follow its widespread journeys. Such journeys have taken wigeons to the Siberian river Ob, tufted ducks elsewhere in Asia, and teals from the Arctic to places as far apart as Newfoundland, Venice and the Azores.

DUNBIRD. Local name for Pochard (*q.v.*), which is the only duck in which the male presents an all-grey, or dun, appearance apart from the chestnut head and neck.

DUN DIVER. Local name for young or female Goosander (*q.v.*). The bird in flight bears a marked resemblance to a Diver (*q.v.*)

Eric Hosking

DIVER FAMILY, *the Red-throated, commonest of British divers, is an unsociable bird, preferring solitude*

For text see pages 181 and 458

To face page 184

DUNGENESS BIRD SANCTUARY. This reserve comprises nearly two square miles of the ten square miles of the Dungeness shingle area, and belongs to the Royal Society for the Protection of Birds. When Dungeness was in danger of exploitation from building speculators, Mr. R. B. Burrowes, in 1929, took up the task of preserving it. With financial and legal help from the R.S.P.B.—each contributing about £4,000—and with substantial help from the Dungeness Preservation Fund Committee (presided over by the late Sir Leslie Probyn), the whole place was at last made secure for bird preservation in 1937.

Most of the land is covered with sparse vegetation — lichens, broom, and gorse ; although there are parts which are completely devoid of plant life. Dungeness is in one of the main paths of bird migration, where the great stream of birds from Scandinavia joins the western stream from the west coast of Denmark, Germany, the Netherlands and Belgium. Dungeness Bird Sanctuary has now become one of the main observation stations in the country for migrating birds.

Some rare birds have visited the reserve : a few pairs of Stone-Curlew nest annually, harrier-hawks are not uncommon, and even an Osprey has been known to settle on the shingle. Among more common birds settling at Dungeness are the Ringed Plover, many wheatears and other small birds. Up to the beginning of the Second World War, the R.S.P.B. watcher, Mr. John R. Tart, had preserved fine colonies of sea-birds on the reserve's west beach, comprising four different species of terns and of gulls.

During and since the war an invasion of foxes has driven off all colonies of gulls and terns except for a few herring-gulls ; but this trouble is now being met. Marauding crows, too, have been reduced in numbers by R.S.P.B. watcher Mr. H. E. Axell, who has done fine work in rebuilding the sanctuary, so that by 1954 a few pairs of terns and gulls were again nesting there.

Bird-watchers are confident that once they have destroyed the foxes and reduced the numbers of crows, there is every reason for the vast, desolate, unfrequented stretches of Dungeness shingle becoming a valuable resort of many of the rarer British birds.

DUNLIN—Calidris alpina. Any large congregation of birds on a sea-shore will probably include a majority of dunlins for these are the most common and widespread of our small waders. Two types, the Southern (*C. a. shinzii*) and Northern (*C. a. alpina*), come to Britain as summer visitors, winter visitors and passage migrants, but only the Southern Dunlin stays to breed. To the ordinary observer

W. Farnsworth

DUNLIN. This, the most common of small waders in this country, is but rarely seen alone

both kinds are identical in appearance ; the Southern bird being slightly smaller.

The Dunlin breeds most commonly in Scotland, especially in the Hebrides, Orkneys and Shetlands ; in England and Wales, it nests only on the moors of Breconshire and Derbyshire and the Lancashire coast. Within recent years it has, however, been recorded in other places and it also breeds in small numbers in Ireland. As passage migrants and winter visitors both Southern and Northern dunlins are abundant, and can be seen in their hundreds on all coasts, mud flats, and estuaries. Abroad, dunlins breed in northern Europe and Asia, Canada and Greenland.

In appearance the Dunlin is a plump bird. Its plumage varies with the seasons, but, on the whole, the predominating colour is brown. It is more conspicuous in Summer, for it is then the only small wader with a black patch on its breast. Its back is chestnut flecked with black, and its undertail coverts are white. Its wings are greyish-brown, with a light wing bar. In Winter the white is much more in evidence on both breast and throat. The longish, slightly curved bill varies in length, that of the female usually being longer. The legs are dark olive. Male and female are alike. The length of the Southern Dunlin is 6¾ in., with a tarsus of 0·8 in. The wing span is approximately 1 ft. and the weight 1½ oz. The length of the Northern Dunlin is 7½ in. ; with the other measurements correspondingly larger.

One of the most gregarious of birds, the Dunlin is found in company with other waders ; on the moors, it has a special liking for the company of golden plovers. It is naturally deliberate in its movements ; its walk is unhurried, with short steps, and it runs only when necessary in search of food. At rest it has a huddled pose. It is fond of wading in shallow water and probing the mud for worms ; if necessary, it will also swim.

The individual voice of the Dunlin is a rather harsh note, but the feeding flocks have a conversational twitter. There is also a musical call uttered on the ground, reminiscent somewhat of the Greenshank's alarm. In its display flight, the Dunlin produces a characteristic purring trill, which gives it the local name of " Purre ". It is best heard in May, June and July.

Dunlins indulge in many marvellous evolutions in the air, especially in the breeding season. These are performed en masse, and the rushing wings produce an astonishing humming sound.

Dunlins arrive about April at their breeding sites on the moors, marshes and estuaries—in the central highlands of Scotland often at altitudes as high as 3,000 ft. above sea-level. They leave again for their winter quarters on the Continent as soon as the chicks can fly.

The nest, which is nearly always near water, is a compact little bowl of grass about 3 in. in diameter ; and the normal number of eggs is four, laid in May or June. They vary very much in colour, but are generally brown or yellow with blotches of chestnut or chocolate-brown. The young, which are a beautiful cream colour, are quickly on the run, attended by both parents. One brood is reared a season.

Dunlins get their food by burrowing in the mud of estuaries and sea-shores. It is almost wholly composed of animal matter, and the bird will often be seen to stamp or patter on the mud, presumably in an endeavour to bring worms to the surface—a performance also observable in other birds of the shore.

The Dunlin has many local names, including Stint, Oxbird, Plover-Page and Sea-Snipe.

DUNNOCK. Old English name for Hedge-Sparrow (*q.v.*), meaning " the little greyish-brown bird ".

DUNTER. Name by which the Eider-Duck (*q.v.*) is commonly known in Scotland.

DUSKY THRUSH—Turdus eunomus. There are only one or two records of the appearance of this species of thrush in the British Isles, and few details are available concerning its behaviour and habits. The Dusky Thrush breeds in the outskirts of woods and forests in northern Asia, and winters in north India, China and Japan. Descriptions of its plumage are scanty. Black spots on its breast are its best identification marks ; its upper parts are dark brown, mingled with chestnut, especially on its rump ; chestnut also appears on its underwings, and its throat is white-speckled at the sides. It is 9 in. long, and about the size of the Song-Thrush (*q.v.*).

Its behaviour and habits are said to resemble those of the Fieldfare (*q.v.*), and its voice is likened to that of the Song-Thrush, but less robust. The Dusky Thrush is gregarious in Winter. May and June are its breeding months ; it nests in small trees and on the ground, and four or five eggs, resembling in shape and colour those of the Blackbird, are laid. Worms, insects and seeds form its diet.

DUSKY WARBLER—Phylloscopus fuscatus. Very rare in Britain, this warbler breeds in Russia and winters in China and India. A little brown bird, 4½ in. long, it has whitish-buff underparts, and no green or yellow in its dress. Some of its characteristics resemble those of the Reed-Warbler (*q.v.*). It is restless and skulking in its behaviour. Its call is described as resembling the notes of the Chiffchaff and Red-breasted Fly-catcher, as well as the common call of British warblers of the same family. No reliable report of the song is known. The Editor once heard a caged specimen whose song resembled some calls of the Nuthatch.

The Dusky Warbler breeds, as a rule, near water. Its dome-shaped nest, built of dry grasses and moss, is on or near the ground ; five or six eggs are laid in June. Small insects of many kinds are its chief food.

Jan P. Strijbos

DUNLIN. *This photograph shows clearly the marks made by a Dunlin stamping around in a circle to bring worms—its favourite food—to the surface*

E

EAGLE

EAGLE. True eagles form the genus *Aquila* of the family *Falconidae* of the order *Falconiformes*. There are only two species on the British list : the resident Golden Eagle (*q.v.*), now mainly confined to parts of Scotland ; and the Spotted Eagle (*q.v.*), which occasionally wanders here from the Continent.

These large and majestic-looking birds of prey possess strong, hooked bills with sharp cutting edges ; there is a conspicuous patch of fleshy skin (the " cere ") at the base of the upper mandible, where the large nostrils are situated. The wings are large and broad, and somewhat rounded. The tail is also rounded. The tarsus is feathered as far as the toes ; there are four of the latter, three directed forwards and one behind, all with sharp, curved claws.

The sexes are similar in plumage, but the females are larger than the males. The nesting-site is generally on a crag or in a tree in a remote mountainous area. The eggs are white with reddish-brown blotches, but are greenish internally. The young remain in the nest for some weeks.

Eagles are easily distinguished in flight from other members of the family *Falconidae* by their majestic movements and by the fact that when they are soaring their heads appear much larger than those of buzzards, hawks, kites, harriers and falcons. Most eagles hunt by pouncing on their prey, although some of those not often seen in this country feed on carrion.

The White-tailed Eagle (*q.v.*), also called Grey Sea-Eagle, Sea-Eagle, or Erne, belongs to the genus *Haliaeetus* of the family *Falconidae*. It is a bulkier-looking creature than the true eagles of the genus *Aquila*, its tail is much shorter and wedge-shaped, and its tarsus is unfeathered. It resembles a vulture in its long, soaring flight. The White-tailed Eagle feeds on fish, mammals, birds and carrion.

EAGLE-OWL—Bubo bubo. Rare vagrant to the British Isles, this owl is widely distributed throughout Europe, Africa, Asia and America, where it breeds in forests, cliffs, ravines and valleys. It is easily recognized by its enormous size and its very conspicuous ear

tufts ; the latter have earned it the local name of " eared owl ". It can raise or flatten these " ears " at will.

Above, its plumage is blackish-brown, tinged with yellow, the underparts are a light buff, heavily streaked with dark brown, more boldly so on the lower breast ; the tail and wings are barred, and the tarsus is thickly feathered. The bird's extremely fierce appearance is due in no small degree to its extraordinary flashing yellow eyes. Its length is, over 2 ft., and its tarsus 3 in. Its weight is about 14 lb., and its wing span is on an average about 3 ft. The female has the same appearance but, as is usual with owls, is larger than the male.

The Eagle-Owl has the noiseless flight of its family and hunts by night, except in countries where daylight lingers long in the Summer, where it has perforce to hunt sometimes before dark. It is a solitary bird and roosts on cliffs, in ruins and hollow trees.

The German name for the bird, " *Uhu* " (the " u " being pronounced as " oo " in " mood "), is the best representation of the chief call notes of both the male and female. Under good conditions the sound can be heard

Fox

EAGLE. *Small wonder that the Eagle, here rearing up in all its might, is known as the king of birds*

clearly fifty or even a hundred yards away. The Editor recorded the calls on high, steep rocks, using a cradle.

The Eagle-Owl makes no nest, and lays its two or three eggs on the ledge of a cliff or rock, in a hollow tree or even on the ground. Its breeding season differs according to the country frequented, but is usually from February to May. The eggs are hatched by the hen alone, for well over a month, during which she is fed by the male. The young leave the nest in five or six weeks, and one brood is reared.

The food of the Eagle-Owl consists entirely of animals and birds. An object of terror to all wild life, it will attack any animal it meets and has been known to kill a roe-deer. Birds of all species are also its prey. Eagle-Owls live to a great age and breed well in captivity.

Fox

EAGLE-OWL. *This fierce-looking owl is a great hunter that will attack any wild animal crossing its path. It has even been known to kill a roe-deer*

EAR, Ear Covert and Horn. Feather-covered part underneath and behind the eye of a bird. It is loosely called the " ear ", but its scientific name is " ear covert " or " auricular ", since it covers the ear opening underneath. The soft feathers of the auriculars often contrast in colouring with the rest of the bird's plumage. When they extend beyond the bird's neck, they are described as " horns " : this is particularly marked among grebes, less so among some owls and herons, and least among the shorelarks.

The so-called " ears " of the short-eared and long-eared owls are not ear coverts, but ear tufts at the front or sides of the forehead.

EARED GREBE. Name for the Black-necked Grebe (*q.v.*) in North America.

EASTERN BLACK-EARED WHEATEAR— Oenanthe hispanica melanoleuca. Habits, voice, breeding habits and behaviour of this species show no difference from those of its close relative, the Western Black-eared Wheatear, and it is only by the different shades of the plumage that the birds can be distinguished. In the Eastern type the black on the throat extends over a wider area than in the Western, and the Eastern males are also conspicuously whiter. The length is 5¾ in.

The Eastern type has been recorded only rarely in the British Isles. It breeds in southern Italy, Greece and Asia Minor and winters in tropical east Africa, the Sudan and south-west Asia. *See also* Black-eared Wheatear ; Wheatear.

EASTERN DESERT-WHEATEAR— Oenanthe deserti atrogularis. This species breeds in the barren steppes and desert wastes of the Caucasus at altitudes up to 12,000 ft. and winters in the same kind of country in Africa and India. One or two have wandered to the British Isles at rare intervals.

There are slight differences in the plumage of the three Desert Wheatears, but only an expert could tell one from another. The Eastern bird is 5¾ in. long.

Its nest, built of grasses and roots and lined with wool and hair, is placed in a hole in a wall or under a bush. Four eggs are laid, in April and May. The bird shares the typical Wheatear behaviour and habits. Its chief food is insects. *See also* Desert-Wheatear ; Wheatear.

EASTERN GOLDEN PLOVER. *See* Asiatic Golden Plover.

EASTERN GREAT REED-WARBLER— Acrocephalus arundinaceus orientalis. This is a very rare wanderer to the British Isles from its breeding places in south-east Siberia, China and Japan. As regards its behaviour, habits, voice and breeding, it shows no great difference from its close relative of the west, but at close quarters its legs are seen to be bluish-grey instead of brownish-grey, and it has shorter wings. It is 7 in. in length and its tarsus is 1 in., its wing span is approximately 10 in. *See also* Great Reed-Warbler ; Reed-Warbler ; Warbler.

EASTERN LARGE-BILLED REED-BUNTING—Emberiza schoeniclus tschusii. One specimen only of this bird is recorded as having visited Great Britain ; this was seen in Sussex, in 1912. The bird is scarcely distinguishable from the Western Large-billed type, though some observers state that its plumage is a paler shade of grey. Both types have a stouter bill than the Reed-Bunting (*q.v.*). The length is 6¼ in.

The Eastern bird's breeding places are probably confined to the great reed-beds of the lower Danube and south-west Russia. Of its nests and habits, which are like those of the Western type, few details are available. *See also* Bunting ; Large-billed Reed-Bunting.

EASTERN LITTLE BUSTARD. *See* Little Bustard. Apart from the fact that the Eastern bird is generally darker and has broader black bands on its upperparts than the Western, there is very little difference between the two varieties. The Eastern Little Bustard breeds in south Italy, Sicily, Sardinia, Rumania, Greece, Austria, east Germany, Poland and Russia, including west Siberia.

EASTERN RUFOUS TURTLE-DOVE. Alternative name, used especially in older works, for Eastern Turtle-Dove (*q.v.*).

EASTERN SHORT-TOED LARK—Calandrella brachydactyla longipennis. Few specimens only of this lark have appeared in the British Isles at rare intervals, most of them in Scotland. It breeds in Caucasia, Transcaspia, Persia and Afghanistan, wintering farther south and west.

It differs in plumage from its close relative, the Short-Toed Lark (*q.v.*), its upper parts being a paler grey and less rufous, and in its white eye stripe ; but only an expert could identify it with certainty. Its length is 5 in., and its tarsus ¾ in. Its wing span is about 8 in. Its voice is similar to that of the Short-toed Lark.

EASTERN SKYLARK—Alauda arvensis intermedia. This is the Skylark of Siberia, India and Africa ; only five or six have wandered to the British Isles. In appearance and habits it scarcely differs from our Skylark (*q.v.*), but it is described as having a lighter plumage, both above and below, and its tail-coverts are pure white. The length is 7 in.

EASTERN TURTLE-DOVE—Streptopelia orientalis. This bird, the Turtle-Dove of Eastern Asia, which breeds in such countries as China and Japan, very rarely ventures to the British Isles where, in fact, only one appearance has been recorded. It is very similar in behaviour and habits to, and belongs to the same genus as, the British Turtle-Dove, but is a larger bird and has a much darker plumage, both above and below. The white under tail-coverts of the British species are replaced by grey. The length of the Eastern species is about 13 in. The call is longer drawn and more monotonous than that of our Turtle-Dove (*q.v.*). The Eastern Turtle-Dove is also called Rufous Turtle-Dove or Eastern Rufous Turtle-Dove.

EAST SIBERIAN MEADOW-BUNTING—Emberiza cioides castaneiceps. Very little has been recorded about this extremely rare Bunting, which breeds from the Ural Mountains to Korea and winters in China. Only one has been caught alive in Britain—in 1886, at Flamborough Head, in Yorkshire.

A large chestnut brown patch behind its eyes and over the ear coverts shows up clearly against its grey head, and serves to distinguish this bird from the Rock-Bunting (*q.v.*). The female bird is similar, but has duller plumage. The length is 6¼ in.

In its habits the East Siberian Meadow-Bunting resembles the Yellow Bunting (*q.v.*), but it appears to be much less gregarious even in Autumn and Winter. It generally nests in south China on mountain slopes with scattered trees, but also frequents bushy ground in the plains, and often cultivated hillsides. Its song has not been recorded, but it is said to resemble that of the Yellow Bunting without the final drawling note of that bird. The nest is usually found on the lower branches of a small pine tree, but is sometimes placed on the ground beneath a rock or at the foot of a bush ; it is made of twigs, grass, ferns and leaves,

Eric Hosking

EASTERN SKYLARK. *The British bird (above) is almost indistinguishable from its Siberian cousin*

189

Paul Popper

EDUCATING YOUNG BIRDS. Even young birds must learn how to fly and swim ; and here a Great Crested Grebe is carrying her chick on the back to teach it how to dive

and lined with grass and hair. Four or five eggs, more or less earth-coloured with dark streaks and spots, are laid during May to July. *See also* Bunting ; Emberiza.

ECLIPSE. Name for dull plumage acquired by some ducks which is worn for only a short time, after which the bird moults again and resumes its normal plumage.

In the male bird the eclipse occurs about mid-Summer, when his expectations of a family have been realized. The eclipse is particularly marked among the so-called surface-feeding ducks (*see* Duck). For a short period the drake doffs the gay plumage assumed for courtship and becomes almost indistinguishable from the female, except that the normal colouring on the wings is retained. Full plumage is resumed between September and December, depending on the species.

It has been suggested that the male duck assumes this dull garb as a protection against prowling enemies to give him the same measure of protective colouring as the female during the period when he is renewing his quill or flight feathers. These feathers are not replaced in pairs, as with most birds, but are all lost together ; until they are replaced, he is helpless, or at best can escape from potential enemies only by swimming.

Females go into eclipse slightly later than males, usually after the brood has dispersed, but their eclipse plumage is generally indistinguishable in the field from that worn at other times of the year.

EDUCATING YOUNG BIRDS. Most, but not all, birds have to be given instruction by their parents.

One of the first things they learn is how to keep the nest clean (*see* Sanitation). The hen teaches her chicks to scratch and peck, and even the meaning of her clucks. Similar behaviour is found with many birds, but education is generally applied by way of encouragement rather than by direct teaching. This is particularly so in the matter of learning to fly. Ducklings must be persuaded to take to the water ; divers or grebes have to encourage their young to dive.

The Great Crested Grebe, for example, illustrated above, takes the young ones on her back, then swims away from the shore and dives, until they learn the technique.

Even so, a good deal of the behaviour of young birds is purely instinctive, as, for example, the motionless crouching of the young Grouse pressed to the ground from the moment it hears the warning call of its parents until the " all clear " signal is given by another call. The trend towards self-protection has developed in relation to the number of eggs laid and young ones produced, so as to safeguard the species from extinction. *See also* Behaviour.

AROUSING YOUTHFUL ENTHUSIASM

CAPTAIN (S) SIR LEWIS RITCHIE, K.C.V.O., C.B.E., R.N.

The author, who in recent years has devoted much of his time and energy to encouraging young people to share his interest in Nature, here describes what the R.S.P.B. is doing to persuade youngsters to make an intelligent and accurate study of birds

EDUCATION. One of the foremost aims of the Royal Society for the Protection of Birds is the encouragement among children of an intelligent and accurate study of birds. The purpose is threefold. Firstly, to make young people aware of a hobby which costs practically nothing, which will last a lifetime and can be followed anywhere all the year round—which, moreover, takes them into the open air and, properly pursued, harms no sentient being. For this reason, and also because the objects of study are beautiful and mysterious, it holds immeasurable happiness.

Secondly, it seeks to protect wild birds and their nests from interference and destruction through the ignorance and, all too often, the deliberate cruelty of boys and girls. Legislation can do a great deal, but, alas, the mere existence of a law is often an incentive in the mind of the young hooligan to break it. The accepted policy of the R.S.P.B. is to catch the child, if possible, before he or she becomes a hooligan, at any rate as far as birds are concerned.

Thirdly, the R.S.P.B. tries to teach the scientific value of bird field-observation. Children have made several original contributions to the science of ornithology, and those with a scientific bent like to feel that their observations are taken seriously, and that they can contribute to the sum of scientific knowledge in a number of ways, such as watching lines of migration, or helping to build up a census of a particular species.

With these aims in view, the R.S.P.B. has evolved two organizations :

Junior Bird Recorders Club. Membership of this is confined to boys and girls between the ages of 11 and 18. Members over 14 are sent record forms on which observations are entered and rendered to Headquarters quarterly. These are edited, and any thought to be of sufficient general interest are published in the Club's annual report. There is an annual essay competition open to all members between the ages of 14 and 18, the first prize for which is the complete *Handbook of British Birds* in five volumes. The badge of the Club bears a representation of a Swift.

The Headquarters of the R.S.P.B. and of the Club are at 25 Eccleston Square, (near Victoria Station), London, S.W.1.

Bird, Tree and Flower County Challenge Shield Competition. This is open to all schools in Great Britain and Northern Ireland, and is for children of all ages up to 15. A challenge shield is offered in every county where the number of schools entering is sufficiently large, the shield being held for a year by the winning school in the county. The shield is awarded to the school sending in the three best essays on birds and the three best on a selected tree or flower. There is also an inter-county shield awarded to the leading school in Great Britain and Northern Ireland.

Children who enter for this competition are designated Bird, Tree and Flower Cadets. They are divided into teams of nine. Each Cadet selects a bird and tree or flower to be the subject of his study and observation, and ultimately of his essay. Each Cadet must write two essays, one on the chosen bird and the other on the tree or flower which has been the object of his study during the year. Essays must be the result of personal observation and expressed in the child's own words. The three best essays in both these categories selected by the teacher or other responsible person are sent in from each school.

At present shields are awarded in the following counties : Cornwall, Cumberland, Dorset, Gloucestershire, Hampshire, Lancashire, Norfolk, Northamptonshire, Somerset, Suffolk, Surrey, Warwickshire, Wiltshire and Yorkshire.

There is an Open Class entry for schools in counties not yet having a shield of their own ;

Dursley Gazette (Glos.)

EDUCATION. Mr. Peter Scott (Wildfowl Trust) presents the shield for the Bird, Tree and Flower Competition to the winning school

John Clegg

EDUCATION. One of the many things young bird-watchers must learn is how to use field-glasses, adjusting their focus to keep a moving bird in view

teams over a period of years :

Cadets were chosen from a country village Church of England primary controlled school of about 50 children from the ages of five to eleven. All the children over nine keep nature note books which were read by the team secretary and were a considerable help in choosing Cadets and observing progress subsequently. Selection was made primarily by the head mistress, and numbers were limited to one team of nine.

We were fortunate in three respects. The schoolmistress regarded nature study—particularly that of birds—as an important feature of children's education, and communicated her enthusiasm and much of her knowledge to the children. Close co-operation between schoolteacher and secretary, if one person does not combine both functions, is essential to the success of the scheme.

In our neighbourhood are miles of common land, comprising sandy heaths, several lakes, some marsh and a good deal of scrub and woodland. None of this is in the immediate vicinity of the children's homes, but this is an advantage, as it is found they are much more observant and interested when in unfamiliar surroundings. The team is divided in halves, each being taken out on alternate weeks.

prizes of books, medals and certificates of merit are also awarded, and almost every member of a competing team receives some prize or token.

Children who are selected for entry into a team as Cadets are given an attractive membership card for which they pay one penny and sign the following pledge :

> I, the undersigned, having been enrolled a Cadet in the ranks of the R S P.B., promise that so long as I hold this card I will take part in Bird, Tree and Flower watching, keep the rules of the competition and study how best to guard all wild life.

The Society's first rule is printed on the card : " To discourage the wanton destruction of birds, and to take an interest generally in their protection."

GUIDING YOUNG TEAMS

The foregoing gives an outline of the activities of the R.S.P.B., directed towards the education of children. The Society, having given the initial impetus to the movement and encouraged it with interest and rewards, must leave details of how its main purposes are put into effect to the efforts of individuals who take an interest in birds and children, and can give up some of their time to act as team-secretaries.

The writer will endeavour to summarise some of his experiences in guiding a succession of

Cadets in the Field. The majority of country children have eyes like a hawk's, and rarely miss anything that moves. They are very quick to note the behaviour of birds, and have prodigious memories. Ability to distinguish song and memorise it is, on the whole, poor and needs patient cultivation. They are better at the songs of migrants than at those of resident birds, because they take the latter for granted and ordinarily do not listen to them. Although they do not possess field-glasses, our Cadets are taught to pick up a bird through a glass, both perching, swimming or on the wing, and to adjust the focus. The purpose of this is to teach them the possibilities of good field-glasses in the hope that later they will save up and buy a pair for themselves if their interest in birds continues.

The detailed observations of birds which Cadets make preparatory to the annual essay are carried out without the help of field-glasses. This necessitates a close approach, and the first lesson they are taught is to refrain from cries and gestures. " Coo ! Look ! " is the invariable shrill comment on sighting an unusual bird, accompanied by an outflung arm and forefinger. The necessity for the minimum noise and movement seems the hardest of all lessons.

It has been found desirable to take on excursions a bird book with good coloured illustrations. This enables the children to see at close quarters a bird of which they may have caught only a glimpse on the wing. We also take handbooks, with coloured illustrations, on trees, flowers and fungi—the latter chiefly to help in identifying the poisonous ones.

Outings continue, weather permitting, throughout the year. On winter days with a north-east wind, when birds are scarce, we learn to " box " the compass, drawing a circle on the ground. We learn " flag wagging ", the morse code and warm ourselves with a quick game of hide-and-seek. It has been found desirable to carry a whistle. Small people, engrossed in a pursuit, occasionally get out of touch in high scrub and may be lost.

Beyond approving of nature study in a general way, parents do not, as a rule, actively encourage their children to take an interest in the subject, probably because they themselves had no such training and are not particularly interested. When they are, the results in the children are very marked. Born ornithologists are rare, but they occur. The writer has been fortunate enough to have experienced one, a boy.

The debt owed by the country to the R.S.P.B. for fostering these interests among children is very great ; supplemented by enforceable legislation, it must bring home to an ever-increasing number of British people a sense of responsibility for their lovely heritage.

For the encouragement given by museums to young naturalists, *see also* Bird Room and Bird Gallery ; for adult education in bird-lore *see* Study, Facilities for.

EDWARD GREY INSTITUTE. An Institute of Field Ornithology was set up at Oxford in 1932, and received its University statute in 1938, when it was named after Viscount Grey of Fallodon, famous statesman, amateur ornithologist and late Chancellor of the University.

The Edward Grey Institute of Field Ornithology, to give it its full name, was founded, and in its early years maintained, primarily by the British Trust for Ornithology (*q.v.*). Its first director was Mr. W. B. Alexander, succeeded in 1945 by Dr. D. Lack. From 1947 onwards the Institute has been maintained primarily by Oxford University. It has a small research staff and several students working for advanced degrees, and it includes the Alexander Library of bird books and journals, which may be used for reference by members of Oxford University, the British Trust for Ornithology and the British Ornithologists' Union (*q.v.*).

John Clegg

EDUCATION. *Three little girls find that a stuffed specimen can tell them many things about a bird that flew away too quickly to be studied in the field*

THE EGG AND ITS CHARACTERISTICS

R. S. R. FITTER

Once the egg has been laid, its shape and colour play an important part in the battle for survival. In the plate f.p. 196 fifty eggs are shown in colour. For clutch size see Breeding Tables. See also Anatomy ; Breeding Season ; Embryo ; Reproduction

EGG. The development of the egg from the time of fertilisation is described under Reproduction, and of the chick within the egg under Embryo. This article is concerned with the egg after it has been laid. It is laid (broad end first) by a series of contractions of the muscles in the wall of the oviduct, aided by a mucous secretion.

An egg consists of a nucleus of living cells from which the chick develops ; the yolk, a relatively enormous food supply which is gradually absorbed by the developing embryo ; and a number of protective coverings (*see* Fig. 1, page 201). Rising from the centre of the yolk is a flask-shaped portion with a flared neck, known as the " white yolk " (really pale yellow), on top of which rests the nucleus. Irrespective of how the egg is turned, this is always uppermost.

More " white yolk " is disposed in thin concentric layers through the " yellow yolk ", the final layer being just under the vitelline membrane (enclosing the yolk) and continuous with the neck of the flask. Surrounding the yolk is the white of egg, or albumen, also in layers separated by fibrous networks, which acts as a shock-absorber and insulator. Further support is given by the chalazae (*q.v.*) attached at one end to the vitelline membrane, and at the other to the double membrane lining the two-layered shell. At the broad end this forms an air chamber in which the chick takes its first breath.

The eggshell is very largely calcareous, and this necessitates a large calcium intake by the laying bird. The shell varies in thickness according to the size of the egg, so that an ostrich's egg has a shell nearly two millimetres thick, a pheasant's a quarter of a millimetre thick, and a finch's less than a tenth of a millimetre.

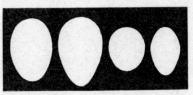

EGG. *The four main shapes—ovoid, pear-shaped, round and elliptical*

WEIGHT, SHAPE AND COLOUR

In relation to their size, the largest birds lay the smallest eggs, and the smallest ones the largest eggs. A small song-bird's egg weighs about one-ninth of its own weight, but in the largest species the egg's weight is about one twenty-fifth of the bird's. It would be impossible for a swan or an eagle to lay an egg one-ninth of its own weight ; since a Mute Swan weighs over 15 lb., and a Golden Eagle 9-10 lb., their eggs would have to be about 1½ lb. and 1 lb. in weight respectively. In fact, a swan's egg weighs about 10 oz. and an eagle's about 5 oz. It is also clear that there is a limit to the smallness of an egg if it is to be a viable unit at all. A Goldcrest weighs only one-sixth of an ounce. If its egg weighed only one-twenty-fifth of its own weight, it would be about 0·2 grams. In fact, a Goldcrest's egg weighs 1 gram, i.e. about 15·4 grains.

The following table shows the weights of some British birds' eggs :

Weight of Eggs
(After A. L. & A. J. Romanoff, *The Avian Egg*, 1949.)

	Grams		Grams
Mute Swan	285	Pigeon	17
Canada Goose	135	Plover	15
Golden Eagle	140	Jay	8·5
Buzzard	60	Starling	7
Mallard	60	Cuckoo	3
Leghorn Fowl	58	Robin	2·5
Pheasant	32	Hedge-Sparrow	2
Partridge	18	Goldcrest	1

Eggs are of four main shapes : the normal ovoid of the domestic hen's egg, which is somewhat less blunt at one end than at the other ; pear shaped, like a Wader's egg ; elliptical or biconical (i.e. elongated but equally blunt at both ends), like a Grebe's or Cormorant's ; and spherical or almost so, like an Owl's.

The colourings of the eggshell are all from the red or green parts of the spectrum, or else white, which is considered to be the most primitive colour (reptiles' eggs are all more or less white). Some eggs are marked with various spottings and streakings, others have the ground colour unmarked. Most, if not all, species that have marked eggs occasionally produce either unspotted or pure white eggs. Reddish (erythristic) varieties of many eggs are also known, but are less common.

EDIBILITY OF EGGS

Thanks to the researches of Dr. Hugh Cott of Cambridge University, we now have a large body of information about the edibility of British birds' eggs. The survival value of a species is naturally linked with the edibility of its eggs, for predators are less likely to take an inedible egg. Experiments with both man and mammals (mainly rats and hedgehogs) have shown a considerable degree of agreement in their tastes. If

John Markham; John E. M. Sumner

EGG. All these eggs are about one-third of their natural size. Thus the first egg, measuring just over ½ in. in the photograph, in actual fact is 1⅝ in. long. From left to right, reading downwards, the following birds are represented : Carrion-Crow, Common Sandpiper, Blackbird, Corn-Bunting, Meadow-Pipit (including a Cuckoo's egg), Blackcap, Redstart. Photographers frequently have to go to much trouble to obtain satisfactory shots of birds and their eggs, as is further described in the article on Photography. Compare this page also with the page of pictures, to the same scale, in Nests and Nesting

a rating of 10 signifies ideally edible, and one of 2 inedible, the eggs of certain British birds are ranked by Cott as follows :

8–9 : Domestic fowl, Coot, Lesser Black-backed Gull, Kittiwake.

7–8 : Fulmar, domestic goose, domestic duck, common and red-legged partridges, Pheasant, Moorhen, Lapwing, Oystercatcher, Curlew, Snipe, Herring- and Greater Blackbacked gulls, Stock-Dove, domestic pigeon, Bullfinch, Dipper, Razorbill, Guillemot.

6–7 : Dabchick, Heron, Mallard, Kestrel, Black-headed Gull, Puffin, Wood-Pigeon, Little and Tawny owls, Rook, Carrion-Crow, Magpie, Jackdaw, Starling, Jay, House-Sparrow, Skylark, Robin.

5–6 : Gannet, Cormorant, Sparrow-Hawk, Buzzard, Turtle-Dove, Cuckoo, Raven, Hooded Crow, Goldfinch, Chaffinch, Yellow Hammer, Mistle-Thrush, Blackbird, Swallow, martins.

4–5 : Shag, Kingfisher, Greenfinch, Linnet, Great and Blue tits, Blackcap, Whitethroat.

3–4 : Green Woodpecker, Reed-Warbler.

2–3 : Wren.

The general rule seems to be that the larger the bird, the more edible the egg.

ADAPTATION

Both the colouring and the shape of eggs are highly adapted by evolution to suit the life and habits of the various species. Thus, the eggs of birds that lay four eggs on the ground, like the waders, are pear-shaped, so that they fit neatly into a square, and well camouflaged by markings so that they are not easily seen by predators ; on the other hand, those of a bird that lays eggs well hidden in a hole, like an owl or a Kingfisher, are usually round and white. The following review of the principal groups of British birds shows how their eggs are adapted to their life.

Song Birds. The majority of these birds build cup-shaped nests, either in trees, bushes or tall vegetation, or more or less well hidden on the ground. Most of them lay four to six eggs of the ovoid shape, which is the most convenient for brooding in a cup-shaped nest. Where there are many small eggs in a deep hole-nest, as with the tits, the eggs are rounder.

Most song birds' eggs are more or less marked with spots, blotches or streaks. Those of the buntings—Yellow Hammer and Corn-, Cirl and Reed-buntings—are noted for their squiggly streaks, which have earned the Yellow Hammer a variety of local names.

Among the few unmarked song-bird eggs are those of the Starling, common Redstart, and Hedge-Sparrow, which are blue ; those of the Nightingale, which are olive ; and those of the Black Redstart, Dipper, House-Martin and Sand-Martin, which are pure white. Of these eight birds, the only one which normally has an open nest in a bush is the Hedge-Sparrow. On the other hand, many song birds build well-hidden or even hole-nests and yet have marked

eggs—the Grasshopper-Warbler, for instance. In this group of birds, therefore, there is no simple relationship between the marking of the eggs and the degree of concealment of the nest.

Near-Passerines. The eggs of this miscellaneous assemblage of birds, consisting of the Swift, Nightjar, Kingfisher and woodpeckers, have little in common, except a tendency to be round or elliptical and white. The Swift lays a somewhat elliptical, pure white egg in a well-concealed nest. The Nightjar's egg, also somewhat elliptical, is well mottled and laid on the ground in the open. The pure white, round egg of the Kingfisher, and the white, elliptical eggs of the woodpeckers, are laid deep in a hole.

Cuckoo. This is one of the most interesting eggs in the whole British avifauna. Its two salient characteristics are that it is very small for the size of the bird, and extremely variable in colour. A Cuckoo weighs about 4 oz. and its egg only three grams, so that it has the extraordinarily small egg-weight/body-weight ratio of about one-fortieth. If the cuckoo's egg were in normal proportion to the bird's weight it would be as large as a Mistle-Thrush's, and any small bird which the Cuckoo parasitised would desert its nest immediately. Therefore, the Cuckoo has evolved an egg only a little larger than that of the bird in whose nest it is laid.

In countries where there is only one possible fosterer, the eggs of the Cuckoo acquire an extraordinary resemblance to those of that fosterer. But in the British Isles there are several common fosterers, notably the Meadow-Pipit, Hedge-Sparrow, Reed-Warbler and Pied Wagtail and, although individual female cuckoos do, in fact, usually specialise in one of these, the British Cuckoo population has developed an extreme variability in egg colour. The ground colour may be bluish, greenish, reddish, brownish or greyish, usually fairly heavily marked with brown or grey spots or speckles. The pure blue egg found in some parts of the Continent is very rare in Britain, and a pure white Cuckoo's egg seems not to have been recorded. It seems possible that the variability of some song-birds' eggs may have evolved as a protective measure against a mimetic Cuckoo's egg, while on the other hand the uniformity of such eggs as the Hedge-Sparrow's would afford some protection against a variable Cuckoo's egg. There is clearly still a fairly fluid state of evolution between the Cuckoo and its fosterers in this matter.

Owls. Our owls' eggs, which are mostly laid in holes, are all white, and more or less spherical. Though the Short-eared Owl always, and the Long-eared and Tawny owls sometimes, lay their eggs on the ground, there has been no adaption of spotting the eggs to camouflage them. Perhaps the reason is that the owls

EGGS OF THIRTY-SIX BRITISH BIRDS

Specially painted by Percy J. Billingshurst

A detailed key to this plate will be found on the next page

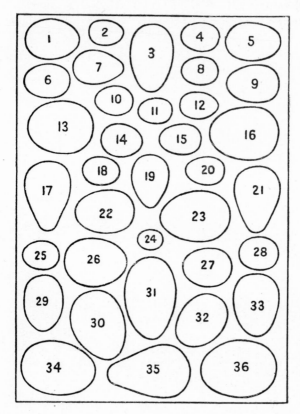

KEY TO EGG COLOUR PLATE

1. Magpie 2. Robin 3. Herring-Gull 4. Nightingale 5. Jay 6. Song-Thrush 7. Starling 8. Nuthatch 9. Blackbird 10. House-Sparrow 11. Swallow 12. Hedge-Sparrow or Dunnock 13. Kestrel 14. Cuckoo 15. Red-backed Shrike 16. Sparrow-Hawk 17. Ringed Plover 18. Tree-Pipit 19. Golden Plover 20. Bullfinch 21. Dunlin 22. Jackdaw 23. Rook 24. Willow-Wren 25. Chaffinch 26. Corncrake 27. Quail 28. Kingfisher 29. Mallard 30. Barn-Owl 31. Great Northern Diver 32. Heron 33. Partridge 34. Moorhen 35. Guillemot 36. Red Grouse. The eggs are in their natural size, apart from Nos. 3, 19, 29, 31 and 32 which are drawn to half-scale

EGGS—Great

Variety in

Pattern

and Design

The eggs illustrated overleaf are typical examples, but many species show considerable variations—although each hen appears to produce the same coloration and design throughout her laying life. For example, the eggs of the Song-Thrush are normally blue with blackish spots, more crowded towards the larger end : but they may, occasionally, be greenish, bluish white, or even pure white, sometimes unmarked, or with reddish spots. With the possible exception of the eggs of the Cuckoo, who endeavours to match those of prospective foster-parents, the greatest variability is found among the eggs of the Guillemot. Their ground-colour may range through white, creamy yellow and deep ochre to blue and deep greenish blue, with an extraordinary variety of markings—spots, blotches, scribbles or uniform masses of colour—varying from red or brown to deep black and greenish black or they may be completely unmarked. Information on the laying period, clutch size, length of incubation and so on of individual species will be found in the tables on pages 96 and 97 ; and on nesting (habitat, site, etc.) and the share taken by both sexes in incubation in the tables between pages 378 and 381

themselves are exceptionally well camouflaged, and are unlikely normally to leave their eggs uncovered in the daytime.

Hawks and Falcons. The eggs of our birds of prey are all either broadly elliptical or nearly spherical, and, except for those of the three harriers, which are white and laid on the ground, are usually well marked and laid in an open nest in a tree or on a ledge. In some species the white ground-colour is often wholly suffused by reddish or brownish markings, but the amount of such marking is very variable.

Herons. The two British breeding members of the Heron family have more or less elliptical and unmarked eggs. The Heron lays blue eggs in an open nest in a tree, and the Bittern lays olive-brown eggs in an open nest on the ground.

Ducks, Geese and Swans. All our ducks, geese and swans lay unspotted eggs, varying from elliptical to somewhat ovoid in shape, and whitish, buffish or greenish in ground-colour. The great majority have well hidden nests on the ground, but a few species, notably the Mallard and Goosander, will sometimes nest in trees, and the introduced Mandarin Duck always does so. Geese and ducks cover their eggs with down when they leave the nest.

Cormorants and Gannets. The Cormorant, Shag and Gannet all have large elliptical eggs, pale blue and unspotted, but so heavily overlaid with a chalky white deposit that the true colour shows through only in patches or not at all. They readily become stained, however, and thus have the appearance of dirty white eggs with darker blotches. All are laid in open nests on rock ledges.

Petrels and Shearwaters. The Storm- and Fork-tailed petrels and the Manx Shearwater each lay a single elliptical white egg in a burrow or crevice. The only marked egg of the three, the Fork-tailed Petrel's, is usually finely spotted with red-brown at one end. The Fulmar's single white ovoid egg is laid openly on a ledge.

Grebes and Divers. Our four breeding grebes and two breeding divers have more or less elliptical eggs. The grebes' eggs—unspotted and white at first—are laid in open nests, either floating on the water or on tufts of vegetation surrounded by water. They are covered with waterweed by the bird when it leaves the nest, and thus very soon becomes discoloured. The divers' eggs, olive-green, or olive-brown, with dark brown spots, are laid in open nests very close to the water's edge.

Pigeons and Doves. These birds all lay elliptical, pure white, unspotted eggs, openly on platforms of sticks in trees (Wood-Pigeon,

Turtle-Dove), or in holes (Stock-Dove), or on more or less hidden ledges on cliffs or in buildings (Rock-Dove, Feral or London Pigeon). The conspicuous white eggs of the Wood-Pigeon and Turtle-Dove form one of the principal exceptions to the general rule that white eggs are laid in holes or other well-concealed sites.

Waders. Nearly all our waders lay four pear-shaped eggs, which fit neatly together with the thin ends towards the centre so as to form the most convenient grouping for the brooding bird. Among the few waders which have more ovoid eggs are the Woodcock, Curlew, Stone-Curlew, and Oystercatcher, the last two of which usually lay fewer than four eggs. All our regularly breeding waders nest on the ground, and their eggs are consequently well camouflaged, with a ground-colour of brown or buff and a heavy spotting and blotching of darker brown or blackish.

Terns, Gulls and Skuas. These birds quite openly nest either on the ground or on cliff or rock ledges. Their ovoid eggs are consequently well camouflaged, with ground-colour varying from buff through olive and brown to bluish or greenish, and a heavy spotting and blotching of dark brown and blacks.

Auks. The Guillemot, laying openly on ledges with no nesting material, has a strong pear-shaped egg which does not fall into the sea (as a rounder egg would) when the disturbed bird flies off suddenly. It is one of the most variable of all British birds' eggs, the ground-colour being anything from pure white, through cream, buff, yellowish-brown and reddish brown to pale blue or deep bluish-green, with or without markings of all shapes and sizes, from lines to blotches in a variety of colours from black to reddish, or yellowish-brown. The Razorbill, Black Guillemot and Puffin, which nest either in crannies or holes, have much more ovoid eggs. The Razorbill's is almost as variable in colour and markings as the Guillemot's ; the Black Guillemot's is still more ovoid but less variable ; the Puffin's—white with brownish markings which may or may not be visible through the thick chalky covering—recalls that of the Cormorant and Gannet.

Crakes and Rails. These birds, which include the Moorhen and Coot, all have ovoid eggs, mostly with a buff ground and darker brown spots. They are laid in open but often well hidden nests, on the ground or in tufts of vegetation over water.

Game Birds. All game birds nest on the ground, and have more or less ovoid eggs, usually speckled or spotted, but in two cases (Pheasant and common Partridge) unspotted.

G. K. Yeates

EGRET. *This seems a first-class picture of a truly hen-pecked husband—namely, the Cattle Egret*

EGG-TOOTH. Calcareous protuberance developed by the bird-embryo on the upper surface of the bill to enable the young bird to hack its way through the egg-shell on hatching. It is shed soon afterwards. *See also* Bill.

EGRET. Three of these birds are on the British list—the Cattle Egret or Buff-backed Heron, the Large Egret and the Little Egret. Only the last two are true egrets belonging to the genus *Egretta* (*q.v.*), while the Cattle Egret is a member of the genus *Ardeola* (*q.v.*) and is closely related to the Squacco Heron. All these birds are described under their own names.

Egrets are similar to herons in many ways. Both types have long, pointed bills, though those of egrets are the more slender ; both have long legs and necks ; and both tuck the head back on the shoulders (the neck thus forming an " S ") in sustained flight. The plumage of egrets, however, is always white or very nearly white and their scapulars are greatly elongated in the breeding season and form a thin, drooping cloak, extending below the birds' tails.

Egrets nest in colonies, showing a preference for marshes, reed-beds and swamps, though they are often seen in open country. This is particularly true of the Cattle Egret, which feeds in meadows among cattle—hence its name. None of the egrets breed in this country in the wild state, and all are seen but occasionally. The rarest of them is the Large Egret. *See also* Ardea ; Ardeiformes ; Heron.

EGRETTA. Genus of the family *Ardeidae* of the order *Ardeiformes*. Its members are distributed over eastern and southern Europe, Asia, Africa, Australasia, and north and south America. It includes two species on the

British list : the Little Egret and the Large Egret (also known as the Great White Heron), which are both described under their own headings. The former is an irregular visitor to the British Isles, and the Large Egret has been recorded here fewer than a dozen times.

These are rather large, mainly white birds ; with long, pointed bills, which are more slender than those of the *Ardea* genus (Heron and Purple Heron). They have slender plumes projecting beyond the nape, and there are elongated feathers on the back with thin, hair-like ends.

EGYPTIAN GOOSE — **Alopochen aegyptiacus.** Breeding throughout Africa, except for the desert regions, and in southern Palestine, this bird is by nature non-migratory. But it has been kept in captivity and as an ornamental waterfowl in England since the 18th century, and escapes and wanderers have led to its establishment in the wild state in Great Britain. There are breeding colonies in Norfolk and elsewhere, and it is recorded that a pair bred in Hertfordshire in 1938.

The Egyptian Goose is a very beautiful bird, especially in flight, with its colourful wings in chestnut, green and white contrasting with its black tail. Its mantle is dun-coloured above, but much paler on breast and underparts ; it has dark chocolate patches round its eyes, and one very noticeable dark patch at the centre base of its breast. Its bill and legs are pink. In movement and size it resembles the Sheld-Duck (*q.v.*), and it likes to perch in trees. It breeds well in captivity, but is inclined to be quarrelsome in company with other species.

Its voice is a harsh and repeated bark, and the male is recorded as having a curious rasping and puffing call during the breeding season. The nest is placed in a tree, and constructed of twigs and lined with grass. But an old nest of another species is often used. In the British Isles the breeding season of the Egyptian Goose is from March to May ; five to nine eggs are laid, and the period of hatching is about a month. Grasses of various kinds are the normal diet, but a variety of other vegetable and animal food is also consumed.

Despite its name, the Egyptian Goose is not a goose but a Sheld-Duck, resembling particularly the Ruddy Sheld-Duck (*q.v.*).

EGYPTIAN NIGHTJAR — **Caprimulgus aegyptius.** This bird of the desert wastes is confined to Egypt and Iraq ; only one has been identified in Great Britain. Its appearance lacks much of the rich colouring of the Nightjar (*q.v.*) ; for its much paler and greyer plumage is adapted, for camouflage purposes, to its drab surroundings.. It is 10 in. in length, and its tarsus is not quite 1 in. long. Its wing span is approximately 1½ ft.

From information available, its general behaviour, voice and habits seem to resemble fairly closely those of the European bird. It builds no nest, and its two eggs, which are much paler than the Nightjar's, are merely laid in a scraped hollow on the ground. The length of the breeding season—from April to July—suggests that two broods may be reared.

EGYPTIAN VULTURE — Neophron pere-nopterus. Many years have passed since the Egyptian Vulture has been seen in the British Isles : two are recorded, one killed in Somerset in 1825 and another in Essex in 1876. It breeds in southern Europe, north Africa and Asia, frequenting mountainous districts in India, Egypt and Turkey. A large vulture-like black and white bird, it has mantle and underparts of snowy white ; the wedge-shaped tail is black, and the white wings shade to black on the quill ends. There is a ruff of long white feathers round the neck, and the face and front neck are yellow and wrinkled ; the legs and feet are flesh-coloured. The length is 25 in.—much less than that of the Griffon-Vulture (*q.v.*) ; and there is no difference in size between male and female. Its tarsus is 3-3½ in. long, and its wing span is about 3½ ft.

On the ground and when feeding on decayed carrion and refuse, the Egyptian Vulture is far from attractive, but seen in the air as it soars to great heights, it is a magnificent bird. Usually it is silent, but in the breeding season many strange noises are heard near the nest. Small caves and holes in cliffs are its breeding-sites. The nest is a large construction made from all kinds of material ; hair, wool, rags, sticks and the remains of dead animals are only a few of the items used. Two dirty white eggs are laid in March or April (in Europe). Both birds hatch out the eggs—during 42 days—and one brood is reared.

Decaying matter of all kinds—the carcasses of dead animals and rotting fruit is greedily devoured. The bird flourishes in the neighbourhood of primitive and undeveloped towns and villages, where garbage and refuse dumps abound. The Egyptian Vulture is also known as the " Alpine Vulture ", " Pharaoh's Chicken " and " White Crow ".

EIDER-DUCK — Somateria mollissima. This is the sea-duck par excellence which is but rarely found inland. Probably one of the best known of our resident duck—in name at least—it breeds on the Northumbrian coast, especially Holy Island and the Farne Islands, and in Scotland is quite common in the Orkney and Shetland Islands, the Outer Hebrides and other parts. In Ireland it is rather rare, although it has bred of late years on one or two islands ; otherwise it is a scarce winter visitor. In the Far North it breeds in great numbers, especially in Iceland and Greenland.

The Eider has always been given protection, though not for the benefit of the bird. The grey down with which it lines its nest has great commercial value, and in the past nests were robbed of this just as the ducks were ready to lay their eggs, so that they had to pluck their breasts all over again. Today, only the most expensive quilts and cushions contain real eider-down ; most of what passes for eider-down is now obtained from the carcasses of domestic ducks.

The Eider drake, a shy bird, is not difficult to identify, for he is large and handsome with a pure white mantle and breast ; his head, tail and underparts are black, and some green feathers decorate his nape and the sides of his neck. It is some years before he gains the full beauty of his adult plumage, and during his moult, which is roughly from August to November, he loses most of his white. The female is also large, but she is completely brown, with bars of a darker shade on her breast. The bills of both birds are unique, for they slope straight down from their foreheads—but this cannot always be seen except at close quarters. Both duck and drake are 23 in. in length, with bodies of 15 in. ; the tarsus is under 2 in. The weight is about 3½ lb. ; the wing span approximately 2½ ft.

Eiders are gregarious, but only with their own kind. They are excellent swimmers and

Erica

EGYPTIAN GOOSE. *The gosling is in its proper element, although its ancestors came from Africa*

divers, and obtain much of their food in that way. Their walk is an awkward waddle, with the running take-off common to sea-ducks. Outside the breeding season, eiders spend most of their time at sea, but they may often be seen resting on shores and rocks. The drake's call is unique among ducks: a loud, eerie crooning, it is uttered usually while swimming with others of his kind. The female has the harsh alarm note common to ducks.

The winter parties of eiders break up during March, and the birds begin to pair; but it is not until some weeks later that the nest is completed and laying begins. Eiders usually nest in colonies on islands off the coast; in the Shetlands and Outer Hebrides they will also nest on inland hills and lochs, but they are never far from the sea. The parent birds select the site together, but after that the drake seems to take little or no interest in the proceedings, and this indifference seems to continue throughout the nesting time and the rearing of the chicks—only if the nest is isolated does he ever remain within call.

A mere hollow on the ground in some sheltered nook, the nest has a foundation of grass and seaweed and is lined with a plentiful supply of the famous grey down. Four to six pale-olive eggs are laid in May or early June, the duck hatching them out alone over a period of about a month; during that time she rarely leaves the nest and seems to take very little food. The ducklings are taken to the water as soon as their down is dry. Once in the water, they are very independent, and will seek protection only when danger is near. Then they will hurry

not particularly to their own parents, but to any near-by duck. One brood is reared in a season. The food of eiders consists of marine insects of all kinds and some vegetable matter.

In Northumbria, the Eider is known as " St. Cuthbert's Duck " and in Scotland as the " Dunter ". *See also* King Eider ; Duck.

EMBERIZA. Genus of the family *Fringillidae* of the order *Passeriformes*. It contains 28 or 29 species in the Old World, with a number of subspecies. Its members are distributed over Europe, a large part of Asia, and northern Africa. The following species are on the British list (*see also* under separate headings) : Yellow Hammer, Corn-Bunting, Cirl Bunting, Reed-Bunting, Ortolan Bunting, Pine-Bunting, Black-headed Bunting, Red-headed Bunting, Yellow-breasted Bunting, Rock-Bunting, Meadow-Bunting, Rustic Bunting and Little Bunting ; but only the first four birds listed are at all common in the British Isles.

Typical buntings, the members of this genus have shortish, hard, conical and sharp-pointed bills, with the cutting-edges somewhat incurved. In several species, especially the Corn-Bunting, there is a more or less developed hump in the roof of the mouth. The nostrils are close to the feathers and more or less covered by them. The wings are well developed, but have only nine primary feathers, the true first being absent ; in most species the second, third, fourth and fifth are almost equal in length and are the longest of the primaries, but in the Rock-Bunting the sixth primary is almost as long as the previous three and the second is much shorter, while in the Ortolan Bunting the fifth

EIDER-DUCK. Compared with the beautiful black and white drake, the duck (right) is a dun bird, little different, except for its bill, from the more common female Mallard

Erica, Eric Hosking

primary is markedly shorter than the previous three. The tail is rather long and has twelve feathers. The toes have strongly curved claws, and the hind toe is longer than its claw. The sexes differ in plumage, and the young are like the females. *See also* Bunting.

EMBRYO. The development of the embryonic chick begins at the moment when the male sperm, having swum up the oviduct, unites with a ripe ovum, which already contains both " white yolk " and yellow yolk. When this happens, the ovum becomes incapable of uniting with any further sperms it may meet, and at once begins to divide up into a number of cells. It then passes down the oviduct, becoming coated first with albumen, the white of the egg, and finally with the shell, which protects the developing embryo while it is being nourished by the contents of the egg. In the domestic hen, the bird in which the development of the embryo has been studied in most detail, this process from fertilisation to the deposition of the shell takes from 16 to 26 hours. The egg is now ready to be laid and then, after a period varying from species to species, incubation begins.

During the first eight hours of incubation few changes are noticeable in a hen's egg, but before the end of the first 24 hours it is possible to tell that the developing embryo is that of a vertebrate, for the notochord, a strip of gristle which eventually forms the basis of the backbone, and is found only in vertebrates, has appeared. On the second day the beginnings of the head, heart, larger blood-vessels and digestive organs can be discerned, the whole embryo being then scarcely half a centimetre long. On the third day many important changes occur, including the appearance of the lungs and the eyeballs, while the head and digestive organs begin to divide up into recognizable parts. The amount of white in the egg has been steadily shrinking as the embryo grows, and during the fourth and fifth days continues to do so. At this time the embryo is still very much doubled up and might appear to be that of almost any young vertebrate. On the sixth day, however, it begins to be apparent that it will in fact develop into a bird, for the limbs develop the typical characters of avian wings and feet, the gizzard appears, and the nose starts to elongate into a rudimentary beak. All this time the white is diminishing and the yolk increasing, as it absorbs the water from the white, until finally there is no white left and all the yolk has disappeared into the abdomen of the chick. Up to about the seventh day the head grows much faster than the rest of the body. Feather-buds appear on the ninth day, and are recognizable as feathers four days later, by which time the skeleton has become more or less bony. A soft beak has

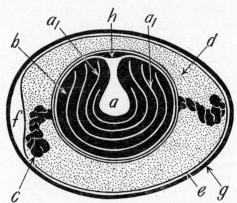

EMBRYO. *Fig. I : Structure of bird's egg, showing the " white yolk " (a_1) disposed in thin layers round the flask-shaped central portion of " white yolk " (a), on top of which rests the nucleus (h) which, after fertilisation, grows into the chick during incubation. Yellow yolk (b) lies between the different portions of " white yolk " ; the two together, forming the complete yolk, are enclosed in the vitelline membrane and kept in place by the chalazae (c). Surrounding the yolk is the white of egg, or albumen (d) ; and the whole is covered by a double membrane (e), which forms a small air chamber (f) at the broad end, where the chick will take its first breath. A two-layered, calcareous shell (g) acts as a protective covering to the egg*

appeared by the twelfth day, and soft claws by the thirteenth ; both are almost horny by the sixteenth. All this time the chick has been getting oxygen (from the air which has been seeping through the shell) through a mass of tiny blood vessels. On about the twentieth day, now fully developed, it breaks the membrane separating it from the shell and breathes the air directly. With its breathing and blood circulation system now fully normal, the chick is able to peck at the egg-shell with the special " egg-tooth " at the tip of its beak. As the shell falls apart, the still wet chick is born. *See also* Anatomy ; Egg ; Reproduction.

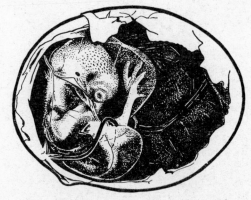

Fig. 2 : *Embryo of domestic fowl, 15 days after incubation began. The head is well-defined, and the whole embryo is seen to be curled up tightly*

EREMOPHILA. Genus of larks of the family *Alaudidae* of the order *Passeriformes*. Its members are distributed over northern and central Europe, Asia Minor, northern and mid-Asia, parts of north Africa, north America and the Andes (Colombia). The only species on the British list, the Shore-Lark (*q.v.*), occurs as a winter visitor.

ERITHACUS. Genus of the family *Turdidae* of the order *Passeriformes*. It contains only one species, with a number of subspecies, distributed over Europe, western Asia and north-west Africa. The genus is well represented in the British Isles by the Robin (*q.v.*), often known as Redbreast.

ERNE. Local name for White-tailed Eagle (*q.v.*), also called Sea-Eagle or Grey Sea-Eagle.

ERYTHRISM. Abnormal or excessive redness (Gr. *erythos*, " red ") found in certain species of birds ; e.g. the Barn-Owl, which has two distinct plumage-phases—one greyish and the other red. There is also a rare red-brown form of female Cuckoo.

Erythrism may be induced artificially in some species. For example, if very young canaries are fed with cayenne pepper the plumage may become orange or red instead of the usual yellow. Some white breeds of fowls are similarly affected by a diet of cayenne, the flight feathers becoming streaked with orange and the breast feathers red.

For generations, the natives of the Amazon Basin have been in the habit of feeding the common Green Amazon Parrot with the fat of certain Silunoid fishes to produce in them a plumage beautifully variegated with red and yellow feathers. In the Malay Archipelago, the natives of Gilolo similarly change the colour of another parrot, thus producing the " King Lory ". *See also ;* Albinism ; Melanism ; Xanthochroism.

ESKIMO CURLEW—Numenius borealis. This bird last came as a rare visitor to Great Britain in 1887, and it is now regarded as almost extinct. Formerly a common breeding bird in Arctic north America, it was led to extinction by its natural tameness, for thousands were slaughtered ; once it had become rare, egg collectors completed its destruction.

In appearance, it was very like a small Whimbrel (*q.v.*), a close relative of the Curlew (*q.v.*), but it was smaller, and had a shorter bill and no white rump. Its length was about 14 in., and its bill was $2\frac{1}{2}$ in. long. In the breeding season, it frequented the barren wastes of Arctic America and was never found in or near woods. Its nesting habits followed the pattern of its kind, the nest being a mere hollow in the ground where four eggs were laid in June and July. One brood was reared in a season.

EUROPEAN CORMORANT. North American name for the Cormorant (*q.v.*).

EUROPEAN HAWK-OWL. North American bird-literature always refers thus to the Hawk-Owl (*q.v.*) to distinguish it from the native American variety, which is described here under American Hawk-Owl (*q.v.*).

EVERSMANN'S WARBLER. Alternative name, used in all older works of reference, for the Arctic Warbler (*q.v.*), a very rare visitor.

EUROPEAN CORMORANT. While the hen broods the eggs, the male Cormorant stands guard to ward off intruders—a needful precaution, as these birds nest in colonies

Eric Hosking

CONTINUING THE UPWARD CLIMB

W. E. SWINTON, Ph.D., B.Sc.

This article, which is complementary to Ancestry and Fossil Birds and should be read together with these, discusses how the various species of modern birds evolved from their primeval forebears. See also *Classification ; Geographical Distribution*

EVOLUTION. The evolution of birds is a long and complicated story, part of which is told in the article Ancestry. But, even without a knowledge of fossils or of the principles of flight, something of this story can be seen merely by looking at the birds of today.

There are, for example, the amphibious birds that can fly well but have webbed feet—like the pelicans, puffins and gulls. Then there are the great sea-birds, like the Albatross, who are also amphibious but can spend days in the air and weeks away from the sight of land. On the other hand, the Penguin has carried amphibiousness perhaps too far, for while it is a powerful swimmer, its wings are reduced and it has lost the power of flight. Penguins can be claimed as aquatic animals though most of them can still walk, even the Emperor Penguin—the only bird never to come on land though it walks on ice. Apart from its aquatic habits, the different appearance of the Penguin's body feathers may be noted.

All birds have two legs, though some are slow walkers (penguins), others can run or hop well for short distances (starlings and thrushes), while ostriches are among the speediest of land animals. All these birds differ greatly in size and in wing-development, and hence in their flying ability.

Different Ways of Life. Birds are adapted for many ways of life : some are nightfliers (owls, nightjars) ; some are fruit and grain eaters (finches, buntings), including the very specialised frugivorous birds of paradise and bee-birds ; others are flesh and fish eaters (vultures and sea-birds) ; still others (crows) are notorious egg-stealers who will even run off with a golf ball in mistake for an egg. Birds may live in trees, or in bushes, or on the ground, and one or two nest in caves. Cases of burrowing are rare, but there is a burrowing owl, and the Cliff-Swallow does something similar.

When one considers this enormous divarication, the many habits and properties affected by

By permission of the Trustees of the British Museum
EVOLUTION. *Diatryma, a large flightless creature from the Lower Eocene, was 7 ft. high*

evolution become clearer. There is, for instance, the additional evidence of coloration (*see* Pattern and Colour) which renders sea-birds like the sky, when seen from below, and like the sea, when viewed from above. The richness of colour of many other birds, their differences in song and nesting habits are all part of the same story. And all these habits, properties and appearances are overlaid on a skeleton that shows in itself the evolutionary advances of at least 100 million years.

All birds have some type of feathers and all have forelimbs modified as wings, whether these are used for flying or not. They are all warm-blooded animals and have many special arrangements to maintain body-heat. Modern birds also have hollow bones and air-spaces (*see* Anatomy ; Air-Sac ; Flight ; Wing). No living bird possesses teeth, but a horny beak has been developed which performs similar functions and, in addition, serves as a hand (*see* Bill).

The major evolution of birds can be seen in two very different ways. Firstly, as has been done so far in this article, by observing the variety of different forms and functions, habits and habitats. Secondly, by examining the fossil (*q.v.*) remains. It is found from such combined observations that the first bird appeared in the geological record about 150 million years ago, and that the main distribution and diversification of birds into their modern profusion and variety occurred in the last 60 or 70 million years—that is, geologically speaking, in quite recent times.

The origin of birds has already been discussed (*see* Ancestry), and the conflicting theories of the origin of flight have been mentioned. This issue can only be decided if some spectacular new discovery is made, but there can be no doubt that birds are descended from reptiles. This conclusion is abundantly clear from studies of *Archaeopteryx* (*q.v.*), the first-found bird, represented by specimens in London and

Berlin (the latter sometimes and probably incorrectly differentiated as *Archaeornis*). Some authorities have suggested that the flying birds are directly descended from one of these, and the running birds from the other ; a theory which the near relationship between the two specimens puts out of court.

There is a long gap in the geological record after *Archaeopteryx* until the Niobrara chalk of Kansas bears tangible witness to further stages in avian evolution. Two kinds of skeletons of aquatic birds were discovered there—*Hesperornis*, a flightless bird which must have been rather like a large Diver, and *Ichthyornis*, a much smaller flying creature. Both birds had toothed jaws (*see* Ancestry, including drawing in p. 20).

We now come to the geological period known as the Tertiary which covers the last 60 million years. Here bird remains, though never numerous except in the latest stages, very obviously approach the modern forms. The skulls of these fossils show a close-knit arrangement of bones, and there are ball and socket vertebrae producing a more stable yet flexible backbone and ending in a short tail. These vertebral characteristics are probably due to the development of stable flight (*see* Ancestry). There is also much evidence that loss of flying ability occurred several times during the Tertiary period. Further, there are many evidences of giantism among flightless birds, with the development of fantastic forms, judged by present standards (*see* Diatryma, page 203).

Flightless Birds. Two important lines of flightless birds can already be seen at the very beginning of the Tertiary. The first is represented by a very large, big-headed creature, *Diatryma*, from the Lower Eocene of Wyoming in the United States. This bird was nearly 7 ft.

high and shows by the reduction of its wings and the ratite-like shoulder girdle that it did not fly. But it was well suited for running on the ground, and the powerful beak and evidence of strong muscles on the neck suggest that it was well able to look after itself. Although *Diatryma* is well known and specimens are exhibited in the London Natural History Museum, its exact position in the systematics of birds is uncertain.

More certainly placed is the other line, that of the Impennes or penguins, whose earliest member is known from the Eocene of New Zealand and the Antarctic. The penguin paddle, which serves as a highly efficient swimming organ, is the modified and reduced wing, but because it is still used, though not for flying, the keel on the sternum is retained. Certain fossils found in the Eocene of Patagonia suggest that the ancestors of the penguins were terrestrial, and the true penguins may therefore have readapted themselves with great success as swimming forms. Certainly before long some of them had attained great size, and fossils are known showing some of them were 5 ft. and 6 ft. high.

The penguins are characteristic of the Southern Hemisphere and all the known fossils come from there, many from the Miocene of Patagonia. It is interesting to note that these fossils also suggest that the hind legs and feet were much more adapted for running than those of the forms living now, whose abilities have more and more been concentrated on swimming.

There is no intimate relationship between the penguins and the flightless birds of south America, south Africa and Australia and New Zealand. The very distribution of these well known cursorial forms suggests a long history and relationship dating from the time when

---

SEQUENCE OF EVOLUTION
(compare with diagram in opposite page)

I. ARCHAEORNITHES (ancient birds)
Represented by *Archaeopteryx* and the doubtfully separate *Archaeornis*. All birds are probably derived from these Jurassic ancestors of 150 million years ago

II. NEORNITHES (modern birds)
These have either keeled or flat sternums and are represented by the four groups which are outlined below

Odontognathae	Birds with toothed jaws. *Hesperornis* and *Ichthyornis* from the American Cretaceous. Although their habits are not unlike those of modern Divers, there is no evidence to connect them with any modern form
Palaeognathae	Birds with a palatal structure of primitive character. Represented by the Ratites or flightless birds
Impennae	Penguins, showing a combination of primitive and advanced (specialised) characteristics
Neognathae	All modern flying birds, represented by 20 orders

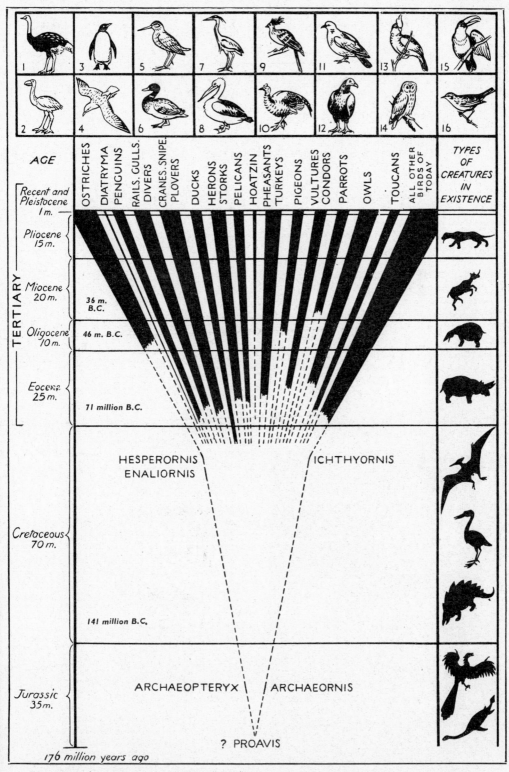

EVOLUTION. *The dotted lines show the possible steps in bird development, whereas the start of the heavy black lines indicates the period to which the earliest known fossils belong. Thus, remains of the Ostrich have been found in the Oligocene deposits of the Tertiary, of about 45 million years ago*

these continental areas were more closely related than now, though fossil evidence for most of this is lacking.

It has been maintained that some of these never originated from flying birds, but Dr. Robert Broom long ago suggested that one proof against this was that, as New Zealand appears to have been separated off from neighbouring lands since at least the Jurassic geological period, i.e. about 180 million years ago, the only way in which the ancestors of the existing birds could have got there would have been to fly. There are certain objections to Broom's theory. The geological relationships of these areas and their probable continental drift are far from being acceptable to all geologists, but the osteological characters of the flightless birds would themselves seem to be inexplicable unless they were of flying origin. To suggest a complete separation of the ratite and the carinate birds would therefore also suggest that bird flight has been attained more than once, for which at present there is no real evidence.

Modern flightless birds are the direct descendants of these fossil southern continental forms. *Dinornis*, an 11 ft. high giant " Moa " from the Pleistocene of New Zealand and *Aepyornis* from Madagascar, are examples very well known through skeletons and other relics. Some of the evidence, especially of the ostriches, shows that in the past their distribution was much greater, extending through India, Persia and Russia to China and Mongolia. The present

W. S. Berridge

EXTINCT BIRDS. *The Crane has been extinct as a breeding species in Britain for about 400 years*

series of flightless birds is poor in size and variety as compared with their ancestors and predecessors of a million years ago.

Flying Birds. During the developmental period of their larger and flightless relations, the flying birds had increased in number and variety. Some of them too attained considerable size, and the Albatross of today was outdone by *Gigantornis*, from the Eocene of Nigeria, which was twice its size.

On the whole, the flying birds are part of a very homogeneous group, and their evolution, of habit and colour, of beak and size, are matters of detail as compared with the greater division of the class.

Today, the highest and most modern group of the birds consists of those comparatively small, perching kinds that belong to the order *Passeriformes*. This order includes nearly half of the bird species we know, and attains its greatest size in the Raven. In a very real sense the size of the birds characteristic of the modern avifauna has returned, after 150 million years, to that of the only bird ancestor we know.

EXTINCT BIRDS. Only one British species, the Great Auk, has become completely extinct within historic times, but several others which once nested in this country no longer do so, although they are far from extinct elsewhere.

Volumes have been written about the Great Auk, but most of them are little more than obituary notices. The last Great Auk ever recorded was killed off Iceland in 1844, and the last British records are of one off Waterford, Ireland, in 1834 and one on Stac-an-Armin in the St. Kilda group in 1840. About 80 skins of the bird have survived, showing how it must have looked, and there are also many parts of its skeleton and about 75 eggs preserved in museums. The Great Auk was a near relation of the Razorbill and resembled it in appearance, though it was as large as a goose. It spent most of its time at sea, coming ashore in May to nest on rocky islets and sea-cliffs. On land it apparently moved awkwardly, and, its legs being set rather far back, it sat erect very much like a penguin. It seems to have been a fairly unintelligent, or perhaps a too trustful, bird with the result that it was regarded as fair prey by sailors, merchants and fishermen in the turbulent and ruthless centuries following the discovery of America. Tens of thousands of great auks were killed for food, for their feathers, for fuel (their fat being melted down for oil), for bait and even for amusement, and, as even the remoter islets of the north Atlantic came within the ken of white men, the species sank quickly into oblivion. The recorded British breeding-sites are St. Kilda and the Orkneys, but remains of the bird have been found on various parts of the coasts of Scotland, Ireland and northern England ; and it may have nested on Lundy and the Isle of Man.

Birds of Fens and Moors. The Crane is almost as extinct in Britain as the Great Auk, certainly as a breeding species. It still breeds, however, in northern and eastern Europe and in Asia, and very rarely occurs in this country on migration. Prehistory for birds is not so very long ago, few written records being available beyond the past 200 years, but it appears that the Crane probably became extinct here about the 16th century, when the great regions of fen and swamp which once covered much of England were beginning to be reclaimed. In Scotland and Ireland it probably lingered longer. Inexpert reports of cranes often prove to refer to the common Heron, which bears a superficial resemblance to the Crane. The latter, however, is much larger, is of a uniform grey and has a black and white head and neck, with a red patch on the back of the crown.

Several other extinct British species belonged to the vanished Fens. The Spoonbill was once fairly common in southeast England. In the 16th and 17th centuries it is recorded as breeding not only in the Fens but in Sussex, Suffolk and even in London, where it apparently nested in the Bishop of London's park at Fulham. As its former breeding haunts disappeared through land drainage, it was subjected to increasing persecution until it was finally exterminated. However, wandering Spoonbills visit our shores almost every year, and isolated birds have even stayed throughout the summer.

Savi's Warbler is another Fenland bird which has disappeared, chiefly through the reclamation of the Fens, though once it had become scarce, its end was hastened by egg-collectors. In this country, however, it was at the edge of its normal range, for it is rare even in northern France and Belgium, its territory extending from Spain through Central Europe to Russia.

British Museum (Natural History)
EXTINCT BIRDS. The Great Auk has become completely extinct little over 100 years ago

Savi's Warbler is a small warbler of reeds and sedges, looking very like the Reed-Warbler.

The Black Tern is a species that became extinct but is now promising to return. It once nested in Lincolnshire and Norfolk, and continued to do so until just over 100 years ago. After its extinction as a breeding species this marsh-tern continued to visit Britain fairly regularly on migration, and was recorded as nesting in south-east Sussex and Nottinghamshire in the early 1940s.

Another species which disappeared because of the destruction of its habitat was the Great Bustard, though this was a bird of the open prairie and moors rather than of the Fens. Its strongholds were the brecklands of Norfolk and Suffolk and the chalk downs of east Yorkshire and southern England, especially Salisbury Plain.

A very large and handsome bird—being as big as a Turkey—the Bustard needed such spacious uplands and was exterminated when the plough and the increasing human population encroached on them. The last breeding pairs were recorded in the 1830s, at Great Massingham, Norfolk, and there seems little likelihood of the bird ever returning to breed, though it is still an irregular visitor from Europe.

Birds of Prey. There are three birds of prey which have been exterminated through human persecution. The White-tailed Eagle, or Sea-Eagle, once nested on almost all the coastal cliffs of Britain as well as some inland crags, but was harried to extinction. It last bred in Shetland in 1908. The bird took lambs as well as game-birds, so every man's hand was against it. The Osprey has a roughly parallel history, the last nest being recorded at Loch Arkaig in 1908. There was, however, less justification or excuse for the extermination of that lovely bird, which is almost exclusively a fishing-hawk. Both ospreys and white-tailed eagles appear occasionally in their former haunts, the Osprey with some regularity, and there are rumours that the Osprey may have nested in the High-lands again of recent years.

The Goshawk used to breed in the British Isles, but it is not known how commonly. The situation is confused because it was a favourite hunting-hawk in the days of falconry, when hawks were often imported and turned loose to breed. However, it seems a likely resident of the vast forests which once covered the greater part of Britain. Equally natural was its gradual extermination at the hand of Man when the country became more thickly popu-lated, for the Goshawk resembles an outsize Sparrow-Hawk, both in appearance and behaviour, and so is no welcome neighbour for farmers and gamekeepers. Goshawks are occasionally seen in Britain, though it is usually impossible to say whether they are genuine stragglers from abroad or have escaped from captivity. The bird is believed to have bred here in 1949-50.

An anomalous species is Pallas's Sand-Grouse, a bird of the steppes of Asia, subject to mysterious impulses which send it migrating westward in vast hordes at irregular intervals. On one such occasion, in 1888, it arrived in Britain in considerable numbers, and sub-sequently a few pairs nested. The species soon died out, though. There is always the chance of another irruption and of seeing Pallas's Sand-Grouse establishing itself in a temporary colony, but it is not likely to become a permanent resident in the British Isles.

EYE. Since birds have hardly any sense of smell and very little, if any, of taste, and since their very nature compels them to cover great distances, their eyes are perhaps their most important sensory organ.

The most remarkable fact about bird's eyes is the relatively large size of the eyeball ; this is obvious in the owl, for example, but it is also true of species in which the greater part of the eye is hidden in the head. In fact, the eyes in some species are so large that the backs of the eyeballs roll on each other when the eyes are moved. In some species the eye departs from the normal spherical form ; the swan, for instance, has a comparatively flat eye, and the owl an elongated one.

Another striking feature of a bird's eye is the " third eyelid " (or nictitating membrane). Vestiges of this exist in most mammals, even in Man, its function being to clean the eye. But in birds it is mostly transparent, and presumably is often drawn across the eye during flight to protect it against the pressure of the air. This third eyelid accounts for a bird " winking ".

Contrary to what one might expect, birds' eyes are not very mobile ; it is the mobile neck which enables birds to look in almost any direction. Their eyes are necessarily adapted for horizontal vision, and birds must turn their heads to view anything apart from that direction.

The most striking feature of birds' eyes is their power of instantaneous alteration of focus, from the " telescopic " to the " microscopic ", as it were. This remarkable feature developed as a result of the need of birds not only to search for food on the ground but to scan the sky for enemies or other prey, which necessitates a frequent change of focus at very short intervals.

Harold K. Whitford

EYE. *The third eyelid or nictitating membrane is almost transparent in most birds and is probably drawn across the eye for protection during flight*

FULMAR
PETREL

F

FAEROE SNIPE—Capella gallinago faeroe-ensis. Common breeding Snipe of Iceland and the Faeroe Islands and a resident in the Orkney and Shetland Islands, this species is only a winter visitor elsewhere in the British Isles. It is similar in practically all respects to the Common Snipe (*q.v.*), and only an expert ornithologist could distinguish them by the slight variations in plumage.

The Faeroe Snipe nests in much the same type of country as the common species, but its breeding range is naturally more restricted. Its four eggs, laid in April, are similar in colour to those of its relative. The hen hatches them, although her mate is always near the nest. Both parents tend the young, which are able to fly in about a month. One brood is reared in a season. The diet is similar to that of other snipes.

FALCO. Genus of the family *Falconidae* of the order *Falconiformes*. It contains all the real falcons, including peregrines, kestrels, merlins, and gyr falcons ; and its members are distributed over a large part of the globe. The seven species which are on the British list— the Hobby, Peregrine Falcon, Merlin, Kestrel, Lesser Kestrel, Red-footed Falcon, and Gyr Falcon—are described under their own headings. The Greenland Falcon and Iceland Falcon (*qq.v.*) are local varieties of the Gyr Falcon.

These diurnal birds of prey have strong hooked bills ; the upper mandible has a sharp " tooth ", and there is a corresponding notch in the lower mandible. At the base of the bill is a patch of fleshy skin known as the " cere ", where the round-shaped nostrils are situated. The wings are long and pointed and, in most species, the second visible primary feather is the longest ; but in the Merlin the second and third are of about equal length and are the longest. The tarsus is almost completely bare ; the feet have four toes, all with sharp, curved claws. The females are larger than the males.

FALCON. Bird of prey distinguished from all other birds of prey by the relatively large head, broad shoulders, long, pointed wings and longish tail. The wing-beats of falcons are rapid and strong, but shallow, and their flight is very fast ; they kill their prey by swooping down on it from a height at great speed.

The Gyr Falcon (sometimes spelt Jerfalcon), formerly much used in falconry, is the largest and rarest falcon to be seen in the British Isles, having been recorded authoritatively only twice. At a distance it is difficult to distinguish from the Peregrine Falcon, although, apart from its greater size, it has a somewhat longer tail and blunter wing-tips. In flight, the Gyr Falcon has slower wing-beats than the Peregrine ; and, when perching, it can be distinguished by its paler and more uniformly coloured plumage.

Two geographical variants of the Gyr Falcon can be seen occasionally in this country : the Greenland Falcon, whose plumage is basically white with black markings, which may vary from very light, practically invisible, streaks to

Eric Hosking

FALCON. Merlins are the smallest falcons, and hunt birds, small mammals and occasionally insects

heavy blotches making the bird appear grey with streaked underparts ; and the Iceland Falcon which resembles the darker types of Greenland Falcon.

The Peregrine may be identified in flight by its anchor-like silhouette of long wings and relatively short tail, its smaller size and rapid pigeon-like flight broken by occasional long glides ; and, when perching, by its heavy, black, lobe-shaped moustaches. Its size is about that of a crow.

Hobbies are smaller than peregrines (a large female Hobby is only about the size of a very small male Peregrine). There are chestnut patches on the thighs and beneath the tail, and the underparts are heavily streaked—not barred as the Peregrine's.

Kestrels can be distinguished from all other falcons by their habit of constantly hovering with tails fanned out (although merlins will hover *occasionally*) ; also, no other bird of prey has the male's combination of blue-grey head and tail, chestnut mantle, black bar on tail and black wing-tips. The Lesser Kestrel, a very similar bird, is smaller and its mantle is uniformly chestnut, not spotted as the Kestrel's. In general, the Lesser Kestrel is a brighter-coloured bird, more fearless, noisy and greg-arious in its habits than the Kestrel. Young or female kestrels and lesser kestrels are rusty-brown, barred black, and have the characteristic black tail-band of the male.

Merlins are the least distinctive of all small birds of prey. They are very small falcons, not much bigger than mistle-thrushes. Their flight is more vigorous than that of kestrels, though they hover occasionally. The under-parts are boldly streaked and heavily rufous, and the tail has several broad black bands.

The Red-footed Falcon, resembling a small, slender Kestrel, is the only all-grey bird with reddish thighs and under tail-coverts. Its "cere" (fleshy skin at base of bill), eyes and legs are bright red. The female has a rusty crown and belly and a barred grey back.

Falcons prey on birds which are usually a little smaller than themselves ; and the smaller species may also hunt insects and moths.

For more detailed descriptions of the various falcons, *see also* under their individual names.

FALCONIDAE. Family of the order *Falconi-formes*, containing many species found in all parts of the world. The following nine genera are on the British list : *Accipiter, Aquila, Buteo, Circus, Falco, Haliaeetus, Milvus, Pandion* and *Pernis*.

The members of this family are diurnal birds of prey of various sizes. They have strong, hooked bills with sharp cutting-edges ; the palatal surface of the upper mandible has a longitudinal ridge. At the base of the upper mandible is a patch of fleshy skin known as the "cere", where the nostrils are situated. The wings are long and pointed, with ten functional primary feathers, the true first primary being rudimentary. The tail generally has 12 feathers. The feet have four toes, each provided with a strong, sharp, curved claw.

FALCONIFORMES. Order of diurnal birds of prey, including four families, whose members occur in all parts of the world. The two families on the British list are *Aegypiidae* and *Falconidae (qq.v.)*.

FAMILY. Grouping of closely allied genera, considered to have certain similarities in common. This definition has been generally—but not universally—accepted after generations of use by scientists, although, in respect of birds, it is not yet based on biological reality. *See also* Classification.

FANTAIL SNIPE. Indian name for the Common Snipe *(q.v.)*, also called "Bleater".

FALCON. *Hobbies can be distinguished by their unique moustachial stripes and by their fast, dashing flight—fast enough, indeed, to capture swallows on the wing !*

G. K. Yeates

BIRDS AND THE FARM—Friends and Foes

RALPH WIGHTMAN

*The author approaches this vexed problem with the commonsense for which he is noted,
and shows that birds cannot be categorically divided into good and bad, but that it
depends often on circumstances whether a species is regarded as a friend or as a pest*

FARMING, Birds in. In Victorian days most people accepted without question the idea that the universe had been created for Man, or at least that Man held it in simple service fee from the Creator. With such a basis it was natural to think of birds and animals as friends or foes, as servants or rebels. Today our conception of life is more complicated and we realize that every kind of creature is living for itself.

None the less, in the business of food production, it is difficult to think of wild life except in terms of how it influences our food or the food of our tame animals. The trouble is that modern research makes it ever more difficult to draw a firm line between the foe we wish to exterminate and the friend we would encourage. In fact, the thought of extermination has been almost completely given up in favour of control.

It is fairly easy to be dogmatic at the extremes. The Wood-Pigeon is a pest which lives almost entirely on vegetable material which would feed us or our livestock. It eats clover, kale, cabbage, peas, grain and fruit. The fact that it also eats some weed-seeds is only a small point in its favour. At the other end of the scale may be placed the swallows, martins and swifts who live entirely on insects, destroying large numbers of winged aphids, crane flies and blowflies that produce maggots in the living flesh of sheep.

If I had to make a list of common birds which are almost wholly beneficial to Man I think I should start with the insect-eaters already mentioned, and couple with them lapwings, who not only eat insects but large quantities of slugs and snails, the Golden Plover, the Nightjar and the Corncrake, who all have much the same diet. In this class also come wagtails and flycatchers. Next, I should take in the birds who are mainly concerned with weed-seeds, such as the Hedge-Sparrow, the warblers, Chaffinch, Goldfinch and Greenfinch. The

W. Farnsworth

FARMING, BIRDS IN. *Despite its seductive voice, the Wood-Pigeon is the farmer's enemy*

Robin and Wren are possibly not so much beneficial as harmless, although some might dislike the Robin's partiality for earthworms.

Finally, in the list of undoubted friends come the birds of prey who live mainly on such animals as rats, mice and rabbits. This is a short list and liable to some dispute. There is no doubt about the Barn-Owl, the Long-eared Owl or the Short-eared Owl. The Tawny Owl probably should be in this list, although it can develop a taste for poultry chicks. Of the hawks I would include the Buzzard, which in my district lives largely on young rabbits, although it may change its habits if myxomatosis becomes widespread. Of the falcons, the Kestrel is predominantly a rodent-eater, although sometimes he will also eat poultry.

On the side of undoubted foes, the Wood-Pigeon heads the list. Next I would place most of the Crow family, who are all rogues, and could be murderers. Most of them have the smartness of the spiv and the cunning of that class. The Carrion-Crow is always a danger near chickens and has killed plenty of weakly lambs in bad weather. The Raven is bigger, much more intelligent, safe from every natural foe except Man, but sufficiently rare in all but wild country to be no very serious enemy. Magpies, jays and jackdaws are much more common. They all do some agricultural damage, especially the Jay, in crops of peas, but their worst fault is as egg-thieves, and they usually steal from other wild birds. Perhaps it would be fair to make a distinction between agriculture and game preservation. The Jay and the Jackdaw can be a direct nuisance to farming, but both of them, with the Magpie above all, can be a nightmare to the gamekeeper.

Of the birds of prey, I would put the Sparrow-Hawk quite firmly in the category of foes, both from the point of view of the poultry farmer and the gamekeeper. Almost certainly the

FARMING, BIRDS IN. *The Lapwing can be called one of the farmer's best friends, for it will not only eat insects, but a great many slugs and snails*

borderline. Thank heaven, that enough land is not fruit-growing—so we shall never lose the Blackbird's song !

That leaves the Rook, the Little Owl and the Starling, and considering how much time is devoted each Spring to organized Rook shooting, it may seem strange for a countryman to hesitate. I have seen a Rook so gorged with leather-jackets that it could not fly. I have also seen rooks dig up seed-grain and potatoes, beat down standing crops, strip wheat in stook and pull the thatch off stacks. To my mind, it is all a question of numbers. If rooks can get grubs with ease, I believe they will leave crops alone. There are infinitely more leather-jackets, cock-chafers and wireworms in grass-land than in arable land. Our ploughing campaign has reduced the Rook's food and he has turned to crops. Some of the damage he does to crops is when he pulls up kale plants in a search for grubs. I place him as a bird to be reduced, but by no means exterminated.

The Little Owl, to my mind, comes in the same doubtful category, but more from the gamekeeper's point of view than the farmer's. This owl eats game chicks, but also plenty of mice and, in June, a lot of cock-chafers.

The Starling is the hardest case of all. These birds have increased enormously in recent years, and their habit of flocking in terrific numbers means that they may do a great deal of damage in a short time. They eat grain and fruit, but they are also very fond of insects, so that a big flock can quickly reduce the number of leather-jackets in a field. Their greatest danger to Man is something we have not considered in connection with other birds. Enormous flocks migrate to Britain from the Continent each year and there is evidence that they have carried foot-and-mouth disease in the dirt on their feet. Again, starlings suffer from a worm which causes gapes (*see* Disease) and this could be passed to poultry or game. In the size of their flocks alone, they compare with the concentrations of human husbandry, and that in itself is a danger.

A fascinating subject this "friend and foe", with strange complications. I leave it to you to place the larks, the gulls and the waders.

Peregrine Falcon comes in the same class. It is sheer sentiment which makes me hope that this lord of the air will never be exterminated. He is a nuisance to the poultry farmer, to the gamekeeper, and to the townsman whose only contact with nature is in racing-pigeons.

Amongst the other foes of the farmer are the House-Sparrow, which should never be confused with the Hedge-Sparrow. The House-Sparrow eats vast amounts of grain at harvest time and does a lot of damage in gardens by stripping buds. With him, I fear, I must place the Bull-finch, who certainly eats some weed-seeds but is an absolute curse as a bud-eater in fruit plantations. Even his beauty and his song are not enough to excuse some of his habits.

In that list of friend and foe I have tried to stick to fairly common birds with the exception of the Raven and the Peregrine Falcon. A host of other extremely common birds remain which I have not listed. The Thrush, the blackbirds, the Rook, the Starling, the Little Owl and the tits. On the whole I would put the tits in the useful list. They do strip some fruit buds, but there is some evidence that they are more than likely to be after the maggot in an already diseased bud. Their fun with milk bottle caps is not an agricultural problem; it might even force townsmen to buy more milk !

The Thrush and the Blackbird are only foes at certain seasons and to a relatively few specialist farmers. Their fault is a fondness for ripe fruit. For most of the year they eat large numbers of grubs and slugs. The Thrush is particularly fond of snails, and if a distinction must be made, the Thrush goes into the "friend" class, with the Blackbird on the

A FLYING COAT—Warm and Beautiful

C. HORTON-SMITH, Ph.D.

Feathers are far from the simple things they may appear. Of their several forms, some are intricate structures that are a triumph of design. The article ends with a part on how feathers obtain their marvellous colours. See also Flight ; Pattern ; Wing

FEATHER. One of the outgrowths from the skin of a bird. The feathers, taken together, form the body-covering or plumage. Birds are the only creatures that possess these unique structures which, however, belong to the same series of skin outgrowths as do the scales of reptiles; and, although the evolution of the modern feather is obscure, the mode of its development greatly resembles that of the reptilian scale.

Feathers differ from scales in their complex structure and by the possession of a core of blood vessels which at first projects from the surface of the skin. In plucking the feathers from a bird, one soon realizes that each feather is embedded in a pocket, or follicle, in the skin; and, when the bird is completely plucked, these follicles are seen clearly as minute pits scattered over the surface of the skin. Muscles associated with these follicles serve to erect the feathers. Unlike the hair of mammals, feathers are not provided with sebaceous glands but are possibly anointed, especially in water birds, by a secretion of the " preen gland " at the base of the tail.

Feathers undoubtedly evolved from the scales of the early reptilian ancestor of modern birds (*see* Ancestry) ; but when or how the change took place is never likely to be known—it must have been over a hundred million years ago, when Archaeopteryx (*q.v.*), the first known creature to have feathers, lived and flew.

Feathers can be grouped as follows :

(1) the contour feathers (*pennae*) which cover the body ;

(2) the down feathers (*plumules*) ;

(3) the *filoplumes*.

The contour feathers, besides covering the body, also form the well-developed feathers of the wing (*remiges*) and tail (*rectrices*). There are usually six pairs of tail feathers, but there may be more or less than this.

Contour feathers have strong shafts with more or less complete webs (*see* below). The structure of the wing feather is fairly typical of the structure of contour feathers in general.

Structure of Wing Feather. Even a casual examination reveals the beauty, complexity and marvellous adaptations of the feather to combine strength with lightness. A more careful examination shows, first, a tapering central shaft like the midrib of a leaf. Despite its airy lightness this tough horn-like shaft can be bent like a bow and whipped backwards and forwards without snapping ; it gives the feather its strength.

The stem or *scapus* consists of two parts :

(1) the *calamus* or quill, with its root embedded in the follicle ;

(2) the tapering extension of the calamus which is known as the shaft or *rhachis* and carries the two lateral webs of the feather, which together form the vane.

The calamus is cylindrical, transparent and hollow. The rhachis, which extends to the tip of the feather, has a groove along the length of its underside to give it concavity as opposed to the convexity of its upper side. The rhachis is filled with a white pith. The feather is nourished by a pulpy substance which passes through a

PRIMARY FLIGHT FEATHER OF GREEN WOODPECKER

SECONDARY WING FEATHER OF BARN OWL

John Clegg

FEATHER. *Specimens should be mounted on card or thick paper and secured with narrow strips of adhesive tape. They should be labelled carefully*

small opening at the base of the calamus (*q.v.*).

The two webs of the feather, which flare out from the rhachis, are complicated in structure. Tiny branches (*barbs*) which lie closely side by side are given off from the rhachis. If the outer edge of the web is rubbed downwards, the branches tear apart quite easily, and the smooth continuity of the feather's surface is ruined ; but if the webs are smoothed out by pulling them upward between the fingers, the branches lock together and the feather looks normal again. To understand why the feather is so quickly restored to good condition, we must look at it under the microscope. Springing out from each branch or barb are smaller branches (*barbules*). The barbules facing the tip of the feather carry hooklets which engage with scroll-like barbules on the opposite side of the neighbouring barb, i.e. the side away from the tip of the feather as shown in Figs. 1C–1D. When the feather is rubbed downwards, the hooklets disengage ; when the feather is stroked upwards, the hooklets re-engage with the scrolls of the adjacent barb rather like a zip fastener.

This disengaging and re-engaging of barbules is what happens when a bird preens its feathers. The device of hooklets and scrolls produces webs so dense and strong that little or no air filters through them when the bird flaps its wings in flight. The wing feathers of flightless birds, e.g. the Ostrich, possess no hooklets or scrolls, with the result that no compact webs are formed. Contour feathers that serve only an ornamental purpose may have few or no barbules, and the webs are fluffy in texture.

In a typical quill feather a tuft of barbs, with or without barbules, is situated at the junction of the calamus and rhachis : this tuft is the aftershaft (*q.v.*), accessory plume or *hyporhachis*.

Grouping of Wing Feathers.

The remiges or wing feathers are grouped according to the bones on which they are carried. The skeleton of a wing, the bird's forelimb, resembles that of a modified human arm ; the differences are the outcome of evolutionary changes by which the wing has become adapted to flight. In a resting bird the folded wing resembles a flattened letter Z, in which the elbow is directed backwards and the wrist forwards. The wing skeleton (*see* Anatomy), like that of the human arm, consists of three principal parts : the upper arm (*humerus*) ; the forearm, made up of two bones (*radius* and *ulna*) ; and the hand which, in the bird, is built up of fused bones (the *carpometacarpus*) that are separate in the human hand.

A bird's hand consists of a fused wrist and palm, which provide a rigid basis for the long flight feathers. There are fewer fingers than in the human hand, and they are greatly reduced in size—in contrast with the wing of a bat which has a full complement of long fingers to support the flying membrane. A bird's second finger supports the wing tip, the first and third fingers are rudimentary, and the fourth and fifth have disappeared altogether.

The number of the feathers of the hand (*primaries*) varies from 10 to 12. An elastic ligament secured to the calamus enables each primary feather to make its individual adjustment, and maintains equal spacing of the feathers when the wing is extended.

The feathers of the forearm spring from the ulna ; they are known as *secondaries* or *cubitals* and may exceed 30 in number. Other smaller feathers (*coverts* or *tertiaries*) lie in several series on the top and beneath the wing ; they conceal the bases of the primaries, thus forming an almost airtight surface over the calami of primaries which have no webs to provide such a surface. The tiny first finger or thumb carries a group of two to four feathers forming the bastard wing (*q.v.*) or *alula*.

The webs of flight feathers are narrower on one side of the shaft than on the other. The narrow webs provide the leading edges of the feathers in flight, i.e. they always face the direction of flight. The broader hind web of each feather overlaps the web of the feather immediately next to it. As a rule, the narrow and broad webs are of fairly constant width along their length, but in the broader-winged birds some of the webs of the primary feathers which form the tip of the wing are abruptly stepped down in width as the upper third or top of the feather is approached. In the Rook's wing, for example, the narrow webs of the second, third, fourth and fifth primaries are stepped down in width ; the broad webs of the first, second, third and fourth are also stepped down, though only slightly in the first primary. Such stepped-down primaries are referred to as *emarginated feathers*.

When the wing is extended in flight, spaces are left between the emarginated broad webs and the emarginated narrow webs of the feathers immediately behind them. These spaces, which can be seen between the finger-like primaries of the extended wing of a flying Rook, are termed slots and the wing itself is spoken of as a slotted wing. (No wing-tip slots occur in very narrow wings.) These slots and the " wrist-slot " formed between the alula and the leading edge of the main wing are associated with maintaining the aerodynamical stability of the flying bird (*see* Flight). Man has used similar devices to preserve the stability of aircraft. *See also* Wing.

Down Feathers and Filoplumes.

The second type of feather, the down feather (plumule), is usually hidden by the contour feathers. Down feathers are more numerous than contour feathers, and are soft and fluffy in texture ; they

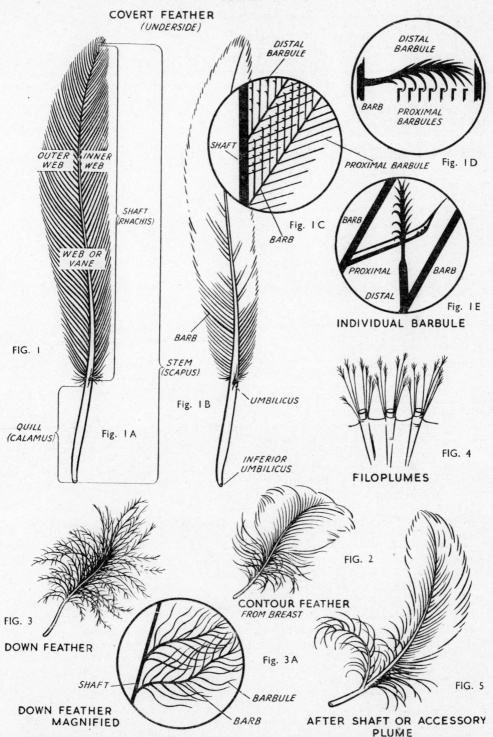

COVERT FEATHER
(UNDERSIDE)

DISTAL BARBULE

DISTAL BARBULE

BARB

PROXIMAL BARBULES

Fig. 1 D

SHAFT

OUTER WEB | *INNER WEB*

PROXIMAL BARBULE

SHAFT (RHACHIS)

Fig. 1 C

WEB OR VANE

BARB

BARB

BARB

PROXIMAL

BARB

DISTAL

Fig. 1 E

FIG. 1

INDIVIDUAL BARBULE

BARB

STEM (SCAPUS)

Fig. 1 B

UMBILICUS

QUILL (CALAMUS)

Fig. 1 A

FIG. 4

INFERIOR UMBILICUS

FILOPLUMES

FIG. 2

FIG. 3

CONTOUR FEATHER
FROM BREAST

DOWN FEATHER

SHAFT

Fig. 3 A

BARBULE

DOWN FEATHER
MAGNIFIED

BARB

AFTER SHAFT OR ACCESSORY
PLUME

FIG. 5

FEATHER. *Typical examples of the three main classes of feather are Contour (Figs. 1 and 2), Down (Fig. 3) and Filoplumes (Fig. 4). Figs. 1 A and B show the main parts of a contour feather, while Figs. 1 C, D, E are progressively greater enlargements showing how the web is constructed and how the barbules interlock (see text). The barbules of down feathers (Figs. 3, 3A) carry no hooklets, do not interlock and are softer. Filoplumes (Fig. 4) are the " whiskers " remaining after plucking other feathers. Fig 5 is a contour feather with (left) the accessory plume or aftershaft springing from it*

FEATHER. *Chaffinch's wing closed (top) and open (bottom), showing the airtight web of the feathers*

have all the structural features of contour feathers except the hooklets. In many instances the rhachis is missing, and the barbs arise from a short calamus. The first feathers of newly hatched chicks resemble the down feathers of adult birds. Down feathers are often used to line the nests of birds.

The third type of feather is the hair-like filoplume, best seen as the " whiskers " that remain scattered over the bodies of birds that have had the other feathers removed by plucking. The filoplume has a short lower shaft (calamus), and the hair-like part is really the rhachis, which carries few or no barbs.

The fully-feathered bird appears to be completely covered with feathers. In fact, there are numerous bare spaces on the body. The feathers are distributed along definite pathways or *pterylae*, and bare spaces (*apteria*) occur between the different pathways.

Colour. Feathers vary in colour from drab and utilitarian shades to hues of startling brilliance and beauty that are almost breath-taking. The colours may be due to the physical structure of the feather and the way it reflects or refracts the light, to the presence of pigments, or to a combination of these. The same colour may also be produced in various ways.

It might at first sight seem strange that colour can exist in the absence of pigment or dye, until one recalls the rainbow effect produced by light falling on a prism, or the scintillating colours of a soap bubble or thin film of oil on water.

Surface markings, provided they are sufficiently fine and closely spaced, also break up the light falling on them to produce colour. Thus, the spectacular patterning in the tail of the Peacock is entirely due to microscopic ridges on the surface of the feathers, which are devoid of either dye or pigment. As the colours caused by the ridging depend partly on the angle of view, they appear to change as either the observer or the Peacock moves, producing an iridescent effect.

Yellows are often associated with absence of pigment, the colour being due to the filtering out of all light-rays except the yellow.

The pigments found in feathers fall into two main classes : the lipochromes or fatty pigments, producing reds and yellows ; and the melanin series, which is responsible for most of the dark colours found in birds.

The actual colour, however, depends partly on the chemical composition and partly on the grain size of the melanin concerned. One member of this series even produces colours varying from reddish-brown to yellow, as the grain size becomes progressively smaller : other melanin pigments provide black, blue and silver coloration. Melanin pigments may also be found associated with lipochromes.

The most brilliant effects are generally produced when the colour caused by pigment is enhanced by iridescence due to the physical structure of the feather, as in the blue plumage of the Kingfisher, in certain parrots, and the prismatic sheen of the Starling. Blue, violet, green and yellow are often produced by a layer of brown (or some other colour pigment) overlaid by a colourless, thin ridged layer, which gives rise to an iridescent effect. This is often found in the tips of feathers where globular pigment grains are overlaid by a transparent layer. Sometimes the dark coloured core is overlaid by a pigmented outer layer. The long waves of the light are absorbed by the dark core, and the shorter ones are scattered back by the grains of pigment and the air trapped between them. The resulting colour is usually blue or green. The feathers of budgerigars exhibit this so-called Tyndall effect.

A few parrots possess a yellow pigment which fluoresces in ultra-violet light, so that these birds look uncannily bright.

Pigments are conveyed to the feathers in the blood, and enter through a small opening in the base of the shaft. They are elaborated in the cells of the developing feather, where they are finally precipitated as grains or suspended in fat. A damaged young feather may be colourless, contrasting with its undamaged neighbour, because the pigment has been stopped in its course and no deposition has occurred.

There may also be a congenital absence of pigment from all or some of the feathers (*see* Albinism), or there may be abnormal redness or blackness, produced by dietary or other causes (*see* Erythrism ; Melanism ; Xanthochroism).

The production or supply of some forms of the pigment is affected by the female sex hormone. This accounts for some of the differences in colour between the two sexes. If the female hormone is given to a brown Leghorn Capon, the breast feathers growing at the time bear the light brown colour of the female plumage instead of the dark brown of the male. A small dose of hormone produces an effect of limited duration, so that narrow bars of female colour appear on feathers otherwise exhibiting male characteristics. *See also*: Autumn Moult ; Flight ; Moult ; Pattern and Colour ; Spring Moult ; Wing.

FERN-OWL. Local name for Nightjar (*q.v.*), because of the bird's preference for heaths, commons and woodland clearings, where gorse and bracken are usually found.

FERRUGINOUS DUCK. *See* White-eyed Pochard. As the bird is only an irregular visitor to this country, this Encyclopedia follows the modern practice of referring to it under the name by which it is generally known in countries where it is more familiar.

FIELDFARE—Turdus pilaris. Like the Redwing, this member of the Thrush family is a winter visitor, arriving in flocks in October and leaving again in April. Its principal breeding haunts are in Scandinavia, but it also breeds fairly regularly in Bavaria. It is also a passage migrant widely distributed throughout the British Isles. It is to be seen in open pastures, farmlands and woodlands, especially where there are many berry-bearing trees and bushes, the fruit of which constitute a great deal of its winter food. Hard Winters often drive the bird into city parks, which usually contain several of these trees. Severe Winters nearly always take a heavy toll of wintering thrushes.

Although resembling the Mistle-Thrush in size and shape, the Fieldfare is a more decorative bird, for it has a bluish-grey head and rump (the latter very conspicuous in flight), and a golden brown mantle. Its rich chestnut breast is spotted in black, and its underparts are light buff, the sides heavily speckled with black. Its under-wing coverts are white (also very noticeable in flight), and it has a blackish tail. Male and female are alike. The Fieldfare is 10 in. long and its tarsus is 1 in. It has a weight of 4 oz. and its wing span is about 1 ft.

Fieldfares are very gregarious and wander about the countryside in flocks, sometimes of several hundreds, in company with redwings. They keep up a constant harsh chattering. When they are disturbed and fly into near-by trees, the birds all face the same way. They roost altogether, mostly on the ground, among the bushes and vegetation in the furrows of ploughed fields, in shrubberies and similar places.

The Fieldfare's chief call—disyllabic and harsh—can be heard all the year. There are various breeding calls which, if accelerated, denote excitement and quarrelling. The song is faint and harsh, and is uttered in flight.

Fieldfares breed in colonies and make little attempt to conceal their nests, which are constructed of grasses and mud, placed in trees (sometimes in gardens) and occasionally on the ground. The breeding season differs according to the country frequented ; in Poland, it is in April, and in Scandinavia from May to July. The eggs vary both in number and colour, but are normally five or six, and generally blue ; they are rather like those of the Blackbird. The hen does most of the sitting, for about two weeks, but both birds tend and rear the chicks. The Fieldfare's natural food where it breeds comprises insects of various kinds.

Local names for the Fieldfare are " Felt ", " Felter " and " Blueback ".

FIELD-GLASSES. Good binoculars, or field-glasses, are essential to successful bird-watching (*q.v.*). It is important to consider the following inter-related factors when selecting glasses : magnification, field of view, light value, resolution (or definition), colour correction, focusing arrangement and weight.

Magnification. Field-glasses are described by and usually marked with their magnification and size of objective ; i.e. the diameter of the lenses at the larger end of the instrument. Thus, 8×40 is an instrument which magnifies objects eight times and whose object-lenses are 40 millimetres in diameter. For general bird-watching, the magnification should be between

Fischer-Wahrenholz

FIELDFARE. *For some reason, a flock of these birds all face the same way on settling in a tree*

$6\times$ and $9\times$, although *experienced* bird-watchers may require an instrument possessing a higher magnification in addition to their general-purpose instrument.

Main objections to too high a power of magnification are that, firstly, as the magnification increases, the field of vision diminishes ; secondly, high magnification increases the effect of the natural shake of one's hands ; and, thirdly, glasses with powers of $10\times$ or over usually do not make any provision for focusing down to short distances.

Field of View. Generally speaking, the wider the field of view, the better ; but this can be obtained only at the expense of other qualities, such as flatness of field, colour correction and definition (especially in higher powers which, other things being equal, diminish the field of view). Measurements of fields of view are usually given in width of area visible in yards at 1,000 yards (or in feet at 1,000 ft.) or in degrees. A general-purpose glass may be expected to have a field of between 120 to 160 yards, or 7 to $8\frac{1}{2}°$.

Light Value. The ability of field-glasses to show up colours and to reveal details in poor light depends on their light-gathering power, which is dependent on the diameter of the exit pupil. This diameter is found by dividing the diameter of the object lens by the magnification.

Thus, a 6×24 glass has an exit pupil of 4 mm. (as have, approximately, 7×30 and 9×35 glasses), but an 8×40 glass has an exit pupil of 5 mm. Since the theoretical light-gathering value increases as the square of the exit pupil, the light value of the last glass is 25, compared with 16 for the others—i.e. an increase of almost 55 per cent.

If, however, the exit pupil is larger than the pupil of the person using it (human pupils average 7 mm.), the eye cannot make use of all the light available. The most efficient instrument, therefore, is one having an exit pupil not smaller than the user's pupil in the worst light in which the field-glasses are to be used. Night glasses have relatively large exit pupils.

Other Optical Considerations. Resolution or definition is that quality which gives crystal clarity to an image. It depends on the optical design, materials and assembly. It is more important than magnification and is the main reason for the difference in price of glasses with the same specifications.

Most new binoculars from first-class makers have coated lenses and prisms (recognized by their bluish or purplish tint). The object of " coating " or " blooming " is to reduce internal scattering of light, to improve transmission (by about 20-25 per cent.), to render the image crisper and to give considerably better contrast.

Flatness of view can best be judged by focusing the glasses on an object about 400 yards away and then slowly swinging round, so that this object moves from the centre to the edge of the field. With good glasses, the object should remain sharply defined. Colour correction and adjustment can be tested in the same way. As colour correction is more important for bird-watching than flatness of view, the image from a distant object should be seen clearly, without blue or orange fringes.

Faulty adjustment will produce a double image or cause a feeling of eye-strain.

Focusing. Independent focusing is lighter, cheaper and more weather-proof ; but the centre-focus is more popular and has the great advantage that the two eye-pieces may be altered simultaneously with one finger. This becomes more important with stronger glasses.

Correct focusing is important. First adjust the bending bars to suit the distance between the eyes—so that only one image is seen—noting the figure on the scale so that, once found, it can be found easily in future.

With separate eye-pieces, close one eye and adjust the other eye-piece to obtain the clearest image. Then repeat with the other eye. Note the readings for infinity and one other distance, say, ten yards. Memorise also the direction of rotation so that, if the glass is at infinity and a bird appears close at hand, time is not lost by turning in the wrong direction.

With centre-focusing, close the eye using the adjustable eye-piece and focus for clearest vision by means of the centre-screw. Then reverse the procedure, and by rotating the adjustable eye-piece, obtain the best result with the other eye. When this position has been

Eric Hosking

FINCH. One of the most colourful finches is the Goldfinch with its red face and yellow wing-band

Eric Hosking

FIRECREST. This tiny, tit-like bird is distinguished from its close relative, the Gold-crest, by its sharp black and white eye-stripes, seen clearly in this photograph

found and noted, all subsequent adjustments can be made by the centre-screw with *eyes open*.

Consult : How to Choose and Use Field-Glasses, J. B. Hebditch, British Trust for Ornithology, *Field Guide No. 2* (revised).

FIGHTING. *See* Behaviour ; Courtship ; *also* Display.

FINCH. Members of the family *Fringillidae* (*q.v.*) are generally called finches although, strictly speaking, this family also includes the buntings, redpolls and crossbills. The Snow-Finch (*q.v.*), despite its name, belongs to the *Passeridae* or Sparrow family.

Finches are distinguished by their stout, conical bills, specially adapted for crushing seeds. Apart from the ordinary, canary-like finch bill, two other forms are found : the exaggeratedly stout, rounded bill of the Haw-finch, Bullfinch and grosbeaks ; and that of the crossbills, which have their mandibles crossed over at the tips.

Most finches are brightly coloured birds, about the size of a sparrow, although the Hawfinch and Pine Grosbeak are somewhat larger, and the Serin, Siskin and Goldfinch smaller. Females are generally duller than the males, and the plumage of juveniles resembles the female's. Finches may also be distinguished by their strongly undulating flight.

The Chaffinch and Bullfinch are found breeding most commonly in this country ; the Goldfinch, Twite, Redpoll and Hawfinch are fairly widely distributed ; and the Siskin and Linnet are only found very locally. Other finches (*see* Fringillidae) are seen here but rarely. *See also* under their individual names.

FIRECREST—Regulus ignicapillus. The Firecrest, or Fire crested Wren, is a welcome annual winter visitor to Great Britain. It breeds in central and south Europe and north Africa, and arrives to winter here in October, staying until April. From a distance it may be confused with its close relative, the Goldcrest (*q.v.*), but close at hand the contrast between the yellow head of the Goldcrest and the yellow-red of the Firecrest is evident ; moreover, the Fire-crest has a black stripe through the eyes, with a white patch above, neither of which appear in the Goldcrest. Both birds have the same yellowish-green mantle and light under-parts, with two white wing bars and a black patch.

Firecrests favour much the same type of country as goldcrests, though they like low bushes and are not restricted to any particular kind of tree. The two species are much in each other's company, along with tits. The song of the Firecrest is not generally heard in Britain, but those who have heard its song in Italy, where it sings from March to June, have noticed its resemblance to the Goldcrest's song ; although the latter's musical call is smoother (*legato*). There are also variations among individual birds.

The breeding season of the Firecrest is in May, and two broods are usually reared. The nest is fashioned with mosses woven together, and lined with feathers, and is suspended under a hanging branch of a tree or bush. It is built by the hen, with her mate in close attendance. The eggs, numbering 7-12, differ only slightly in colour from those of the Goldcrest.

The food of the Firecrest consists chiefly of all kinds of insects ; but it seems to show a special preference for spiders and their eggs.

LOOKING AFTER INJURED BIRDS

W. C. OSMAN HILL, M.D., F.R.S.E., and J. J. YEALLAND

This article is in two parts. The first, by Dr. Osman Hill, gives practical information on First Aid for birds ; the second, by Mr. J. J. Yealland, deals with after-care and convalescence. Both contributors are on the staff of the Zoological Society of London

FIRST AID and After-Care. Almost the only cases in which First Aid to birds is practicable are those of accident and shock. Birds show little resistance to the effects of shock and haemorrhage (*see* Anatomy), though they do not seem to be susceptible to pain in the mammalian sense.

It is, therefore, essential to reduce shock and to stop haemorrhage. Shock is increased by handling the victim and by manipulating damaged parts. Such manipulations as are essential are best carried out if the bird's eyes are screened, so that it does not know what is taking place. Even large birds become quite amenable once they have been hooded ; they stop struggling and therefore have not to be restrained by force to the same extent.

Bleeding may be reduced or stopped by a weak solution of ferric chloride. All wounds *must* be disinfected after washing, preferably with antibiotics, such as penicillin powder. In cases of fracture of a limb, amputation may become necessary. Many wild birds (e.g. gulls) have been known to survive long periods with one leg only. Loss of a wing, or even part of a wing only, is more serious, except for ground-nesting birds. If amputation is decided against, the fractured limb must be splinted or put in plaster ; a broken wing may be bound to the body in its natural position, the body acting as splint.

Wounds of the head may prove more serious, but birds have survived even injuries necessitating removal of part of the brain. Conjunctivitis and other eye-troubles must be treated by repeated washing and syringing with disinfectant lotions ; but more drastic treatment is needed for mycotic lesions (*see* Disease).

Fouling of the plumage is a serious disability, and seems to produce profound depression in

Eric Hosking

FIRST AID. An injured Bittern, whose leg is in plaster, here poses with his good Samaritan

birds. If the victim cannot clean its feathers and preen itself, it becomes extremely unhappy and may even die. The worst cases, unfortunately all too frequent, are those of pollution by marine oil (*see* Oil Pollution).

Oiled birds should be cleaned with warm water and soap-flakes or any of the milder detergents, and should then be rinsed in warm water. This involves loss of the bird's natural grease from the feathers, which become pervious to water ; as a result the body itself becomes chilled and the bird may die from pneumonia. It is, therefore, essential to keep the patient in artificial heat, to keep the feathers dry and the body free from chill. The application of olive oil, butter or any other grease is not recommended ; though patients may benefit by a short warm bath daily, for, as a result of the bird preening himself after a bath, the feathers gradually regain their normal state. Another feature of oiling may be loss of appetite caused by oil that has entered the crop or the gizzard. This usually must be got rid of slowly. Artificial feeding may be necessary for a short while, but in such cases the prognosis is usually poor. For the after-care of oiled birds, *see* below, page 222.

AFTER-CARE AND FEEDING

The catching of many species of British birds formerly kept in captivity is now prohibited and it is illegal to offer for sale any of these birds unless they have been bred in aviaries and carry closed leg rings which can only be put on when the birds are nestlings (*see* Ringing). It often happens, however, that injured birds or fledglings in distress are found, and the feeding and care of these may present some difficulty.

Most fledglings are unable to feed themselves for some time after they have left the nest, so they must be offered suitable foods by means of tweezers at frequent intervals. Members of the Crow family are easily catered for : they thrive on a diet of small pieces of raw meat, including a little fat, puppy-rearing meal softened by being soaked in water or milk, a little wholemeal bread, a little ripe fruit and as many large insects and their larvae as can be obtained. Young mice, mealworms, gentles (the cleaned maggots used as bait for fishing), snails and earthworms are all good foods. Adult crows appreciate raw eggs ; also young rats, mice, nut kernels, a few sunflower seeds and mixed corn which has been soaked for 24 hours in water. If tame enough, these birds may be let out in the garden during the day, but should not be allowed into the house. Choughs are almost entirely insectivorous : jays are largely vegetarian and are particularly fond of green peas, ripe cherries and acorns.

Disabled starlings and blackbirds are often found, particularly in towns, and perhaps the most conveniently provided food for them is any ready prepared insectile food obtainable, like the mealworms and gentles, from pet stores. Fruit and berries, together with insects (including earwigs), woodlice, spiders and larvae (such as leather-jackets, mealworms and gentles) should also be offered. Earthworms are a good food, but these should not be collected from ground on which poultry have been kept, mainly because of the risk of gape-worm infestation. Thrushes would also thrive on this type of diet, with the addition of snails from which the shells have been removed.

House-sparrows eat a great variety of food and, in towns at least, seem to thrive largely on white bread ! They need a good seed mixture—canary seed, white and brown millet (Indian millet is rather small for them), hemp and groats—together with a little insectile mixture and a few mealworms and gentles. Greenfood such as lettuce, watercress, dandelion leaf, flowers and seeding heads (before they have opened, the tips being first clipped off to prevent a mess being made in the room by the fluffy part by which the seed becomes airborne) and small turves of grass are valuable foods. The fledglings could be reared on a little of the insectile mixture, mixed with chopped hard-boiled egg ; also wholemeal bread and milk, some well-masticated greenfood (the mixture to be given warm) and such live food as mealworms and gentles. Buntings need the same types of food (with a higher proportion of live food) and, in the adult stage, wild seeds such as seeding grasses, shepherd's purse, chickweed, dandelion, milk thistle and many others will be appreciated.

Good finch seed-mixtures can be bought from pet and corn stores. Goldfinches are fond of thistle and teazle seeds ; bullfinches of seeds of buttercups, ripe berries and buds of fruit and other trees.

Tits like seeds of sunflower and nut kernels (but do not give coconut) ; to these add a little suet, some insectile mixture, and live food.

The small insectivorous birds (including swifts, swallows and martins) do well on a good insectile mixture, mealworms, gentles, spiders, earwigs and suchlike, and some of them like small ripe berries. All birds should be kept very clean and must be provided with a shallow dish of water for bathing, for they are miserable if their plumage is soiled.

Sea birds whose plumage is covered with oil are, like so many of the others, generally far gone when they reach the stage of allowing themselves to be picked up, and even then their main concern is to get themselves clean. For

FIRST AID. *Thousands of sea-birds, their feathers polluted with oil, are cast up on our shores every year. Unless they are rescued in time, they die a miserable death*

Eric Hosking

FLAMINGO. His full glory is but seen in flight with his wings magnificent in scarlet and black

G. K. Yeates

methods of cleaning, *see* above, page 220. After they have been cleaned, they should not be let free until their feathers have regained their normal waterproofing. During this time, the birds should be fed according to their kind. Thus gannets, guillemots and similar birds must be forcibly fed with small whole fish or pieces of fish, but they soon learn to feed themselves. Gulls will eat pieces of fish, raw meat and dog biscuit or brown bread put into a dish of water.

The sea-ducks—Scoter, Golden-Eye and others—are not very easy to keep. They should be fed on soaked puppy-rearing meal, minced raw meat and fish and, if obtainable, small marine molluscs and crustacea. They need to be allowed to go on water as soon as the plumage condition permits. Other water-fowl will thrive on soaked mixed corn (wheat being the favourite) and wholemeal bread or biscuit meal ; duckweed and other water weeds.

The birds of prey, particularly owls and kestrels, are quite often found injured. They will feed readily on mice, young rats or sparrows. Raw lean meat can be given, but occasional roughage in the form of fur or feather is necessary. Fledglings must be fed by hand with small pieces of food. In all cases it is advisable to study the natural diet of the birds to be able to provide this wherever possible, or the best available and nearest substitutes.

FLAMINGO—Phoenicopterus ruber roseus. This bird is unlike any other, and most people who have visited a Zoo will be familiar with its appearance. The wild Flamingo from south Europe has not been recorded in Britain and it is quite possible that the few that have been seen alive here in the wild are escaped birds from a Zoo. The Flamingo breeds in large colonies in countries bordering on the Mediterranean, the south of France, especially in the Camargue ; Spain ; and also in tropical Africa, India and Ceylon.

Its main plumage is pale pinkish-white, and its extremely long legs and neck are the most striking features when at rest. It flies with both neck and legs outstretched. Its unique bill is long and pink, black at the tip, and has a curious abrupt downward bend ; its legs are pink, its feet webbed. Although a beautiful bird on the ground, it is in its flight that the Flamingo's full glory is seen, in its gorgeous scarlet and pink wings with their contrasting black tips. Adult flamingoes vary greatly in size, but the average length is 50 in. with a body of 21 inches. The bird has a tarsus of 13 in., and its wing span is approximately $3\frac{1}{2}$ ft.

The Flamingo has a sedate walk, with both neck and legs extended ; it never perches on trees, but spends most of its time wading in the shallow water of the lagoons, lakes and estuaries, searching for food among the mud, with its head often completely submerged. It is said to tread on the mud in an endeavour to induce the organisms on which it feeds to come to the top. When at rest, the Flamingo has a curious habit of curving its long neck round its body and tucking its head into its shoulder feathers, sometimes standing on one leg like a stork. Its voice is a goose-like sound on the ground ; but in flight the Flamingo usually utters a loud, honking call.

For a nest, the Flamingo raises a mound of mud above water level and scoops out a central depression measuring about 15 in. across. As far as is known, both parents help in this operation. In May two white eggs are laid, which the hen hatches, and one brood is reared in a season. It is surprising that the young survive in the closely packed colonies, without being trodden underfoot by their tall parents.

While the Flamingo's food is mainly obtained from the mud of the lagoons and lakes, grasses and water plants, and sometimes small fish, are also taken.

FLEDGLING. Name given to a young bird from the time when it is ready to start flying until it has full-grown wing quills and tail. It is a stage following that of the nestling (*q.v.*). *See also* the article on Young, Care of.

THE MYSTERY OF BIRDS' FLIGHT

C. HORTON-SMITH, Ph.D., and A. S. LONG

Starting from first principles, the joint authors here clear up many past misconceptions and with the aid of numerous diagrams and photographs, including a unique four-page colour sequence, show how birds travel through the air, take off, land and manoeuvre

FLIGHT. The flight of the bird and that of the aeroplane rely upon the same principles. Once that fact is grasped, there is no danger of falling into the (very pardonable) error of believing that the bird's wings operate by simply ' beating downwards " on the air, thrusting against it flatly like a paddle or the blade of an oar.

The fact is that the flapping wing of the bird and the rigid wing of the aeroplane both operate *by meeting the air at an acute angle.* Flapping (in level flight) is merely the bird's mode of propulsion, as the airscrew or jet is the aeroplane's.

It would be broadly true to say that the appreciation of this fact marked a turning-point for the pioneers of human flight. The birds were their obvious examples, but so long as their efforts were confined to mere imitation of bird flight, they failed. It was after serious students had rejected the conception of flapping-wing flight that the study of bird behaviour and construction made its great contribution to the development of flight with rigid planes.

NATURAL and ARTIFICIAL FLIGHT

Systematic study of bird flight was the foundation for the work of the German, Lilienthal, greatest pioneer of gliding flight, who inspired such men as Pilcher and Weiss in Britain and Chanute in America. All of them concentrated upon fixed-wing machines—but it was the birds who had, at the earliest stage, taught Lilienthal the efficiency of the curved wing section, as well as the rudiments of airmanship. It was bird forms which led Weiss to his advanced conclusions upon stability. And it was these men and other experimenters of the late 19th century whose work provided the essential bridge to powered flight by the Wright brothers in 1903.

Today, the wheel has turned full circle and the student of bird flight can find much to help him in the vast amount of research carried out for the benefit of the aircraft designer. For example, there is no need to guess about the pattern of airflow round a body. By the use of smoke and other media, it has been made visible in the wind tunnel and recorded by the camera (*see* illustrations in pages 224 and 225).

We shall take advantage of this by considering first the basic principles which are common to bird flight and to artificial flight. The common ground also extends to gliding and soaring, in which there is an exact analogy between the glider or sailplane and the bird with motionless wings. Finally, we will deal with the " powered " flight of the bird—flapping flight.

THE WING

How It Gives Lift. The bird, although it is so light in relation to its size (and power), is heavier than the air in which it moves. Like all man-made heavier-than-air machines (including helicopters), it is supported by surfaces so shaped that the reaction upon them of a mass of moving air will produce a force at right angles to the direction of the airflow—" lift ".

That definition is ponderous. But it will make things simpler in the long run because it underlines one very important fact : *We must always consider the flow of air—both its speed and its direction—in relation to the wing; in short, the RELATIVE AIRFLOW.*

The same effect is obtained by towing a wing through still air at 40 m.p.h., or by tethering it stationary (like a kite) in a 40-m.p.h. wind, or by towing it at 20 m.p.h. against a 20-m.p.h. wind. In all cases, the speed of the relative airflow would be 40 m.p.h.

The relative airflow is not always horizontal, and the force we call " lift " does not always act vertically. For the present, however, we will consider a wing in normal horizontal flight. Since its object is to produce an upward thrust (lift) by reaction against the air, it has to push a mass of air downwards. This could be done by any plane surface, from a post-card to a timber plank. But what kind of surface is needed to do it efficiently ? Part of the answer is clear if we look at the flow of air past the simplest of all surfaces—a flat plate—when it is set at a small angle to the airflow (*see* Fig. 1).

The total effect is admittedly a downward deflection of the airflow. But it is accompanied by a good deal of turbulence, or eddying, above and to the rear of the plate. This eddying does nothing to help the job in hand, but some-

FLIGHT. *Fig. 1 : Airflow past flat plate*

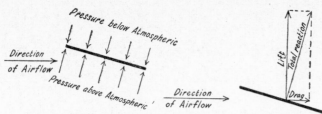

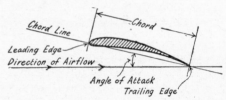

FLIGHT. Fig 2A (left) : Differential air pressures on flat plate
Fig. 2B (right) : Forces produced by airflow on flat plate

thing is having to do work to keep those little whirlpools going. That " something " is whatever power is being used to push the air past the plate. In other words, the turbulence is increasing the plate's resistance. The air, like any mass, tries to keep moving in a straight line, and it cannot flow round a sudden angle like that presented by the front of the plate.

The example of the flat plate is worth considering from another aspect. Over the whole of its under-surface, which faces the airflow, air pressure is raised above normal atmospheric pressure. Over the whole of its upper surface, pressure is reduced below that level (Fig. 2A).

The difference between these two pressures can be represented by a single force acting at right angles to the plate—that is, thrusting upwards and backwards (Fig. 2B). The upward (vertical) part of this force is the *lift* ; the backward (horizontal) part is the resistance or *drag*. The greater the lift and the smaller the drag, the less power will be needed to keep this primitive wing moving forward at a speed sufficient to maintain flight.

The fact that a curved surface could provide a better lift/drag ratio than a flat one was the first great lesson that the pioneers of human flight learned from birds. A glance at the airflow over a wing of curved section (Fig. 3) makes one reason for this quite clear. The airflow is cleanly divided and follows the wing's smooth contours without drag-producing (and lift-reducing) eddies.

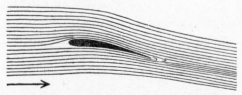

Fig. 3 : Airflow over wing of curved section

Moreover, the shape of the upper surface, especially towards its front edge, induces *a considerably greater reduction of pressure* than was obtained above the flat plate. The true explanation of this is too complex to give here ; it is sufficient to state merely the fact established by experiment that the reduction in pressure

above a surface of aerofoil section is considerably greater than the increase of pressure below it.

How Can Lift be Altered. A few technical terms must be defined here :

The *leading edge* is the front of an aerofoil (facing the airflow). The *trailing edge* is the back. The *chord line* is a straight line passing through these edges. The *chord* is the distance between them. *Span* is distance from wing-tip to wing-tip.

The *angle of attack* is the angle between the chord line and the direction of the airflow. This is the most important of these " shorthand " terms, for changes in this angle are critical. Between certain limits *increasing the angle of attack increases lift ; and reducing the angle of attack reduces lift.*

Fig. 4 : Illustration of technical terms used

Clearly the bottom limit is reached by reducing the angle until there is no lift at all (with a flat plate, this would happen at 0 degrees ; with an aerofoil section, at a slight *minus* angle—a fact easier to accept if one remembers that the upper-surface curvature is responsible for the bigger pressure variation).

The top limit is reached at an angle of attack of about 15° for the average aerofoil. Up to that point, both lift and drag rise with each increase in angle of attack. But any further increase in angle now produces a *reduction* in lift. The photographs (Figs. 5A–C) show what has happened They picture the airflow (traced by smoke jets) over a model bird-wing in a

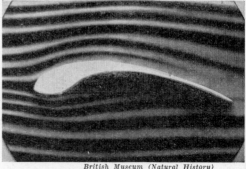

Fig. 5A : Model bird-wing in wind tunnel

FLIGHT—Bluebird coming in to land

This illustration of a Bluebird extending its " landing gear " and
spreading its feather " brakes " introduces a series of pictures
revealing many of the eye-baffling details of a bird's flight.   These
remarkable colour photographs, reproduced by the kind permission
of the National Geographic Magazine, were taken at Mr. H. Roy
Ivor's Song-Bird Observatory for the Study of Emotive Behaviour,
at Erindale, Ontario, Canada.   Despite appearances, they are not
" frames " from a cinematograph film, but still pictures taken for
their sharper image.   Each of them required a separate bird-flight
and prolonged trial and error by Mr. Ivor and the photographer,
Bernard Corby. Even so, the problem could not have been solved
but for the electronic photo-flash, whose 1/5000th-second exposures
appear to freeze the bird in mid-air, showing the minute adjustment of its feathers. From a casual glance, the pictures show only
a single bird, but actually two bluebirds were used to save both
from fatigue.   Further details of the technique involved in obtaining
this series of pictures are given on the last page of this section

I. Bluebird on his perch sights a lure, four feet distant.   Wings start to rise

3. Head up, tail down, legs tucked in, the little flyer strives to level off

5. Eyes focus on the stick, feet take aim.   The body rears upright for balance

2. Lifting pinions to the fullest, he takes off on the downbeat, legs extended

4. Approaching the second perch, he lets down legs. Tail fans out as a brake

6. Feathers pivot to let air through the wings. Springy legs absorb landing shock

In conducting their experiments, Mr. Ivor and Mr. Corby set up two perches four feet apart. Mr. Ivor, proffering a meal-worm, lured the bird to the first perch. A moment later, Mr. Corby, standing behind the second perch, extended another worm, leaving his other hand free to press the switch of the photo-flash. Great skill and patience were needed to take these shots because the photographer had but a fraction of a second in which to act

Reward for
Good Behaviour

The test completed, the bird flies away to eat his well-earned reward in privacy, and his opposite number takes over for the next run. Bluebirds, which are not, of course, British birds, were chosen because not only were they colourful, but small enough to fit into the lens's limit of coverage

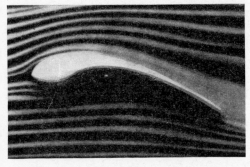 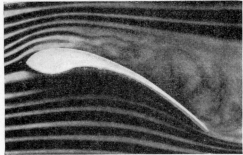

British Museum (Natural History)

FLIGHT. Figs. 5B and 5C : Model bird-wing, showing development of turbulence with increasing angle of attack

wind tunnel. In the first, the angle of attack is 3–4°, and airflow both round and behind the wing is smooth. In the second, at about 10°, a mere trace of turbulence is visible behind the trailing edge. In the third, at about 20°, smooth airflow has definitely broken down ; eddies extend over most of the upper surface and continue, beyond the photograph, for some distance " downstream ".

This breakdown of streamline flow over an aerofoil is called *stalling*. The *stalling angle* is the angle of attack at which lift reaches a maximum. Lift does not *disappear* immediately after the stalling angle. It only decreases—more or less sharply according to the wing section.

Drag also increases with the angle of attack—slowly at first, but at a progressively greater rate, until at large angles it is increasing faster than lift. Clearly, there must be a point at which the amount of lift generated represents the best value for the energy spent in overcoming drag. This angle of attack at which the lift/drag ratio is at its highest is chosen by a bird for normal flight—which helps to explain both the angle at which the wing is set on a bird's body and the bird's attitude in the air.

The section of the wing also affects lift. High-lift sections are deeply curved (like those of birds of prey, which have to bear the additional weight of the " catch "). High-speed, sections, like those of the swift, are flatter.

GLIDING AND SOARING

In gliding flight, the bird is " running downhill," sacrificing height to secure the forward motion which its wings need to give lift. The propulsive force is gravity—that is to say, the bird's weight. This *can* be used to dive steeply and fast, but if the bird wants to save energy by gliding as far as possible it will maintain its wings at the " most efficient angle of attack " referred to above. This will give its best *gliding angle*—and the higher the lift/drag ratio of the whole bird, the flatter that angle will be.

All birds glide—usually, of course, when they want to lose height. Some small birds, like

swifts, sparrows, tits and wagtails, even intersperse their normal flight with short spells of rigid-wing flight. But the specialists of flapless flight are those birds which can *soar*.

Soaring is simply gliding in air-currents which rise at a speed equal to, or greater than, the bird's rate of descent. The bird is still descending relative to the air around it, although it is maintaining or increasing height relative to the ground.

To soar systematically and constantly, a bird must have a very " flat " gliding angle (i.e. low sinking speed). This quality has evolved in those birds which have most needed it—the long-distance fliers, and the birds of prey which patrol over large hunting areas.

The most efficient of these birds can maintain height in up-currents of only 2 or 3 feet per second. They may find these currents where air is deflected upwards by hills, cliffs and similar obstacles ; or they may use " thermals " —rising currents of warmer air above land (such as bare earth, ploughland, or built-up areas) which has absorbed more heat from the sun than its surroundings. Thermals also exist under cumulus cloud and along " storm fronts ". The circling flight so often observed in soaring birds is usually to be explained by the fact that the bird has found an up-current and is staying in it.

Chief of the soaring land-birds are the eagles, vultures, kites and buzzards. To them, endurance and height are of prime importance, for their hunting depends upon a wide range of vision plus the tactical advantage represented by altitude (which can always be converted into speed at will by diving). The soaring powers of the Stork have a different object—to economise effort on its long migrant journeys.

Among sea-birds, soaring is employed by gulls and by that master of the art, the Albatross. This bird remains on the wing during almost the whole of its long sea-passages, and much of its flight is either " flapless " or achieved with a minimum of wing motion—a remarkable feat considering that the only up-currents over the sea caused by deflection are those near ships, and the only " thermals " those caused by suitable cloud formations ; and neither of these sources is sufficiently common to sustain soaring of long duration.

It seems fairly well established that, in fact, the Albatross is able to take advantage of " wind gradient "—that is, the tendency of the wind's velocity to increase with height. The greater the wind speed, the more marked this effect becomes. Given a certain minimum wind velocity, the Albatross can soar by gliding down-wind in the faster-moving upper strata and then, using the momentum it has received, start an up-wind climb after turning in the slower-moving air near sea level. During this up-wind climb, it enjoys the advantage of passing through air strata which have progressively greater velocity *against* its flight path. The total effect is that the bird maintains or increases height virtually without effort, although it drifts down-wind in so doing. In much the same way, the Albatross can take advantage also of horizontal variations in wind speed, i.e. gusts.

The aerodynamic efficiency needed for flight under these conditions is very high. Small wonder that the " design " of the Albatross is concentrated upon flying qualities. Like sailplanes and long-range aircraft, the Albatross has wings of very high aspect ratio (ratio of span to chord) with a considerable taper—a plan form making for high lift/drag ratio. Drag is kept down, too, by the streamlining and small frontal area of the bird's body. The net result is a gliding angle of only 1 in 20, and a forward speed of some 50 m.p.h.

But high efficiency in one direction is only achieved by sacrifices in others. This fact is borne out by comparison of the Albatross with the land soarers. The birds of prey have wings of considerably lower aspect ratio, but they also have the qualities which accompany it—greater manoeuvrability (due to lower turning moments) and greater structural strength. The Albatross could not " pull out " of a fast dive with the Eagle's speed ; nor could it operate happily from a land base with a very irregular surface, or carry a load representing a considerable proportion of its own weight.

FLAPPING FLIGHT

In the air, as on land, Nature's mode of propulsion is reciprocating. Man has applied motive power to the rigid wing ; Nature has evolved the flapping wing with a pattern of movement which provides *forward thrust* as well as *lift*.

How is this thrust obtained ? The answer is simplified if we recall the effect of airflow

upon an aerofoil, and bear in mind that an efficient wing produces a total resultant force which acts chiefly upwards and only slightly backwards (in other words, one that is almost at right angles to the airflow).

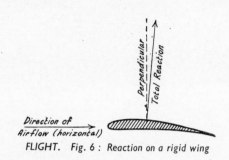

FLIGHT. Fig. 6 : Reaction on a rigid wing

Now imagine that the airflow is meeting the wing *from below*, but the angle of attack remains the same. This simply means that Fig. 6 is tilted bodily downwards.

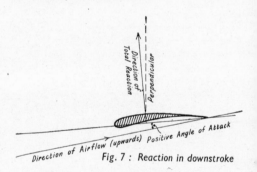

Fig. 7 : Reaction in downstroke

The total reaction is now acting *forward of the perpendicular*—in other words, it is providing a propelling as well as a lifting force. This is the state of affairs over the outer part of a bird's wing during the down-stroke. The primary feathers of the " hand ", which provide most of the thrust in normal flight, can be flexed independently of the inner part of the wing. During the down-stroke, they flex upwards at the trailing edge; so the position of the wing will be similar to that in Fig. 7. The direction of the relative airflow will be the product of the *downward* motion of the wing and the *forward* motion of the bird (assuming level flight)—that is, the air meets the wing in an upward and backward direction, again in the same way as in Fig. 7.

On the upstroke, both the vertical movement of the wing and its flexion are reversed—and so, therefore, is the whole pattern of forces. This time we have Fig. 7 inverted (*see* Fig. 8). The total reaction is still acting forward of the perpendicular, and therefore providing some forward thrust. (For simplicity, these three diagrams show a wing changing its attitude

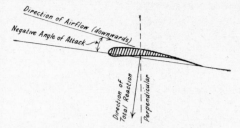

bodily. In fact, a bird's wing bends upwards or downwards at the trailing edge, but the effect is similar.)

To summarise the foregoing broadly : *the wing flexes so that on the downstroke it pushes air downwards and backwards; on the upstroke, upwards and backwards.*

This explains how thrust is obtained. But why does not the upstroke cancel out the downstroke, leaving no net upward force to keep the bird in flight ? The truth is that during the upstroke the bird does lose a little height—visibly, in the case of large, slow-flapping birds—but much less than it has gained on the downstroke. This is due to three things ;

(1) The wing is at a negative angle of attack (to the *relative* airflow), at which its section, designed to give lift at positive angles, is much less efficient—i.e. it is producing a smaller force at right angles to the airflow.

(2) The wing is not only flexed, but is also bent at the "elbow." This can be seen in Fig. 9, head-on outline views copied from a cine-film of a Black-headed Gull in flight. The effective part of the downstroke has been completed in view number 8. Numbers 10–13 show the bending of the elbow during the upstroke, accompanied by a marked drooping of the tips.

The result is not only to reduce the effective span of the wings, but also to permit air to "spill" easily over the tips (the "spilling", of course, is downwards).

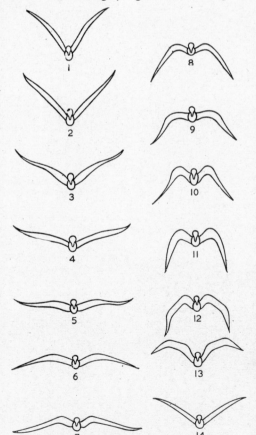

Fig. 9 : Head-on outline views of flying gull

(3) Individual feathers are so designed that the wing-covering itself is less "airtight" on the upstroke than on the downstroke (*see* Feather).

In the cruising flight of larger birds, when the only object is to maintain flying speed, flapping is confined almost entirely to the outer part of the wing. The considerable area inboard can then be considered as virtually a rigid lifting surface, playing no part in propulsion.

TAKE-OFF, LANDING and MANOEUVRE

Take-Off. So far, our discussion of propulsion has assumed that the bird is already in flight. But take-off conditions demand the generation of lift without any initial forward air-speed except that provided by the bird facing into the wind (a few birds unaccustomed to flight, like the domestic fowl, Peacock and several wading birds, add to this by running before take-off).

For lift at take-off, then, a bird must rely upon the vertical force obtained by direct downward displacement of air during the downstrokes, minus the smaller opposing force generated during the upstrokes. During this short period, the wing is not behaving as an aerofoil at all—in fact, it really is "beating the air" or "acting like a paddle".

This is a very inefficient process, demanding great muscular effort, and it has been observed that birds appear to be completely exhausted after repeated take-offs. It is certain that primitive birds were incapable of taking off from level ground, and some contemporary birds will avoid it whenever possible (turkey buzzards, for instance, prefer to take off from an eminence and wait for conditions which give them the added help of up-currents).

All birds keep the period of energy-wasting "direct-reaction" flapping to a minimum by levelling-off as soon as they have enough height to permit

Eric Hosking

FLIGHT. Fig. 10 : Bird on the point of landing, showing how drag is augmented by the fanned-out tail, while wing-tip slots and alula are open

the momentary dip as they gain flying speed. Under favourable conditions, the take-off can be so short as to be hardly perceptible.

Landing. Landing involves an approach to the chosen spot at an angle of glide sufficiently steep to clear obstacles, followed by the checking of both horizontal and vertical speeds. Landing into the wind assists both objects. Apart from that, a bird can secure low sinking speed and steep glide path by gliding at a large angle of attack (high lift plus very high drag). Drag is augmented by the fanned-out tail and the bird's body, both at an angle which sometimes approaches the vertical (Fig. 10). The wing angle is often so acute that it must be at or beyond the stall. The problem which this raises is not that of sudden loss of lift—for the stall of the average bird's wing is gentle—but that of control. Near the stall, a slight increase of tip angle, intended to raise a wing, not only might be ineffectual, but might have an opposite effect by accelerating the stall of that wing.

Nature's answer to the problem has an exact parallel in the device used in some air-

craft, the Handley Page slot. If a small aerofoil is placed just ahead of a wing's leading edge, the "downwash" from it will "smooth out" incipient eddying over the upper surface of the main aerofoil. Fig. 11 shows the effect upon the model wing which was shown stalled at the same angle of attack in Fig. 5C.

The effect is to maintain lift *and* control at angles which would otherwise be beyond the stall, permitting steeper climbing and gliding. In birds, slotting at the wing tips is often multiple. Several of the tip feathers are partially separated, and are capable of flexion about their leading edges. At high angles of attack, the airflow causes these feathers to flex upwards at the trailing edge and thus to separate completely, forming a series of "slots" (Fig. 12). Slot effect at the elbow is provided by the alula (*q.v.*), or bastard wing. In normal flight, this lies so closely against the main wing as to form part of its leading edge. At large angles of attack, the alula is raised and separated (again automatically) by the reduction of pressure upon its upper surface.

Fig. 12 : Multiple wing-tip slots

Extensive wing-tip slots are found in birds which live in woods (game-birds are good examples), or among reeds or bushes. Short, broad wings are necessary for their constant passage through obstacles and manoeuvring in confined spaces. Their slots serve to avoid the large tip losses caused by low aspect ratio, as well as assisting take-off, landing and control.

Birds of prey, also, have multiple tip slots. For them, flight at large angles of attack is necessary (i) when they wish to "hover" almost stationary relative to the ground by soaring against the wind ; and (ii) when lift must be increased to sustain the additional weight of their catch.

Manoeuvre. Both for diving and for making a steeper glide path before landing, a bird can lose lift simply by folding the wings upwards. Kestrels and buzzards dive upon their

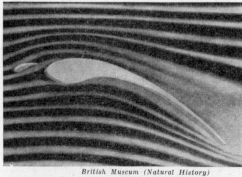

British Museum (Natural History)

Fig. 11 : Airflow over model slotted wing

prey in this way ; so do the fish-eating birds. The hunters can recover from the dive very quickly by spreading their wings again and using the speed gained either for fast level flight or for rapid climbing attack.

In general manoeuvring, the wings play the principal part. Lateral control is provided by differential tip flexion—chiefly, it seems probable, upward flexion at the trailing edge of the tip on the inside of the turn. It seems likely that trailing-edge flexion may also supplement the very short tails of some birds for control in the vertical plane (climbing and diving).

Aerodynamics also enter into the formation flying employed by many species of gregarious birds and by most birds on migration (q.v.). Flight in " V " formation, or staggered, or in a straight line at different levels as in the flock-flight of starlings, assures that a following bird avoids the turbulent wake of the bird ahead.

PERFORMANCE

The variation of wind speed with height makes it difficult to estimate bird speeds accurately. Direct observation is possible only from aircraft flying at the same height and on the same course. Attempts have been made, however, to correct for wind speed, and the results may be accepted if allowance is made for a 5–10 m.p.h. error either way.

The Swift has been credited with 90 m.p.h., and the Mallard with 65 m.p.h. Other speeds recorded are: gulls, 50–58 m.p.h. ; ducks, 44–59 m.p.h. ; stock-doves, 40–59 m.p.h. ; turtle-doves, 41–51 m.p.h. ; swallows, 29–32 m.p.h. ; green-finches, 35 m.p.h. ; thrushes, 30 m.p.h. ; and rooks, 24–35 m.p.h.

Casual judgments of speed are deceptive. The speed of a large bird travelling at height always tends to be under-estimated. The leisurely wing-beat of the wild goose or wild swan, for example, may be propelling the bird at about 75 m.p.h. ; yet the darting low-altitude flight of the Kingfisher does not exceed 45 m.p.h.

Birds on migration appear to increase their average speeds ; that of the Swallow, for example, may go up to 38 m.p.h. But migratory birds make all possible use of wind trends, so that point-to-point speed and air-speed may be completely unrelated. It is on record that marked lapwings made a trans-oceanic flight, with the wind, at about 100 m.p.h., nearly twice their normal air speed.

Diving speeds can be extremely high. The Peregrine Falcon, it is said, " stoops " at nearly 200 m.p.h., and the dive of the Gannet on a fish is given as more than 100 m.p.h.

The final test of flying efficiency is flatness of glide—a direct reflection of the lift/drag ratio.

One authority gives the gliding angle of the Albatross as 1 in 20, that of the Eagle as 1 in 17, and that of the Pigeon as 1 in 9 (the first two are, of course, soaring birds).

There are on record a fair number of observations of the heights at which birds fly. The difficulty lies in attempting to separate the random from the typical. It seems that the average height at which the majority of birds fly does not exceed 1,000 feet, but there are many exceptions.

The Golden Eagle, the Imperial Eagle, the Raven, the Hooded Crow and the Peregrine Falcon have been observed at 6,000 ft. Vultures are said to attain heights of 2 to 4 miles, and the " ceiling " of the Condor, largest of the vulturine birds, has been given as 6 miles. The White Stork can reach an altitude of about 2 miles. Cranes are other habitual high fliers. Finally, one may recall that choughs and curlews have been seen flying at the 20,000-ft. mark on Mount Everest, and that a photograph of the eclipse of the sun even recorded a flock of geese at a height of 29,000 ft. (see Speed).

FLYCATCHER. These little birds, members of the family *Muscicapidae* (q.v.), are usually seen perched *upright* on some vantage point watching for flies and suchlike. No other small bird shares their habit of so persistently sallying forth after insects—which are caught with an audible snap of the bill.

Of the five flycatchers on the British list, described under their own names, only the Spotted Flycatcher is at all common ; while the Pied Flycatcher, though a breeding visitor, occurs but locally. The Brown and the White-collared species are stragglers, while the Red-breasted bird is but an irregular winter visitor.

John Markham

FLYCATCHER. *Watching from some vantage point the little bird will suddenly dart after an unwary fly*

FOOD AND FEEDING HABITS OF BIRDS

J. A. GIBB, M.A., D.Phil., M.B.O.U.

The author here gives a fascinating account of the feeding habits of different species of birds. He describes the types of food birds like and for which they are adapted, how they prepare it for eating, and how they may store it against their future needs

FOOD and Feeding Habits. Through the gradual process of evolution (*q.v.*) birds have fitted themselves to live in almost every habitat wherein life exists, so that here in Britain we take them for granted as our constant companions. The directing force behind their evolution, which has produced the startling variety of bird life now confronting us, ranging from swallows to swans and from wrens to eagles, has surely been the ever-pressing struggle for birds to win their food from the environment.

Size, shape and structure of birds have been determined largely by their food requirements ; and different kinds of birds have evolved to exploit the opportunities presented by the environment. Each species of bird is adapted to a particular mode of feeding, at which it excels. As a rule, no two species of birds living together in the same habitat (*q.v.*) have identical food demands ; for if the demands of two species were identical, they would compete with each other for food, and one would eventually drive the other out of existence.

Search for Food. Birds search for food by sight, sound or touch, but probably never by smell (though nuthatches were once said to

distinguish full from empty hazel-nutshells by means of the " fine sense of smell " which was erroneously attributed to them).

Sparrows picking crumbs at our back door and swallows rushing over the meadows ; the Kestrel hovering over the downs and the Sparrow-Hawk fleeting through the woods ; the Kingfisher watching by the lake-side and the Dipper walking submerged along the stony bottom of the stream ; gulls jostling in the harbour and gannets sailing out at sea—all these are examples of birds hunting by sight. Oyster-catchers and some other waders habitually probe for food in mud and sand, relying on the sensitive tip of their bill to detect edible matter.

Owls, with their specially softened plumage, silently quarter the hedgerows by night listening for the faint rustlings and squeakings of mice. Woodpeckers tap on dead wood, sounding it for the hollowed chambers of wood-boring larvae beneath the surface ; and blue tits behave in the same way on dead twigs. It has been suggested that song-thrushes listen for squirming worms when they stand still, with head on one side ; but this is altogether unproven, for they may equally be watching for slight movements on the surface of the ground.

Pursuit and Capture. Once the food has been detected, it must be pursued and captured. This phase, which provides us with some of the finest spectacles in bird-watching (*q.v.*), often demands great skill, and many birds are specially adapted for its execution. The Peregrine stooping on its quarry has the rare but essential ability to focus with both eyes on objects lying immediately ahead. Gannets plunging headlong for shoaling fish could never withstand the impact of their dive without the cushioning given by the inflated air-sacs (*q.v.*) beneath their skin. The Crossbill is peculiar in having the tips of its mandibles crossed over ; with a scissor-like action of this unique tool, it wrenches open the scales of unripe cones to disclose the seed at the base of the scales. Swifts and nightjars have immensely wide gapes to catch insects in flight. *See also* Bill.

The pickaxe bill and powerful neck muscles of woodpeckers make them efficient wood-hacking machines ; and their stiffened and pointed tail feathers support them against the trunk of the tree as they climb. The woodpecker's fantastically long, sticky tongue explores the channels of wood-boring larvae ;

W. Farnsworth

FOOD. *Kingfishers swallow their prey usually at one gulp, but large fish are dashed to pieces first* while the Green Woodpecker, which has partly forsaken its tree-climbing habits, uses its tongue to extract ants and their pupae from ants' nests.

Many wading birds, like the Curlew, have long slender bills for probing in the mud, and long legs for wading. The Avocet combines long legs with a strongly upturned bill. It feeds on small animals skimmed from the surface of shallow water with a side-to-side motion of its upturned bill. Many surface-feeding ducks, like the Mallard and Shoveler, have bills adapted for straining small particles of food from water or mud. The sides of their mandibles are provided with a fine, comb-like structure of lamellae, which act as a sieve.

The most elaborate sieve of a bill is possessed by the Flamingo, for the inner sides of its abruptly angled bill are finely grooved (lamellated) towards the tip, forming a complex sieve. The Flamingo feeds with its head submerged and upside-down, so that the upper side of the angled part of its bill is nearest the bottom. It sucks up quantities of water and liquid mud with a pumping action of its tongue, sieving out the solid food particles in the lamellae of its bill. Surplus water is squirted out sideways from the base of the bill by the same pumping action. For sheer efficiency in a specialized field, the Flamingo must reign supreme. But such acute specialization makes it unadaptable, and the Flamingo might be among the first to succumb in a changing environment if its accustomed food were lacking.

Food Preparation. Some foods are not immediately edible when captured and must be prepared ; they may be too big, too tough or even too active, or certain parts may be unpalatable. Birds of prey and carrion-feeders

FOOD. Hawk (top) is settling on his prey to tear it into pieces ; Woodpecker (centre) has caught a mouthful of insects on its long sticky tongue ; Nightjar (below), yawning, shows its enormously big gape

Lynwood M. Chace; Eric Hosking

tear up bulky foods, for which they are equipped with strong, hooked beaks. Finches must crush large seeds to obtain the kernels : thus the Hawfinch splits open cherry stones with one squeeze of its pincer bill.

Nuthatches and woodpeckers hammer open hazel nuts, first wedging the nut in a crevice in the bark. The Nuthatch then stands upside-down above the nut to bring the whole weight of its body behind the smashing blows. Of the tits, only the Great Tit can open hazel nuts, and takes up to 20 minutes to do so.

The ability to hold food between the feet is possessed only by certain birds, notably the birds of prey, shrikes, tits (except the Long-tailed Tit and Bearded Tit) and the crows ; other species occasionally place a foot upon food but fail to grasp it. When birds which cannot grasp food in their feet have to break up large morsels, they usually hold them in their bill and thrash them against a branch or rock. The Song-Thrush, for example, has solved the problem of extracting snails from their shells by smashing them against stone " anvils ". The battered snail, withdrawn from its shell, is then wiped in grit to remove the slime before being eaten. Heaps of empty snail shells littered around the " anvils " give witness to the thrush's success. Several species of gulls and crows break open hard-shelled molluscs by dropping them to the ground from a height. As a last refinement, many waders wash dirty food taken from mud or sand.

Most young birds receive their food more or less in its original state, brought by their parents either in the bill or in the crop, from which it is regurgitated after a preliminary softening. Some foods, however, need special preparation. Parent birds usually break up large morsels or select smaller morsels for their young than they would normally eat themselves.

Pigeons and doves feed their young at first on a fatty substance, known as " pigeon's milk ", produced in the crop. Young birds which can leave the nest shortly after hatching, such as young waders and game birds, may receive little or no food direct from their parents, but are simply led to suitable feeding grounds where they forage for themselves. *See also* Nestling ; Young, Care of.

Storing of Food. Many birds commonly store food for short periods in their crop before swallowing it. This enables a bird to gather more food than it could otherwise cope with immediately. Digestion does not take place in the crop, though the food is slightly softened. An altogether different phenomenon is displayed by a few birds which hide surplus food ; for instance the Nuthatch and some of the tits and crows do this. The Red-backed Shrike impales surplus food on thorns or the barbs of barbed wire ; these stores being known as " larders ". Similarly, birds of prey assemble surplus food at their nests or roosting places. Such stored food is sometimes eaten later if other food becomes short.

Jays hide vast numbers of acorns in the ground in Autumn, often carrying them many hundreds of yards. The Jay apparently re-members exactly where at least some of the acorns, which it buries singly or in small groups, were hidden, and recovers them several weeks or months later. Coal-tits and marsh-tits hide various seeds and nuts, as well as more perishable foods like caterpillars and aphids, in Spring and Autumn. Each morsel is normally hidden singly, though aphids are hidden in beakfuls of about 50 at a time. The most common sites for hiding food are in the ground or in a bark crevice. The morsel is poked well in and very often covered with a small piece of lichen or moss. It is impossible to believe that each tit remembers just where it has put even a small proportion of the hidden food, for one bird may well hide several hundred morsels daily for weeks on end. More likely,

FOOD. *A sparrow picking up crumbs at somebody's backdoor is a familiar sight in both Summer and Winter alike, and here one of them can be seen making himself at home*

Ronald Thompson

FEEDING HABITS OF SELECTED BIRDS

Bird Family	Feeding Place	Food	Feeding Habits
Colymbidae (Divers : 4 spp.)	Freshwater in Summer ; sea, Winter	Fish ; also other aquatic animals	Dive from surface
Podicipidae (Grebes : 5 spp.)	Mainly freshwater	Aquatic animals ; fish, insects, crustaceans, molluscs.	Dive from surface
Procellariidae (Petrels : 16 spp.)	Marine	Small fish, offal from fishing vessels, flotsam	Feed on surface of sea. Settle, or dive in, from flight
Sulidae (Gannet)	Marine	Fish	Fish sighted from air ; dive into water from heights to 140 ft. Sometimes settle on water
Phalacrccoracidae (Cormorant, Shag)	Coastal	Fish	Dive from surface
Ardeidae (Herons : 10 spp.)	Marshes ; some spp. on dry land	Fish and aquatic animals, mammals ; also insects	Some spp. crepuscular. Food stabbed with bill
Anatidae (Ducks, geese, swans : 42 spp.)	Most spp. breed near freshwater ; many partly maritime in winter.	Surface-feeding ducks, geese and swans, chiefly vegetarian; sea-ducks, more animal food ; sawbills, fish	Surface-feeding ducks and swans " up-end " in shallow water ; sieve food in bill. Diving ducks (incl. sawbills) dive from surface. Geese graze turf
Falconidae (Diurnal birds of prey: 22 spp.)	Aerial, ground ; also arboreal	Larger spp., birds and some mammals; small spp., also insects. Osprey, fish	Falcons and Sparrow-Hawk feed on wing ; others on ground. Kestrel hovers. Osprey plunges
Tetraonidae (Grouse, Ptarmigan, Capercaillie ; 4 spp.)	Ground, esp. mountain and moorland; some arboreal	Shoots of conifers, buds, fruits or moorland plants ; insects	In flocks (" packs ") in Winter
Phasianidae (Partridges, Quail, Pheasant : 4 spp.)	Ground, esp. on agricultural land	Mainly vegetable, some insects	Partridges in flocks (" coveys ") in Winter
Rallidae (Rails, crakes, Moorhen, Coot : 8 spp.)	Ground, esp. marshes; mainly freshwater	Rails, crakes : aquatic insects, worms, molluscs. Moorhen, Coot ; aquatic vegetation, animal food	Largely crepuscular and secretive (except Moorhen and Coot). Coot dives from surface of water
Haematopodidae (Oystercatcher)	Ground ; coastal mud, sand, rocks.		Molluscs levered or hammered open. Probe with part-open bill
Charadriidae (Plovers, Dotterel, Turnstone : 12 spp.)	Ground, near water ; many inland in summer, coastal in winter		Lapwing patters with feet to bring worms to surface. Turnstone turns over stones, etc.
Scolopacidae (Snipes, Woodcock, Curlew, godwits, sandpipers : 41 spp.)	Ground and shallow water. Many inland in summer; coastal, Winter	Mainly animal : worms, molluscs, crustaceans ; also many insects	Short-billed spp. feed from surface, long-billed probe. Long-legged wade. Some patter with feet to bring up worms
Recurvirostridae (Avocet, Stilt)	Avocet is coastal ; Stilt, inland		Avocet skims food from water with side-to-side action of bill
Phalaropodidae (Phalaropes : 2 spp.)	On water surface ; also ground, mud		Feed from surface of water ; " up-end " in shallow water, like duck. Habit of spinning like top on water may stir up food
Burhinidae (Stone-Curlew)	Dry ground in open country	Insects, molluscs, worms ; small mammals and birds	Largely nocturnal
Stercorariidae (Skuas : 4 spp.)	Maritime ; some inland in summer	Fish, mammals, birds ; insects; some seeds, berries	Typically harry other birds, forcing them to disgorge food
Laridae (Gulls and terns : 27 ssp.)	Coastal, estaurine; some inland. In ground and water	Very variable ; omnivorous. Larger gulls : carrion; refuse ; small mammals, birds ; also vegetable food. Smaller gulls : largely insects. Terns : mostly fish	Gulls often predatory on other birds. Several spp. drop molluscs on rocks to break open ; also patter with feet to bring worms to the surface, or to stir up food. Terns fish by plunging into water from up to 20ft.
Alcidae (Auks, guillemot, puffin : 7 spp.)	Marine	Mainly fish ; also marine crustaceans, molluscs, worms	Dive from surface
Columbidae (Pigeons : 5 spp.)	Ground ; also arboreal	Mainly vegetable, but also some animal	Large flocks in Winter

To face page 232

FEEDING HABITS OF SELECTED BIRDS

Bird Family	Feeding Place	Food	Feeding Habits
Cuculidae (Cuckoos : 4 spp.)	Ground and arboreal	Insects	
Strigidae (Owls : 10 spp.)	Mainly ground. also arboreal	Mainly small mammals, birds ; insects, worms	Most spp. nocturnal ; but some hunt by day
Caprimulgidae (Nightjars : 4 spp.)	Aerial	Insects	Crepuscular. Feed on wing close to ground
Apodidae (Swifts : 3 spp.)	Aerial	Insects	Feed on wing, often high up and at great speed
Alcedinidae (Kingfisher)	Mainly freshwater	Small fish; aquatic insects	Dive into water from perch ; or hover before diving
Picidae (Woodpeckers Wryneck : 4 spp.)	Arboreal; also ground, esp. Green Woodpecker	Mainly insects, esp. wood-boring larvae ; also nuts, seeds, fruits	Hack at dead wood; probe with tongue. Green Woodpecker digs into ants' nests with bill
Alaudidae (Larks : 8 spp.)	Ground, esp. in open country	Small seeds ; insects	Sometimes flocks in Winter
Hirundinidae (Swallows : 4 spp.)	Aerial	Insects	Feed on wing in fast flight. Often in flocks
Corvidae (Crows : 9 spp.)	Mainly ground : also arboreal	Very varied. Larger spp., carnivorous and carrion ; insects. Much vegetable food	Heavy-billed spp. tear up flesh ; spp. with slenderer bills probe in soil. Nutcracker smashes nuts
Paridae (Tits : 8 spp.)	Mainly arboreal ; also herbage and ground	Very varied. Mainly insects ; also many seeds, nuts, fruits	Very agile among twigs ; often feed upside-down. Hack and tear at food
Sittidae (Nuthatch, Wall-Creeper)	Nuthatch arboreal ; Wall-creeper on ground, cliffs	Mainly animal ; but Nuthatch eats many nuts, esp. hazel nuts	Nuthatch hacks and probes ; smashes nuts ; stores surplus food ; Wall-Creeper probes
Certhiidae (Tree-creeper)	Arboreal	Insects	Ascend trunks and stouter parts of tree. Accompany tit-flocks
Troglodytidae (Wren)	Low vegetation : also ground	Insects	
Cinclidae (Dipper)	Shallow running water ; ground	Aquatic insects, molluscs, crustaceans	Unique in walking submerged on bottom of stony streams
Turdidae (Thrushes : 25 spp.)	Largely on ground; also arboreal	Very varied. Most spp. mainly animal	Song-Thrush smashes snails on stones. Wheatears hover, etc
Sylviidae (Warblers : 38 spp.)	Mainly arboreal and low vegetation	Mainly insects ; some fruits, seeds	Insects sometimes taken on wing in short sallies ; often hover
Regulidae (Goldcrest, Firecrest)	Arboreal and low vegetation	Insects	Often hover in foliage ; sometimes hang upside-down
Muscicapidae (Flycatchers : 5 spp.)	Arboreal and low vegetation	Mainly adult insects	Typically feed on wing, in short sallies from prominent look-out
Prunellidae (Hedge-Sparrow and Alpine Accentor)	Mainly ground ; also low vegetation	Mainly insects in Summer, small seeds in Winter	
Motacillidae (Pipits : 10 spp.)	Ground, esp. in open places	Insects	Dart at food with rapid run ; sometimes feed on wing
Bombycillidae (Waxwing)	Arboreal; also ground and aerial	Many kinds of berries ; also insects	Sometimes catch flying insects in short sallies. Flocks in Winter
Laniidae (Shrikes : 5 spp.)	Ground ; also aroreal	Large insects; also small mammals and birds	Scan ground from look-out and pounce. Impale surplus food
Sturnidae (Starlings : 2 spp.)	Ground ; also arboreal	Very varied. Many insects, worms, molluscs, crustaceans ; also fruits, cereals and other seeds, root-crops; household refuse	Probe shallowly in soil with open bill. Large flocks in Winter
Fringillidae (Finches : 33 spp.)	Arboreal ; buntings mainly on ground	Mainly vegetable; also animal, esp. in Summer	Seeds crushed in bill. Crossbill extracts seeds from cones
Passeridae (Sparrows : 3 spp.)	Ground; some arboreal	Mainly vegetable ; also animal, esp. in Summer	In flocks in Winter

Eric Hosking

FOOD. The Redstart, who belongs to the Thrush family, has just captured an insect in flight and is seen here about to land on a branch to devour his tasty bit of food

the birds happen on the hidden food accidentally, though they may well later search the same sorts of places as those in which they have earlier hidden food. There is evidence from Norway that some tits may rely in Winter largely on food hidden during the previous Autumn ; but this merits closer study in Britain.

On the Continent, too, the Nutcracker hides hazel nuts in Autumn, placing several nuts together in caches in the ground. It then returns to the caches in Winter and apparently digs down to them without hesitation despite thick snow. Not only do the stored nuts sustain the bird through the Winter, but the Nutcracker feeds them to its young early in the Spring before other foods are available.

Discovering What a Bird Eats. Remarkably little is known about the food of most British birds, and although there exist lists of known foods for each species, these are often misleading. The food of birds can be studied by the inspection of their crops and gizzards, from the contents of " pellets " (indigestible material cast up through the mouth) and faeces, and by direct observation of wild birds (*see* Pellet).

Examination of a bird's crop, if it has one, and gizzard provides the clearest proof of what it has been eating. But this method necessitates killing the bird, and is therefore permissible only with certain suspected pests, such as the Wood-Pigeon and Rook, with game birds, and occasionally with other birds in small numbers.

The habit of casting pellets is perhaps commoner among birds than is generally suspected, but the pellets are of little value unless they can be collected regularly. This has been done successfully with herons, owls and hawks. The main drawback to the examination of gizzards, pellets or faeces is that indigestible matter in the diet is more readily detected than is digestible

matter, and conclusions about a bird's diet may therefore be seriously distorted. Examination of a bird's crop, on the other hand, is much more reliable, as digestion has not yet begun.

Direct observation of feeding birds can be usefully employed as a means of studying their food when the food morsels are sufficiently distinct to be recognized ; unfortunately this is rarely possible. Direct observation is, however, a very valuable method when used together with crop, gizzard, pellet or faeces analysis, and should always be used in these studies.

Even less is known about the quantity of food consumed by a bird than about its composition ; this field remains almost unexplored. During an invasion of waxwings in the Winter of 1943-44, one observer estimated that a single bird ate about 500 *Cotoneaster* berries on a December day, and little else. The present writer estimated the consumption of a Rock-Pipit in December as about 825 isopods (*Idotea*, similar to woodlice) and just over 1,000 minute winkles (*Littorina*) on one day ; about 12,000 winkles and 5,000 midge larvae (*Tanypus*) on another day ; and about 15,000 midge larvae and 2,500 winkles on a third day. The dry weight of the food eaten varied from about 8 to 25 grammes (i.e. from about $\frac{1}{4}$ oz. to roughly $\frac{7}{8}$ oz.) per day.

It is generally rather easier to study the food brought to the nest for the young than that eaten by adult birds. A small tent, or " hide ", can sometimes be built in easy stages close to the nest to conceal the observer (*see* Photography), so that the food may be identified from close quarters. In the same way, the amount of food brought to the young can be measured by counting the number of visits paid to the nest by the parent birds.

See also Nests and Nesting ; Young, Care of.

FOOT. Like the bill, the feet show countless modifications or adaptations according to the habits of the various species. Most birds possess three front toes, and a backwardly-directed hind-toe. In the perching birds of the order *Passeriformes*, such as the Blue Tit, the hind-toe is strong and well developed, thus enabling the bird to obtain a firm grip on the object on which it is perching. Furthermore, an automatic muscular " mechanism " in the legs controls all four toes, causing them to close tightly round such an object as a twig or a branch for as long as the bird remains sitting with its legs bent. Skylarks are unusual among the *Passeriformes* in having an exceptionally long claw attached to the hind-toe. This helps them to maintain their balance when running over rough grassy land, their usual habitat.

Birds spending much time on the wing, like the Swift and Swallow, possess small and weak legs and feet. The Swift, for example, has very small feet with four forwardly-directed toes, admirably adapted to its habit of clinging to rough vertical surfaces or to its nest, but almost useless for ordinary perching.

Climbing birds, such as the woodpeckers, have two front and two hind-toes. The latter provide additional support when the bird is climbing a tree-trunk, and all four toes are equipped with strong, curved claws, which help the bird cling to the bark. Strangely enough the Cuckoo, though primarily a perching bird, has a similar toe arrangement. This is of great assistance to the young Cuckoo when it climbs up the wall of its foster parent's nest to push out the other young birds or eggs, while the adult Cuckoo finds its feet perfectly suitable for perching in the ordinary way.

Most aquatic birds, such as the ducks and gulls, have webbed feet, which they use as paddles for propelling themselves through the water. No doubt, they also find their webbed feet helpful for walking on soft mud. Usually, the front toes are fully united by webs, and the members of the Cormorant group, including the Shag, are unusual in having all four of their toes fully webbed, the hind-toe pointing forward for this purpose. Many aquatic birds (as well as certain ground birds) possess only a very small hind-toe, which is often elevated, and in some cases completely absent.

Several aquatic or semi-aquatic birds, such as the Heron, have only partially webbed feet ; and in a few cases the toes have no webs at all. The toes of grebes and coots, for example, are fringed by lobes which are shaped rather like paddles, and are very efficient both for swimming and for walking over soft muddy ground.

Aquatic birds which are in the babit of running over floating plants have rather large feet, with long " spindly " toes which have neither webs nor lobes. An example is the Moorhen. The large feet of this bird, with their long toes, spread its weight evenly over a wide area and enable it to run over floating vegetation without sinking through or becoming entangled in it.

When we come to the birds of prey and the owls, we find a direct link between the form of their feet and their feeding habits, for they use their legs and feet for catching, gripping and killing their prey. Thus they all possess strong legs and feet, with extremely sharp and powerful claws. The feet of owls, however, differ in one respect from those of such typical birds of prey as eagles and hawks. Like the latter, owls have three front toes and a hind-toe, but they are able to turn the outer front toe right back so that it meets the hind-toe, enabling them to hold and crush their prey in a truly vice-like grip.

Birds which scratch on the ground for their food (Partridge, Pheasant, Pigeon and domestic Hen, for example) are equipped with particularly strong legs and feet. They generally have three front toes and a hind-toe, all with strong blunted claws.

The Capercaillie is another bird which sometimes scratches on the ground for food, but it is mainly a bird of the pinewoods, and spends much of its time among the branches of tall conifers and other trees, feeding on pine-needles, buds and berries. Thus, it is equipped with strong " general-purpose " legs and feet.

Most ground birds, and particularly the so-called " running birds ", do not need to be able to grip with their feet, and so they have only a very small hind-toe, or none at all. The Great Bustard is a typical example, with its long, sturdy legs and large hoof-like feet, which have only three toes, all pointing forward.

FOSSIL BIRDS. Although many fossil birds are known, their number does not compare with that of living species. Despite this fact and the lines of descent that can therefore be traced, there is no fossil evidence for the origin of birds and the early stages of their evolution (*q.v.*). Consequently much interest and value centres on the first bird remains. These include a tail feather, known from a part in the Munich Museum and its counterpart in the Berlin Natural History Museum, and the skeletons of the same bird ancestor, *Archaeopteryx* (*q.v.*), in the London and Berlin Natural History Museums. These remains are of Upper Jurassic (Kimmeridgian) age and are at least 120 to 150 million years old.

The next fossil form is shown by fragmentary remains from the Cambridge Greensand of England (deposited over 100 million years ago). These remains, called *Enaliornis*, have been preserved in the Sedgwick Museum, but they are of

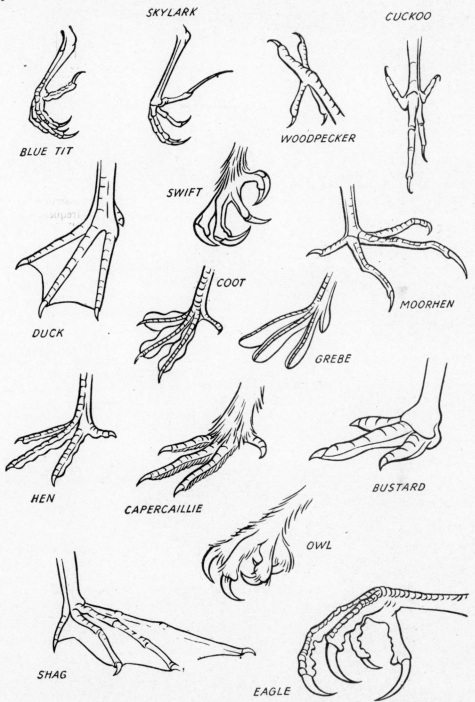

FOOT. *Diagrams show how bird's feet are adapted to different modes of life (see text opposite)*

little importance compared with the famous fossils from the Kansas Chalk of the American Upper Cretaceous, known by the toothed swimming birds *Hesperornis* and *Ichthyornis*. There is a blank from then till the beginning of the Tertiary (Lower Eocene), but the latter yields remains of representatives of no fewer than 11 of the 15 suborders into which toothless birds are classed.   Many of these remains are of great importance, though much of this is in the evidence for the evolution of birds that had occurred by that time, rather than the steps by which the diversification was achieved. Some of the specimens are well preserved and indicate gigantic forms as compared with the modern representatives, and they also throw light on the wider geographical range of genera now alive.

To list these fossils would take up much space and they are now preserved in museums in many parts of the world, but the main interest of palaeontologists must remain essentially with those mentioned above. *See also* Ancestry ; Evolution ; Geographical Distribution.

English readers may be reminded that the discovery of fossil bird bones is by no means uncommon today in the London Clay (Eocene) of the Isle of Sheppey and in the Eocene and Oligocene deposits of the Isle of Wight.

FRATERCULA. Genus of marine birds of the family *Alcidae* of the order *Charadriiformes*. It is distributed over north-west Europe, the north-east of north America, and Greenland ; and, when not breeding, in the Mediterranean area, the Atlantic islands, and Massachusetts. Only the Puffin (*q.v.*), is on the British list.

FRENCH PARTRIDGE, or Frenchman. Local names for Red-legged Partridge.

FREQUENCY RANGE. To make accurate recordings and reproductions of birds' songs, it is essential to know the range of frequencies covered by the sounds uttered by birds.

From the point of view of a listener, the frequency of a sound is defined as the number of sound waves (pulsations or vibrations) reaching the ear in a second; the higher the rate at which they strike the ear drum, the higher the pitch of the note, and vice versa (e.g. the middle " C " of a piano, or other instrument, has a fundamental frequency of 261, and a note an octave higher, has a frequency of 522).

Very few sounds consist of vibrations of a single frequency, but have, superimposed on the fundamental, notes of higher frequency, usually much fainter, which give the note the characteristic timbre of a particular instrument or voice. Only if the instrument, human or mechanical, receiving the vibrations is capable of responding to the full range of frequencies in the sounds emitted, can it faithfully interpret the original.

A young human adult can hear frequencies of from 16 to 20,000 cycles per second (c/s), but as people get older they find it increasingly difficult to hear the higher frequencies, and an

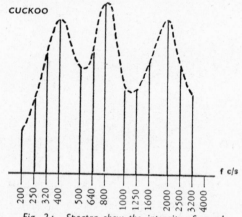

Fig. 2: Spectra show the intensity of sound at different frequencies (cycles per second)

elderly person may find it impossible to hear sounds with a frequency greater than 5,000.

This limited range still permits them to hear speech and most vocal and instrumental music, the practical upper limit of frequency for which is about 4,000 (the upper limit of a normal piano is 4,186), but they may find it difficult to hear some, if not all, the notes of certain birds. Moreover, the songs of some species of birds contain notes of such a high pitch that they cannot be heard by the human ear at all.

But it is now possible to obtain on the screen of a cathode ray tube either a complete picture of the sound waves comprising a bird's song, which can be photographed and compared with others, or pictures similar to those illustrated here which show the songs of three different birds analysed, or broken down, into their frequencies. The instrument used for obtaining such pictures is called a *frequency spectrometer*, and the pictures themselves *spectra*. An analysis of

FREQUENCY RANGE
Fig. I. Sound spectrum
of the Blackbird's song

Pure Note

Chuck Chuck →

f c/s

Sound spectra are visual records produced by apparatus that breaks down sound into its constituent frequencies

records obtained in this way shows that it is misleading to give the frequency range for different species, because there are individual variations within the species. In the following table the frequency range of two individual birds from each of the selected species are given:

| Species | Frequency Range (cycles per second) Note: Middle C=261 c.p.s. | |
	1	*2*
Wren	3,000–5,100	6,100–8,000
Blackbird ..	620–4,500	1,000–8,000
Song-Thrush ..	730–5,000	2,500–16,000
Chaffinch ..	1,000–4,000	1,000–8,000
Cuckoo	620–780	200–3,200
Nightingale ..	620–4,500	800–6,400

The Editor writes :

As a further proof of how misleading it is to generalise, I may quote the case of the Robin. For many decades I recorded the spring and summer song of the male Robin, and found that the limits of its frequency range were about 1,400 to 4,500 ; but in 1948 I recorded the autumn song of a Robin, probably a female, and found that, as far as I could hear, most of the song was covered by a frequency range of from 4,000 to 8,000, but some notes went to over 10,000.

I was unable to discover the ultra-sonic notes, but it was interesting to find that the sub-song began at about 5,000 and had an upper limit so high that I was unable to detect it.

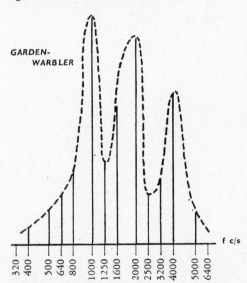

GARDEN-
WARBLER

FREQUENCY RANGE. *Fig. 3: Spectra allow various birds' songs to be compared at leisure*

FRIGATE BIRD — Fregata magnificens rothschildi. This bird of the Caribbean was added to the British list in 1953, an immature male having been found dying on the Hebridean island of Tiree, on July 10. This was later placed in the Royal Scottish Museum. Only twice before had any Frigate Bird been recorded in Europe—the first on the German coast in 1792, and the second on the French coast in 1902.

The Frigate Bird is an oceanic bird related to the Cormorant, and has a similar long, slender, hooked bill, short legs, webbed toes, and usually black plumage. Unlike the Cormorant, however, it has exceedingly long wings, and a forked tail of twelve feathers. It has a small pouch on the throat, and catches its prey on the surface of the sea, and not by diving. It frequently pursues other birds until they disgorge their prey, which is then deftly caught.

The different branches of the *Fregatidae* family vary somewhat in size and colour. Some have red bills, others blue-grey. The specimen found on Tiree had a white head, brownish back, and much white on the underside, usually characteristic of the female. It measured 3 ft. from bill to tail; fully-grown males normally measure more than $3\frac{1}{2}$ ft. in length, and have a wing span of over $7\frac{1}{2}$ ft.

Frigate birds nest in trees and cliffs by the sea shore, and usually lay one white egg ; Folklore connects the bird with all sorts of disaster at sea ; and it is often regarded as an ill omen.

FRIGATE-PETREL — Pelagodroma marina hypoleuca. This very rare visitor to the British Isles has been recorded once or twice within comparatively recent years. It is an Australasian and Atlantic species of a truly marine family, and breeds on the islands of the southern oceans and in the Salvages and Cape Verde Islands. In appearance it differs from all other petrels likely to be seen in Britain, for it has pure white underparts, and is also white under its wing coverts; above, its mantle and the back of its head are brownish-grey, with a paler grey in wings; its tail is black. It has a dark eye stripe, showing very conspicuously against the surrounding white. Its legs—longer than those of its relatives—are black, with orange webs. The length of the Frigate-Petrel is 8 in., and its tarsus is 1 in. Its wing span is about 1 ft.

FRINGILLA. Genus of the family *Fringillidae* of the order *Passeriformes*. Its members are widely distributed over Europe, northern Asia, north-west Africa, the Azores, Madeira and the Canary Islands. It includes two species on the British list : the Chaffinch (*q.v.*) and the Brambling (*q.v.*).

FRINGILLIDAE. Family of the order *Passeriformes*, comprising all the finch-like birds on the British list, excepting the House-Sparrow and the Snow-Finch. It contains a large number of genera, and its members are distributed throughout the world, except Australia and New Zealand, though several European species have now been successfully introduced there, too. The family includes the following 12 genera on the British list : *Calcarius, Carduelis, Carpodacus, Chloris, Coccothraustes,*

Emberiza, Fringilla, Loxia, Pinicola, Plectro-phenax, Pyrrhula and *Serinus.*

The members of *Fringillidae* have rather short, hard, conical bills, with the cutting-edges smooth, or strongly toothed, or angulated. All species moult completely in the Autumn, and some also have a partial spring moult.

The sexes generally differ in plumage, the young being very like the females in appearance.

FULICA (Latin, " coot "). Genus of the family *Rallidae* of the order *Ralliformes.* One species, the Coot (*q.v.*) is on the British list.

FULMAR PETREL—Fulmarus glacialis. Charles Darwin is said to have held that the Fulmar Petrel was, in his time, the most abundant sea-bird in the world. It is true that its spread within recent years has been one of the most spectacular events in the bird world.

Great numbers breed on the sea cliffs of Iceland, Spitzbergen, Bear Island, Franz Josef Land and elsewhere in the Arctic North, and its spread to the British Isles has been phenomenal. As early as 1697 the Fulmar was breeding on the Island of St. Kilda, but it was not until 1878 that it definitely took up breeding quarters in Shetland. From that date, it has spread in an extraordinary way, until now there are well over 200 colonies of fulmars up and down our coasts ; the cliffs of the Scillies, Cornwall, Lundy Island, Norfolk, Yorkshire, Devon and Pembrokeshire, also the west coast of Ireland all support colonies of hundreds of breeding birds.

Largest of the petrels, the Fulmar varies in colour. Of the three phases—the pale, the

dark and the blue—the species usually seen in the British Isles is the first ; the other phases are occasionally seen, but they are generally only passing visitors coming south from their breeding haunts in the Arctic.

At a distance, the Fulmar might be taken for a gull, for its mantle is pearl-grey, shading to darker grey on its long and narrow wings, which have no black tips. It has a white neck, head and underparts, and in front of the eye there is a small dark patch. The yellowish-green bill has the tubular nostrils of the petrels. The bird is 19 in. long, with a tarsus of 2 in. It weighs almost 2 lb., its wing span is $3\frac{1}{2}$ ft.

The Fulmar is not a particularly gregarious bird, and, except during the breeding season (which is roughly from May to August), it spends most of its time wandering over the ocean, rarely coming to land. Like all petrels, it has a free, graceful and abandoned flight, gliding along effortlessly with its narrow wings fully extended, and with few wing beats. It seems to have difficulty in settling, and will make several attempts to do so.

Outside the breeding season the Fulmar is a silent bird. I was fortunate enough, however, to be able to watch the display at its breeding site for some days and nights in one of the Shetland bays, and to note the variation in the Fulmar's voice. In each nest a female was sitting, and when the male came on a visit she displayed ; it was then I heard the wonderful mating call. This display went on for hours. Then the male flew away and did not return for a long time ; when he did come back, it was an unforgettable experience to see the two birds more excited than before, and hear the cooing notes becoming quicker and quicker.—EDITOR.

When frightened or disturbed, the Fulmar can discharge oil through its mouth and aim it to a distance of 3 or 4 ft. (hence its name, which is old Norwegian for " foul gull ").

The Fulmar nests in crowded colonies. One white oval-shaped egg is normally laid, but there are many records of two. The egg is laid in a crevice or on a cliff-ledge—sometimes on a grassy slope—and little or no effort is made to build a nest ; but some bits of grass or little stones are put round the egg. Hatching takes place in May, both parents sharing in the work for about four weeks. The young chick is usually fed only once a day, the male tending it during the day, while the hen feeds it at night.

The Fulmar's varied diet is taken almost wholly from the floating refuse of the sea ; a good deal is probably secured from the ships it likes to follow, fish (dead or alive) are also taken, and oil of all kinds is eagerly devoured.

FULMARUS. Genus of oceanic birds of the family *Procellariidae* of the order *Procellariiformes.* It includes only a single species, the Fulmar Petrel, which is described above.

Eric Hosking

FULMAR PETREL. The tremendous spread of this bird in recent years is a puzzle to ornithologists

GANNET

G

GADWALL—Anas strepera. Successfully established in 1850 by pinioning birds captured in decoys (*q.v.*), the Gadwall, a fresh-water duck, now breeds regularly in East Anglia and some parts of Scotland ; elsewhere, it seldom appears in Great Britain, except as an autumn migrant.

Abroad, the Gadwall is found in northern Europe (not common), palaearctic Asia, north-west Africa and north America ; in the non-breeding season it migrates to Abyssinia, southern Asia and the Gulf of Mexico.

In appearance, the Gadwall is not unlike a small Mallard (*q.v.*) but both duck and drake can always be recognized by the black and white speculum (*q.v.*) and white underparts. In general, the drake's plumage is a speckled greyish-brown, with darker upper and under tail coverts. The wings are more pointed than the Mallard's and have a chestnut patch ; the Gadwall's breast is covered with crescent markings ; his legs and feet are dull orange ; his bill dark grey. The duck much resembles the Mallard duck, but the orange sides to her bill are a good distinguishing mark. The length is 20 in. and tarsus 1·8 in. ; the wing span is about 2 ft. and the weight is 2-3 lbs.

The Gadwall is gregarious and is usually found with other surface-feeding ducks. Its speed of flight is similar to the Mallard's, but the wing beats are faster and produce a whistling sound. Gadwalls swim buoyantly.

More shy and retiring, the Gadwall is nevertheless very similar to the Mallard and other surface-feeding ducks in its habits and courtship. The drake has a deep, hoarse, croaking note ; the duck, a quack rather softer than that of the Mallard duck.

Quiet lakes, ponds, marsh pools, meres, reservoirs and, indeed, fresh water of all kinds, attract the Gadwall. The thick vegetation, close to the water, is chosen for the nest which is well concealed. The eight to twelve creamy-buff eggs are laid in May in England ; in June, in Scotland. The duck begins to sit when the clutch is complete and hatches the eggs alone for 27 to 28 days. Once the ducklings are dry,

they are led to the water and take to it at once ; they can fly in about seven weeks. The drake takes little or no interest in the rearing of his family. One brood is reared a season.

The Gadwall, like all surface-feeding ducks, lives chiefly on vegetable matter.

GALERIDA. Genus of the family *Alaudidae* of the order *Passeriformes*. Its members are distributed over Europe, south-west Asia including India, and parts of northern and tropical Africa. The only species on the British list is the Crested Lark (*q.v.*), which has been recorded here about a dozen times.

GALLIFORMES. Large order of birds, containing the game-birds. It is divided into seven families, its members being distributed over all continents. The two families, *Tetraonidae* (*q.v.*) and *Phasianidae* (*q.v.*), occurring in Europe, are on the British List.

The members of this order are terrestrial or arborial four-toed land birds, medium or large-sized, with stout, arched bills and broad wings. The legs and feet are strong. The male birds of this order are often brightly coloured.

Eric Hosking

GALLIFORMES. The Red-legged Partridge shows by its shape that it is a member of this order

239

GALLINULA. Genus of the family *Rallidae* of the order *Ralliformes*. It contains one species in various forms, distributed over Europe, Asia, Africa, the Atlantic islands, north and south America, the Pacific and Indian Oceans, and, casually, Greenland. The British form of this species is the Moorhen (*q.v.*).

GANNET—Sula bassana. This magnificent sea-bird—one of the largest in the British Isles—is unique in both appearance and performance. Its older name, " Solan Goose ", refers to its size, for in no way does it resemble a goose. The type occurring in the British Isles, the Northern Gannet, is related to the tropical birds called boobies, and the Gannet is sometimes known as Booby in this country. Although their colonies can rarely be visited, the Gannet is one of our best-known birds, thanks to public interest aroused by the investigation of ornithologists into its history.

It was estimated in 1939 that approximately 169,000 gannets were breeding in 22 gannetries in the world, and over 109,000 of these birds in the British Isles. Scotland has at present eight colonies of which the desolate and wind-swept Bass Rock (*q.v.*), rising steeply out of the Firth of Forth, is one of the most famous, as well as the oldest, having been first mentioned in 1447. It is now the breeding place of some 4,370 pairs of gannets (*see* Gannetry).

The Gannet's plumage is a brilliant white, tinged with yellowish-buff on its head and neck. Its wings are long and narrow, tipped with black,

and it has a pointed tail. Its bill is long, straight and pointed, and there is a bare patch round its eyes. Dark legs and feet, all four toes of which are included in the web—a characteristic of the pelicans, to which the Gannet is related—complete the appearance of this handsome bird. Male and female are alike. The total length of the Gannet is 36 in., with a body of 23 in.; its tarsus is 2 in., and it has a wing span of 6 ft. It weighs about $7\frac{1}{2}$ lb.

The Gannet is the perfect diving bird, and secures all its food in this way. On sighting its prey, it plunges swiftly down, often from a height of 100 ft., its wings closing just before its violent impact with the water. The dive gives it great speed under the water, where it fastens on its prey, swallowing the fish (unless it is too large) there and then.

Like so many sea-birds, the Gannet is clumsy on the ground, but its performance in the air is almost unrivalled. It flies with power and grace, turning and twisting in the wind, gliding and soaring. Some difficulty seems to be experienced in landing, for a Gannet may circle round many times before actually touching down. But another reason for this may be difficulty in finding space on the crowded ledges, for the birds already settled there inevitably resent another pushing in. The Gannet is a fine swimmer, and sails high in the water, propelled by its feet. But it rises with what seems an effort, flapping over the surface before taking off. It has a variety of calls, naturally most in the breeding season. The male and female are both very noisy, and the calls of a pair of gannets multiplied by thousands can make an awesome clamour at a colony. A typical special call is the " diving note ", sounded when the bird leaves its ledge to enter the sea for food. Young gannets have a chirping note.

> During the Second World War fishermen discovered that a Gannet colony of about 600 pairs had settled in Ortac, near Alderney. This islet is almost inaccessible, and even on a fairly calm day I could not land on it. Recording from the sea also proved to be impossible because of echoes from the rocks.
> In 1942 another colony was discovered by fishermen on the Garden Rocks, a few miles off Alderney. There were about 250 pairs nesting there. On our arrival at the gannetry for a recording, the birds took no notice of our activities nor of our microphone and recording apparatus. We had only an hour to wait before the birds began to call.—EDITOR.

The Gannet is essentially an oceanic bird and rarely comes inland, unless in very stormy weather. But it does not wander far at sea, and can be seen round our coasts more or less at all times of the year. The birds may return to their breeding sites on the rocky and precipitous cliffs as early as February, some having ventured as far as the Spanish coast and the Azores.

John Markham

GANNET. *This, one of the largest British sea birds, is never found far inland, except in gales*

GARDEN-WARBLER, *would be unnoticed but for its song*

To face page 240

For text see page 242

W. Farnsworth

GANNETRY. The so-called " Solan Geese " always nest closely together in crowded colonies, found on a more or less inaccessible cliff, their nests being untidy structures

The courting display of this sea-bird has always held great interest for ornithologists, and much has been written about it. Both sexes take part, the birds facing each other with wings outspread, their heads wagging vigorously from side to side. What is termed " false drinking actions " are also indulged in—a habit the Gannet shares with the Smew.

Gannets nest very close together. On arriving at the colony in the Spring, a pair will immediately stake their claim, and one of them always remains to guard the spot, for there is constant competition and quarrelling for the best ledges. These birds are also great thieves and will, in the absence of the rightful owners, steal the nesting material that has been laboriously got together. It usually consists of seaweed, grass and anything else that might "come in useful", and the nest is an untidy accumulation which, since it is used year after year, becomes in time a bulky mass. One egg, oval-shaped and white, but later stained dark brown, is laid in the middle of May. Both birds take part in hatching. They have a peculiar way of carefully placing one webbed foot over the other before settling on the egg. It is about 45 days before the chick emerges. At first, it is ugly and naked, but it soon acquires a covering of white down. It is fed by regurgitation, the parent helping the weak little creature to get the food out of its bill.

As is usual among some sea-birds, the young bird is abandoned by its parents as soon as it can reach the water, and it probably starves for some days until it can catch fish for itself. One explanation of this seemingly unnatural practice is that the young Gannet is very fat and heavy, and can live for some days on its surplus fat while it develops its wings and plumage. In any case, it is soon able to catch fish for itself. The Gannet takes about four years to become adult.

Gannets have always provided food for the inhabitants of the Scottish Islands and men have risked their lives to reach the birds' breeding haunts. Within recent years, however, this traffic has ceased to a large extent ; the only colony still habitually raided is that of Sula Sgeir in the Hebrides, and even there the practice is decreasing.

In some parts of the world, the excreta of gannets has become a useful product for the manufacture of fertilisers.

Oil discharged from vessels at sea is probably the greatest enemy of the Gannet, as it is of other sea-birds. If the bird is not too badly oiled, there is every hope of recovery. For a method of cleansing the plumage, recommended by the Royal Society for the Protection of Birds, *see* the article on First Aid.

GANNETRY. Term applied to a colony of gannets. There is only a limited number of gannetries in the world; in 1939 there were 22 and in 1954, when the last census was made, there were 29, of which 13 were in the British Isles. The largest is at St. Kilda (about 17,000 breeding pairs). Other important colonies are at :

Little Skellig, off Co. Kerry (9,500 pairs)
Grassholm, off Pembroke (6,000 pairs)
Ailsa Craig, off Ayrshire (5,500 pairs)
Bass Rock, Firth of Forth (4,500 pairs)
Sula Sgeir ⎫ north of Scotland ⎰ (4,000 pairs)
Sule Stack ⎭ ⎱ (3,500 pairs)
Herma Ness ⎫ east of Shetlands ⎰ (2,500 pairs)
Noss ⎭ ⎱ (2,000 pairs)

Note: *Breeding pairs to nearest 500, subject to fluctuation.*

Smaller colonies are occasional at Bull Rock, Scar Rocks, Great Saltee and Bempton (Yorkshire).

Eric Hosking

GARDEN-WARBLER. This secretive little songster's name is a misnomer, for it does not show any special preference for gardens

GARDEN-WARBLER—Sylvia borin. Were it not for its outstanding performance as a songster, the Garden-Warbler might pass its summer residence in the British Isles almost unnoticed, for in appearance it is one of the dullest of the warblers. A late arrival, it comes at the end of April and leaves again in September or October. Its breeding is confined to certain districts of England and Wales ; in Scotland, it is not present beyond the Highland line, and it is rare in Ireland. The Garden-Warbler is also a passage migrant, principally on the east coast. Abroad, it nests in most parts of Europe, wintering in central and south Africa.

The name " garden " is somewhat of a misnomer, for this warbler shows no particular preference for gardens. It haunts much the same type of country as its close relative, the Blackcap (*q.v.*), and is found on heaths and commons, in woods and large gardens—in fact, wherever dense bushes, brambles and briars abound. The Garden-Warbler is often confused with the Blackcap, but the latter's black cap is distinctive enough when seen in the open.

The very dullness of the Garden-Warbler seems to set it apart. The mantle, wings and tail are dark brown above, the underparts being paler ; over the eye appears a light streak. Male and female are alike. The length is 5½ in., and the tarsus ¾ in. The wing span is about 6½ in., and the weight less than an ounce.

Secretive and shy, the Garden-Warbler spends most of the time under cover of trees and undergrowth. The movements, flight and courtship display resemble closely those of the Blackcap. The Garden-Warbler excels as one of our loveliest songsters. Some people consider the Blackcap a finer performer, and it is not surprising that confusion arises between the songs of these birds since they haunt the same type of country. But a trained ear can distinguish between them. The Garden-Warbler's call frequently used as an alarm is harsh, as is that of all the *Sylvia* genus heard in this country. The Garden-Warbler's song, delivered from among trees and bushes and often when the bird is moving about, is a mellow and sweet warble, poured out in a series of well-sustained repetitive phases, and lasting some minutes, with brief intervals. When it is heard in the quiet of the evening, there are few more beautiful and touching bird songs. It can be heard best from late April until June ; a sub-song of inferior quality can be heard in August and September before the bird departs on its long journey to the south.

Thick undergrowth is the chosen site of the Garden-Warbler's nest. Built by both birds, the nest is composed of grass stalks and bents, and lined with finer grasses and hair. The male will often indulge in building a " cock's nest " (*q.v.*). During late May or early June, four to six eggs, very like those of the Blackcap, are laid. Most of the hatching is done by the hen ; both parents share in the rearing of the chicks.

Insects form the main food of the Garden-Warbler, except during the Autumn, when it enjoys berries and fruit of all kinds.

GAREFOWL. Scottish name for the Great Auk (*q.v.*). *See also* Auk ; Extinct Birds.

GARGANEY—Anas querquedula. This surface-feeding duck is one of Britain's summer residents, arriving in March and leaving sometimes as late as October. Although slightly larger than the Teal (*q.v.*), it has much in common with that bird and is, in fact, often called the " Summer Teal ". The Garganey is confined to the eastern counties, and breeds regularly in Cambridgeshire and the coastal counties from Norfolk to Dorset. It is a rare visitor elsewhere and a spring migrant throughout the country, but there is reason to believe that it has extended its range within recent years and is on the increase.

The Garganey breeds almost everywhere in Europe and in some parts of Asia. It winters in Africa, India and in China.

Its general colouring is dark brown, but there is a distinctive white stripe passing from eye to nape, which shows up conspicuously against the dark head, even at a distance. The rest of the head and neck is reddish-brown ; the wings are blue-grey, the speculum being greyish-green. The Garganey is dark brown above, but its underparts are whitish, with a clear demarcation line round its speckled, dark brown breast. The duck very much resembles the female Teal, but is distinguished by the white stripe above the eyes, her greyer wings and by her obscure speculum. The Garganey is 15 in. in length, with a body of 10½ in. ; its tarsus is 1 in. It weighs 12 oz., and its wing span is about 1¼ ft.

Its flight is swift, very like that of the Teal but with fewer twists and turns. Both the drake and duck quack, and the drake's breeding call note is a curious grunting or rattling sound, which has earned it in some districts the name of " Cricket Teal ". The Garganey does not " up-end " so frequently as the Teal or Mallard, if it does so at all. Much of its courting display resembles the Shoveler's rather than the Teal's. It is usually seen in pairs or small parties, in company with other ducks.

In Britain the Garganey chooses a nesting place among the green vegetation of a mere, pond, fen or marsh. The nest is built of grass and water plants, and lined with grey down. Six to twelve creamy-buff eggs are laid in late April or early May. All domestic duties are borne by the duck, although the drake is never far away. One brood is reared in a season.

Apart from aquatic plants, the Garganey eats the spawn of fish and frogs, and, when wintering in India, it feeds in the rice fields.

GARRULUS (Latin, " noisy "). Genus of the family *Corvidae* of the order *Passeriformes*. It contains about half-a-dozen species, distributed over Europe, north-west Africa, northern Asia, south China, Japan and Formosa. Only one species, *Garrulus glandarius*, occurs in Europe. This is divided into several subspecies, three of which are on the British list : the British Jay, occurring mainly in England ; the Irish Jay, almost entirely confined to Ireland ; and the European Jay, an irregular visitor to the British Isles. *See also* British Jay ; Irish Jay ; Jay.

GELOCHELIDON. Genus of terns of the family *Laridae* of the order *Charadriiformes*. It contains only one species, the Gull-billed Tern, of which there are a number of subspecies. The members of this genus are distributed over Europe, Asia, north-west Africa, Australia, north and south America, and, outside the breeding season, tropical Africa. A form of the Gull-billed Tern (*q.v.*) occurs in the British Isles (mainly along the south and east coasts) as an irregular summer visitor.

GENUS (pl. *Genera*). Grouping of species considered to have obvious similarity and close relationship. The term has been made by Man for his convenience and has come to be generally accepted after generations of use by scientists. The generic name of any plant or animal might, in fact, be considered its surname, while its specific name might be likened to its Christian name. Thus the Raven, Carrion-Crow, Rook and Jackdaw all share the " surname " *Corvus* (meaning Raven *or* Crow in Latin), but can be distinguished at once by their " Christian names " of *corax*, *corone*, *frugilegus* and *monedula*.

Apart from giving much concise information at a glance, the " binomial " practice, described above, serves as an international language, although, in a few cases, final agreement has not yet been reached. The generic name is always spelt with a capital letter, and is followed by the specific name, with a small initial.

This international scientific language was finalised by the great naturalist Linnaeus in his *Systems of Nature*, first published in 1735, and is being expanded and modified constantly as our knowledge about the world we live in increases. *See also* Classification ; Order.

At the end of this Encyclopedia a very special kind of index of bird names will be found to enable any reader, whatever his language, to see at a glance what birds are listed in this work. It is, in fact, an index in four languages—English, Latin, French and German—but, as each bird's international (or scientific) name has been given, too, a person who speaks any other language than the four listed here will be able to know which birds have been included in the *Encyclopedia of British Birds*.

Erica

GARGANEY. *The best distinguishing mark of the drake is the white stripe, starting above the eye*

BIRD COMMUNITIES OF THE WORLD

JAMES FISHER, M.A., F.L.S.

The world can be divided into six regions, each with a characteristic pattern of bird life, and the author explains with the aid of maps (plate f.p. 244) how birds came to be thus distributed and why Britain can boast so many species. See also *Classification*

GEOGRAPHICAL DISTRIBUTION. The meaning of this term, in scientific ornithology, has changed considerably in the last fifty years. In the days of Sclater and Wallace, who laid the foundations of the study of the distribution of animals a century ago—chiefly from the study of birds—the science consisted of an examination of the world, area by area, and a descriptive catalogue of the animals that inhabited each area. Nowadays, it is concentrated upon *communities* of animals, and upon the areas that these communities inhabit ; to this study our knowledge of evolution, and of fossils, has provided an historical approach.

Therefore the study of Geographical Distribution has now become the study of faunas. Each of the great avifaunas, or bird communities, of the world is dominated by particular orders and by families of birds—different from those which dominate the communities elsewhere— which have evolved in its area.

Birds have existed since the Jurassic period, 150 million to 120 million years ago. Since then great changes have taken place in the distribution of the land-masses, and in the climate of the earth. For instance, in the Eocene and Oligocene periods (about 65 million to 33 million years ago) a great land-bound water, the Tethys Sea, occupied the non-Arctic part of the north Atlantic, most of central and south Europe, the Mediterranean and north Africa. It communicated with the Arctic Ocean ; with the Indian Ocean by a fairly broad gap across Persia and India ; and with the Pacific through narrow gaps in Panama and Colombia. It was barred from the south Atlantic by a land-bridge from west Africa to Brazil ; the south Atlantic was probably also barred from the Pacific by a land-bridge from Patagonia to Antarctica. The climate of the Bering Sea area, an easy bridge from the Old World to the New, was temperate.

During the succeeding Miocene and Pliocene periods (about 33 million to 1 million years ago) the Tethys Sea shrank, and the north Atlantic and Mediterranean nearly reached their present form. However, it is probable that the African-south-American land-bridge persisted for a long time, as did the Persia-India channel between the Mediterranean and the Indian Ocean ; and there was at least one gap through central America between the Pacific and the Atlantic until the upper Pliocene, about 2 million years ago. This cut off a big area in southern north America which was climatically tropical, and in which some important tropical families evolved. The present arrangement of continents and oceans finally became stabilised during the Pleistocene period (in other words, during the last million years).

Such surface changes on the earth have obviously had an important effect on the distribution of both land-birds and sea-birds, and the fact that the distribution of land and sea masses was at one time very different from what it is today helps to explain why some members of a particular group of birds may now be widely severed from their nearest kindred, and why the birds of northern north America resemble those of Europe more than they do those of south America. Perhaps in this connection one of the best examples of the influences of the past on the present distribution is provided by the Gull family. As will be seen from the maps facing pages 244 and 245, it seems highly probable that the present distribution of light and dark-headed gulls in distinct, if overlapping regions, may best be accounted for on the supposition that the evolutionary home of the light-headed gulls was on the north shore of the Tethys Sea, and that of the dark-headed gulls on the east and south shores.

Changes still continue, and have even been observed in historical times. But these are very small in comparison with those that have taken place in geological time, and are the consequence of climatic, not geographical, changes. Within the present century, for instance, there has been a detectable penetration of the central American fauna into Mexico and the southern United States, and in the Old World a north-westerly movement into the Palearctic sub-region of some elements of the Oriental sub-fauna. We should therefore think in terms of avifaunas whose boundaries are always fluctuating, rather than of the static regions outlined by the great zoo-geographers of a century ago.

Nevertheless, the geographical regions which Sclater and his successors described so lucidly must serve as our basis. It has been estimated that in the middle of the 20th century the number of living bird species known is about 8,600 and, to judge from the diminishing rate at which new species are being discovered, it is unlikely that as many as a hundred remain to be found. Nine-tenths of the total had been found a hundred years ago. Thus P. L. Sclater could make

WORLD DISTRIBUTION OF WHITE-HEADED AND HOODED GULLS

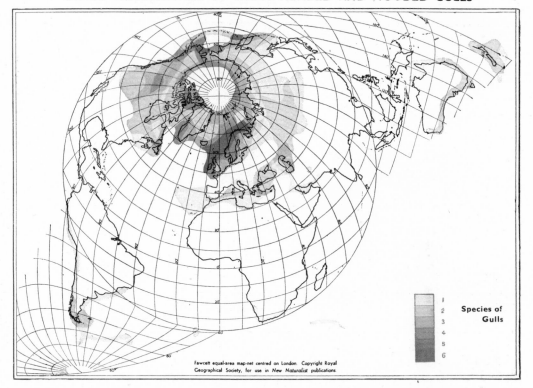

Species of
Gulls

Fawcett equal-area map-net centred on London. Copyright Royal
Geographical Society, for use in *New Naturalist* publications.

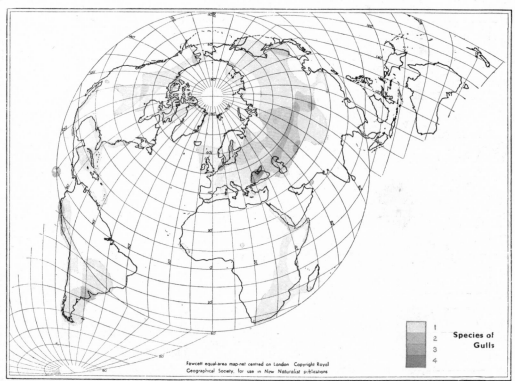

Species of
Gulls

Fawcett equal-area map-net centred on London. Copyright Royal
Geographical Society, for use in *New Naturalist* publications

*Distribution of white-headed (upper map) and hooded (lower map) gulls. Present bias of world distribution
suggests an original evolutionary centre for the former north of the Tethys Sea (upper overlay); and
for the latter, east and south of this (lower overlay) at a time when the Tethys Sea had begun to shrink*

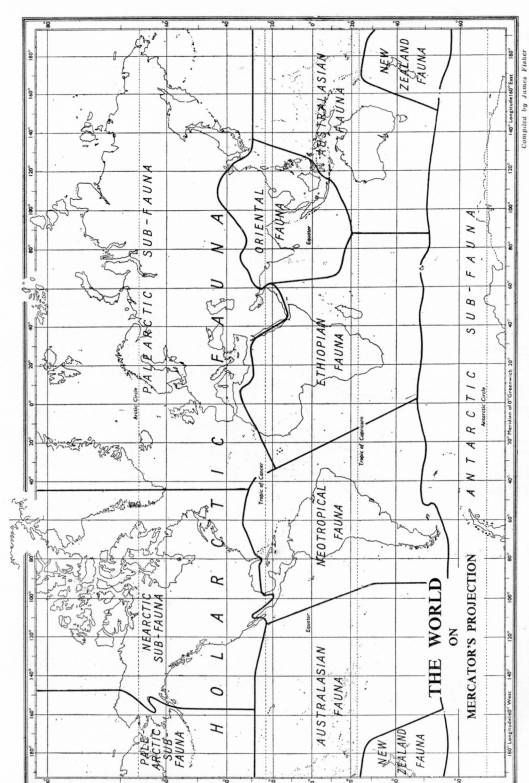

GEOGRAPHICAL DISTRIBUTION. Map of areas at present occupied by the world's principal avifauna

Compiled by James Fisher

n 1858 a classification of the geographical regions of the world which has never been subsequently modified in any radical way, though it was refined in important particulars by Alfred Russel Wallace, when he published his *Geographical Distribution of Animals* in 1876.

THE MAIN REGIONS

Most authorities recognize six principal geographical regions, each possessing a characteristic avifauna. *See* facing plate

1. **NEW ZEALAND REGION** : New Zealand and its satellite islands.
2. **AUSTRALASIAN REGION** : Australia, the East Indies from Lombok (" Wallace's line ") eastwards, and most Pacific islands.
3. **ORIENTAL REGION** : India, most of China, and the East Indies to Borneo and Bali. Celebes has a fauna with both Australasian and Oriental elements.
4. **ETHIOPIAN REGION** : Africa south of the Atlas mountains, Madagascar, and some islands in the Indian Ocean.
5. **NEOTROPICAL REGION** : the Americas from tropical Mexico southwards, including the Caribbean islands.
6. **HOLARCTIC REGION** : the rest of the land surface of the world. Arabia has considerable Ethiopian and some Oriental elements, but R. Meinertzhagen's *Birds of Arabia* (1954) shows that its fauna is predominantly Holarctic.

Sclater divided the area occupied by the Holarctic fauna into two : Nearctic (New World) and Palearctic (Old World) Regions. But the faunas of these two regions are rather similar, and they are classified by many as subregions supporting sub-faunas. It is generally held now that the Palearctic sub-fauna extends into two small parts of the *New* World—Alaska west of the tree-line, and east Greenland.

There is justification for considering that the Antarctic and sub-Antarctic regions support a distinct sub-fauna.

Britain. The British Isles represent a small area of the region occupied by the Palearctic sub-fauna. In 1954 about 430 species are generally accepted as having been seen at least once in the British Isles, though the total may become higher after a reconsideration of the claims of certain small birds, drift migrants from north America, to be included on the British list. The total of 430 species is a twentieth of the number of species in the world, and represents almost half the species that have been found in the Holarctic Region. There are various reasons for this rather large figure. Britain is a natural trap for wind-drifted wanderers, both from Siberia and from north America ; it is particularly attractive to seabirds ; and, with its varied climate and scenery, it can maintain a wide variety of forms, from nightingales, which have a warm temperate distribution, to Arctic and tundra species such

as the Snow-Bunting, Dotterel and Ptarmigan, which nest on Highland mountain tops.

Of the 134 resident species, which breed regularly in some part of the British Isles, no less than 50, or three-eighths, are Holarctic, nesting in the northern New World as well as in the Old. The remaining 84 are purely Old World species, and 70 of them are members of the Palearctic sub-fauna only.

There are very few cosmopolitan birds found in Britain. The Dabchick is a member of all the Old World faunas, and the Heron, Bittern, Great Crested Grebe, Coot and Rock-Dove are found in most of the regions. Of cosmopolitan birds that belong to New World faunas as well, the Barn-Owl has perhaps the widest distribution, and the Short-eared Owl, Peregrine, Cormorant and Moorhen belong to many faunas. The Manx Shearwater has recently been shown to belong to a species which has a curiously wide scattered distribution over most of the oceans of the world.

If we consider Britain's summer visitors—those migrants which come from the south to breed in our islands and winter in southern Europe or, more usually, Africa—we find not unnaturally a greater preponderance of Old World elements than among our residents. Thus the warblers belong to a family that is practically confined to the Old World.

The Yellow Wagtail is only a New World species by reason of the fact that its summer distribution extends from Siberia into Alaska (it thus remains a member of the Palearctic sub-fauna). Among the summer-visiting members of the gull-wader order there are, however, more Holarctic elements, including the Whimbrel, Red-necked Phalarope, Dunlin, Kentish Plover, five species of tern, one skua and a gull.

Two of Britain's summer visitors are nonbreeding sea-birds, which during our Winter nest in the Southern Hemisphere—the Great and Sooty shearwaters. The majority of Britain's 128 winter visitors are water-birds or waders, most of which are Holarctic. The list contains only six passerines. Britain has 22 passage-migrants (birds which do not regularly breed or regularly winter, but are recorded every year) ; half of these are waders. The remaining British birds, 190 or more, are either extinct (Great Auk) or scarce or irregular visitors and vagrants ; they include over 20 species recorded on only one occasion.

The possibility that small Passerine birds can survive wind-aided crossings of the Atlantic had been seriously underrated until recently. The following north American species have claims to be included on the British list which will have to be carefully considered at its next revision : American Goldfinch, Slate-coloured

Junco, White-throated Sparrow, Red-eyed Vireo, Yellow Warbler, American Robin and Grey-cheeked Thrush. Rather inconsistently, some small or smallish American birds have already been accepted, such as the American race of the Rock-Pipit and the Yellow-billed and Black-billed cuckoos.

No important lessons about the nature of the world's principal avifaunas can be learned in Britain. But it is a valuable centre for the elucidation of the more detailed problems of distribution, which are becoming increasingly important with the advance of the study of evolution and speciation. Thanks to the astonishing network of amateur ornithologists in western Europe, and in Britain in particular, our knowledge not only of breeding-ranges but also of actual breeding populations has increased to a remarkable extent. For instance, the marked amelioration of the late spring and early summer climate of 1920-50, with its consequent changes in the ranges of a very large number of European birds, has been under close observation. It has thus been possible to follow in some detail the spread of the Great Spotted Woodpecker through Scotland, and the gradual withdrawal, also to the north, of the area of overlap in the breeding distribution of the Hooded and Carrion-crows. Patiently, observers await the arrival of the Serin and the Collared Turtle-Dove, which have reached the Channel coast after spreading across Europe (the latter has moved over a thousand miles in only 20 years).

Our commonest large Passerine bird, the Rook, has been the subject of a nest-census covering two-thirds of the entire area of England, Wales and Scotland. The nesting population of many sea-birds has been assessed—e.g. Great Skua, Gannet, Fulmar, Leach's Petrel and Puffin—and of most others at least the location of all the important colonies has been mapped with pin-point accuracy. Fluctuations in the numbers of some accurately countable species like the Great Crested Grebe and the Heron are carefully followed year by year. Many of these advances in our knowledge of what might be called micro-geographical distribution can be credited to the British Trust for Ornithology, which celebrated its twentieth birthday in 1954.

Recently there have been notable advances in the study of visible migration in Britain. Organized in a new way, with a chain of observation stations, migration watchers are returning, with improvements, to the techniques and interests of such pioneer students as Eagle Clarke, Barrington and Harvie-Brown. A new school of behaviour studies is also rising. There is no doubt that in Britain the study of geographical distribution, once cultivated to the exclusion of almost everything else, and later neglected and almost deserted, is returning to its own.

METHODS OF DISPERSAL

Outside Europe and north America our knowledge is mostly at the stage of museum collection and study of facts. It is only by field work that we can fully understand the *methods* by which birds become dispersed. In the main, the dispersal-mechanisms of birds are of two kinds : active and passive.

Active. Undoubtedly active dispersal has been the more important, and is responsible for the general pattern of world distribution ; but passive dispersal has produced some spectacular local results, and has played a part whose importance has been properly recognized only recently. With a few exceptions (such as some ducks), birds tend to return to their breeding-places every year, or, if they have not previously bred, to their birthplaces. Active dispersal can take place only if the species has the capacity to pioneer, and take advantage of opportunities of settling new ground. Usually, of course, this new ground is at or near the edge of its previous range. Pioneering of this kind is in contradiction to most species' natural tendency to home-conservatism, or *Ortstreue*, as it is widely called ; and it now seems clear that most pioneering is undertaken by young birds that have not previously bred—often males, but occasionally females.

Many young that home to their birthplace encounter there aggressive displays from their parents—or their parents' adult successors— that is, of older birds with greater territorial drive. They are thus displaced into vacant ground. In most cases the tendency will be to occupy ground as near as possible to other occupied territories, for these probably continue to hold a strong attraction. This kind of dispersal can only be gradual, yet it must be adequate to enable a species to follow the movement of climatic and other environmental conditions, across hundreds, sometimes thousands, of miles.

Active dispersal may be a quicker process, or at least capable of exploiting remoter opportunities, among species which show marked differential migration. Of many species only a part of the population is migratory, or some parts are more migratory than others. The differentiation may be by age or sex, or both. The young of many species make longer journeys than the adults, and quite a number of young birds make journeys towards the Poles and not the Equator in the Autumn of their year of birth.

Passive. Passive dispersal is of two main kinds —Man-aided and wind-aided. Man-aided dispersal has occurred in little more than the last 1,000 years ; while it has affected 100 bird species or more, it has been accompanied so far by very little evolutionary change. But gales and hurricanes, and even some days of lesser winds, often carry birds across thousands of miles of ocean. While the vast majority of these birds have died, the laws of chance have inevitably brought some to new havens to which they are already adapted and in which there are few, or no, indigenous species to compete with them. All over the world are islands populated by the descendants of such drift species. In the last 25 years at least two species have established breeding populations in new faunal areas by drift : the Cattle Egret, from Africa, in both south and north America, and the Fieldfare from Norway, in west Greenland.

On two archipelagoes drift immigrants have had time to evolve subfamilies (some workers make them families). The *Geospizidae* (Darwin's birds) of the Galapagos, according to the study of Lack (1947), have evolved into 14 species in four genera, with remarkably different structure and feeding-habits, all putatively descended from some drift immigrant bunting species, probably from central America. The *Drepaniidae* (honey-creepers) of Hawaii, according to Amadon's study (1950), have evolved into 22 species in nine genera, with even more differentiation than the *Geospizidae* (the *Drepaniidae* deserve family status), all putatively descended from an unspecialised tanager, also probably from central America.

A list of the world's orders of birds, and the numbers of their members belonging to the British avifauna, is given under Classification (p. 130). The table (above) gives the world distribution of certain selected orders and families.

Evolutionary Centres. All orders and families have a geographical " evolutionary centre," which in many has been clearly identified with one particular region, though the order or family has subsequently spread into others. Thus the penguins (*Sphenisciformes*) and petrels (*Procellariiformes*) probably originated in or near the Antarctic, and the pelican-cormorants (*Pelecaniformes*) either in the Indian Ocean or the Tethys Sea. In the diurnal birds of prey order, the New World vultures probably originated in a once tropical area in the southern part of *north* America, as possibly also did the order *Trogoniformes* (trogons), and the motmot family of the roller order, the turkey family of the game-birds, the limpkin family of the rails, and, among passerines, the New World warblers.

Tropical *south* America was the evolutionary home of the guan family (game-birds), humming-birds (swift order) and, in the passerines, the tyrants and tanagers. In the gull-wader order the evolutionary home of the gull-tern family was probably on the shore of the Tethys Sea—the light-headed gulls on its north shore, the dark-headed gulls on the east or south, and the terns perhaps at its eastern, Indian Ocean, end. The pigeon order was quite possibly of Australasian origin.

Of probable Old World origin are the flamingo order, the game-bird order, the cuckoo order, the bustard family, the crane family, the courser family, the parrot order, the owl order, the bee-eater, roller, kingfisher, hoopoe and hornbill families, and the song-birds (the largest suborder of the passerines).

Some British birds belong to groups, not so far mentioned, which originated in the Americas ; such are the grouse family (or subfamily), which probably originated in northern north America, the buntings from north America, and the woodpecker order and wren family which came originally from somewhere in the New World.

WORLD DISTRIBUTION

COSMOPOLITAN. Grebes (*Podicipidiformes*) ; cormorants, pelicans, etc. (*Pelecaniformes*) ; diurnal birds of prey (*Falconiformes*) ; herons, etc. (*Ardeiformes*) ; geese and ducks (*Anseriformes*) ; game-birds (*Galliformes*) ; cranes, rails, etc. (*Ralliformes*) ; waders, gulls, etc. (*Charadriiformes*) ; pigeons (*Columbiformes*) ; cuckoos (*Cuculiformes*) ; owls (*Strigiformes*) ; nightjars (*Caprimulgiformes*) ; swifts (*Apodiformes*) ; rollers, kingfishers, etc. (*Coraciiformes*) ; woodpeckers (*Piciformes*) ; and the great order of *Passeriformes* : all these are now found in every principal avifauna.

NEW ZEALAND FAUNA. The extinct moas and living kiwis (*Apterygiformes*), two families of parrots and two Passerine families are (or were) entirely confined to this avifauna.

AUSTRALASIAN FAUNA. The cassowaries and emus (*Casuariiformes*), one family of game-birds, one of the crane-rails, two of parrots, one of nightjars and ten of Passerines are confined to this fauna.

ORIENTAL FAUNA. Only one Passerine family is peculiar to this fauna, but quite a number of bird families are only Oriental and Australasian, or Oriental and Ethiopian.

ETHIOPIAN FAUNA. The ostriches (*Struthioniformes*) and mouse-birds (*Coliiformes*) are purely Ethiopian (the Ostrich extended into Arabia until 1941), as are one family of the diurnal birds of prey, one of storks, one of cuckoos, one of crane-rails, one of pigeons, one of woodpeckers and two of Passerines.

NEOTROPICAL FAUNA. The world's most strange and varied avifauna, with two peculiar orders—rheas (*Rheiformes*) and tinamous (*Tinamiformes*), and peculiar families in the goose-duck order (one), game-birds (two), cranes (three), gull-waders (one), nightjars (two), rollers, etc. (two), woodpeckers (three) and Passerines (nine).

HOLARCTIC FAUNA. One peculiar order, the divers (*Colymbiformes*), and peculiar families in gull-waders (one, the auks), and Passerines (two).

ANTARCTIC SUB-FAUNA. One peculiar family in the gull-wader order (sheathbills).

GIBRALTAR POINT. Nature Reserve (*q.v.*) managed by the Lincolnshire Naturalists' Trust on behalf of the Lincoln (parts of Lindsey) County Council. It is situated a few miles almost due south of Skegness, and consists of 300 acres of sand dunes and salt marshes. Although the succession of plant life is of great interest to the botanist, the Reserve is chiefly important as a sanctuary for migrant and wintering birds, and is widely recognized as being one of the important stations for the observation and study of bird migration.

GIZZARD. In birds, the second, or bulbous stomach in which the food is ground (with the aid of a horny lining, swallowed grit or small stones) after being softened in the first, or glandular, stomach. *See* Anatomy.

GLAREOLA. Genus of the family *Glareolidae* of the order *Charadriiformes*. It contains seven species, two of which are distributed over southern Europe, the others occurring mainly in the arid regions of the Eastern Hemisphere. The species on the British list are the Collared Pratincole (*q.v.*) and the Black-winged Pratincole (*q.v.*), the former an irregular visitor, and the latter only a rare vagrant.

GLAREOLIDAE. Family of the order *Charadriiformes*, comprising the pratincoles, coursers and their allies. It is divided into about half-a-dozen genera, and its members are mainly distributed over the more barren and arid regions of Africa and Asia. There are only two genera, *Glareola* and *Cursorius* (*qq.v.*), on the British list.

The members of this family of terrestrial birds have shortish, curved bills, and their oblong nostrils are protected by a membrane. The wings are long and pointed, and there are eleven primary feathers, the outermost of which is much reduced. The tail is forked or square-shaped, and has twelve feathers. The legs are generally long and slender, and the tarsus is covered with scutes (horny scales) both at the front and back. There are three front toes and an elevated hind-toe. The plumage is mainly sandy or rufous in colour, but there are generally some conspicuous black and white markings on the wings. There is down on the feathered and featherless tracts.

GLAUCOUS GULL—Larus hyperboreus. This is a regular autumn and winter visitor to the east coast, especially to the Orkney and Shetland and other islands in the north, from its breeding haunts in the Arctic. Its appearance has much in common with that of the Iceland Gull (*q.v.*), but it is a stouter and larger bird and its bill is longer. Along with the Iceland Gull, it is the only gull likely to be seen in this country with a pure white plumage, except for its pale silver-grey mantle and wings. The absence of black from wings and tail distinguishes both the Glaucous and Iceland gulls from all other sea-birds. The Glaucous Gull's lemon-yellow eye contrasts with the brick-red of the Iceland Gull's. The Glaucous Gull varies in size, but its average length is 27 in. ; its tarsus is 3 in. Its weight is 4 lb., and its wing span is about 3 ft.

In habits and behaviour the Glaucous Gull does not differ greatly from the Greater Black-backed Gull ; though perhaps less fierce, it is equally destructive to other sea-birds, and is greatly feared by them. Saxby, in his *Birds of Shetland*, states that the Glaucous Gull is much less quarrelsome than the Greater Black-backed Gull. He adds that it is neither shy nor wary.

Its flight is powerful, speedy and soaring, but slower than that of the Iceland Gull. It is on the whole a silent bird, but in the breeding season it has a large vocabulary of harsh, raucous and rather plaintive notes.

The Glaucous Gull breeds on the coasts of the far north and builds a large nest of whatever materials—such as moss and seaweed—are available. Its breeding season varies with the temperature, but is usually in May or June. The number of its eggs is three and both male and female take a share in the hatching and in the rearing of the single brood. The young are buff-coloured, and gradually become whiter ; they do not assume the complete adult plumage until about their fourth year.

No animal food or refuse comes amiss to the Glaucous Gull. Dutch fisherman call it the " Burgomaster ", and in the north it commonly goes by the strange name of " Iceland Scorie ".

R. P. Bagnall-Oakeley

GLAUCOUS GULL. *This and the Iceland Gull are the only pure white gulls to be found in Britain*

GLEAD. Old name for Kite (*q.v.*), derived from the Old English word *glidan*, meaning "glide". The bird was named thus after its buoyant, effortless gliding in the air, during which it makes good use of its flexible tail.

GLOSSY IBIS—Plegadis falcinellus. At irregular intervals in Autumn, and occasionally in Spring, small parties of the Glossy Ibis— a very beautiful visitor—appear on the coasts of the British Isles, most frequently in the south-west and east, but occasionally also in both Scotland and Ireland. They rarely come inland. The Glossy Ibis breeds in colonies, sometimes very large, in the swamps, estuaries, marshes and lagoons of central and southern Europe, north Africa and north America.

This bird has the size and build of the Curlew, and sportsmen have named it the "Black Curlew". From a distance its appearance is that of a large black bird. Nearer observation, however, reveals the rich brownish-purple mantle, darker towards the wings and tail, which both have a beautiful green and purple lustre. Its winter plumage, in which the bird is most likely to be seen in Britain, is much duller, and some white appears on the head and neck. The curlew-like, down-curved brown bill is 5 or 6 in. long, and the long legs are greenish-grey. Male and female are alike. The length is 22 in., the body measuring 12 in., the tarsus is 4 in. The weight is 1½ lb., and the wing span something over 2 ft.

On the ground, the walk of the Glossy Ibis is stately and heron-like, but it will often be seen perching in trees. It can perform some marvellous feats of flight, swooping down at speed from a great height with the rounded wings half-closed and the feet and neck outstretched. It is not a solitary bird, and is normally seen in small groups and in company with herons and egrets. On the whole, the Glossy Ibis is a silent bird, but at breeding time it emits some harsh and grating croaks.

The breeding season varies according to the country frequented, but is normally in May and June. The nest is built in a reed bed or tamarisk bush, or in a tree growing in water, and is composed of small sticks and lined with leaves. The three or four eggs are blue and are 2 in. long. As far as is known, one brood is reared in a year. Both male and female take part in hatching, which lasts about three weeks, though the hen takes the larger share. The chicks, clothed in black down at first, are very helpless and are fed by regurgitation. After they leave the nests, the feeding of the young is a communal responsibility of the colony.

On its rare visits to Britain, this bird finds its food by wading in the mud and ooze of estuaries and marshes and probing for insects with its

G. K. Yeates

GODWIT. The two godwits are very alike, but the larger Black-tailed bird (above) has longer legs

useful long bill. Its diet is more varied in its breeding haunts and includes leeches, snails, snakes, frogs and shrimps.

The ancient Egyptians revered and honoured this beautiful bird, and the embalmed remains of ibises have been found in their tombs.

GOATSUCKER. Local name for nightjars (*q.v.*). In German these birds are occasionally known as "Goat-milkers".

GODWIT. Familiar name of a genus (*Limosa*) of birds, which used to be grouped in the same family as the plovers (*Charadriidae*), but now belongs to the family *Scolopacidae*, which also includes, among others, snipes, woodcocks, curlews and sandpipers.

Godwits are distinguished by their long slender bills and legs, with a large part of the tibia bare. All the species frequent marshes and shallow waters, chiefly coastal, where they seek their food, like snipes, by plunging the long bill into water or mud. They sometimes also run after small crustaceans, and catch them on the sand after the tide has withdrawn. The two species on the British list, Black-tailed Godwit and Bar-tailed Godwit, are fully described under their own names.

As birds of passage they are not infrequent visitors to the marshy parts of the east coast of England, where the former used to breed regularly, and, after a break, irregularly again after 1927. The females are larger than the males, and the whole length of the female Black-tailed Godwit is about 17 in., the bill being 4 in.

Though similar in appearance, the two godwits may be distinguished not only by their tails but also by the fact that the Black-tailed bird is, generally, slightly larger, has much longer legs and a straight (*not* upcurved) bill, and, moreover, it also sports a broad white wing-bar.

Eric Hosking

GOLDCREST. *This, the smallest bird breeding here, weaves its nest together with spiders' webs*

GOLDCREST—**Regulus regulus anglorum.** This charming little bird, often called the Golden-crested Wren, is the smallest of all British breeding birds. A popular favourite, it is with us all the year round, wherever there are conifer trees, except for the Orkney and Shetland Islands. The Goldcrest is also a winter visitor and passage migrant.

A severe Winter takes a terrible toll of this tiny bird, and it has often been on the verge of extinction ; but the large numbers of nestlings safely reared every year ensure its survival as a species. As it flits in and out of the branches, the Goldcrest is easily recognized by its small size alone. The only bird with which it could possibly be confused is the Firecrest (*q.v.*), a winter visitor, but at close quarters various distinguishing marks can be seen. The cock Goldcrest is a dull green above and a creamy-buff below, and its wings have two white bars and some black patches. Its crest is bright orange, with a distinct black surround. It has a slender dark bill and brown legs. The hen is similar, except that her much less distinctive crest is lemon instead of orange. The Goldcrest is 3½ in. long and its tarsus is 0·7 in. Its wing span measures 5 in., and its weight is only ⅛ oz.

It is a tame little creature, heedless of human observation as it flits about on its various activities. During the courtship display, the brilliant crest of the male is much in evidence ; the quivering bird raises and spreads it out in great excitement. The crest is also erected when a rival enters the territory.

The voice of the Goldcrest befits its size, for it is a feeble, high-pitched squeaky note ; its song is a combination of two notes lasting a few seconds and ending with a little flourish. It has little or no carrying power, and only a keen ear can detect it in the open, unless one is actually listening for it. The tiny call may be heard all the year round ; the song, however, is said to be at its best during March, April, May and June. During Winter goldcrests go about in flocks, in company with firecrests and tits, foraging for food and roosting in trees.

The nest, a real work of art, is always cleverly concealed. It is built with green moss, woven together with spiders' webs and feathers, and is suspended beneath the thick branches of a tree. Both birds assist in its intricate construction. The seven to ten tiny, dirty-white eggs with reddish-brown spots, laid in April or May, are hatched out by the hen alone. From then on, the devoted little parents tackle the feeding and rearing of their large family tirelessly for about a fortnight. It is not unusual for a second brood to be hatched out.

Insects are the staple diet of the Goldcrest; it is thus of benefit to farmer and forester.

Large numbers of migrating goldcrests used to succumb to wind and weather. Today the perches which have been fitted to lighthouses, and are maintained by the Royal Society for the Protection of Birds, enable thousands of these tiny birds to complete their arduous journey.

GOLDEN EAGLE—**Aquila chrysaëtos.** This magnificent and noble-looking bird may well bear the title of " King of Birds ", and certainly no other bird is surrounded so much by romance, for the eagle represents all that is fierce, powerful and terrible in the bird world. Legend even tells of its thefts of babies, and it does, in fact, carry off sick lambs and other animals weaker than itself, crushing the life out of them with its cruel talons. It has been known to carry off food weighing as much as 12 lb. Eagles will even attack a man when roused or angry, but as a rule humans are recognized as enemies and given a wide berth.

Centuries of persecution and the depredations of egg collectors have driven the Golden Eagle from its former haunts in England and Wales, and it is now only a very rare vagrant there. It is still, however, a resident and breeding bird— and increasing in numbers—in the highlands of Scotland and in the Hebrides, thanks entirely to the rigorous application of bird protection laws and the efforts of nature-lovers throughout the British Isles.

Many owners of deer forests now encourage their gamekeepers to leave the Golden Eagle unmolested, since it keeps down the grouse which often disturb the deer. In Ireland, where it was once widespread, the Golden Eagle has suffered the same fate as in England, and it was last recorded there in 1930. *See also* Conservation.

The Golden Eagle is of huge size and its general appearance is a blackish-brown ; its head feathers are a lighter shade and, when seen in sunshine, have a golden hue, whence its name. Its head and neck are small for its great size. Its short tail is deep grey with brown bars. Its legs are feathered their whole length to its yellow feet. It has a very powerful-looking hooked beak, with yellow cere. Male and female are alike, but the hen is the larger. They attain sometimes as much as 3½ ft. in length, with a wing span of 7 or 8 ft., their weight is about 13 lb., and their tarsi 3 or 4 in.

No other bird can compete in the air with the majestic Golden Eagle, which soars to a great height, gliding with its great and powerful wings scarcely moving. But it has an awkward and clumsy walk on the ground, and likes to perch on crags and trees, sitting motionless for hours on end. On the whole, it is a silent bird, but three different notes are recorded : a yelping scream, a whistling alarm note and a barking cry. The Golden Eagle is usually seen alone, but in Winter it will hunt for food in pairs.

Formerly the Golden Eagle bred on sea cliffs in many parts of the country; but today it nests only on the moorlands and in the deer forests of the Highlands. Its eyrie, usually on the ledge of a cliff, is not always as inaccessible as it seems, for egg collectors have robbed many a nest, and some wonderful photographs and films have likewise been taken of the Golden Eagle at its home. Sometimes the same nest is used year after year, fresh material being added until it becomes a very unwieldy structure. It is built by both male and female of sticks, branches of trees, and other suitable material. Throughout the nesting season the b'rds continue to add to it, and decorate it with ferns and fresh green leaves. The two eggs are laid during the latter half of March, at an interval of two or three days. They are oval-shaped and either white or mottled, and blotched in reddish-brown and violet. The eggs are hatched almost entirely by the hen for about 40 days, but the male takes his part in feeding and rearing the young. The food brought in the male's talons is given to the chicks by the hen until they are about two months old. The Golden Eagle is single-brooded, but when one clutch has been stolen, a second one has sometimes been laid. The white in the tails of the young has led to their confusion with the White-tailed Eagle (*q.v.*).

The Golden Eagle is entirely carnivorous, and lives on a variety of animals and birds; but carrion of all kinds is eagerly devoured and apparently enjoyed, however putrid it may be.

GOLDEN-EYE—Bucephala clangula. This diving duck does not breed in the British Isles, but comes only as a winter visitor and passage migrant, arriving in October and leaving again in early May for its breeding haunts in the forests of nearly every part of the world. There is, however, some evidence that it has bred in England; nests were found in Cheshire in 1931–32, and the bird has often been seen in Scotland in the Summer. In Winter the Golden-Eye is widely distributed round our coasts and estuaries; a number make their way further inland, and some have even penetrated as far as London.

The short, squat body of this buffle-headed duck is quite distinctive. The main dress of the drake is a study in black and white; its head is completely black, showing a purplish-green sheen when seen close at hand; against this, the striking white patch between its eye and bill is very conspicuous. Its back and tail are both black, with sides and underparts in pure white. Its wings are black with white patches. Its eyes are yellow but, in spite of its name, this is not a particular distinction as other ducks have golden eyes. Its legs are orange-yellow. The duck is much smaller, and dark brown above instead of black, with white patches on its wings. It lacks the white patch on the face of the drake, and has a yellow tip to the bill. The length of the Golden-Eye is 18 in., the body measuring 12 in.; its tarsus is 1 in. It weighs 2 lb. and its wing span is approximately 1½ ft.

The Golden-Eye is a hardy little duck and is little disturbed by severe weather. It delights

Harold K. Whitford

GOLDEN EAGLE. *This huge bird, majestic in its soaring flight, likes to sit motionless for hours*

in swimming and much prefers water to land; it is an excellent diver and reaches a good depth. It rises easily from water, and flies with more rapid wing-beats than some other ducks. Golden-eyes are not at all sociable; they prefer their own kind, and are seldom seen in company with their relatives.

" Whistler " is one of the bird's local names, but this does not refer to its voice but to a unique whistling sound made by the swishing of its wings. It is a silent bird, except for a harsh, rasping breeding call, and a guttural croak uttered by the duck.

Its choice of nesting site is unusual, for it prefers a hole in a stump or a tree—sometimes at a considerable height—or a rabbit burrow; it would probably use a nesting box if one were provided. Very little material is used for the nest beyond little bits of wood, some down and feathers. The breeding season varies; it is April in Germany, and scarcely before June in Scandinavia. The 6–15 bluish-green eggs are hatched by the duck, though the drake is never very far away, the period being 26 days. The duck is left alone to tend and rear the chicks, which are able to swim and fly in about 57 days. One brood is brought out in a season.

The Golden-Eye procures the greater part of its food by probing in the mud at the bottom of water; it feeds almost entirely on animal matter. It is a wary bird and, to avoid detection, it will completely submerge itself in the weeds at the bottom, holding on to them, it is thought, by its bill. " Morillon " is another name by which it is sometimes called.

GOLDEN MOUNTAIN-THRUSH—Turdus dauma aureus. Formerly called White's Thrush, the Golden Mountain-Thrush in Winter occasionally wanders to the British Isles from its home in the deep forests of eastern Siberia and Japan. It is very similar to the Mistle-Thrush in build, but its plumage is quite distinct from all other thrushes (*see* Turdidae). The upper parts are yellowish, the underparts white, and the bird is patterned all over with small black crescents at the feather-tips. The undersides of the wings have broad black and white bars, most conspicuous in flight. Both male and female are alike. The length is 10½ in., the wing span about 13 in., and the tarsus is 1·3 in.

Extremely shy and therefore difficult to observe, the Golden Mountain-Thrush is a solitary bird. Its flight is very similar to the Green Woodpecker's. It appears to be a very silent bird, but observers who have heard its voice describe the song as quite different from that of the Song-Thrush and somewhat reminiscent of the Redwing's.

The Golden Mountain-Thrush breeds in dense forests with thick vegetation and the large nest is built in the fork of a tree some 12 to 20 ft. from the ground. The nest consists of moss and twigs, lined with pine needles and dead leaves. The four to five eggs are laid from mid-May to late June in Japan. The bird is thought to be double-brooded.

GOLDEN ORIOLE—Oriolus oriolus. Ornithologists believe that, given some encouragement, this rare and handsome summer visitor might remain to breed in the British Isles, for there have been instances of its doing so in places where it was unmolested by the " man with the gun " and the egg collector. In the 1830s it was a regular visitor and by no means rare, and it is hoped that the day may not be far distant when this lovely and unusual bird will become, if not an ordinary sight in our countryside, at least a fairly frequent one. At present it is only an occasional summer visitor to England from Africa, arriving in April and May. Kent seems to be one of its favourite spots, but the Editor has had the great pleasure of watching golden orioles on the Norfolk Broads, near Horsey, for three days in succession.

The bird's appearance is most striking, the male being bright yellow with black on wings and tail. W. H. Hudson described the sight of it among other birds as a " gleaming topaz in a necklace of little brown and green and freckled stones ". Dr. Koch has never forgotten the sight, early one morning, of the display of a pair of golden orioles gleaming in the sunshine " like a see-saw of golden balls ". The female has less brilliant colouring ; the yellow is subdued to a greenish tint, with darker head, tail and lighter underparts. The young birds resemble the female.

The Golden Oriole has sometimes been mistaken for the Green Woodpecker, for in flight the yellow colouring of both birds shows clearly. Its flight is long, graceful and undulating ; but on the ground, where it rarely rests, its walk is

W. S. Berridge

GOLDEN-EYE. One of the " buffle-headed " ducks which has even been seen in London during Winter

a clumsy hop. The length of the Golden Oriole is 9 in., and its tarsus is 0·85 in. Its wing span is approximately 12 in.

During the courtship period, the male and female birds dash swiftly in and out of the trees together, the male following the female, imitating her movements.

The nest of the Golden Oriole is a work of art. Suspended between the branches of a tree in parkland or a large garden, it is made of grass, tree bark, sedges and wool, and lined with grass and sometimes pieces of paper. Both birds take part in the building but the hen alone lines the nest. The eggs, generally three or four in number, have a whitish ground, with brown and purplish spots. Both birds assist in hatching them for about a fortnight. The young are fed by both parents, and are ready to fly in about 14 days. The Golden Oriole has one brood in a season ; some believe it has two, but there is no confirmation of this.

G. K. Yeates

GOLDEN ORIOLE. *Compared with others, this bird has been called " a gleaming topaz in a necklace of little brown and green and yellow stones "*

> The song of the Golden Oriole, which may be heard in May, June and July, is a far-carrying note of incomparable sweetness. On the Continent the bird is foremost in the dawn chorus. Over many years of observation I have proved that at the beginning of the nesting season the birds cannot be seen or heard.
> On one occasion, a special day-and-night watch in May, in a wood where these birds habitually bred, had proved that no Golden Oriole had been seen or heard ; but when I played a record of their song every half-hour the birds responded and then continued singing. On the Continent the song is said to sound like the words " die Kirschen sind reif " (the cherries are ripe). The call note is short and harsh, with no carrying power.—EDITOR.

Insects of every kind are its favourite food, but in the Summer much fruit is taken.

GOLDEN PLOVER—Charadrius apricarius.

Two races, the Northern (*C.a. altifrons*) and the Southern (*C.a. apricarius*), are to be found in the British Isles. The Northern bird, breeding in northern Europe and Asia, is merely a winter visitor and passage migrant to this country ; whereas the Southern variety, though distributed very locally, also breeds here.

The Southern Golden Plover nests in the high moorland country of England and Wales ; throughout Scotland, though only rarely in the Outer Hebrides ; it also occurs in small numbers in many boggy and mountainous districts of Ireland. This bird has a greater liking for inland districts than its closest relative, the Grey Plover (*q.v.*) and is not found on the coasts during its breeding season.

A strikingly beautiful and interesting bird, the Golden Plover, with its round head and slender, pointed bill, is typical of the plovers. The Northern bird in summer plumage is especially handsome in its mantle spangled black and gold and its black cheeks, breast and underparts. A broad white stripe runs from the forehead round behind the eye, down the sides of the breast and along the flanks.

The Southern bird has lost the distinctive white stripe and its colouring is altogether much less clear-cut, the black of its cheeks and underparts being partly obscured and gradually merging into the beautiful spangled mantle ; and the white showing only as blurred, yellowish patches here and there.

In Winter the two races are indistinguishable, with paler upperparts and whitish face and underparts, mottled golden on the breast. The rump and tail are dark in both races, the underwing has a patch of white and, unlike the Grey Plover, there is no wing-bar. The legs are greenish-grey and the bill black. Both male and female are similar in Summer, though the latter is duller and has less black on her breast ; in Winter they show no difference. The length is 11 in., with a wing span from 14 to 15 in. ; the weight is 9 oz. and the tarsus 1·6 in.

A shy bird, the Golden Plover has been provided by nature with a marvellous camouflage. It can merge itself completely into its background and, unless it moves, can evade observation successfully. Even the chicks are difficult to discover, for when danger is near they " freeze " (*see* Protective Coloration).

The Golden Plover has a rapid and direct flight. Outside the breeding season it is one of the most gregarious of its family and shows a special liking for lapwings. Towards evening, large flocks of these birds assemble to perform astonishing aerial acrobatics, often rising to a great height. As the flocks settle again, the birds emit the low and unique whistling notes that have earned the Golden Plover the name of " Whistler ".

On the ground, the Golden Plover has the characteristic tripping run of plovers, stopping a moment to gaze around, then continuing its search for some insect. Should an intruder appear, the bird stops dead, head erect, to gaze steadily at him. During the breeding season golden plovers like to stand on the top of stones, rocks or hummocks.

The spring display of the Golden Plover has been widely studied and is of much interest to ornithologists. From mid-February to July the males indulge in " advertisement flights ", slowly gliding high in the air, with their wings raised at an angle of 45°, and repeating their curious whistling call. They also tend to have display gatherings or "leks" of their own. Both male and female perform all sorts of mating antics, such as chasing, leap-frogging, dipping and diving.

Apart from the display and mating calls, the voice of the Golden Plover is a liquid, far-carrying and musical piping, with many variations. It can be heard at all seasons.

Upland moors, peat mosses and bogs are the nesting haunts of this bird and, in Scotland, it has been known to breed at an altitude of 2,800 to 3,000 feet. The nest is only a depression among the moss or heather. Four buff and brown mottled eggs are laid in April and early May. Nest and eggs merge marvellously into the ground and are very difficult to find. Both male and female incubate for four weeks and tend the young, which are out of the nest in a few hours, for the same period. The chicks are golden brown with dark mottlings and attain their adult plumage by their first breeding season.

The Golden Plover feeds on insects, molluscs, worms, spiders and so forth, but some vegetable matter is also taken.

Formerly the Golden Plover was classified as belonging to the genus *Pluvialis* (Latin, " rainy "). It is interesting, therefore, to note the following remark in Saxby's *Birds of Shetland ;*

> My own note-books remark that in most cases rain has not been far distant when the flocks of golden plovers were wheeling about noisily and at random, without any apparent cause.

For the American and Asiatic golden plovers, which, however, belong to the species *Charadrius domenicus, see* under these names.

GOLDFINCH—Carduelis carduelis britannica. The Goldfinch is one of the loveliest of British native birds, and it was no doubt its beauty, coupled with its natural tameness, that so long attracted the attentions of the bird-catcher before legislation put a stop to his unpleasant trade. Today a " charm " of goldfinches can flit about garden and orchard and add its decoration to the thistles of roadside and waste land without fear of capture and cage.

In spite of the increased cultivation, which has meant the disappearance of many of its favourite haunts, the Goldfinch is on the increase. But it is still confined to certain districts; it is a rare bird in many parts of Scotland, and seldom or never visits the Hebrides or the Orkney and Shetland Islands. In Autumn and Winter it roams about the countryside, in company with redpolls and siskins and other seed-eating birds, foraging for food and roosting in the trees; some goldfinches may even emigrate to the Channel Islands.

This beautiful little bird is immediately recognizable, for no other of our resident birds has such a dainty coat of so many colours. The top of its head is black with white at sides and throat, and it has a red face. Its tail is black, and its black wings are decorated with a band of brilliant yellow. Its mantle is light brown with white underparts, and a light brown demarcation line runs across its breast. Male and female are alike, but the young have no colouring on their heads. The length of the Goldfinch is $4\frac{1}{2}$ in., and its tarsus is 0·6 in. Its wing span is about 7 in., and it weighs $1\frac{1}{2}$ oz.

A " fairy bird " in the air, the Goldfinch has the graceful undulating flight of the finches,

Eric Hosking

GOLDEN PLOVER. The Southern Golden Plover, seen above, is found breeding in England and Wales

and moves restlessly among the hedges and bushes. It is not at home on the ground, where it hops. In his mating display the male moves his body from side to side, showing his golden wing-band to the best advantage.

The song of the Goldfinch, a gay and liquid performance and full of musical notes, is usually uttered from a tree or a hedge some 10 ft. from the ground. The song is composed of three or four phrases delivered without a pause. The

Eric Hosking

GOLDFINCH. *Chestnut and fruit trees are the favourite nesting sites of this finch ; and the beautiful nest is built of roots, bents, moss and feathers*

Goldfinch is perhaps not so strictly territorial as some of our small birds, for it does not seem to mind the intrusion of another one in its vicinity and, indeed, they perform wonderfully together in the Spring. The song is heard at its best from March to June.

The breeding season is in early May. The nest, hidden in a thick hedge, in a garden or orchard or in open woodland, is one of the most beautiful ones of our breeding birds. It is composed of roots, bents, moss and feathers, and lined with vegetable down and feathers. The five or six eggs are bluish-white, spotted and streaked with reddish brown ; they are hatched by the hen alone, but the cock feeds her while she is sitting. The chicks are fed in turn by both parents by regurgitation for a fortnight. Two broods are brought out in a season.

The Goldfinch is one of the most useful friends of the farmer, for it lives on small insects, larvae, and the seeds of many injurious weeds and plants, its favourite being the thistle.

One of our most popular birds, the Goldfinch has several local names, including " King Harry ", " Redcap ", " Proud Tailor " and " Draw Water " ; the last refers to its ability, when caged, to draw water up for itself from a small receptacle.

GONYS. The keel of a bird's lower mandible (from Greek *genys*, chin). *See also* Anatomy.

GOOSANDER—Mergus merganser. The group of ducks which includes the Goosander, Merganser and Smew comprises the only ducks which live entirely on fish, and Nature has endowed them with long and narrow saw-edged bills, well adapted for catching their slippery food. The Goosander is the largest of the group. It was first mentioned as breeding in Scotland in 1871 ; since then, it has increased

in numbers, and is widely distributed throughout the Scottish highlands ; and in recent years its range has extended further south. A regular winter visitor to England, it often visits the reservoirs of the Thames valley. Abroad, it breeds in many parts of north and east Europe, migrating south in Winter, sometimes as far as India.

The handsome Goosander drake has a large elongated body. Its general appearance, especially in flight, is a study in black and white. Its head and neck are dark green, with a glossy sheen, and its mantle and wings are black ; the sides and white underparts are tinged with pink. Its rump and tail are grey, and its beak and legs red. The duck is a smaller, greyer bird, with a rich brown head from which a crest flows down the back ; its legs and beak are red, but paler than the drake's. The Goosander is 26 in. long, with a body of 18 in., its tarsus is slightly over 1 in. It weighs 4 lb., and its wing span is from 1¾ to 2 ft.

Flying low over the water, the Goosander is a rapid and expert swimmer and diver, but finds difficulty in taking off quickly from the water. On the ground, it is less awkward-looking than most diving ducks, but it normally prefers to remain on the water. Goosanders fly high in small flocks, their wings making a whistling sound. They are very sociable, but rarely seen in huge flocks, preferring to wander in small parties. Their voice is seldom heard, except in the breeding season, when it has several notes from a harsh croak to a soft call.

The Goosander haunts both salt lochs and freshwater lakes, and shows some preference for wooded districts. Its nesting season in Britain is in April, but further north—in Iceland, for instance—it is in June. The eggs, 7-13 in number, are a smooth creamy-white, and are

Erica

GOOSANDER. *The drake is a handsome fellow with his glossy, dark green head and neck, black mantle and wings, and the delicately pink-tinged sides and underparts*

laid in a hole or crevice in a hollow tree or bank, never far from water. Almost no nesting material is used. The duck alone hatches the eggs and tends and rears the young, the drake taking little or no interest. After about five weeks the young can scramble down to the water, and they are soon swimming about.

The Goosander feeds entirely on animal matter, principally fish. It is said to be so greedy that it will devour many fish at one meal ; as a result of its feeding habits its activities have had to be checked in some districts in Scotland, because of its interference with the freshwater fisheries industry.

GOOSE. Large, heavily-built birds of the *Anatidae* or Duck (*q.v.*) family, with fairly long necks, long pointed wings and short rounded tails. Geese found in the British Isles are divided into two main groups—the Grey Geese of the genus *Anser* (*q.v.*) and the Black Geese of the genus *Branta* (*q.v.*).

Geese swim little and never dive. They rise easily from land into the wind, but have difficulty in taking off from water. They fly surprisingly fast, with regular powerful wing-beats, and seldom glide, except when alighting.

There are nine species on the British list, described under their respective headings : Grey Lag-Goose, White-fronted Goose, Lesser White-fronted Goose, Bean-Goose, Snow-Goose, Brent Goose, Barnacle-Goose, Canada Goose and Red-breasted Goose. The Pink-footed Goose (*q.v.*) is a geographical race (subspecies) of the Bean-Goose species.

Grey Geese. These are chiefly inland and diurnal feeders, with bills (*q.v.*) well adapted for cropping grass or biting off plant stems. They roost in shoals and mudbanks in estuaries or low-lying coasts, and usually pass to and from their feeding grounds at dawn and dusk. On long flights, they fly in characteristic V-

formation behind a single gander. These geese are generally greyish-brown, with lighter margins to the body feathers, and with tail coverts and rectrices tipped with white.

The most common—though somewhat scarce —resident is the Grey Lag, from which the domestic goose is descended. This breeds in parts of north-west Scotland and is also a non-breeding visitor. The White-fronted Goose is a regular visitor, mainly to Ireland and the Western Isles, but a few hundred visit the Wild Fowl Trust (*q.v.*) each year, arriving after the Pink-footed Goose, which comes in September.

The Bean-Goose is browner than other Grey Geese, and has a relatively longer neck and larger bill. It is the least common of the regular visitors. The Snow-Goose is an irregular visitor.

Black Geese. Those found in Britain are easy to identify. Except for the Canada Goose, their feeding habits differ from those of the Grey Geese; and they seldom fly in V-formation, preferring long lines transverse to the direction of flight, or packs.

The Barnacle-Goose is a non-breeding winter visitor, mainly to the western islands of Scotland and the Solway Firth. It is rarely seen inland and feeds chiefly at night. The Canada Goose, introduced in the 17th century, is now widely distributed in England, except in the north and south-west, and occurs in parts of Scotland and the east and south of Ireland.

Dark-breasted and Light-breasted Brent geese occur as winter visitors, the former preferring south-east Scotland and the east and south of England. The Dark-breasted Brent is the smallest and darkest of British geese, with sooty black head, neck and shoulders.

Finally, there is the Red-breasted Goose, which is a straggler from north-west Siberia and the Caspian Sea, and which has been recorded on only nine separate occasions in this country.

GOSHAWK—Accipiter gentilis. Although never a common bird in the British Isles, the Goshawk bred in many parts until the early 19th century. Its extinction was in great part due to the cutting down of forests in the interests of game preservation ; moreover, since it is the enemy of every game bird, gamekeepers usually shot it on sight. For over a century the Goshawk only visited Britain as a rare vagrant, but within recent years, under rigid protection, it has once more shown an inclination to return and breed in suitable country. Some form of Goshawk is found in the forests of both the Old and New Worlds, and it breeds across all Europe and Asia.

This noble and handsome bird resembles a large Sparrow-Hawk but has shorter legs. The mantle and long rounded wings are dark brown ; underneath it is much paler and boldly barred in brown ; the white-tipped tail is long, with dark bands. The bill has the typical hook of the hawks, and there is a white stripe running over the eye and ear coverts. The legs are yellowish. Male and female are similar in plumage, but the female, as is usual in birds of prey, is the larger ; it is also the fiercer and more formidable, especially when on the prowl. The measurements are : *Male*—length 18 to 20 in. ; tarsus 3 in. ; wing span about 2½ ft. *Female*—length 23 in. ; tarsus 3 in. ; wing span about 3 ft.

While hunting, the Goshawk has much the same agility and mastery of the air as the Sparrow-Hawk, but when soaring it is distinguished by the breadth of its wings. Outside the breeding season, it is a silent bird. When disturbed, and near the nest, it has a plaintive mewing note ; other variants are a hoarse warning call and another call uttered when passing food to the female at the nest. Goshawks are essentially birds of the forest, and their nests are substantial affairs of sticks, branches and small twigs, built (chiefly by the hens) in holes in trees or walls, sometimes on the ground or on the foundation of an old nest. Three or four whitish eggs are laid from April to May, the date depending on the country frequented. The hatching is done almost entirely by the hen ; the male brings food, clasped in its feet, for the young, the female preparing it at the nest. In about three weeks young goshawks are to be seen in the branches of the trees, and soon afterwards the young are on the wing. One brood is reared a year.

No small animal or bird comes amiss as food to the Goshawk. It usually prefers to seek its prey in the evening or early dawn, when anything moving is hunted down and attacked.

The Goshawk is still captured and trained for falconry especially in the east. In olden times it was named the " Falcon Gentil " and was the falconer's favourite. Many tales are related of its cunning, daring and cruelty in pursuit of prey ; when trained, it is said to become very devoted to its master. Irish goshawks were considered the best for hawking and were much sought after. The name " Goshawk " means " goose hawk ".

GOWK. Regional name, used chiefly in Scotland and Ireland, for the Cuckoo (*q.v.*).

GRASSHOPPER-WARBLER—Locustella naevia. This summer resident, arriving in April and leaving again in September, is generally distributed throughout the British Isles, except for the north of Scotland, where it is rarely seen. It is, however, by no means abundant, being confined to certain suitable districts. Abroad, it breeds in most parts of Europe, wintering in north-west Africa and west Asia.

Only its peculiar voice—which has earned it the name of " Reeler "—reveals the presence of the Grasshopper-Warbler, for it is the most secretive of the warblers, worming its way among the dense undergrowth like some small rodent. Apart from its cry, there is little to distinguish this sombre-looking little bird. The mantle is streaked in brown, darker towards the wings and tail ; the underparts are light brown. The graduated tail is slightly different from that of others of the family. Male and female are alike. The length is 5 in., and the tarsus 0·8 in. The wing span is about 6 in., and the weight a fraction of an ounce.

The flight is typical of the warblers ; but the bird rarely flies, spending most of its time skulking among the bushes. As the nesting season approaches, the male runs or walks about excitedly, often carrying in his bill a leaf or

Eric Hosking

GOSHAWK. *Falconers called this bird " Falcon Gentil " and prized it above others for its daring*

John Markham

GRASSHOPPER-WARBLER. *Sure that the coast is clear, the hen quietly slips back to her nest*

stem of grass which he presents, with quivering wings and expanded tail, to his mate.

The Grasshopper-Warbler can scarcely be said to have a song in the proper sense of the term. No other British bird utters such a truly remarkable sound. Anyone unaware of its presence and unfamiliar with the voice probably attributes the sound to some insect (but *not* to its namesake) or to some purely mechanical process, such as an angler slowly unwinding his fishing reel or the winding of a clock. The rapid rise and fall of the high-pitched trill is uttered with wide open bill, the bird turning its head from side to side, and consequently making it difficult for the listener to trace the direction of the strange noise. The song goes on for hours, especially after midnight, with short intervals between the phrases ; its carrying power is remarkable. Heard at close range, the pitch is so high as to be beyond the range of some human ears. The song is at its best in the evening or early morning, but it can be heard at any time of the day or night from late April until well into July.

Built by both male and female on a foundation of dead leaves and composed of grasses and bents and lined with hair and moss, the nest of the Grasshopper-Warbler is carefully concealed in the dense undergrowth of bushes. The six eggs are laid during May or early June ; they are a creamy ground-colour, spotted in reddish-brown. The parents share both the hatching and the rearing of their two broods.

All kinds of insects and their larvae form the chief food of the Grasshopper-Warbler.

GREAT AUK—Alca impennis. This extinct bird was quite common in the western Isles of Scotland a century ago. Its disappearance was due to the fact that both the bird and its eggs were taken for food and because the bird was relatively tame. The last British specimen was killed near the island of St. Kilda in 1840.

From all accounts—and there is much literature on the subject—the Great Auk was a harmless and attractive bird. In appearance it resembled a Razorbill, but was much larger. Its wings, with a span of only about 1 ft., were useful for swimming but useless for flying, and no doubt contributed to its extinction. Records reveal that the Great Auk was heard to utter only a croaking note.

According to Coward's *British Birds*, the Great Auk bred in Iceland and Greenland, in the Faeroes, Orkneys and Outer Hebrides, and off the coasts of Newfoundland and Labrador. *See also* Auk ; Extinct Birds.

GREAT BLACK-HEADED GULL—Larus ichthyaetus. This gull, a very infrequent wanderer to the coasts of the British Isles, nests in colonies on the coasts, rivers, estuaries and lakes of south Russia and parts of Asia, and winters in the south. It is a much larger bird than the Black-headed Gull (*q.v.*), and its breeding hood is really black, and not dark brown. It has a heavy orange bill and green legs. Its length is about 25 in., and its tarsus 3 in. ; its wing span is about 5 ft.

It resembles the other larger gulls in behaviour and habits. The breeding season is from the middle of May to early June and, the bird is apparently single-brooded. *See also* Gull.

GREAT BUSTARD—Otis tarda. Once a common resident in the British Isles, where it roamed over the wide moorland country of England and south Scotland, the Great Bustard is no longer included among our breeding birds and has become a very rare winter visitor. Many causes seem to have contributed to its disappearance. Chiefly responsible was the advancement of agriculture, made necessary by increasing population and involving the reclamation for food-growing of many of the bird's haunts in Yorkshire, Norfolk, Suffolk and Scotland. But the fact that this large bird was good to eat also contributed to its extermination.

The last breeding bustard was shot in Scotland about 1830. Some attempt to reintroduce it was made at the beginning of the 19th century by bringing birds from Spain ; but these birds shared the fate of their predecessors, and the Great Bustard now breeds only in central and south Europe and all across Siberia.

The great size of this bustard makes it unique among European birds ; some specimens weigh

258

as much as 30 lb. The male bird has a mantle of speckled chestnut brown down to its tail, with very light grey underparts and grey neck and head ; the upper part of the breast is also chestnut. Under its chin it has a tuft of bristles. The end feathers of its tail are white and very prominent in flight. The female is much smaller, and has no bristles on her chin and no chestnut on her breast. From a distance, a group of bustards could be mistaken for a flock of turkeys or even sheep. The length of the male is 40 to 45 in., and his tarsus is 6 in. ; his wing span is 7½ ft. The length of the female is about 30 to 35 in., and her tarsus is 4 in. ; her wing span is over 7 ft. The weight varies from 28 to 30 lb.

In behaviour the Great Bustard has some relation to the Stone-Curlew. It has a very stately and deliberate walk, but it is a shy and wary bird, and when alarmed runs away swiftly on its long legs. With regular beats of its huge wings, it flies faster than one would think possible for a bird of its size.

A silent bird, the Great Bustard gives vent to mere grunts and barks in the breeding season, but the young are supposed to have a pleasant whistling note. The breeding display of the male is one of the most extraordinary in the whole range of bird behaviour ; for, by turning over its wing coverts and tail feathers, this huge and awkward-looking bird suddenly becomes a billowing cloud of white, with its breast puffed out like that of a Pouter-Pigeon.

The Great Bustard frequents open rolling country, steppes, moorlands, heaths and downs. Some selected spot among cornfields, with a few scattered feathers trampled down, suffices for its nest. The number of eggs varies, but is usually two. The sitting is done by the hen alone for nearly a month ; it takes about the same time for the hen to rear the one brood.

The Great Bustard's diet consists mainly of vegetable food from crops and gardens, but it also takes voles, young birds and hares. *See also* Bustard ; Conservation ; Extinct Birds.

GREAT CORMORANT. Local name for Cormorant (*q.v.*), also known as Black or Common Cormorant.

GREAT CRESTED GREBE—Podiceps cristatus. The shooting of the Great Crested Grebe for the sake of its beautiful plumage threatened the bird with extermination in Great Britain in the 19th century and in 1860 only about 40 pairs remained throughout England, Wales and Scotland (the slaughter in Ireland was far less wholesale). Since that time legal protection has been responsible for a really wonderful recovery in the numbers of this species, and over 3,000 pairs now breed in safety on our lakes, meres and reservoirs. Recent surveys also report an increase in range. England and Wales have the greatest population, Norfolk, Cheshire and Northamptonshire being the favourite counties ; but there is also an encouraging number now breeding in Scotland and Ireland. The Great Crested Grebe is found in most parts of Europe, and in north Africa and Asia. Grebes are water birds similar to divers in many of their habits, but their feet, instead of being webbed, have characteristic lobes on the toes.

Of the five grebes to be seen in Britain, the Great Crested Grebe is the largest. No difficulty should be experienced in recognizing this handsome and attractive bird, for no other resembles it, except the very rare Red-necked Grebe. The habits and behaviour of the Great Crested Grebe have always held much interest for the ornithologist, and recent years several surveys and investigations have been carried out ; but much information has yet to be added to its life history.

Its most distinguishing feature is the quaint bonnet of dark tufts on each side of the ears, and the long rich chestnut feathers, shading darker at the tips, which hang down on each side of the head and form a kind of tippet. The long slender throat, breast and underparts are snowy white ; the mantle is greyish-brown ; the wings are a darker shade, and have two very conspicuous white patches. There is little or no tail;

Eric Hosking

GREAT BUSTARD. *This bird of the downs and moors was driven away by the advance in farming*

Eric Hosking

GREAT CRESTED GREBE. The grebe's floating nest is one of the marvels of the bird world

the cheeks are whitish ; the bill long, straight and red. The legs are greenish. Male and female are alike. The total length is 19 in., the body measuring 12 in. ; the tarsus is 2 in. The weight is 2 or 3 lb., the wing span about $1\frac{1}{4}$ ft.

An awkward bird on the ground, where it shuffles along, the Great Crested Grebe prefers to spend most of its time on the water. It swims low and fast on the surface, with head erect and turning from side to side as if ever on the watch. An expert diver, it will suddenly disappear for some seconds and come to the surface some distance away.

The Great Crested Grebe is not a distinguished performer in the air. It rises from the water with a pattering effect before taking off, but, when really necessary, it can fly with both speed and strength.

These birds have an extraordinary display in the mating season, sometimes beginning as early as January. In the " penguin dance " the two birds meet on the water, with necks outstretched and reared up to display the lovely snowy breasts. The " ears " are erected and the " tippets " spread out as they waggle their heads rapidly from side to side. At other times, both birds will dive for weeds, which they present to each other.

More or less a silent bird outside the breeding season, the Great Crested Grebe is noisy when mating and has a very large vocabulary. At the beginning of the display a very low call is heard as the male and female meet ; this becomes faster and faster but finally degenerates into a grating quacking. On approaching a lake or mere, a rambler may often be surprised to hear the sound of many crying voices coming from a hidden colony of grebes.

The breeding season depends on the growth of water vegetation, but is usually in May.

The bulky nest looks like a floating heap of water weeds, moored to plants and reeds on the surface of the water. It is constructed by both male and female, the male seeming to show the greater activity. The eggs, usually three or four, are an elongated oval shape, and chalky white in colour but, later on, much stained. They are laid every other day, and both birds take their share of the work during the month of incubation ; should the eggs have to be left for a short time they are carefully covered up. The young are very pretty little creatures, clad in stripes of black and white down. They take to the water and are carried cradle-wise on the backs of their parents almost the same day as they hatch. They can look after themselves in a few weeks and attain full plumage during their first season. Normally one brood is reared.

The food of grebes consists of fish of various kinds. They have also a curious habit of eating and digesting their own feathers. They rarely form colonies, and are usually seen in pairs ; in Winter they are generally distributed throughout the country.

The term " grebe " comes from a Celtic word meaning " comb " and refers to the crest—which, however, is not possessed by all grebes. The Great Crested Grebe's local names include " Tippet-Grebe ", " Loon ", " Gaunt " and " Diver ".

GREATER BLACK-BACKED GULL — Larus marinus. The largest of the six gulls breeding in the British Isles, the Greater Black-backed Gull is in size equalled only by the Glaucous Gull, a winter visitor. Although it is still not so plentiful as some other gulls, its population has greatly increased within recent years, especially in the Orkney and Shetland Islands and the Outer Hebrides. In Winter it is to be seen on almost all coasts, but it rarely goes inland except in very severe weather, when it has been known to venture as far as the Thames. Abroad it breeds all over the northern parts of both the Old and the New Worlds. The Greater Black-backed Gull is not gregarious by nature, but during the autumn herring season on the Norfolk coast it is by far the most numerous of the gulls congregating there, and its rapacious and vicious nature make it a danger to other birds.

The Greater Black-backed Gull is a noble and fierce-looking bird. It is often confused with the Lesser Black-backed Gull (*q.v.*) because it breeds in much the same areas, but it is considerably larger, and its mantle and wings are much darker and more distinctly mottled ; its neck, head and underparts are whiter, and its bill stouter and more formidable-looking with a red patch at the end. Its legs are flesh-coloured. In winter plumage the head takes on brownish-grey streaks. The length of the Greater Black-backed Gull is between 25 and 27 in., and its tarsus is 3 in. Its wing span of over 5 ft. supports a weight 4-5 lb.

Its voice has the typical gull-like sound, but is stronger, deeper and more raucous than that of its relatives, and dominates any congregation of gulls either in the air or at their breeding sites. Its flight is very similar to the Herring-Gull's and it can reach a great height and perform wonderful evolutions in the air.

Greater black-backed gulls nest in colonies when they are found in great numbers, otherwise they nest in single pairs or small groups. Rocky coasts, islands in fresh or salt water, and sometimes moors, are their favourite nesting sites. Their nests, built by both male and female, are large constructions of heather, sticks, seaweed and mosses. The three eggs are olive-buff, copiously marked and blotched in grey and umber. They are laid on alternate days in May or early June, and both male and female take a share in hatching them, beginning before the clutch is complete. The young are out in about 26 days, and they are fed and reared by both parents for about 50 days. One brood is reared in a season.

The Greater Black-backed Gull is a ruthless forager for food, and no smaller bird or animal is safe from it. It also feeds on carrion. It is said in Shetland that this is the only gull that will attack a human corpse. This gull is also said to keep an association with the seals which abound in the coastal waters.

Its numerous local names include " Corpse-Eater ", " Bougie " and " Saddleback ".

GREATER REDPOLL—Carduelis flammea rostrata.

A larger finch than the Lesser Redpoll (*q.v.*), the resident of this species in the British Isles, the Greater, or Greenland, Redpoll visits only the northern islands of Scotland, especially Fair Isle, as a more or less regular passage migrant from its home in Greenland. Identification is difficult, even for the expert ornithologist, for there is little in its appearance to distinguish it from other redpolls.

The birch and willow bushes of the Arctic tundra are its breeding sites, and in behaviour and habits it follows closely the pattern of its relatives. The song is said to resemble that of the Lesser Redpoll. A seed-eater, the Greater Redpoll forages for its food among birch, alder and coniferous trees.

GREATER SPOTTED WOODPECKER—Dendrocopos major anglicus.

Often referred to as the Pied Woodpecker, the Greater Spotted Woodpecker is an even more ardent lover of woodlands, especially coniferous trees, than the Green Woodpecker. A resident bird, confined to the British Isles, it breeds throughout England and Wales, but is by no means common. It is scarce in Scotland—at one time it was never seen there but it is extending its range. The British form is unknown in Ireland. Another form, the northern Greater Spotted Woodpecker (*Dendrocopos major major*), similar in every way to the British bird, breeds throughout Europe and northern Asia ; it is a winter visitor to Britain, arriving sometimes in large numbers.

The variegated black and white plumage of the Greater Spotted Woodpecker is both beautiful and distinctive. Black predominates

GREATER BLACK-BACKED GULL. *Reaching a length of over two feet, this, the most predatory of gulls, is feared by all other birds for its fierceness and cunning*

Eric Hosking

above, but a large white patch appears on each wing, and the under tail-coverts are crimson ; the breast and underparts are a light buff. The cheeks and throat are white, separated by the black of the mantle, and another white patch appears on the side of the neck. The central tail feathers are black, the others decorated with white dots and bars. The crown is black. The cock's nape exhibits a prominent red patch ; the female lacks this colour, but otherwise the sexes are alike. The young have a crimson crown. The length is 9 in., and the tarsus 0·9 in. The wing span is about 12 in., and the weight 2¾ oz.

Few differences in behaviour or habit separate the Greater Spotted from the Green Woodpecker (*q.v.*). Less inclined to come down to the ground, the Greater Spotted is even more shy of observation, and is rarely seen in the open. Its flight is undulating, with the wings closely folded to its sides after each forward bound.

But if the Greater Spotted Woodpecker is rarely seen, its presence is well advertised by its " drumming " on the dead wood of trees with its powerful bill. This produces an extraordinary sound which echoes through the woods and can be heard some distance away. Variations in the pitch of this noise are produced not by the bird but by the kind of tree attacked : an oak, for instance, gives out a different sound from a pine. Other woodpeckers " drum ", but the Greater Spotted Woodpecker is the most proficient and regular performer ; its drumming starts during the latter part of February and continues until late April, occasionally into May. Only near the nest and in the breeding season

is the voice of the Greater Spotted Woodpecker heard at any length. The young in the nest make a peculiar rasping noise.

Nesting habits of this species resemble those of the Green Woodpecker in every detail except that the nesting hole is usually farther from the ground. The four to seven creamy white eggs are laid in May on the wood chips resulting from the bird's excavations. Both male and female take a share in all the domestic duties connected with the one brood.

The larvae of wood-boring insects are the main diet of the Greater Spotted Woodpecker, but spiders, nuts and many varieties of berries are also eaten when insects are not available. *See also* Woodpecker.

GREATER WHITETHROAT. Name sometimes given to the Whitethroat (*q.v.*) to distinguish it from the Lesser Whitethroat (*q.v.*).

GREATER WHITE-WINGED GULL. Local name for Glaucous Gull (*q.v.*), which, together with the smaller Iceland Gull, is the only all-white gull, except for its pale silvery-grey wings and mantle.

GREATER YELLOW-LEGS — Tringa melanoleuca. Except that it is one-third larger, this bird is similar in appearance, habits and behaviour to the Lesser Yellow-Legs—also a bird of north America. It has the size and build of the Greenshank (*q.v.*) and, were it not for its conspicuous yellow legs, might be taken for that bird on its rare visits to the British Isles. Its voice is described by those who have heard it, as much longer and clearer than that of the Lesser Yellow-Legs (*q.v.*).

The Greater Yellow-Legs breeds on the treeless tundra, never far from water ; the nest is a mere scrape in the ground, where four olive-buff eggs are laid at the beginning of May. The bird feeds entirely on animal matter. In Britain this bird is often called the Greater Yellowshank, but this Encyclopedia follows the practice of the British list in adopting the name by which the bird is generally known in the area where it breeds.

GREAT GREY SHRIKE—Lanius excubitor. Arriving in October, the Great Grey Shrike is a regular autumn and winter visitor to Great Britain ; also, but less frequently, a passage migrant in Spring. Essentially a bird of north Europe, it rarely ventures farther than the south of Europe even in Winter. A fierce species, it is the largest of the shrikes, and its size, combined with a distinctive pattern of both plumage and tail, makes identification easy. The mantle is grey, and the tail and wings black, the latter having either one or two white wing bars. Underneath, it is white, tinged with grey. A

W. Farnsworth

GREATER SPOTTED WOODPECKER. *Nearly everybody has heard the drumming of this shy bird*

Eric Hosking

GREAT GREY SHRIKE. *One of the less attractive habits of the " butcher bird " is to spike its prey on sharp thorns or wire, the corpses thus resembling a butcher's shop*

black stripe runs from the forehead through the eye to the ear coverts. The legs are blackish, and the beak hooked. The female is duller, and the young are clad in greyish-brown with barred underparts. The length is 9½ ins., and the tarsus 1 in. The wing span is about 10 ins., and the weight 3 oz.

The Great Grey Shrike's most characteristic position is a perch on the highest branch of a tree, or pole, where it keeps watch for its prey, whether mice, insects or other birds. Suddenly it swoops down, and the largest of the catch is carried away to be impaled on some sharp point, such as a thorn or barbed wire. A row of little corpses hanging in some thorn bush forms the " larder " of the " butcher bird ", as the shrike is often called.

The Great Grey Shrike seldom settles on the ground. Its flight is undulating and it has, in common with its relatives, a habit of constantly bobbing the tail up and down. All shrikes have a varied vocabulary of harsh, chattering calls, and the song is a medley of these. The calls of other birds are imitated.

In company with other shrikes, the Great Grey Shrike breeds in wooded country, heaths, plantations, orchards and gardens, and the nesting site varies accordingly. Both birds share the building of the bulky nest of twigs, moss and leaves, lined with wool, hair and feathers. The five or six eggs are laid in April and May, later in higher altitudes. Incubation

(chiefly by the hen) takes about 15 days, and both parents rear the young. Normally, there is only one clutch but, should disaster overtake the first nest or eggs, they will be replaced.

Small birds of many species form the diet of the Great Grey Shrike ; small animals and insects are also taken.

At one time, especially in Holland, this bird was trained to help in the catching of hawks. Tethered in some spot where it could take refuge, it was able to warn the watchers of the approach of a hawk before they could see it.

GREAT NORTHERN DIVER—Colymbus immer. This is the largest diver, and a common winter visitor to all coasts of the British Isles from September to May. It is most frequent in the north of Scotland, especially the Outer Hebrides and Shetland Islands, where it has been suspected of nesting but this has never been proved. Its breeding haunts are in Europe, mainly Iceland, north America and Canada.

In summer plumage, the Great Northern Diver is a very beautiful and striking bird. It is speckled black and white above, and is allwhite below ; its head is black, and the thick neck is banded with collars in black and greenish-purple glowing with a glossy sheen. The middle collar is striped evenly in black and white and a smaller black and white patch appears across the front of its throat. Its beak is very straight and powerful looking. Its legs are black and grey and the eyes red. The winter plumage is dark brown above, the white underparts remaining. Male and female are alike. The total length is 27 to 32 in. with a body of 17 to 20 in. The tarsus is 3·6 in., the weight 15 to 16 lb. and the wing span measures approximately 2½ ft.

The Great Northern Diver has a remarkable flight, despite the fact that the wings, set far back on the large body, seem quite inadequate to carry its weight. It rises with much difficulty from the water but, once on the wing, it can fly to a great height, the short wings beating rapidly. This flight is best seen in the Spring. Like all divers, it is awkward and clumsy on the ground and quite incapable of adapting itself to movement on land. In an emergency, however, it can get along surprisingly quickly, using its wings as well as its feet. An inquisitive bird, it is not difficult to attract its attention and there is a curious movement of its head from side to side. It is not very gregarious and little more than half-a-dozen birds will be seen at a time ; even on migration, great northern divers are only rarely seen in large flocks.

But the most remarkable accomplishment of the Great Northern Diver is its ability to dive and swim at speed under the water, again using its wings to help drive it along. One observer has reported that to catch flat fish, the bird turns on its back and puts its lower jaw beneath the fish. The longest and deepest dive recorded is for 69 seconds at a depth of 33½ ft.,

but dives lasting as long as two to three minutes have been claimed.

I went to Iceland in the Spring of 1953 to attempt to make a first recording in Europe of this remarkable bird. I was quite alone and after spending a few days in the capital of Reykjavik, I came to the conclusion that it was quite hopeless to find anyone who could give me information about the nesting haunts of the Great Northern Diver.

At this point, it is as well to remember that Iceland is a very wild country with an area of about 39,700 square miles. People tried to persuade me to go some thousands of miles north to the Arctic Circle, but as my time was limited, I went about 25 miles from Reykjavik to Lake Thingvallavatn, Iceland's largest lake, with an area of 25 square miles. How I managed to find some kindly person who took me in a boat sailing in all directions in an effort to find the nest of the " Himbrimi "—the Iceland name of the Great Northern Diver—was indeed a miracle.

My quest was ended when far away in the desolate wilderness, and on the last and smallest of the lake's eight islets we searched, I saw the two chocolate-brown eggs I was seeking ! A pair must be breeding ! And sure enough, in the far distance I saw the two birds peacefully swimming about. A day later, my tent and recording gear were established ten yards from their nest. I was marooned for 12 days and nights, and I often wonder now which were most on the watch, myself or the two birds which doubtlessly regarded me as some rare species !

The real recording started after five days when the strong wind, which had been blowing since my arrival, dropped. It is an experience which will remain with me always. The birds were silent and always swimming together. At three o'clock in the afternoon, they were both swimming very peacefully about 100 yards away, very often turning their necks towards me. Suddenly, I heard some very excited calls from both male and female, interspersed with a far-carrying laughing note. I would never have imagined that any bird could perform exactly like clockwork, but that is just what happened. Precisely for half-an-hour, the male and female would swim around, turning their necks towards me, uttering a large variety of their unique calls. This lasted for five hours, and I got many perfect recordings of the voice of a bird which few people have heard or are ever likely to hear.—EDITOR.

The Great Northern Diver breeds in large, deep lakes in lowland and mountainous

G. K. Yeates

GREAT NORTHERN DIVER. It was a case of patience being rewarded when the Editor went to Iceland to obtain a recording of this unique bird

districts, and one pair will lay claim to a whole lake. The breeding season is at the end of May and in early June in Iceland, but in some parts of America it may be earlier. The nest is usually on a small islet on the lake, or on a mound of tufted grass near the water's edge. Little trouble is taken to build a nest and any flat bit of ground suffices to house the two large, elongated eggs, chocolate-brown or olive-green in colour, with dark brown spots ; the second egg is laid about two days after the first, and hatching takes about 30 days. The young are fed for 45 days—at first by regurgitation and later with fish.

The Great Northern Diver feeds entirely on fish of various kinds. In north America the bird is known as the " Common Loon ".

GREAT REED-WARBLER — Acrocephalus arundinaceus. A close relation of the Reed-Warbler (*q.v.*), the Great Reed-Warbler has been recorded about a dozen times in the British Isles. It breeds throughout central Europe and in north Africa and Asia, wintering in the south. Only in size does it differ from the Reed-Warbler, but, owing to its heavier build, its movements are less agile. Its characteristic song is louder and harsher. The length is 7½ in. and the tarsus 1 in. The wing span is about 8¼ in. Insects of various kinds form the food. *See also* Eastern Great Reed-Warbler.

GREAT SHEARWATER—Procellaria gravis. The lovely South Atlantic island of Tristan da Cunha is the only known breeding place of this shearwater, but outside the breeding season, in company with other shearwaters, it wanders over the Atlantic Ocean. As a regular summer and autumn visitor to the British Isles, it is met frequently in Hebridean waters, off the south-west coast of Ireland and, less frequently, off the coasts of Devon and Cornwall. Only when storm-driven is it seen inland.

One of the larger shearwaters, the Great Shearwater is easily recognized by the black cap, formed by the white of the throat and breast extending almost round the back of the neck. A prominent white patch at the base of the tail is another distinguishing mark ; both these features can be seen from a distance. The mantle is dark brown and the underparts white ; the wings are long and narrow. The hooked bill, with its tubular nostrils, is dark, and the legs are brown. The length is 17 or 18 in., and the tarsus 2 in. ; the weight is 2 lb., and the wing span approximately 2½ ft.

The Great Shearwater can dive both from the air and from the surface of the water ; beneath the surface it swims with the wings. Its flight is typical, the bird gliding with rigid wings for long intervals over the sea. Especially when the migration season draws near, great

G. K. Yeates

GREAT SKUA. Famed for its dive-bombing tactics, the skua does not scruple to attack curious humans

shearwaters may often be seen in long rows on the water, all facing one way. The harsh and unmusical voice is heard when the bird is feeding—an unusual characteristic.

Few reliable details are available concerning the breeding habits of the Great Shearwater. It breeds in large colonies ; the one smooth white egg is laid in a burrow on the steep slopes of Tristan da Cunha, its only known breeding place. The open sea is its feeding ground ; but large numbers often assemble with much noisy quarrelling at fishing stations and dash greedily for the offal, showing little fear of Man. Fishing boats are also followed.

GREAT SKUA—Stercorarius skua. At one time the Great Skua, or " Bonxie " as it is often called, was almost, if not quite, extinct in the British Isles. Within recent years, however, largely thanks to the efforts of a local land-owner, it is once again an established summer resident in the Orkney and Shetland Islands. Indeed, it is so increasing its range, that it now threatens the strongholds of the Arctic Skua. It is essentially a maritime species, and Iceland and the Faroes are its chief home. It does not breed in America. In Winter, it wanders over a large area of the Atlantic Ocean, rarely being seen inland unless driven there by storms.

Large, fierce and powerful, the Great Skua is a sturdy-looking bird, clad in dark brown speckled plumage ; the colouring varies considerably, but the dark wings have a conspicuous white patch under and towards the tips. Underneath, the brown is lighter, with a reddish tinge. The bill is lightly hooked, and the legs are black. The length is 23 in. and the tarsus 2 in. ; the wing span is 4½ ft., and the weight 3½ lb.

The " dive-bombing " attacks of the Great Skua are well known to visitors to its breeding haunts in the Orkney and Shetlands. They are fierce enough to intimidate the boldest intruder. The normal flight is gull-like, but in attack—on human or bird—it is relentless, swift and powerful. The bird swoops down from a great height uttering just one grunt ; and, when attacking a human, just misses the head, though often dealing a blow with the feet as it flies past. The Great Skua both swims and walks, and it delights in bathing in, and drinking, fresh water.

During courtship both male and female practise wing-raising, accompanied by harsh, loud cries. Many other calls and shrieks of alarm or anger echo round the nesting sites. But outside the nesting season, the bird is almost silent. The breeding haunts are deserted in the Autumn until the approach of Spring.

The Great Skua breeds in colonies, and activity begins at the nesting site about April, though the main business does not get under way until May. In common with other skuas, a colony of great skuas always has a permanent look-out—a bird that is sitting at the entrance of the territory to give warning of any intruder. *See also* Skua ; Arctic Skua.

GREAT SNIPE—**Capella media.** Also called the "Woodland Snipe", "Solitary Snipe" and " Double Snipe ", this is a larger and darker bird than the Common Snipe (*q.v.*). The two birds closely resemble each other, but the Great Snipe is a rare passage migrant, principally in the Autumn, to the south and east of England ; it is only occasionally seen in Scotland and Ireland. It breeds in northern and middle Europe and Asia, wintering in Africa.

In addition to having a darker brown and more heavily barred plumage than the Common Snipe, the Great Snipe also has conspicuous white feathers at the sides of its tail, clearly seen in flight. The long bill is brown, and the legs grey. The length is 11 in., the bill being 2½ in., the tarsus is 1 in. ; the wing span is about 12 in., and the weight is 8 oz.

The Great Snipe has a unique spring display. At the assemblies which take place at dusk, the excited males run backwards and forwards exhibiting the white feathers in their raised tails. Usually silent on passage, the bird will utter only a guttural croak when flushed ; but in the breeding season it has a very individual warbling song, although it does not " drum " like the Common Snipe.

The Great Snipe chooses drier districts for its breeding than the Common Snipe. It will even frequent woodlands, as well as swamps, grassy marshes, wet meadows, and birch and willow scrub. The nest is only a depression in the ground, lined with grass and sheltered by the surrounding vegetation. The four eggs, laid in May, June, or July, according to the country, are buff, well marked in various shades of brown and grey. As far as is known, only one brood is reared annually.

Small slugs, insects and some vegetable matter form the food of the Great Snipe.

GREAT SPOTTED CUCKOO—**Clamator glandarius.** This member of the Cuckoo family breeds in countries near the Red Sea, north Africa and parts of Asia, and is very rare as a breeding bird in Spain, Portugal and the Balkans. It wanders infrequently to Britain ; but five only have ever been recorded here.

This is the cuckoo with the most striking appearance. A much more colourful bird than the common Cuckoo (*q.v.*), it is slimmer and sports a very conspicuous crest ; its upper parts are dark brown, liberally spotted with white, and the grey of its head merges into a large yellow throat and paler, unbarred breast. The bird's length is about 15 in.

Its calls in Spring are raucous, and have nothing in common with those of the common Cuckoo. The bird is also a parasite, its principal victims being the Crow family, and its eggs resemble theirs ; but the chicks of the Great Spotted Cuckoo do not always attempt to push out the rightful occupants of the nest, and all the young may be reared together.

GREAT TIT—**Parus major newtoni.** Although perhaps not quite so popular as the little Blue Tit, the Great Tit—also called " Ox-Eye "—is probably equally well known. The largest and most colourful of the tits, it is a species confined to the British Isles ; it is very generally distributed, but is less abundant in the north of Scotland and unknown in the Outer Hebrides. Woodlands, heaths, orchards, gardens and city parks are among its favourite haunts.

The Great Tit is attractively dressed in olive-green above and bright yellow underneath. The head and throat are a lustrous blue-black, which extends round the nape to form a circle round the conspicuous white cheeks. Down the centre of the yellow underparts runs a broad band of black. The rump, tail and wings are blue-grey, the latter having a white wing bar ; the outer tail feathers are white. As is usual among tits, the male and female are alike at all seasons ; but in the Great Tit the black band down the centre is narrower in the female. The young have a duller coloration. The length is 5½ in., and the tarsus is 0·8 in. The wing span is about 6½ in., and the weight 1 oz.

All tits have very similar habits, and the Great Tit follows the usual pattern of behaviour,

Eric Hosking

GREBE FAMILY, *Little Grebe on the floating nest which is favoured by all members of this family*

For text see pages 267 and 334

To face page 266

Gösta Hakansson; John Barlee

GREAT TIT. Great tits differ from all other tits in their belly-stripe, just discernible
in the Continental bird (left). On the right is the practically identical British bird

but is more inclined to be aggressive. It hops on the ground and has a weak flight, preferring to linger among the trees where it flies from branch to branch ; its longer flights are undulating. In the courtship and spring display, the male moves to and fro among the branches with his wings dropped, tail erect and feathers fluffed out ; much display of the black throat is also made.

Tits have a fine vocabulary, but the Great Tit's is the loudest, most extensive, and most varied of them all. It has, in fact, the distinction of using more notes than any other British bird ; and, so far, the Editor has counted 68 different ones. One of the most familiar notes has been rendered as " teacher, teacher ", and another reminds one of a saw being sharpened ; but there are many other variations, among them imitations of other birds, especially the Chaffinch. A continuous, low, whispered sub-song is closely related to the courtship season. Although there are excellent recordings of many of the calls of the Great Tit, it has so far proved impossible to record them all. Great tits can be heard in almost every month of the year, but their best performance is from the end of January until the first half of May.

The Great Tit often begins its breeding activities as early as the end of March. Almost any hole or crevice is regarded as suitable for the nest, including holes in walls, trees, rocks and stumps ; nests have been found in pumps, flower pots and letter boxes, and nesting boxes are greatly favoured. The nest is made of moss and well lined with hair and feathers. The eggs number from six to twelve, and are white, blotched with reddish spots. Hatching begins on the completion of egg-laying, and is done by the hen alone, the cock feeding her for a

fortnight. Both parents show great devotion in the exhausting duties of rearing their numerous family. Normally there is only one brood, but two have been known.

It cannot be denied that the Great Tit works some havoc among the buds of Spring and the fruit of Autumn, but the enormous amount of injurious insects eaten counter-balances this damage. One authority puts the number of insects taken by one pair in three weeks at 8,000.

The Continental Great Tit (*q.v.*), almost indistinguishable from the British bird, is an irregular visitor to this country.

GREAT WHITE HERON. *See* Large Egret. This work follows the modern practice of referring to the bird under the name by which it is generally known in countries where it commonly breeds, such as India.

GREBE. Family of exclusively aquatic diving birds (*Podicipidae*), usually frequenting rivers and fresh-water lakes, except on migration or sometimes in Winter, when they visit the sea.

The feet of grebes are broad, flattened and *lobed*, i.e. there are separate membranes on each toe. The wings are short and rounded, and there is virtually no tail. The legs are placed so far back that the bird stands erect like a Penguin. Its movements on land are ungainly, but it swims gracefully and is among the most expert divers, propelling itself downwards solely with the aid of its paddle-like feet.

Grebes seldom leave the water and usually build floating nests, moored to reeds and grasses. They can swim under water for considerable distances.

There are five species on the British list, described under their own names. The largest of them is the Great Crested Grebe, a common resident easily distinguished by its *blackish ear tufts* and, in the breeding season, its prominent chestnut frills on the side of its head. Perhaps the best known and most popular British species is the Little Grebe, or Dabchick, one of the most beautiful river birds, which is widely distributed throughout England and Ireland, and is also found in Scotland.

The Slavonian (or Horned) Grebe is another resident, distinguished by a broad golden stripe through the eye. The Red-necked Grebe visits our shores in Winter, and the Black-necked Grebe in Spring and Summer.

GREEN CORMORANT. Alternative name for Shag (*q.v.*), a bird very similar, though smaller, than the Cormorant.

GREENFINCH—Chloris chloris. Next to the Chaffinch, the Greenfinch or Green Linnet is the most common of the Finch family and can easily be spotted by any rambler in the country. A resident in Britain all the year round, it is also a visiting migrant, flocks of greenfinches arriving on the east coast of Britain in the Autumn and Winter and departing in the Spring. The Greenfinch is also a " two-way " local migrant in Autumn, for the British species has been observed in some Continental countries and vice versa.

The Greenfinch frequents almost any part of the countryside which is well supplied with trees, hedges, bushes and evergreens. It is easily identified by the bright yellow of the body under the wing and towards the tail, the rest of the bird being olive-green. It has the strong, solid bill of the finches. The female is more brownish in colour, with the yellow much subdued. The young are greyer, with brown streaks. The length of the Greenfinch is 6 in.,

S. C. Porter

GREENFINCH. *Apart from the Chaffinch, this is the most common finch to be seen in this country*

and its tarsus is only 0·7 in., with a wing span of 7 in., its weight is about 1 oz.

Sociable in its habits, this bird is found in company with sparrows, buntings and others. It also roosts in parties with other birds.

The flight of the Greenfinch is undulating, and resembles to some degree that of other finches. On the ground it is always said to hop, but the Editor has also seen it running.

Vocally this bird has characteristics which cannot be compared with those of any other British bird; its vocabulary has some remarkable variations, and there is no great difference between its calls and its songs. The long-drawn-out notes of the Greenfinch, repeated over and over again, are pleasant and familiar sounds on a warm summer day. Another typical note is a cheerful song reminiscent of an electric bell. Apart from these well-known songs, there are many other varying notes based on the same theme. Singing continues from about mid-March to August.

The courtship of the Greenfinch is marked by a peculiar " batlike " song-flight, in which the male circles round and round with wings flapping slowly. The bird also displays with an expanded tail and with wings opening and closing, and offers food to the female.

The Greenfinch's rather untidy nest is built by the hen alone in a tree, hedge or evergreen; it is constructed of twigs, moss, grass and wool, and cosily lined with hair and feathers. The breeding season begins in late April or early May; the eggs, numbering four to six, are a dirty white colour, tinged with brown and green, and vary considerably in shape. Hatching, which takes about 14 days, is done by the hen alone, but the male feeds her on the nest. Both birds feed the young for about 16 days. It is recorded that some young have remained in the nest until Autumn. There are two broods and sometimes three.

The Greenfinch is one of our most useful birds; for its diet consists of seeds of all kinds, and although it occasionally nips off the buds of fruit trees and flowers, it amply makes up for this by clearing arable land of many weeds. Insects are also eaten and are the principal food of the young.

GREEN-HEADED BUNTING. Local name for Ortolan Bunting (*q.v.*), because of the cock's greyish-olive head.

GREEN-HEADED WAGTAIL. One of the five known geographical races of the Yellow Wagtail (*q.v.*) group, and the only one to breed in this country. The Yellow Wagtail group (*Motacilla flava*) is at present under revision, and a new classification may have been formulated by the time this Encyclopedia is published.

GREENISH WARBLER—Phylloscopus rochiloides.
The inclusion of the Greenish Warbler in the list of British birds rests on one appearance in Lincolnshire in 1896. It breeds in Russia and Siberia, wintering in India and Ceylon. The green in the plumage is deeper than in that of the Willow-Warbler (with which it has otherwise much in common), and a distinct yellowish-white bar appears on the wings. The voice is louder and more powerful. The length is 4½ in., the wing span is 6 in. and tarsus ¾ in.

GREENLAND FALCON—Falco rusticolus candicans.
One of the three gyr falcons (q.v.), the Greenland Falcon breeds in north Greenland and Arctic Canada, and is an irregular autumn and spring visitor to the British Isles—principally to the Scottish islands and the north and west coasts of Ireland but it rarely visits England. It is an extremely handsome and noble-looking bird, in white plumage covered with dark bars and markings. Its plumage varies in detail, but no similar bird is likely to be seen in the north, save perhaps a Snowy Owl, which could be confused with it, although certainly not at close range. The Greenland Falcon's beak is hooked, with yellow cere, and it has yellow legs. Its behaviour, habits and size are similar to those of the other gyr falcons. Its weight is 2½ lb., the female being the larger.

The breeding sites of the Greenland Falcon are on the wild and desolate rocky cliffs of the Arctic, and this type of country is always frequented. The bird has the typical flight of the falcons, but observers report that the Greenland has not the speed or mastery of the air of either the Gyr or the Iceland Falcons. Its voice has the high-pitched screaming note of its kind, but outside the breeding season it is generally silent.

There are few trees in the solitary wastes where the Greenland Falcon breeds, and it must of necessity lay its eggs on the steep cliff-sides. It builds no nest, but as the same spot is used year after year, the debris left from all the broods forms a heap which can be seen from some distance. Three or four eggs, closely resembling those of other falcons, are laid in May ; only the female appears to hatch them, the time being about a month. The food for the young birds is provided by the male, and it is only possible for one brood to be reared in a season.

Small animals and birds of all kinds form the food of the Greenland Falcon, which seems to have a special liking for the domestic pigeon ; in Saxby's *Birds of Shetland* an instance is recounted of a Greenland Falcon in pursuit of a pigeon, which it chased into a kitchen where farm labourers were having their meal.

Eric Hosking

GREENLAND WHEATEAR. *This is altogether a darker and larger bird than the common Wheatear*

GREENLAND REDPOLL. Alternative name, commonly used in older ornithological works, for Greater Redpoll (q.v.).

GREENLAND WHEATEAR — Oenanthe oenanthe leucorhoa. It is only as a brief passage migrant in Spring and Autumn that this wheatear appears in the British Isles. It breeds in north-east Canada, Labrador, Greenland and Iceland, wintering in the U.S.A. and west Africa. This subspecies so closely resembles the common Wheatear (q.v.) that identification, even by an experienced watcher, is often difficult. It is, however, a slightly larger bird and is distinctly darker on the mantle and wings, while the underparts are a deeper shade of buff. In every other respect—flight, behaviour and breeding habits—it resembles other wheatears. The breeding season is in June, and two broods are often reared. The length is 6 in., and the tarsus 1 in. The wing span is about 10 in., and the weight less than ½ oz.

There has always been argument as to how the hard sharp note of the Greenland Wheatear is produced—whether it is, in fact, vocal or mechanical. In the isolation of an uninhabited island the bird is not very shy, and I have been able to get quite close to its calling post. I have thus been able to establish the fact that the first note of its call is produced by a clipping of the bill ; this is followed by a whistling note which, naturally, is vocal.—EDITOR.

GREEN LINNET. Alternative name for Greenfinch (q.v.), a common British resident.

GREEN PLOVER. Local name for Lapwing (q.v.), a member of the Plover family, whose black and white plumage appears a brilliant green (and white) in bright sunlight.

G. K. Yeates

*GREENSHANK. This solitary wader seems to be ever on the watch for intruders;
yet the Editor managed to get close enough to its nest to record a Greenshank's birth*

GREEN SANDPIPER—Tringa ocrophus. As a passage migrant in the Autumn and Spring, the Green Sandpiper is fairly frequently seen throughout the British Isles—but not in Ireland during the Spring. It is also an occasional visitor in Summer and Winter and has, in fact, been recorded in every month of the year. In 1917 it bred in Lakeland; although no other occasions have been proved, several suspected attempts have been reported from various counties. The species breeds across Europe and temperate Asia, wintering in the south.

Its name is rather misleading, for the only tinges of green about the bird are the greenish legs and bill. In the main, the general appearance and behaviour are very like those of the Common Sandpiper (*q.v.*). The Green Sandpiper is, however, a larger and considerably darker bird, and its white rump, tail and underparts, in contrast to the dark brown mantle, are easily recognizable, especially when it rises. The length is 9 in., and the tarsus $1\frac{1}{4}$ in. The wing span is about 12 in., and the weight $3\frac{1}{4}$ oz.

The Green Sandpiper is rarely seen on the seashore; it is essentially an inland species, haunting the vicinity of rivers, streams, lakes and ponds. It has an erratic flight, rising easily to great heights and tumbling and twisting in the air much in the manner of snipes. On the ground it walks or runs.

The courtship display is typical of the waders: the birds bow with lowered heads, wings dropped, and tails outspread and raised, and both male and female indulge in the game of " leap-frog ".

The Green Sandpiper will almost always utter its individual, clear and musical call on rising. Many other variations are heard on the ground and on migration.

Its breeding season varies with the country frequented from April to June—even July in

Siberia. A peculiar breeding habit of the Green Sandpiper is its preference for the old nests of other species; nests of the Fieldfare, crows, thrushes, Blackbird, Jay and Shrike (to name a few) are taken, little fresh material being added. Forks in trees, where pine needles have lodged, are also used. The hatching of the four olive-brown and spotted eggs, taking 20-23 days, is done chiefly by the hen, as well as the first attention to the young; later, the cock takes on *all* the domestic duties. One brood is reared.

Insects and their larvae form the chief food of the Green Sandpiper. *See also* Sandpiper.

GREENSHANK — Tringa nebularia. Only in the wild and desolate regions of the Highlands and islands of Scotland does this bird breed in Great Britain—and even there it is far from abundant. It is, however, a widespread passage migrant along the south and west coasts of England, Wales and Ireland, and sometimes one or two may remain to winter. The Greenshank is widely distributed through Europe, breeding in Scandinavia, Finland, the Baltic States and in many countries in Asia. It winters in the south, reaching as far as Australia and the Cape.

The chief distinctive marks of the Greenshank are its long green legs and feet—whence its name. It has much the same build as its close ally, the Redshank (*q.v.*), but it is larger and taller, and has a slightly curved bill. The mantle, head and wings are greyish-brown, the latter showing no white. The underparts, breast, tail and rump are all snowy white. In Summer the throat and neck have very conspicuous dark spots. The length is 12 in., the tarsus $2\frac{1}{4}$ in. The wing span measures about $1\frac{1}{2}$ ft. and the weight is 7 oz.

A solitary and shy bird, the Greenshank seems to be ever on the watch; outside the breeding season it is usually seen alone, or with only one or two others. On migration, however, considerable flocks have been seen. The flight and movements have much in common with those of the Redshank ; there is the same nervous habit of bobbing the head when scenting danger or intrusion, and both male and female will mob an intruder. At times the bird stands for long periods on one leg. Nature has provided the Greenshank with perfect camouflage, and it is almost impossible to see the hen when she is sitting ; one can be actually within touching distance and she will not rise.

The Greenshank's call notes are lower than the Redshank's and, when it is flushed, there is a typical alarm note. The breeding calls are many and varied, with long repetitions of the normal " excitement call". There are also several short calls for communication between parents and young. The song in early Spring, uttered perching or in flight, is a wonderful wavering sound, especially if heard coming nearer and nearer, then fading again in the distance. Otherwise the male has a very long, constant and sustained call. The female's vocal contribution is not impressive in the last stages of hatching ; when the egg shells are on the point of cracking, she has a totally different, almost raucous note. A whistling is heard from the chicks some 24 hours later, when they are out of the nest ; this can be heard ten or more yards away.

The Editor journeyed twice to the Scottish highlands to obtain the first records of the Greenshank's song. In May, 1946, after almost insuperable difficulties his patience was finally rewarded :

> History was made within the next twenty-four hours, for at last I managed to record the birth of a Greenshank. I heard the burst of the egg-shells, the piping of the young, and the mother talking to them.—EDITOR.

But it was not until his second journey to the same spot in the following Spring (mid-May, 1947), that real success came, again after much patient waiting :

> My Scottish engineer friend and I placed the microphone near a little greenish-yellow water, a possible Greenshank feeding ground. But the bird may sing anywhere within a radius of 20 miles or more. Would he oblige me by flying over the tiny microphone, and should we be able to pick up his song ? No sound was heard in the first 24 hours. Then Jimmy was walking on the moor about 4 a.m., when he suddenly heard the Greenshank's familiar alarm call about half a mile from our recording machine. Without hesitation, we decided to shift our studio, and the effort was rewarded. We recorded a beautiful display song within a fair distance of our position.—EDITOR.

Desmond Nethersole-Thompson's recent book on the Greenshank has added much to our knowledge of this rare bird. The courtship follows to some extent the wader pattern : the male and female rise excitedly in the air with wings shivering, soaring high ; uttering their breeding calls as they glide down. There are bowing and wing-lifting ceremonies, and " leap-frog " is one of their favourite games.

March sees the arrival of the Greenshank at its breeding place on the lonely Highland moors and loch-sides, often near boggy land. The nest, a hollow in the ground and never far from water, is made by the hen, with the cock in attendance ; it is lined with heather, leaves, pine needles and bits of wood. The breeding season is in May, and the long-pointed eggs with their whitish ground colour are laid at intervals of two days. They are hatched out by both male and female, the duration being 25 days. The chicks are striped buff and black, with white underparts. Both parents tend and rear the one brood. The chicks are able to fly and look after themselves in about a month, and attain adult plumage after a year.

The Greenshank feeds entirely on animal matter, and in contrast to many other members of the Sandpiper family, will chase and catch fish. *See also* Sandpiper.

GREEN WOODPECKER—Picus viridis pluvius. Of all woodpeckers likely to be seen in Great Britain the beautiful Green Woodpecker is the largest and best known. Once seen— and this is not easily done even when the bird can be heard—its appearance is unmistakable. Essentially a bird haunting ancient trees in woods, heaths, commons, parks and large gardens, it breeds throughout England and

John Markham

GREEN WOODPECKER. *The nest, a round hole bored in the decayed trunk of a tree, is unique*

G. K. Yeates

GREEN WOODPECKER. A typical shot, showing the bird using his tail and claws to climb trees

Wales ; it is rarer in Scotland, but in recent years has shown a tendency to widen its range. In Ireland it is practically unknown, the last appearance being in 1854. Abroad, it breeds in many parts of Europe and south-west Asia.

The Green Woodpecker is rather stoutly built and has a most decorative dress—dark olive-green above, with underparts in a paler shade, and with a brilliant red cap extending to the nape. The eye has a surround of black and, in the male, the centre of the moustachial stripe is bordered in red ; in the female the stripe is wholly black. Apart from that, the sexes are alike. The rump is a bright yellowish green, most conspicuous in flight. The young are a lighter colour, mottled and barred, but with the adult plumage well defined. The bill is massive and chisel-like, well suited to its work. The length is $12\frac{1}{2}$ in. and the tarsus 1 in. The wing span is a little over 12 in., and the weight is 6 oz.

All woodpeckers behave in much the same way. Their mode of progress up the trunks of trees is well known, and that of the Green Woodpecker is typical. With its four strong, clawed toes—two in front and two behind—it climbs in a series of jerks, the stiff tail feathers pressed against the trunk to act as a support. It descends in the same way, tail first.

The Green Woodpecker is more inclined than other woodpeckers to feed on the ground, where it moves along in clumsy hops, and, although it avoids observation, it shows a greater tendency to come out into the open. Usually seen in pairs or singly, it is not gregarious. Although a heavily built bird, it has an easy undulating flight. At night it roosts in a hole in a tree.

It is difficult to get a glimpse of the Green Woodpecker, but its loud, rather demoniacal "laugh" or "yaffle", uttered in flight and echoing through the wood, proclaims its presence. One of the most prolonged bird calls, it is a curious and unique sound, and has a far-carrying quality. Most frequent from January to June, and again in the Autumn, it can be heard at all seasons. The alarm call is a prolonged note equal in tone to the "yaffle". The young make an astonishing variety of noises in the nest. Instances of "drumming" during the breeding season (a characteristic of the Greater Spotted Woodpecker) have been recorded, but it is not a regular habit of the Green Woodpecker. In display the male pursues the female round the trunks of trees. The rival males sway from side to side, with wings outspread, tail fanned and crest raised.

The nest of the Green Woodpecker is unique. It bores a circular hole in the trunk of a decayed tree—sometimes only a yard from the ground but usually higher—and here, on some wood chippings as the only nesting material, the five to seven white eggs are laid at the end of April. Both male and female share the duties of hatching, which takes about three weeks, and of rearing the one brood.

In common with other woodpeckers, the chief food of the Green Woodpecker is insects dug out of the trunks of trees ; its "tapping" as it progresses along the trunk is a familiar woodland sound. It captures insects with its long tongue, which is specially adapted for this work. It has also, however, a special liking for ants, and this no doubt explains its frequent appearances on the ground. During Winter, berries, acorns and nuts also form part of the diet.

Local names for the woodpecker are "Rain Bird" and "Yaffle"—the latter from its call.

GREY CROW. Local name for Hooded Crow (*q.v.*), the only member of the Crow family to have a grey rump, shoulders, mantle and underparts. Another local name is "Hoodie".

GREY FLYCATCHER. Alternative name for Spotted Flycatcher (*q.v.*), the most undistinguished-looking of all flycatchers.

GREY - HEADED WAGTAIL — Motacilla flava thunbergi. This bird sometimes visits the British Isles as a rare vagrant from its breeding grounds in the Scandinavian countries, the Baltic States, Russia and Siberia. It winters in tropical Africa. Experienced observers identify it from the pattern of the head plumage, which is slate-grey with dark ear coverts ; it does not possess the white eye stripe which is a distinguishing mark in many of its family. In all other respects—behaviour, habits and size—the Green-headed Wagtail resembles other wagtails, its voice having a close resemblance to that of the Pied Wagtail. *See also* Yellow Wagtail.

GREY LAG-GOOSE—**Anser anser.** This is the only " grey " goose to breed in the British Isles. A century ago it used to nest on the moors and marshes of England, but today it breeds only in a few districts of the north of Scotland and some islands in the Hebrides, and it is said to be decreasing even there. It still comes to England, however, as a winter visitor and passage migrant from October to March. Abroad it breeds in many European countries, especially in Scandinavia and Iceland.

All grey geese are extremely difficult to identify at a distance, and the Grey Lag is no exception. It is the nearest relative of the domestic goose, and is very like it in build, although smaller and slimmer. Its chief characteristics are the pink legs and feet, and the orange bill, which has no black on it ; the nail (the tip of the upper mandible) is white or brownish. The head and neck are light brown, the mantle is greyish-brown, darkest on the wings. The breast and underparts are a light bluish-grey, the breast being sometimes spotted with black. The grey tail is tipped with white, and the upper and under tail coverts are pure white, very conspicuous in flight. The drake and the duck are alike but the duck is smaller. The Grey Lag-Goose is 30–35 in. long, the body being 20 in. ; its tarsus is 3 in. Its weight is about 10 lb., and its wing span varies from 2¾ ft. to just over 3 ft.

In general the habits and behaviour of all grey geese are more or less similar. In the air the Grey Lag seems at first glance to be slow, but its measured wing beats actually carry it along faster than one would imagine. Grey lags fly in " V " formation, and it is said that each bird has its appointed place, with the leader at the head of the flock. Often a group will perform some wonderful aerial evolutions, including plunging through the air with half-folded wings.

The Grey Lag has a stately and graceful walk and can run with some speed. It is a good swimmer. Its voice is reminiscent of the farmyard goose's hiss. Outside the breeding season, grey lags are gregarious, forming flocks which number hundreds and even thousands.

This bird of the open country haunts salt- and fresh-water marshes, bogs, lakes, lagoons and any inundated land. In Scotland, the breeding season (which is in April) finds the Grey Lag on the heather moorlands and on islands in lochs or off the coast. Its large nest, placed among rushes or thick heather, is built of heather, sticks, grass and moss, with down added until the eggs are concealed. The dull creamy-white eggs vary in number, but four to six are usual. The female hatches them alone, but both parents look after the young for approximately eight weeks. One brood is brought out in a season.

The Grey Lag feeds by day on grasses and vegetation of various kinds. It is said to be very fond of grain, but the bird usually visits cornfields only at night.

GREY PHALAROPE—**Phalaropus fulicarius.** Of the two phalaropes—the Grey and the Red-necked—likely to be seen in the British Isles, the Grey is only a passage migrant in the Autumn, occasionally in the Spring, to the east and south coasts of England, and is rarely seen in Scotland or Ireland. It breeds in the Arctic region, and its haunts nearest to Britain are Greenland and Iceland. After a strong south-west gale, many are driven on to the sea shore in the south of England and Wales. In Winter the Grey Phalarope travels as far south as Chile and New Zealand.

The behaviour of the Grey Phalarope is unique, for it completely reverses the usual status of the sexes. It is the hen which is clothed in bright colours and makes the " advances " in the Spring ; the dull-looking cock takes on all the arduous domestic duties

G. K. Yeates

GREY LAG-GOOSE. *Our domestic geese are descended from this stately bird of marsh and mere which is, unfortunately, becoming increasingly rare*

of hatching, rearing and tending the brood, with the hen in complete control of operations.

In summer plumage, the female Phalarope has a rich chestnut breast and underparts, and a dark brown head with conspicuous white patches round the eyes. The mantle is dark grey with brown streaks and there is a white bar on the wings. The bill is yellow, with a dark tip. The male is duller in colouring, and has a black bill with a yellow tip. In winter plumage, both male and female are grey above, with white head, breast and underparts. Unlike those of many wading birds, the feet of the Grey Phalarope are not webbed, but have lobes on the points of the toes similar to those of coots and grebes. The length of the bird is 8 in., and the tarsus 0·9 in. The wing span is about 11 in., and the weight 1 oz.

An extremely tame bird, the Grey Phalarope appears indifferent to human approach and can, therefore, usually be watched with ease. It delights in swimming—which is not at all usual among sandpipers whom, despite its small size, it much resembles—and rides buoyantly on the surface, bobbing up and down and darting here and there after insects, like a tiny gull. Its flight is erratic and weak over short distances, but it must possess great stamina to carry it over the immense distances of its journeys to the south. The voice is a low whistle with some unpleasantly grating variations ; a continual chattering is heard in the vicinity of a flock.

The Grey Phalarope breeds in small colonies on marshy ground near freshwater pools, on fjord islands, and on shingle banks. The nest is a mere hollow among stones, sometimes, but not often, lined. The four eggs, laid in June or July, vary in colour from ground to umber. The hatching of the eggs, and the tending and rearing of the one brood, is done by the cock, occasionally assisted by the hen.

The food of the Grey Phalarope when inland comprises chiefly insects and molluscs taken from water weeds.

Sportsmen name this bird the " Coot-footed Sandpiper ". In north America it is known as the Red Phalarope.

GREY PLOVER—Charadrius squatarola. This regular winter visitor and passage migrant can be seen in most months of the year on all coasts of the British Isles, most abundantly on the east. It breeds in all Arctic regions of the world and in Winter is widely distributed, reaching as far south as Africa, Australasia and south America.

The Grey Plover resembles the resident Golden Plover (*q.v.*), but is larger and more stoutly built. In place of the gold spangles on the back of its relative, its summer plumage of dark brown is spangled in silver grey—a fact which has given it the name of " Silver Plover ". The cheeks, throat and underparts are black, and the white of the forehead extends behind the eye, becoming broader and very conspicuous against the dark breast and underparts. Further distinguishing marks are a black patch on the underwing, and the white rump and under tail coverts. The bill is black, and the legs are blue-grey. The Grey Plover has also a tiny hind toe which is absent in the Golden Plover. The winter plumage is a more uniform brownish-grey, with white in place of black underneath. The length is 11 in., and the tarsus 1 in., the weight is 7 oz. and the wing span about 1½ ft.

Essentially a shore bird, the Grey Plover is rarely seen inland. It is gregarious, and goes about in small parties, in company with other shore birds. Although shy by nature, it will defend its nest and young against any intruder. Its flight is swift and powerful, with deliberate wing beats ; on the ground it runs quickly, catching insects along the shore.

At times, the Grey Plover is a noisy bird, especially when in company with others. Its

R. P. Bagnall-Oakeley

GREY PHALAROPE. *In its winter plumage, this bird is a study in grey and white ; in Summer, however, the underparts are a beautiful chestnut*

R. P. Bagnall-Oakeley

GREY PLOVER. Unlike the Golden Plover, its close relative, this shore-bird is merely a winter visitor and passage migrant to the British Isles, breeding only in Arctic lands

voice bears some resemblance to that of the Golden Plover, but the tone is shriller and higher-pitched. Much of the courtship display takes place on the wing, the male plunging to the ground and rapidly rising again. This is one of the species that use "injury feigning" to distract attention from the nest.

The breeding season is from May to July, according to the country frequented. The boggy parts of the Arctic tundra form the breeding ground, and the nest, usually placed on the top of a ridge, is a circular hollow scraped in the ground, lined with moss and lichen. The four eggs are very similar in shape and colour to those of the Golden Plover. Male and female share the hatching for 23 days, and both also tend and rear the one brood.

Little is known of the food taken when breeding, but on passage the Grey Plover feeds on insects and vegetable matter. In north America the bird is known as " Black-bellied Plover ".

GREY-RUMPED SANDPIPER — Tringa brevipes. Only two specimens of this sandpiper have been recorded in Britain. It breeds in north-eastern Asia, and winters in the south, sometimes as far as Australia. The same size as the Redshank, it is very like the Knot, but an expert would recognize it by its uniform grey mantle, shorter bill and dull yellow legs. The length is 9½ in., and the tarsus 1 in. The wing span is about 16 in.

Very little information is available concerning the habits, behaviour and voice of this Sandpiper, but they are presumed to be similar to those of its American counterpart, the "Wandering Tattler ", which breeds on Alpine river banks. Four eggs are laid in a hollow of a shingle bed in June or early July. The hen hatches the eggs, but the male takes the chief part in

rearing and tending the young. Little is known about the bird's food, but one shot in Siberia had insect larvae from the icy water of glacier streams in its stomach. In north America the bird is called " Polynesian Tattler ".

GREY SEA-EAGLE. This is the American list's name for the White-tailed Eagle (*q.v.*), also sometimes known as Sea-Eagle.

GREY SHRIKE. *See* Greater Grey Shrike ; Lesser Grey Shrike.

GREY WAGTAIL—Motacilla cinerea. One of the most attractive and charming of small birds, the Grey Wagtail is present in the British Isles all the year round. It is necessarily confined to the neighbourhood of water, and in Summer, wherever swift-flowing, rocky becks and streams are found among the hills and mountains, this graceful and active wagtail will delight the eye as it flashes past, bounding from rock to rock. In Winter, it moves to lower ground and haunts weirs, streams and cress-beds, even appearing in pools or waterways in town. The Grey Wagtail is found in all suitable country in Europe, Asia and Africa.

This is the most graceful of all wagtails— those lovely and delightful birds—not only because of its colouring, but also because of its dainty and elegant body and slender tail, which is exceptionally long even for a wagtail. It could be, and often is, confused with members of the Yellow Wagtail (*q.v.*) group, but the latter more often frequent meadows and pastures.

The Grey Wagtail is blue-grey on both head and mantle, and the underparts are a brilliant yellow ; the dark brown wings are tipped with white. The outer feathers of the long tail are also white, and a white stripe appears above and below the eye. In Spring and Summer the

S. C. Porter

GREY WAGTAIL. *Streams, specially fast-moving ones in hilly country, are its favourite resort*

male has a black throat, replaced by white in Winter. The female has less brilliant yellow colouring, and her throat is always white. The bill is thin and darkish grey. The length is 7 in., the long tail accounting for 3 in. ; the tarsus is 1 in. The wing span is about 8 in., and the weight a fraction of an ounce.

All wagtails are cheerful and lively, and the Grey Wagtail is no exception as it flits from boulder to boulder or perches on overhanging trees. When it is running swiftly on the ground, the tail moves constantly up and down, a characteristic that gives the wagtails their name.

Grey wagtails are no songsters. Unless one is near at hand, the feeble trill can scarcely be heard above the sound of rushing water. The call note, resembling that of the Pied Wagtail (*q.v.*), consists of a series of shrill notes run together, often uttered on the wing. The song is best heard in April, but a very sweet sub-song can be heard as early as March.

The courtship is a pretty sight : the male flits from perch to perch in pursuit of his mate, displaying his black throat, and brings gifts of food to the female who receives them with quivering wings and gestures.

The Grey Wagtail is usually seen alone or in pairs, rarely in flocks. Late April or the beginning of May is the breeding season. The nest is cleverly concealed in some crevice of the rocks, or on a ledge or in a hole of the river bank with over-hanging vegetation. Roots, moss and leaves are the materials used for the untidy nest, where four to six stone-coloured and brown-mottled eggs are laid. Both male and female hatch the eggs during a fortnight, and both also share the rearing of the young. As a rule only one clutch is brought out, but two are by no means unknown.

Great activity is displayed by the Grey Wagtail in getting its food. Insects are pursued on the ground and caught on the wing.

GRIFFON-VULTURE—Gyps fulvus. Breeding in the mountainous regions of southern Europe, in Africa, and as far east as India, the Griffon-Vulture rarely appears in the British Isles. In 1943 one young specimen was captured alive in Cork Harbour ; its body is now in a Dublin museum. There is another mention of one seen near Southampton, and two others appeared in 1927 in Derbyshire. These are the only recorded appearances.

A large bird of prey, the Griffon-Vulture has sandy-brown plumage, broad dark wings and a very short, dark, squared tail. The head and throat are pale buff and featherless ; round the neck is a large whitish ruff of long straggling feathers. The underparts are a lightish buff. Male and female are alike, and do not seem to differ much in size ; this is unusual among birds of prey, in which the female is usually the larger. The length is over 40 in. and the tarsus 4 in. ; the wing span is approximately 5 ft., and the weight is 18-20 lb.

However unprepossessing the bird may appear on the ground, in the air it is a magnificent sight as, with its great wings outspread, it soars and glides to great heights. It is generally silent, but weird sounds emanate from the breeding site. It is troubled with few enemies and may live for many years.

The Griffon-Vulture breeds in colonies in mountainous country. The nest is placed on the face of cliff ; material for its construction is almost non-existent, and only a few twigs and grasses are gathered together by both male and female. One large white egg is laid in February, and both birds share the hatching for nearly two months. The chick is fed on half-digested carrion by regurgitation, and remains in the nest for almost three months.

Carrion and putrified matter of all kinds are eaten. Long periods are spent on the wing searching for food, and a carcase will in a few seconds attract many vultures to quarrel around it. However disgusting the feeding habits of the Griffon-Vulture may be, it is a useful scavenger.

GROSBEAK. Birds belonging to the Finch (*q.v.*) family, or *Fringillidae* (*q.v.*) ; but, as their name implies, their bills are large and stout, unlike those of most finches.

Of the two grosbeaks on the British list (both described under their own names), the Scarlet Grosbeak, which is about the size of a sparrow,

GROUND BIRDS, *the smallest British one is the Quail*

For text see pages 277 and 440

is an irregular visitor from eastern Europe and is chiefly found in Scotland.

The Pine Grosbeak is a much larger bird, a little bigger than the Swallow, with a bill whose mandibles show a tendency to cross over at the tips—a tendency much exaggerated in the cross-bills (*q.v.*). The Pine Grosbeak has been recorded only four times in the British Isles.

GROUND BIRDS. Term loosely applied to the game-birds of the order *Galliformes* (*q.v.*). Members of this order are chiefly ground-dwelling birds who tend to take to the air only when flushed or alarmed. As the Latin name ("like a cock") implies, these birds, despite variations in size and in length and shape of tail, have chicken-like characteristics.

The two families of this order, *Tetraonidae* and *Phasianidae*, are described under their own headings; they differ chiefly in that the former have feathered tarsi, while the latter have unfeathered legs. Sizes of birds vary from the huge 34-in. long Capercaillie to the 7-in. long Quail.

The following ground birds (*Galliformes*) are on the British list (*see also* separate entries); Black Grouse; Capercaillie; Partridge; Pheasant; Ptarmigan; Quail; Red Grouse; Red-legged Partridge.

GROUSE. Familiar name of the *Tetraonidae*, one of the two families of the order *Galliformes* (*q.v.*). These are plump, chicken-like birds, chiefly ground-dwelling (*see* Ground Birds).

The following grouse appear on the British list and are described under their own names: Red Grouse; Ptarmigan; Black Grouse; Capercaillie. Of these, the Red Grouse is the most common bird breeding here; the Ptarmigan is found only in parts of the Scottish highlands; the Black Grouse, although resident in many places in the British Isles, is steadily decreasing in numbers; while the Capercaillie, a huge bird, has been successfully re-introduced in some parts of Scotland in comparatively recent years.

GUILLEMOT — *Uria aalge.* Two variants, the Northern Guillemot (*U. a. aalge*) and the Southern Guillemot (*U. a. albionis*), breed on many suitable cliffs in the British Isles. There is also a " bridled " or " spectacled " form—so called from a conspicuous white ring round the eye—which increases in numbers and in proportion to the common forms as one goes farther north, until in Iceland over half of all members of the *Uria aalge* species are found to be "bridled". The Bridled Guillemot is not, however, a separate species nor has it been listed as a separate race. Northern, Southern and Bridled Guillemots interbreed.

The Southern Guillemot is resident in Ireland and Great Britain as far north as St. Abb's Head in Berwickshire, but is not found generally between Yorkshire and the Isle of Wight. The Northern Guillemot breeds on the east coast of Scotland, in the Inner and Outer Hebrides, in the Orkney and Shetland Islands, and is also a winter visitor. Abroad, guillemots breed in many countries of northern Europe and in north Africa.

The Southern Guillemot is dark greyish-brown on the head and mantle, but on the wings there is a pure white bar. The underparts are pure white. The black bill is long and sharply pointed. In Winter the bird becomes browner, with white cheeks, chin and throat, and with a dark line running from behind its eye over its ear coverts. Its legs and feet are olive. The sexes are alike. The Northern form is similar, except that its plumage is darker. The length of the Guillemot is 18 in., and its tarsus is $1\frac{1}{4}$ in., its weight is $1\frac{1}{2}$ lb., and its wing span is $1\frac{1}{4}$ ft.

Outside the breeding season, guillemots spend their lives at sea, unless driven inland by storms. Their behaviour has a great deal in common with that of the Razorbill. The colonies of the Guillemot are, however, even larger, and thousands of the birds may be seen together, sitting upright on the narrow

GRIFFON-VULTURE. Not a pretty sight on the ground, these big birds of prey are magnificent in flight as, wings outspread, they soar effortlessly to great heights

G. K. Yeates

Eric Hosking

GUILLEMOT. *Spectacled guillemots are by no means rare, particularly further north. These awkward-looking birds are always found in huge colonies*

ledges of steep cliffs. The Guillemot is an expert swimmer, and spends most of its time playing and splashing on the surface, sometimes diving to a depth of as much as 30 ft. and disappearing for more than a minute. Like many other sea-birds, it shuffles along the ground with an ugly and awkward gait.

In proportion to its size, the Guillemot has the smallest wings of all British sea-birds, but its flight is fast and direct. It usually flies low over the water where it flaps noisily along, but it can travel at great speed. It has the whirring movement of the wings common throughout the Auk (*q.v.*) family. Although a silent bird at sea, the Guillemot has a great variety of barking and growling call notes, one of which has earned it the name of " Willock ". Guillemots are very restless birds during the breeding season, and a continual clamour echoes from their crowded colonies.

They arrive early at their breeding haunts for what appears to be preliminary survey, the Southern form sometimes as early as December ; but they soon go back to the sea, and it is not until the end of April that they return permanently to their cliff ledges. Further north the colonies are not full until much later in the Spring. Then begins the mating ceremony, the two birds bowing to each other with neck outstretched and, sometimes, intertwined. Mated birds rub bills, and pluck at each other's neck and throat.

The Guillemot makes no attempt to build a nest, and its one egg is laid precariously on a crowded ledge, very rarely in a crevice. Many eggs are lost, for, apart from the fact that at some colonies they are taken by the inhabitants for food, many are kicked into the sea when the birds rise in their thousands at some alarm.

The egg is large and varies greatly in colour ; some are a beautiful deep blue-green, others

are reddish-brown, and all have various streaks and blotches on them. It is a miracle that the egg is ever hatched out in so small a space, but this is finally accomplished by both parents after about four weeks.

The downy chick is looked after by the parents for some time, but it is very active, for in a few weeks it is in the water. Fish is the main diet of the Guillemot, but some vegetable matter is also eaten. The greatest enemy of the Guillemot, as of almost every other sea-bird, is the refuse oil which is discharged from vessels at sea and drifts to the shore. *See also* Oil Pollution ; First Aid.

The Guillemot has many local names besides " Willock " ; it is called " Scout ", " Wilmot ", " Longie " (in Shetland) and " Murre " (in America).

For other species, *see also* Black Guillemot ; Brünnich's Guillemot ; *further see* Cline.

GULL. Name applied to several genera of sea-birds belonging to the family *Laridae*, which also includes the terns (*see* Tern), to which the gulls are closely related. There are 15 species on the British List : Ivory Gull, Greater Black-backed Gull, Lesser Black-backed Gull, Herring-Gull, Common Gull, Glaucous Gull, Iceland Gull, Great Black-headed Gull, Mediterranean Black-headed Gull, Bonaparte's Gull, Little Gull, Black-headed Gull, Sabine's Gull, Ross's Gull and Kittiwake—all described in detail under their own names.

Gulls are long-winged swimming birds, with webbed feet and stronger, more robust bodies than terns, compared with which they have also broader wings for sailing through the air, and longer legs. The wings are not normally fully extended, but held with the joints markedly flexed so that the angles of the wrist are clearly apparent. The shape of the wing and the way in which it is held differentiates them from the Fulmar, which, like the shearwaters, flies with its narrower wings rigid and fully spread. Gulls have stout wedge-shaped bills, with the upper mandible slightly hooked at the tip, and usually square or rounded tails. Most of them are white with grey or black backs and wings, and most have dark wing tips.

They are beautiful to look at as they glide on the updraught of cliff or ship, masters of the wildest weather. We think of them as marine birds, but several species live inland for most of the year, and some also breed there.

During the day gulls forage at sea, often behind fishing ships or collecting the offal as it is expelled from some great ocean liner, or along the shore in search of shellfish and small marine life, or by lakes and rivers. Most species follow the plough eagerly. At night they withdraw to safe roosting places. In Summer, from April to July, the adult breeders live in their gulleries.

With the exception of the pelagic Kittiwake, which freely crosses the Atlantic, gulls remain within sight, or within a day's flight, of land. Some gulls will follow a ship across the narrow Straits of Dover, but not, for example, over the hundred miles between Southampton and the Channel Islands. Each gull has its territory of sea or land, a wide one in Winter, and smaller one centred on the gullery in Summer.

Herring-gulls are among the first to return to the gullery in spring, when the males take up their old nesting-sites—sometimes as early as January in the mild south-west. The females arrive later, and by habit approach the familiar ledge of rock or shingle where they nested the previous season. There is no evidence that the gull pair remain together all Winter.

The situation is different for the young gull breeding for the first time. After two or more years of immaturity, which is also the period of its greatest wandering, it returns towards the gullery, to find old birds in possession and hostile towards any intrusion upon their territory. It may take the young would-be breeder another year to establish a niche for itself, and to attract a partner. It may not find a niche at all in an over-populated gullery; in that case it may wander away and found a new colony.

Gulls are, however, gregarious by nature, and breed most successfully when they are in large numbers, which afford protection, stimulation and greater watchfulness against enemies. But although gregarious they are not really sociable, and vigorously defend a certain area round the nest, even to the extent of killing a neighbour's chicks. Gulls will also swoop down and strike the human intruder.

Gulls lay three richly coloured eggs (the Kittiwake two), which hatch in three to four weeks. The chicks are down-covered, open-eyed and precocious at birth, and in a day or two will run from the nest of seaweed and grass when disturbed; excepting again the Kittiwake, which is born on a tiny ledge nest stuck against a cliff. After a somewhat longer period the young gulls in their drab brown plumage are able to fly, and their parents gradually lose interest in them.

Largest of British breeding gulls, the Greater Black-backed, has greatly increased in numbers in the last hundred years. It nests on rocky islands and cliffs. Its black back, large size and whitish legs distinguish it from the smaller Lesser Black-backed Gull.

Commonest British gull is probably the Herring-Gull, as large as the Lesser Black-backed, but with pale legs and a delicate French blue mantle; it breeds preferably on steep cliffs, but sometimes, as abroad, it establishes its gulleries among sand-dunes and shingle. Almost as common is the Black-headed Gull, wearing a chocolate-coloured hood (in Summer only), and breeding by mountain pools and reedy lakes.

The true Common Gull, like the Black-headed, is a small bird, and frequently feeds inland. Resembling the Herring-Gull in colour, its bill is slender and legs are yellow-green.

Smallest and most charming of all is the Kittiwake, so named from its pretty wailing call familiar to those who have gazed on its gullery of nests clinging to niches on steep cliffs. It is exclusively a marine feeder, dipping lightly to pick up small fish, and pelagic larval forms of organisms living close to the surface. Unlike other young gulls, the young Kittiwake has a distinctive first plumage, with white head and striking wing and tail pattern of black bands known as the " tarrock " dress.

In this dress it has been known to cross the Atlantic; marked birds from Britain having been recovered in Canadian waters. *See also* Gullery.

Eric Hosking

GULL. The Lesser Black-back is one of the six gulls to breed in Britain. Its mantle, usually slate-grey, may vary from pale grey to nearly black

GULL-BILLED TERN — Gelochelidon nilotica. Breeding in many countries both of the Old and New Worlds, this bird, although it bred in Great Britain in 1949-50, is still only a rare vagrant here, appearing chiefly during May. Although larger, it closely resembles the Sandwich Tern (*q.v.*), the chief difference appearing in the gull-like bill which, as well as being shorter and stouter, is all black and lacks the yellow tip of the Sandwich Tern's. Both birds have the same silver-grey mantle, dark head and white underparts. The tail is dark and, in the Gull-billed Tern, perhaps less deeply forked. The legs are black. In Winter the head is almost white. The length is 15 in., and the tarsus 1 in. ; the wing span is about 2½ ft., and the weight 7 oz.

In the main this bird's behaviour and habits follow the pattern of other terns, but its flight is more gull-like and consequently less swift. Its voice is a characteristic laughing chatter.

Salt marshes and lagoons are the breeding haunts of the Gull-billed Tern, and the nests are grouped close together. A mere hollow in the sand or earth, lined with grasses, is all the preparation made for the four or five creamy-white eggs, which are laid in May. Both male and female bring out the eggs and rear the one brood. The food is varied and includes small animals, fish and insects.

GULLERY. Name given to nesting colony of gulls. Gulleries are very numerous in Great Britain, and are found inland as well as all along the coast line at all sea-bird stations. It is therefore more difficult than with some other colonial birds to specify individual localities, but the following list gives an indication of where large colonies of some of the more common species may be found :

Black-headed Gull ; Ravenglass, Cumberland, probably the largest (up to 10,000 pairs) in Britain. Many colonies in the Fen Country, Scottish, Welsh and Pennine mountain lakes and pools, often altering in size and situation.

Common Gull ; Small colonies, chiefly in Scotland and Ireland, low coasts, rivers, lakes, moorland pools.

Herring-Gull ; Breeds everywhere on cliffs and islands, sometimes on beaches and low ground. One of the biggest gulleries is on Lambay Island (probably 10,000 pairs), near Dublin.

Lesser Black-backed Gull ; Gulleries on Skomer and Skokholm Islands, off Wales, and on Lundy Island. Also many islands and cliffs and some moors in Scotland, Ireland and northern England. Often in small settlements with larger colonies of herring-gulls.

Greater Black-backed Gull ; Few large colonies. One of 100 pairs on Middleholm, Pembrokeshire, and several large ones on Scottish and Irish islands and cliffs, notably North Rona, Outer Hebrides. Also Channel Islands. Likes to breed on rocky islets and high cliffs.

Kittiwake ; St. Kilda, many Shetland Isles, Orkneys, Hebrides (Shiant Isles), Scottish and Irish islands have large colonies. Skomer Island has the biggest colony in Wales (about 2,000 pairs). Also Channel Islands.

GULLET. The passage from the mouth to the stomach. The oesophagus. *See* Anatomy.

GYPS. Genus of the family *Aegypiidae* of the order *Falconiformes*. It contains four species, mainly distributed over southern Europe, Africa and Asia. The only species on the British list is the Griffon-Vulture (*q.v.*).

GYR FALCON—Falco rusticolus. Of the three forms of Gyr Falcon—the Greenland, Iceland and Gyr—the last is an exceedingly rare visitor to the British Isles. None has been identified in recent years. It lives and breeds in Scandinavia, frequenting open country near cliffs where it can nest. It is somewhat like the Peregrine Falcon (*q.v.*) in appearance, but at a close view is seen to be larger, with a shorter tail and paler plumage. It is about 22 in. in length, with a tarsus of 3 in. As is usual among birds of prey, the female Gyr Falcon is larger than the male.

The habits and behaviour of the Gyr Falcon show little difference from those of the Peregrine, and its flight, too, is very similar as it swoops down from a height on its prey, though slower wing beats are recorded. Its voice is similar to the Iceland Falcon's. Four eggs, less colourful than the Peregrine's, are laid on a cliff ledge in late April, and one brood only is reared in a season. Small animals and many species of birds form its food. *See also* Falcon ; Greenland Falcon ; Iceland Falcon.

R. P. Bagnall-Oakeley

GULLERY. Colonies of kittiwakes, the prettiest gulls, are mostly in the Scottish and Irish isles

HERON

HABITAT. Most standard dictionaries define this in some such terms as " a locality where a species, race, person, animal, or plant usually lives or is found ". Ornithologists, however, draw a distinction between locality and habitat, and, as is explained under the heading Birdsnesting, between habitat and nesting site.

Although not every ornithologist attaches precisely the same *shade* of meaning to these terms, and in practice it is sometimes difficult to draw an exact boundary between them, the most generally accepted definitions are :

Locality. The geographical region or area in which a particular species is likely to be found, usually given in handbooks, etc., under such headings as " distribution ", " local distribution ", or, when applicable, " foreign distribution ". Thus one field guide gives for the distribution of the Nightingale, the " lowlands of southern England north and west to line Humber-Severn (though a few south Wales) and south across Somerset and Devon ".

Habitat. The type of *environment* in which a particular species likes to dwell, and for which it is structurally adapted. Thus the same guide says of the Nightingale : " Essentially a bird of the ' thickets ' in England, whether these are found as a bush storey in deciduous woods (e.g. hazel coppices with oak standards), along the woodland edge and deep lanes, or as a stage in botanic succession on their own, etc.".

It has been suggested that all primitive birds probably lived in trees. This is open to question, but one thing is now quite certain—that each kind of bird now has its individual prefer-

ences regarding places in which to live, and the type of environment it favours. Except during migration (*q.v.*), when they may be found in the most unlikely places, birds have strict limits of geography, habitat and vegetation, and are seldom discovered outside these limits. It is therefore essential for the bird watcher to know what these limits are. Furthermore, a knowledge of habitat may be helpful in distinguishing between species of somewhat similar appearance. Thus the Long-tailed Duck is likely to be seen only on salt water, but the Pintail, a duck which also has a longish, pointed tail, frequents fresh water. Similarly, the Wood-Warbler, which is a bird of the upper leaf canopy of beech and oak woods, will not be found on the low, bushy scrub where one would seek the Grasshopper-Warbler.

It is still a mystery why a bird should select one type of habitat in preference to another. James Fisher suggests in his *Watching Birds* that " psychological preferences for things like the height of song-posts, open or closed woodland, type of nest site and material and so on

John Markham

HABITAT. Redstarts are widespread, but locally distributed in this country. Their chosen habitat is scrubwood, like this one in Inverness-shire

281

may be as important in determining a bird's choice of world as his food preferences or tolerance of climate ".

Britain is rich in types of habitat, which may be broadly grouped as follows : (1) Woodland ; (2) Park or Garden Land ; (3) Agricultural Land ; (4) Heath and Moor ; (5) Alpine ; (6) Water ; (7) Coastland ; (8) Built-up Areas.

All of these, with the possible exception of (5) and (6), may be still further sub-divided. Thus, Woodland may be divided into coniferous deciduous, and mixed plantations, and again into the type of wood—alder, ashwood, beech-wood and so on. Not only may different species be found inhabitating different parts of the wood, or preferring certain types of trees, but they may also be in different layers. In some tropical forests there are as many as seven or eight such layers, one on top of the other, with special bird fauna in each. The woodland in such a situation is a typical example of what has been termed a " gross habitat " (i.e. it offers a dwelling place for many different species), within which may be found the specific habitats of several distinct species.

Because of changes in the vegetative covering of an area, birds either have to leave that area or change their habits. Thus, according to Lack and Venables, at one time, shortly after the last Ice Age, pine and birch forests extended well down to the south of Britain and were inhabited by the Crossbill, Siskin, Lesser Red-poll, Tree-Creeper, Coal-Tit, Willow-Tit, Crested Tit, and Black Grouse. When the coniferous belt retreated to Scotland, the crested tits, crossbills and black grouse retreated there also, whereas the more adaptable tree-creepers, coal-tits and goldcrests remained behind to colonise the oak. Similarly, black-birds and robins, who probably were originally birds of deciduous forests, have adapted them-selves to a man-made environment, as have bullfinches, hawfinches and greenfinches, who naturally frequent scrubland ; and pied wagtails, whose " natural " habitat is water meadow.

Information on the habitat of various species may be found in this Encyclopedia, in Witherby's *Handbook of British Birds*, in the various field guides, and in many other sources.

HAEMATOPODIDAE. Family of large wading birds of the order *Charadriiformes*. Its members are distributed over many of the sea-coasts of the world. It contains only one British genus, *Haematopus* (see below).

HAEMATOPUS. Genus of the family *Haematopodidae* of the order *Charadriiformes*. Its members are distributed over Europe, Asia, Africa, Australasia and north and south America, but only one species, the Oyster-catcher (*q.v.*), occurs in the British Isles.

HALF-CURLEW. Local name for Whimbrel (*q.v.*) This bird is closely related to, and in general appearance much resembles the Curlew, although it is much smaller in size.

HALIAEETUS (Latin, " sea-eagle "). Genus of large eagles of the family *Falconidae* of the order *Falconiformes*. Its members are dis-tributed over most parts of the globe except south America. It includes one species on the British list, the White-tailed Eagle (*q.v.*).

HARLEQUIN-DUCK — Histrionicus histri-onicus. This duck has been recorded only eight times in the British Isles — six times in England and twice in Scotland. It breeds in the north of Europe, Asia and Canada. There is no mistaking the gaily-coloured drake in his dark blue-grey plumage with rich chestnut flanks and a dash of the same colour over his eye. But his most dis-tinguishing features are the patches of white on the sides of face and neck, his white collar, the white line on his breast continu-ing over his back, and the white on his wings. The female Harlequin-Duck is much less

John Markham

HABITAT. Chiffchaffs, garden-warblers and the Nightingale all favour a woodland-edge habitat, and often the Nightingale may be heard near London

colourful. She is uniformly dark brown with two white spots in front of her eye and another, brighter, patch behind the eye and on the breast. In some ways she resembles the Long-tailed Duck with which she is sometimes confused. Both drake and duck are the same size and are 17 in. long, with a body of 11½ in. The tarsus is 0·47 in., the wing span about 1¼ ft. It weighs about 1¼ lb.

Harlequin-ducks are very sociable in breeding and many will nest together, especially on rocky islands in the middle of fast flowing rivers, sometimes even preferring to be near waterfalls. They are usually silent birds, but during the nesting season they have various display calls ; and they are also heard in Winter.

HARRIER. These birds of prey of the genus *Circus* are distinguished by their long tails, long wings (which are not pointed like those of the falcons) and by their long bodies. Their flight is more languid and gliding than that of the falcons and somewhat resembles the kites'. Harriers usually fly low over the ground, holding their wings in a shallow " V ".

Of the four harriers on the British list (described under their own names), the Marsh-Harrier breeds sparingly in England though it is known to have bred in Wales and Ireland ; while the Hen-Harrier breeds only in northern Scotland and possibly in Ireland. Both are also occasional visitors. Montagu's Harrier is a breeding visitor from April to October, with a rather local distribution in England and Wales ; and the Pallid Harrier has been recorded only three times in this country.

HARUSPEX (pl. *Haruspices*). Diviner of ancient Rome who interpreted the will of the gods from the entrails of slaughtered animals, or from extraordinary portents. The way in which the animals died, the flames caused when they were burnt and other particulars of their sacrifice were also taken into account by the *Haruspices*. The latter are not to be confused with the *Augurs* who were primarily concerned with approving or disapproving of a given course of action (*see* Auspices).

The *Haruspices*, were never so important politically as the Augurs, nor were they directly connected with the chief magistrates.

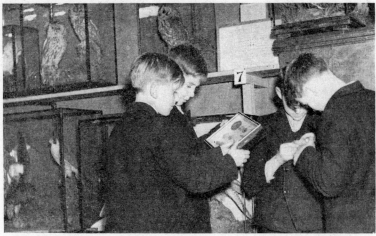

John Clegg

HASLEMERE. Children learn more from handling an object than from observation. Here the youngsters are deeply immersed in the study of owl pellets

HASLEMERE. Since it was opened in 1888, the Haslemere (Surrey) Educational Museum has set itself the task of explaining the countryside to the ordinary visitor, both young and old. While, as befits a museum, it maintains excellent collections of stuffed specimens, the accent in its teaching has always been on the living rather than the dead.

Children, for example, are encouraged to regard the splendid " Newdigate Collection of British Birds " (almost complete in species on the British list) as reference material to check or confirm some aspect of bird study encountered in the field. Perhaps the greatest value of such a collection lies in establishing the size of particular birds; and often the sight of a stuffed specimen, hitherto known only from illustrations, comes as a surprise. Thus the Kingfisher fails lamentably to come up to expectations, although some compensation is afforded on the one hand by the huge Golden Eagle, and on the other by the minute Goldcrest. Uncased specimens are also kept, since most children learn far more from handling an object than from merely looking at it.

Live birds that have, perhaps, been brought in damaged or have fallen from their nests are often on show for visiting school parties during the Summer. These birds are reared until they can fend for themselves, when they are released; but during their stay they earn their keep by providing interesting lessons on bird biology, which would be difficult with stuffed specimens.

In Spring and early Summer gramophone recitals of bird song are given, after which the children are taken into the museum's extensive wooded grounds to hear the actual birds. Other children's activities in the museum itself are : the dissection and examination of owl and other

S. C. Porter

HAWFINCH. *The young do not leave their nest for about eleven days, and during that time both parents are busy to keep their hungry offspring fed*

pellets and of pine-cones opened by crossbills, as an incentive to the outdoor study of the food of birds; games involving the identification of bird feathers; migration studies in which the children make their own maps, marking on them the routes of particular migrants and measuring the distances flown by referring to the ringing returns in the magazine *British Birds;* competitions with such questions as " Find and draw a bird in the gallery with two toes pointing forward and two backward " or " Find and draw a bird with a saw-edged bill ".

Daily nature items of interest are recorded on a notice board in the entrance hall; and children are encouraged to note down the arrival of summer migrants and the like, care being taken that the information is reliable.

Ornithological activities are not confined to children, for there are many lectures for adults by some of the leading bird authorities, special exhibits and, in recent years, residential week-end field courses on bird study which attract ornithologists from a wide area.—JOHN CLEGG.

HATCHING. This word is used in various senses, meaning (1) the emergence, or production, of a young bird from an egg ; (2) the incubation, or brooding, of an egg by a parent bird ; (3) also, it may describe a brood hatched from a single clutch (*q.v.*). *See also* Reproduction and Development.

HAVERGATE ISLAND. This bird-reserve of about 240 acres consists of low islets and shallow lagoons, whose water levels are controlled by sluices. It is famous as Britain's only breeding ground of the Avocet (*q.v.*). A few pairs first bred here in 1947 and, under careful preservation, a colony has grown steadily, numbering over fifty pairs.

Other breeding birds include Common and Sandwich terns and black-headed gulls. In late Summer and Autumn the bird-reserve is often crowded with passage waders of many species (including godwits, dunlins, ringed plovers, oystercatchers, spotted redshanks, redshanks, greenshanks, Common, Wood- and Green sandpipers, ruffs and reeves, red-necked phalaropes, little stints, curlews and whimbrels and some interesting transient species of birds.

In the winter months thousands of duck usually find sanctuary on the reserve, including Mallard, Wigeon, Teal, Shoveler, Pintail and Sheld-Duck ; while Pink-footed and Brent geese are occasional visitors.

The island belongs to the Royal Society for the Protection of Birds (*q.v.*). It was constituted a Nature Reserve (*q.v.*) in 1954 by an agreement concluded between the R.S.P.B. and the Nature Conservancy (*q.v.*).

HAWFINCH—Coccothraustes coccothraustes. Because of its extreme shyness, this resident British finch is often thought a rare bird. It is, however, well distributed, though somewhat locally, throughout England, except Devon and Cornwall ; but it is only found in certain areas of Wales and Ireland, and of Scotland.

Hawfinches are fond of company once their families have started to fend for themselves, and in Winter are found in flocks in wooded districts. They are not, however, always welcome in gardens and orchards, for they have a bad habit of raiding fruit trees and vegetable beds.

In appearance, the Hawfinch is unmistakable with its dumpy body, huge beak, which seems to out-balance the head, and its short tail. At close range, its plumage has most beautiful colourings of brown, russet, gold and white, the latter being very conspicuous when the bird is in flight or on the ground. The bill is gun-metal blue in Spring, horn-coloured outside the breeding season and in juveniles. The female Hawfinch has a duller plumage. The length is 7 in. and the wing span about 10 in., with a tarsus of 0·9 in. The bird weighs about 2 oz.

On the ground the bird moves in a series of hops with its top-heavy body held very upright. The Hawfinch flies with an undulating movement with wings beating rapidly. It is most attentive in courtship, the male bird constantly pursuing his mate with eager hops.

The song of the Hawfinch is simple compared with that of other birds and resolves itself into a sudden whistle which is not unmusical when uttered from the top of a tree—its favourite perch. Even this, however, is only heard in February or March, seldom later.

Hawfinches frequent woods, parks, gardens and orchards. The nest is a shallow construction in a tree or bush, sometimes on a horizontal branch and at a good*height from the ground. It is made of twigs and roots, lined with roots, wool and hair. The four or five eggs are laid in April or May ; they have a light-blue ground with bold, irregular spots of dark brown. They are hatched by the hen alone ; but the cock feeds her during her nine or ten days of sitting, and the young are fed by both parents for a period of about eleven days.

Its food consists of kernels and seeds of many fruits and trees. It is very fond of peapods.

HAWK-OWL—Surnia ulula. This rare visitor to the British Isles from its home in the northern European forests can be recognized, especially in flight, by its short, pointed wings and long, rounded tail. Its plumage is wholly brown, barred with white, lighter underneath and almost white on its throat. Its face is more hawk-like than owl-like, and is bordered with black, except under the chin. The length of the bird is 14–15 in., the tarsus 1 in., and the wing span about 2 ft. *See also* American Hawk-Owl.

HAWK, SPARROW. *See* Sparrow-Hawk.

HEARING. Next to sight, hearing is the most acute of all the senses in birds. Not only is their hearing much keener than that of Man, but they also have a wider frequency range (*q.v.*) so that they can detect sounds which are inaudible to us. It is also clear from the great variety of song and call notes in the bird world, as well as from the skill in mimicry shown by certain birds, that they can distinguish differences in pitch and tone. *See also* Song.

As in mammals, the organ of hearing consists of an outer, middle and inner ear ; but there is no external flap, or *pinna*, such as most mammals have, and in this birds exhibit their reptilian origin. The opening to the outer ear is generally surrounded by fine, hair-like feathers, arranged to collect sounds and pass them on to the ear drum. The outer ear itself consists mainly of a short membranous passage. leading to the middle ear.

The middle ear consists of the tympanic cavity, containing the tympanic membrane (or " drum ") and the *columella*, which together form a sensitive sound-conducting apparatus. They have the same arrangement as in the lizard. The columella, a tiny " rod " extending across the tympanic cavity, transmits vibrations from the tympanic membrane to the inner ear.

As in mammals, the inner ear is the most important part of the hearing organ. It contains the sound perceiving apparatus. The auditory nerve-endings are contained in a cavity called the *cochlea*, which differs from that of mammals in being only slightly, instead of spirally, coiled. The cochlea is most highly developed in owls and parrots.

As in mammals, there is in the inner ear a system of semicircular canals which function in connection with the sense of balance. There would appear to be some relation between these canals and a bird's flight habits, for they are most highly developed in " aerial " species like the Swallow, and less complex in the ducks.

HEART. *See* Anatomy.

HEATH-HEN. Local name for Black Grouse (*q.v.*), because of its preference for nesting near moorland or marshy ground.

HEBRIDEAN WREN—Troglodytes troglodytes hebridensis. Apart from the common Wren (*q.v.*) inhabiting the mainland, the Shetlands, St. Kilda and the Outer Hebrides have all their own peculiar Wren, which is confined to that part. All the island wrens are larger than their mainland relative. Smaller than the Shetland form, the Hebridean Wren has also lighter, less heavily barred underparts, but the behaviour and habits remain the same. *See also* Wren ; Shetland Wren ; St. Kilda Wren.

HEDGE-SPARROW—Prunella modularis. One of the most abundant of our song-birds, the Hedge-Sparrow has a most misleading name, for it has nothing whatever to do with the Sparrow family (*Passeridae*), which includes the House- and Tree-Sparrow. It is, therefore, usually called the *Dunnock* or *Hedge-Accentor*. It frequents nearly every part of the British

John Markham

HEDGE-SPARROW. *This songster has nothing in common with the House-Sparrow—despite its name*

Paul Popper

HELIGOLAND TRAP. *The entrance to the trap is on the right, hidden by bushes to provide the cover necessary to induce birds to " feel at home "*

constantly repeated, which can be heard easily from 50 ft. away. The song is at its best from January until July.

The Hedge-Sparrow may nest in any type of country abounding in commons, heaths, quiet roadside hedges, copses, spinneys and gardens, and it is often found in suburban shrubberies and gardens. The nest is built by the hen—while the cock looks on—of twigs, moss and leaves, lined with moss, wool and feathers. Four to five sky-blue eggs are laid in April, and are hatched by the hen for about a fortnight, while the cock feeds her. Both parents rear the two broods, which are regularly brought out each season, for another fortnight.

Isles, except some remote islands in the north of Scotland. Autumn sees some movement south, and some British birds cross the Channel, but the resident population of hedge-sparrows keeps fairly steadily at about three million.

The Hedge-Sparrow is dressed in shades of glowing browns and greys, and is as familiar to the countryman as the House-Sparrow is to the town-dweller. The wings, tail and back are brown; the head, neck and breast are slate-grey with brownish streaks; and the underparts merge into a paler grey. The thin bill is brownish-black and the legs flesh-brown. Both male and female are alike. The length is 5¾ in. and the wing span about 7 in.; the tarsus is 0·8 in. and the weight ¾ oz.

Quietly, attracting little notice, the Hedge-Sparrow is always there moving about the roadsides, hedgerows, copses, spinneys and gardens, foraging among the fallen leaves or perching on low bushes. It hops on the ground in an individual jerking manner, but does not run ; while feeding, it has a characteristic way of flicking its wings which has in some districts earned it the name of " Shuffle-Wing ". The flight is low, never for a long distance nor at any great height.

Early in the year, the male Hedge-Sparrow begins his courting, chasing his mate with wings outspread and constantly jerking, the female responding with much the same attitudes.

The voice of the Hedge-Sparrow is not so inconspicuous as its appearance. In the Spring, a short, high-pitched, most insistently repeated call note proclaims the bird's presence everywhere. It also has another short, warbling song,

One of the most useful of small birds, the Hedge-Sparrow feeds in Summer almost entirely on insects, many of them injurious to the farmer and gardener ; in Winter, seeds of various kinds take the place of insects.

The Continental Hedge-Sparrow is a spring and autumn passage migrant to the British Isles, and is so similar to the British bird that even an expert can distinguish between them only in the hand. The same applies to the Hebridean Hedge-Sparrow, except that the plumage of this bird is darker both above and below than that of either the British or Continental races. The song of the Hebridean bird is also thought to be lower-pitched than that of the mainland variety.

HELIGOLAND. This small island, about 28 miles north-west of the German mainland, lies exactly at the cross-roads of two of the main paths of bird migration (*q.v.*). It is here that, in Autumn, the southward-moving stream of birds migrating from western Scandinavia joins the westward-moving stream from Germany and the Low Countries before passing on to either Britain or France.

For this reason, the Heligoland migration station, established in 1910, proved of great value to British ornithologists. It is estimated that by the outbreak of the Second World War, when the station was transferred to Wilhelmshaven, on the mainland, over 1½ million birds had been ringed and registered at Heligoland.

Apart from ringing (*q.v.*), German scientists also used to mark certain birds with indelible ink.

HELIGOLAND TRAP. This type of trap, evolved by the Heligoland migration station, consists of an immense tunnel tapering gradually into a reception chamber, from which the birds may be taken for observation and ringing (*q.v.*).

The mouth of the tunnel, which may be over 30 ft: in diameter, is usually covered with bushes, shrubs and suchlike. The ease with which birds can be induced to enter the trap has led to its general adoption at migration stations. *See also* Observatory ; Research ; Trap.

HEN-HARRIER—Circus cyaneus. The end of the 19th century saw the virtual extinction of the Hen-Harrier as a breeding bird of the British Isles, a fate it shared with many other birds of prey, including the Marsh- and Montagu's harriers. The disappearance of the Hen-Harrier was not only due to the cult of game preservation, but also to the growing development of agriculture.

Today, the bird confines its breeding almost entirely to the Orkney Islands and to a few favoured haunts in the Outer Hebrides. It has, however, occasionally bred elsewhere in recent years, both in the Scottish Highlands and in England and Wales ; it is also a winter visitor and autumn and spring migrant. Abroad, the Hen-Harrier breeds in northern Europe, northern Asia and north America, wintering in Mediterranean islands, north Africa, India, the West Indies and Colombia.

This is the most handsome of British harriers. The male Hen-Harrier is predominantly blue-grey above, with paler throat and breast which merge into white. There is a prominent white patch on the rump which serves as a distinguishing mark from Montagu's Harrier whom the Hen-Harrier otherwise resembles closely.

The grey wings have black tips and the broad grey tail is tipped with white.

As is usual in birds of prey, the female Hen-Harrier is larger than the male, but she is also so different in appearance as to appear almost a different species. She is mainly dark brown, streaked paler on the head, with a conspicuous white patch over the eye and chin. Her underparts are streaked dark and pale brown and she also has the white rump patch. Her long, slender tail is barred in different shades of brown and has white tips. These differences in plumage have led to different local names ; the female Hen-Harrier is often called " Ringtail ", and the male " Blue-Hawk " or " Dove-Hawk ".

The beaks of both male and female are black and hooked, and the legs and eyes are yellow. The length of the male is 19 in. and the tarsus 2 in. ; his wing span is about 2½ ft. and the weight 1 lb. The female is 21 in. in length and the tarsus, wing span and weight are proportionately larger.

The habits and behaviour of the Hen-Harrier are typical of all harriers. It walks easily and quickly on the ground, often perching on a convenient rock or post. The flight is easy, buoyant and leisurely, usually low over moorlands or hillsides while hunting for prey. An expert in hovering, the Hen-Harrier frequently interrupts its progress in doing so. When gliding, the wings are held in a shallow " V ". The display flight of the male includes such antics as somersaults and dives, interspersed with chasing after the female. Rarely heard outside the breeding season, the voice of the Hen-Harrier is a series of quick, chattering cries and squeals.

Desolate moorlands and valleys are the Hen-Harrier's chosen nesting sites and the breeding

HEN-HARRIER. *The growth of farming led to the virtual extinction of this harrier in Britain. It is now breeding only in the Orkneys and, sometimes, the Outer Hebrides*

John Markham

season, in the Orkneys, is in May. The nest is merely a hollow in the ground and is lined, chiefly by the hen, with a thick layer of grasses, roots and heather; the whole is often surrounded by small branches of birch and heather sticks. Four to five bluish-white eggs are laid on alternate days. The hen incubates for three weeks, during which time she is called off by the male to feed on prey passed from foot to foot or "airborne". The young resemble the female. Both birds tend the young of the one brood for five or six weeks.

Small animals and birds of all kinds, chiefly caught unawares on the ground, form the Hen-Harrier's main food.

HERON—**Ardea cinerea.** Locally known as the Grey Heron, this is a breeding bird of the British Isles and also a winter visitor and passage migrant. Heronries are scattered throughout the country: Sussex, Surrey, Northants, Norfolk and Kent are favourite counties for breeding, but there is also a well-known heronry at Ravenglass (*q.v.*) in Cumberland. Many heronries, containing from five to 100 pairs, have been used for centuries. The common Heron is distributed throughout Scotland, but has never been known to breed in the Shetland Isles; it is comparatively common in Ireland. Abroad, it breeds in parts of Europe, Asia and Africa.

One of the largest of British resident birds, the curiously gaunt appearance of the Heron is unmistakable. Its plumage is predominantly grey, shading to darker, almost black on the rounded wings and under feathers. Its white head is adorned with a black crest running down the back, ending in a trailing tuft of feathers. Its breast and long neck are white, with dark, blue-black markings and a kind of breast-shield of feathers below. Its bill is thick, pointed and yellow, its legs are long. The Heron is 36 in. long, its body being 16 in; its tarsus is about 6 in. It weighs 4 lb., and its wing span is approximately 4 ft.

Herons have a large vocabulary of notes, mostly raucous and harsh, and many queer sounds emanate from heronries, especially in the breeding season. One of the most typical sounds is the unmistakable "clipping" of the hungry chicks. The alarm note of the Heron, which sounds like "frank", has given it the local name of "Old Franky". Individual birds have various distinctive calls. The courtship and pairing ceremonies of the Heron have been much studied by ornithologists (*see* Courtship; Display).

> I have studied and recorded the Heron many times; and believe that, by patient watching and waiting, I have managed to record this bird's full vocabulary, including the "clipping" noise made by the young with their bills.—EDITOR.

The Heron is seen in its most characteristic attitude when resting; it stands quite motionless looking the picture of patience—and incidentally of misery as well—with its neck and head sunk into its haunches. But the appearance is deceptive, for if prey is sighted, the bird will rapidly spring to attention, and the fish's or frog's fate is sealed with a stab from the powerful bill. The Heron has a slow and deliberate flight, with its neck well drawn in and its legs stretched straight out behind, but it can cover considerable distances with surprising speed. It can swim, but does not often do so, preferring to spend a good deal of its time on the ground. When not standing motionless, it walks with a deliberate air. It is fond of perching on trees, stumps or dead branches, and is inclined to activity by night.

There is a coating of "powder down" on the bill and legs of the Heron — often on its plumage as well—resembling the bloom on fruit. Various theories have been put forward as to its use: at one time it was thought that the powder had a luminous quality to help attract fish by night! Probably the powder is used for the bird's toilet,

G. K. Yeates

HERON. One of the largest resident birds, the Heron will stand for hours with its head and neck drawn into its body, looking a picture of misery

HOBBY, *one of our rarer birds of prey, with young*

For text see page 291

R. P. Bagnall-Oakleley

HERRING-GULL. This gull bids fair to outstrip all other gulls in its aerial grace, gliding and soaring with ease in the teeth of a high wind

.g. for removing fish lime after a meal. It may also have some water-proofing property.

Herons frequent any type of country where water will supply their food—lakes, meres, rivers, reservoirs and ponds being the favourite sites. They nest in colonies in high trees, and several nests may be seen in one tree. As they are used from year to year, the nests eventually become large platform erections of branches, sticks and dead leaves. The male fetches most of the material, while the hen does the building. The Heron is an early breeder and the greenish-blue eggs, usually numbering from three to five, are laid at intervals of two days, during February and early March. Sitting starts with the first egg, and both male and female take turns.

The chicks are fed with regurgitated food taken from the parents' bills ; they are ready to fly in a couple of months or even less. As a rule, only one brood is reared in a season. The British Trust for Ornithology (q.v.) has done much research into the Heron's breeding habits and has produced an index of heronries in Britain.

The Heron's diet consists mainly of fish, including eels. The fish is swallowed head first. If it is too bulky to be eaten at one gulp, it is carried to the bank and stabbed with the bird's powerful beak.

See also Ardea ; Ardeola ; Egretta ; Night Heron ; Purple Heron ; Squacco Heron. The Great White Heron and Buff-backed Heron of older ornithological works are described respectively under Large Egret and Cattle Egret.

HERRING-GULL—Larus argentatus. Of the six gulls breeding in the British Isles, the Herring-Gull—also called " Sea-Mew " and, in Shetland, " White-Mew "—is the most common and widespread. It is both a resident and winter visitor, many gulls arriving from the Continent in Autumn. Abroad, the Herring-Gull breeds right across the Northern Hemisphere, and in Winter is found as far south as the Mediterranean and West Indies.

" Common " would really have been a more fitting name for the Herring-Gull, for this is the bird found everywhere in our coastal towns and seaside resorts. It will become amazingly tame, especially in Winter. The Herring-Gull has always been abundant and has recently been increasing in numbers. It is now found even on London's Thames Embankment in Winter.

Confusion between the herring- and common gulls frequently arises, for both birds are similar in appearance and habits. Seen together, however, the Herring-Gull is much the larger bird, and its heavy, rather ugly, hooked yellow bill, with the bright red spot, is an unmistakable mark of distinction. In Summer, the whole plumage is snowy white, except for the silver-grey mantle and wings, the latter having black tips with white " mirrors ", like the Common Gull's. The legs and feet are flesh-coloured, whereas the Common Gull's are yellowish-green. The winter plumage is much less decorative and the whole bird presents a dirty-white appearance, especially on the head and neck, then streaked with brown. Herring-gulls only attain to their full adult plumage after three to four years, and immature herring-gulls in their various stages of development are almost indistinguishable from young lesser black-backed gulls. The length of the Herring-Gull is 22 in. and the tarsus 2 in. ; the wing span is something over 4 ft. and the weight is 2 lb.

The Herring-Gull walks easily on the ground and is a fine swimmer. It dives from the air plunging into the water after food. Like other gulls, it will trample the ground to bring up worms and it will drop crabs and molluscs from a height of from 15 to 25 ft. to break their shells.

All large gulls are marvellous performers in the air, but the Herring-Gull bids fair to outstrip

Eric Hosking

HIRUNDINIDAE. Like its cousin, the Swallow, the Sand-Martin spends much of his time in the air

them all. Best seen when following in the wake of a steamer or fishing smack, it glides and soars, even in the teeth of a high wind, with ease and grace, the wings seeming almost motionless. Ever on the watch, the keen eyes will mark the least morsel thrown overboard and the bird will plunge to snatch it.

Herring-gulls, many already paired, arrive early in the year at their breeding sites on all coastal cliffs and rocks, shingle beaches, sand dunes and grassy slopes of islands—but never far from the sea. Their display has been widely studied and includes such ceremonies as grass plucking, false brooding, aerial dances and the like. These antics may go on for hours on end and are communal.

All gulls are very sociable, even communal, in their behaviour at their breeding sites, and herring-gulls prove no exception. At their colonies, they can produce a tremendous clamour, particularly when frightened or disturbed. The Editor has watched herring-gulls for many years, sometimes for six months on end, and has recorded about 70 different calls —some of which are on gramophone disks. The chief call of these gulls is their well-known wailing sound, repeated several times.

Sometimes the gulls clear away rough earth or small stones before building their nest—a

substantial and untidy structure, built with any available material, such as grass, heather, sea weed and moss. Both male and female share the nest-building. Three eggs are laid on alternate days, usually in May. They vary much in colour from olive-green to green or buff, and are covered with spots and blotches of dark brown. The hen takes the bigger share of the hatching, beginning with the first egg laid. The chicks, clad in dusky brown down, are out of the shell in about a month and are tended by both parents for six weeks ; after that time they soon learn to fly. One brood is reared but should disaster overtake the first clutch another will be laid.

The Herring-Gull is an inveterate scavenger for food and nothing comes amiss in the way of garbage or refuse. In that, no doubt, lies some usefulness, but unfortunately it will loot an unguarded nest of any other sea-bird of both young and eggs, not excluding those of its own kind. When fish is not available all sorts of small animals—even rabbits—are devoured. Vegetable matter—turnips, potatoes, apples grain—all find their way into this gull's crop. *See also* Scandinavian Herring-Gull ; Gull.

HIMANTOPUS. Genus of very long-legged wading birds of the family *Recurvirostridae* of the order *Charadriiformes*. Its members are distributed over Europe, Asia, Africa, Australasia, and north and south America. Only one species is on the British list, the Black winged Stilt (*q.v*), which mainly occurs as an irregular visitor in Spring and Autumn, but which bred in England in 1945.

HINDHEAD. Although these popular Surrey playgrounds of Hindhead and the Frensham Ponds are much frequented by visitors, especially at weekends, they are, nevertheless, of much interest to serious bird-watchers.

In the well-known Devil's Punchbowl area of Hindhead, a region mainly of dry, sandy heath but with a stream running through the bottom of it, some 64 species of birds have been recorded —including the Woodcock, Stonechat, Nightjar and Grasshopper-Warbler.

Not far away to the north nests the Curlew and there is every hope that the Dartford Warbler, which nested on adjoining heathland until the Second World War, may re-establish itself. Two miles to the north-west, at Witley, a small nesting colony of buzzards survives—the species having been introduced in 1939 by Mr. Edgar Chance.

Frensham Great Pond and Frensham Little Pond are favourite spots for local bird-watchers. The wildfowl population of the Great Pond (which has an area of 77 acres and was made originally by damming streams and flooding a natural basin) has been the subject of continuous study for some years by a bird-watching group of the Haslemere (*q.v.*) Museum.

Both stretches of water afford nesting sites for various water birds, including the Great Crested and the Little Grebe, Tufted Duck, Mallard and, of course, Coot and Moorhen. Many passerine birds frequent the trees and bushes fringing the ponds. In Winter the population of water birds increases and it is then that such rarities as the Osprey, Slavonian Grebe and Great Grey Shrike are recorded. During the spring and autumn migration the ponds serve as resting places for some 25 species of birds, including waders, terns and gulls. There is open access to both ponds from the main Hindhead-Farnham road.

HIPPOLAIS. Genus of the family *Sylviidae* of the order *Passeriformes*. Its members are distributed over Europe, northern and western Asia, northern Africa, and also occur in tropical Africa and in India outside the breeding season. This genus includes four species on the British list which are described under their own headings : the Icterine Warbler, Melodious Warbler, Olivaceous Warbler and Booted Warbler. The first of those is an irregular summer visitor, while the others occur here only very rarely.

Structurally the members of this genus are very similar to those of the genus *Acrocephalus* (*q.v.*)—Reed-Warbler, Marsh-Warbler and many others—but their tails are more square-shaped, and they have wide, flattish bills. Their wings are comparatively short, and males and females are alike in plumage.

HIRUNDINIDAE (Latin, " swallow "). Family of the order *Passeriformes*. Its members occur in almost all parts of the world, except New Zealand. Species breeding in the higher latitudes of both hemispheres migrate to tropical or sub-tropical regions for the Winter. The family includes three genera on the British list, described under their own names—*Hirundo* (swallows), *Delichon* (house-martins) and *Riparia* (sand-martins). Like the members of the Swift family (*Apodidae*), these birds spend much of the day time on the wing catching insects.

HIRUNDO (Latin, " swallow "). Genus of the family *Hirundinidae* of the order *Passeriformes*. It comprises the true swallows and contains several species, distributed over much of the globe, except New Zealand. There are two species on the British list, the common Swallow and the Red-rumped Swallow (*qq.v.*). The former is a common breeding visitor to these islands from March to October, but the latter has been recorded only five times.

Members of this genus have very wide mouths, with flattish, triangular bill. Their long and pointed wings have nine primary feathers, the

second of which is the longest, the first being very small. The tail is forked and has twelve feathers, the outer pair of which are very elongated. The unfeathered tarsus is very short and the weak feet are also bare. The three front toes are more or less united at the base. All the toes have strong claws.

HISTRIONICUS. Genus of ducks of the family *Anatidae* of the order *Anseriformes*. It contains only one species, the Harlequin-Duck (*q.v.*) which is mainly distributed over north America, Greenland, Iceland and northern Asia, but occasionally wanders to the European continent. The Harlequin-Duck has been recorded in Britain only eight times.

HOARY REDPOLL. Name for Coues's Redpoll (*q.v.*) in the American list.

HOBBY—Falco subbuteo. One of the rarer birds of prey, the Hobby arrives in May as a summer visitor. It breeds sparingly in some southern counties of England, but seldom goes farther north, although it has occasionally bred there, and there is even a record of a nest in Perthshire. Otherwise, it is only a rare vagrant to the British Isles. It breeds throughout Europe, except in the extreme north, migrating in Winter to India and Africa.

Most graceful of British falcons, the Hobby is about the size of the Kestrel (*q.v.*), but its long, swallow-like wings, reaching to the end of the tail, give the impression of greater slenderness and length. The Hobby's mantle is slate-grey and the underparts are whitish, profusely streaked in black. The sides of the cheeks and chin are white and there is a well-defined, black, moustachial stripe. This, and the long, slender wings, serve to distinguish

Eric Hosking

HOBBY. This, the most graceful falcon, boasts swallow-like wings reaching to the end of the tail

the Hobby from other falcons. Rusty-red breeches and under tail coverts complete the dress. The hooked bill is blue-grey. The legs, cere and skin round the eye are yellowish.

The female is generally larger than the male ; the young are browner and have no red on the thighs. The length of the male Hobby is 12 in. and the tarsus 1·25 in. ; the wing span is about 2 ft. and the weight 8 oz. The length of the female is 14 in. and the tarsus 1·4 in. ; the wing span is about 2½ ft. and the weight 10 oz.

This is essentially the falcon of the woodlands. It spends much of the day perched among the trees where it also roosts at night. The Hobby hunts over the open countryside in the early morning and late evening, and is usually seen in pairs or alone. Occasionally several hobbies may be seen together.

In the air, the Hobby performs the most wonderful feats, which equal those of any other falcon, and even surpass those of the Peregrine (q.v.), though the Hobby will often use some of that bird's tactics. The speed of the Hobby in flight is such that it can catch swifts and swallows on the wing. The Hobby has a most remarkable spring display, the male and female soaring to great heights, wheeling and circling in the air, uttering excited calls. The presentation of food to the female by the male while in the air is part of the courtship ceremonies.

Noisy at its nest, the Hobby has several distinct and individual calls, including a clear repeated call, similar to the Kestrel's, and a high-pitched single note. Away from the nest, the Hobby is more vocal than its relatives.

Like other falcons, the Hobby does not build a nest but occupies those of other birds, chiefly the Carrion-Crow's. Here the hen lays her three eggs, varying in ground-colour from white to yellow, and streaked and mottled in brown. These are laid at intervals of from two to three days towards the end of May or in June, and are hatched, chiefly by the hen, for 28 days. The chicks are at first brooded by the hen, the male providing the food for the young. Later both parents provide the food until the young are able to fly. One brood is reared each year.

Unfortunately, small birds of all species provide the main diet of the Hobby and its young—swifts and swallows caught on the wing are the chief victims. Small animals, including bats and mice, are also taken, together with many insects. Like other falcons, the Hobby ejects pellets (q.v.) containing the indigestible remnants of its food.

HOMING. *See* Navigation.

HONEY-BUZZARD—Pernis apivorus. This handsome bird, at one time a common resident in the woodlands of Britain, suffered persecution by gamekeepers and egg collectors to such an extent that it has now become an extremely rare summer resident. A pair will nest very occasionally in the New Forest or some other suitable district. The bird breeds throughout central Europe and Asia.

In flight, the Honey-Buzzard could be mistaken for one of the other buzzards, but at close range its tail is quite different—besides being longer, it has two broad dark bars, one close to the body and the other at the tip, with narrow bands between. Instead of bristles, there are rounded feathers between eyes and beak— another distinguishing feature. The female is similar to the male. The length is about 23 in., and the tarsus 2 in., the wing span is 4 ft., and the weight 1½—2 lb.

On the ground, the Honey-Buzzard walks and often runs. Its flight resembles that of the common Buzzard, but it does not soar so often or so long. Its voice varies from sounds like whistling, spitting and screaming, to various soft wader-like call notes and quickly repeated phrases.

This is essentially a woodland and forest bird. Unlike the common Buzzard, the Honey-Buzzard, when it had been driven from woodlands in

Arthur Christiansen

HONEY-BUZZARD. *This handsome bird lives almost entirely on insects, but will also eat honey, fruit and berries and, sometimes, small animals*

Britain, could not take to the mountains, but had to leave the country. The bird uses the nest of some other species as foundation for its own, which it decorates and lines each evening with fresh green leaves. The one or two eggs have a white ground and are richly coloured in purple, red and brown ; they are among the most attractive birds' eggs.

The Honey-Buzzard lays very late in the season (usually in June) and at intervals, and both parents take part in hatching the eggs, as soon as the first one has been laid, for 30 to 35 days. It is about 52 days before the young are able to leave the nest, and one brood only is reared in a season.

Paul Popper

HOODED CROW. This is the resident crow of Scotland, Ireland and the Isle of Man. It is much disliked because it will eat nestlings and eggs

The bird's diet consists almost completely of grubs and insects, mainly wild bees, wasps, bumble-bees and hornets. Honey, fruit, berries and some small animals and birds, however, are also taken occasionally.

HOODED CROW—Corvus cornix. This is the common and resident crow of Scotland, the Orkney and Shetland Islands, the Isle of Man and Ireland ; it is a non-breeding visitor to England, but is scarce in Wales. It is so similar in its habits to the Carrion-Crow (*q.v.*), and there are so many instances of inter-breeding between the two crows in all countries where their geographic ranges overlap, that some experts regard them as two forms of the same species. Abroad, the Hooded Crow is even more abundant than in Britain, and in the Autumn large flocks arrive from Europe on the east coasts of England.

There can be no confusion between the two crows, for the Hooded Crow is unmistakable in its grey mantle, breast and underparts, with black head, wings and tail. It is, indeed, the only large " black " bird with so much grey in its plumage. Both sexes are alike, though the male is said to be a little larger, and the young birds are browner. The length of the Hooded Crow is about 19 in. and its wing span 2½ ft. ; its tarsus is 2 in. and its weight 1¼ lb.

Its courtship and display, flight and habits are similar to those of the Carrion-Crow. There is every reason for believing that these birds mate for life.

Although the voice of the Hooded Crow shows its close relationship with its family,

a well-trained ear would never confuse the calls of the Hooded and Carrion-Crow, even though the latter occasionally uses one call similar to one used by the Hooded Crow. The common call notes of the two, however, differ.

The Hooded Crow prefers trees and cliffs as its nesting-sites, but it will nest on the ground in treeless districts—for instance, in Scotland. The nests and the material used for building them are also similar to the Carrion-Crow's.

Hooded crows are much detested because of their ravages among the eggs and young of other birds. One might expect a decrease in their numbers, but this crow is a wary and cunning bird that seems to be able to evade all Man's efforts to destroy it.

The Hooded Crow is variously known as Grey Crow, Royston Crow, Hoodie and, in Scotland, as Corbie.

HOODED MERGANSER—Mergus cucullatus. Unique in appearance, this bird sometimes wanders to Britain from its American home. At least four authentic visits have been recorded. It breeds in north America, wintering in the south. The male is adorned with a wonderful black and white fan-shaped crest, not unlike that of the Hoopoe in shape. At the sides of the pure white breast, just in front of the black wings, run two black marks. The underparts are white and the flanks light brown. The neck and head are dark, glossed with green and purple. The female is much less colourful, having brown plumage above, white underparts, and her brown breast is much less conspicuous. The total length is 18 in., the body being 12 in. and the tarsus 1·3 in. The wing span is about 1¼ ft.

Less socially inclined than other mergansers, the Hooded frequents lakes and pools in

Eric Hosking

HOOPOE. This beautiful and rare bird has been trying for years—without success—to breed here

wooded country, and the flooded areas adjoining the great rivers of north America. It prefers fresh to salt water. Often on the wing, the flight is very rapid with quick wing beats. During courtship, the crest is always erected. A very silent bird, the Hooded Merganser's voice—a guttural, purring-like croak—is heard only in the breeding season.

Fish, insects, snails, frogs and tadpoles are the main food of the Hooded Merganser, but vegetable matter is also taken.

HOOPOE—Upupa epops. It is sad to think that this beautiful bird would breed in the British Isles—and, indeed, has been endeavouring to do so for many years—if it were not for egg collectors and " sportsmen ". So far, its various attempts to nest in southern England have always been frustrated, but now that public opinion has been better educated and better reception and protection is given to our rare visitors, the Hoopoe may one day succeed in establishing itself as a British breeding bird.

At present, it is a regular passage migrant in Spring and Autumn to south and east England and east Ireland ; elsewhere, it is still a rare vagrant. Quite a common bird in the Mediterranean countries, it breeds across Europe, north Africa and temperate Asia, wintering as far south as India.

The Hoopoe is one of the most striking-looking birds with its wonderful fan-like crest of pinkish-brown feathers, tipped with black and its pinkish-brown mantle and breast ; its tail and wings are beautifully barred in black and white. The bill is long and curved and the legs are grey. Both male and female are alike, but the young are less colourful with shorter

bills. The length of the Hoopoe is 11½ in. and the bill 2½ in. ; the wing span is about 12 in., the tarsus 0·8 in. and the weight 3 oz.

Almost too tame—a fact which has proved a decided disadvantage—the Hoopoe walks in much the same fashion as the Starling (q.v.), with which it appears to have some affinity, for it is often seen in its company, bobbing its head up and down as it moves restlessly along. The Hoopoe's flight is slow and undulating. Its curious, soft " hooping " note is responsible for its name. The call is uttered either from a perch on a tree or from the ground, and has considerable carrying power. It is heard best in Italy during part of May and during June.

The Hoopoe breeds in open country, parks and gardens during late April and early May in south Europe, and May to June in middle Europe. The nesting sites are varied—any kind of hole in trees, buildings, walls and suchlike. A nesting box will also attract it. Little or no material is used for the nest, and filth is accumulated to form, in time, an evil-smelling mass. There the five to eight unspotted eggs, varying in colour from white to grey or green, are laid and the young are brought out by the hen alone, the cock feeding her on the nest for 18 days. Both parents rear the chicks. Two broods per season are not unusual.

All kinds of insects are eaten by the Hoopoe —woodlice, centipedes, worms and beetles. The Hoopoe will hammer large beetles to pieces, throw them in the air and catch them again.

Once, legend relates, the Hoopoe's crest was a crown of gold, given reluctantly by wise King Solomon when a flock of hoopoes had given him shade in the desert from the heat of the sun. Fowlers discovered the value of the crown and persecuted the bird. Wearied and ashamed, the Hoopoe returned to the king asking for the crown to be taken away, and was given instead the beautiful crest of feathers.

HORNED GREBE. American name for Slavonian Grebe (q.v.), whose ear-tufts point up, like horns, when the bird is in breeding dress.

HORNEMANN'S REDPOLL—Carduelis hornemanni. This Arctic Redpoll (q.v.) has only very rarely wandered to the British Isles from its home in north-west Greenland, but experts have, from time to time, been able to record its visits, mainly to the Shetland Isles. It differs from other redpolls in its white underparts and white, unstriped rump ; but, apparently, does not differ in either habits or behaviour. Its length is 5 in. ; the wing span about 7 in., and the tarsus 0·7 in. *See also* Redpoll.

HORN. This term is applied to ear coverts (*see* Ear) when they are conspicuous and point upwards, as in certain grebes, owls and herons.

HOUBARA BUSTARD—Chlamydotis undulata macqueenii. Only four birds have been authentically recorded in Britain, the last in 1898. The Houbara Bustard breeds in extreme south-east Europe and south-west Asia, and winters in India, where it feeds on the mustard and oil-seed fields. " Houbara " is its Indian name, whereas in older British ornithological works it is called " Macqueen's Bustard ".

It is a large bird, about the size of a female Great Bustard (*q.v.*), and its most distinctive feature is its crest of long white feathers. Seen from the front, the bird looks as if it were wearing a black and white stole. The bird's length is 28 in. and its tarsus 4 in. Its wing span is about 3½ ft., and its weight about 2½ lb.

Houbara bustards resemble other bustards in habits and nesting procedure. In Winter they go about in small droves of up to a dozen, but the autumn migrations bring very large numbers together.

HOUSE-MARTIN—Delichon urbica. Among the sure signs of Spring are the return of the House-Martin from its sojourn in the south and its activity to repair or replace its nest of former years. Arriving in April, a little later than the swallows, the House-Martin is well distributed throughout the British Isles until September, when it begins to move south again ; it is also a passage migrant. Abroad, it breeds in all temperate parts of the Old World and winters in South Africa and India. House-martins have somewhat declined in numbers in recent years, probably because modern tarmac road surfaces make it more difficult for the birds to obtain mud for building their nests.

Often mistaken for the Swallow, the House-Martin has several differences : its forked tail has no " streamers " like the Swallow's, its underparts are wholly white and the feet and legs, conspicuous when the bird is clinging to the outside of its nest, are feathered in white. Its mantle and wings are dark blue. Both male and female are alike, the young are similar, but browner. The length of the House-Martin is 5 in. and the wing span about 10 in. ; the tarsus is 0·45 in. and the weight less than ½ oz.

Like the Swallow, the House-Martin is constantly seen in the air, wheeling and circling round its nesting site in the eaves of some building in town or country. The House-Martin always roosts in its nest, and is hardly ever seen in trees, but it delights in perching on buildings and telegraph wires. Long rows of these birds may be seen perched on telegraph wires in Autumn, together with swallows, in preparation for their long journey to the south. Rarely seen on the ground, the House-Martin walks in an awkward, waddling way.

A shrill alarm note—a constant excited chirping and chirruping, uttered both on the wing and near the nest—is the main feature of the House-Martin's vocal efforts. A sweet twittering of no carrying power and infrequently uttered may be heard, often before the House-Martin takes to the air or before it perches.

More gregarious than the Swallow, the House-Martin breeds in colonies (*see* Colonial Nesting). A nest from the previous year generally suffices, but if a new one is made, it is composed of wet mud mixed with feathers. The nest, built by both male and female, is shaped like a half-cup, with a small entrance at the top. The whole structure is attached to the wall, preferably in a corner of the eaves. When finished—it takes about a fortnight to allow the mud to dry— it is indeed a work of art. Old nests are repaired with wool and feathers. House-sparrows will appropriate forcibly the House-Martin's nest for their own eggs and young,

HOUSE-MARTIN. A gregarious little fellow, the House-Martin, though only rarely seen on the ground where its movements are awkward, delights in having a bath

W. Farnsworth

S. C. Porter

HOUSE-SPARROW. A familiar bird, nesting by human habitations, it does great damage in fields

and there have been instances of a whole House-Martin colony being evicted.

Three to four white eggs are laid in the latter part of May or in early June. Both birds take their share in hatching, which takes about 14 days. The young are fed by both parents by regurgitation for about three weeks. Two clutches—three are not uncommon—are brought out each season, and often the young of the first brood feed those of later broods. If the last brood are very late in the season, they are left to die by their migrating parents.

Insects, caught on the wing, are the main diet of the House-Martin and its young.

HOUSE-SPARROW—Passer domesticus. Wherever Man chooses to build, the ubiquitous House-Sparrow will appear sooner or later. Called by some a pest and parasite, its presence and cheerful chirp are part of everyday life. Although the House-Sparrow is probably the most common land bird in the world—except perhaps the Starling—it is not the most common bird of the British Isles. Its numbers are considerably below those of the Chaffinch and Blackbird (*qq.v.*) and, in some hilly districts, the House-Sparrow is far from common. Throughout Europe, except parts of Italy, the British House-Sparrow is found everywhere, and allied forms are as abundant in other continents.

It scarcely seems necessary to describe such a familiar and undistinguished bird. The only bird it could be taken for is the Tree-Sparrow, a smaller and slimmer species. The male House-Sparrow's upper parts are brown, streaked with black, with crown and nape in dark grey. The throat is black, the cheeks and underparts greyish-white and the dark wings have a white bar. The female and young are a duller brown without the grey, and with the wing bar less conspicuous. The length is 6 in. and the wing

span about 7 in. ; the tarsus is 0·7 in. and the weight ½ oz.

At all times gregarious, the House-Sparrow breeds always near human habitations in small colonies, and, domestic duties over, a great number roam the countryside consorting with other seed-eaters, such as chaffinches and yellow hammers. The House-Sparrow has a perky, cheeky air, but at the same time is very wary as it hops along, flicking its tail. It has a bounding and direct flight. At night it roosts in company with other sparrows on trees, bushes, eaves of houses and buildings, or in holes of any kind.

The House-Sparrow has various song- and call-notes. Its cheerful, noisy chirping is heard all the year round—both single birds as well as a chorus of birds performing. Apart from that, there is a courtship song in the breeding season—a love song of little carrying power, dropping as the bird attacks others or defends itself, but always louder and more sonorous than in Winter. The House-Sparrow is a quarrelsome little bird and frequently engages in squabblings. It delights in sand or water baths.

Any hole or niche near a house or building—in ivy, creeper, under the eaves or even in water spouts—suffices for the House-Sparrow's nesting site. Often it will use the House-Martin's nest, ousting the rightful owners. As three broods in a season are quite usual, the numbers of the House-Sparrow are not really surprising, and the parents are kept busy from March onwards. The untidy nest is built of straw by both male and female, but often a hole is merely lined with wool, hair and feathers. The four to six eggs, greyish-white with dark spots, are hatched for two weeks, chiefly by the hen.

It is little wonder that efforts are yearly made in agricultural districts to keep down the numbers of the House-Sparrow. It is estimated that grain constitutes 75 per cent of its food but, on the other hand, it also devours some injurious insects, and its young are fed entirely on these. In towns, it lives chiefly on household scraps, refuse and insects. In Spring, for some unknown reason, the House-Sparrow has an annoying habit of attacking yellow flowers, showing a particular liking for crocuses.

Hedged about with so many dangers, the House-Sparrow's expectation of life cannot be great, but W. H. Hudson records one which lived for 18 years and recently a pet House-Sparrow was kept for 16 years.

Dr. Saxby in his *Birds of the Shetlands* relates that in one district there the House-Sparrow was persecuted and driven away. In its absence, the potato crop failed year after year, until the bird was allowed to return.

HYBRIDS and HYBRIDISATION of BIRDS

R. S. R. FITTER

After explaining what is a hybrid and describing different types that can exist, the author discusses conditions favouring cross-breeding and the obstacles in the way of universal interbreeding that would eventually lead to the production of a common type

HYBRID. This is the offspring of animals or plants of different kinds. Among birds, interbreeding takes place most often between members of different subspecies or geographical races, less often between members of different species, occasionally between birds of different genera, and very rarely between birds of different families. In Britain, wild hybrids are most often found among the ducks, geese, game-birds, crows and finches.

Hybridisation in birds is of two kinds. First, where the territories occupied by two subspecies or closely related species (and often the line between species and subspecies is a matter of personal opinion) are adjacent, there will often be a narrow belt where the two interbreed, and hybrids are frequent. These hybrids are usually fertile. Second, there are random or occasional hybrids resulting from the breeding of birds of less closely related species, or of different genera; these hybrids are usually unable to reproduce themselves.

If interbreeding of different species were general, and the resultant hybrids were all fertile, it is easy to see that all species would soon get mixed up, as happens with the feral pigeons in our towns, few of which now show the pure plumage of their wild progenitor, the Rock-Dove. There must, therefore, be a series of obstacles interposed by the process of evolution to keep different species apart. The most important of these is difference of habitat. Birds which, like the Meadow-Pipit and the Rock-Pipit, though closely related, never normally meet in the breeding season, have little opportunity to interbreed. For those birds of different species which do chance to meet at

the right time of year, the next obstacle is difference in courtship behaviour and sometimes also in breeding season. Thus a female Wood-Pigeon would pay no attention to a courting male crow, because he would be unable to produce the motions or sounds that stimulate her; and the breeding seasons of the closely related Kestrel and Hobby are so far apart that individuals of the two species are unlikely to be in breeding condition at the same time. The third obstacle is the purely physical one that widely different birds would experience in the act of mating. The fourth and most important obstacle is the genetic difference that either prevents the development of offspring of a mixed union, or makes them sterile.

When hybrid swarms occur in narrow belts along the junction of the territories of two subspecies or closely related species, some other mechanism is needed to prevent the spread of these fertile hybrids throughout one or both the main populations. This is to be found in adaptation and natural selection, which give each of the two main forms the greater advantage in its own territory. Sometimes the balance of advantage may shift either one way or the other, and the belt of hybridisation will then shift with it accordingly.

Daily Mail

HYBRID. Dark-brown, with the head and neck of its mother —a duck, and the body and beak of its father—a gander

The only example in the British Isles of a belt of hybridisation between species is that of the Hooded Crow and Carrion-Crow, which interbreed along a strip of territory from Galloway to the Moray Firth. North of this line and in Ireland the Hooded Crow is the common species and the Carrion-Crow normally absent, while the reverse is true of England, Wales and south and east Scotland. Occasionally carrion-crows

297

may mate with " hoodies " in Hoodie territory, and *vice versa*. Thus a few carrion-crows occasionally breed around Dublin, and hooded crows have bred with carrion-crows in East Anglia. There is some suggestion that the hybrid zone has been moving westwards within the past fifty years, at any rate in Morayshire.

Random or occasional matings occur in Britain mainly in the game-birds and ducks. It is significant that among the commonest species to hybridise are the Black Grouse and Capercaillie, which have a communal courtship behaviour. The early pairing and " engagement period " of most birds is one of the obstacles to wrong matings, but an individual of the wrong species which happens to get caught up in a communal courtship ceremony, such as the " lekking " of the Black Grouse, may mate or be mated relatively easily. The Capercaillie was a spreading species in Scotland during the last century, and individual birds would often arrive in a district and mate with one of the local Black Grouse.

On the island of Bute a stray hen Capercaillie reared a brood with a Blackcock for three years running, about 1914. Wild crosses between Black Grouse and Ptarmigan, Black Grouse and Pheasant, and Pheasant and Capercaillie are also on record.

Among the ducks there have been wild crosses of Mallard with Teal, Pintail with Eider, and Golden-Eye with Smew. Wild crosses recorded among song-birds include Swallow with House-Martin, Goldfinch with Greenfinch, and common Redstart with Black Redstart.

Among domesticated birds interbreeding is, of course, much easier, and there have been recent instances of hybrids resulting from the breeding of domestic geese with both ducks and swans. Among ducks and pheasants in captivity, double crosses can be bred ; for example, there was at one time in the Natural History Museum, South Kensington, the offspring of a Silver Pheasant which had mated with a cross between a common and a Reeves's Pheasant.

HYDROBATES. Genus of sea-birds of the family *Procellariidae* of the order *Procellariiformes*. It contains only one species, the Storm-Petrel (*q.v.*), which is mainly distributed over the eastern north Atlantic area and the Mediterranean, and also occurs off south-west Africa and eastern north America outside the breeding season. The Storm-Petrel breeds in colonies on many islands off the west coast of Britain.

HYDROPROGNE. Genus of the family *Laridae* of the order *Charadriiformes*. It contains one species only, the Caspian Tern (*q.v.*), which is mainly distributed over the Baltic area, the Mediterranean and Black Seas, Africa, Asia, Australasia and north America. The Caspian Tern has been known to wander to this country on migration.

HYPORHACHIS. *See* Aftershaft.

HYBRID. *The parents of the little fellow in the previous page. Interbreeding among domesticated birds, especially members of the Duck (q.v.) family, is by no means rare*

Daily Mail

I

IBIS

IBIS, GLOSSY. *See* Glossy Ibis, also known as Black Curlew.

ICELAND FALCON—Falco rusticolus islandus. This very rare visitor to the British Isles breeds in Iceland and south Greenland. It is seen from time to time in the north of England, but more often in the Scottish Highlands and Islands.

Paler and larger than the Gyr Falcon (*q.v.*), to which it is closely related, the Iceland Falcon has a whiter head and no moustachial stripe. The upper parts are barred in light and dark grey ; the underparts are whiter with dark streaks ; and the flanks are conspicuously barred. As in all falcons, the female is larger than the male. The length of the male is 21 in., and the tarsus $2\frac{1}{2}$ in. ; the wing span is approximately 3 ft., and the weight $3\frac{1}{2}$ lb. The length of the female is 24 in., and other measurements are in proportion.

In common with others of the family, the Iceland Falcon is a silent bird apart from the breeding season. Its nest is usually in desolate and mountainous country, where trees are rare ; often no material is used beyond a few gathered twigs, feathers and the remains of prey.

In Iceland birds of various species, large and small, provide this falcon's main diet. Though it is swift and powerful, the Iceland Falcon is now not greatly favoured by falconers.

ICELAND GULL—Larus glaucoides. This is a scarce and irregular visitor from October to March to the north of Scotland, Shetland and the Outer Hebrides, and also in severe Winters to the east coast of England. The Iceland Gull has much in common with the Glaucous Gull, another winter visitor. Despite its name, the Iceland Gull does not breed in Iceland but in Greenland, but during the Summer it also occurs in Baffin Island, Canada. Outside the breeding season, its home is in Scandinavia, the Faroes, Iceland and the U.S.A.

The Iceland Gull at all seasons resembles a small Glaucous Gull (*q.v.*). The mantle and wings are a uniform pale grey ; the head, tail and underparts are white (tinged with brown in Winter). The long slender wings, reaching well beyond its tail, are, apart from its size, the only reliable distinguishing marks. The bill is less massive than the Glaucous Gull's and the ring round the eye is brick-red, instead of yellow. The length of the Iceland Gull is 21 in., the tarsus 2 in. ; the wing span is up to $3\frac{1}{2}$ ft. ; and the weight 2 lb. In flight the Iceland Gull has the rapid wing beats of the smaller gulls. Its behaviour and habits resemble those of the Herring-Gull—as does its voice, although this is considerably shriller.

The Iceland Gull breeds in colonies, often with other species, on rocky coasts and islands. The breeding season is from May to early June. The nest, built probably by both male and

Eric Hosking

ICELAND FALCON. *This rare guest from Arctic lands has been seen here only about thirty times*

female, and usually placed in a ledge of the high cliffs, is composed of moss and grass. The two or three eggs are similar to, but rather smaller than, those of the Glaucous Gull. As far as is known, they are hatched by both parents, and both take part in rearing the young. The nestlings are pale grey, with buff bars, and attain their adult plumage in three or four years.

Like all the Gull (*q.v.*) family, the Iceland Gull has a very varied diet, a good proportion of which is garbage and offal ; small fish are caught, and much vegetable matter is also eaten.

ICELAND REDSHANK—Tringa totanus robusta. A rare winter visitor to the British Isles from its breeding grounds in Iceland and the Faroes, the Iceland Redshank is darker and more boldly marked than the British species, but is difficult to identify in the field.

In size, habits, behaviour and song, it does not materially differ from the British Redshank ; although the Editor does not consider its vocabulary as rich as that of the British species.

Placed usually in a marsh or on the edge of moorland or heath, the nest is a well concealed hollow in the ground, lined with dry grass. Four eggs are laid, in late May and early June. The hatching of these and the rearing of the single brood are presumed to follow the family pattern. The food comprises both animal and vegetable matter. *See also* Redshank.

ICELAND REDWING—Turdus musicus coburni. A darker form of the Continental Redwing and, like it, a winter visitor and passage migrant in the British Isles, the Iceland Redwing breeds in Iceland and the Faroes. Evidence that it has visited the British Isles is provided by the identification here of birds ringed in Iceland ; but it is doubtful whether any

G. K. Yeates

ICELAND REDWING. *Though darker, this bird is almost indistinguishable from the common Redwing*

ordinary observer could distinguish it from the Continental Redwing.

Iceland has no forests, but in its few hedges and bushes as well as in the gardens of its capital Reykjavik and of Akureyri, the northern capital, the Editor heard the Iceland Redwing ; and so he did on the isolated island in Lake Myvatn in the north. Its voice is pleasant yet harsher than that of our thrushes. Its nest is placed among the rocks and boulders of tree-less country, but its breeding habits and behaviour are the same as those of its near relative. In Iceland, this bird feeds mainly on insects and berries. *See also* Redwing.

ICTERINE WARBLER—Hippolais icterina. It is surprising that this bird, which breeds quite commonly just across the English Channel in France and Holland, has remained only a rare visitor to the British Isles. Its one attempt to breed here, made some years ago, has not been repeated. But of recent years its visits have tended to increase.

Very like a large, sturdily built Wood-Warbler (*q.v.*), the Icterine Warbler has yellow underparts (instead of white), olive upper parts and a pale eye stripe. The tail and wings are browner, and the legs bluish-grey. When it is singing, the red inside its mouth is quite visible and forms a good distinguishing mark. The length is $5\frac{1}{4}$ in. and the tarsus 0.8 in. ; the wing span is 7 in. and the weight well below 1 oz.

Like all warblers, the Icterine is a lively bird and spends much of its time flitting among the foliage of trees, often quite near human habitations. It is rarely seen on the ground. When it is excited or curious, the head feathers are fluffed up, giving the appearance of a crest.

Its song, delivered either from an exposed perch or from under cover, is among the most varied of warblers' songs—loud, rich and musical at times, at others full of harsh and discordant notes. The Icterine Warbler is an accomplished mimic, and the Editor, who has watched this bird without interruption for many months on end, reports that, to his great surprise, he once heard it repeat his Christian name " Ludwig " five times ! The song is best heard during May and June.

The Icterine Warbler breeds during May or early June in orchards, hedgerows and gardens. The nest, placed in the fork of a bush or tree, and built by both male and female, is cleverly put together with down, grasses and wool, interwoven with roots, and lined with grass and hair. The four or five eggs are rose-coloured, streaked with black. Both parents share the hatching and rearing of the one brood, each of which takes about a fortnight. Insects are the chief food of this warbler, but ripe fruit and berries are largely taken in the Summer months.

HOW TO RECOGNIZE BIRDS

R. A. BAYNTON, T.D., B.Sc.

The present article is intended as an introduction to what is undoubtedly a very long and involved subject, but one that has to be mastered by anyone wishing to be a bird watcher. It shows what clues to look for to discover the identity of a strange bird

IDENTIFICATION. The identification of birds has been termed the A.B.C. of bird watching (*q.v.*), and is one of the first things that a beginner has to learn. This does not mean, however, that before starting to enjoy his hobby he must first be able to recognize immediately the several hundreds of species on the British list, but rather that he should aim to recognize a fair number of the more common varieties and learn how to set about identifying a bird previously unknown to him.

There are several ways of acquiring this art, and the best and easiest way is, undoubtedly, to have the continual help of an experienced ornithologist. But this, obviously, is not possible for all beginners, and many have to learn the hard way, with the aid of books, museum exhibits, and perhaps the occasional assistance of experienced bird watchers.

Some enthusiasts with photographic memories can retain mental images of illustrations they have seen in books, and in this way they are able to identify in the field birds previously unfamiliar to them. But the scientific method of dealing with a strange bird is to sketch it in a field note-book, marking all details about its

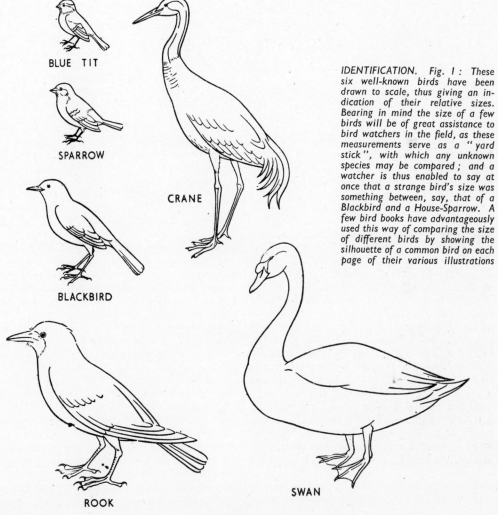

BLUE TIT

SPARROW

CRANE

BLACKBIRD

ROOK

SWAN

IDENTIFICATION. Fig. 1 : These six well-known birds have been drawn to scale, thus giving an indication of their relative sizes. Bearing in mind the size of a few birds will be of great assistance to bird watchers in the field, as these measurements serve as a " yard stick ", with which any unknown species may be compared ; and a watcher is thus enabled to say at once that a strange bird's size was something between, say, that of a Blackbird and a House-Sparrow. A few bird books have advantageously used this way of comparing the size of different birds by showing the silhouette of a common bird on each page of their various illustrations

TAIL WAGGING
FROM SIDE TO SIDE
Wagtail

TAIL QUIVERING
Redstart

TAIL USED IN
CLIMBING
Woodpecker

CLIMBING
IN
SPIRALS
Tree-creeper

RUNNING
UP AND DOWN
TREES
Nuthatch

HOPPING
Sparrow

WALKING
Pigeon

PAUSING AFTER EVERY FEW PATTERNS   *Plover*

IDENTIFICATION.   *Fig. 2 : Different ways of walking often give a clue to a strange bird's identity*

appearance which will help in its subsequent identification, as is shown in page 309. It is better to include too much information than too little, because nothing is more infuriating than to find too late that some important point has been overlooked.

It helps in describing a bird correctly if one knows the names of the principal parts and areas of the body, as shown on the *Plate facing page* 1.

In addition to these details on the sketch, notes should be added about the general shape or look of the bird (its " habit ") ; its size in comparison with the sizes of known birds, how it moves on the ground ; whether it walks or hops and, if it is a water bird, how it behaves on the water or in taking off (*see* Figs. 2 and 3) ; and how it flies, preferably with a silhouette sketch. Notes should also be added on its locality and habitat (*q.v.*) and, if possible, on its song or call notes.

Armed with this information, and with the aid of a knowledgeable friend, by consulting books or by visiting the bird gallery or bird room (*q.v.*) of a museum, one can proceed to identify birds at leisure.

Thus the art of identification is to know what to look for, and how to look for it, and then to reach an exact diagnosis by a process

of elimination, by comparison with other species which the particular bird may resemble (*see* opposite page onwards).

The whole subject is very wide, and can only be touched on briefly here. For further information the reader is recommended to obtain a good book which specialises in identification. There are many to choose from, but two useful ones, available at reasonable prices, are : *Collins' Pocket Guide to British Birds* and *A Field Guide to the Birds of Britain and Europe*, also published by Collins. The former, in addition to the usual coloured and black and white Plates, ranges birds by size under three headings—land, waterside and water birds— and, under each species, gives details of plumage, structure, movement, voice, fieldmarks, flocking, habitat, range and status. It also includes a migration table and a " key " which tabulates plumage and field marks by colour, and gives details of structural and behaviour features and habitat. This information enables one very rapidly to locate a strange bird from records in the field note-book.

A feature of the *Field Guide* is the way in which it draws attention to *essential* field marks by a system of arrows.

To learn how to apply the method, it is a good idea to start with some familiar birds.

Most people, even without any specialised training, can recognize at sight about 25 common varieties, but it is doubtful if many could name all of the distinguishing features of any one of them, any more than they could describe accurately so familiar an object as a florin. Therefore, armed with a field note-book, one can venture into the garden or visit the pond in a local park and make a start.

POINTS TO LOOK FOR

Below are given briefly some of the things to look for when attempting to identify birds :

Size. Acquire the habit of comparing the size of a strange bird with that of any of the familiar ones. It is an advantage if these can be seen at the same time, but as this is not always possible, keep in mind some well-known bird, such as the House-Sparrow, Blackbird or Rook, to act as a " yard stick ". One can then say that the unknown is, perhaps, as large as a sparrow, slightly larger, or twice as large, as the case may be. This idea is applied in the *Pocket Guide*, in which the silhouette of a sparrow, drawn to scale, appears on every Plate, as a standard of comparison.

Fig. 1 on page 301 shows the relative sizes of six well-known birds. The whole range of sizes is not quite covered, because there are about half-a-dozen British birds slightly smaller than the Blue Tit, but they are less familiar. The Mute Swan holds the honour of being the largest British water bird.

The absolute and relative sizes of various *parts* of the bird's structure, are also useful

aids in recognizing birds, and one system of identification has brought this method of comparison to a fine art by working out the ratio between one part and another ; e.g. the *neck ratio* is the proportion of the head, neck and bill to the overall length. Beginners, however, may find this method a little complex.

Shape. What is its body shape ? Is it plump like a Robin, or slender like a Wagtail ?

The shape of the bill, or beak, is another aid to identification (*see* illustrations on pages 52-54). Note how the short, stubby, conical bill of a sparrow differs from the more delicately pointed bill of the Wren, and the still conical, but longer and stronger bill of the Starling ; and how, in some species, the upper mandible is longer than the lower, and curves over it, as in owls, grouse, falcons and eagles. Note also the strong, but flattened, beaks of the ducks, geese, and swans, particularly the toothlike processes of the mergansers ; and the remark-ably long, curved bills of some of the waders, the upward curving bill of the Avocet, and the downward curving one of the Curlew. These are only a few of the many examples that could be quoted. The distinctive colour of some bills is a further aid to recognition.

Examples of distinctive head and neck features are illustrated in Fig. 5, which shows several different crests, varying from the " slicked-back hair style " of the Waxwing to the headdress of the Hoopoe, which resembles that of a Red Indian chief. With some crested birds, such as the Crested Tit, Woodlark, Skylark and Lapwing, the crest is of the same colour as the

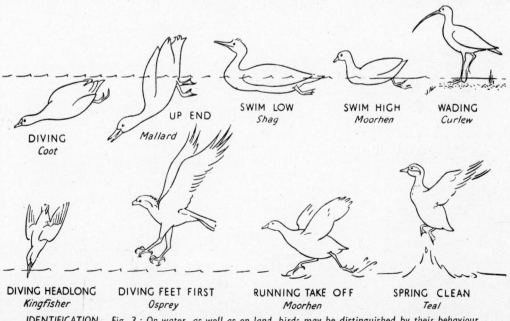

DIVING
Coot

UP END
Mallard

SWIM LOW
Shag

SWIM HIGH
Moorhen

WADING
Curlew

DIVING HEADLONG
Kingfisher

DIVING FEET FIRST
Osprey

RUNNING TAKE OFF
Moorhen

SPRING CLEAN
Teal

IDENTIFICATION.   Fig. 3 : On water, as well as on land, birds may be distinguished by their behaviour

head or crown, but in others, like the Goldcrest and the male Smew, it is of a different colour.

Several species have "ears" or "horns" (e.g. Long and Short-eared Owl and some grebes) ; and the owls, Montagu's Harrier and the Hen-Harrier have facial discs. Also shown in Fig. 5 is the characteristic ruff of the bird of the same name, and the ruff or "mane" of the Red-breasted Merganser and the Mandarin Duck—an ornamental waterfowl.

Then again, of what shapes are the bird's wings ? Are they pointed like those of the Swallow or of a tern (see Fig. 4) ; rounded like a warbler's or an owl's ; or short and broad like those of the Partridge ? Do the end feathers spread like those of an eagle ? What is its tail like ? Is it square like the Starling's (Fig. 4) ; rounded like the Cuckoo's, slender like a wagtail's, or extra long like the

Pheasant's ? It is notched like the Linnet's or forked like the Swallow's or Swift's ?

In the field it is frequently less easy to observe the feet than some other characteristic features, but if they can be seen they may serve as a useful aid to identification, because there are so many different types (*see* illustrations on page 235).

Behaviour. Some birds have very character- istic habits, which sometimes, alone, provide sufficient clue to identity. Selected examples of distinctive types of behaviour, on land, water and in the air, are illustrated in Figs. 2, 3 and 7 respectively.

Land. Dealing first with behaviour on land, it can be noted whether the bird has a character- istic stance. The Song-Thrush, Mistle-Thrush, Blackbird, Fieldfare and Redwing have a habit of standing with the head on one side, as if listening—possibly for worms. The Shag and

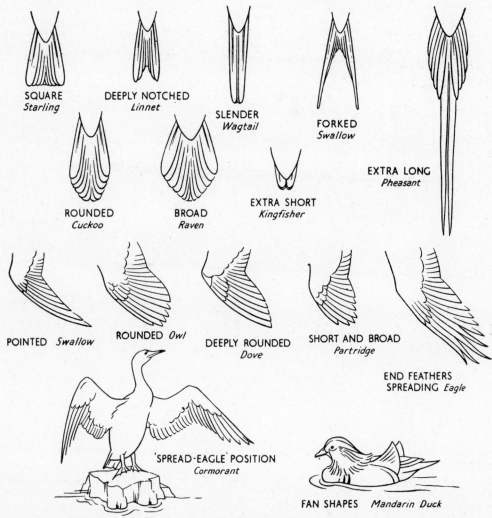

IDENTIFICATION. Fig. 4 : The shape of the tail or wing are good pointers for identifying a bird

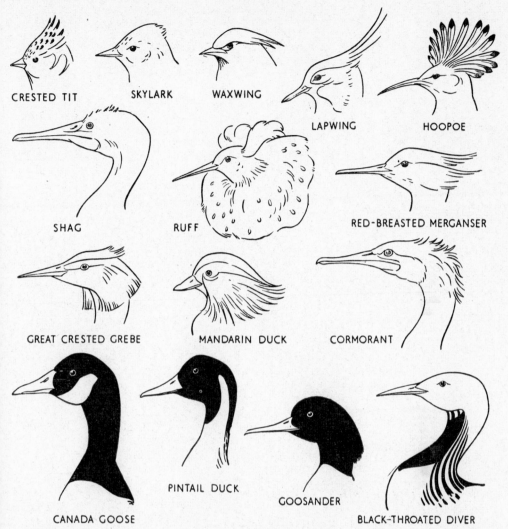

CRESTED TIT　　SKYLARK　　WAXWING

LAPWING　　HOOPOE

SHAG　　RUFF　　RED-BREASTED MERGANSER

GREAT CRESTED GREBE　　MANDARIN DUCK　　CORMORANT

PINTAIL DUCK

GOOSANDER

CANADA GOOSE　　BLACK-THROATED DIVER

IDENTIFICATION. *Fig. 5 : Some birds' heads are unmistakable, due either to their colour or their shape*

the Cormorant (*see* Fig. 4, opposite) often stand with their wings " spread-eagled ".

Notice how the bird moves on the ground. Does it walk like the Blackbird or a pigeon, hop like the House-Sparrow, run spasmodically like a wagtail, shuffle along close to the ground like the Hedge-Sparrow, often also called the Dunnock, or move from side to side, with a pause after each pattern, like the members of the Plover family ?

Does it use its tail in a characteristic way, wagging it from side to side like a wagtail, quivering it up and down like the Redstart, cocking it up like the Wren or Dipper ; or does it sit bolt upright, with the tail downwards, like the Spotted Flycatcher ? If it climbs trees, does it move in short jerks, using the tail as a prop, like a woodpecker ; run up and down, without using its tail as a prop, like the Nut-

hatch, or climb upwards in spirals, like the Tree-Creeper ?

Water. Fig. 3 illustrates some things to look for when observing water and waterside birds. Some of these birds, like the Moorhen, swim high in the water, others, with the body almost submerged, like the Coot and Shag. There are distinctive diving methods : the Kingfisher dives head first, the Osprey feet first ; the Mallard upends, and the Coot dives cleanly from the surface, immersing completely. Some species, including land birds, dip down to the surface of the water without immersing.

If the bird takes to the air, note how it does so. Does it spring clear in one jump, like the Teal, or does it first splash along the surface of the water like the Moorhen or have the pattering take-off of the grebes ? Is it a wading bird ? If so, does it stand motionless in the

Eye stripe above eye

Moustachial streak

Orbital ring and moustachial streak

GREAT GREY SHRIKE   GREEN WOODPECKER   GOLDCREST

IDENTIFICATION. Fig. 6 : Eye stripes and moustachial streaks may be the only means of distinguishing species which appear otherwise identical

shallows for long periods like the Heron, run quickly along the margins, like a sandpiper, or chase receding waves like the Sanderling ?

Air. How does it fly ? Has it a straight flight, like the Starling, an undulating one like a woodpecker, or a dipping one like a tern ; or does it, like the Snipe, zig-zag at first and then fly direct ? Does it beat its wings slowly like the Heron, with laboured beats like grey geese, rapidly like the Mallard ; with alternate periods of wing beating and stooping like the Fieldfare, or soar with splayed-out wing tips like the Buzzard ; hover motionless or, like the Kestrel, with tail fanned out and wings flapping vigorously ? Does it dangle its legs in flight like the Corncrake or the Corn-Bunting, or trail them behind like a grebe ? Does it somersault in flight like the Raven and Chough, or birds of prey when sparring, or pursue other birds to make them disgorge their food, like many gulls and the even more persistent skuas ?

Plumage and Field Marks. A few birds can be recognized instantly by colour alone, but with most species it is usually necessary to look for specific features or field marks. First, note the *general colour*—whether it appears, say, chiefly black or blackish, brown or buff, or perhaps one main colour combined with another ; for example, chestnut and grey. Then, note the *colour of the various parts*—upper and under parts, head, crown or cap, crest, bill, neck, mantle, rump, tail, wings, throat, breast, flanks, belly, legs and feet.

The next step is to look for *field marks.* Some birds are more or less spotted or streaked above and below. The Song-Thrush has these marks nearly all over the under parts ; the Skylark has them only on the upper breast, and the Redpoll only on the flanks. Others show barred effects : the Cuckoo and Barred Warbler on the under parts, the Hoopoe on the tail and mantle, the Gadwall on the breast. In some birds, part of the plumage is the same colour, but a darker or paler shade than other parts, e.g. the head and neck of the Coot are darker than the body, and the crown of the Dotterel and Gadwall is darker than the rest of the head. In other species the field mark consists of one or more bars, lines, spots,

patches or streaks of a distinctive colour. Bar or bands may appear as neck collars (Ringed Plover), or breast band (Arctic Skua), at tip of tail (Siskin), or a wing bars—forewing (Avocet), midwing (Brambling), hindwing (London Pigeon, *two long bars*). Wing bars are very important help to identification in such families as the warblers.

Eye stripes are equally important in many small passerines. Does the bird have a stripe above, through, or below the eye—or a combination of two or three of these stripes ? Some birds have distinctly coloured eyes, or eye rims, or " moustachial " stripes (*see* Fig. 6).

Other places to look for stripes or streak are between cheeks and nape, on the neck and shoulders, side of mantle, between throat and breast, and breast and flanks. Patches and spots may be found in similar positions and also on the bill (Surf-Scoter—white patches on bill).

In *Collins' Field Guide* attention is drawn to the important field marks by a system of pointers, and in the *Pocket Guide* they are listed by colour, feature by feature.

Songs and Call Notes. The bird's voice is often the best, and sometimes the only, clue to its identity. The ability to recognize the various songs and call notes is of the greatest help at night and in the height of Summer, when the cover is thickest. It is one of the most satisfactory aids to finding nests. The beginner should, therefore, follow the expert's example and learn to use his ears as well as his eyes.

As explained under the heading Song, it is impossible to express bird song in any musical notation, and not very satisfactory to attempt to express it by some system of phonetics, as so many bird books do—particularly as nearly everyone has a different system.

The best method of learning is to listen to the actual birds themselves, preferably in company with some one who really knows the songs, or, failing this, by going out on some spring morning, before the trees have acquired their foliage, and tracking down some familiar birds and listening patiently to their songs. The finest substitute for the real thing are gramophone records of birds' songs, either bought or " home-made." These may be played repeatedly until the different songs become familiar. Next come the B.B.C. broadcasts which millions of listeners have found invaluable

Much practice is required, and many pitfalls have to be avoided. Some birds are great imitators, and delight in mimicking members

SOARING *Eagle*

SLOW, FLAPPING, SILENT *Owl*

HOVERING *Kestrel*

LEGS TRAILING BEHIND
Grebe

Pigeon FAST, WITH
COOING CLATTER

LEGS DANGLING
Corncrake

ZIG-ZAGGING AT START, DRUMMING

Snipe

AERIAL EVOLUTIONS *Raven*

UNDULATING
Woodpecker

DIPPING *Tern*

STRAIGHT *Starling*

NECK TUCKED BACK *Heron*

HUNCHBACKED *Diver*

IDENTIFICATION. *Fig. 7: Apart from the actual flight silhouette, watch the way a bird moves in the air*

of other species. Moreover, the calls of juveniles often prove very troublesome.

Habitat, Range and Season. Sometimes, when it is difficult to distinguish a bird by appearance or behaviour only, it is possible to place it from a knowledge of its habitat, range or season. For example, the "Blue Chequer" London Pigeon and the Rock-Dove are almost identical in appearance ; moreover, the Blue Chequer plumage of the *London* occurs as a genuine wild variant in some colonies of the *Rock*. But the Rock-Dove is found only on sea cliffs, and feeding up to a few miles inland ; it is confined to the Scottish and Irish coasts,

307

north and north-west islands, and occurs locally in the Isle of Man ; whereas, the London Pigeon is typically an inland bird, showing a preference for towns and built-up areas, where it feeds in squares, streets and docks, and for the shores of tidal rivers—although it may also be found near sea cliffs or sand dunes. Most colonies of wild pigeons on the coasts of England and Wales consist of London pigeons.

In some circumstances, the Cuckoo, in spite of its many distinguishing features, is sufficiently like a bird of prey—particularly the male Sparrow-Hawk—to have been shot by keepers and mobbed by small birds ; but, unlike the Cuckoo, whose tastes in habitat are very catholic, the Sparrow-Hawk is seldom seen in open country. On the other hand, it may be seen in Winter, whereas the Cuckoo is mainly a summer visitor.

An example of how to apply the method of identification, outlined in this article, to recognize an unknown bird is shown opposite, in the Page *torn from a Field Note-Book.*

INCUBATION. Hatching of a clutch of eggs. The period of incubation varies with different species (*see* Breeding Tables), being generally longer for those birds that are hatched fully covered and able to leave the nest after a comparatively short time. *See also* Egg ; Embryo ; Young, Care of.

INJURY-FEIGNING. Parent birds often pretend that they have been injured in order to draw enemies away from nests containing eggs or young. The injury-feigning bird may flutter on the ground as if it had a broken wing, or hobble as if lamed—always only just out of its pursuer's reach—until it deems to have reached a safe distance from its nest, when it will suddenly take wing or otherwise disappear.

Ground-nesting birds which conceal their nests or scrapes only very little or not at all, are particularly prone to this type of " distraction display," as it has been termed (*see* Display). Among these, special mention must be made of the ducks and plovers, particularly the Dotterel. An illustration of the latter, pretending to a broken wing, will be found in page 179, Fig. 9, of this work.

INTER-BREEDING *See* Cross-Breeding ; *also* Hybrids and Hybridisation.

INTESTINE. *See* Anatomy.

INTRODUCED BIRDS. The two main reasons why birds have been introduced into the British Isles have been to provide sport or to embellish a landowner's estate. The great majority of naturalised birds therefore are either game-birds or waterfowl. It is important to distinguish between birds which have become so fully naturalised that they now breed without any protection from Man and often spread widely from the point of introduction, and those which have merely become acclimatised under the protection of keepers on a large estate, from which they show no tendency to spread. There have been many unsuccessful attempts at naturalisation, and the successful attempts have often followed many fruitless efforts.

Three of our seven breeding species of game-birds are introduced species, though one of them, the Capercaillie, was actually reintroduced from Swedish stock in 1837 after the native Scottish birds had become extinct about 1785. The last two native Scottish capercaillies are said to have been shot on the occasion of a marriage feast at Old Balmoral in that year. The successful reintroduction of the bird began at Taymouth, Perthshire, reinforced later in other places, and by 1914 it was widely distributed over the whole of the Highlands. When a survey was made in 1949, however, the bird had retreated somewhat, and was only really common in the eastern Highlands, especially the valleys of the Spey and the Dee.

The Pheasant (*Phasianus colchicus*) is one of the most successful of introduced birds, and would clearly be able to maintain itself in most of our wooded and marshy districts if it were not so tasty to the human palate. P. R. Lowe was able to find no authentic bones of the Pheasant in Romano-British deposits (all the previously reported ones were actually those of the domestic fowl) and, as there is no convincing evidence of the bird's presence in prehistoric western Europe at all, it is presumed that it was introduced to Britain at about the time of the Norman Conquest. The first written reference to it occurs in a bill of fare of some monks in Essex in 1059, but this is, of course, no proof that the bird could then be found wild.

The original English Pheasant was the Caucasian race (*colchicus*), but the overshooting of game preserves in the 18th century made necessary the introduction of fresh blood, which consisted mainly of the ring-necked Chinese race (*torquatus*). This race is known to have been enlarged prior to 1785 by the Duke of Northumberland at Alnwick and by the Dowager Duchess of Portland at Bulstrode, Bucks, and soon became as common as, and in some districts commoner, than its " old English " relative. Since then, several other races of Pheasant have been introduced, notably the Mongolian (*mongolicus*), and also several other species, including the Japanese Pheasant (*P. versicolor*), the Golden Pheasant (*Chrysolophus pictus*), Lady Amherst's Pheasant (*C. amherstiae*) and Reeves's Pheasant (*Syrmaticus reevesi*).

Continued in page 310.

PAGE TORN FROM A FIELD NOTE-BOOK

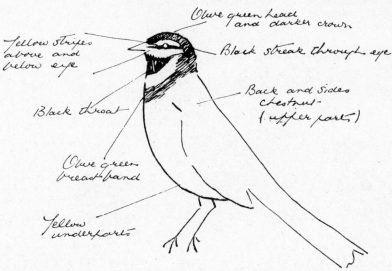

Tall hedge bounding farmland
Maidenhead
21st June 1954

About same size as a Sparrow

Olive green head and darker crown

Yellow stripes above and below eye

Black streak through eye

Black throat

Back and sides chestnut (upper parts)

Olive green breast band

Yellow underparts

The only British Birds with
Chestnut upper parts are : Cirl-Bunting,
Yellow Hammer, Turtle-Dove, and, in Summer,
Dunlin and Turnstone. Of these the only
ones with
Black eye-stripe through eye are Cirl-
Bunting (m.) and Turnstone, but the Turn-
stone is a much larger bird than a Sparrow,
and it is also a wader (i.e. not found in
hedges), so the unknown bird is probably a
CIRL-BUNTING. For further confirmation,
the only bird of those listed above with
Yellow eye-stripe above eye is Cirl-bunting
                                        (m.)

Green breastband   is Cirl-bunting

Eric Hosking

INTRODUCED BIRDS. *So many types of Pheasant were introduced that the present British population has become an extraordinary mixture of races*

which now frequents wooded lakes and ponds in Berkshire, Surrey, Bedfordshire and Shropshire, its chief stronghold being Virginia Water and Windsor Great Park. Gadwalls, which breed naturally in Scotland, are introduced in England, where the Breckland colony originated in birds turned down about 1850 ; escaped birds from St. James's Park, London, started a colony at Barnes, Surrey, in the 1930s.

The Grey Lag-Goose is another native and introduced bird, which is found " wild " (i.e. in feral colonies) in Norfolk, Essex, Western Ross, Caithness and in County Fermanagh. In the past, private col-

The result is that our present population of pheasants is an extraordinary mixture of races and species. Pure populations of Reeves's pheasants existed for many years in Inverness-shire and the Cotswolds, and typical golden pheasants may still be seen at large in many parts of the East Anglian Breckland.

Overshooting in the 18th century also led to the successful introduction of the French or Red-legged Partridge, which is now quite common in eastern England. Innumerable attempts have been made to acclimatise the Red Grouse in the south and east, but except for a few on Exmoor, none has survived. Equally fruitless have been the attempts to restore the Black Grouse to the many southern heaths from which it was exterminated by over-enthusiastic sportsmen. Among various other game-birds which have been introduced from time to time, never lasting for more than a few years, have been the Virginian Colin (*Ortyx virginiana*), the Rufous Tinamou (*Rhynchotus rufescens*), the Indian Chukor (*Alectoris graeca chukar*), and the Barbary Partridge (*Alectoris barbara*).

Undoubtedly the most successful of the introduced waterfowl has been the Canada Goose, which escaped from various ornamental waters in the 18th century and is now established in many parts of England and Scotland, notably the Home Counties, East Anglia and the west Midlands. More recent has been the escape and naturalisation of the Mandarin Duck,

lections, notably those at Foxwarren (Surrey), Woburn (Bedfordshire), Netherby (Cumberland) and Fallodon, the late Lord Grey's estate in Northumberland, have been responsible for many introductions or attempted introductions of waterfowl. In future the Wildfowl Trust's collection at Slimbridge, Gloucestershire, is likely to perform the same function ; already Gadwall, Mandarin ducks and Carolina ducks are breeding in or near the Trust's grounds.

The Little Owl was repeatedly introduced from Charles Waterton's 1843 attempt onwards. When at last it began to spread from Northamptonshire in 1889 and from Kent in 1896, it soon appeared in almost all parts of England and Wales, and is now beginning to spread into the south of Scotland. In its first explosive phase it was widely regarded as harmful, but it now seems to fit quite well into the countryside. No other non-sporting land bird has been successfully introduced, though many attempts have been made with other species ; e.g. the American Robin and both the Budgerigar and the domesticated Turtle-Dove (*Streptopelia risoria*) have frequently been acclimatised.

Mention must also be made of the Mute Swan, whose origin is obscure—it may well be a case of a wild bird half-domesticated and then allowed to go wild again. A similar case is that of the Feral, or London, Pigeon, which is the domesticated form of the wild Rock-Dove, and has now gone wild in our cities and on our cliffs.

BIRD WATCHING IN IRELAND

ARNOLD BENINGTON, B.Sc.

This article by a well-known Irish ornithologist, broadcaster and founder of the Copeland Bird Observatory, discusses the bird life of Northern Ireland and of Eire, and mentions the contribution these two countries are making to the study of ornithology

IRELAND, Birds in. Ireland has been likened geographically to a saucer, with a shallow depression in the centre, and cliffs all round the coast. The central plain is marshy and boggy, and there are few warblers and no woodpeckers or tawny owls in the sparse woodlands. But on the hundreds of smallish lakes, and the few larger ones, thousands of wild ducks and Whooper- and Bewick swans forage in Winter, many staying to breed in Summer.

On Lough Neagh as many as 120 Tufted Duck nests have been observed on a 10-acre island, along with a few nests of Shoveler, Mallard, Teal, Merganser, and sometimes that of a Pintail or a Gadwall.

The new Copeland Bird Observatory, on Old Lighthouse Island off the mouth of Belfast Lough, is not intended for the study of migrants, but mainly for the observation of the breeding biology of the large colonies of Manx Shearwater, Greater and Lesser Black-backed Gull, Herring-Gull, the Sandwich, Common, the Arctic and Roseate tern, and many other species that breed in smaller numbers or are met with occasionally. Up to 1954, 76 species had been recorded and interesting results were obtained from a ringing, weighing and measuring programme, that had been carried out persistently.

The best opportunities for a student of bird migration are to be found at the bird observatory on Saltee Island off the Wexford coast, where, as well as the usual pipits, warblers, chats, etc., and some very unusual visitors like the Tawny Pipit, a good representative collection of breeding sea-birds is easily accessible. Probably, the greatest single-species sea-bird colony in Ireland

is the gannetry at Little Skellig, but this is by no means always accessible on account of the poor landing facilities.

The south of Ireland also boasts one of the finest waterfowl haunts, in the north slob (mudflats) in Wexford, where in Winter thousands of white-fronted geese may be seen, along with a smaller number of brent, barnacle-, grey lag-, and an occasional Snow-Goose.

Dublin ornithologists are fortunate in having several places of interest within a few miles of their city centre : not least of these is Phoenix Park, where a flock of at least 100 hooded crows roosts throughout the Winter. There is also a flock of about 500 pied wagtails which roosts regularly in small lime trees in the full glare of the lights in busy O'Connell Street. Also within easy reach is the small peninsula, covered with rough herbage and salt marsh pools, called the North Bull. This is excellent for the observation of migrants, especially perhaps, waders, in the Spring and Autumn.

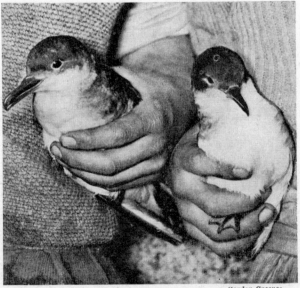

Gordon Greeves

IRELAND. *Two shearwaters from one burrow—the first to have reached Lighthouse Island one Spring for breeding*

Except in a few small areas where mechanised farming is carried out on an extensive scale, the Corncrake is quite common in Ireland, and in many places it is still possible on a June night, to hear as many as three or four corncrakes calling together at the same time.

Along the grand rocky coast of the west and north-west, one cannot go far without seeing ravens, peregrines, choughs and eiders. Here, too, was the last stronghold of the Golden Eagle, which a relentless war of shooting and poisoning cleared out completely early in the present century. The attitude of countrymen also prevents its re-establishment, for almost every year Scottish birds come over, which would doubtless remain to breed if unmolested. In this case, however, the traditional Irish hospitality is lacking. Fortunately, the people of Northern Ireland feel differently on this matter, and in 1953 and 1954 a pair of golden eagles bred successfully in north Antrim. Recently buzzards have also re-established themselves in the north-east province, after an equally long absence from Ireland except for one unsuccessful attempt to nest in 1933.

Sixty miles north of Belfast lies Ballycastle, from where on three days in the week the mail boat goes to Rathlin. This island, six miles long and bounded almost everywhere by cliffs to a height of 200–400 ft., makes a good centre for bird watchers. As well as the dense sea-bird colony of auks, gulls, fulmars, kittiwakes, shearwaters, shags, etc., there are in the west good opportunities of watching buzzards, peregrines, ravens, eiders, and, above all, choughs. The latter are less aggressive and more vivacious than the Jackdaw ; and to watch a family party of six or eight choughs in early Summer, diving and playing aerial tag over their native cliff with screams of obvious delight, is an experience not easily forgotten.

In Winter small flocks of barnacle-geese graze on Rathlin and the neighbouring Sheep Island, but larger flocks may be seen on the islands off Donegal and Mayo. Perhaps the best place in Ireland at which to study the dark, shy Brent Goose is the north end of Strangford Lough. Here one may stand on the low shore on some frosty morning and watch upwards of 1,500 Brent feeding before the incoming tide, their chorus of short, high-pitched barks swelling occasionally to a roar, as the flock takes wing.

Less than 12 miles to the south-west, in the Downpatrick marshes, with certain conditions of flooding during Winter, one may have an unusual opportunity of watching at a few yards' range from the county road, hundreds of teal, mallard, wigeon, shovelers, lapwings and moorhens ; all these birds are protected here except for two shoots during the Winter. Further into the marsh, with permission from Lord Dunleath, one may see Pintail, Tufted Duck, Pochard, and an occasional Gadwall. Here, too, at evening flight may be seen the finest sight of the winter months. From a certain chosen spot, by arrangement with the keeper, one can hide and watch enthralled up to 500 grey lags and maybe 100 Greenland whitethroats flying close overhead to their respective roosts. To stand there in the eerie half-light, "between duskus and day-la-gone," as the Tyrone man calls it, with the wild clamouring chorus just overhead, ringing in one's ears, is an experience at once thrilling and unique.

Also in County Down, on some of the hundreds of islands in Strangford Lough and the surrounding sea, there are several good colonies of the rare and dainty Roseate Tern ; and on several of those islands it is possible, without elaborate hides, to sit quietly among the rocks and watch, at close range, the delightful displays and breeding habits of this beautiful bird.

IRELAND. A shearwater is ringed at Copeland Bird Observatory. This observatory, on Old Lighthouse Island at the mouth of Belfast Loch, is justly famous for sea-birds

Gordon Greeves

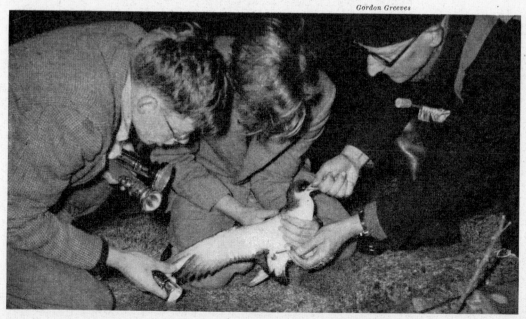

IRISH JAY—Garrulus glandarius hibernicus. This bird is almost indistinguishable from the common British Jay. Irish bird watchers mention as a particular trait that, when the young are almost on the wing, any intruder is mobbed with angry imitations of other birds.

The Irish Jay's plumage appears to be slightly darker in colouring, but its nest, nesting habits, courtship posturing, and voice follow the British pattern (*see* Jay). The eggs differ somewhat in number, but the periods of hatching and feeding the young birds are similar. The breeding season is a little later in May. The Irish Jay's measurements are the same as those of the British bird, and the same food is eaten.

ISABELLINE WHEATEAR — Oenanthe isabellina. An occasional wanderer to the British Isles—five have been identified in England—this bird breeds in south-east Russia and Asia and winters in north Africa and south-west Asia. Its larger size and paler sandy appearance distinguish it from other members of its family, but in general habits and behaviour it follows closely the common Wheatear pattern. The sexes are alike. The length is 6½ in. and the tarsus 1·2 in.; the wing span attains to a length of 8 in.

The song, delivered from a height or on the wing, is described as " rich and powerful ", and is distinctive for its mimicry.

The bird breeds in the desert and barren tracts of steppe country. Its bulky nest is built of dried grass, and four to six pale-blue eggs, closely resembling those of the common Wheatear (*q.v.*) are laid in March, April or May, according to the country frequented. Two broods are probably reared each season. Insects are the chief food of adults and young.

IVORY GULL—Pagophila eburnea. One of Britain's rarest autumn to spring visitors from the Arctic, the Ivory Gull has been recorded some 70 times. Chiefly seen in the Orkney and Shetland Islands, it has also occurred from time to time in England and Ireland. It breeds in such places as Spitzbergen, Franz Josef Land and Greenland, and winters south on the Arctic coasts of Europe, Asia and America.

About the size of the Common Gull, the Ivory Gull in adult plumage is a beautiful bird, pure white with the breast tinged with pink. The black legs and feet, and greyish-green bill with a bright red tip, are its only dark marks, although in their first year the young have greyish plumage with black spots on back, wings and tail. The sexes are alike. The length is 17½ in. and the tarsus 1½ in., the wing span is up to 2½ ft., and the weight about 1½ lb.

Tern-like in flight, the Ivory Gull is extremely graceful in the air, but on the ground walks and runs in an awkward fashion. Essentially a

Eric Hosking

ISABELLINE WHEATEAR. *Paler than the bird from Greenland (right), this is a rare straggler*

creature of the open Arctic seas, it rarely comes inland unless driven by unusually stormy weather, and, unlike most gulls, it rarely settles on, or swims in, the water, although it may occasionally do so in search of food. On ice, ground or rocks, it lands easily and gracefully.

The Ivory Gull is fierce and aggressive by nature and more than a match for its enemies ; human intruders near the nest may encounter the strength of its powerful legs. Its voice has the harsh and discordant note of the tern and is often repeated on the wing. In anticipation of food, this gull is described as uttering a " shrill, excited squeal ".

Known to Arctic explorers and visitors as the " Snow-Bird ", the Ivory Gull breeds in colonies in the Far North. It is, of necessity, a late nester, for the rocky shingle shores and cliffs, where it nests, are ice-bound until late June or July. The nest is made of seaweed, grass, moss and feathers, and two eggs—sometimes only one—very like those of the Common Gull, are laid. The hatching is shared by both parents, who also rear and feed the one brood.

In contrast with its spick-and-span appearance, the Ivory Gull has the disgusting habits of the scavenger and feeds on the filth of various animals as well as on the flesh of carcases. Some fish and insects are also eaten.

IXOBRYCHUS. Genus of the family *Ardeidae* of the order *Ardeiformes.* It contains about a dozen species, distributed over much of the globe. Only one species, the Little Bittern (*q.v.*), breeds in Europe ; this is on the British list, occurring as an irregular passage migrant.

J

JACK CURLEW. Alternative name for Whimbrel (*q.v.*), a close relative of the Curlew.

JACKDAW — Corvus monedula spermologus. Although it has many of the characteristics of the Crow family (*see* Corvidae), the Jackdaw is smaller than any of its relatives. A popular and very sociable bird, it is often seen in towns, although it prefers to congregate in colonies with rooks and crows. Jackdaws will also assemble in huge numbers on cliffs, nesting in the holes there : this is unusual among the Crow family, and only the Jackdaw does so.

The Jackdaw is a common resident in Britain, but is scarcer in Scotland and Ireland. There is evidence that some birds leave in the Autumn, returning in the Spring ; of two ringed birds, one, which had wintered in England, was recovered in Holland, and the other, ringed in Denmark, was recovered in Norfolk.

The Jackdaw has a glossy black plumage with an over-all blue tinge, but its nape and the back of its head are in a contrasting silvery-grey, evident in all adult birds. The Jackdaw is the only black bird with this characteristic.

On the ground its walk is far less pompous than either the Rook's or the Crow's, and it has a very amusing, not to say cheeky, air as it struts along, its body jerking up and down as it goes. The length of the bird is 13 or 14 in., and its tarsus 2 in. ; its wing span is $1\frac{1}{2}$ ft., and its weight about 9 oz.

Its flight is less direct than the Crow's, but its movement is faster. During the nesting season the Jackdaw's fantastic aerial displays are accompanied by a wild and continuous clamour. The Crow family have no pretension of being songsters, and the Jackdaw is no exception ; during display it produces a kind of song, not unmusical to the human ear. The common call, which can be heard throughout the year, is a single short high-pitched note, usually uttered in chorus flight, also together with crows and rooks.

In the courtship and mating displays, which resemble those of the Crow, bowing is the main feature, but the Jackdaw has some individual movements this season, such as raising its crown feathers and showing off its grey hood.

Jackdaw's nests can be found in many different places, but are usually placed very close together in holes in trees, buildings, rocks, or even in rabbit-holes. Jackdaws have sometimes built on the old foundations of rooks' and magpies' nests. Both cock and hen take part in nest-building, the material used varying according to the site chosen.

The number of eggs is four to six, but this varies and as many as seven are not uncommon. The eggs, bluer than those of other crows and less marked, are laid in April. They are hatched by the hen alone, but she is fed by her mate ; hatching takes about 18 days. The young birds are fed by both parents for about 30 days. There is only one brood in the season.

The varied diet consists chiefly of insects, but jackdaws also like young birds, eggs and suchlike. The Jackdaw is very gregarious, and will roost at its breeding place all the year round.

Its habit of concealing food is well known ; it will also steal jewellery, as witness the story of the Jackdaw of Rheims that stole the cardinal's ring and was cursed with bell, book and candle.

John Markham

JACKDAW. The smallest of the Crow tribe, this bird is known for its thefts of bright jewellery

Maslowski & Goodpaster

JACK SNIPE. Smaller than the Common or the Great Snipe, the Jack Snipe is not known to have bred in Britain, although it is one of our commonest winter visitors

JACK SNIPE—Lymnocryptes minimus. Although never proved to have bred in the British Isles, the Jack Snipe is one of our most common and widely spread winter visitors from September to March. A few non-breeding birds will even remain all Summer. Northern Europe and parts of Asia are its breeding places, and it winters mainly in Africa and southern Asia.

It is thoroughly snipe-like in build and appearance, but its smaller size is sufficient to distinguish it from other snipe. On its crown it has two narrow, light stripes instead of the one broad stripe of the others, and this is another good distinguishing mark. The Jack Snipe's plumage is warm brown, the mantle streaked in darker shades, with an over-all gloss of green and purple. The underparts and under tail coverts are white, and on either side of its back there are two conspicuous light stripes ; over the eye two pale stripes are separated by a black one. The bill is long and straight, though relatively shorter than in other snipe, and the legs are greenish-grey. The length is 7½ in., the bill being 1½ in., the tarsus is 0·8 in. The wing span is about 10 in., and the weight 2 oz.

Although a small " wisp " of Jack Snipe may sometimes be seen, it is normally solitary in habit, and delights in swamps, bogs and water-logged expanses. The perfect camouflage of its plumage enables it to merge completely into its surroundings, and it will remain in concealment until an intruder is dangerously near. On being flushed, it rises silently and usually alone, but soon again sinks into hiding once the danger is past. The flight is slower and less zig-zag than that of the Common Snipe.

The Jack Snipe's " drumming " is softer and more subdued than that of the Common Snipe ; as with the latter, it is a purely mechanical sound. A low, soft and weak call, uttered when flushed, is also recorded ; this has never been heard in Great Britain.

Low scrub of willow and birch, and water-logged stretches of sedge and cotton grass are the breeding sites of the Jack Snipe from early June to August. The four eggs, very like those of the Common Snipe, but smaller, are laid in a hollow scraped in a heap of moss and occasionally lined with leaves. As far as is known, the female hatches the eggs alone for about 24 days.

With its long bill the Jack Snipe probes in the mud for the worms which are its staple diet, but it will also take seeds and various insects.

JAEGER. This is the American name for some skuas. The Arctic Skua is thus known as Parasitic Jaeger ; the Pomatorhine Skua as Pomarine Jaeger ; and the Long-tailed Skua as Long-tailed Jaeger. Strangely enough, the British list's Great Skua is usually called only Skua in north America. The word is probably derived from *Jäger*, which is German for "hunter"—an excellent description of the Skua.

JAY—Garrulus glandarius rufitergum. The British Jay is one of our most colourful birds, and the ordinary observer would never associate it with the Crow family of which it is a member. In game-preserving districts it is, like the Magpie, much persecuted because of its ravages among young birds and eggs. This persecution, however, has had very little effect upon its numbers. The Jay is a resident, generally distributed throughout England ; in Scotland it is on the increase, although still confined to certain districts. In Ireland the Irish Jay (*q.v.*) replaces the British variety ; and the Continental Jay (*q.v.*), an irregular visitor to Britain, breeds on the European mainland.

The Jay is rarely found outside woodland districts during the nesting season, but later on it frequents orchards and gardens.

This is a bird of striking beauty, with its wine-coloured body and erect black-and-white crest ; its colourful wings are bright blue, barred with black, and its underparts are pure white. This variety of colour makes the bird especially conspicuous in flight. The male and female birds are alike, and the young show little difference in plumage from their parents. The length of the Jay is 15 in. and its tarsus about 1 in. ; its wing span is about $1\frac{1}{2}$ ft. and its weight 7 oz.

Similarity to the Magpie and other members of the Crow family is evident in the Jay's behaviour and breeding habits. On the ground, its movements are clumsy hops, its body jerking as it goes ; its flight is weak, but it can move from tree to tree with astonishing agility and speed. It is a shy, restless bird and easily alarmed, which makes it very difficult to watch at close range. It shares the habit of concealing surplus food with the rest of the Crow family.

The call of the Jay is a harsh and discordant sound which can be heard at some distance ; but there is also a typical, very rhythmical double-call, resembling a double-bass. The Jay also imitates other birds—much to the confusion of bird watchers. It is generally held to be no songster, but the Editor has heard a sweet musical song from a Jay in April and May, but not carrying more than ten yards.

The ceremonial spring gatherings of jays are not quite on the scale of the Magpie's but they follow much the same procedure, the birds chasing each other excitedly among the branches and flapping their wings to show the conspicuous white of their bodies.

Plantations, woods and orchards are the Jay's chosen nesting sites. The nests are built in April of sticks, roots and earth, and lined with earth, roots and sometimes hair. Both birds help in the work, the male bringing the material. The nest, though bulky, is well concealed when complete. The hatching of the five or six sage-green mottled eggs is done by the hen alone, and takes about 17 days. Both birds feed the young until they are on the wing in about 25 days. There is only one brood in a season, but sometimes broods have been recorded as late as June.

In spite of the fact that the Jay is regarded as a menace to many other birds and their young, much of its food consists of injurious insects, especially the destructive winter moth, and it also eats large quantites of acorns.

JERFALCON. *See* Gyr Falcon (*q.v.*).

JUVENILE. Young fledged bird up to time of first autumn moult (*q.v.*). *See also* Moult.

JYNX. Genus of the family *Picidae* of the order *Piciformes*. It includes the Wryneck (*q.v.*), which occurs in several forms in Europe, northern and western Asia, north-west Africa, and, outside the breeding season, in tropical Africa and southern Asia.

The Wryneck occurs in England and Wales as a breeding summer visitor, especially in the southern half of the country, though it is decreasing in numbers. It is but rare in Ireland, and in Scotland occurs as a passage migrant.

JAY. It is surprising that the usual sounds of these bright and beautiful creatures are but harsh and discordant, although some softer calls may be heard at breeding time

Eric Hosking

K

KESTREL

KENTISH PLOVER—Charadrius alexandrinus. Never common nor widely distributed in the British Isles, this bird bred in small numbers along the coast of Kent until about 1780. Protection came too late to save it in many of its haunts, but it still breeds irregularly and under careful watching on the east and south-east coasts of England. Otherwise, it is a passage migrant in the Spring, mainly in the south, and only a rare vagrant in Scotland and Ireland. Abroad, the Kentish Plover has a wide breeding range in Europe, Asia, north Africa, and north and south America.

The Kentish Plover can be distinguished from its near relative, the Ringed Plover (*q.v.*), by its smaller size, but it also has different plumage markings. Where the Ringed species has distinct black ring across the breast, the black on the Kentish appears only in patches on the crown, cheeks and sides of the breast ; in the female, the male's black patches are replaced by dark brown, and the young have none at all. The Kentish Plover is sandy-brown above with a white wing bar, and the underparts are white. The bill is black. The blackish-grey legs also distinguish it from the Ringed Plover, which has orange-yellow legs. The length of the Kentish species is 6¼ in., and the tarsus 0·9 in. ; the wing span is up to 9 in., and the weight about 2 oz.

Like all plovers, the Kentish Plover is a graceful and attractive little bird. Its behaviour and habits are like those of its ringed relative, but it is even more active. It progresses on the ground in the same manner—running a little way and then stopping—but it is faster. The flight is also similiar.

Outside the breeding season, Kentish plovers go about in small flocks, seldom greater than 20 or 30 birds, and will mingle with other waders. Like all its relatives, the Kentish Plover has a rich variety of breeding calls, some not unlike the Ringed Plover's, but less shrill. During the spring display, it has a curious bat-like, warbling song, and a special short call when alarmed.

Kentish plovers arrive at their breeding sites during March and April, and leave again about the end of July. The nest is merely a hollow in the shingle above high-water mark, and no attempt is made to prepare it for the three eggs. These are very like those of the Ringed Plover ; their wonderful protective coloration makes it so difficult to see them on the shingle that a walker might well tread on them unintentionally. For 24 days both male and female hatch the eggs, and both also rear the young, which resemble the young of the Ringed Plover, except for their dark legs. Insects, molluscs, spiders and worms make up the food of this plover.

KERMADEC PETREL—Bulweria neglecta. This is a very rare straggler from its home in the sub-tropical zone of the South Pacific, where it nests in huge numbers in the Kermadec and Lord Howe Islands, and has only once been recorded in Great Britain, namely in 1908. It is about the same size as the Manx Shearwater. The plumage has both a light and a dark brown phase ; in the light the underparts are white, with a pale head and throat ; and in the dark the whole plumage is almost black, with some lighter patches on the throat. The length is 14 in., and the tarsus 1½ in. ; the wing span is 2½ ft.

Eric Hosking

KENTISH PLOVER. *Once a breeding bird, this wader has become mainly a migrant to our shores*

Eric Hosking

KESTREL. *Not so long ago a pair of kestrels chose a West End hotel in London as nesting site*

KESTREL—Falco tinnunculus. The only common resident falcon remaining in Great Britain, the Kestrel is very widely distributed. Even the citizens of London and Manchester have heard, above the traffic, its curious shrill cry and glanced upwards to see the " Wind-Hover " poised almost motionless above them. A pair of kestrels recently nested on a well-known hotel in the West End of London, the nest being placed at the feet of a statue 40 ft. above the ground. In due course one young was safely hatched, and the voice of the mother and her nestling were recorded through the din of the traffic below.

Other falcons (*q.v.*) *can* hover, but none practises the art with such perfection as the Kestrel. It is its favourite pastime, and an infallible sign of its identity. In addition to the resident kestrels, Britain also shelters passage migrants and non-breeding visitors from August to May. Abroad, the Kestrel is found all over Europe, Asia and Africa.

The handsome male Kestrel has chestnut mantle and wings, spotted with black, and buff underparts also streaked in black ; his head and rump are grey. The long pointed tail—quite as long as that of the Sparrow-Hawk—is also grey, but bears a black band across the end and is tipped with white. The female does not differ greatly in size, but is less colourful ; her mantle and head are reddish-brown, barred in black, and her long tail is also barred ; her underparts

are pale, with dark streaks. In both sexes the bills are hooked, and the legs, " cere " and skin round the eyes are all yellow. The young resemble the female. The length is 13 or 14 in., and the tarsus 1½ in., the wing span is 1½ or 2 ft., and the weight 9 oz.

A solitary bird, always seen alone or in pairs, the Kestrel haunts many different types of country—woodlands, marshes, hills, rocky coasts and often the vicinity of old buildings and ruins. It is seldom seen on the ground, but will perch in trees, on telegraph wires and on buildings. Its flight is easy and graceful, especially in its spring display, when the male can be seen pursuing the female, circling round her in the air or even while she perches.

But it is the Kestrel's ability to hover some 20 to 30 ft. above the ground which is its outstanding characteristic. Its ordinary flight is suddenly checked, and it hangs, motionless except for its rapidly quivering wings, with its tail outspread and depressed, searching the ground below. On sighting its victim—it may be a field-mouse, vole, worm, beetle or some small bird—down it swoops headlong, its wings almost closed, to seize the quarry in its claws ; then it rapidly mounts again, to look for some perch on which to devour its prey.

On the whole a silent bird, though sometimes noisy during the breeding season, the Kestrel has a shrill and peevish-sounding cry near its breeding places. During courtship and when excited, the male has a soft musical note as it offers its gift of food to the female.

While recording the Kestrel, I discovered that this bird could be very silent, even at the height of the breeding season. Once I waited from 3.0 a.m. until 7.55 a.m. until the clear call of the male came through the recording apparatus. After that, there was complete silence again for 14 hours.—EDITOR.

The breeding sites are varied. In wooded country the old nests of crows and magpies, or of other birds of prey, are used ; elsewhere holes in ruins, the ledges of old buildings, and quarries are chosen ; and only very occasionally does it nest on the ground. No attempt is made to build a nest, but like many birds of prey the Kestrel ejects pellets (*q.v.*) and these are often used as nesting material.

Five or six is the normal number of eggs laid every two days during April or May ; they are whitish, much mottled and blotched in reddish brown. The hatching, which lasts about a month, is done chiefly by the hen. The young of the one brood are clad in white down. Both parents provide food and tend the young even after they can fly.

Animal food is the staple diet of the Kestrel, which rids the country of many harmful small animals and insects. *See also* Lesser Kestrel.

KILLDEER PLOVER—Charadrius vociferus. This rare visitor, which has occurred only 13 times in the British Isles, has its home in north and south America. It is larger than the Ringed Plover (*q.v.*), and the upper parts are browner ; across the breast are two conspicuous black bands, one forming a collar. The rump and wedge-shaped tail are reddish, the latter having a subterminal black band. The bill is black, and the legs yellow. The length is 9½ in. and the tarsus 1·4 in. ; the wing span is 12 in., and the weight 3 or 4 oz.

In its general behaviour and habits, the Killdeer resembles the Ringed Plover. The rapid flight is generally low, and on the ground it runs and stops in the same way. If not molested, it will become very tame. A noisy bird, the Killdeer owes its name to one of its loud clear calls ; it has several varieties of call, especially in the breeding season.

Meadows, pastures and cultivated land, often near human habitation, are its breeding grounds. The nest is a hollow scraped in the ground, where four eggs, rather larger than those of the Ringed Plover, are laid in March and April. Both parents apparently assist in the hatching, and both tend the chicks, which leave the nest as soon as they are dry.

Vegetable and animal matter, chiefly insects, constitute the food of this plover.

KING-EIDER—Somateria spectabilis. A rare winter visitor to Britain, sometimes seen in the Orkney and Shetland Islands in company with the common Eider-Duck (*q.v.*), the King-Eider breeds in the far north of Europe and Asia and on the Arctic coasts of Canada and Greenland, and winters on the coasts of north Russia, Finland, Norway and Iceland. Although it usually breeds near fresh water, this duck is never found far from the sea.

The drake can be recognized at once by his distinctive yellow forehead and bill, made even more prominent by its edging of black. He is smaller and sturdier-looking than the common Eider drake and the white on his black-and-white mantle is much less in evidence. A white patch appears from under his black wing, and his head and cheeks are white, with a greenish tinge on his nape. The duck, although rather more buff or rufous, is so like the female common Eider that only an expert observer would be able to distinguish between them. The total length of both drake and duck is 22 in., the bodies measuring 14 in. The tarsus is 1·8 in. and the wing span not quite 2 ft.

The down of the King-Eider is much darker than that of the common Eider-Duck, and is regarded as even more valuable in commerce.

KINGFISHER—Alcedo atthis ispida. The Kingfisher is at once the most beautiful and the most elusive of the resident birds in the British Isles. All the ordinary observer sees of it—and then only if he is on the alert—is a sudden meteor-like flash of brilliant blue, as the bird darts along the bank of the stream. With patience and perseverance, however, it is possible to watch the Kingfisher closely, for it will sit for long periods on a branch or rock overlooking the water, watching intently for a fish or other water creatures.

Generally distributed and fairly common in some counties of England and Wales, the Kingfisher is rare in Scotland, where it is seldom seen north of the Grampians. It appears in most counties in Ireland. It is found all over Europe, north Africa and Asia.

Clad in a perfect riot of colour, the Kingfisher has upper parts of brilliant cobalt-blue and green, and underparts of warm chestnut. Through the eye runs a broad chestnut band ; the throat is white, and there is also a white patch on the side of the neck. The legs are red, and the long, thick, dagger-like beak—almost as long as the tail—has a red base. The rounded head is disproportionately large. The sexes are alike, and the young are similar but a little duller in colour. The length is 6½ in., the bill measuring 1¾ in., and the tarsus is 0·3 in. The wing span is approximately 7 in., and the weight 1¼ oz.

Clean fresh-water streams, canals and fen drains are the favourite haunts of the Kingfisher, but Winter may find it on estuaries and rocky sea shores. Its flight is extraordinarily

Lynwood M. Chace

KILLDEER PLOVER. *This bird—a rare visitor—is not named after its feeding habits but because one of its many calls resembles the sound "Killdeer"*

KINGFISHER. No wonder that legends were woven round this bird of startlingly beautiful plumage

swift and direct, with rapidly whirring wings, but it often hovers low over the water. When uneasy or excited, the bird's head moves up and down, accompanied by flicks of the tail.

As an angler the Kingfisher is an expert rivalling even the Heron. Sitting motionless for hours on some branch or stump or hovering over the stream until it sights its victim, it plunges down with perfect aim to catch it. If too big to be swallowed whole, the fish is beaten on a branch or similar object.

During the Spring much play takes place round the stream banks and in the near-by trees, the male chasing his mate from place to place, uttering his high, shrill call note. The Kingfisher is no songster, but from February until April the male has a sweet and trilling series of repetitive musical whistles.

A tunnel, ending in a circular plateau, which is a yard or more from the opening, is excavated in a river bank by both male and female with their feet and beaks. This forms the nest of the Kingfisher, and no nesting material is used. In contrast to the Kingfisher's beauty, the nest is extremely filthy ; the depository of all the bird's food in the shape of fish pellets, it eventually becomes an evil-smelling mat. Here the six to ten glossy white eggs are laid from April to May. Both birds share the hatching for some three weeks, and also rear the young, which emerge completely naked from the shell. Two broods are usually brought up each season, often in the same malodorous tunnel.

Fish, including minnows, sticklebacks, gudgeon, small trout and roach, and insects form the food of the Kingfisher. Although not always " persona grata " where the waters are preserved, it is in reality a harmless bird and should be welcomed for its beauty wherever it appears. At one time it was much pursued for its plumage, but it is now rigidly protected.

Around the Kingfisher is woven the legend of the " halcyon days ". This is the story of Alcyone, daughter of Aeolus, the wind-god. She was changed into a bird and built her floating nest on the open sea. Each year she was granted a period of mid-Summer calm so that her brood might be brought off in safety. All seafarers knew that during the " halcyon days" tranquillity would reign.

KITE—Milvus milvus. As a resident bird of prey, the Kite—also called Red Kite or Glead—has almost disappeared from Britain, for it is doubtful whether even a dozen pairs now breed in the remote valleys of central Wales. The few that remain are rigidly protected, and their nests are watched over almost day and night. Natural history societies are offering annual rewards to farmers and others on whose land the birds breed, so that the efforts of egg collectors may be frustrated. But despite all this, it is doubtful whether the Kite can ever again be more than one of our rare birds. Abroad, it is found all over central and southern Europe, western Asia and north-west Africa.

In the 15th and 16th centuries the Kite was as common in the cities of Great Britain as in forests and woods. It was even then protected because of its value as a scavenger when the streets served as refuse dumps. Records reveal that kites were then as common along the Thames in London as gulls are today. Thus it was not only due to the advance of agriculture but also to the progress of sanitation in the cities that the Kite joined the ranks of rare birds. The preservation of game, which made game keepers its relentless enemies, also played its inevitable part in the bird's decrease. By the end of the 19th century it was a rare bird and thus a target for the egg collector.

The deeply forked and rufous tail of the Kite serves to distinguish it from all other birds of prey. The upper parts are dark brown, with lighter edges to the feathers ; the underparts are reddish and the head grey—almost white in older birds—with dark streaks ; and there is a conspicuous pale patch on the underwing. The hooked bill is black, and the legs are yellow. The young are duller, with browner heads. Male and female are similar. The length is 24 or 25 in. and the tarsus 2·3 in. ; the wing span is approximately $3\frac{1}{2}$ ft., and the weight $2\frac{3}{4}$ lb.

Kites are magnificent and powerful performers in the air. Gliding is their special delight, and from this was derived the ancient name of " Glead " or " Gled ". Far above its solitary home in the remote and wooded Welsh valleys, the Kite soars for hours, wheeling and

KINGFISHER, *most beautiful and elusive of our residents*

To face page 320

banking ; the long, narrow wings are almost motionless, and the forked tail seems to direct all its movements. Both male and female join in the spring display flights, circling round each other, and hovering somewhat like the Kestrel.

The voice of the Kite is a shrill mew, recalling that of the Buzzard, but higher pitched and less frequently heard. The Kite is, in the main, a silent bird, but in the Spring it has a variety of whinnying and trilling call notes.

Both male and female build the massive nest, placed in a tall oak. This is composed principally of sticks and grass, but all kinds of material find their way into it. In Shakespeare's day the Kite seems to have been a stealer of clothing from the washing line for in *A Winter's Tale*, Autolycus, who is himself " a snapper up of unconsidered trifles ", utters the warning : " When the Kite builds, look to the lesser linen ".

Normally two or three eggs are laid at intervals of three days in mid-April and onwards ; they are an unglossed white, marked in varying shades of reddish and purple brown. The greater part of the month-long hatching is done by the female, the male bringing her food. The young are clad in white down, but later become a creamy buff ; it is not known how long they take to become adult. Both parents tend and feed them, and they are able to fly in about six to eight weeks. One brood is reared.

The Kite's food is mostly taken from the ground and but rarely snatched from the air, for it is not a good attacker. Where it breeds in some cities abroad, it is still a scavenger, but in Wales it must depend on carrion, small animals —such as rabbits and squirrels—poultry and many kinds of birds. *See also* Black Kite.

KITTIWAKE—Rissa tridactyla. Of the six gulls breeding in the British Isles, the Kittiwake is the smallest and the most attractive ; it is also the least familiar, for it breeds only on steep and inaccessible cliffs, and is seldom seen inland. The breeding season over, it disappears out to sea and makes the wide ocean its winter home. All the suitable coasts of Great Britain and Ireland form the spring and summer quarters of the Kittiwake, but it especially favours the west and is much rarer on the east coast. It is also a winter visitor. It breeds in thousands all round the northern coasts of the world, from the Gulf of St. Lawrence through Greenland and Arctic lands to Spitzbergen, Norway, Heligoland and France.

In form and build, the Kittiwake is not unlike a smaller and lighter Herring- or Common Gull, but its eye has a milder expression and it lacks the fierce predatory look of other gulls. Its grey mantle is slightly darker, and the head, breast and underparts are snowy white ; the nape and crown are greyer in Winter. The

black wing has no white tips or " mirrors ", and this and the almost black legs are two reliable distinguishing marks. The hind toe on all gulls is very small and of little use ; in the Kittiwake it has all but disappeared. The bill is greenish-yellow. The sexes are alike. The young " tarrocks ", as they are called, are white, with a grey mantle spotted in black, and a black band across neck and wings. This variation is kept until the second Autumn, when they take on the winter appearance of an adult ; it is three or four years before they can breed. The length of the adult Kittiwake is 16 in., and the tarsus $1\frac{1}{2}$ in., the wing span is up to 3 ft., and the weight 7 or 8 oz.

The Kittiwake's graceful and buoyant flight, with rapid wing-beats, is faster than that of the larger gulls. Although so small, it will follow ships across the Atlantic Ocean, even in the teeth of a strong gale. Unlike its relatives, it can drink salt water. The Kittiwake rarely alights on land, except at its breeding site. A fine swimmer and diver, it plunges ternlike from the air, often completely submerging in the water, where it propels itself along with its wings.

For a gull, the Kittiwake is on the whole a silent bird, except during breeding, when its colonies echo to the rather pleasant but mournful " kittiwaking " sound which gives it its name. During the Spring, the call is important in the mating ceremony ; the two birds face each other, uttering their calls with bills wide open to show the orange interior and indulge in

W. Farnsworth

KITTIWAKE. *This is the gull of the open sea and follows ships even across the Atlantic Ocean*

many bowings and bill-scissorings and much begging and feeding.

Kittiwakes leave the sea during March and early April, and come inland to form their colonies on steep and precipitous cliffs. The nest, built on the narrowest of ledges, looks most insecure, but is really a solid construction and a marvellous work of art. Built by the male and female, it is composed of seaweed, moss and grass and moulded with mud into a firm cup fixed to the ledge.

The normal number of eggs is two, but three frequently form a clutch, especially in the south. They are laid during May and June, and vary in colour from bluish-white to yellowish-brown, blotched and spotted with brown and grey. Both birds hatch them over a period of 23 days ; observers have noted that the female performs this duty during the day and the male by night. The chicks, which are clad in long, silky down, are tended for at least five weeks.

Kittiwakes feed chiefly on fish obtained from the surface of the sea. Unlike other gulls, they are not scavengers and never feed on dry land, nor are they ever seen among other gulls at fishing stations or harbours. The Kittiwake has few enemies, but is sometimes attacked by the Skua and the Greater Black-backed Gull (*qq.v*). *See also* Gull.

KNOT—Calidris canutus. Of the countless thousands of waders landing on all coasts of the British Isles during their autumn migration, the little knots are some of the most attractive. Many stay to spend the Winter, and some remain all Summer to haunt the more northerly coasts, but they are seldom seen inland. A bird of the Far North, the Knot breeds in the Arctic regions of Europe, Asia and north America.

Little was known of its breeding haunts and habits until the late 19th century and much still remains to be investigated.

It is difficult for the casual observer to single out the different waders which crowd the mud-flats and estuaries during migration—Dunlin, Curlew-Sandpiper, Ringed Plover, Sanderling, Redshank, godwits (to name but a few)—but the Knot can be recognized by its intermediate size : it is larger than the Dunlin and Sanderling, and looks small beside the long-legged godwits and bulky Curlew. From a distance, when feeding in flocks, knots can also be picked out by their closely packed appearance; they move together in one mass, stopping now and then to probe for food in the wet sand. They feed by night and day, on both the ebbing and incoming tides.

In Summer the Knot has breast, underparts and cheeks of deep chestnut; the head and upper parts are browner and streaked in chestnut, with lighter edgings to the feathers. The wings are grey, with a pale bar and dark tips. In Winter, the Knot becomes a grey bird, neatly mottled with darker streaks ; the underparts are then white, and the wing bar and dark tips remain. In Summer the female is less colourful than the male; during the Winter they are indistinguishable. The bill is black and straight, shorter than that of the Dunlin. The legs are rather short. The length is 10 in.; the tarsus $1\frac{1}{4}$ in.; the wing span is approximately 1 ft. ; and the weight 2 oz.

The Knot is very similar to the Dunlin in its movements. Its flight is swift and strong and well sustained on its long migration journeys. The mass evolutions of knots in the air at their favourite mud flats form one of the finest sights on our coasts. The huge flock rises and falls as it flies low over the water—forming at one moment a long line, at the next a cloud—and often returning to the spot whence it came.

Outside the breeding season—when its voice is likely to be heard in Britain—the Knot utters a note sounding rather like its name. From a settling flock there rises a collective low and musical twitter.

Knots breed among the sparse vegetation of the barren Arctic, chiefly in the fells, but also on lower ground. A hollow with a lining of lichens provides the nest, where the four greenish-grey to olive-buff eggs of the single brood are laid in June. As far as is known, both male and female share the hatching, but the male appears to show more interest in tending the young than the female.

In Britain the Knot feeds on marine insects of all kinds, which it obtains by probing in the shallow water and wet sand ; but in its breeding quarters it lives largely on vegetable matter.

G. K. Yeates

KNOT. *These waders love company and are always seen in one huge mass on mud flats and estuaries*

LAPWING

LAGOPUS. Genus of game birds of the family *Tetraonidae* of the order *Galliformes*. It contains four species, which are mainly distributed over the Arctic regions and the mountain areas of the Northern Hemisphere, extending south to the Pyrenees in Europe and to New Mexico in America. Two species, the Red Grouse (*q.v.*) and the Ptarmigan (*q.v.*), are on the British list.

These birds have rather stout, arched bills, and their nostrils are covered by feathers. They have broad wings and shortish tails. Both the tarsus and the toes are feathered, more thickly in the Winter than in the Summer. There are no spurs. The sexes are usually different in colour, but are about the same size.

LAMELLA. A thin plate or disc. Particularly applied to tooth-like serrations in the upper and lower mandibles, developed especially in species of ducks and geese, and used for sifting water from food when feeding. *Pl.* lamellae; *Adj.* lamellated. *See also* Bill.

LAMINA. Term applied to any thin sheet or scale; such, for example, as the scales found on the legs of some birds, and the plates of which the vane of a feather is composed.

LANDRAIL. Local name for Corncrake (*q.v.*), a member of the Rail (*q.v.*) family.

LANIIDAE (Latin, " butcher-birds "). Family of the order *Passeriformes*. It comprises the shrikes, and its members are distributed over Europe, Africa, Asia as far as Australia and the Pacific, and north America as far south as Mexico. Five members of this family are on the British list, in the genus *Lanius*.

LANIUS (Latin, " butcher-bird "). Genus of the family *Laniidae* of the order *Passeriformes*. It includes five species which are on the British list : the Great Grey Shrike (with a closely allied form, the Southern Great Grey Shrike), the Lesser Grey Shrike, the Woodchat-Shrike, the Masked Shrike and the Red-backed Shrike ; these are described under their own names.

The members of this genus are medium-sized birds, with distinctively-coloured plumage. They possess strongly-hooked bills, near the tip of which is a notch forming a kind of " tooth ". The nostrils are more or less covered by bristly feathers. The wings are rounded; as is the tail, which is fairly long. The tarsus is rather short and covered with scutes in front. The diet of these birds consists of insects, reptiles, frogs, small mammals and small birds ; and the name, " butcher-bird ", is derived from their habit of impaling their dead victims on thorns.

LAPLAND BUNTING—Calcarius lapponicus. Also known as the Lapland Longspur, this bird is more or less a passage migrant, arriving in Autumn on the Scottish Islands of the north and west, and on the east and south-east coasts of England. It could easily be over-looked, except by an expert bird watcher, as it is a gregarious bird and is often found in company with other seed-eaters.

The Lapland Bunting may, however, be distinguished from both the Reed-Bunting and the Snow-Bunting, for its plumage is brown with darker streaks, and in Summer the cock has a

H. N. Southern

LAPLAND BUNTING. The cock is a handsome bird in Summer, in Winter he resembles a Reed-Bunting

LAPWING. *One of our most beautiful as well as useful birds, the " Peesweep " is a familiar sight*

bright chestnut collar and black face, head and breast, with a white stripe running from the back of his eye round his cheek down to his breast.

He has a stout yellow bill. The female is similar, but duller. In Winter male and female look much alike, both having light buff underparts. Although likewise breeding in Arctic regions, the Lapland Bunting is found at lower altitudes than the Snow Bunting. Its length is about 6 in., tarsus 0·75 in., and wing span about 7 in. It weighs about ½ oz.

Its song is a short whistle not unlike some notes of the Skylark ; this is not, however, ever heard in Britain.

The breeding season of the Lapland Bunting in Arctic or sub-Arctic regions, is in May or early June, later in the higher altitudes. It frequents treeless country and rough ground, preferably near the sea. The nest, which is placed on the ground, is built by the hen alone, of grasses and moss and lined with feathers. The eggs, which have a ground colour ranging from greyish-green to olive-brown, are usually thickly clouded and blotched with chestnut, sepia, or ochreous brown, with a few dark streaks or spots. The normal clutch is five to six, sometimes seven, occasionally only four eggs ; and one brood is brought out in a season. The hatching is done chiefly by the hen, but the cock has been known to take part.

The Lapland Bunting's food consists mainly of insects in the Summer, and seeds and grasses in the Winter. *See also* Bunting ; Fringillidae.

LAPWING—Vanellus vanellus. Found throughout the British Isles, the Lapwing—also often known as the Green Plover or Peewit—is one of the most decorative and useful of our birds. At all seasons of the year it is a familiar sight ; in Summer, breeding in the fields, farmlands and pastures, and in Winter, sometimes assembling in huge flocks on the margins of fresh waters, especially if muddy, and on estuaries and mud flats. Some of the British birds emigrate in the Autumn ; at the same time, many thousands arrive in Britain from the Continent to join our residents. Abroad, the Lapwing breeds throughout Europe and Asiatic Russia, wintering in Africa and Asia.

Both the plumage and the voice of the Lapwing are characteristic and distinctive. Its most prominent feature is the long curved crest. Superficially, it has the appearance of a black and white bird, but nearer inspection reveals a mantle and breast of beautiful all-over dark green with a purplish sheen. The underparts, cheeks and back of the head are white ; the throat black in Summer, white in Winter. The wings are broad and rounded and the white tail is crossed at the end with a broad black band. Chestnut upper and under-tail coverts complete the dress. The bill is black and the legs flesh-coloured. In the female, the crest is shorter and the wings narrower and less rounded. The length is 12 in., the tarsus 1·6 in., and the wing span 14 to 16 in. The weight is 8 oz.

Characteristic in its actions, the Lapwing has what is described as a " wobbly " flight, moving along, slowly flapping its broad rounded wings and, although the progress can be swift enough, it lacks the agility and dash of the true plovers. As evening falls, the flocks of lapwings delight in wonderful aerial manoeuvres, wheeling, turning and twisting in the failing light. On migration, they fly very high and one airman has recorded that he ran into a flock at a height of some 6,000 ft.

On the ground, the Lapwing has the typical walk of the plovers ; a short run, a pause, another short run, and so on. It can swim, and does so when necessary. It roosts on the ground in fields and pastures. The least disturbance will bring the shy flock to the edge of the field.

As the Spring approaches, the Lapwing indulges in an extraordinary display flight during which the wings produce a loud pulsating or " lapping " sound, no doubt responsible for the name. With this performance is combined its wonderful spring song, a sound quite impossible to produce in human language.

The ordinary call of the Lapwing is a wheezy " pee-wee ", a sound familiar to everyone. On this theme, with many variations, both its call note and song turn. Its song, uttered usually in flight, is best heard during March, April and May, and again during September and October.

Meadows, fields, arable land, marshes and moors are all favourite breeding sites. The nest is a hollow on the bare ground, usually lined with some dry grass, where four olive or dark buff eggs, blotched and spotted with brown, are laid in late March or early April. Both male and female incubate, but the female takes the greater share. The period varies but is usually 24 to 26 days. The chicks, dainty little creatures clad in buff down with a dark breast-band and a short crest, are looked after by the female, with the male keeping guard. They become fully fledged in 33 days. One brood is reared in a season.

The Lapwing is one of the most useful of birds, for it clears the ground of all kinds of injurious insects. Some vegetable matter including seeds, grass, cereals, etc., is also eaten.

Apart from Green Plover and Peewit, the Lapwing is also called Black Plover, Peesweep and Pyewipe. In Scotland, it goes by the name of " Teuchat ".

The Lapwing and its eggs have in the past suffered much persecution, but it is now protected under the Protection of Birds Act, 1954.

LARGE-BILLED REED-BUNTING. *See* Eastern Large-Billed Reed-Bunting. *See also* Bunting ; Reed-Bunting.

LARGE EGRET—Egretta alba. This bird is also known as the Great White Heron. It and the Little Egret are the only two herons with pure white plumage. Confusion between them consequently often occurs, but the Large is both bigger and slimmer, and also lacks the distinctive crest decoration of the Little Egret, Both have been, and still are, much sought after for their plumage. The Large Egret pays only rare visits to the British Isles ; so far only seven instances have been recorded.

Its distribution is world-wide, and colonies exist wherever suitable swamps, meres and river beds are to be found. It is a silent bird, even in the breeding season. In behaviour and habits it follows closely the pattern of the common Heron. The nest is usually built in dense reed-beds—sometimes in a few feet of water—and is of the usual heron type. The four eggs are hatched by both male and female, and both also feed and rear the one brood.

The total length is 36 in., the body measuring 15 in. ; the tarsus is 7 in. The weight is 2½ lb., and the wing span is over 3 ft.

LARIDAE. Family of the order *Charadriiformes*, comprising the gulls and terns. The following genera are on the British list : *Pagophila, Larus, Xema, Rhodostethia, Rissa, Chlidonias, Gelochelidon, Hydroprogne* and *Sterna*.

All the members of this family of aquatic birds have long wings. The bill is generally almost straight and sometimes quite slender, but in the gulls the culmen (*q.v.*) is more or less decurved. Neither gulls nor terns have a cere (*q.v.*) at the base of the upper mandible. In the terns the tail is generally forked, whereas in the gulls it is usually squarish or only very slightly rounded, and it is rarely forked. The terns have shorter legs and smaller feet than the gulls, but in both cases the three front toes are generally webbed.

Most of the members of this family are greyish coloured above, and white below ; the plumage of the young is mottled with brown. Often they have a dark-coloured cap or hood, and the wing-tips also are often black.

LARK. These birds belong to the family *Alaudidae* (*q.v.*) and are, apart from the male Black Lark, brown-streaked song-birds, somewhat like pipits, though stouter. Their varied, musical song is delivered chiefly on the wing.

There are eight species on the British list, described under their names. Of these only the Skylark and Wood-Lark are at all common ; the Shore-Lark is a winter visitor while the Black Lark, Calandra Lark, White-winged Lark, Short-toed Lark and Crested Lark are merely stragglers.

LARUS. Genus of gulls of the family *Laridae* of the order *Charadriiformes*. It contains about 35 species, distributed over the greater part of the globe, and 11 of these are on the British list : the Greater Black-backed Gull, Lesser Black-backed Gull, Herring-Gull, Common Gull, Glaucous Gull, Iceland Gull, Black-headed Gull, Great Black-headed Gull, Mediterranean Black-headed Gull, Bonaparte's Gull,

Eric Hosking

LARUS. *Despite its name, the Common Gull is by no means the most typical gull of the genus Larus*

G. K. Yeates

LESSER BLACK-BACKED GULL. *Two types of Black-Back are found here—the Scandinavian, with slaty-black back, and the lighter British bird*

lined with grass, roots, moss and wool. One egg, larger than the Storm-Petrel's, is laid early in June. The incubation, which lasts for at least 50 days, is shared by both male and female. They sit for spells of about four days, and during that time the sitting bird neither leaves the nest nor takes any food ; the other roams the wide ocean seeking food. As far as is known, both parents tend and rear the one chick for as long as 60 days. When it is ready to fly, it follows its parents to the sea and is then left to fend for itself.

Leach's Petrel feeds on plankton from the sea's surface, small fish, crustacea and molluscs.

LEAST SANDPIPER. American name for the British list's American Stint (*q.v.*).

and Little Gull. These are separately described under their own headings. *See also* Gull.

All these species have strong, laterally compressed bills, with the tip of the upper mandible pointed and curving down over the lower. The nostrils are longitudinal. The wings are long and pointed and the tail is short and squarish.

LEACH'S PETREL—Oceanodroma leucorhoa. This is a rare resident in the British Isles, breeding in Europe only in the Hebrides, some islands off the Irish west coast and on the coast of Iceland. Elsewhere it is only likely to be seen in the open seas of the north Atlantic and Pacific oceans, unless driven inland by storms. The most oceanic bird of the north Atlantic, it is also the most elusive of petrels.

Leach's Petrel is larger than its close ally the Storm-Petrel, but very similar in behaviour and habits. At close quarters its forked tail is a reliable identification, but it also has a characteristic darting and erratic flight, quite different from that of other petrels, and is never seen following vessels at sea. It has much the same sooty plumage and white rump and under-tail coverts as the Storm Petrel. The legs are black, and the slightly hooked bill has the tubular nostrils of the family. The length is 8 in. and the tarsus 0·9 in., the wing span is 12 to 14 in., and the weight between 1 and 2 oz. Unlike the Storm-Petrel, Leach's Petrel calls on the wing.

An interesting and uncommon feature is its display of wild and excited nocturnal flights, with both male and female calling in their characteristic guttural voices over the breeding burrow. Mating takes place in the burrow, and a special trilling note issues from it on one night only and is never repeated that season. Various guttural notes are heard at the nest.

Leach's Petrel nests on coastal islands. The burrow, which is excavated by the male alone for three days, is sometimes, but not always,

LESSER BLACK-BACKED GULL—Larus fuscus graellsii. A smaller and slimmer edition of the Greater Black-backed Gull, the Lesser Black-backed is a summer breeding visitor to the British Isles, arriving in February. Most of the visitors leave again in November for the coasts of France, Spain and Portugal, and north Africa, but some may remain to winter in the south of England. More migratory in habit than either its larger relative or the more common Herring-Gull, it is widely distributed on the north and west coasts of England, the north of Scotland, including the Orkneys, Shetlands and Hebrides, where it is very abundant, and the west coast of Ireland ; it is more often seen inland than the Herring-Gull.

The two black-backed gulls closely resemble each other. Both are white, except for the dark mantle and wings, the latter with white " mirrors " near the tips. The legs and feet of the Lesser Black-backed Gull are, however, bright yellow, in contrast to the flesh colour of the Greater Black-back and the Herring Gull. Its bill is less massive, and, in Winter, its head and neck are streaked with grey. The sexes are alike ; the young birds, which are similar to the young of the Herring-Gull, do not attain their adult plumage for about three years. The length is 21 in. and the tarsus 2·6 in. ; the wing span 4-5 ft., and the weight $2\frac{1}{4}$ lb.

The habits and behaviour of the Lesser Black-backed Gull resemble those of the Herring-Gull, but it is even bolder and more aggressive. It is much seen in company with herring-gulls and joins in following ships, staying on the wing for hours on end. A scavenger like other gulls, it forages round harbours, sewage outlets, and rubbish dumps, and is a common visitor to the North Sea fishing stations, where it quarrels with, and bullies, less bold birds. But it does not have the habit, common to many of its family, of dropping molluscs to break them.

Its typically gull-like voice, resembling that of the Greater Black-back, is even louder and more raucous than the Herring-Gull's. Like all gulls, it is fierce in defence of its nest and young. No other bird dares approach too close to a colony, for one alarmed bird will rouse the whole population to drive off the intruder.

Marshes, upland moors and grassy islands in lochs are among the chosen sites for the colonies which may also be on low ground near the sea. The nest is built of any material at hand—heather stalks, seaweed, lichen, etc.—and the normal number of three eggs, with a ground colour ranging from olive brown to very dark brown, with splotches of dark sepia, are laid, at intervals of two days, in May. Both male and female share the hatching, which takes from three to four weeks. The chicks, clad in grey down spotted over in dark brown, are exactly similar to the chicks of the Herring-Gull. They are fed in the nest for a few days, but soon leave it to wander among the stones and grass, carefully watched and guarded by their devoted parents for at least six weeks.

The food of the Lesser Black-back is varied. Besides what it picks up when scavenging, all kinds of animals, birds and eggs, and fish find their way into its voracious crop. The Scandinavian Lesser Black-backed Gull (q.v.) is similar except that its mantle is darker.

LESSER GREY SHRIKE—Lanius minor. A wanderer from its home in Europe and Asia, this bird has been recorded some 20 times in the British Isles. Smaller than its near relative, the Great Grey Shrike, it is also distinguished by a black band across its forehead, broad in the cock and narrower in the hen. The shoulder feathers, head and upper parts are grey—rather darker than those of the Great Grey Shrike—and the underparts are whitish, tinged with rose-pink on breast and flanks. The wings are black with a white bar, and the tail is shorter than the larger bird's. The length is 8 in., the tarsus 1·15 in. and the wing span approximately 9 in.

The behaviour and habits of the Lesser Grey Shrike closely follows those of the Red-backed Shrike. It is quarrelsome and fearless in driving intruders—often larger than itself—from its nest but is less inclined to impale its prey on thorns.

Like all shrikes' calls, those of the Lesser Grey Shrike are discordant. Its song, described as an " unmusical succession of broken discordant noises ", is usually delivered from a high perch.

LESSER KESTREL—Falco naumanni. This rare vagrant to the British Isles has been recorded about a dozen times. It breeds in south Europe, Asia and Africa, and winters in south Africa and India. More gregarious than the common Kestrel, it nests in colonies of 15-20 pairs in the neighbourhood of ruins and old buildings in towns and villages, as well as in the open country. It is rather smaller than the common Kestrel, and the male is more colourful with a richer and unspotted chestnut mantle ; in the sunlight, its grey head and tails shine with a blue tinge. The female is so like the common Kestrel in plumage that only the smaller size distinguishes her. The claws of both are whitish. The length is 12 in., the tarsus 1·2 in., and the wing span up to 1½ ft.

At its colonies the Lesser Kestrel is noisy, with calls more varied than those of its relative. *See also* Kestrel ; Falcon.

LESSER REDPOLL—Carduelis flammea cabaret. Of the three redpolls of this species to be seen in Britain—the Mealy, the Greenland and the Lesser—the Lesser Redpoll is the only resident and breeds, though somewhat locally, throughout the country. It is perhaps more familiar as an autumn and winter visitor, as large flocks of these birds arrive on our east coasts from the Continent in September and October, leaving again in March and April. Abroad, the Lesser Redpoll breeds in the mountains of central Europe, wintering in the Mediterranean countries.

Smaller than any of its relatives, the Lesser Redpoll is similar to the Linnet in that its crown and forehead are crimson, but it has a black chin. The mantle is brown with darker streaks, shading into grey further down the back;

Eric Hosking

LESSER REDPOLL. This is the only Redpoll to breed—even if somewhat locally—in Britain

the underparts are whitish and, in Summer, the male's breast is dark pink and the rump is tinged with pink. Across the wings are two buff-coloured bars. The female has no pink on breast or rump, but retains the crimson on the head. The tail is cleft, the stout beak yellow and the legs dark brown. The length is 4¾ in. and the wing span 6 in. ; the tarsus is 0·55 in. and the weight considerably less than ½ oz.

The Lesser Redpoll is very gregarious and in Autumn and Winter roams the countryside in flocks in company with other finches. Like the rest of its family, it delights in all sorts of acrobatic manoeuvres.

In its erratic and bounding flight, it has all the liveliness and buoyancy of the finches. Often it will fly to a greater height than other finches. It hops on the ground and roosts chiefly in bushes and hedges.

But for its very characteristic song-flight— if one can call its twittering love-call, often uttered at considerable height as it flies round in circles, a song—the Lesser Redpoll might pass unnoticed. Many of his ordinary notes resemble those of the Linnet and Siskin, but have been described as being less musical. His charming trill begins in late March and continues until August and sometimes even later.

The Lesser Redpoll breeds among the birch woods and conifer plantations. It will, however, also nest in large gardens and shrubberies in suburban towns and cities. The nest is cup-like and is made of small twigs with a lining

Eric Hosking

LESSER SPOTTED WOODPECKER. *Also called "Barred", this bird is extremely shy and elusive*

of moss, grass, wool, etc. The four to six darkish blue eggs, with markings in shades of brown, and rather darker and smaller than those of the Linnet, are laid usually in May or early June. The hatching, which takes 10–11 days, sometimes longer, is done by the hen alone, with the cock feeding her and watching nearby. The young are fed by both parents for a similar period. One brood is normally reared.

In common with the finches, the Lesser Redpoll feeds chiefly on the seeds of alders and birches ; some insects are also eaten.

LESSER SPOTTED WOODPECKER— Dendrocopos minor comminutus.

Its small size and black-and-white barred dress—which gives it its other name of Barred Woodpecker—make recognition of this bird easy. It is, however, very elusive and keeps to the higher branches of the trees it haunts, so that, if it were not for its " drumming " and call, it might easily be overlooked. A resident in the south and Midlands of England and in east Wales, it is rarer farther north and in the west. No reliable records exist of its having bred in either Scotland or Ireland. Various allied races breed in Europe, Asia, and north-west Africa.

Its upper mantle is black, copiously barred in white; its under-parts are brownish-white, and lack the crimson of the larger Greater Spotted Woodpecker (q.v.). The face and sides of the neck are white, the forehead lightish brown. The male's head is crimson and the female's white, but both sexes of the young have dull crimson caps. Neither male nor female have any marked seasonal changes. The straight bill and legs are slate-coloured, and the eyes reddish-brown. The length is 5¾ in., the tarsus 0·55 in. and the wing span 7 or 8 in. ; the weight is 1 oz.

The Lesser Spotted Woodpecker spends most of its time climbing about the high trees, it is seldom seen on the ground ; its flight has the usual slow, hesitating movement of woodpeckers. It haunts much the same type of country as its relatives, and its general behaviour and habits closely resemble theirs. But it has a typical loud call note, harsher than the Wryneck's, but easily confused with it because it follows the same succession of notes. A single call note, similar to that of the Greater Spotted Woodpecker, can be heard mostly near the nest. The " drum " is as loud as, but longer sustained and more pleasant to hear than, the abrupt drum of the Greater Spotted Woodpecker.

A cavity chipped out of the decaying wood of trees at varying heights—sometimes as high as 60 or 70 ft. from the ground—provides the nest, and no material beyond a few chips is used. The four to six white eggs, are laid in May, rather earlier than the Greater Spotted Woodpecker's. Both birds share the 14-day hatching,

John Markham

LESSER SPOTTED WOODPECKER, *a shy and elusive bird*

the night watches being taken by the male. The chicks are fed frequently by both parents for three weeks. One brood is reared.

The food of this bird consists chiefly of wood-boring insects and their larvae, and spiders.

LESSER WHITE-FRONTED GOOSE—Anser erythropus. A rare vagrant to the British Isles, this goose has been recorded at least nine times ; it breeds in northern Europe and Asia (Lapland, Siberia, etc.). The species is smaller than the White-fronted Goose (*q.v.*), and also has darker plumage, and a much larger area of white on its head ; its bill is shorter and smaller, and round the eye appears a rather swollen yellow ring. The total length is 21–26 in., the body being 16 or 17 in. ; the tarsus is $2\frac{1}{2}$ in. and the wing span about $2\frac{1}{2}$ ft.

The behaviour and breeding habits of the Lesser White-fronted Goose resemble those of other grey geese. Its voice, which is described as " higher and more squeaky " than its near relative's, can easily be distinguished when a single Lesser White-fronted Goose flies amongst a flock of White-fronted. Both male and female have a special alarm call, the male's being a characteristic high-pitched, far-carrying and frequently repeated call similar to that of the Pink-footed Goose ; the female's being fainter.

This species breeds among swamps and peat mosses at higher altitudes than most other geese, often even above the snow line in places where the snow has melted.

The food of the Lesser White-fronted Goose is thought to be like that of other grey geese—that is, chiefly vegetable matter (grain in the Autumn). Huge flocks of lesser white-fronted geese, sometimes numbering as many as 50,000, assemble in Winter on the mud flats of great lagoons, often mingling with White-fronted.

LESSER WHITETHROAT—Sylvia curruca. This summer visitor arriving in April and May is more restricted in range and fewer in numbers than its relative the common Whitethroat (*q.v.*), which it resembles in many ways. The Lesser Whitethroat is not uncommon in the south and Midlands of England and some parts of Wales, but is rare in the rest of England. Reports of its breeding in the south of Scotland have been received, but none from the north, and it appears in Ireland only as a rare vagrant. It is also a passage migrant on the east coast and the northern islands. Abroad, it breeds throughout Europe and western Asia, spending the Winter in Africa and southern Asia.

The Lesser Whitethroat is smaller than its close relative, and has a greyer mantle and whiter underparts (especially the throat), but the most reliable distinguishing mark is the lack of chestnut edgings to the wing feathers. The ear coverts are also conspicuously darker than the

Erica

LESSER WHITE-FRONTED GOOSE. *This rare visitor may build its nest far above the snow line*

cap, and the outer tail feathers are white. Male and female are alike. The length is $5\frac{1}{4}$ in., the tarsus $\frac{3}{4}$ in., and the wing span about 6 in. ; the weight is less than $\frac{1}{4}$ oz.

Habits and behaviour are similar to those of the common Whitethroat, but the Lesser Whitethroat, being more secretive than its relative, is inclined to seek the shelter of trees, dense shrubs and suchlike in more thickly wooded country.

Its song, unique among the warblers, is a soft warbling, interspersed with (usually four) strong far-carrying. rhythmical, rattling notes, repeated several times per minute. This is uttered from a concealed perch among bushes and thickets from the time of the bird's arrival in April until well into June. Its call notes resemble the common Whitethroat's. It has no special song flight, but a low warbling sub-song is heard in the Autumn.

The nest is placed 2–5 ft. above the ground in a dense bush, hedge or shrub. It is a frail structure built of dry stalks, roots and dry leaves by the cock, the lining and decoration of spiders' cocoons and hair being added by the hen. Four to six eggs, with a creamy-white ground and sepia-brown markings, are laid in May. Both birds share the hatching period of 10 or 11 days, and tend the young for the same period. One brood—occasionally two—is reared.

Insects, often captured on the wing, form the main food of the Lesser Whitethroat, but in Autumn it finds its way to gardens and orchards, where it will revel in soft fruit, especially red currants. *See also* Siberian Lesser Whitethroat.

LESSER YELLOW-LEGS—Tringa flavipes.
A much smaller edition of its " Greater "
relative, the Lesser Yellow-Legs has been recorded in the British Isles fifteen times.   It is a
bird of north America, breeding in woodlands
interspersed with lakes and wintering in grassy
marshes, lagoons and coastal mud flats.

The Lesser Yellow-Legs resembles the Redshank, but is rather smaller and has longer
and more slender bright yellow legs.   In
summer plumage, its back is dark brown,
copiously mottled and spotted in a lighter shade.
Its head, neck and breast are grey, the rest of
the underparts are white.   Its wings are grey
and its tail white.   Both sexes are alike.   The
length is 10 in., the wing span up to 12 in. and
the tarsus 2 in.

Its flight is strong and swift, with erratic
movements.   Its voice is described as having a
yodelling note and the song, uttered by both
male and female in their display flight, as being
a long-continued whistle.

The Lesser Yellow-Legs breeds on dry open
woodland.   Four buff or olive coloured eggs,
blotched and spotted in purplish-brown, are
laid in mid-May or June—usually later than
those of the Greater Yellow-Legs—and, as far
as is known, both the male and female incubate.

The Lesser Yellow-Legs feeds exclusively on
animal matter picked up on the surface of the
mud or from the bottom of the shallow water.
Locusts, grasshoppers, ants, molluscs and
crustacea of many varieties are all included in
its diet.   *See also* Greater Yellow-Legs.

LIBRARY.   Although the active part of
bird watching (*q.v.*) takes place " in the field ",
the enthusiast who wishes to make any real
progress in his chosen hobby will need to
devote some of his time to the quiet study of
books in his home or local library, in order to
benefit from the accumulated knowledge of
others.   Many beginners will want to build
up a reference library of their own, and a wide
choice of books is available to them.   In doing
so, they had best start with essential books,
and add to them as interest and taste dictate.

A good book on identification must be
numbered among those which are absolutely
essential.   Many books on this subject fail,
because their illustrations are not true to
colour—the various tints and shades in bird
plumage are very subtle and difficult to reproduce, except by the most expensive processes.

The five-volume *Handbook of British Birds*
(Witherby) is the standard reference work,
and is above reproach in this respect, but it
is expensive.   The beginner may consider it
beyond his means, but most serious students
feel that they must have it at any price or, at
least, ready access to it in a public library.

It contains everything of importance that is
known about every bird on the British list.

A one-volume *Popular Handbook of British
Birds*, based on the *Handbook*, has been published under the editorship of P. A. D. Hollom.

Most of the older generation of orncholo-
gists were brought up on the late T. A. Coward's
Birds of the British Isles and Their Eggs (Warne),
which has been through many reprints and
editions.   It is now published in two editions—
a full one in three volumes, of which the last
deals mainly with migration and habits, and
a short, pocket-size edition, which is an abridge-
ment of the first two volumes of the full edit'on.

Spotting British Birds, by Vere Benson, also
published by Frederick Warne, contains several
special aids for easy recognition, and his
Observer's Book of British Birds (Warne),
is a small, modestly-priced book for novices.

Two other moderately-priced books recommended for beginners are *Collins' Pocket Guide
to British Birds* and the *Field Guide to Birds
of Britain and Europe*, also published by
Collins.   Some of their useful features are
mentioned under Identification (*q.v.*).

In James Fisher's *Bird Recognition*, published in four volumes in the Pelican series, the
illustrations by *Fish-Hawk* are in wash, which
is better than bad colour plates.   *Wing-Tips :
The Identification of Birds in Flight*, R. Green
(Black) deals with one aspect of recognition.

Books on the general technique of bird
watching are comparatively rare.   The best
one of its kind is Nicholson's *The Art of Bird
Watching* (Witherby), but it is out of print
(1955) and not easy to obtain.   A thoroughly
sound and practical one for beginners is *Bird
Watching for Beginners* in the Puffin series,
and Stuart Smith's *How to Study Birds* (Collins)
is also good, as is *Bird Watching for Everybody*,
R. Harrison (Black).   Covering slightly different ground is James Fisher's *Watching Birds*
(Collins).   Two sound books on finding nests
are *Finding Nests* by Bruce Campbell (Collins),
and *Eggs and Nests of British Birds*, R. C. R.
Ford (Black).

All serious students will require a copy of
the latest *Check-List of the Birds of Great
Britain and Ireland* (B.O.U.).   A remarkably
full and authoritative, but expensive, work is
Birds of the British Isles, by D. A. Bannerman
and the late G. E. Lodge (Oliver & Boyd), of
which only three of the six volumes projected
have so far been published (1955).   Another
fine work in one volume is *British Birds*, by
F. B. Kirkman and F. R. C. Jourdain (Nelson).

For those who wish to specialise, there is
a fascinating selection of books to choose
from, of which only a brief number can be
given here.   The fact that many equally

excellent works have had to be omitted, is no reflection on their merit.

Behaviour. *Territory in Bird Life,* E. Howard (Collins) ; *Bird Watching and Bird Behaviour,* J. Huxley (Dennis Dobson) ; *Bird Behaviour and Display,* E. A. Armstrong (Lindsay Drummond) ; *Adaptive Coloration in Animals,* H. B. Cott (Methuen) ; *Social Behaviour in Animals,* N. Tinbergen (Methuen).

Bird Song. *Songs of Wild Birds* and *More Songs of Wild Birds,* E. M. Nicholson and L. Koch (Witherby)—with records.

Individual Species. *The Life of the Robin,* D. Lack (Penguin) ; *The Life of the Rook,* G. K. Yeates (Philip Allan) ; *Shèarwaters,* R. M. Lockley (Dent) ; the following *Monographs* on individual birds have all been published by Witherby—*Petrels,* F. Du Cane Goodman, *Pheasants,* W. Beebe, *Home Life of the Golden Eagle,* B. Macpherson, *The Osprey,* C. C. Abbot, *Terns,* W. Bickerton ; *Reed-Warblers,* P. E. Brown and M. G. Davies (Black) ; and the *New Naturalist Series,* published by Collins, includes among others—*The Redstart,* J. Buxton, *The Yellow Wagtail,* Stuart Smith, *The Greenshank,* D. Nethersole-Thompson.

Migration. *Bird Migration* and *Problems of Bird Migration,* both by A. Landsborough Thomson (Witherby).

Habitat and Locality. *Birds of the Coast* and *British Sea Birds,* C. A. Gibson Hill (Witherby) ; *Birds and Men,* E. M. Nicholson (Collins) ; *London's Birds,* R. S. R. Fitter (Collins) ; *Birds of the Green Belt,* R. M. Lockley (Witherby). Nearly every important British county has had a book written about its birds.

Photography. *The Art of Bird Photography,* E. Hosking and Cyril Newberry (Country Life) ; *Bird Photography,* G. K. Yeates (Faber).

Popularly Scientific. *The Biology of Birds,* J. A. Thomson (Sedgwick & Jackson) ; *Bird Biology for Beginners,* B. Vesey-Fitzgerald (Cassell) ; *History of Birds,* J. Fisher (Hutchinson).

The excellent series of modestly-priced *Field Guides,* published by the British Trust for Ornithology, on such subjects as ringing methods, nestboxes, field glasses, and trapping, will be found of great use by practical bird watchers.

The B.T.O. also publishes a list of bird books for beginners, and periodically book-lists are published in the *Ibis.* For the latest information on bird life, one must have recourse to the various journals published by ornithological associations. Among these are :

Ibis. British Ornithologists Union. Quarterly.
Bulletin. British Ornithologists Club. Monthy, except July-September.
Bird Notes. Royal Society for the Protection of Birds. Quarterly.
Bird Study. British Trust for Ornithology. Monthly.
Birds and Country Magazine. Quarterly.
British Birds. Witherby. Monthly.

LIMICOLA. Genus of the family *Scolopacidae* of the order *Charadriiformes.* It contains only one species, the Broad-billed Sandpiper (*q.v.*), which occurs in two forms in northern Europe and northern Asia, and, outside the breeding season, in the Mediterranean area, India, Borneo and Australia. It has only been recorded in the British Isles about twenty times.

LIMNODROMUS. Genus of the family *Scolopacidae* of the order *Charadriiformes.* It contains only two species, the members of which are chiefly distributed over north America, but also occur in south America and the West Indies outside the breeding season. A few members of this genus also wander to Europe occasionally. One of the two species, the Redbreasted Snipe (*q.v.*), is on the British list, but it has only been recorded authoritatively in the British Isles on about thirty separate occasions.

LESSER YELLOW-LEGS. Despite its name, this is one of the most typical of sandpipers, and it bears a very strong resemblance to the Redshank, a common resident

Maslowski & Goodpaster

C. W. Teager

LINNET. *The cock's forehead and breast are a
beautiful crimson only during the breeding season*

LIMOSA. Genus of wading birds of the
family *Scolopacidae* of the order *Charadriiformes*.
It contains four species, which are distributed
over much of the globe. Two species, the Bar-
tailed Godwit (*q.v.*) and the Black-tailed
Godwit (*q.v.*), occur in the British Isles, both of
them as non-breeding visitors, and as passage
migrants in Spring and Autumn.

These birds have long bills with a bluntish tip.
The wings are long and pointed, and the tail is
squarish. The legs are long and the tarsus is
covered with scutes (horny scales). There are
three front toes and a well-developed hind toe.

LINNET—Carduelis cannabina. This is a
member of the genus which also includes the
Goldfinch, Siskin, Twite, the redpolls and the
Citril Finch. The Linnet is widely distributed
in Britain and throughout Europe. It is rarer
in the Highlands and islands of Scotland,
where it is replaced by the closely allied
Mountain-Linnet or Twite (*q.v.*). The Linnet
is migratory to some extent, and many of the
home birds move south across the Channel in
the Autumn, returning in the Spring ; at the
same time, large numbers arrive from the
Continent to spend the Winter here, returning
home in the Spring. A bird of uncultivated
country rather than of the garden, the Linnet
frequents gorse-strewn commons, hillsides
covered with scrub, coast marshes and sandhills.

In his summer plumage, the male is a handsome bird with his mantle of warm chestnut
brown, underparts of fawn merging into white,
and grey head ; but his great beauty is the
crimson breast, crown and forehead. The wing
quills and tail feathers are dark, with conspicuous edgings of white. The tail is cleft, the
stout conical bill horn-coloured, and the legs

dark brown. The female is less colourful and
lacks the crimson. The length is 5¾ in., and
the tarsus ¾ in. ; the wing span is about 8 in.,
and the weight 1 oz.

The Linnet hops on the ground ; and bushes,
walls and fences, rather than high trees, are its
favourite perches. Its flight is rapid and
undulating, with the airy, dancing motion common to the finches. Gregarious at all seasons,
linnets roam the countryside in Winter—often
in hundreds—searching the fields for food, in
the company of other seed-eaters. Although
not a brilliant songster, the Linnet has a pleasant
and musical song, and its airy, twittering notes
are usually uttered from a tree perch but also
often on the wing. The cocks often join and
sing in chorus, for they are less inclined to have
an exclusive territory than many other small
birds. The song is heard in almost every month
of the year, but is at its best from the beginning
of April until early June.

Any rough ground with low bushes serves as a
breeding site for the Linnet. The nest, cun-
ningly put together by the hen alone, is made of
fine twigs, grass and wool, and lined with wool,
hair and sometimes feathers. Four to six eggs,
bluish-white in ground-colour and spotted and
streaked in purple and red, are laid from the
middle of April onwards ; two, and even three
clutches are hatched in a season. The incubation, which lasts 12–13 days, is carried out almost
wholly by the hen, but the male occasionally
relieves her. The young, which are very like
the female, are fed by both parents for nearly
another fortnight.

The seeds of weeds of many kinds constitute
the Linnet's food, but some insects are also
taken ; the chicks are fed chiefly on insects and
crushed seeds.

The Greenfinch — *Chloris chloris* — (*q.v.*) is
sometimes known locally as the Green Linnet.

LITTLE AUK—Plautus alle. The smallest
of its family, this is also the smallest diving bird.
Its usual home is the open sea, but in the Winter,
during stormy weather, hundreds of little auks
are sometimes driven on to our shores, usually
on the east coast, and occasionally inland.
Little auks breed in huge, closely packed
colonies in the Arctic ; according to some, they
rival the Fulmar as the commonest bird there.

The single egg is laid in mid-June in crevices
and holes in cliffs and rocks. The ground colour
of the eggs is pale bluish, often unmarked or with
faint yellowish brown spots or distinct streaks
and spots, chiefly at the big end. The incubation
period is 24-27 days, and is shared by both
sexes, who feed and rear the young chick for
about the same time. There is only one brood.

The small size and round, short bill of the
Little Auk prevent confusion with other auks.

In Summer, its plumage is principally black, with white underneath ; but in Winter, when it is likely to be seen here, there is also white on its throat and cheeks. The length is 8 in. and the tarsus 9 in., the wing span is less than 1 ft. and the weight 1 oz.

Away from their breeding haunts, little auks are silent birds, but in the nesting season they have various different noisy calls. The noise that arises from their colonies resembles the " alle " of their Latin name. *See also* Auk.

LITTLE BITTERN — Ixobrychus minutus. There is evidence that during the past 60 years this bittern has bred at some time in Norfolk and Suffolk, but at present it is known only as a rare visitor on migration in May and June. It has been seen in nearly every county of England and Wales, and occasionally in Scotland and Ireland. Its natural home is Africa and parts of Asia.

The smallest of the Heron family, it has the general Heron shape, but the white feathers on its wings, clearly visible when it is flying, distinguish it from all other herons. It is about 14 in. long, its wing span is just over 1 ft.

The Little Bittern has the same secretive nature as its larger relatives, and even an expert bird watcher may find difficulty in locating it. It is rarely seen by day, and feeds at night. As well as the marvellous camouflage (*q.v.*) with which Nature has endowed the Bittern (*q.v.*), it has the ability to " freeze " into a state of complete motionlessness ; even young birds have been seen to do this.

Its flight and movement on the ground are faster than the Bittern's, but its voice is quite different. The Little Bittern has various call notes—in Spring it frequently utters a deep, not very loud note, but one which, nevertheless, can be heard from several hundred yards away. The nest, which is built among the reeds, is a floating mass of roots and reeds, not unlike that of a Moorhen. The eggs, usually five to six, are white. There is one brood in a season and the rearing of the young follows the same lines as in the common Bittern—i.e. the hen does all the work.

LITTLE BUNTING — Emberiza pusilla. This bird occurs as a passage migrant on the east coast of England in the Autumn, and is usually recorded at isolated islands and migration stations ; for instance, it is a regular visitor to Fair Isle. It breeds in northern Russia, Siberia and Finland, wintering usually in India and China.

It is so similar to other buntings, that it may often be missed. In general appearance it is rather like a small Reed-Bunting, but it has rufous cheeks and duller underparts than its very near relative, the rare Rustic Bunting, in whose company it is sometimes found. Its length is about 5 in., tarsus 0·75 in., and its wing span about 6–7 in.

The song of the Little Bunting, sweeter and more varied than the usual monotonous bunting note, is not unlike that of the Robin. The call note is high-pitched, while the alarm note is low. *See also* Bunting.

LITTLE BUSTARD — Otis tetrax. The two types of this bird—the Eastern Little Bustard (*Otis tetrax orientalis*) and Western (*Otis tetrax tetrax*)—are nearly identical and appear in Britain only as very rare winter vagrants : the Western type has been recorded only three times, but the Eastern has appeared more often. The former breeds in south-west Europe and north-west Africa, and the latter in eastern Europe and south-west Asia.

The Little Bustard, as the name shows, is considerably smaller than the Great Bustard (*q.v.*). The males of both types have very distinct black-and-white collars, but the same grey heads and light underparts as the Great Bustard. The females of both are duller above and below, and lack the black-and-white collars in the Spring. The length of both birds is 17 in., and the tarsus 2 in. ; the wing span is 2½ ft.

Like the Great Bustard, the Little Bustard is a silent bird. A kind of humming can be heard on the ground as well as in flight; but there is scope for studying its vocal production further. *See also* Bustard.

LITTLE CRAKE — Porzana parva. An occasional vagrant visitor to Great Britain, this crake has been recorded in every month from March to November, but chiefly in the earlier part of the year ; Norfolk and Sussex are the counties most favoured. Abroad it breeds in central Europe and Asia.

It is a smaller bird than any of its relatives, with brown plumage streaked with black above;

Eric Hosking

LITTLE BITTERN. *This bird is as shy as its large relative and " freezes " when danger is close*

the underparts are grey, with black-and-white bars under the tail but no white above it. The bill is pale green, with some red at the base ; the legs are green, and the eyes red. The female has a distinctive buff face and underparts. The length of the Little Crake is 8 in., the tarsus 1·5 in., and its wing span 10 in.

It would certainly be well worth-while to study the voice of this bird further. The Little Crake can be heard day and night uttering its different calls, which vary from a soft sound to louder poly-syllabic trills and a fast dog-like barking, heard only occasionally, which sounds rather like laughter from a distance.—EDITOR.

The behaviour and nesting habits of the Little Crake hardly differ from those of the Spotted Crake (*q.v.*). It is fond of swimming and diving and will walk and wade over swampy places, but it never ventures far from its hiding place. *See also* Crake.

LITTLE EGRET—Egretta garzetta. Only one authentic record exists to show that this beautiful bird has ever wandered to Great Britain ; but the name " egret " is familiar, for this is, of course, the bird which produces the plumes so highly valued in the millinery trade. It is only in the breeding season that the Little Egret is adorned with this rare plumage, and in the 19th century. when feather ornaments in women's hats became fashionable hundreds of these birds were ruthlessly slaughtered.

Since male and female are alike, both were indescrimately killed, and the young were thus left to die a lingering death of starvation. Protests against the practice by ornithological and preservation societies began in 1908 ; but it was not until 1921 that the Plumage Act, brought forward by the Royal Society for the Protection of Birds, became law and the im-portation of skins or feathers of any wild bird was prohibited, except of birds usually used for food, birds imported alive or certain birds in-cluded in the Schedule of the Act. Some years earlier a similar campaign had been waged in the U.S.A., and the law there is now also on the side of the birds ; but Great Britain and the U.S.A. are the only countries which have attempted to check the trade by law.

The Little Egret breeds in many parts of southern Europe, south Russia, Africa, Aus-tralia and Asia. It has the typical appearance of a heron, but with a long, slender neck, and in Summer its plumage is dazzlingly white. On its back and breast are the long and much-sought-after plumes and from its nape, two long, thin crest feathers hang down. Its bill and long legs are black, and its feet yellow. The length of the Little Egret is 22 in., the body being 11 in., and the tarsus is 4 in. The wing span is about $2\frac{1}{2}$ ft., and the weight only 1 lb.

Resemblance to the Heron is shown in its walk, flight, breeding habits and voice. Outside the breeding season it is a silent bird.

The term " osprey ", often applied to egret plumes, is an ornithological misnomer, since the egret has no relationship whatever with the bird called the Osprey, which is a member of the Falcon family. *See also* Egret.

LITTLE GREBE—Podiceps ruficollis. Popu-larly known as the Dabchick, this is the smallest and most familiar of the British grebes. A resident, generally distributed throughout the British Isles though less abundant in Scotland and only a winter visitor to Shetland ; it breeds on all kinds of fresh waters which provide some cover of vegetation—lakes, ponds, meres and lochs, not excluding the ornamental waters of urban parks. In Winter, many find their way to reservoirs and estuaries. The Little Grebe is found all over Europe, although it is less abundant in the northern countries ; an allied form, very similar to the British bird, breeds in Asia, Africa and Australasia.

No crest or tippet adorns the head of the Little Grebe, and this fact chiefly distinguishes it from all other grebes. The round and stumpy body, with little or no tail, is dressed in dark brown, paler on the underparts. In Summer, the cheeks and throat are chestnut, and the base of the bill and gape yellowish-green; in Winter, the upper parts are paler brown, and the chestnut vanishes. The bill is black, and the legs greenish. The sexes are alike. The young are striped and mottled in dark brown.

S. C. Porter

LITTLE GREBE. *The Dabchick is the smallest of British grebes and the only one not to bear a crest. It is also less shy than the other grebes*

The length is 10 in. and the tarsus 1¼ in. ; the wing span is about 9 in. and the weight is 5 oz.

More often seen in the open than is usual with grebes, the Dab-chick flies with rapid wing-beats, spattering low over the water before the take-off. It is ·skilful at swimming and diving and spends much time doing so, submerging sometimes without a surface ripple, and at other times with a splash. This habit is no doubt responsible for the name of " Dab-chick " or "Dipchick". In common with its family, the Little Grebe, if alarmed, submerges under the water, with its head alone showing among the vegetation. Though it is seldom seen to do so, the Little Grebe can, if it becomes necessary, both walk and run.

Lacking a crest, which is always a prominent feature of the display of other grebes, the Little Grebe gives its voice first place in its courtship-display. Both male and female take part chasing each other over the water with many trillings, head stretchings and offerings of food and nesting material. The characteristic shrill trilling and whistling notes can scarcely be said to form a song. Usually heard on the water during the breeding season from March to May, they are frequently also audible during July and August and, occasionally, until October.

The breeding habits of the Little Grebe closely resemble those of the Great Crested Grebe (q.v.). Floating on the water, and sheltered by the over-hanging branches and vegetation of the lake or pond, the nest is built from weeds and plants brought up from the bottom, both male and female taking their share. The four to six chalky-white eggs, later much stained in buff and brown, are laid during April and onwards, two—and often three—broods are reared in a season. Hatching begins with the first egg, and both birds take part, the duration begin about three weeks. The delightfully pretty little chicks are tended by both parents and, like those of the Great Crested Grebe, are often carried on their parents' back. It is charming to watch them left to swim on the surface when the parents submerge, looking anxiously round and then scrambling back when the bigger birds reappear. Marine insects, small fish and some vegetable matter form the diet of little grebes.

Arthur Christiansen

LITTLE GULL. *The smallest gull breeds in Baltic countries and northern Asia, but is a more or less regular winter visitor to the English coasts*

LITTLE GULL—Larus minutus. As a winter visitor and passage migrant, the Little Gull is more or less regular in its visits to the British Isles. These chiefly occur from August to March on the east and south coasts of England, and the bird is rarely seen in Scotland and Ireland. It breeds in the Baltic countries and throughout European Russia and Asia, wintering in the Mediterranean, Black and Caspian Seas. Within recent years, a new colony has established itself in Holland.

This is the smallest of the gulls. Although somewhat similar to the Black-headed Gull, it can be distinguished by the absence of black on the tips of the pale grey wings ; the undersides of the wings are dark and slaty rather than grey and white, a further difference most conspicuous in flight. The rest of the plumage is white, but the tail has a black tip. The whole of the head and nape is black in Summer, and white with dark spots at the back in Winter. The bill is dark red and the legs red. The Little Gull is 11 in. long, and the tarsus is 1 in., the wing span is approximately 1½ ft., and the weight 3½ oz.

The flight of the Little Gull shows similarity to that of the terns rather than of the gulls, and has a curious wavering and hesitating quality not at all like that of the Black-headed Gull. Its voice is a little less harsh and strident than those of some gulls, and intruders near the nest hear an angry rattling note as it swoops down.

I have watched hundreds of little gulls feeding and discovered that these birds shift their position constantly, at the same time calling to each other, uttering a short, deep call, reminiscent of the Jackdaw's. In flight, they produce calls lasting 20 seconds or more.—EDITOR.

During the breeding season the Little Gull is found among marshes and marshy lakes ; the

LITTLE OWL. Unlike other owls, this plumpish bird may also be found hunting during the daytime

rest of the year is spent on both inshore and sea-coast waters, estuaries, etc. Built of reeds and rushes, the nest is set among the reeds and water plants. The three eggs, laid in May or early June, are like those of the terns. Incubation is shared by male and female. Little appears to be known about the behaviour of the young.

The major part of the Little Gull's food is taken in flight from the surface of the water, and consists chiefly of insects of many varieties and small fish. *See also* Gull.

LITTLE OWL—**Athene noctua vidalii.** The astonishing spread of this bird since it was introduced to Britain from the Continent in 1889 and again in 1896 has been one of the most remarkable events in the field of ornithology. Before those dates it was only a vagrant ; today, there is no corner of England and Wales, as far north as Lancashire and Yorkshire, where it has not established itself (although there have been recent reports of its decrease in some counties). In Scotland and Ireland it has always been fairly uncommon. The Little Owl breeds throughout the Old World, and has recently been introduced into New Zealand.

Whether the activities of the Little Owl were harmful or not from the economic point of view was for long a matter of much controversy. Until recently it was blamed for the decrease of such birds as blackbirds and nightingales, as well as for the death of game chicks, and had to face much persecution. But the result of investigations into its food, involving the examination of hundreds of ejected pellets (*q.v.*), has cleared its reputation, and the Protection of Birds Act (1954) names the Little Owl as a protected bird.

The smallest of British owls, the Little Owl is a plump round bird, with the appearance char-

acteristic of the Owl family. It has a flat head and short tail ; the upper parts are greyish-brown, streaked and barred in white ; the underparts are much lighter—almost white—and streaked in dark brown. The wings are round, and the large yellow eyes, surrounded by the flat facial disk, give it a fierce expression. The hooked bill is greenish, and the feet and legs are feathered. The length is 9 in., the tarsus 1·1 in., the wing span is about 1 ft., and the weight 5-8 oz.

The Little Owl runs rapidly on the ground, but rarely hops. Trees, hedges, fences, walls and posts are its favourite perches, on which it sits erect. A solitary bird, it is usually seen alone or in pairs. It roosts in the holes of trees or walls, or in some other sheltered nook. Most of its hunting is done at dusk or in the early morning, but, unlike other owls, it also goes about by day, especially in the breeding season and when the young are in the nest.

The Little Owl has the characteristic noiseless flight of its family, its motion in the air having a striking likeness to that of the woodpeckers. Except for various special mating calls, it has no proper spring display. Its ordinary voice, which is often heard by day, is a monotonous plaintive hoot, with many varying pitches. But one call is very like the beginning of the Curlew's song, and a curious snoring sound is often heard from its perch during the day. Often one may hear two little owls calling to each other for minutes on end—a very pleasant sound. The young have a continuous wheezing call.

The nesting sites are varied : holes in trees, and buildings, rabbit warrens, quarries and even the old nests of other birds, such as the Jackdaw, are all taken. No nesting material is used, and three to five white eggs are laid in April or May. The hen hatches them for about a month. The chicks, which are covered with white down, are at first fed by the male, but later both parents take a share. Normally there is one brood, but two are not uncommon.

Insects, mammals, earthworms, reptiles, fish, spiders, centipedes, and other birds are eaten.

LITTLE RINGED PLOVER—**Charadrius dubius curonicus.** A rare passage migrant until 1938, this plover has now the status of a breeding summer resident. It has bred sparingly in south-east England, and has shown some evidence of extending its range ; it has also bred in Scotland ; but in other parts of the country it remains exceedingly rare, although now reported to be more widespread on passage to and from its breeding grounds. Europe, Asia and Africa are its normal breeding places.

Its smaller size distinguishes it from the Ringed Plover (*q.v.*), but this is not always apparent unless both birds are seen together. The most noticeable difference in the plumage is the

John Markham

LITTLE OWL, *a falsely maligned bird—now protected*

For text see pages 336 and 399

absence in the Little Ringed Plover of the conspicuous white wing bar of the larger bird. Then again, the Little Ringed has a narrow white line above the black forehead-stripe, lacking in the Ringed species. Other differences, only to be seen at close range, are the blackish bill, yellow on the lower mandible, and the flesh colour of the legs and feet, which are never bright yellow or orange as in the Ringed Plover. Both sexes are alike in Summer, though during the Winter some slight differences may appear. The length is 6 in., and the tarsus 0·9 in., the wing span is approximately 10 in., and the weight 1½ oz.

In general behaviour and habits the Little Ringed is similar to the Ringed Plover, but it is more inclined to frequent fresh-water areas, and it is more excitable, demonstrative and noisy. Its voice is higher pitched and less musical than the Ringed Plover's, but the ordinary calls of the two birds are much alike. Delivered during courtship on its bat-like flight and also on the ground, the song of the male is a repetition of the ordinary notes, slow at first and culminating in a combination of trills.

Low sandy coasts and the sand and shingle banks of rivers are suitable nesting sites. As with other ground-nesting birds, the nest and eggs are zealously guarded by the parents, but even so are often unwittingly destroyed by the feet of passers-by. A hollow scraped in the sand or shingle, lined or unlined, suffices to house the four greenish-buff eggs, which are marked and streaked all over with brown spots. In England in April, these are laid on alternate days ; incubation is shared for 24 days by both male and female. The chicks, which soon leave the nest, are tended and fed by both parents. One brood only is reared in Great Britain.

Insects, caught while the bird is running along the shore or shingle, form the chief food.

LITTLE SANDPIPER. Local name for Temminck's Stint (*q.v.*).

LITTLE SHEARWATER—Procellaria baroli. This bird of the Atlantic, Indian and Pacific Oceans much resembles a small Manx Shearwater (*q.v.*), except that its feet are dark, not pink. Two races occur very rarely as stragglers in the British Isles, the Cape Verde Little Shearwater (*Procellaria baroli boydi*) and the Madeiran Little Shearwater (*Procellaria baroli baroli*), both described under their own names. The two vary only in the colour of their under-tail coverts, those of the Cape Verde race being black as against the Madeiran bird's white ones. Both races or subspecies are also found occasionally in France, Spain, Italy and Holland.

The voice of the Little Shearwater, though smaller in volume and much higher-pitched, resembles that of the Manx Shearwater.

LITTLE STINT—Calidris minuta. The stints, smallest of all the waders, are members of the Sandpiper family. Of the two which visit the British Isles as passage migrants in Spring and Autumn, the Little Stint is better known than its rarer relative, Temminck's Stint, although the latter is reported to have bred in the north of Scotland. A third variety, the American Stint, is only a very rare vagrant. The Little Stint breeds in northern Europe and north-west Asia, and winters in south Africa and southern Asia.

The Little Stint is often seen in the company of the Dunlin, and bears some resemblance to it, although the Stint is smaller. In Summer, the upper parts are a warm reddish-brown and buff, mottled darker on mantle and breast ; the underparts are white, and the wings have a pale bar and dark tips. In Winter—when the bird is likely to be seen here—the warm reddish-brown gives place to greyish-brown on both mantle and breast. The straight bill and legs are black. The length is 5¾ in., the tarsus 0·6 in. ; the wing span is approximately 8 in., and the weight a fraction of an ounce.

One of the tamest of the waders, even in the breeding season, the Little Stint is constantly on the move ; it is swifter on the wing than many of its larger companions (*see* Sandpiper), and does not probe among the mud and water for food as many waders do.

As heard on passage in Great Britain, its voice is a sharp and repeated trill ; when they are together on the shore, little stints give out a low twittering note. There are many variations on this, but the most characteristic is a humming, undulating sound, covering a fairly wide frequency range (*q.v.*).

The food, mainly taken from the surface of the water, consists of insects of many kinds, worms, small molluscs. sandhoppers and shrimps.

Eric Hosking

LITTLE STINT. *One of the smallest and tamest of waders, the Little Stint is always on the move*

LITTLE TERN—Sterna albifrons. One of the five terns to breed regularly in Great Britain, the Little Tern arrives from the Continent on the south coast in April and leaves again in September. It is also a passage migrant on our coasts, but is rarely seen inland. Abroad it breeds in Europe, Asia, Africa, Australia and north America, also the Caribbean region.

The smallest of the sea terns, this is also the only one with a white forehead and a yellow bill with a black tip in the breeding season. In Winter the crown is mottled, but the head remains black. The legs and feet are orange-yellow. Otherwise, the general appearance is similar to that of other terns. The female and young have a much duller bill, feet and legs. The length of the Little Tern is 10 in., and the tarsus 0·6 in. ; the wing span is approximately 16 in., and the weight 2 oz.

In the air it has the same buoyant and graceful flight as the other terns, but its wing beats are quicker, and it is not capable of such long flights on its journeys to its winter home as the rest of its family.

In behaviour and habits, the Little Tern follows the family pattern, plunging to secure fish and catching insects on the wing. It is valiant in defence of its nest and young, but, although it will occasionally dive at an intruder, it rarely attempts to strike. Its spring display and posturing are more or less the same as the Common Tern's (see Courtship ; Display). Its voice, less harsh and strident and less sustained than that of the Common Tern, is oftener heard on the wing. The Little Tern utters short calls of different pitches. These calls are louder and harsher than, but similar to, those of the Swallow. Sometimes a soft conversational, but hurried, sound may be heard from a number of little terns assembled on the shore.

Little terns are less gregarious than other terns ; their colonies are smaller and their nests more widely scattered. They arrive at their chosen nesting sites on sands and shingle banks, never far from the sea, during April and May. A hollow in the sand, made by the female, is the only preparation for the two or three eggs, which are very variable in colour, and match their surroundings extraordinarily well. If disaster should overtake the first clutch, a second is usually laid. Both male and female share the hatching, for three weeks. The chicks, which are clad in thick grey or yellowish down, with dark mottlings on the top and white underneath, leave the nest in a very short time—sometimes after only 24 hours. Tended by both parents, they begin to fly in about four weeks.

The food of the Little Tern consists of fish, worms, molluscs, etc. See also Tern ; Ternery.

Paul Popper

LITTLE TERN. The only one of the sea terns to keep its white forehead during the breeding season

LOCUSTELLA. Genus of the family *Sylviidae* of the order *Passeriformes*. It contains nine species distributed over Europe, northern and western Asia, and north-west Africa—and, outside the breeding season, in southern Asia and tropical Africa. There are four species on the British list—the Grasshopper-Warbler, Temminck's Grasshopper-Warbler, Savi's Warbler, and Pallas's Grasshopper-Warbler—none of which, except the first, has been recorded here more than a very few times. They are fully described under their own headings.

These birds possess slender, pointed bills, rounded wings of medium length, and rounded tails. The under-tail coverts are at least as long as the lateral tail feathers. The tarsus is rather long. Males and females have similar plumage.

LONG-EARED OWL—Asio otus. Since it is the most devoted to woodland and also completely nocturnal, the Long-eared Owl is less well-known than either the Tawny or the Little Owl. It is, however, a common and widely distributed resident throughout the British Isles, and breeds in most suitable wooded areas, although inclined to be very local in some of its haunts. In Ireland, where the Tawny, Little and Short-eared Owl are all absent, it is the commonest owl. A number arrive on the east coast and in the northern isles as passage migrants in Spring and Autumn. It is found throughout Europe, Asia, north-west Africa and north America. Pines are its favourite trees, and when these covered a larger area of Great Britain, the Long-eared was probably our commonest owl. Today it breeds freely in oak and beech as well as pine woods.

The Long-eared is smaller and slimmer in build than the Tawny Owl. The ear-tufts which give it its name are very conspicuous when erected ; but when—as they often are—they are kept flat and quite invisible, the wings and tail, which are longer than the Tawny or the Short-eared Owl's, together with the bright yellow irises of the eyes, are the best identification marks. The upper parts are a warm buff, mottled in brown and grey and streaked in darker brown ; the underparts are buff streaked in dark brown, and have bars forming faint crosses and arrows. The hooked bill is dark, and the legs and feet feathered. The length is 14 in., and the tarsus 1·6 in. ; the wing span is approximately 2 ft., and the weight 11 oz.

Various calls are typical of the Long-eared Owl. The most common is a sort of mixed whistling and squeaking. The love call of the male, though smaller in volume, otherwise much resembles that of the Eagle-Owl. The young utter a loud, plaintive whistling.

The Long-eared Owl is usually seen alone, except on migration and in Winter. It ejects pellets (q.v.) both when roosting and hunting.

Noiseless and leisurely as it sallies forth on its nightly hunting forays, its flight is typical of the larger owls. During courtship, both male and female indulge in zigzag flights among the branches, with much " clapping " of their wings, reminiscent of the Nightjar. An angry Long-eared Owl is a terrifying sight ; with its feathers raised and its wings forming a frame for its head, its yellow eyes glaring and its cruel beak snapping, it spits defiance at intruders.

During the day the Long-eared Owl is very difficult to detect, for it roosts hidden among branches with its slim, upright body pressed against the tree trunk so that it merges into the surroundings. Only when disturbed, or unmercifully mobbed by other birds that have discovered its presence, is it brought into the open.

The Long-eared Owl builds no nest, but uses the old nests of other birds (principally those of the Jay, Magpie, Sparrow-Hawk or Wood-Pigeon), or a squirrel's " drey ", in which it lays three to five white eggs, on alternate days in March or early April. Occasionally it will nest on the ground. The hatching, which commences with the first egg laid, is normally done by the hen alone, but the male has been known to take some part. The period of incubation is 25 to 30 days. The young at first are clad in white down, but later become barred in grey and brown. Both parents tend them for three to four weeks, when they are able to leave the nest. One brood is reared, but occasionally two.

Flying silently by night, the Long-eared Owl seeks its food among small animals and birds. Voles, mice, rats, moles and shrews are among the mammals that it pursues and kills. It is more destructive to bird life than the Barn-Owl. Some insects are also included in its diet.

LONG-TAILED DUCK—Clangula hyemalis.

A winter visitor, principally to the Orkneys, Shetlands and Hebrides but also, though less frequently, to the east coast of Great Britain and the north-east coast of Ireland, the Long-tailed Duck, also known locally as " Old Squaw ", is rarely seen inland, for it is one of the most marine of ducks. It is reported to have bred in the north at least once, and it may have done so more often unobserved. It breeds in the northern countries of Europe and Asia, in north America, Greenland and Iceland.

In Winter, when he is likely to be seen in Great Britain, the strikingly handsome drake is dressed in dark brown and white : head, neck, underparts, flanks and shoulders are white, while the rest of the plumage—and a patch on the side of the face—are dark brown. In Summer, except for his underparts and under-tail feathers, he changes to all brown. His orange bill, with dark base and tip, is distinctive, and, at all times, he can be identified by his long, slender and dark tail feathers. The duck's tail is much shorter, and she is much browner both in Summer and Winter, only her underparts being white. Her head is whitish but brown on top, and her bill has no orange. The legs of both are greyish. Before they attain adult plumage, which they do in their third season, the young resemble the winter duck.

The length of the drake is 17 in., excluding the tail, which is 5 in. long ; the tarsus is 1·1 in. ;

Eric Hosking

LONG-EARED OWL. *Once roused, this owl is a fearsome sight as it spits defiance at its enemies*

the wing span is about 1½ ft., and the weight 2 lb., the female weighing rather less.

At home in the open sea, the Long-tailed Duck swims buoyantly and is an expert diver. Dives to a depth of nine fathoms, lasting from 30 seconds to 1½ minutes, have been recorded.

The Long-tailed Duck is gregarious and not shy, but is seldom seen in company with other than its own relatives. Its carriage on land is upright, and it does not patter when taking off from the surface of the water. The flight is characteristic : the wings are held almost level with the body, which sways from side to side.

In the spring display, which may often be seen before the birds leave for their breeding grounds, numbers of drakes will surround one duck, with their tails erected and necks outstretched, uttering their extraordinary mating calls—followed by much quarrelling and chasing of one another.

> The oft-repeated call of the Long-tailed Duck, which has earned it the name of " Calloo " in Scotland, is heard at all hours on the water and in the air. This is one of the most romantic and musical sounds made by water birds.
> When I journeyed in 1953 to Iceland in the hope of recording the voices of the Long-tailed Duck and the Great Northern Diver, the success I achieved made ornithological history, and through the medium of broadcasting this duck's unforgettable call was brought to the ears of thousands who could never have had the experience of hearing it in its native haunts.—EDITOR.

Islands in lakes and fiords are the favourite breeding sites of the Long-tailed Duck. Little preparation is made to house the six to eight olive-buff or yellowish, elongated eggs, laid at the end of May, or in June or July farther north. For 24 days the hen incubates them alone, with the drake never very far away. Only the female looks after the young of the single brood for a period of five weeks.

The food consists mainly of animal matter— small crabs, shrimps and small fish—but in the Summer insects and their larvae are taken.

LONG-TAILED SKUA—*Stercorarius longicaudus.* This is a purely Arctic species, breeding in such countries as Iceland, Greenland, Siberia and Labrador, and visiting British waters only as a rare and irregular Autumn visitor, usually on the east coast of England.

Although a smaller and more elegant bird than the Arctic Skua (*q.v.*), its plumage much resembles the latter's lighter phase, except that it is somewhat greyer and, in Summer, has no dark patches on the breast. The long central feathers, which project about 8 in. beyond the others, are the best identification. The length is 23 in., including the tail ; the tarsus is 1·8 in., and the wing span is about 2½ ft.

Except that it is said to be less sociable than either the Arctic or the Great Skua, the Long-tailed Skua scarcely differs from them in habit or behaviour. It is the most graceful in the air, and will often hover in the manner of the Kestrel. Its calls are harsh and totally unlike those of its relative, the Arctic Skua. Outside the breeding season it is a silent bird.

The Long-tailed Skua breeds in small and scattered colonies on tundras or high barren land. The two greenish or olive eggs are laid in June in a rounded hollow in the moss or peat. Both male and female hatch them during 23 days, and tend and feed the chicks for three weeks ; after which the young are capable of looking after themselves.

Lemmings (small mammals similar to, and slightly larger than, voles) form a large proportion of its food, and the birds apparently breed where these are likely to be available. Other food includes insects, worms, fish, birds and various mammals. At sea it often obtains its food by compelling terns and gulls to disgorge their prey. The " Long-tailed Jaeger " is the name given to this bird in north America. It is also occasionally called " Buffon's Skua " in some older ornithological works of reference.

LONG-TAILED SKUA. This is the most graceful of all skuas with its beautiful long tail. Its plumage otherwise closely resembles the light phase of the Arctic Skua

H. N. Southern

John Markham

LONG-TAILED TIT. From its wonderfully constructed nest this tit has earned the name of " Bottle-Tit ". Male and female take a fortnight to complete its structure

LONG-TAILED TIT—**Aegithalos caudatus rosaceus.** Hard Winters wreak terrible havoc among our rarer small birds. The Long-tailed Tit suffered so severely in the eight weeks' frost of early 1947 that it was almost exterminated. But it is amazing how, given a series of normal Winters, the surviving remnant will recover their former status and even increase their numbers, and the Long-tailed Tit has proved no exception to this rule.

This is a British resident, widely distributed throughout the country, although much rarer in the north than in the south. It also breeds in Europe and Asia. Unique among the tits, and belonging to a different genus from the rest, this charming bird is easily recognized by its long narrow tail—longer than its body—and its colourings of black, pink and white. The underparts and head are white, the latter with a conspicuous black band over the eye extending to the mantle. The upper parts are dark, shaded in pink, with rump and shoulders in rose colour. The wings have white edges to the secondaries, and the dark tail is decorated with white on the outer feathers. The bill is short and small, and the legs blackish-brown. The eyes and irises are pink. The sexes are similar in appearance. The length of 5¼ in. includes the 3-in.-long tail; the tarsus is 0·6 in. The wing span is approximately 6 in., and the weight is ⅛ oz.

The most woodland-loving of the tits, the Long-tailed is best seen during Winter when it roams the countryside in company with other tits and small birds. Flitting restlessly among the trees and bushes of wood and coppice, it performs the graceful acrobatics of its kind, making great play with its long tail. Seldom seen on the ground, it has the typical flight of the tits. Although not shy, it is less inclined than other tits to haunt gardens, city parks and suburbs. The male's courtship chase of the female in the Spring is full of grace and activity, a striking characteristic being the strength and speed of the flight at that period in comparison with the birds' ordinary performance in the air.

The Long-tailed Tit has a number of varied and characteristic calls and songs. These are, however, mostly so quiet and high-pitched that they are only audible within a few yards.

The beautiful nest, which has earned it the name of " Bottle-Tit ", is an amazing effort for so small a bird. Built in thorn bushes, furze and brambles—sometimes also quite high in trees—it is fashioned with moss, woven together with hair, spiders' webs and lichens. The hole and centre of the dome-like construction are lined with a fantastic number of feathers—over 2,000 have been counted in one nest—a marvel of compression. The building of the nest, by both male and female, takes two weeks.

Here the 8-12 white eggs, spotted and streaked with red, are laid in March and April. Most of the sitting is done by the little hen, the cock roosting above. Both parents feed their numerous progeny for 15 or 16 days. How a dozen or so youngsters and their parents can squeeze into such a small space is one of the mysteries of Nature ; certainly the chicks have little room for development, for they are ugly and naked when they emerge from the nest. One brood, occasionally two, are reared.

Insects and their larvae, spiders and buds form the chief foods of the Long-tailed Tit.

The Northern Long-tailed Tit (*Aegithalos caudatus caudatus*), confined entirely to northern European countries and Asia, comes to Britain as an occasional rare visitor. A completely white head, whiter underparts and more white on the wings distinguish it from the British bird ; it is, however, not known to differ in either its habitat, behaviour or habits.

LOON. This is the American list's name for the Diver (*q.v.*) ; thus the Common Loon is the British list's Great Northern Diver (*q.v.*), and the Black-throated, Red-throated and Yellow-billed Loon are respectively the Black-throated, Red-throated and White-billed Diver (*qq.v.*).

In Britain, "Loon" often serves as local name for the Diver, specially in Norfolk and Suffolk.

LORES. Space between eyes and beak.

LOXIA. Genus of the family *Fringillidae* of the order *Passeriformes*. The three European species, which occur in a number of forms, are the Crossbill, the Parrot-Crossbill and the Two-barred Crossbill. These are all on the British list, but only the first-named is at all abundant in the British Isles.

The members of this genus are unique among British birds in having the upper and lower mandibles of their compressed bills crossed at the tip. In nestlings the bill is at first quite straight, but, as the birds grow, the tips of the mandibles begin to cross. The crossing may be either way, the lower mandible being turned either to the left or to the right.

The wings are long and pointed and the tail rather short, as is the tarsus. The males and females have differently coloured plumage, and the young are generally brown, streaked darker.

LULLULA. Genus of the family *Alaudidae* of the order *Passeriformes*. It contains only one species, the Wood-Lark, which occurs in a number of very similar forms in Europe, northern and western Asia, and north-west Africa. One form of the Wood-Lark (*q.v.*) occurs as a local resident in England and Wales.

LUNG. *See* Air-Sac ; Anatomy.

LUSCINIA (Latin, " nightingale "). Genus of the family *Turdidae* of the order *Passeriformes*. It comprises the nightingales, and its members are distributed over Europe, northern and western Asia, and north Africa ; outside the breeding season they are found in other parts of Africa and in tropical Asia. The genus includes two species on the British list, the Nightingale (*q.v.*) and the Thrush-Nightingale (*q.v.*).

These birds have rather short, slender bills, rounded wings of medium length, and shortish tails. In general appearance they are not unlike the Robin, to which they are related.

LUSCINIOLA. Genus of the family *Sylviidae* of the order *Passeriformes*. It contains only one species, the Moustached Warbler, which occurs in a number of forms, distributed mainly over southern Europe, Tunisia and western Asia. Outside the breeding season these are to be found as far south as Lake Chad in French West Africa. The Moustached Warbler (*q.v.*) is on the British list ; although it has been recorded here only once or twice, it is believed to have bred here in 1946.

LYMNOCRYPTES. Genus of the family *Scolopacidae* of the order *Charadriiformes*. It contains only one species, the Jack Snipe, distributed over much of northern Europe and northern Asia, and also parts of Africa and southern Africa outside the breeding season. The Jack Snipe (*q.v.*) is on the British list.

LYRURUS. Genus of the family *Tetraonidae* of the order *Galliformes*. Of the two species which are mainly found in Europe and northern Asia, one—the Black Grouse (*q.v.*)— is on the British list.

Eric Hosking

LUSCINIA. *Genus to which our loveliest songster, the Nightingale, belongs. Strange to tell, this rather drab-looking bird is related to the Robin*

MOORHEN

MACQUEEN'S BUSTARD. Local name for Houbara Bustard (*q.v.*), a rare straggler.

**MADEIRAN LITTLE SHEARWATER —
Procellaria baroli.** Eight specimens of this shearwater—most of them picked up dead on the coasts of Kent and Sussex—have wandered to Great Britain from their home in the Azores, Madeira and the Canary Islands. The variety belongs to a group of ocean-going birds similar to, but much smaller than, the Manx Shearwater. Little shearwaters are all very much alike, and only an expert can detect the minor differences in their plumage and behaviour.

The Madeiran Little Shearwater is distinguished from its fellows by having completely white tail-coverts. The length is 11 in., the tarsus 1·4 in., and the wing span about 1½ ft.

These birds are usually seen in small parties within reach of their home islands. They breed in holes and crevices in the rocks and boulders. Their flight is low over the water ; although excellent divers, they feed on the surface.

MADEIRAN PETREL — Oceanodroma castro. Recorded three times off the south coast of England and once on the coast of Mayo, Ireland, the Madeiran Petrel differs from that other rare visitor, Leach's Petrel (*O. leucorhoa*), only in having a less conspicuously forked tail, on which the white band is even in width and goes straight across.

The nearest breeding sites of the Madeiran Petrel are in the Azores, Madeira and the Salvages. Its length is 8 in., tarsus 0·82 in., and wing span about 12 in.

As far as is known, the habits and behaviour of the Madeiran Petrel resemble those of its close relative, except that it follows in the wake of vessels at sea. On the wing its voice is typical of that of other petrels.

MAGPIE — Pica pica. A member of the Crow family, the Magpie is one of our most distinctive birds. Owing to its fondness for the eggs of game birds, it is much persecuted in game preservation areas. In those parts of the country, therefore, it has become almost a rare bird, but in other districts it is a common

and familiar sight. Resident and well distributed in England and Wales, it is less frequent in Scotland, but in Ireland it has been a common bird since the 17th century.

Found in open grassland, hedges and the outskirts of woods, the Magpie attracts attention at once by its distinct black and white colouring and long tail ; indeed, it is the only large British land bird with this combination of features. Its head, neck and breast are black, with a green and violet sheen, and its under parts are white, showing conspicuously in flight. The young have the same appearance, but with a less glossy sheen. Magpies are seen in pairs and in small flocks, but they do not congregate in such numbers as the other crows.

The Magpie is 18 in. in length, with a tail of about 10 in. ; its tarsus is 2 in. The wing span is about 15 in., and the weight 8 or 9 oz.

On the ground, it walks when feeding, but if it is agitated or alarmed, it breaks into a peculiar, quick, sideways hop. It is fond of perching on trees, and has a direct, slow and rather laboured flight, with wings beating rapidly. During the Winter the Magpie becomes a wanderer, but at night it shares a

A. R. Thompson

MAGPIE. *This handsome member of the Crow tribe has the reputation of being of evil portent*

roosting place with others of its kind. It often conceals its food, and, like the Jackdaw, will steal and hide any coloured or shining object which attracts its attention.

The Magpie's call, which is quite distinct from those of the rest of the Crow family, is a loud chattering sound, with many variations during the nesting season. A soft musical song, which carries only ten or twenty yards, can very occasionally be heard.

The courtship displays are particularly interesting, and ornithologists believe that there is still much to learn regarding their meaning. Noisy groups are formed, the birds jumping about among the trees and chasing each other with much chatter. Some authorities hold that the gatherings are not specially connected with the mating season, but are purely social and take place at other times of the year.

The Magpie usually builds its large nest in a tall tree, but occasionally it chooses a bush or hedge row. Both parents assist in building ; the male bird brings the material—chiefly sticks for the main body of the nest, which is then lined with earth and roots. When complete, it looks like a dome of branches, with the opening well hidden. The eggs vary in number from five to eight, the usual colour being blue-green, with spots of brown and grey. The hen sits alone for 17 days, and the young are fed by both parents for 27 days. The Magpie rears only one brood each year.

This bird is an omnivorous feeder, but is particularly addicted to taking the young and eggs of small birds.

The Magpie has the reputation of being a bird of ill-omen, and many legends are told of it. A well-known couplet tells what omens are portended by various numbers of Magpies seen together at one time :

" One for sorrow, two for mirth,
Three for wedding, four a birth,
Five heaven, six hell,
Seven the deil's ain sel'."

Sea-Magpie is an alternative name for the Oystercatcher (q.v.), a black and white wader.

MALAR. Cheek-bone (from *mala*, the Latin word for " cheek ").

MALLARD—Anas platyrhynchos. The most familiar of wild ducks, the Mallard has the distinction of being the ancestor of all British domestic ducks. Few people can fail to recognize the Wild Duck, as it is often called, for it is the most abundant occupant of the ponds in every town and city throughout the British Isles, and so tame that it is almost willing to be touched. In addition to our residents, there are passage migrants and autumn visitors, and many which arrive to spend the Winter in Britain. It is almost as familiar throughout the Northern Hemisphere as in Britain, and the various forms differ very little in appearance. It is also popular as a sporting bird.

The drake is a handsome bird, with his beautiful dark-green head glistening with a violet and purple sheen, and his white collar and tail. His breast is dark purplish-brown, and his back grey, shading to brown above his grey flanks. The upper and under tail-coverts are black. The female, much less colourful, is dressed in brown and buff. Both sexes have grey wings, with a black-edged purple speculum bordered on both sides with white. During his summer " eclipse " (q.v.) moult, the drake's sombre dress is not unlike the duck's. The drake's bill is yellow, that of the duck greenish or reddish ; the legs of both are yellow. The young resemble the duck. The length is 23 in., and the tarsus 1¾ in. ; the wing span is about 2 ft., and the weight 2 or 3 lb. Among mallards a so-called albino (q.v.) often occurs, especially among those on the waters in the London parks ; these usually have bright yellow bills.

R. P. Bagnall-Oakeley

MALLARD. *The drake is a handsome fellow in his metallic-glistening plumage, while the duck is but drab-looking and well-camouflaged to escape foes*

John Markham

'MAGPIE AND STUMP', *a not uncommon name for Inns*

Karl H. Maslowski

MALLARD. This, the most familiar of British ducks, is also called the " Wild Duck " and few people would fail to recognize the drake with his glossy head and white collar

The Mallard is gregarious, and moves about in pairs ; even outside the breeding season it is unusual to see a duck without a drake in attendance. They flock with other surface-feeding ducks, and show a special liking for the company of teal. While the ducks are busy hatching the eggs, the drakes enjoy themselves by having small " parties " on their own.

The Mallard's swift and direct flight produces a kind of whistling sound. At home on the ground, it walks with a less awkward waddle than the domestic duck. On the water it frequently "up-ends" and feeds on the surface. Although it belongs to what are called the non-diving ducks, the Mallard can and does occasionally dive, especially if wounded, and the young are quite good divers.

Much study has been given to the Mallard's spring display, in which several drakes crowd round one duck, bowing, bobbing up and down, neck-stretching and chasing. The " quack " of the Mallard is well known. The duck gives voice much more frequently than the drake, but during the breeding season the latter has a subdued whistling call.

The haunts of the Mallard are many and varied. Winter finds it abundant on shores, marshes, tarns and lochs among the hills, and on small or large sheets of water everywhere. It pairs early in the year—sometimes as early as January—and breeds near any kind of fresh water. The nest is placed among the thick vegetation of bushes and hedgerows, in a pollarded willow, a tree hole, or the old nest of another bird, such as the crow. The nest is fashioned by the duck alone, and lined with leaves, grasses, down and feathers. The eggs, 10-12 in number, vary in colour from greenish-grey to greenish-buff and sometimes pale blue. On completion of the clutch, the duck hatches them alone for 28 days, but the drake is never very far from the nest. The ducklings are clad in dark olive-brown above and yellowish-white below. They are carefully guarded by their mother ; should danger be imminent, she will indulge in every kind of manoeuvre to attract the intruder's attention to herself and away from them. As soon as the ducklings are dry, they are guided to the water, to which they take at once ; from then on, the duck tends them alone. As a rule, only one brood is reared.

The Mallard eats almost any available food, whether it be animal or vegetable, culled from mud, soil or the surface of the water.

MALLIE. Name for Fulmar Petrel (*q.v.*).

MANDIBLE. The two mandibles (upper and lower) form the beak (*see* Bill).

MANTLE. Term for the feathers of the back ; i.e. the scapulars (feathers over the *scapulae* or shoulder-blades—between hind neck and rump) and wing coverts taken collectively. *See Plate facing* Page 1.

MANX SHEARWATER—Procellaria puffinus. This is the only species resident in the British Isles of the family of shearwaters—those nocturnal sea birds whose habits and behaviour remain more or less a mystery. The Manx Shearwater breeds in large colonies on such islands as the Scillies, Lundy, Skokholm, Skomer, the Orkneys and Shetlands and some

Eric Hosking

MANX SHEARWATER. *This bird was named after its low curving flight, skimming the wave-crests*

islands in the Hebrides ; also on several islands off the west coast of Ireland, and even on some mainland cliffs. Although at one time it flourished abundantly on the Isle of Man—whence its name—it no longer breeds there. At all seasons of the year it is present in most of our coastal waters, even if no known breeding site is in the neighbourhood. It is by no means a rare bird, but it is an unusual sight for people living inland or on the east coast. Abroad, it breeds on the islands of the Atlantic Ocean and the Mediterranean Sea.

Larger than the storm-petrels, to which all shearwaters are closely related, the Manx Shearwater is black above and white below, the white merging into greyish-brown on head and neck. Its bill is black and slightly hooked and has the typical tubular nostrils of the family. Its wings are long, pointed and narrow. The legs are pale pink. The length is 14 in. and the tarsus 1·9 in. The wing span is 2 ft. 6 in., and the weight 17 oz.

Like all shearwaters, the Manx rejoices in great beauty of movement in flight. Sweeping low over the water, it glides along, with its long and graceful outspread wings curving first to one side, then the other, as if " shearing " the waves. Outside the breeding season, its home is the wide ocean, where it is met either singly or in small groups. It neither follows nor collects round ships, as does the Storm-Petrel. The Manx Shearwater swims easily ; it occasionally dives for fish from the air, propelling itself in the water by its wings, but this is not one of its favourite pastimes. In contrast to its lovely movements in the air, it walks with great difficulty and is exceedingly awkward on the ground, where it shuffles along upright for only a few paces. It gets

along well enough on level ground but, if any obstruction is met, flutters over it.

No special spring display is evident ; what little courtship there is takes place mainly in the burrow, where the mating pair " scissor " bills and nibble at one anothers' head feathers. Mating usually takes place in the burrow, whence the various noises of male and female come clearly to the listener's ear.

At sea, the Manx Shearwater is silent, but at their large colonies a tremendous clamour generally fills the air.

No verbal description of the nocturnal flight of the Manx Shearwater is possible : one must see and hear it. The hundreds of burrows are quiet during the day and during a starlit night. As you go closer to the burrows, just before midnight you hear an eerie sound from under the ground, mostly from a single bird.
" One dark night full of drizzling rain, I was suddenly surrounded by hundreds of shear-waters, flying towards my recording gear, between my feet, close to my face, always uttering, whether close or distant, a nocturnal symphony—an indescribable cacophony which cannot be compared with any other bird noises. Those who heard my recording will remember the din. The birds' performance started at 12.30 a.m., and at 2 a.m. the shearwaters flew away towards the sea, the sound becoming fainter until it finally disappeared.—EDITOR.

Manx shearwaters reach their breeding haunts sometimes as early as February, and all will have arrived by the end of March. They seem reluctant to leave the sea to begin the business of breeding, and for a time they remain on the water, dispersing to feed. Finally they settle to their domestic duties, beginning by excavating a burrow, 2–4 ft. long, in soft earth. Both birds take part in this. A nesting chamber is made at the end of the burrow to house the one white egg, measuring 2½ in., which is laid in May. The same musty smell emanates from the burrow as from the Storm-Petrel's, but it is less strong.

At their colonies, Manx shearwaters are strictly nocturnal, and all comings and goings take place during darkness ; even a fine moonlight night will keep them at home. Both male and female take turns at incubating, in sessions of two or three days, the absent bird going south, often to a great distance, to feed. The period of incubation is seven to eight weeks. The chick, which is clad in grey-brown and grey-white down, is fed and visited by its parents by night for a further eight or nine weeks. It is then abandoned. It lives for about 10 days on its surplus fat, then makes its slow and arduous way, under cover of darkness, to the sea and, like the parent birds, disappears from sight.

Shearwaters leave their breeding sites in August. Their exact destination is unknown ; for the rest of the year they must wander over the vast ocean, until the call of another Spring lures them back.

The Manx Shearwater feeds chiefly on small fish of various kinds—young sprats, herrings, pilchards and small squids—picked up from the surface of the sea as it flies along.

Its chief enemies are gulls, rats and humans. At one time thousands were killed to provide animal manure, with the result that several colonies were exterminated or their numbers very much reduced. In the past 30 years, however, where they have been unmolested, these birds have flourished and increased.

MARSH-HARRIER—Circus aeruginosus.

All three harriers—the Marsh-, Montagu's and Hen-Harrier—are now included among the rare British birds of prey ; but the Marsh-Harrier is the rarest and, if it were not for a few pairs still attempting to breed in England and Ireland, would be extinct as a British breeding species. A dweller in swamps and marshes, the " Moor-Buzzard " nested at one time in all suitable parts of the country, but it fared badly, as did many other birds of similar habitat, when so much land was drained and cultivated in the 19th century. As a rare bird, it naturally became a victim of the egg collector. Today, apart from the few still breeding, it is only a rare and irregular autumn and winter visitor. Abroad it breeds in Europe, Asia and Africa.

The largest of the European species, the Marsh-Harrier is very variable in plumage ; the predominating colour is dark reddish-brown, with darkly streaked head and shoulders of light buff—a reliable distinction from the other harriers, which are grey. The long rounded black-tipped wings and unbarred tail of the male Marsh-Harrier are grey. The female is slightly larger and has lighter buff on head and shoulders, but does not otherwise differ much from the male. The bill is black and hooked, the yellow eyes are set in an owl-like face. The legs are yellow. The length is 19-22 in., the tarsus 3½ in. ; the wing span is about 3 ft., the weight 1¾ lb.

Solitary in habit and heavier in flight than its relatives, the Marsh-Harrier ranges over the marshes and reed beds, flying low with leisurely and graceful wing-beats, and hovering now and

then in order to track the prey on which it swiftly pounces. Like other birds of prey it ejects pellets (q.v.).

Spring brings an extraordinary display of spectacular air acrobatics. Soaring to a great height, the male dives down through the air, somersaulting and " looping the loop " on the way, and uttering his plaintive shrill mating note. The female meets him in the air to receive her gifts of food.

Outside the breeding season the Marsh-Harrier is silent, but during it, apart from the mating call, many varying mews and whistles are heard from both male and female in or near the nest.

The Marsh-Harrier confines its breeding to large tracts of marshland and reed beds. The bulky nest is well concealed among dense vegetation, often surrounded by water several feet deep. Built by the hen alone, it comprises a platform made of sticks, roots, reed stems and sedges. Occasionally the male will assist, but usually he builds a " cock's nest ". Three to five eggs are laid at intervals of two to four days during May, and are an unglossed white or pale-blue colour. The incubation is done largely by the hen, beginning with the first egg ; the period of hatching is 33-38 days. The male provides the food for the mother and nestlings, bringing it in his feet to the nest or passing it to his mate in the air. The chicks are clad in white down ; almost two months elapse before they are fully fledged. The female chick attains adult plumage in the second season, the male in the third. One brood only is reared each season.

The Marsh-Harrier has a varied diet of voles, frogs, toads, rats, mice, and birds of various species ; eggs are also taken during the Spring.

Eric Hosking

MARSH-HARRIER. *Rarest of harriers to be found in this country, this is a solitary bird of prey, breeding in marshlands and large reed beds*

MARSH-SANDPIPER—Tringa stagnatilis.

This bird of eastern Europe and central Asia has been seen in the British Isles eleven times, eight of its visits being to Sussex and Kent. A slender and graceful bird, it is about the size of the Green Sandpiper, but with plumage not unlike that of the Greenshank. Its greenish legs are rather longer than those of the latter, and project conspicuously behind it in its typical sandpiper flight. In Winter, when it is likely to be seen in Great Britain, its mantle is grey and its underparts and lower back white. But in Summer it wears a very different garb, for its mantle and lighter underparts are then richly speckled and streaked in dark brown. The length is 9 in. and the tarsus 2 in. The wing span is about 1 ft. Apart from size, the Marsh-Sandpiper is distinguished from the Greenshank by its very fine, straight bill.

Many of the agile and graceful movements of the Marsh-Sandpiper are like those of the Greenshank, especially when it is feeding, but its spring display closely resembles the Green Sandpiper's. Observers describe its voice as a weaker version of the Greenshank's.

Grassy marshes, meadows and pools are the favoured sites of the Marsh-Sandpiper, which breeds either in separate pairs or in small colonies. The nest is only a hollow in the grass, lined with bents. The four or five buff or yellowish-brown eggs, blotched and spotted in purple, are laid in May or June, according to the place of breeding. Both birds appear to take part in the hatching, but the period is unknown. One brood is reared.

Aquatic insects and their larvae, probed from marshy ground, are this sandpiper's chief food.

John Markham

MARSH-TIT. *Despite its name, this little tit shows no special preference for swampy districts*

MARSH-TIT—Parus palustris.

So alike are the Marsh- and Willow-Tit that it was not until 1900 that ornithologists decided that they belonged to different species, and there seems no doubt that they must at some time or other have had a common ancestor. No particular significance attaches to the title of "Marsh", for this bird shows no preference for damp districts. Both species live and breed in much the same type of country, a fact which adds to the difficulty of distinguishing between them.

Although not so abundant as the Great, Coal- or Blue Tit, the Marsh-Tit is a resident in England and Wales; in Scotland and Ireland, except where it has been introduced, it is practically unknown. Except in Greece and some parts of Spain, it breeds all over Europe.

The only recognizable mark of difference in plumage between the Marsh- and Willow-Tit lies in the fact that the former has no white patch on its wings and has a glossy, not sooty, black crown. But these marks are not always apparent, and the young of both tits are exactly alike. For the rest, the Marsh-Tit is a sober-looking little bird, with a brown mantle and paler underparts. The head, nape and chin are black, the cheeks and sides of neck whitish, and the bill black. The legs are bluish-green. Male and female are alike. The length is $4\frac{1}{2}$ in., and the tarsus 0·55 in. The wing span is 5 or 6 in., and the weight is $\frac{1}{8}$ oz.

Following the family pattern in behaviour, breeding habits and flight, the Marsh-Tit flits actively about the bushes and branches, often hanging upside down by one leg. It is not really gregarious, but in Winter will be found seeking food with others of the family.

Like other tits, the Marsh-Tit has a wide variety of vocal notes; almost all of them—but especially the song—are totally different from the Willow-Tit's, and in that fact lies a safe distinguishing mark for those who are familiar with the sounds of the two birds. The Marsh-Tit has several differing nasal calls, including a harsh breeding note. Its song, usually delivered from a tree, is a simple repetition of notes with a liquid bubbling quality. This can best be heard during March and April, but there is no time of the year at which the bird is entirely silent.

Woodlands, hedgerows, copses, orchards and gardens are all favoured nesting sites of the Marsh-Tit, and, although not so easily attracted to a nesting box as some other tits, it will also use one, especially if food is provided. The nest is placed in a ready-made hole in the ground, in a tree or stone wall; the Marsh-Tit rarely makes a hole for itself, but it will enlarge an existing one. On a closely packed foundation of moss, wool, hair, fur and down, the seven or eight white red-spotted eggs are laid in April or May. The little hen hatches them alone for 13 days, but the young are fed and tended by both parents for over a fortnight. Normally one brood is reared, but occasionally two.

Insects form the main food of the Marsh-Tit, but many kinds of seeds are also taken

MARSH-WARBLER—*Acrocephalus palustris.* A close relative of the Reed-Warbler, the Marsh-Warbler is a summer visitor and one of the rarest of British breeding birds. Only a few of the southern counties of England, including Somerset, Gloucester, Dorset and the valleys of the lower Severn, are favoured with its presence, though from time to time there are records of its occurrence in other counties. As far as is known, the Marsh-Warbler has never bred in Wales or Ireland, and Scotland sees it only as a very rare vagrant. A late arrival, it seldom appears before late May or June. Abroad it breeds in many parts of Europe and Asia, wintering in Africa.

So similar is the plumage of the Marsh-Warbler to that of the Reed-Warbler (another summer visitor), that only those very familiar with both species can tell one from the other. The Marsh-Warbler has a paler shade of olive in its brown mantle and lighter underparts, and lacks the reddish tinge which appears on the rump of the Reed-Warbler. It has a thin, brown bill, and legs of pale flesh colour. The sexes are alike, and the young are similar to those of the Reed-Warbler. The length is 5 in. ; the tarsus 0·9 in. ; the wing span about 6 in. ; and the weight less than ¼ oz.

The Marsh-Warbler's habits and general behaviour are the same as its close relative's, but it is somewhat less secretive. Its favourite haunts are willow and osier beds with dense vegetation, especially those overrun with meadow-sweet and willow herb ; on the Continent it sometimes nests in cornfields.

The Marsh-Warbler's song—one of the loveliest to be heard in England—is its chief distinction, excelling in beauty and tone both that of the Sedge- and Reed-Warbler.

Its performance as a mimic has no rival ; I have recorded imitations of the Great Tit, Skylark, Linnet, Blue-headed Wagtail, Whinchat, Nightingale, and Redstart.—EDITOR.

The Marsh-Warbler often sings by night. The song is usually uttered from a tall bush, plant, or small tree, and is best heard before the nest is completed at the end of May or early June. The British Marsh-Warbler's song is not usually heard for longer than the best part of a week, in contrast with its Continental relative's, which can be heard for a month or two.

The nest is placed in a willow or osier bed, on the banks of a stream or at the foot of a

G. K. Yeates

MARSH-WARBLER. *This, one of the rarest of British breeding birds, is found only in the south*

hedge, not necessarily near water. Its clever construction differs from that of the Reed-Warbler, for it is shallower, and fixed by " basket-handles " rather than woven round adjacent vegetation. It is built by both male and female, the hen taking the larger share, with dry grasses and dead weeds, and lined with roots and hair. Four or five whitish eggs, blotched and streaked in purple and olive, are laid in June. Both birds hatch them over a period of 12 days, and the single brood is reared by the parents for 10-14 days.

Insects form the chief food of both adults and young, but some berries are also taken.

MARTIN. Name applied to certain members of the Swallow family (*Hirundinidae*), of which only two are resident in Great Britain ; the House-Martin (*Delichon urbica*), sometimes called the " Window-Swallow ", to distinguish it from the " common " or " Chimney-Swallow ", and the Sand-Martin (*Riparia riparia*). The Purple Martin, also called Purple Swallow, has been reported as an occasional visitor from north America. The Crag-Martin (*Ptyonoprogue rubestris*) frequents southern Europe, but has not been reported in this country.

Like other members of the Swallow family, martins are distinguished by their slim, streamlined form and graceful flight. They have long, pointed wings, a long head, slender bill, small legs and feet, scutes on the front of the tarsus, and, usually, a forked tail.

The House-Martin is glossy bluish-black above, white below and on the rump ; the feet are covered with short downy feathers. Its length is a little over 5 in. ; the sexes are similar. The nest is built of mud or clay, like that of the

Eric Hosking

MARTIN. *These relatives of the Swallow may be recognized by their slender bodies and aerial grace*

Swallow, but is hemispherical, with its entrance on the side, and is attached to a rock or the wall of a house, frequently under the eaves or in the upper angle of a window.

The Sand-Martin is slightly smaller than the House-Martin and has naked toes and a moderately forked tail. The plumage is brown on the upper parts and across the breast ; the underparts are white. It nests in sandy river banks, sides of sand banks, etc., excavating with its bill tortuous galleries, ranging from 18 in. to 5 ft. in length.

The general colour of the Purple Martin, both of upper and underparts, is shiny purplish-blue ; the wings and tail are black.

MARTIN, PURPLE. *See* Purple Martin.

MASKED SHRIKE—Lanius nubicus. Only one Masked Shrike, identified in Kent in 1905, has ever wandered to Great Britain from its home in south-east Europe and south-west Asia. Smaller than any of the British shrikes, it has black and white plumage, with reddish underparts. Its length is 6¼ in.

Two broods are reared a season. Little difference is shown in behaviour and habits from other shrikes, but the Masked Shrike is described as being " more lively and graceful ".

MASKED WAGTAIL—Motacilla alba personata. A subspecies of the Continental White Wagtail, which is a spring and autumn passage migrant to the British Isles, the Masked Wagtail was once identified and recorded at St. Leonards, Sussex, in 1919. Its normal home is central Asia. A white line behind its eye and darker ear-coverts are its distinguishing marks. The length is 5½ in. Its breeding habits and behaviour are similar to the White Wagtail's.

MATING. This term is used rather loosely to mean either the general association of two birds of the opposite sex (in which sense it is considered here) or, more specifically, the sexual union of two birds. The sequence of events covering the actual selection of a mate is called pair-formation, or pairing (*q.v.*) ; the latter word is also sometimes used as a synonym for mating. A similar difficulty exists in defining courtship (*q.v.*), which some ornithologists take as the whole period from the beginning of pair-formation until fledging and sometimes beyond, while others think of it as the period immediately before, and leading up to, coition.

It is quite impossible to generalise about the mating habits of birds ; not only do the species themselves differ, but often individual pairs behave in a way that is not typical of other members of their species. But on one point most authorities are agreed—that however active the male may be in courtship, he does not seek out and select a mate ; the female does that. Why she chooses one particular male, and rejects another, is still a mystery.

Darwin thought that " the females are most excited by, or prefer pairing with, the more ornamental males, or those which are the best songsters, or play the best antics ". But species which have been studied closely show many instances of a female preferring what, at least, by human standards, appears to be one of the less well-favoured males, in respect of either his dress or song—although it must be admitted that a bird's assessment of the quality of a song may be entirely different from our own.

Furthermore, although a male may be rejected by one female it does not follow that he will fail to appeal to another. Moreover, a male that is unmated one season may be successful in the next, and vice versa.

As in human relationships, the selection may be made for purely personal reasons ; although there are indications that among certain territorial birds, some of the females have a predilection for a particular territory—returning to the same one year after year—irrespective of its male occupant.

Most song-birds pair for one season only ; this is due to the fact that the sexual urge is seasonal, being entirely dormant for a large part of the year (*see* Breeding Season), but the Marsh-Tit has been proved to pair for life, and other tits, and the Nuthatch and Stonechat are suspected of forming life-long associations. Life-pairing has also been proved or claimed for members of the Crow family, moorhens, little grebes, geese, swans, parrots and others.

With the exception of the Wren and the Corn-Bunting, which may have up to six or seven wives, European birds are monogamous. This is probably because the male—particularly where the clutch is large—finds it impossible to feed more than one family.

Occasionally, bigamous males are found in species (e.g. Robin) that are normally monogamous, but in such cases the male usually deserts one or both of his spouses round about the time of incubation, usually to be supplanted quickly from among the unmated cocks. Instances of " divorce " have also been recorded ; according to Lack, among robins about 10 to 18 per cent of the hens deserted their mates either in the engagement period or between the first and second broods.

As mentioned under courtship (q.v.), the family life of birds follows a sequence very different from that of human beings. First comes the selection of the mate (pair-formation), a period of excitement which may last a few hours or several days, and this may precede courtship proper (leading up to coition), by several months or only a few days. In the first case, the excitement of pairing may be followed by a period during which the male ignores his mate.

Both at pairing and during courtship proper, one or both sexes may indulge in what Darwin called antics (see Display ; also Behaviour ; Dance), aerial acrobatics and chasing (in some species the male, towards the end, chasing the female towards the nest). With some species coition is attended by great excitement, whereas, in others it arouses comparatively little interest, the preliminaries apparently being far more emotionally satisfying to the birds concerned.

During copulation the female usually takes up a crouching position, lifting her tail. The male mounts her and applies his cloaca (see Anatomy) to hers, and male fluid then passes into the female cloaca from little widenings in the sperm ducts of the male, where it has been stored (see further illustration of Mechanisms of Reproduction, in page 94). Some males, which might have difficulty in passing sperm in this way—e.g. ducks, which copulate on water— have a small penis ; but this is unusual.

The building of a nest is part of the essential work of many species during the mating period, sometimes performed by both sexes, sometimes by the female alone—the male acting as builder's labourer and carrying the material. Similarly, sometimes both sexes assist in incubation, and sometimes only one, and during this period the male may, in certain species, caress his mate and feed her, either actually or symbolically, in the so-called bond-forming display.

MAVIS. Local name for Song-Thrush (q.v.).

MEADOW-BUNTING. See East Siberian Meadow-Bunting, an extremely rare straggler.

MEADOW- PIPIT—Anthus pratensis. Though included in the Wagtail family (Motacillidae) because of their similar body, bill and walk, pipits have, in habits and behaviour, more in common with the larks—and " Titlark " is another name for the Meadow-Pipit.

This is an abundant resident throughout the open country of the British Isles, though apparently scarcer in the south and east. In Winter, many of the northern birds move south, and some emigrate ; at the same time, many more arrive from the Continent. The Meadow-Pipit also breeds all over Europe and west Asia.

It closely resembles the Tree-Pipit. Its upper parts are a warm brown, streaked darker ; its underparts are much paler ; and its white outer tail feathers are very conspicuous in flight. Its hind claw is much longer than that of the Tree-Pipit. It has a thin dark bill, and flesh-brown legs. The length is 6 in., and the tarsus 0·85 in., the wing span is 7 in., and the weight 1 oz.

A gregarious bird outside the breeding season, the Meadow-Pipit moves about low pasture lands, marshes, sewage farms, etc., in company with other pipits and wagtails. It walks and runs on the ground, rarely perches on a tree, except occasionally when on migration.

> In general, the song of the Meadow-Pipit is not particularly noteworthy, and, though it is delivered from the ground, a shrub bush or post, the air seems to be its most natural place. Nevertheless I have recorded on a Scottish moor an individual Meadow-Pipit with a beautiful musical song which included a perfect rendering of the characteristic notes of its kind.—EDITOR.

It is a great joy on a spring day on high moorland or heath to watch dozens of these delightful

MEADOW-PIPIT. Known as " Cuckoo's Servant " in Welsh, this bird hatches many a Cuckoo's egg

H. N. Southern

MEALY REDPOLL. This is the Redpoll of the north, breeding in northern and central Europe, northern Asia, Canada and even in inhospitable Greenland

little birds revelling in their courtship. Rising from the heather they fly with fluttering wings to a height of between 10 and 100 ft., singing as they rise a typical and musical little nuptial song—quite different from the Tree-Pipit's—and then descend again almost to the same spot. The average time of the ascent and descent ranges between 17 and 23 seconds. The song, which persists throughout the breeding season until July, is often heard when the songs of other birds are stilled.

The Meadow-Pipit breeds on every kind of uncultivated country—moors, bogs, heaths and sand dunes. The Cuckoo seems to have a particular liking for it as a foster mother, for the Meadow-Pipit probably brings up more Cuckoo chicks than any other bird ; indeed, in Wales, it goes by the name of *Gwas-y-gog* (" Cuckoo's servant ").

The nest, well concealed among the heather, is built of dry grasses and bents, and from late April, two, and even three clutches of three or four eggs, very variable in colour, are laid. The hen hatches them for 13 or 14 days, and both parents rear the young for another fortnight.

Insects of various kinds form the chief food of the Meadow-Pipit but it is also said to take seeds, and Saxby in his *Birds of Shetland* remarks that it is very fond of eating the seeds of rye-grass. " Hill-Sparrow " and " Teetick " are two of the names given to this bird in the north.

MEALY REDPOLL—Carduelis flammea.
Unlike the Lesser Redpoll, which is a British resident, the Mealy Redpoll—which is the sub-species common in north America—comes to Great Britain only as a very irregular visitor, arriving from October to May. In some years, the influx is very great. It appears along the whole of the east coast, but is more likely to be

seen farther north, especially in the Shetlands. It breeds in northern and central Europe, northern Asia, Greenland and Canada.

It might be as well to state here that three subspecies or races of the common Redpoll species (*Carduelis flammea*) occur in the British Isles. These are the Lesser (*C.f. cabaret*), Mealy (*C.f. flammea*) and Greater (*C.f. rostrata*) Redpoll.

Recognition of the Mealy Redpoll is difficult, since it closely resembles the Lesser Redpoll. It is, however, larger, and has a distinctly paler appearance (especially in its underparts) that is very noticeable when it is seen in large numbers. Its crown is brighter, but in winter plumage this is not distinguishable. Above, it is brown, streaked in light grey ; its brown tail and wing feathers are tipped with white ; and it has a whiter wing bar than the Lesser Redpoll. The cheeks, throat and breast are pale pink, which in Summer becomes a deep rose colour. The female is almost indistinguishable from the Lesser Redpoll hen. The length is 5 in., and the tarsus 0·6 in. ; the wing span is 7 in. ; and the weight a fraction of an ounce.

In Autumn, when it is likely to be seen here, the Mealy Redpoll haunts birch copses, conifer plantations, hedgerows and open spaces. The bare stony hillsides and rocky ground of the Shetlands are also a favourite haunt, a characteristic which has earned it the name of " Stone Redpoll ". But it will resort to garden and cultivated land in search of food. Like all redpolls, the Mealy Redpoll is gregarious and associates with other finches. It shows little difference in behaviour and habits from the Lesser Redpoll, but its song is said by those who are familiar with the trills of both species to have a fuller and deeper tone.

The nest is placed in the fork of a tree, and five or six eggs are laid, generally in June or later, the date depending on the altitude and the region. As far as is known, the hatching and rearing of the chicks follows the family pattern. Seeds form its main diet, and Saxby in his *Birds of Shetland* remarks that when the common sorrel is abundant, a flock of mealy redpolls will become so intent on seeking its seeds that an approach can be made to within a few feet of them. Some insects are also taken.

MEDITERRANEAN BLACK-HEADED GULL—Larus melanocephalus.

The Balkan countries, the shores of the Black Sea and Asia Minor are the homes of the Mediterranean Black-Headed Gull, but it occasionally wanders to the British Isles and at least ten visits have been recorded. Closely related to the British Black-headed Gull, it is the same size, and only differs in plumage by having no black on its wings; in the breeding season, its hood is black and not dark brown. Its bill also is stouter. The length is 15 or 16 in., the tarsus about 3 in., and the wing span about 3 ft.

In behaviour and habits, this gull is similar to the British species, but its voice is described as harsher and more reminiscent of the terns'. It breeds near salt- or fresh-water swamps and lagoons, where its single brood of three chicks is hatched in May or early June. Few details of its food are known, but fish are presumed to comprise the main diet.

MEDITERRANEAN SHEARWATER—Procellaria diomedea.

The single specimen of the Mediterranean Shearwater picked up on the Sussex coast in 1906 was the only recorded visitor to the British Isles of this species, which breeds on the islands of the Mediterranean. It has whiter underparts than the Manx Shearwater, and lacks the " capped " appearance. There is no white band at the base of its tail, and its bill is yellow instead of dark. In general behaviour and breeding habits, it follows the shearwater pattern. Its length is 17 or 18 in.

This shearwater belongs to the same species as the North Atlantic Shearwater (*q.v.*), which is also known as Cory's Shearwater.

MEGALORNIS.

Genus of the family *Balearicidae* of the order *Ralliformes*. It contains only one species which is on the British list, the Crane (*q.v.*), which, although it once bred in this country, now occurs only as a rare passage migrant.

MELANISM.

An abnormal development of black pigment in the feathers; as opposed to albinism (*q.v.*). The abnormality may be congenital (i.e. present at birth), or it may, in certain species, be induced by artificial feeding on a special diet. For example, as is well-known, bullfinches become darker, and their plumage may even become black, if they are fed on a diet of hempseed. *See also* Albinism; Erythrism; Xanthochroism.

MELANITTA.

Genus of the family *Anatidae* of the order *Anseriformes*. It contains only three species, distributed over the northern parts of the Northern Hemisphere, but all three —the Velvet Scoter duck, the Surf-Scoter, and the Common Scoter—are on the British list.

These are separately and fully described under their individual headings.

Structurally, the members of this genus closely resemble those of the genus *Aythya* (Scaup and Tufted Duck, etc.) and *Bucephala* (Golden-Eye, etc.). They have a wide bill, slightly shorter than the head, which has a compressed tip. The nail occupies the whole of the tip, and in the male birds there is a rather prominent " knob " at the base of the culmen. The nostrils are situated a little under halfway down the bill. The wings, of medium length, are somewhat pointed. The short, stiff, wedge-shaped tail has 14–16 feathers. The plumage of the drakes is black, of the ducks dark brown.

MELANOCORYPHA.

Genus of larks of the family *Alaudidae* of the order *Passeriformes*. It contains some six species, which are mainly distributed over the Mediterranean area, western and central Asia (including northern India) and south-east Russia. There are three species on the British list—the Black Lark, Calandra Lark, and White-winged Lark—but none has been recorded here more than a very few times. They are described under their own headings.

The bill in this genus is strong and rather high. The nostrils, which are covered by bristly feathers, are situated close to the forehead. The wings are long and pointed, and the tail comparatively short. The tarsus is a little longer than the middle toe with its claw, and at the sides is covered with scutes (horny scales). The hind toe is shorter than its claw.

G. K. Yeates

MELANOCORYPHA. No lark of this genus is more than an exceptionally rare visitor to this country

MELODIOUS WARBLER—Hippolais polyglotta. An occasional visitor to the British Isles from its home in Italy, France and other European countries and north-west Africa, the Melodious Warbler has been authentically recorded five times. Closely resembling in appearance the Icterine Warbler, another of our rare visitors, it chiefly differs from it in its shorter and more rounded wings, and less blue legs. The length is 5 in., the tarsus 0·85 in., and the wing span not more than 6 in.

The varied notes of its song are described as being more richly musical than the Icterine Warbler's; less hurried in delivery, the bird continues singing for several minutes.

MERE-HEN. *See* Moorhen.

MERGANSER. " Sawbills " or fish-eating ducks belonging to the genus *Mergus* (*q.v.*) of the family *Anatidae*, having long slender spike-like bills, hooked at the tips and with toothed edges. The genus embraces six species, nearly all inhabitants of the sea and coasts and distributed over the northern regions of the Old and New World, also in Brazil and the Auckland Islands. The Goosander (*q.v.*) is the largest and best known British species. The Red-breasted Merganser (*q.v.*) is resident in Scotland and Ireland, where it breeds not only on the coasts of Ross, Sutherland and the Hebrides, where it is abundant, but also on inland lochs and rivers. It is also a non-breeding visitor and passage migrant, from September to May. It feeds chiefly on small fishes, and its flesh is unpalatable. The Hooded Merganser (*q.v.*), a smaller species, is a very rare visitor to Britain from north America. The Nun or Smew (*q.v.*), a still smaller species, is a non-breeding visitor which passes the Summer in the northern parts of the Old and New World.

Another species, *Mergus australis*, has as yet been found only in the Auckland Islands.

MERGUS (Latin, " a diver "). Genus of the family *Anatidae* of the order *Anseriformes*. It contains seven species, mainly distributed over Europe, northern Asia and north America and, in some cases (outside the breeding season), north Africa and southern Asia. There are four species on the British list : the Red-breasted Merganser, Goosander, Smew, and Hooded Merganser, the last-named being extremely rare in the British Isles. These are described under their own headings.

The members of this genus differ from other birds in the family *Anatidae* mainly in the structure of the bill, which is narrower and slenderer than that of the others and, instead of lamellae, has sharp, saw-like " teeth " along the edges of both the upper and lower mandibles ; these help the bird to capture and hold its slippery aquatic prey. The upper mandible does not overlap the lower, and there is a large decurved nail occupying the whole of the tip of the bill. The large nostrils are located close to the middle of the upper mandible. The wings, which are of medium length, are somewhat pointed, and the tail, which has 16-18 feathers, is more or less wedge-shaped. *See also* illustration under Bill in page 53.

MERLIN — Falco columbarius. The smallest of resident British falcons, the attractive little Merlin dwells in the wild and desolate northern moorlands and mountain hillsides far from human habitation, and has consequently escaped much of the persecution which in the past has been the lot of many of our birds of prey. It is widely distributed throughout Scotland, Wales and Ireland, and all suitable parts of northern England. It is also a winter visitor, many arriving in August from the Continent. Abroad, it breeds throughout Europe, northern Asia and north America.

It is rather similar in appearance to the Hobby, but confusion between them is unlikely to arise, for the Hobby is the falcon of the south, while the Merlin —or Stone-Falcon—is the falcon of the north. In its home region its small size is its chief distinction, and should prevent confusion with any other bird. The upper parts are slate grey, and the under-parts a warm reddish buff, streaked in dark brown. The barred tail has a broad black band in front of the white tip. The Merlin lacks the moustachial stripe

Eric Hosking

MERGANSER. The Red-breasted Merganser is probably the most typical of all mergansers, which are also known as the sawbills or fish-eating ducks

of both the Hobby and the Peregrine, and its wings are more rounded than the Hobby's. The female, the larger bird, has dark brown upper parts and whitish, not reddish, buff underparts, streaked and mottled darker. Her tail is distinctly barred in black and brown. Very old females may assume male plumage. The young take after the female, but are rather more rufous. The bill is bluish-grey ; the legs and cere are yellow ; and the irises dark brown. The length of the male is 10-13 in., the tarsus 1·45 in., the

G. K. Yeates

MERLIN. Smallest and most agile of British falcons, the Merlin — or Stone-Falcon—spreads terror among smaller birds which it kills in mid-air

wing span about 1¼ ft., and the weight 5 or 6 oz. The length of the female is 12-14 in., the tarsus 1·5 in., the wing span is about 1½ ft., and the weight 7 or 8 oz.

Most agile of the falcons, the Merlin probably holds the record for speed among these expert performers in the air, and flies even faster than the Kestrel or Peregrine—though it lacks much of the latter's beauty of movement. With a stop-watch the Editor has put the speed of a Merlin at approximately 240 miles per hour ! It glides less than other falcons, but will sometimes hover.

Its bold and predatory nature spreads terror among the smaller inhabitants of the air. When hunting it flies low, pursuing its quarry with extraordinary speed. A victim has little chance of escape : however it may turn and twist, its pursuer follows its every movement until, drawing level, it moves above and strikes its prey with its feet.

As a rule, the male precedes his mate to the selected nesting territory, moving from perch to perch, often soaring, and uttering his shrill falcon cry. When he is joined by the female, both birds wheel and circle over the site throughout the breeding season. Ceremonial feeding of the female on the nest is part of the Merlin's behaviour. When alarmed, or at the approach of an intruder, it has a shrill and grating chattering note. The call of the female for food is quite individual.

Moors and rough mountain pastures are the favourite nesting sites in Scotland and the north of England, but in Wales the Merlin is found breeding on cliffs and sand dunes. The nest, like all falcons', is a mere hollow scraped

among the heather, where its three or four whitish eggs, spotted in purplish dark brown, are laid early in May. Both birds assist in hatching the eggs, the female taking the greater share, for three to four weeks. The young, clad in yellowish-white down, are tended by both parents for another three to four weeks ; the male provides almost all the food, often passing it to the female in the air.

Birds of many species and their young find their way into the crop of the Merlin, for they are its chief food ; even birds as large as lapwings and rock-doves are attacked and killed. When these fail, insects, mice and voles may be eaten.

In olden times the Merlin was much used for hawking ; apparently it was easily tamed and would become a docile and intelligent pet.

MEROPIDAE (Latin, " bee-eaters "). Family of the order *Coraciiformes*. It comprises the bee-eaters, and its members are mainly distributed over Africa, Asia and southern Europe. Only one genus in this family, *Merops* (*q.v.*), is on the British list.

MEROPS (Latin, " bee-eater "). Genus of the family *Meropidae* of the order *Coraciiformes*. It contains about twenty species, mainly distributed over Africa, Asia and southern Europe. The only species on the British list, the Bee-eater (*q.v.*), occurs as an irregular summer visitor from April to October.

MEW. Local name for Gull (*q.v.*).

MEW-GULL. Alternative name for the Common Gull (*q.v.*), derived from one of its various characteristic, high-pitched call notes.

THE PROBLEMS OF BIRD MIGRATION

SIR LANDSBOROUGH THOMSON, C.B., D.Sc.,
and A. J. MARSHALL, D. Phil. (Oxon)

In the first part of the article, Sir Landsborough Thomson summarises present knowledge of migration ; while in the section on Physiological Factors, Dr. Marshall discusses the bodily changes causing the urge to migrate. See also *Navigation; Observatory*

MIGRATION. The migration of birds is well exemplified in the British Isles. Even among the resident species some individuals perform movements within the country—including journeys from Great Britain to Ireland—while others migrate beyond our boundaries. But the true migrants comprise : (*a*) species which visit this country in the breeding season ; (*b*) species which come in Winter ; and (*c*) species which pass through twice a year on their travels between a breeding area farther north and winter quarters farther south.

Migration as we know it is thus an immense phenomenon, involving many species and countless individuals. It is also a complex phenomenon, because our climate is such that the country presents different opportunities to birds having different requirements ; because the dates of the various movements are spread over a very large part of the year ; and because, owing to their geographical position, the British Isles receive migrants from several different directions. Yet it is a remarkably regular phenomenon, repeating itself year after year in accordance with a constant pattern.

In grouping species according to their migratory status in this country, let us first note that the difference between a local migrant and a long-distance traveller is mainly one of degree rather than of kind ; also that the difference between a summer visitor and a winter visitor is purely relative to the geographical area which we are considering, since our winter visitors are summer visitors somewhere else and vice versa.

Examples of species which are *wholly resident* in the British Isles, or at most perform only slight local movements, are : Tree-Creeper, Nuthatch, Coal-Tit, Green Woodpecker, Mute Swan, Rock-Dove, Red Grouse, Partridge and Pheasant.

Examples of *summer visitors* are : Ring-Ouzel, Nightingale, Wheatear, Whinchat, Redstart, warblers of many species, Spotted Flycatcher, Yellow Wagtail, Tree-Pipit, Red-backed Shrike, Swallow and martins, Wryneck, Swift, Nightjar, Cuckoo, Turtle-Dove, Corncrake, Quail, Stone-Curlew, Common Sandpiper and terns of several species. In a few of these, individuals may exceptionally remain in Winter in some parts of the country.

Examples of *winter visitors* are : Redwing, Fieldfare, Brambling, Waxwing, Rough-legged Buzzard, geese of several species, Bewick's Swan, Golden-Eye, Long-tailed Duck, Velvet Scoter, Smew, Grey Plover, Turnstone, Jack Snipe, Purple Sandpiper, Knot, Bar-tailed Godwit, Glaucous and Iceland gulls, Great Northern Diver, Red-necked Grebe and Little Auk. In a few of these, non-breeding individuals may remain in Summer, e.g. the Turnstone.

Species which are only *passage migrants* include no very common birds, but examples are : Blue-throat, Lapland Bunting, Great Snipe, Ruff, Little Stint, Black-tailed Godwit and Long-tailed Skua. Individuals may appear irregularly out of season, and in many of the examples given of summer and winter

Royal Society for the Protection of Birds

MIGRATION. Many lighthouses, like that of St. Catherine's, Isle of Wight, provide perches where weary birds may rest during their long journeys

Arthur Christiansen

MIGRATION. Whooper-swans from Lapland and Finland migrating westwards along the coast of North Sealand (Denmark) and bound for western Europe—maybe for Britain

visitors, some individuals are passage migrants.

There remains a very small group of oceanic birds which are non-breeding visitors in our Summer, having their own breeding season in the Southern Hemisphere during the other half of the year. The least irregular in appearance off our coasts are the great and sooty shearwaters.

Apart from the foregoing more or less definite groups, there is a host of species of "mixed" status. In some species one status predominates ; thus the Snow-Bunting and Whooper-Swan are mainly winter visitors, although a very few breed in the north of Scotland.

Many examples could be given—a few must suffice—of species which are common in the British Isles throughout the year, but in which some individuals are definitely migrants. Thus, in the Great Tit, Starling and Mallard, our native birds are almost entirely resident within the country, but birds breeding on the Continent visit us in large numbers in Winter and on passage. In other species some of our native birds are resident, others are summer visitors, and still others are winter visitors or passage migrants. The Song-Thrush is a good example of this threefold status : the ringing of native individuals has shown that some remain through the Winter while others migrate to countries farther south, and there is also an autumn influx from the Continent. The same is true of the Lapwing ; some of our native birds are stationary, some perform a local movement from the northern parts of Great Britain to Ireland, and others migrate as far as Portugal and even north Africa.

Seasons of Migration. Late Summer and Autumn see local movements of native birds within the British Isles, the departure of summer visitors, through-migration of passage visitors, and the arrival of winter visitors.

The migrating season begins in July, with local movements within the country and a beginning of the departure of some of our summer visitors, notably the Cuckoo (adults) and the Swift. September, however, is the chief month for the departure of summer visitors, and October for the arrival of winter visitors. In November, migration proper reaches its end; but at any time during the Winter there may be late "weather movements", differing from typical migration by varying in nature and extent according to the year's meteorological characteristics.

The spring movements are the counterparts of those just mentioned. The season begins in the latter part of February, but it is not until March that even the earliest species which are known only as summer visitors begin to arrive— Wheatear, Chiffchaff and Sand-Martin, for instance. May is the peak month for spring migration, both coming and going. In June there is still considerable passage of birds bound for farther north ; and our tardiest summer visitor, the Marsh-Warbler, may not put in its appearance until this month. (The dates mentioned refer to the country as a whole ; there are of course many differences in timing between one part of the area and another.)

It will be seen that there is some migration in every month of the year, with a slack period in late June and early July, and with little but possible "weather movements" in December and January. "Spring" and "autumn" migration are thus rather loose terms.

There are, of course, considerable variations in the dates of first and last arrivals or departures. There are, for instance, some differences in respect of sex and age. The males of some of our summer visitors tend to be earlier in arrival than the females. In Autumn the young of many species are on the move before most of the adults, the latter waiting to complete their moult. In some species of which not all the members migrate, the tendency may be greater among the young birds ; and these may go farther, as the results of ringing gannets in the British Isles have shown.

Directions of Migration. It is convenient to consider the directions of autumn migration ; those of the Spring are merely the opposite. In Autumn, we have migration from the north-west (Greenland, Iceland and the Faroe Islands), from the north-east (northern Europe and Spitsbergen), and from the east (northern Germany and the Low Countries).

This last migratory movement is largely on an east-to-west line, striking particularly the English counties on either side of the Thames estuary. Finally, we have the outgoing migration

Eric Hosking

MIGRATION. *Sanderlings, seen usually in Great Britain only on sandy beaches, resting during their travels on a rocky, boulder-strewn sea-front*

going in a southward direction ; most of this follows the western seaboard of Europe, but some of it goes across country, and a few species —Wood-Warbler and Red-backed Shrike— seem to go south-eastwards.

Recent work indicates that migrants have an innate capacity for flying in what is called a "standard direction", which is constant for the species, or at least for a particular population of a species. Experiments suggest that orientation in such a direction is by the position of the sun, and that in this regard birds are able to allow for the time of day. There is, however, a tendency to be diverted by topographical features such as coasts, which often serve as " leading lines " for a stage of the journey, even if they lie at a considerable angle to the standard direction. Thus migrants crossing the North Sea south-westwards on a broad front may be diverted to the south by the east coast of Great Britain, with a resulting concentration along that route (*see* Navigation).

On the other hand, migrants flying by night— or by day across open sea—are liable to be blown off course by side winds. Contrary to earlier views, there is now reason to believe that this " lateral drift " plays an important part in determining just what movements will, at a particular time, in a particular year, reach our coasts instead of the opposite side of the North Sea.

Irregular Phenomena. Although migration is in the main characterised by a high degree of regularity, there are some interesting phenomena of an irregular nature. We have already noted that certain late " weather movements " vary according to the severity of the Winter ; and that the wind prevailing at the time may influence the volume of a particular movement reaching our shores.

There is also the occurrence of " stragglers " of species which are not normally members of the British avifauna at any season, but properly

belong to, for example, north America or northern Asia. These are individual birds, or perhaps small parties, which wander, or are blown off, their usual course. Some of these " vagrant " species are recorded with such regularity, although in very small numbers, that the occurrence must be regarded as almost normal. Others have been recorded in the British Isles only once, or perhaps on very few occasions. In a different category are the large-scale " invasions " (or " irruptions ") of certain species. At intervals of from three to ten years, our relatively small resident stock of crossbills is reinforced by a large invasion from northern Europe in the late Summer ; to some extent this movement is irreversible, in that many of the birds remain to breed here in the following spring. Again, the Waxwing is usually a very uncommon winter visitor, but in some Winters considerable numbers appear in Great Britain, particularly on the eastern side. Such occurrences may be due to the migration of a greater than usual number of birds, possibly owing to unusually severe weather or scarcity of food in the native area, or to the diversion by strong easterly winds of a movement which would normally miss our shores.

Still more remarkable are the occasional invasions of southern birds in the breeding season. The classical example is Pallas's Sand-Grouse, a species native to south-east Russia and west central Asia, which at irregular intervals migrates in large numbers westwards through Europe as far as the British Isles (where it has even, exceptionally, bred). The greatest recorded invasions took place in 1863 and 1888 ; there have been several lesser invasions, but the species has not been seen in the British Isles since 1909. A somewhat similar but less spectacular instance is that of the Rose-coloured Starling.

Flight of Migrant Birds. In an inland district little may be seen of actual migration beyond the disappearance and reappearance of various species, or perhaps fluctuations in the numbers of birds present. Moreover, much migration takes place at night, even of species that are at other times diurnal in their habits. On the coast and at off-lying islands, however, migration can often be seen in progress ; and at night, when the weather is not too clear, migrants are sometimes attracted in large numbers to lighthouse beams.

When observing a diurnal migration, we are impressed by the direct, purposeful flight of most of the birds ; but some species tend to fly only at cruising speed, and birds of prey often circle to pick up a meal on the journey. We note also the tendency to fly in flocks—often compact—even in species which are not in other circumstances notably gregarious. The migrants often fly very low, sometimes just clearing the wave-tops ; and they commonly fly within a few hundred feet of ground or sea level. Migration at great altitudes (except when crossing mountain ranges) is exceptional.

The other side of Migration. We are concerned here with migration in the British Isles, but it is not irrelevant to ask where our visitors spend the other part of the year. First, where do our winter visitors breed ? Some travel no vast distances, and are native to neighbouring European countries in the same latitude but subject to the more severe Continental Winter. Others belong to more northerly lands, and some to the Polar regions where—in the brief Summer of perpetual daylight—they have their only breeding places.

Secondly, where do our summer visitors spend their " off-season " during what is Winter for us ? There are three main areas, representing journeys of greatly different lengths. Some of the hardier species seek no more than the milder Winter of southern Europe and the Mediterranean basin. Others—some of our warblers, for instance—cross the Sahara to the forest belt of tropical Africa. The third group—for example, the Swallow—fly beyond the Equator and find a second Summer, in which they do not breed, in south Africa.

A form of behaviour so costly in life and effort as migration must be of advantage to the species. This advantage lies in the ability to exploit the opportunities of two different areas at the most favourable season in each—one for breeding and one for non-reproductive life. Of the factors that make an area favourable, food-supply is probably more important than the direct influence of climate ; at one season,

the availability of suitable breeding-places is another factor.

Migration must not be thought of as undertaken with a conscious purpose ; nor is it actually forced on the birds by external conditions (except for " weather movements "). We must regard the behaviour as an inborn tendency, originated and developed in the past by factors the precise nature of which can be a matter only for speculation. This tendency must be stimulated to active expression twice a year by factors in the cycle of the seasons and also in the physiological cycle of the bird's life. Below are discussed the endocrinological factors involved. How migrating birds are able to find their way is described in the article on Navigation.—A. LANSBOROUGH THOMSON.

PHYSIOLOGICAL FACTORS

The prime utility of migration is to spread the bird population over the world's available food supply. There is no fundamental physiological difference between the post-nuptial flocking, dispersion and subsequent return to the breeding area of numerous " stationary " or " dispersive " species and the more or less precise long-distance migration of swallows (for example) from Britain to Africa and back.

Each individual of a species seems to behave in accordance with innate behaviour patterns incorporated within its central nervous system. These characteristic patterns of activity have been developed during the evolution of the species just as surely as have its distinctive song and plumage. Both dispersive and truly migratory movements occur after the post-nuptial gonad metamorphosis (*see* Breeding Seasons) and the extinction of territorial behaviour and

Eric Hosking

MIGRATION. Redshanks (foreground) and oystercatchers (back) assemble in huge flocks on the shore, preparing to leave for their winter-quarters

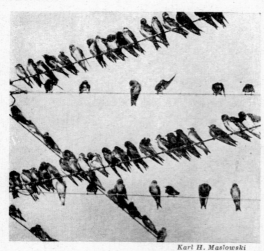

Karl H. Maslowski

MIGRATION. *Crowding on telephone wires before migrating is a habit of the martins and swallows*

parental activity at the nest site. Although the weather may remain warm, and for several weeks at least there may be abundant food left in the breeding area, the movement is always to a traditional " winter " feeding ground. This outward movement is part of an annually recurring behaviour pattern, probably established in times climatically very different from today. Whether the train of behaviour that leads to movement away from the breeding area is part of an autonomous internal rhythm or whether it is set in motion by a combination of external stimuli is not yet known.

On the other hand, the annual spring movement *back* to the breeding grounds seems to be primarily dictated by the seasonal secretion of sex hormones, as suggested by Rowan's epochmaking work a generation ago. The possible environmental factors which stimulate the exterceptor organs (*see* Breeding Seasons) and set in train the nervous and hormonal events which cause this seasonal liberation of sex hormones remain undetermined. It has been generally considered that increase in day-length is responsible, but that could not cause the seasonal initiation of the sexual cycles of numerous birds which spend the Winter on or very near the Equator. The possibility that an autonomous rhythm is responsible for the seasonal liberation of sex hormones, the accumulation of depot fat and the movement towards the breeding grounds must be carefully considered.

If such is the case the breeding cycle must be " anchored " in time by factors governing nesting-time on the breeding ground.

There is proof that the secretion of sex hormone is heavy long before passerine spring migrants arrive in Britain. Eight species— Willow - Warbler, Sedge - Warbler, Blackcap,

Whitethroat, Wheatear, Redstart, Spotted Flycatcher and Pied Flycatcher—so far examined all possess actively-secreting interstitial cells and contain spermatozoa in their testes when they kill themselves against St. Catherine's Lighthouse, Isle of Wight, each Spring on their way to England. (As in " stationary " birds, the male cycle far outstrips that of the female.) Stomach contents prove that the migrants have recently touched down en route (e.g. in Portugal or France). So, even though pairing and song have been recorded in some species during the passage flight, and some males contain bunched spermatozoa, these birds have passed apparently suitable Continental breeding places in their inherent urge to reach Britain where they themselves were probably bred. The highly advanced sexual condition achieved by the time of arrival enables the migrant males quickly to claim and defend territory : they are at little disadvantage, compared with residents, after their journey.—
A. J. MARSHALL.

" MILK " OF BIRDS. Most birds feed their young on insects, larvae and other foods similar to their own, but there are a few exceptions. Pigeons, for instance, feed their young with the substance popularly termed " pigeon's milk ". This consists of a creamy fluid (sometimes called slimy, as it is not really fatty), produced by the cells lining the adult's crop, and is given until such time as the young are able to digest heavier food. Similarly, the Storm-Petrel gives its young a daily dose of oil from its crop ; this so-called oil is derived from small sea fish and crustaceans.

MILVUS (Latin, " kite "). Genus of the family *Falconidae* of the order *Falconiformes*. Its members are distributed over many parts of the Old World. There are only two species on the British list : the Kite (*q.v.*), which is a scarce resident breeding only in parts of Wales, and the Black Kite (*q.v.*), which only very occasionally wanders to this country.

These birds may be distinguished from other members of the family *Falconidae* by their comparatively long, forked tails. Like other members of the family, they have a well hooked bill, with a " cere " at the base of the upper mandible. The nostrils are longitudinal in shape, and are obliquely placed. The wings are long, and these birds are capable of powerful, and very graceful, flight.

MINSMERE. This large reserve of some 1,500 acres, including the Minsmere Level marshes and the Westleton heath, near Eastbridge, Suffolk, is leased by the Royal Society for the Protection of Birds (*q.v.*).

One of the most remarkable British reserves, it has not only a very dense but also a very

MIGRATION OF

BRITISH BIRDS

The plate overleaf shows pictorially the
general direction from which some of the
more important visitors to this country make
their approach. The actual routes followed
are shown in greater detail in the diagram
facing page 353. The British Isles are
remarkably well situated, as regards both
position and climate, for the reception and
study of migrants, who may be divided into
three main groups: (i) species that visit
Britain in the breeding season—spring
arrivals (summer visitors); (ii) autumn
arrivals (winter visitors); and (iii) species
passing through twice a year on their journeys
from breeding areas in the north to their
winter quarters in the south. The normal
periods during which some of the species in
the first two groups stay in this country are
tabulated overleaf. Much is now known
about the question of migration, but many
problems are still unsolved—including that
of navigation (q.v.), the problem of how birds
are able to find their way over vast distances

MIGRATION OF BRITISH BIRDS

In this plate, showing the general direction taken by bird migrants to the British Isles, we see the so-called summer visitors arriving between March and May from their winter quarters in Africa and other southern lands, and, approaching along a wide sector stretching from north-west to east, the autumn arrivals, known as winter visitors, which make their homes in Britain until April, when they return to their breeding haunts in the lands to the north and east.

These waves account for the presence within our shores of the great majority of our bird visitors, but in addition numerous "passage migrants" pass straight across Britain to and from their nesting haunts in Iceland, the northern islands, and Scandinavia.

A number of the birds included among the spring arrivals, e.g. Song Thrush, Lapwing, and Skylark, are not only spring but also autumn arrivals, as well as residents, and many birds that are normal residents may also at times be passage migrants.

SPRING ARRIVALS

SPRING ARRIVALS

1 Ring Ouzel *(Mar.-Oct.)*
2 Wheatear *(Mar.-Oct.)*
3 Chiffchaff *(Mar.-Oct.)*
4 Sand Martin *(Mar.-Oct.)*
5 Willow Warbler *(Mar.-Sep.)*
6 Swallow *(Mar.-Oct.)*
7 Tree Pipit *(Apr.-Sep.)*
8 Blackcap *(Mar.-Sept.)*
9 Wryneck *(Mar.-Sept.)*
10 Yellow Wagtail *(Mar.-Sep.)*
11 Whitethroat *(Apr.-Sept.)*
12 Nightingale *(Apr.-Sept.)*
13 Redstart *(Apr.-Sept.)*
14 House Martin *(Apr.-Oct.)*
15 Cuckoo *(Apr.-Sept.)*
16 Stone Curlew *(Mar.-Oct.)*
17 Common Sandpiper *(Mar.-Sep.)*
18 Lesser Whitethroat *(Apr.-Sept.)*
19 Wood Warbler *(Apr.-Sept.)*
20 Sedge Warbler *(Apr.-Sept.)*

21 Reed Warbler *(Apr.-Sept.)*
22 Grasshopper Warbler *(Apr.-Sept.)*
23 Whinchat *(Apr.-Oct.)*
24 Corncrake *(Apr.-Oct.)*
25 Dotterel *(Apr.-Aug.)*
26 Kentish Plover *(Apr.-Sep.)*
27 Common Tern *(Apr.-Sept.)*
28 Little Tern *(Apr.-Sept.)*
29 Garden Warbler *(Apr.-Sept.)*
30 Spotted Flycatcher *(Apr.-Sept.)*
31 Pied Flycatcher *(Apr.-Sep.)*
32 Swift *(Apr.-Aug.)*
33 Nightjar *(Apr.-Sept.)*
34 Turtle Dove *(Apr.-Oct.)*
35 Red-backed Shrike *(Apr.-Aug.)*
36 Sandwich Tern *(Mar.-Sep.)*
37 Song Thrush *(April)*
38 Lapwing *(April)*
39 Black-headed Gull *(April)*
40 Skylark *(April)*

AUTUMN ARRIVALS

41 Snow Bunting *(Sept.-Apr.)*
42 Redwing *(Sept.-May)*
43 Teal *(Sept.-April)*
44 Mallard *(Sept.-Mar.)*
45 Pink-footed Goose *(Sept.-Apr.)*
46 Little Auk *(Sept.-Apr.)*
47 Hooded Crow *(Sept.-Apr.)*
48 Brambling *(Sept.-Mar.)*

49 Heron *(Sept.-Apr.)*
50 Starling *(Oct.-Mar.)*
51 Waxwing *(Oct.-May)*
52 Fieldfare *(Oct.-May)*
53 Kestrel *(Oct.-Mar.)*
54 Woodcock *(Sept.-Apr.)*
55 Wood Pigeon *(Sept.-Apr.)*
56 Curlew *(Sept.-Apr.)*
57 Pochard *(Sept.-Apr.)*

AUTUMN ARRIVALS—

Main paths taken by these migrants along our shores

This map, showing the main paths of the autumn migration along the shores of north-west Europe, has been adapted from Sir A. Landsborough Thomson by James Fisher. Autumn migrants follow four main streams along the shores of Great Britain. The most important is from Scandinavia down the east coast of Britain, from the Shetlands to Kent, where this stream combines with a second from the west coast of Denmark, Germany, Holland and Belgium. The joint stream, diminished by birds that have taken up residence in countries along their route, then passes along the south coast of Britain and the north coast of France. The third stream comprises birds from the Shetlands and Orkneys, together with some from the Faeroes, Iceland and Greenland. These birds pass westwards along the north of Scotland and down the west coast to Northern Ireland; where they divide into two streams— one passing down the east coast, the other down the west coast of Ireland, until they re-combine and their remnants continue until they join the remnants of the other two and proceed down the west coast of France

varied bird population. This variety is due to the fact that the reserve consists of four distinct habitats—sand and shingle by the shore, reedy marshland, heathland and mixed woodland.

Minsmere is one of the few remaining strongholds of the very rare Bearded Tit, considered by many to be our most beautiful small bird. Other rare or uncommon birds which breed on the reserve include the Garganey, Gadwall, Bittern and Stone-Curlew.

Access to the reserve is by permit only. Permits, which are usually issued for certain days during the summer months, can be obtained from the Royal Society for the Protection of Birds, 25, Eccleston Square, London, S.W.1. *See also* Nature Reserve ; Sanctuary.

MISTLE-THRUSH—**Turdus viscivorus.** It is its fondness for mistletoe berries that has given the Mistle-Thrush the name which it has borne since medieval times. Even more telling is its other name, " Stormcock ", for no songster delights more in the storms of early Spring.

The largest of the thrushes, and less plentiful than the Blackbird and Song-Thrush, the Mistle-Thrush is a resident throughout the British Isles, though less common north of the Tweed. Since 1800 it has been resident and generally distributed in Ireland. It occurs all over Europe, Asia and north-west Africa. It is a partial migrant, and many British birds leave in the Autumn to winter on the Continent, while as many arrive at the same time to winter here.

No difficulty should be experienced in distinguishing the Mistle- from the Song-Thrush. Not only is the former much larger but its plumage is greyer, and the spots on its breast are larger, darker and more prominent. Its outer tail feathers have white tips, and it has a white underwing which shows conspicuously in flight. It has a horn-coloured bill and palish brown legs. The sexes are alike. The length is 10½ in. and the tarsus 1·3 in. ; the wing span is about 1 ft., and the weight is 5 oz.

During the breeding season the Mistle-Thrush frequents well-wooded country, gardens and orchards, but Winter finds it roaming over moorlands and wild and open country. Much of its time is spent on the ground, where it hops and has a characteristic stance, with head raised, ever on the alert for worms. It is a pugnacious and quarrelsome bird, and will fiercely drive off any intruder near its nest. It is not afraid of attacking birds larger than itself and will even come to grips with a Sparrow-Hawk ; indeed, it is known to attack Man.

The characteristic strong and direct flight of the Mistle-Thrush differs from those of all other thrushes except the Fieldfare ; it holds its wings now open, now closed, showing its white underwing. The mating display takes place chiefly among the branches of the trees, where the male and female chase each other—often for hours—from perch to perch.

The mild and clear song of the Mistle-Thrush is usually uttered from a high tree ; it has been likened to that of the Blackbird, but lacks that bird's beauty of tone and mellowness. One of the earliest spring performers, the Mistle-Thrush is also one of the first to lose his full volume. Beginning as early as November, the song continues until April, but from then on, although still heard in practically every month of the year, it is but a feeble echo of its early power. The call note is a harsh scream, also used when the bird is alarmed or angry. The song of the Mistle-Thrush need never be confused with that of the Song-Thrush, for it has none of the latter's characteristic repetitive notes.

The Mistle-Thrush is an early breeder and normally places its nest in the fork of a tree at some distance from the ground. The nest is fashioned with bents, roots and moss, lined with dry grasses, and often decorated with wool and feathers. The hen does most of this work. Her four eggs, greenish-blue or greyish white and blotched with brown and violet markings, are laid usually in March or early April, but sometimes as early as February. The hen sits for 13 or 14 days, with the cock on guard near by. The chicks—yellowish, spotted over in buff—are fed and reared by both parents for 14-16 days. Two broods are usually reared.

Ripe berries of all kinds, including those of ivy, yew, hawthorn and mistletoe form the chief food of the Mistle-Thrush, but worms and snails —the latter smashed on stones—are also eaten.

C. W. Teager

MISTLE-THRUSH. *The largest of thrushes got its name because it likes to eat mistletoe-berries*

G. K. Yeates

MONTAGU'S HARRIER. *The smallest harrier to be found in this country, this bird performs the most fantastic aerobatics in its breeding season*

MOLLYHAWK. Sailors' name for Albatross (*q.v.*), a bird which was formerly regarded with much superstitious awe and fear.

MONTAGU'S HARRIER—Circus pygargus. Owing to its similarity to the Hen-Harrier, Montagu's Harrier—also known as the Blue Hawk and the Ring-Tail—was not recognized as a separate species until the 19th century. A summer breeding visitor to the British Isles, arriving in April and departing again in October, it was formerly much commoner than today, but seems to have fared rather better than the Marsh-Harrier, no doubt because it does not require such large areas of marshland on which to breed. It is estimated that, since their recent protection, 50 pairs breed annually in parts of England and Wales. Scotland and Ireland see this bird only as a rare vagrant. Abroad it inhabits Europe, Asia and Africa.

Montagu's Harrier is the smallest of the three harriers. The male is blue-grey, with a black bar across the wings and black wing tips. The rump patch, so conspicuously white in the Hen-Harrier, is greyish in Montagu's Harrier, and the tail and upper tail coverts are also grey. The outer tail feathers are barred. The underparts are whitish, with rufous streaks on the flanks. The bill is black, and the cere, legs and irises are yellow. The female, very like that of the Hen-Harrier, is dark brown, paler and streaked on head and neck, and with a white line above the eyes. Her underparts are buff with reddish streaks and her irises are hazel. A darker melanic—almost black—form also occurs.

There is little difference in size between the male and female. The length is 18 in., and the tarsus 2 3 in. ; the wing span is from $2\frac{1}{2}$ ft. to 3 ft., the weight 11-15 oz.

Montagu's Harrier has the typical grace and buoyancy of the harriers as it flies and glides close to the ground. During the breeding season it performs fantastic aerial acrobatics, but these are less strenuous than those of the Hen-Harrier. Its voice, heard mainly during breeding, is a fairly far-carrying, chattering note, uttered at the nest and in flight. It is said to be higher-pitched than that of the Hen-Harrier, but the ordinary observer would probably hear little difference between the two. The food-call in the air is similar.

Montagu's Harrier has a wide variety of breeding sites ; heaths, moorlands, commons, sand dunes, salt- and fresh-water marshes, reed-beds and even cornfields and cultivated land on the Continent are all suitable. Elsewhere many pairs will breed together in one area, but in England, where so few nest, only one or two pairs will breed in the same district. The nest varies in size and material according to its position. If among marsh vegetation, it is built of rushes, sedges and grasses ; if on the ground, it is well concealed among beaten-down vegetation. The female usually does all the work. Four or five eggs, similar to those of the Hen-Harrier, are laid in May at intervals of two or three days. They are incubated by the hen, the period being 28 or 29 days for each egg. She leaves the nest several times a day to receive food from her mate in the air ; she then feeds each chick in turn, eating the remainder herself. The nestlings are covered with light buff down. The females attain adult plumage in their second season, the males in their third. When almost fledged, the chicks move away and hide ; they are then fed by both parents separately for about a month. One brood is reared.

Much the same kind of food is taken as by other harriers, though Montagu's Harrier is recorded as being less likely to chase its victims.

MONTICOLA (Latin, " mountaineer "). Genus of the family *Turdidae* of the order *Passeriformes*, whose members are distributed over Europe, Africa and Asia. The Rock-Thrush (*q.v.*) is the only species on the British list.

MONTIFRINGILLA (Latin, "mountain-finch"). Genus of the family *Passeridae* of the order *Passeriformes*. Its species are mainly distributed over the more mountainous regions of Europe, central and northern Asia and north America. That rare visitor, the Snow-Finch (*q.v.*), is the only species on the British list.

MOORHEN—Gallinula chloropus. Almost every one of the smaller stretches of fresh water throughout the British Isles has its complement of the abundant and familiar Moorhen. A British resident, it is also a winter visitor, arriving on the east coast in the Autumn ; almost a cosmopolitan species, it is found all over Europe, Asia, Africa, north and south America, and on many islands of the Atlantic.

Sometimes confused with the larger Coot, the Moorhen is in fact very easy to recognize for, in place of the white frontal patch so conspicuous in the Coot, its frontal patch is red, as is also the base of its bill, the tip of which is yellow. Above its general colour is dark brown, almost black. The underparts are grey, and along the flanks runs a white line ; the undertail coverts are white and very conspicuous in flight. There is no wing bar. The legs are green with a red "garter", and the long thin toes are unwebbed. The length is 13 in., and the tarsus is 1¾ in., the wing span is 13 or 14 in., and the weight 15 oz.

Although it may be seen in Winter feeding with several others, the Moorhen is not gregarious. Extremely graceful on both the water and the ground, it walks daintily along, flirting its short tail and nodding its head. It swims easily and buoyantly, and is an expert diver, usings its legs for propulsion under water. When scenting danger, it will vanish under cover of the water, clinging to the vegetation, with only its bill appearing on the surface. Like the other rails in its family, the Moorhen has some difficulty in rising from the water, and flies a short distance on the surface before getting away ; but once on the wing, its action is strong and well sustained. It delights in flying high by night.

Less secretive and skulking than the rest of its family, the Moorhen will become quite tame. But it is a very territorial bird, so much so that no two pairs can peacefully exist on the same stretch of water, and, especially in the Spring, fighting is frequent, with the males constantly creating an uproar and rising from the water to strike each other with their feet.

The courtship of the Moorhen begins early in the year, when both male and female indulge in varied water acrobatics. The bird has many vocal sounds, the chief being a croak, which is far-carrying and heard often. A softer note is used during courtship and when tending the chicks.

Any fresh water that affords some sort of sheltering vegetation is suitable for nesting.

February sees the beginning of the construction of the sturdy " platform " near the water's edge, or in an over-hanging bush or sometimes high in a tree on the foundation of an old nest of Rook or Magpie. The " platform " is built of flags, reeds and sedge, cleverly woven together, by both birds, the male taking the larger share. The 5-11 eggs of whitish-grey or greenish-buff, covered with purple spots, are laid on consecutive days in March or April. For 19 to 22 days both male and female hatch the eggs. The young, clad in dark olive-brown down with whitish underparts, are extremely active, and take to the water in two or three days. They can fly in six or seven weeks. Both parents tend them, but the chicks of the first brood are very often feeding and tending those of later broods.

The Moorhen's varied diet is chiefly of vegetable matter, but some insects are taken, and the eggs of other birds are sometimes stolen.

MOTACILLA. Genus of the family *Motacillidae* of the order *Passeriformes*. It comprises the wagtails. Containing many different species, distributed over Europe, Africa and Asia, it is represented in the British Isles by the Pied Wagtail, White Wagtail and Masked Wagtail, which all belong to the same species ; the Grey Wagtail ; and the Yellow Wagtail, five forms of which occur in the British Isles. These are described under their own headings.

Wagtails belong to the same family as pipits, but they may easily be distinguished from the latter by their long tails, which are at least as long as the wing, with twelve rather narrow feathers. Also, unlike the pipits, none of the wagtails has striped or spotted plumage. The wings have nine primary feathers, and the secondaries are almost as long as the primaries. The bill is thin and slender. Like the pipits, wagtails *run* along the ground.

Eric Hosking

MOORHEN. *Related to the Coot as is seen from its frontal shield, coloured red in the moorhens*

MOTHER CAREY'S CHICKEN. Sailor's name for Storm-Petrel (*q.v.*). Mother Carey is a corruption of *mater cara* (" dear mother "), meaning the Virgin Mary, possibly because She was thought to send Her " chickens " as a warning of impending storms.

MOULT. 1. The shedding and renewal of all or part of the plumage; 2. The season or period of moulting.

During its life a bird has three separate and distinct types of plumage (*q.v.*) : (a) nestling, usually one, but sometimes two successive coats; (b) juvenile, that of the fully fledged but immature bird—usually lost at the first autumn moult, and (c), the adult stage, renewed periodically each year. At the end of each of the first two stages, the feathers are shed and replaced by those of the next stage. All adult birds, except in certain very special circumstances, renew all their feathers at least once a year, at the autumn moult (*q.v.*), and some species have a second, partial moult in the Spring or early Summer.

Feathers (*q.v.*) begin to form long before the bird is hatched, each feather rising from a nipple at the bottom of a small pit in the skin of the embryo (*q.v.*) still in its shell. Around the nipple a small cap of horny material is formed, which is presently loosened and pushed up by another horny cap forming beneath it. This finally leads to the formation of the shaft of the feather, in which, on close inspection, the successive caps can often be seen. When the feather is fully grown, the small hole at the root of the quill, through which nutriment passes, becomes sealed, and the feather, previously a living thing, becomes dead and is finally, at moulting time, pushed out by the new growth.

This is the general picture, but it is dangerous to generalise. In some species, where there are two generations of nestling plumage, the second lot of feathers starts to grow before the growth of the first has ceased. Thus, the bases of the first feathers are organically connected to the tips of the second, so when eventually these appear through the skin, they are surmounted by the down feathers that preceded them. Similarly, the tips of the first contour feathers may at first bear the second generation of down feathers. Sometimes all three feathers may for a time be found joined together.

In the adult bird the complete renewal of the feathers in the Autumn is the most important. Although called the autumn moult, and occurring typically from August to October, there are many variations, but it usually starts just after the rearing of a family, and some birds succumb to the strain.

With healthy birds, moulting is, in most species, a gradual process, only a few feathers being shed at a time, and these are replaced before others are shed, so that the power of flight is never lost. The feathers are generally shed in pairs, starting at a definite place on the bird's body and being lost in a regular order. The whole process of renewal usually takes from one to two months, but some species may take as long as six months, or even most of the year. The order probably varies from one species to another, but in the wing the first feather to be lost appears to be the innermost primary feather, and when the new feather replacing it is about half grown, the next one is shed, and soon. The tail feathers are also shed successively in pairs, starting from the centre. In a few swimming and diving birds (e.g. Mallard) all the flight quills are shed at one time, and for a period the birds are unable to fly. Ducks are also unusual in that drakes reassume their breeding dress in the Autumn after a short period of eclipse (*q.v.*).

Although some species, such as kingfishers, parrots, swans and geese, petrels, cranes, bustards and birds of prey, moult only once a year, others, such as many of the wading birds—dotterels, dunlins, turnstones, grey and golden plovers, phalaropes, terns,

Dragesco

MOULT. *Young tit—showing the nestling down with which it was hatched on the back and head. The beginnings of growing feathers can also be seen*

John Markham

MUTE SWAN, *the ' Bird Royal ',*

the very embodiment of quiet dignity and grace

To face page 364   *For text see pages 1, 365 and 542*

starlings, ptarmigans, and several species of pipits, wagtails and buntings, undergo a partial moult in the Spring, often both sexes, but sometimes the males only, adopting a brighter dress preparatory to the breeding season.

Many brighter-coloured species with only a single moult, have a distinct brightening of plumage as the critical period of courtship approaches, the tips of the feathers and the outer surfaces of the barbs and barbules being shed (*see* Breeding Dress; Spring Moult).

MOUNTAIN FINCH. Alternative name for the Brambling (*q.v.*).

MOUNTAIN-LINNET. Alternative name for the Twite (*q.v.*).

MOUSTACHED WARBLER — Lusciniola melanopogon. History credits this rare warbler with one visit to the British Isles (in 1915), and the Check-List of the British Ornithologists' Union records that it bred here in 1946 (sight record). Its home is in south Europe, Tunisia and Asia. Similar in appearance to, but smaller than, the Sedge-Warbler, the Moustached Warbler has a distinctly darker chestnut tinge in its upper parts, the crown is also darker, and the eye stripe and throat whiter. The length is 5 in., the tarsus 0·7 in., and the wing span about 6 in.

In the reed beds of swamps and the borders of lakes—its favourite haunts—it perches on the reeds and moves restlessly among the vegetation. The unusual movement of its tail is quite unlike that of the Sedge-Warbler. Those who are familiar with the songs of both birds describe the Moustached Warbler's as the sweeter and more varied.

The nest is placed among the reeds or among small bushes growing out of the water.

MURRE. American name for guillemots; the common Guillemot is called Atlantic Murre and Brünnich's Guillemot, Brünnich's Murre.

MUSCICAPA (Latin, " flycatcher "). Genus of the family *Muscicapidae* of the order *Passeriformes*. Of its many species, distributed over almost all parts of the Old World, five are on the British list: the Spotted Flycatcher, Pied Flycatcher, Red-breasted Flycatcher, White-collared Flycatcher and Brown Flycatcher. These are described under their own headings.

MUSCICAPIDAE (Latin, " flycatchers "). Family of the order *Passeriformes*, comprising the flycatchers. These birds are mainly distributed over the tropical regions of the Eastern Hemisphere, but some also occur in New Zealand and the Pacific islands and in parts of Africa, and a few journey to northern Asia and to Europe in the Summer. The only genus that appears on the British list is *Muscicapa*.

Eric Hosking

MUSCICAPA. The Spotted Flycatcher is the only member of this genus to be seen often in Britain

MUTE SWAN—Cygnus olor. The largest and probably the most familiar water bird in the British Isles, the Mute Swan is a resident, unlike Bewick's and the Whooper-Swan. A Royal bird, it is said to have been introduced by Richard Coeur-de-lion. Before 1186 the Mute Swan bred in a wild state, but through the centuries it gradually has been semi-domesticated. Mute swans fall into three groups:

(1) The common and familiar breeding occupant of our lakes, ponds and rivers which, though tame enough to accept tit-bits from children, will, on the other hand, attack any human being or animal going too close to its nest.

(2) The so-called semi-domesticated swan, full-winged, almost wild and quite unresponsive to any human approach, which goes year after year to breed in such swanneries as the unique and and world-famous twelve-hundred-year-old one at Abbotsbury (*q.v.*).

(3) The really wild Mute Swan breeding in parts of Europe (e.g. Hungary) and in Asia. This wild swan is known to fly several thousand of miles to its breeding haunts.

Outside the breeding season, all three groups are found wherever their natural food, and in particular the marine grass *Zostera marina*, is in plentiful supply.

From the 13th to the 18th century, every swan belonged to the Crown and was protected by laws made in the reigns of Edward IV and Henry VII. If a private person or corporation wished to keep swans, a Royal licence for which payment had to be made, was necessary. The keeping of swans was governed by a code of Royal statutes, which were enforced by the King's Swan-master or his servants, and any infringement was severely punished. Penalties included imprisonment and heavy fines. Licensed owners were granted the use of a special mark, usually a notch on each bird's bill or a mark on the foot.

All swans on the River Thames belong to the Crown or to the Dyers' or Vintners' Companies, both granted their charters in the time of Edward IV. To this day, under the supervision of the respective swan-keepers, the ancient ceremony of " swan-upping " is carried out in July or August of each year, to determine the ownership of all the cygnets between the City of London and Henley. This is done by the time-honoured practice of cornering the birds and their young. Swans are not Royal birds in Scotland, and no details are available of their history in Wales or Ireland.

A bird so well-known scarcely needs description. The plumage is pure white, and the neck is carried in an elegant and graceful S-shaped curve. The Mute Swan is distinguished by its having an orange bill, with a conspicuous black knob at the base, from either Bewick's or the Whooper-Swan, which have black bills, yellow at the base. The legs are blackish. The sexes are alike, but the knob is less prominent on the female's bill. The male is called a " cob " and the female a " pen ".

The total length of the Mute Swan is 5-6 ft., its body accounting for about half of this. The tarsus is 4·5 in. The wing span is also between 5 and 6 ft., and the weight from 20 to 50 lb. (it is thought to be the heaviest flying bird).

The flight of the Mute Swan is typical of its family. With its neck fully extended, it flies with slow, deliberate and very powerful wing beats, which produce a musical humming sound audible for some distance. Its take-off is awkward, the huge bird flapping along the surface of the water, head erect, before getting clear. When landing on water, it produces a " bow-wave ". Like so many waterbirds, the Mute Swan is full of grace and elegance while swimming, but

Eric Hosking

MUTE SWAN. *Swan and shadow, floating double, are a familiar sight, figuring much in literature*

its bulky body and short legs give it ungainly movements on the ground ; it rarely dives, but will do so in face of danger. When feeding, its long neck often disappears completely, and it can also " up-end " like a duck.

During the breeding season, the chief display takes the form of a unique dance on the waves of the water, the birds circling and swaying round and round.

The Mute Swan—even the so-called semi-domesticated bird—is by nature extremely vicious and aggressive in defence of its young and nest. No bird has a more formidable and frightening appearance as it sails along, with wings outspread and arched over its back, ready for its dangerous attack.

Despite its name this is by no means a silent bird. I am strongly of the opinion that its name should be changed from " mute " to " silent ". I am one of the few in these islands who have studied the life of the Mute Swan and watched it through every season of the year, both before and during the breeding season, and I have been amazed at its great vocabulary. I have recorded fourteen totally different notes, and heard many others. The most astonishing is that made by the pen after the birth of a cygnet ; this is like the barking of a dog, and has to be heard to be believed. But I have only once heard a Mute Swan make a very loud trumpeting call, and that was, of course, a wild swan.—EDITOR.

The nests are placed near water and, if in a protected area, quite close together. An enormous circular construction, composed of reeds, roots, sticks and rushes, the nest is built by both male and female, the cob bringing the material which is arranged by the pen to form the hollow for housing the five to seven greyish or bluish tinted eggs laid in April. Hatching begins on the completion of the clutch, and both birds take their share during 34-38 days. The cygnets are clad in silvery-grey down ; they become brown later, but two years must elapse before they attain their pure white dress. They remain in the nest for a day or two, but soon become completely at home sailing along on the water, or perched on the back of the pen, where the Editor has seen as many as fourteen. They are looked after by both parents for some four or five months, until fully fledged. One brood is reared in a season.

The Mute Swan finds its chief food among under-water weeds and marine plants, especially *Zostera marina* grass. Some animal matter is also taken, including frogs, toads, tadpoles and worms. Swans seem to know instinctively where food is available, for when the water freezes, in a severe Winter, they have been seen to make endless efforts to break the ice in order to reach their food.

A collection of swans is called " herd " on land, " flight " in the air, and " fleet " on water.

NIGHTINGALE

NAIL (or Dertrum). A hard, horny plate found on the end of the bill of members of the Duck family. *See* Plate facing page 1.

NAPE. Name given to the area at the back of a bird's neck. *See* Plate facing page 1.

NARES. Nostrils (*q.v.*). *See also* Bill.

NATURALISED BIRDS. *See* article on Introduced Birds.

NATURE CONSERVANCY. Government organization, constituted under Royal Charter in March 1949, charged with the conservation and control of natural fauna and flora in Great Britain (i.e. exclusive of Northern Ireland). It is directly responsible to a Committee of the Privy Council, composed of Ministers and presided over by the Lord President of the Council, who is directly responsible to Parliament for Nature Conservancy.

A special Scottish Committee, membership of which requires the approval of the Secretary of State for Scotland, is appointed to look after affairs in Scotland. For the acquisition of land, and only for this purpose, the Conservancy has the power of a Government department, and the land acquired has the status of Crown land. Otherwise, the Conservancy is a Government organization, and, apart from a small administrative section, the staff is recruited from among scientists.

The Conservancy's functions are threefold :
(1) To provide scientific advice on conservation and *control* of natural fauna and flora.
(2) To establish, maintain and manage Nature Reserves (*q.v.*)—including maintenance of physical features of scientific interest (i.e. by establishment of geological reserves).
(3) To organize and develop scientific research relating to ecological problems.

The Conservancy was brought into being largely as the result of the efforts of private and semi-official bodies, the members of which were far-sighted enough to see that much of the country's natural flora and fauna was disappearing, either because of environmental changes brought about by men (e.g. agricultural and building developments, drainage schemes

and so on), or because of the injudicious control of so-called weeds or pests. The second of the three objects listed above is fully discussed under Nature Reserve *and* Scientific Site.

In order to be able to advise public authorities and others on how to conserve and control the flora and fauna in their charge, the Conservancy has first to learn what causes the rise and fall of natural populations—both generally and specifically. Consequently, population studies of different kinds of plants and animals form an important part of the research work. In general, the different populations are intermingled, affecting one another directly or indirectly, so that upsetting the " balance of Nature " often leads, at present, to unpredictable results, sometimes with disastrous effects.

To stimulate interest in this work, which is of the greatest importance to the nation, the Conservancy makes about 12 research grants a year for post-graduate study ; a high proportion of these have gone to young ornithologists.

Robert M. Adam

NATURE CONSERVANCY. Beinn Eighe was our first National Nature Reserve to be established

NATURE RESERVE. A tract of land which has been publicly declared a Nature Reserve by the Nature Conservancy (*q.v.*) or by a local authority, and which has been set apart for the preservation and study of animals, birds and insects ; trees, plants and vegetation ; and geological and other physical features ; thus being safeguarded for all time from " development " other than that necessary to enhance its natural value.

Many years ago naturalists began to appreciate the importance of selecting and acquiring suitable places as reserves for studying and preserving plants, birds, butterflies and other insects, particularly as it was known that some rare or valuable species had disappeared, or were fast disappearing, at the hands of the hunter or collector, or because their habitat had been destroyed by building, industrial development, or the needs of agriculture. Thus, in this country the Great Auk and Great Bustard are now extinct ; the Black Grouse is rapidly vanishing because it is prized for the table, and the Avocet was exiled for about 100 years, until it made its spectacular return in 1947.

Apart from the efforts of such societies as the National Trust, the Society for the Promotion of Nature Reserves and the Royal Society for the Protection of Birds (*qq.v.*), enlightened private landowners often managed places of scientific interest as if they were virtually Nature Reserves. It was some time before the Government was brought to realize that the safeguarding of the natural life of this country was too big a task to be entrusted entirely to voluntary effort, and that it must take official action if an important part of our heritage was not to be swept away on the floodtide of development. When, however, the Government did come to this realization, things moved quickly, culminating in 1949 in the foundation of the Nature Conservancy, whose charter empowered it, among other things, to acquire and manage Nature Reserves for the nation. Since its inauguration it has acted with commendable speed in surveying the whole of the country for possible reserves, in an endeavour to discover those of the highest standard and importance.

There are two forms of Nature Reserve—National and Local. A National Nature Reserve is one that is preserved for the nation, and comes directly under the control of the Nature Conservancy, which may have acquired it by purchase, voluntary or compulsory ; by a long lease ; as a gift ; or by agreement with the owner. Where possible, the Conservancy prefers to obtain a Reserve as a gift or by purchase.

Except when the Conservancy enters into an agreement with an owner that he shall manage the estate in accordance with the Conservancy's

wishe
respo
and ir
time or h
station ana
bourhood oi
visiting scientist
Crown property, a.
an Exchequer grant.

A Local Reserve is created in
after declaration by the council of a co
borough (in Scotland a large " burgh ") or, certain conditions, the council of a county district. Local Authorities may exercise their powers in this direction only after consulting the Conservancy. All expenses have to be borne out of the local rates and no grant is made from the Exchequer. In spite of this, some local authorities have already used their powers. Thus, in 1952, the Lincoln County Council requisitioned Gibraltar Point, which, together with other parts of the dune-saltmarsh system in the neighbourhood, has been a centre for the study of bird life for many years. Similarly, Aberlady Bay, on the southern shore of the Firth of Forth, which is of ornithological and botanical interest, has been declared a Reserve by the East Lothian County Council, and the Cumberland County Council did the same regarding Ravenglass Gullery and Ternery.

In addition to what may be termed official Reserves, there are a number of unofficial reserves maintained and managed by private individuals or trusts with an interest in wild life —for example, Abbotsbury (*q.v.*), which belongs to the Earl of Ilchester, and the Wildfowl Trust (*q.v.*), at Slimbridge.

A Reserve differs from a " sanctuary " in that it is *not necessarily* an area in which nothing may be killed or taken. Sometimes shooting rights which existed before the creation of a Reserve are permitted to continue ; in other cases a protective belt round the actual Reserve may be necessary to protect wild life against disturbance or persecution (e.g. to safeguard wildfowl flying to the Reserve).

A Reserve must also not be confused with a National Park. Such confusion is likely to arise, particularly as some of the powers for dealing with Reserves are derived from The National Parks and Countryside Act, 1949. A National Park is essentially a large area selected because of its scenic beauty and designed for the enjoyment of the general public, who are free to enter it at will. A Nature Reserve, on the other hand, is a relatively small, sometimes very small, area, selected and maintained because of its high scientific value and to enable research work beneficial to the nation to be carried out within its boundaries. Nevertheless, the Nature

Air Ministry (Crown Copyright)

NATURE RESERVE. The flats at Bridgwater Bay, Somerset, provide an ideal roosting
place for many waders and wildfowl, including several types of goose and duck

Conservancy has stated that it keenly desires the Reserves to be, as far as possible, accessible not only to scientific workers and students, but to all members of the public who are prepared to respect them and to avoid interfering with scientific work that may be in progress. In order to visit a particular Reserve, a free permit must first be obtained from the Nature Conservancy; (address: 19 Belgrave Square, London, S.W.1.) ; when applying for this it is necessary to state for what period (not exceeding one year) it is required, and also if it is desired to take away any specimens. Permits are issued for organized parties of students, school-children, Natural History Societies and members of the general public, but special responsibilities are imposed on the organizers concerned in view of the serious damage which can often be unwittingly inflicted by parties.

The *Beinn Eighe National Nature Reserve*, in Ross and Cromarty, declared in 1951, holds the honour of being the first National Reserve to be established in this country. By December 1954, 19 National Nature Reserves, totalling 72,358 acres, had been declared, the largest being the *Cairngorms*. The first Welsh Nature Reserve, and the first to be declared in a National Park, is at *Cwm Idwal*, about four miles north of Snowdon. Other National Reserves of particular interest to ornithologists and bird lovers are :

Bridgwater Bay and Steart Island. The flats at Bridgwater Bay, Somerset, are of considerable ornithological interest as a roosting place for wildfowl, including wild geese, and for waders. Steart Island, off the mouth of the River Parret and about half a mile from the mainland. is a roosting place for hundreds of geese, mainly the White-fronted Goose, and is

the only area in Britain where moulting Sheld-Duck are known to gather each Summer.

Cairngorms. This area, which occupies 62 square miles (approximately 40,000 acres), and includes four of Scotland's highest peaks, has a widely varied and interesting selection of wild life and vegetation. Of particular interest to ornithologists are the Golden Eagle, Ptarmigan, Dotterel, Snow-Bunting, Black Grouse, Greenshank, Crested Tit and Scottish Crossbill which are to be found there.

Morton Lochs, Fife. These shallow, artificial lochs in a belt of arid ground lie directly on the main migration route of wildfowl and waders, and for this reason, and because there are no other stretches of fresh water for several miles, are visited by many species, including some rarely seen in other parts of the country. Besides being a resting place for wildfowl on migration, the lochs are an important breeding ground.

Orfordness/Havergate, Suffolk. Havergate Island was constituted a Nature Reserve in 1954 by an agreement concluded with the Royal Society for the Protection of Birds ; and the shingle spit at Orfordness is leased from the War Office.

Havergate Island has become famous in post-war years because of the establishment there of a successful breeding colony of avocets. Under protection, this island has acquired colonies of Sandwich terns and other interesting species. Access to the island is restricted to the holders of special permits, for which a fee is charged.

Scolt Head, Norfolk. The Conservancy holds most of this island on lease from the National Trust, and is negotiating a lease with the Norfolk Naturalist Trust for the remainder of the island. It is renowned for the variety of its plant and bird life, and particularly noted as being one of the main terneries on the North Sea coast of Britain, and as a wintering area for shore-larks and other rare birds.

See further under individual reserves ; *also* Conservation ; Nature Conservancy ; Observatory ; Research ; Sanctuary ; Wildfowl Trust.

HOW DO BIRDS FIND THEIR WAY?

G. V. T. MATTHEWS, M.A., Ph.D.

This article discusses the various theories advanced to explain how birds find their way with uncanny accuracy over hundreds of miles, and shows that recent tests indicate birds navigate by the sun. How they do this, is still a mystery. See also *Migration*

NAVIGATION. There are two main aspects of the problem of bird navigation :

1. How do young birds find their way on their first migration to winter quarters which they have *never* seen ?

2. How do older birds regain the home area, which they *have* seen before, on subsequent migrations or, more particularly, when they are removed from it in such a way that they cannot observe what is going on ?

UNKNOWN GOAL

In a few species the family unit remains intact on migration, and the young will simply have to follow the guidance of the parents and remember the route for future occasions. But in many cases the young migrate independently of their parents ; the young Cuckoo is, of course, an extreme example of this. The results of very extensive ringing studies have shown that such youngsters nevertheless arrive in the somewhat circumscribed area typical of the geographical group from which they came. They must, therefore, have some " information " as to where they are to go.

Many experiments have been made of rearing young birds in areas entirely foreign to their stock. These have demonstrated quite clearly that there is no inherited memory of an " ancestral home "—winter or summer. Thus British Mallard reared in Finland returned there to breed, after migrating with their Finnish foster-parents to the latter's wintering area. This was all the more striking since the British stock is normally non-migratory. If, however, migratory birds are used, and the young foreigners held back until all the locals of that species have left, we find strong indications of an inherited tendency to migrate in a particular compass *direction.* For example, white storks from east Prussia, which normally migrate to the south-south-east, were reared in the Ruhr, in which storks migrate to the south-west. When the young foreigners were left to their own devices, they migrated in the direction which would have been appropriate in east Prussia, but which now brought them up against the barrier of the Alps. (Fig. 1).

Similar results have been obtained by catching young birds in transit between their summer and winter quarters. If these birds are transported some hundreds of miles to one side of the migration axis, they will on release continue flying in the original direction, say south-west. They will thus follow a course parallel to the normal, and arrive in an area quite outside the usual range of their stock.

The conclusions drawn from such experiments are strongly supported by field observations of uninterrupted migration. The records of teams of observers scattered over wide areas show that migrant birds pass through on a broad front. They fly in a " standard " or preferred direction until some obstacle, such as a range of hills or the coast, acts as a temporary diversion. For a time this may result in a condensed stream of migrants along such features, which earlier observers had considered to be evidence of rigidly fixed, hereditary migration routes. But when the obstacle is passed the original direction of migration is resumed once again.

This basic " information " of compass direction suffices to bring the young birds to

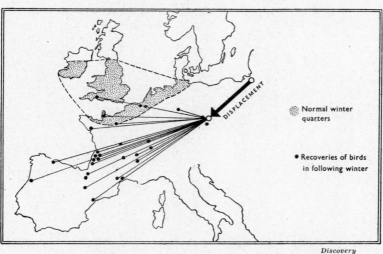

Discovery

NAVIGATION. *Fig. I : In this experiment, it was found that young starlings, transported from their home area, had a natural tendency to migrate on courses parallel to their normal direction (after Kratzig & Schuz)*

Normal winter quarters

Recoveries of birds in following winter

the normal haunts of their kind. The factors which terminate the flight there are less well understood. Probably a limit is imposed by the relatively short duration of the impulse to migrate, coupled with the appearance of suitable conditions ; but we can no more explain the inheritance of such directional tendencies and migratory urges than other " instincts ".

Bearings from the Sun. It has been shown that if a day-migrant, such as a Starling, is kept in a cage at migration time, it shows great restlessness. More important, its hoppings and flutterings have a strong directional tendency, even though care is taken that there are no fixed landmarks by which the bird could orientate itself. The direction in which the bird " points " is that in which it would fly if it were free. Even outside the migration season, the bird can be trained to point in one direction by arranging for it to find food there. But the bird shows this ability for direction finding only if the *sun* is visible to it ; with heavily overcast skies its movements become random. The strong suspicion that the sun is used as a compass can be confirmed by changing its apparent position with mirrors. The direction shown by the bird then moves through an equivalent angle, bearing the same relation to the new sun as it did to the old (*see* Fig. 2, in this page).

Other laboratory experiments of this kind have shown that the bird will point in the right direction when brought into the open at different times of day. Alternatively, when presented with an artificial *fixed* sun, the angle that the bird makes with it changes progressively according to the time of day. Lastly, if the bird's " day " is advanced by means of

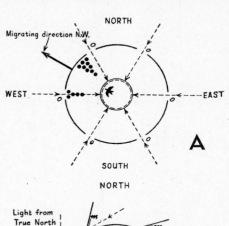

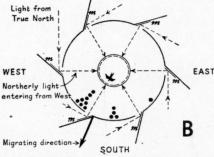

NAVIGATION. *Fig. 2: In a series of experiments to determine whether migrants navigate by the sun, light was permitted to enter an enclosure containing a captive Starling only through a series of openings (0-0, in Fig. A). When light entered these normally, the bird attempted to fly off in a north-westerly direction, as shown by the heavy arrow (average direction of dots, each of which represents 15 seconds of activity in a particular direction). But when mirrors (m-m, in Fig. B) were used to deflect the incoming light and thus alter the sun's apparent position, the Starling tried to adjust its direction of flight accordingly. Thus in Fig B, where the light was rotated 90° ; in an anti-clockwise direction, the bird tried to fly off in a south-westerly direction (heavy arrow), which it quite evidently took to be the north-west*

artificial lighting, the angle the bird makes with the sun is changed by an equivalent amount ; namely, 15° per hour. We must therefore conclude that the bird can allow for the movement of the sun across the sky.

This particular ability is innate, since it has been demonstrated in starlings reared by hand which have never seen the sun in all their lives. The use of the sun as a compass has also been demonstrated in the laboratory with homing pigeons. This can be confirmed by field experiments in which the pigeons are repeatedly released in one direction at increasing distances ; indeed, this is actually the normal technique used in racing these birds. The training direction is taken up regardless of the time at which the birds are released. With poor homers and/or considerable over-training in the chosen direction, the pigeons will show a strong tendency to fly in that direction when released in quite another one—for instance, at right angles.

Once a direction has been determined from the sun, it is not necessary for the birds to keep the sun in view in order to maintain that direction. Migration can thus continue even if the sky becomes overcast. Further, the sun compass mechanism has been demonstrated in typical night-migrants, such as warblers and shrikes. The direction of flight is probably determined by such birds about sunset, before the night's movements begin. They have to maintain that direction as best they can through the darkness, by topographical features or, perhaps, by the general star pattern. If the sky clouds over when it is above the sea, the bird has no outside clues to correct its track, and is liable to be drifted to one side by a beam wind (the effect of wind cannot be appreciated by a bird in flight, if it has no points of reference below or above). The striking correlation between the arrival of Continental migrants on our east coasts and the occurrence of easterly winds strongly supports this conclusion.

KNOWN GOAL

The navigational abilities of birds are by no means limited to determining one fixed direction from the sun's position. This suffices to carry the young bird on its first complete migration, and in pigeons makes their return home so certain that the breeders can concentrate simply on those birds that will fly the fastest. But after a wild bird has bred, it will " home " if captured and displaced from either summer or winter quarters, or while on transit between them. A great many such homing experiments have been carried out with a wide variety of species, involving the release of birds in areas of which they could not have had any experience. Only some strictly non-migratory species showed a complete lack of ability to return to the appropriate area, Winter or Summer. Some extraordinary feats have been recorded—Alpine swifts returning from 1,000 miles, swallows from 1,150 miles, and white storks from 1,400 miles. *But all these were completely eclipsed by a Manx Shearwater which was released in Boston, U.S.A., and flew well over* 3,000 *miles back to its burrow on Skokholm Island, Wales, taking only* 12½ *days to complete this journey.*

RP = **Release Point**

Home

RP

Discovery

NAVIGATION. Fig. 3: Pigeons were released in unknown territory (at RP), and their direction of flight observed. Arrows show bearings at which individual birds disappeared—note tendency towards home

Effects of Distance. Despite some outstanding performances, the general run of pre-war experiments showed a rapid fall in the proportion of returning birds as the distance was increased. Moreover, the time elapsing between release and return was usually much greater than what it would have been if the bird had flown straight home. These facts led to the theory that birds released in areas unknown to them simply wander at random until, by chance, they enter territory familiar to them from migratory experience. Mathematical formulae were derived which showed that the results could indeed be fitted into such a simple conception. In one experiment the actual tracks

taken by homing birds were observed from an aircraft and appeared to be of a wandering, random nature. In this particular case the birds concerned (gannets) may have been searching for good soaring conditions rather than making directly for home.

This relatively inefficient method of homing *may* be employed by some species. But it is definitely not the method of at least three very different species—Lesser Black-backed Gull, Manx Shearwater and Homing Pigeon (not subjected to overtraining in one direction). Large numbers of these birds have been released, one at a time, in unknown country, and watched with powerful binoculars until out of sight. When the bearings at which they are lost from view are plotted, they are found to be scattered about the line of the home direction. This means that, even in the few minutes while they are in sight, these birds become orientated towards home—they " know " where they are. This is true, whether the bearing of home is north, south, east or west. Further striking evidence of navigational ability of a high order has been given by pigeons and shearwaters that have returned home so quickly that they must have continued to fly straight over intervening unknown country. In addition, consistent individual variations in the accuracy of orientation and speed of return are found in different birds, as would be expected if we were dealing with some definite " faculty ".

There is thus no doubt that at least some birds are gifted with a remarkable orientation mechanism which enables them to find their way home in the absence of known landmarks—to navigate, in the strict sense of the word. Once again we must for the present simply accept the fact that this mechanism is inborn. Young pigeons with no training at all will show a strong homeward orientation. Experience gained from training flights, or migration, considerably increases the chances of a bird completing the homeward journey, but this is readily explicable on such grounds as an increase in " confidence " and of the area of known country round the home.

Possible Explanation. There are many theories regarding the physical factors on which orientation is based ; but there is no evidence at all to suggest that there is a direct physical or non-physical link with home, any "thread of Ariadne". One theory has suggested that a bird could register all the changes in direction and acceleration imposed on it during its involuntary outward journey, and, by triangulation, fuse these into one component—the direction of home. Theoretically this is beyond the capacity of the inner ear apparatus which would be concerned, and in practice homing has not been disturbed after elaborate attempts to disrupt the working of this apparatus. These have included direct damage to the structure, transport in a state of narcosis, and transport in continuously, but irregularly, revolving cages.

It seems more probable that birds can detect and use some form of navigational *grid*, much as human navigators do. If some geo-physical factor, which a bird can both detect and measure, varies regularly in a quantitative manner over the earth's surface, the bird could move along the gradient and so approximate more nearly to the value obtaining at home. Two such gradients at an angle to one another would constitute a grid, along the resultant of which the bird could proceed directly home. It has often been suggested that the earth's magnetic field could provide at least one of the co-ordinates of such a grid. But when examined in detail, the changes in the field are too slight to be measured by any organ at the disposal of a bird. Moreover, homing has not been disturbed, as it would be on this theory, by attaching powerful magnets to pigeons' wings. Nor are pigeons attracted to a "false home" having the same magnetic

characteristics as the true home. At one time it seemed that the effects of the earth's rotation—what is known as the "Coriolis Force"—which vary with latitude, could provide a navigation co-ordinate. But again careful examination showed its effects on the bird would be far too small for it to detect them.

The only theory remaining is that which proposes that both co-ordinates are provided by the sun position. This is strongly suggested by the well-established fact that homeward orientation and swift returns occur only when the sun is fully visible ; with overcast skies the birds scatter at random or drift downwind, and returns are much slower and less complete. But if a bird *fixes* its position by the sun, it must do much more than simply use it as a compass. In some way it would have to measure the sun's height (altitude) and displacement round its arc and it would have to compare these values with those obtaining at home at the same time of day. Then if the sun were, say, lower in the sky than at home, the bird would correct this by flying south. If the sun had moved round the arc more than it would have at home, the bird would correct this by flying west. In other words, the bird would obtain its position relative to home in terms of latitude and longitude, and then act accordingly.

Besides the effect of overcast on orientation, there is other experimental evidence which supports this theory. Pigeons kept for a period of days out of sight of sun and sky gave, on release, an orientation which suggested that they had treated the interim seasonal change in the

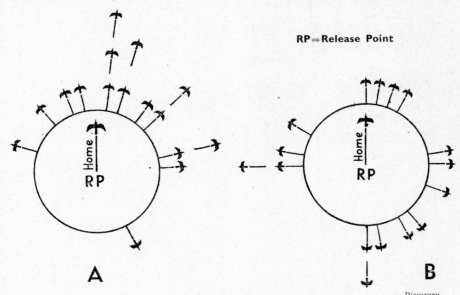

RP=Release Point

A

B

Discovery

NAVIGATION. Fig. 4 : Pigeons released from the same point (RP) as in Fig. 3, and observed in the same way. When wing-magnets were attached to the birds (Fig. A), orientation was unaffected : but with cloudy skies (Fig. B), the birds were found to scatter in all directions

sun's altitude as being due to a change in their own latitude. Other pigeons were kept in an artificial " day " shifted in time by several hours from the normal ; on release the majority treated the change in time as being due to a change in longitude.

The accuracy of initial orientation is greater at greater distances, as would be expected on a grid navigation, since the difference between the home and release co-ordinates is more marked and more easily detectable. Even at only 50 miles from home, the differences in the sun's co-ordinates are big enough to be well within the theoretical capacity of the bird's eye. At short distances, of course, this form of

a small part of its arc and then, by extrapolation, to determine the highest point of that arc. This point is reached at local noon, and is due south. That a bird can make such an estimation, particularly in a minute or two, is difficult to credit, although it is not outside the bounds of possibility. Final assessment of this theory will have to await laboratory experiments in a form of solarium, in which the sun's appearance and *movement* can be faithfully reproduced.

NEEDLE-TAILED SWIFT — Chaetura caudacuta. Credited with being one of the fastest fliers of the bird world—for a speed of about 200 m.p.h. has been claimed—the Needle-tailed Swift has twice visited the British Isles : one was seen in Essex in 1846, and the other in Hampshire in 1879. Another is thought to have been sighted at Fair Isle in 1931. This bird is a native of Japan, Manchuria and north-east Asia.

The Needle-tailed Swift, which is larger than the British Swift, gets its name from the long thin tips of feathers which project from its short tail, though these are not always visible in flight. A better distinguishing mark is the large white patch on the hind part of its belly. It has a dark brown mantle and breast, with metallic green wings and tail. Its throat and under tail feathers are also white. The sexes are alike. The length is $7\frac{1}{2}$ in. ; the tarsus 0·7 in. ; the wing span about 16 in.

Like other swifts, the Needle-tailed is aerial in habit. It breeds in steep and rocky districts on cliffs and both bare and wooded mountains. Its cup-shaped nest is built with feathers caught in the air and glued together with saliva.

M. R. Raut
Prince of Wales Museum of Western India

NEEDLE-TAILED SWIFT. After scouring the world to obtain a flight picture of this Swift—one of the fastest birds—we had to be content with stuffed specimens, which we finally tracked down to an Indian museum

navigation will not work, and the bird will have to home by means of landmarks.

The main difficulty in the way of accepting the idea of sun navigation is that, in an unknown area, the bird will have no independent reference point from which to measure the sun's co-ordinates. Such a reference point would, it seems, have to be provided from the sun itself, and the only way a bird could do this would be to observe the sun's movement along

NEOPHRON. Genus of vultures of the family *Aegypiidae* of the order *Falconiformes*. It contains only one species, the Egyptian Vulture (*q.v.*), which is mainly distributed over southern Europe, Africa and western Asia, and has been recorded twice in Great Britain.

NERVOUS SYSTEM. *See under* Anatomy.

NESTS and NESTING of BRITISH BIRDS

J. A. GIBB, M.A., D.Phil., M.B.O.U.

This article includes two tables of valuable information—one giving the nests, nesting habits and sites of about 100 species, and the other the parts played by both sexes in nest building, incubation and care of the young. See also *Breeding Tables ; Egg*

NEST. Less than half the four hundred-odd species occurring in Great Britain breed here, and of these only about one hundred are common. The number and variety of birds breeding in a habitat depend on its capacity in terms of food, nest sites, song perches, and cover from predators.

Birds normally pair for the breeding season, but a few, such as the Pheasant, Cuckoo, Wren and Corn-Bunting, are habitually polygamous. Long-lived birds often pair for life. Mortality among short-lived birds may be so severe that the chances are against the survival of both members of a pair for a whole year.

Most birds nest solitarily. These include all those which stake out and defend a breeding territory (*q.v.*). The Robin is perhaps the most notoriously aggressive member of this group. Although the maintenance of a territory is primarily associated with breeding, certain birds hold territories also in Winter.

At the other end of the scale are colonial nesters, whose " territory " extends for only a few feet or inches round the nest. Colonies of rooks and house-martins may contain hundreds of nests cheek by jowl, but to see colonial nesting (*q.v.*) at its most impressive we must visit the teeming sea-bird colonies of cliffs and rocks.

Birds breed when feeding conditions are at their best : for instance, thrushes, blackbirds, and rooks, which feed earthworms to their young, can breed in March and April ; while tits, which could hardly tackle worms, must wait until late May for the caterpillars on which they specialise. Swallows and martins breed even later in the Summer, when winged insects are most plentiful. Some generalised feeders can rear young over a longer span by exploiting different foods for successive broods. Wood-pigeons and other doves produce a fatty substance known as " pigeon's milk " for their young. This makes them so independent of special foods that they can breed from April to September, with occasional nests found throughout the year. Crossbills normally nest in February and March, but in Winters when pine seeds—their main food—are abundant, they sometimes nest in Autumn and mid-Winter.

The conventional bird's nest is cup- or saucer-shaped. It ranges from the Reed-Warbler's deep cylinder to the Wood-Pigeon's shallow plate ; and in size from the Gold-crest's gossamer casket to the Golden Eagle's solid platform on which a man can stand. Yet some nests lie outside even these wide bounds.

Sites and Materials. Wrens and long-tailed tits build a domed nest with a small circular entrance. The Long-tailed Tit's nest is a masterpiece of delicate construction, lined with as many as two thousand feathers. Of the birds which nest in holes, some take over more or less ready-made homes, whilst others excavate their own. Puffins and wheatears nest in rabbit burrows. Owls, many tits, nut-hatches, starlings and jackdaws will all breed in suitable nestboxes, as well as in natural sites. A Jackdaw may select a hollow tree or chimney which it fills with enormous quantities of sticks. Woodpeckers excavate their own holes ; British species usually choose dead wood, unlike the larger Black Woodpecker on the Continent. Most birds which breed in ready-made cavities add nests of their own, while those that excavate their own holes are often content with an un-lined chamber. Nuthatches cement up draughty cracks in the nest cavity and round the entrance with a mixture of mud and mammal dung

Mud is used in the nests of many birds. Song-thrushes make a smooth inner lining with mud and soft decaying wood. Swallows and house-martins depend on mud for the outer shell of their nests and for sticking them against a beam or vertical face. Swifts are so clumsy on the ground that they rely on picking up nesting material on the wing ; the few straws, feathers and wisps of light material are stuck to the floor of the nest cavity with saliva.

Birds' eggs long exercised a fearful fascination over naturalists, but today serious egg collecting has been driven underground by a more enlightened public opinion. Yet we can still appreciate the subtle shapes, texture, and endless variety of markings of birds' eggs. Eggs of birds nesting in the open are often beautifully camouflaged : see for example the deeply mottled eggs of gulls and waders. Some birds laying bright-coloured eggs are often themselves unobtrusively coloured, and so sit tightly in the face of danger. Thus the Song-Thrush crouches on its bright blue, black-spotted eggs until an outstretched hand almost touches the nest. Birds which lay in dark holes or in domed nests have no need of camouflage ; so it is that owls, Kingfisher, Swift and Wren have pale eggs. The Wood-Pigeon's glaring white eggs, laid conspicuously on the exposed nest, suggest that it has taken comparatively recently to nesting in the open. The nearly-spherical eggs of owls and Kingfisher contrast strangely with the pointed eggs of waders. The long, pointed shape of Guillemot's eggs probably makes them less liable to roll off narrow ledges. *See also* Camouflage ; Egg ; Pattern and Colour.

Laying and Incubation. Small birds lay one egg daily, often at about dawn, until the clutch is completed. Occasionally days may be missed, but it is rare for two eggs to be laid in much less than twenty-four hours. Larger birds have longer intervals between eggs : e.g. three days in the Shag, and three to four days in the Golden Eagle. Eggs laid by one female tend to be similar, so that successive layings can sometimes be recognized.

A few birds, including waders, pigeons and gulls, always lay the same number of eggs. But usually the number of eggs in a clutch differs widely, not only with the species, but within one species from district to district, year to year, and week to week. The average clutch size of a species probably represents the greatest number of young that the parents can hope to rear. Thus owls lay larger, and more frequent, clutches when mice are abundant than when they are scarce. Birds are capable of laying more eggs than they usually produce ; for if the eggs are taken one by one as they are laid, the bird often goes on laying far in excess of its normal clutch. Many small birds attempt to rear two, three or four broods in one season, though some will come to grief. A great many birds that are ordinarily single-brooded will lay a second clutch if the first fails. Large birds, whose breeding cycle occupies several months, may be unable to produce two broods in one summer. *See also* Breeding Tables.

Birds develop a bare, inflamed " brood-patch " on their breasts, against which the eggs are pressed during incubation. Brood-patches may be present in one sex or both, according to their share in incubation. Female birds almost invariably participate, and usually take the major share of incubation. Three waders, the Dotterel, Grey-necked Phalarope and Red-necked Phalarope, have reversed the normal routine, and the male alone incubates the eggs and tends the young. Incubation most commonly begins as soon as the clutch is completed. In some species, such as the birds of prey and crows, incubation begins when only one or two eggs have been laid. Eggs laid after start of incubation hatch correspondingly late, so that one brood may contain young of different ages. The onset of incubation is often gradual, and it may be impossible to say exactly when it began ; thus measurements of the length of the incubation period are rarely precise. The heat

required to hatch the eggs of a particular species, and the time for which this must be applied, probably vary little in nature.

The Young. Fully-developed chicks become quite active inside the egg, and cheep before the shell is " pipped ". A young bird has a horny growth, the " egg-tooth ", on the tip of the upper mandible, with which it fractures the shell. It rotates slowly within the egg, cutting the shell as it goes ; when it has turned completely round, the cap of the shell falls off, and the chick can wriggle clear.

Birds fall into one of two fairly distinct groups according to the length of time their young stay in the nest after hatching. Those species—by far the larger group—in which the young are born blind, helpless, and either naked or with sparse down, and therefore must remain in the nest for a long time, are called ridicolous species. Species in which the young are born with their eyes open and clad in thick down, and run about shortly after hatching, are called nidifugous species ; they include game birds, waders, ducks and geese.

The care of the young is usually undertaken by both parents. According to the weather, the chicks are given warmth by brooding, or are sheltered from rain or sun beneath a parent's wing. Young grebes are carried upon the back of a parent when swimming, and young woodcocks are carried in flight between a parent's legs. Nestlings of nidicolous birds are completely dependent on their parents for food, and partially dependent even for some weeks or months after they have flown.

The feeding of their offspring generally occupies by far the greater part of the parents' time during the nestling period. As the young grow, they need an increasing amount of food. A normal-sized brood of tits may be fed about 200 times a day for the first few days, but by the time they are a fortnight old they may receive 600-800—or even 1,000—feeds a day. By the end of the nestling period the parents are tired and dishevelled from so much work.

Tits probably feed their young more often than any other British bird ; for they have large families and breed when the early summer flush of woodland caterpillars is at its peak. Moreover, tits ordinarily bring to the nest only one or a few morsels of food at a time. This contrasts with the Swift, for example, which visits its young only two or three times an hour, but at each visit brings several hundred morsels stuck together in a ball, the size of a marble, carried in its throat. The slowest rate of feeding is perhaps that of the Manx Shearwater, whose single chick may be deserted for several days during unfavourable feeding periods. Manx shearwaters sometimes travel huge distances

John Markham

NEST, *simplest of several types built by the Lapwing*

John Markham

NESTS AND NESTING. Nests and eggs of seven British birds, shown at about one-third of their natural size (compare also with the seven nests shown under Egg, in page 195, to the same scale). Reading downwards, from left to right, nests of the following birds are shown : Black-throated Diver, Curlew, Capercaillie, Black Guillemot, Bittern, Black-headed Gull, Coot. The nests in page 195 are, for the most part, those of the smaller landbirds and, on the whole, prove to be far greater feats of construction

to collect enough food for their young. Those breeding on Skokholm Island, off Pembrokeshire, fish the seas off Finistère, 300 miles away, where they catch shoaling sardines, which they bring back in a semi-digested state for their chicks. Young of many nidifugous birds receive little or no food from their parents, but are merely led by them to suitable feeding grounds where they forage for themselves. They follow their parents closely, and learn quickly by copying them and by trial and error.

Nests of nidicolous birds are kept clean through the attentions of parents and young. The parents carry all faeces from the nest, or eat them when they are small. Faeces of nestlings are mostly enclosed in a gelatinous sac, so that they can be removed intact. The nestlings co-operate by defaecating over the edge of the nest ; smaller young turn their hindquarters towards the parent, who takes the faeces as it emerges. Nests of some sea-birds compare unfavourably in the matter of sanitation (*q.v.*) with those of most land-birds. A nauseating stench hangs over a colony of cormorants on a hot, breathless day ; and in places abroad platforms have been provided for them so that the guano can be collected conveniently.

The breeding of the Cuckoo, which differs from the conventional pattern described above, is described under Cuckoo.

See also Breeding ; Egg ; Sanitation ; *further,* the description of nest given under each bird.

HABITAT, SITE AND DESCRIPTION OF NESTS OF SELECTED BRITISH BIRDS

Species	Nesting Habitat	Nest Site	Nest
Avocet	Brackish lagoons	In colonies. On ground in open ; near water	Shallow scrape
Blackbird	Very variable, mostly in bushy places	Usually within 10 ft. from ground ; or on ground	Cup-shaped, substantial
Blackcap	Deciduous woods with shrubs and bushes	Usually 3–10 ft. above ground ; bushes, tangled vegetation	Cup-shaped, flimsy
Bullfinch	Thickets, tall hedges, shrubberies	Usually 3–10 ft. above ground ; dense shrubs	Cup-shaped, shallow
Bunting, Reed-	Near water, reed beds	Close to ground in thick vegetation	Cup-shaped, untidy
Bunting, Yellow	Commons, hedges	Usually within 2 ft. of ground, in dense cover	Cup-shaped, untidy
Buzzard	Chiefly in hilly districts ; also cliffs	Usually 20–50 ft. above ground in trees, on cliff-ledges or on mountain-side	Cup-shaped, bulky and untidy. Often decorated with green foliage
Chaffinch	Woods, hedges, gardens	Usually 3–20 ft. above ground in rather dense cover	Cup-shaped, deep and very neat
Chiffchaff	Deciduous trees with undergrowth	Usually ½–3 ft. above ground, in dense undergrowth	Domed, with side entrance
Coot	Still or very slow-running fresh water	Anchored to aquatic vegetation in shallow water ; usually close to verge	Cup-shaped, bulky
Cormorant	Mainly maritime, occasionally fresh waters	In colonies. Usually on ground, rocky islets	Cup-shaped, broadly based
Corncrake	Grassland where not too closely cropped	On ground, hidden in long grass and low herbage	Saucer-shaped pad of grass and dead stalks
Crow, Carrion-	Cultivation, woods, parks, moors, mountains and coasts	Usually 30–60 ft. above ground in stout fork of tall tree	Cup-shaped, bulky
Cuckoo	Open woods, bushy places, hedges, commons and heaths	Builds no nest, but lays in nests of other birds, especially of Meadow-Pipit, Hedge-Sparrow, Reed-Warbler, Pied Wagtail and Robin	
Curlew	Mainly hill country ; bogs and marshy pastures	On ground in open, with little cover	Shallow scrape
Dove, Turtle-	Edges of woods, thickets, overgrown hedges shrubberies	Usually 5–20 ft. above ground in fairly dense cover	Shallow saucer-shaped platform of fine twigs ; very scanty
Duck, Eider-	Rocky and sandy shores, rarely on fresh waters	Often in colonies ; also singly. Fairly close to water	Saucer-shaped depression
Duck, Tufted	Fresh waters with good cover	Often social. On ground in cover of vegetation ; usually close to water's edge	Cup-shaped depression
Eagle, Golden	Remote mountains	Cliff- or mountain-ledge ; sometimes in tree	Cup-shaped, very large and bulky, rather untidy
Falcon, Peregrine	Mainly coastal and inland cliffs	Ledge or crevice on cliff ; sometimes in tree	None, but sometimes takes over nest of other bird
Flycatcher, Spotted	Gardens, farms, parks and edges of woods	Usually 5–20 ft. above ground ; shelf-type of nestbox	Cup-shaped, rather slight
Gannet	Maritime ; rocky coasts and cliffs	In colonies, usually on small islets. Ledges on cliffs	Cup-shaped, fairly bulky
Goldcrest	Commonest in conifers	Usually 5–50 ft. above ground ; nest suspended from extremity of bough	Cup-shaped, very deep and finely made

Species	Nesting Habitat	Nest Site	Nest
Goldfinch	Hedges, orchards, gardens	Usually 5–30 ft. above ground; especially in fruit trees	Cup-shaped, compact and tidy
Grebe, Great Crested	Fresh waters more than c. 7 acres; still or very slow-running	Floats on water close to shore	Low, saucer-shaped platform, anchored to aquatic vegetation
Grebe, Little	Fresh waters of all sizes; also on slow-running rivers	Floats on water, usually close to shore	Low, saucer-shaped platform, anchored to aquatic vegetation
Greenfinch	Bushy places with some trees	Usually 5–20 ft. above ground in dense cover	Shallow, cup-shaped; rather untidy
Grouse, Red	Upland moors, usually heather or crowberry	On ground in open, sheltered in low herbage	Shallow scrape
Guillemot	Coastal; rocky cliffs and stacks	In colonies. Ledges in vertical cliffs, tops of stacks	None
Gull, Black-headed	Wide variety inland and coastal	In colonies. On ground in open or in low vegetation	Cup-shaped, fairly substantial
Gull, Greater Black-backed	Coastal, especially with cliffs	In colonies and solitarily. Prominences on cliffs, stacks or coastal islands	Cup-shaped, large and untidy
Gull, Herring-	Coastal, especially cliffs or extensive dunes	In colonies and solitarily. Mostly on steep grass slopes above cliffs	Cup-shaped, rather large and untidy
Hawk, Sparrow-	Woods; cultivation with hedgerow trees	Usually 20–40 ft. above ground in main tree-crotch	Saucer-shaped
Heron	Within feeding range of shallow waters	In colonies. Most commonly in tall trees	Saucer-shaped, straggling
Jackdaw	Woods, well-timbered parks, urban districts near pasture; coastal	In colonies and singly. In holes in trees, buildings or cliff; nestboxes	Cup-shaped; size depends on site
Jay	Woods, timbered parks and hedges	Usually 7–20 ft. above ground in smallish trees	Cup-shaped
Kestrel	Open country	Usually 30–70 ft. above ground in tall tree; cliffs	Builds no nest, but often takes over nest of others
Kingfisher	Fresh water, with steep banks	Steep or vertical bank, usually beside water	Spherical chamber at end of 1–3-ft. tunnel in soil
Kittiwake	Rock coasts with steep cliffs	In colonies. Very small ledges on vertical cliffs	Cup-shaped; small, neat against other gulls'
Lapwing	Open country; rough pasture, arable, heaths, commons	On ground in open	Shallow scrape
Linnet	Commons, uncultivated land with bushes, gardens, hedges	Social, but not in colonies. Usually 1–6 ft. above ground in thick bush	Cup-shaped
Magpie	Grassland with some trees, edges of woods	Usually 30–60 ft. above ground in tall tree	Cup-shaped base, domed with entangled sticks
Mallard	Fresh waters, still or slow-running, fairly shallow	Usually on ground in dense low cover, fairly near water	Cup-shaped
Martin, House-	Largely confined to human habitations	In colonies. Usually under eaves of house	Nests cemented in angle formed by vertical and horizontal surfaces; shaped as half a cup
Moorhen	Fresh waters with dense cover; not fast-running	Anchored to aquatic vegetation in shallow water	Cup-shaped; water-weeds, especially leaves of reeds
Nightingale	Thickets, tangled hedges	On or very close to ground, in dense vegetation	Cup-shaped, deep and substantial
Nightjar	Open woodland, commons, heaths with scattered trees	On ground in woodland clearings; open patches of heaths, especially where recently burnt	None. Eggs laid in shallow scrape
Nuthatch	Deciduous woods; timbered gardens, parks and hedges	Hole in stout part of tree, usually 10–40 ft. above ground; nestbox	Saucer-shaped
Owl, Barn-	Mainly cultivation, especially near farms	Shelf in old building; also hole in tree or cliff	None. Eggs laid in shallow scrape in debris
Owl, Little	Cultivation with timbered hedges; parks	Hole in tree or building; low stone walls, rabbit burrows	None. Eggs laid in shallow scrape in debris
Owl, Tawny	Woods; well-timbered parks, hedges and gardens	Hole in tree; sometimes on open platform of old nest of other bird or squirrel; large nestbox	None. Eggs laid in shallow scrape in debris
Oystercatcher	Mainly coastal, all sorts of shores	On ground in open	Shallow scrape
Partridge	Cultivation with hedges or waste land	On ground in cover of low vegetation	Shallow scrape
Petrel, Fulmar	Maritime; cliffs, occasionally some distance inland	In colonies. Ledges and steep slopes near cliff-top	None, or shallow scrape
Petrel, Storm-	Marine; small and remote islands	In colonies. Beneath piles of boulders, in stone walls; burrows hole in soft soil	Normally none

Species	Nesting Habitat	Nest Site	Nest
Pheasant	Wood edges, hedges, commons, reed-beds	On ground in low vegetation	Shallow scrape
Pigeon, Wood-	Woods, hedges, shrubberies ; parks, often urban	Usually 6–30 ft. above ground, in rather thick cover	Shallow saucer-shaped platform
Pipit, Meadow-	Mainly grassland	On ground in open, often hidden in tussock	Cup-shaped
Pipit, Rock-	Rocky coasts	On ground or in crevice of cliff ; nest partly hidden	Cup-shaped
Plover, Golden	Moors, usually hilly	On ground in open	Shallow scrape
Plover, Ringed	Sandy and stony beaches	On ground in open	Shallow scrape
Puffin	Rocky coasts and islands with turf slopes	In colonies. Usually in burrows	None, or some vegetation scattered in burrow
Raven	Mountains and remote hills, cliffs, woods	Mainly inland and coastal cliffs ; also trees, ruins	Cup-shaped and very bulky
Razorbill	Coastal ; rocky cliffs	In colonies. On ground in crevice or beneath boulder	None
Redshank	Water meadows, marshy ground	On ground, usually hidden in tussock	Shallow scrape
Robin	Bushy places ; woods, gardens, hedges, commons	Usually on ground, especially in banks ; shelf against wall and all sorts holes ; nestbox	Cup-shaped
Rook	Cultivation, with copses or hedgerow trees	In colonies. Usually 30–70 ft. above ground in tall trees	Cup-shaped and substantial, rather untidy
Sandpiper, Common	Stony streams, lochs	Stony ground close to verge, sheltered by low herbage	Shallow scrape
Shearwater, Manx	Marine : rocky islands	In colonies. Burrows in soil or cavity in stone walls	Very scanty
Skua, Great	Coastal ; rough pasture and moorland	In colonies. On ground in open	Shallow scrape
Snipe, Common	Mostly boggy places	On ground in open, in tussock or similar cover	Shallow scrape
Sparrow, Hedge-	Bushy places	Usually 1–5 ft. above ground, in bush or dense twigs	Cup-shaped
Sparrow, House-	Habitations of Man	In colonies and singly. Usually in hole or crevice of building	Spherical where space permits, with side entrance
Starling	Largely in association with Man	Often social. In holes in buildings, trees, cliffs ; nestboxes	Cup-shaped, untidy
Stonechat	Commons, moors, waste land	Usually on or within 1 ft. of ground, in dense herbage	Cup-shaped
Swallow	All types country close to human habitation	Against vertical face, usually supported	Cup-shaped
Swan, Mute	Still or slow-running waters, shallow enough for feeding	Exceptionally colonial. On ground by water	Saucer-shaped, solid mound
Swift	Largely confined to human habitation	Social, colonial, solitary. Crevice under eaves of buildings ; cranny in cliff	Saucer-shaped, very slight
Teal	Mainly small areas of fresh water	On ground, often far from water ; in fairly dense cover	Deep cup
Tern, Common	Mainly coastal, but some inland	In colonies. On ground in open	Shallow depression
Thrush, Mistle-	Woods, open country	Usually 10–50 ft. above ground	Cup-shaped, substantial
Thrush, Song-	Woods with undergrowth, and other bushy places	Usually 2–10 ft. above ground	Cup-shaped, fairly substantial
Tit, Blue	Woods, orchards, tall hedges, gardens	Usually 6–30 ft. above ground in hole, nestbox	Cup-shaped, substantial in large cavities
Tit, Great	Woods, orchards, tall hedges, gardens	Usually within 10 ft. of ground in hole, nestbox	Cup-shaped, substantial in large cavities
Tit, Long-tailed	Thickets, tall hedges, scrubby places	Most commonly 4–10 ft. above ground, but often up to 50 ft.	Domed, rather taller than broad, with entrance hole in top side
Tree-Creeper	Woods, parks	Usually 10–40 ft. above ground. Behind loose slab bark ; nestbox	Cup-shaped
Wagtail, Grey	Usually fast-running water	Cavity in wall or steep bank, shelf in building	Cup-shaped
Wagtail, Pied	Villages and around farms ; gardens	Shelf or cavity on building ; depression in ground, steep bank	Cup-shaped
Wagtail, Yellow	Cultivation, especially water-meadows	On ground in open, usually in thick herbage or tussock	Cup-shaped
Warbler, Garden-	Deciduous woods with undergrowth ; other bushy places	Usually 2–5 ft. above ground, in thick vegetation	Cup-shaped
Warbler, Reed-	Reed and osier beds	Usually 2–5 ft. above ground ; woven to several stems	Cup-shaped, very deep
Warbler, Sedge-	Thick undergrowth near water or damp place	Usually 1–3 ft. above ground, in dense vegetation	Cup-shaped

Species	Nesting Habitat	Nest Site	Nest
Warbler, Willow-	Open woods, hedges and bushy places	On ground, especially in tussock or at base of shrub	Domed, with side entrance
Wheatear	Dry, open country ; commons, heaths	Hole in ground or low wall	Cup-shaped
Whitethroat	Low, dense vegetation, often away from trees	Usually ½–3 ft. above ground, in dense herbage	Cup-shaped, rather deep
Woodcock	Woods within feeding range of soft, damp ground	On ground in shallow depression	Almost lacking
Woodpecker, Greater Spotted	Woods ; less often well-timbered parks, hedges, gardens	Usually 10–50 ft. above ground, dead or dying tree	Pear-shaped chamber about 12 in. deep, 5–6 in. wide, with round side entrance at top
Woodpecker, Green	Open woods ; timbered parks, hedges and large gardens	Usually 8–40 ft. above ground ; similar to the above	Pear-shaped chamber, 12–16 in. deep, 6 in. wide
Wren	Variable ; wherever low vegetation gives cover	Usually within 10 ft. of ground ; nestbox	Domed, with side entrance ; compact

SHARE OF SEXES IN NEST-BUILDING, INCUBATION AND CARE OF YOUNG

(The following abbreviations are used :— M = Male, F = Female, x = Takes part)

Species	Building of nest M.	F.	Incubation of eggs M.	F.	Care of young M.	F.
Avocet		x	x	x	x	x
Blackbird		x		x	x	x
Blackcap	x	x	x	x	x	x
Bullfinch		x	x	x	x	x
Bunting, Reed-		x	x	x	x	x
Bunting, Yellow		x	..	x	x	x
Buzzard	x			x	x	x
Chaffinch		x		x	x	x
Chiffchaff		x		x		x
Coot	x	x	x	x	x	x
Cormorant	x	x	x	x	x	x
Corncrake		x		x	x	x
Crow, Carrion-	x			x	x	x
Cuckoo						
Curlew		x	x	x	x	x
Dove, Turtle-	x	x	x	x	x	x
Duck, Eider-		x		x		x
Duck, Tufted		x		x		x
Eagle, Golden	x	x		x	x	x
Falcon, Peregrine		x	x	x	x	x
Flycatcher, Spotted	x	x	x	x	x	x
Gannet	x	x	x	x	x	x
Goldcrest	x	x		x	x	x
Goldfinch		x		x	x	x
Grebe, Great Crested	x	x	x	x	x	x
Grebe, Little	x	x	x	x	x	x
Greenfinch		x		x	x	x
Grouse, Red		x		x	x	x
Guillemot		x	x	x	x	x
Gull, Black-headed	x	x	x	x	x	x
Gull, Greater Black-backed	x	x	x	x	x	x
Gull, Herring-	x	x	x	x	x	x
Hawk Sparrow-		x		x	x	x
Heron	x	x	x	x	x	x
Jackdaw	x	x		x	x	x
Jay	x	x	x	x	x	x
Kestrel			x	x	x	x
Kingfisher	x	x	x	x	x	x
Kittiwake	x	x	x	x	x	x
Lapwing		x	x	x	x	x
Linnet		x	x	x	x	x
Magpie	x			x	x	x
Mallard		x		x		x
Martin, House-	x	x	x	x	x	x
Moorhen	x	x	x	x	x	x
Nightingale		x		x	x	x
Nightjar		x	x	x	x	x
Nuthatch	x	x		x	x	x
Owl, Barn-				x	x	x
Owl, Little				x	x	x
Owl, Tawny				x	x	x
Oystercatcher		x	x	x	x	x
Partridge		x		x	x	x
Petrel, Fulmar		x	x	x	x	x
Petrel, Storm-	x	x	x	x	x	x
Pheasant		x		x		x
Pigeon, Wood-	x	x	x	x	x	x
Pipit, Meadow-		x		x	x	x
Pipit, Rock-		x		x	x	x
Plover, Golden		x	x	x	x	x
Plover, Ringed		x	x	x	x	x
Puffin	x	x		x	x	x
Raven	x	x		x	x	x
Razorbill			x	x	x	x
Redshank		x	x	x	x	x
Robin		x		x	x	x
Rook	x	x		x	x	x
Sandpiper, Common		x	x	x	x	x
Shearwater, Manx	x	x	x	x	x	x
Skua, Great		x	x	x	x	x
Skylark		x		x	x	x
Sparrow, Hedge-		x		x	x	x
Sparrow, House-	x	x	x	x	x	x
Snipe, Common		x		x	x	x
Starling		x	x	x	x	x
Stonechat		x		x	x	x
Swallow	x	x		x	x	x
Swan, Mute	x	x	x	x	x	x
Swift	x	x	x	x	x	x
Teal		x		x		x
Tern, Common	x	x	x	x	x	x
Thrush, Mistle-		x		x	x	x
Thrush, Song-		x		x	x	x
Tit, Blue		x		x	x	x
Tit, Great		x		x	x	x
Tit, Long-tailed	x	x		x	x	x
Tree-Creeper	x	x		x	x	x
Wagtail, Grey		x		x	x	x
Wagtail, Pied		x		x	x	x
Wagtail, Yellow		x		x	x	x
Warbler, Garden-	x	x	x	x	x	x
Warbler, Reed-		x	x	x	x	x
Warbler, Sedge-		x		x	x	x
Warbler, Willow-		x		x	x	x
Wheatear	x	x	x	x	x	x
Whitethroat	x	x	x	x	x	x
Woodcock		x		x		x
Woodpecker, Greater Spotted	x	x		x	x	x
Woodpecker, Green	x	x	x	x	x	x
Wren	x	x		x	x	x

MAN-MADE HOMES FOR BIRDS

EDGAR STERN-RUBARTH, Ph.D.

After naming the British species that may be induced to use nesting boxes, the author gives practical information on the types favoured by different birds, on how to give protection against the weather, cats and other predatory creatures, and on the best sites

NESTING BOX. One of the very simplest ways of increasing one's interest in, and knowledge of, bird-life is to attract them to one's garden or window ledge by erecting a nesting box. If properly constructed and sited, this will afford endless pleasure to the bird-lover, who can not only watch the activities of a pair of birds throughout the mating season and until the young are reared, but can also welcome visitors year by year.

At least 28 British species regularly occupy such boxes ; they range from five species of tits, the Wren, Robin, House- and Tree-Sparrow, Blackbird and Starling to such supposedly shy birds as the Barn-, Little and Tawny Owl and even the Kestrel. The Jackdaw, Pied Wagtail, Tree-Creeper, Nuthatch, Spotted and Pied Flycatcher, Redstart, Wryneck, Swallow, Swift, House-Martin, Stock-Dove and Greater Spotted Woodpecker complete the list.

Housing Requirements. These vary considerably and the size of the nesting box must be adapted to the species one wishes to attract. The accompanying diagrams will assist in the proper choice. The most widely accepted type of box is that illustrated in Figs. 1a and 1b. For tits the floor should by 4 in. by 4 in., the average depth 5 in., and the hole not wider than $1\frac{1}{8}$ in. in diameter (for marsh-tits even slightly less). With about the same dimensions, a nesting box for the Nuthatch or Pied Flycatcher should have a hole of between $1\frac{1}{4}$ in. and $1\frac{1}{2}$ in. diameter ; for the Tree-Sparrow a hole of about $1\frac{1}{4}$ in. (the box should also be a little deeper) ; and for the Wren a hole of 2 in.

The House-Sparrow needs more space : a floor of 6 in. by 6 in., average depth of 8 in., and a hole $1\frac{1}{2}$ in. wide. The Wryneck needs a similar hole, but is content with a depth of 6 in. and a floor of 5 in. by 5 in. The Redstart may fancy the same lodgings, with a hole $1\frac{1}{2}$ in. to 2 in. wide ; but he also is known to have lodged in—as have some tits—the boxes shown in Figs. 3a, 3b and 4. The Jackdaw, Starling and Greater Spotted Woodpecker have the same taste in ready-made lodgings, but require larger dimensions: the Jackdaw a floor of $7\frac{1}{2}$ in. by $7\frac{1}{2}$ in., average depth of 17 in., and a hole 6 in. or more in diameter ; the Starling a floor of 12 in. by 12 in., depth of 12 in., but a hole of only 2 in. width ; the Greater Spotted Woodpecker a floor of 5 in. by 5 in., a depth of 12 in., and

a hole of 2 in. This last usually prefers the box in Fig. 1b to that in Fig. 1a.

For owls, the Kestrel and the Stock-Dove a large entrance has to be cut in the front panel by simply cutting out the part left in our designs from the hole up to the rim. The Little Owl needs an entrance 4 in. wide, and the Tawny Owl and Stock-Dove one of 8 in; they also need floor of about 8 in. by 8 in., and a depth of 12 in. (but for the Tawny Owl as much as 30 in.). The Barn-Owl prefers a " tray " on the pattern of Fig. 5, with a bottom of 15 in. by 18 in. and an average depth of 12 in. Robin, Swallow, Blackbird, Spotted Flycatcher and Pied Wagtail prefer living " in the open " (Figs. 2, 3a, 3b), and all demand a floor of about 4 in. by 4 in., except the Blackbird which needs 12 in. by 12 in.

There are also specially constructed nesting boxes for swifts made by the Edward Grey Institute (*q.v.*), and variations of the essential and serviceable makes given here. Two which a clever handyman might make for himself, are shown in Figs. 4 and 1c. The first is an artificial nest for house-martins. Placed under a ledge frequented by them, this is made in clay, baked in a pottery oven, from a cast of an original nest carefully taken down ; it is slightly thicker than the original and has flanges for fixing. The entrance holes should be not more than $1\frac{1}{8}$ in. in diameter ; the traps shown are for examination from above.

The second is a cat- and squirrel-proof development of Fig. 1a. It has a swivel top, pivoted and weighted at the back, so that an animal jumping on to it causes it to drop down in front to close the entrance. If it is well balanced and on well oiled hinges, the top snaps back as soon as the cat or squirrel jumps off. This is manufactured under patent by the Greenrigg Works, Woodford Green, Essex.

Siting the Nesting Box. It is important not only to have the right box but also the right place for it. It is not necessary to make the entrance hole face in any particular direction, although one from north through east to south-east is recommended, so as to avoid both strong sunlight from the south and the prevailing west winds. The box can be fastened to any tree, as long as it allows a clear flightway. The box should be slightly inclined forwards to prevent the entrance of rain and sunshine ; it

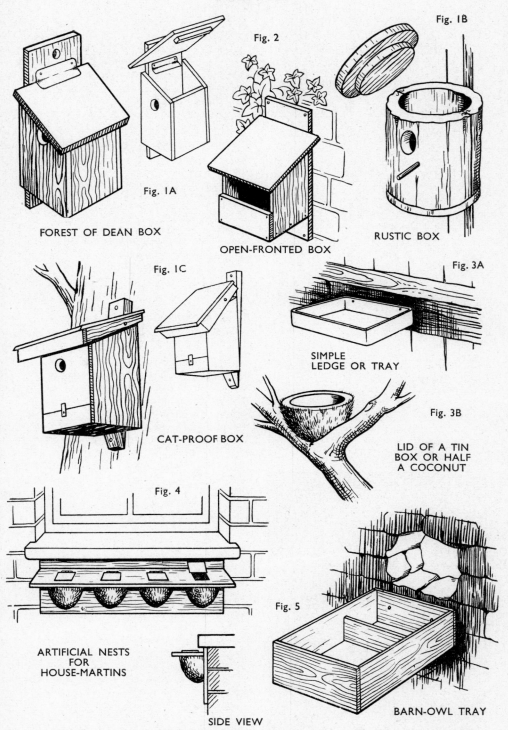

Fig. 2

Fig. 1B

Fig. 1A

FOREST OF DEAN BOX

OPEN-FRONTED BOX

RUSTIC BOX

Fig. 1C

Fig. 3A

SIMPLE
LEDGE OR TRAY

Fig. 3B

CAT-PROOF BOX

LID OF A TIN
BOX OR HALF
A COCONUT

Fig. 4

Fig. 5

ARTIFICIAL NESTS
FOR
HOUSE-MARTINS

SIDE VIEW

BARN-OWL TRAY

NESTING BOX. It is essential to have special boxes for particular types of bird. The most usual ones are those shown in Figs. 1A and 1B, but even here the size of the box will vary according to the species of bird. Thus, most tits need a box with a floor of 4 in. by 4 in., and a depth of 5 in., while the Starling will use the same type of box, provided it be 12 in. by 12 in. by 12 in. Many birds prefer living in the open, in the boxes shown in Figs. 2, 3A and 3B. Special " boxes " (see text) are seen in Figs. 4 and 5 should be carefully planed and nailed—or, better still, screwed—so as to avoid splinters or cracks which are dangerous for a bird's slender feet ; and, generally, it should not have a perch, because this would help a predator's attack.

The height at which boxes should be fixed varies. The Robin, Spotted Flycatcher, and suchlike accept boxes as low as 4 ft. from the ground ; the Great Tit prefers to live at six times that height ; and the House-Sparrow and Starling like a box to be at least above the reach of Man. In general, Passerines take the lower, and stock-doves, owls and woodpeckers the higher boxes. All prefer them to be well away from bushes, and hung so that they can fly in without touching anything with their wings.

The provision of nesting material is not necessary, but some tits and finches seem to be grateful for cotton-wool placed near their prospective home ; if possible this should not be white. For species which do not build nests—the Tawny Owl, Wryneck and so on— some sawdust on the floor of the box is useful. The simple trays or ledges (Figs. 3a, 3b and 5) should have a few small holes for drainage.

> *Consult* How to Feed and Attract the Wild Birds, H. Mortimer Batten, 1933 ; Every Garden a Bird Sanctuary, E. L. Turner, 1935 ; Nestboxes, Cohen & Campbell, 1952.

NESTLING. Young bird until the time it is ready to fly, when it becomes a fledgling. Nestlings in a stage of helplessness, unable to leave the nest for days, are described as *nidicolae* ; nestlings able to run and leave the nest immediately after hatching are called *nidifugae*.

Eric Hosking

NESTING BOX. *Nuthatch, bringing food to its young, is on the point of entering its nesting box*

NET. *See* Trap.

NETTA. Genus of ducks of the family *Anatidae* of the order *Anseriformes.* It contains only one species, the Red-crested Pochard (*q.v.*), which mainly occurs in southern Europe, north-west Africa and northern Asia, but is also found in southern Asia and in other parts of northern Africa outside the breeding season. It is an irregular winter visitor to Britain.

NICTITATING MEMBRANE. Also sometimes called " haw ". The third eyelid found in birds, which springs from the inner border of the eye, and is capable of being drawn across the eyeball. *See illustration under* Eye.

NIDICOLAE (L. *nidus*, " nest "; *colere*, " to inhabit "). Name given to that class of birds which are featherless when hatched and must remain in the nest for some time before being able to live independently.

NIDIFICATION. Term applied to the process of nest building. *See also* Nest.

NIDIFUGAE (L. *nidus*, " nest "; *fuga*, " flight "). Name given to nestlings which are able to leave the nest and run about on the day they are hatched.

NIGHT-HAWK—Chordeiles minor. The bird called the Eastern Nighthawk in the A.O.U. Check-list and known in Great Britain as the American Nightjar, breeds in north America and winters in the south. Only one is recorded as having visited Great Britain : this was in 1927, in the Scilly Isles. It is more a bird of the open country than the European Nightjar, and has longer wings, and a slightly forked tail instead of a round one. Its bill is very small and surrounded by very short and fine bristles. Its general habits are similar to those of the European bird, but it is less shy and is more often seen by day in fields and on moors; it can sometimes be seen even in cities, where it nests on gravel roofs. Its length is about 9 in.

NIGHT HERON—Nycticorax nycticorax. A more or less regular bird of passage on the south and east coasts of England, especially in Spring and early Summer, the Night Heron is native to southern Europe, Asia and Africa, and to north and south America where it is called the Black-crowned Night Heron.

A squat, dumpy bird with its head habitually sunk in its shoulders, it has a generally grey appearance. The crown and mantle are very dark grey, almost black, and have an all-over sheen of bluish-green; its rounded light grey wings and white breast and underparts contrast vividly with the dark upper parts. From the dark crown hang several elongated crest plumes. The bird has a rather long, pointed, green bill,

NIGHTINGALE, *its ' liquid notes close the eye of the day '*

yellow or pink legs, and red eyes. The total length is 24 in., but the bird has the appearance of being much shorter and the tarsus is 3·15 in. The wing span is approximately 2 ft., and the weight between 1½ and 2 lb.

Solitary and nocturnal in habit, the Night Heron roosts silently during the day amid the branches of trees or other dense cover, and seeks its feeding ground as dusk approaches. During the breeding season, it occasionally forages for food for its young by day. On the ground, its walk is slow and elegant.

The flight of the Night Heron is typical of the family, but with rather faster wing beats than the common Heron's ; its neck is always well retracted. Its voice is a harsh croak, usually heard by night. From its breeding haunts many strange noises emerge.

The elaborate mating display of the Night Heron has been the subject of much study, both in Britain and America. The following extract from *The Handbook of British Birds* is worth quoting :

> With head and wings lowered, the male executes a queer sort of dance—treading from one foot to the other with a peculiar weaving action. From time to time he suddenly lowers his head and neck vertically, while his shoulders lift as if in a hiccough, and he utters his courting cry.—Lorenz.

Wooded and bushy swamps and reed beds are the Night Heron's favourite haunts. It forms large colonies, together with little and cattle egrets, squacco herons, Glossy Ibis and other herons. The nests are close together, among bushes or trees growing in the water ; in Egypt many nests are built in high trees. The male, having chosen the site, summons his mate, and the huge nest is begun; it is formed of any materials suitable for the site. Three to four blue-green eggs are laid in April or May, one every 48 hours. The hatching, which begins with the first egg, lasts for 21 days, both birds taking part. The chicks are fed by regurgitation by both parents. They leave the nest in about four weeks, and can fly in six weeks. One brood is normally reared, but two are occasionally brought out.

In common with all its relations the Night Heron feeds largely on fish, water animals and insects. Some vegetable matter is also taken.

G. K. Yeates

NIGHT HERON. This squat, dumpy bird in its dark- and light-grey plumage is a native of southern Europe, Asia and Africa and also of the Americas

NIGHTINGALE—Luscinia megarhynchos. No other bird in the world has inspired so much romance and poetry as the Nightingale, thanks to the surpassing beauty of its song which, borne on the warm air of a summer night, knows no rival. The fact that it sings by night when most other birds are silent is no doubt responsible for its hold on the imagination of the public. In fact it sings just as well during the day, but then the song mingles with those of other birds and passes unnoticed in the volume of spring melody.

A summer visitor, arriving in April and leaving again for its winter quarters in the south in August or early September, the Nightingale is narrowly restricted in its distribution. It nests only in suitable areas of south and east England and the border counties of Wales ; elsewhere it is very rare. In recent years, however, it has been observed farther north, in Yorkshire and the Lake District and in 1953 one was even heard in Scotland. It is not known to breed in Ireland. The Nightingale occurs throughout Europe, western Asia and north-west Africa, wintering in tropical Africa.

A sober-looking bird, rather like a large brown Robin, the Nightingale's appearance bears no relation to the beauty of its voice. Its upperparts are russet-brown, shading deeper on tail and tail coverts ; the underparts are pale greyish-brown, showing whiter on throat and belly. Its bill and legs are brown. The sexes are alike, and the young are very similar to the young robins, with the same mottled plumage. The length is 6½ in., the tarsus 1 in. The wing span is between 9 and 10 in., and the weight 1 oz.

Essentially a bird of woodland copses, spinneys, thickets and woods with dense vegetation, the Nightingale is rarely found in

1 D

John Markham

NIGHTINGALE. Shy and secretive, this little brown bird is the most wonderful songster, though individual birds may differ in their ability

hilly country here, but abroad it will nest at heights of about 3,000 ft. and even at 6,000 ft.

Needless to say, I have spent countless hours recording the many variations in the Nightingale's repertory, and am glad to have been able to bring the song in all its beauty to those who live where it is never likely to be heard. Apart from the song, the Nightingale has many varied notes—among them a soft call rather resembling that of the Chiffchaff and Willow-Warbler, and several harsh and grating alarm notes. The song is of short duration. Rarely heard before the latter half of April or after the middle of June, it ceases as soon as the eggs are hatched.

I have heard and recorded the songs of over 20 nightingales in the last 30 years, and discovered that there were individual variations in the song of even the same bird. Another fact, still less known, is that the Nightingale will imitate other birds. I have recorded it mimicking the Nuthatch, the bubbling call of the female Cuckoo, and other birds.

Once I made a recording of four nightingales singing within 50 yards of each other ; but I have also been surrounded by nightingales night after night, when, though the weather was fine, not one bird would oblige with a song.

Years ago, when the famous Beatrice Harrison played her 'cello to the accompaniment of singing nightingales, Oxted, Surrey, suddenly became known for these birds. I believe that the nightingales inspired Miss Harrison and not vice versa ; for all birds sing louder when they have to compete with other sounds.

An amusing incident once occurred after I had been trying for several nights to obtain a recording of a Nightingale in a deep wood. Somebody must have watched me, for one morning I received an invitation from a family living on the outskirts of a Surrey town. They were sorry, they wrote, that I had gone to so much trouble to try and get a recording near *midnight*. If I cared to come to their place at *midday*, I could obtain a wonderful recording of a singing Nightingale. Needless to say, I went—only to discover that my host mistook a Song-Thrush for a Nightingale. I did not dare shatter his illusion !—EDITOR.

The famous song is the best evidence of the Nightingale's presence. Delivered usually from a low tree or bush, the full song is a superlative performance of unique richness and beauty and reaches a crescendo which no other bird can attain, and which no words could adequately describe. But not every Nightingale is a good songster ; indeed, many are only very indifferent performers.

Many of its habits and movements recall those of the Robin, but the Nightingale has nothing of the Robin's tameness or its liking for human society. Exceedingly secretive, it avoids the open, and at the approach of an intruder will hurriedly dive into the undergrowth. It hops along, pausing at intervals, and now and then flicking its tail and wings. Its flight, which also has much in common with that of the Robin, is a low flitting over the ground, never for any great distance. In courtship, much play is made with the rufous tail, the head is lowered and wings are fluttered.

The Nightingale's nest is placed on, or close to the ground amid the dense undergrowth of roadside spinneys, thickets or copses. Built by the hen alone, it has a foundation of dead leaves, and is lined with grasses, leaves and hair. Four or five olive-green or olive-brown eggs are laid in May, and are incubated by the hen for a period of 13 or 14 days. The young are fed and reared by both parents for 11 or 12 days and sometimes even longer.

Insects of various kinds are the chief food of the Nightingale, but spiders, worms and some kinds of berries are also taken. Long before broadcasting and sound-recording, the news that a Nightingale had honoured a district where it was not usually heard was not infrequently a cause of great excitement. It is related that in 1865 a " Nightingale train " was run from Manchester to Lymm in Cheshire, where a Nightingale was reported to be singing, and in 1896 the crowds endeavouring to hear another became so great that efforts were made to scare the bird from its favourite perch.

NIGHTJAR—Caprimulgus europaeus. Comparatively few people have had the good fortune to see this fascinating and interesting bird for it is purely nocturnal in its habits. Nightjars are among our latest summer visitors to arrive, rarely appearing before May. Except in the Orkney and Shetland Islands and the Outer Hebrides, where it is a rare vagrant, it is generally distributed throughout the British Isles in suitable areas. Abroad, it is found in Europe, Asia and Africa ; in Winter, in Tanganyika, it has been seen at an altitude of 6,000 ft.

When flying at night, the Nightjar is completely unlike any other night bird in shape and flight. Few birds have a finer camouflage (*q.v.*). Its all-over colour is a greyish-brown, finely spotted and barred in dark and light shades of brown, with some parts touched with chestnut ; when at rest the whole bird completely merges into its surroundings. The male has some white tips on his long tail feathers, and three white spots on his outer wing quills, very conspicuous in flight. Both the female and young lack these white marks. The bill is dark brown, and the eyes are very large. The length is $10\frac{1}{2}$ in. and the tarsus $\frac{3}{4}$ in. ; the wing span is between 12 and 18 in. ; and the weight is $2\frac{1}{2}$ oz.

From mid-May onwards, as soon as the Robin has ended his evening song at dusk, a jarring rattle may be heard in the distance, continuing for five minutes or more. This far-carrying sound which, however, is by no means shrill, is the Nightjar's song.

It is usually uttered from a perch on a horizontal bough. Often the sound changes when the bird takes to the air. There are also many other variations—thus, instead of the jarring or churring noise, two notes of different pitch may be heard. On one occasion I even managed to record a gliding note, interspersed with the sound of wing-flapping.

Individual nightjars have songs of different pitch, and sometimes the jarring ends with a soft, clear, bubbling sound. The British Nightjar is said to be silent on migration.

The eerie call note, uttered in flight, is characteristic. I have heard it from the same bird first from a distance and then, within seconds, from close at hand.—EDITOR.

The "churring" is scarcely ever heard in Great Britain before May ; from the middle of that month until the middle of July is the best time to hear it. It is not heard later than September.

During the day the Nightjar remains silent and very low on the ground, so that, unless disturbed, detection is almost impossible. If one is seen, it appears rather like some peculiar reptile with its mottled plumage and round flat head. It walks with short quick steps, but is seldom seen to do so. On a branch it perches lengthwise. Although it migrates in flocks, the Nightjar is not gregarious and, outside the breeding season, is usually seen singly. In its noiseless and erratic nocturnal flight, it wheels, glides and coasts in pursuit of the insects that make up its diet.

Its chosen haunts are heaths, moors, commons and woodlands. No nest is made, the two creamy-white eggs being deposited on the ground. Delicately mottled in brown and dark purple, and oval in shape with both ends rounded, they are laid from mid-May onwards. Both birds share the hatching, the hen undertaking the daytime watch and the cock relieving her in the evening ; the period is 18 days. The chicks are fed by both parents, but the male takes entire charge of the first when the second brood is being hatched. The young birds are able to fly after 16 or 18 days, and in about a month's time are quite independent.

Insects—mostly harmful species—taken on the wing, form the Nightjar's main diet.

"Goatsucker" is the other name commonly applied to the Nightjar, and its Latin name *Caprimulgus* is a translation of this. The name comes from an absurd ancient superstition that these birds suck the milk of goats and sheep. Among local names are "Fern-Owl", "Night Hawk", "Churn Owl", "Wheel Bird" and "Spinning Jenny" (the latter from its call).

NIGHTJAR. *Few birds are better camouflaged than the grey-brown Nightjar, who may often be mistaken for a twig, when roosting lengthwise on some branch during the day*

G. K. Yeates

Arthur Christiansen

NORTHERN BULLFINCH. *Its rose-pink breast is of a much brighter hue than the British bird's*

NORTH AFRICAN BLACK WHEATEAR —Oenanthe leucura syenitica. One specimen of this form of Black Wheatear was identified in Sussex in June 1915. A browner tinge in the black of the plumage is a mark of distinction from its near relative. Otherwise it is similar. Its length is 7 in. *See also* Black Wheatear.

NORTH AMERICAN PEREGRINE—Falco peregrinus anatum. Two young birds belonging to this race of Peregrine Falcon, called the Duck-Hawk in the American Check-list—have visited the British Isles, one in 1891 and the other in 1910. The species breeds in the Far North, including Baffin Land and Greenland. Very similar in appearance to the British Peregrine Falcon, it has some slight difference in coloration. The young have, however, darker plumage than the British young, and it was no doubt this distinction that led to the identification of the two visitors. The length is 15-19 in, and the tarsus 2 in. The wing span is about 2½ ft. and the weight is 3 lb.

The breeding habits of the American Peregrine follow the pattern of its family. The same type of country is frequented, three eggs being laid on a ledge or in a cavity in a cliff, in early March, June or July, according to the latitude.

Birds, usually caught on the wing, form the main diet, but some mammals are also taken.

NORTH ATLANTIC SHEARWATER — Procellaria diomedea borealis. Only in the range of its breeding sites does the North Atlantic Shearwater differ from the Mediterranean Shearwater. One picked up in Sussex in 1914 was definitely identified as belonging to the North Atlantic species. Its length is 17 or 18 in.

This bird is also known as Cory's Shearwater, after the naturalist who first studied its habits.

NORTHERN BULLFINCH—Pyrrhula pyrrhula. An autumn and winter visitor to Great Britain, usually seen in Scotland, especially in the Orkney and Shetland Islands, this Bullfinch breeds in Scandinavia, Finland, Russia and other countries of northern Europe. Imported into Britain as a cage-bird, this is the bullfinch seen for sale in shops. It is a larger bird than the British Bullfinch (*q.v.*), being about 6 in. long, and its plumage, especially the rose-pink of its breast, is much brighter, even at a distance. Essentially a bird of the woodlands, it often builds its large nest in a cone-bearing tree. Five or six greenish-blue eggs are laid from May to July, according to the country frequented. The Northern Bullfinch's characteristics do not differ materially from those of the resident British bird.

NORTHERN CRESTED TIT. *See* Central European Crested Tit.

NORTHERN DUNLIN. *See* Dunlin.

NORTHERN GOLDEN PLOVER—Charadrius apricarius altifrons. The Golden Plover of Iceland, Scandinavia and Russia, this Northern species comes to Britain as a passage migrant and winter visitor. *See also* Golden Plover.

NORTHERN GREATER SPOTTED WOODPECKER. This bird is closely related to, but rather larger than, our Greater Spotted Woodpecker (*q.v.*).

NORTHERN PHALAROPE. American name for the Red-Necked Phalarope (*q.v.*).

NORTHERN RAZORBILL — Alca torda. Only two birds of this species of Razorbill, one picked up dead in England and another found in Scotland, have occurred in Britain. It is, however, so similar to the British Razorbill, that it may occur much more often off our coasts than generally suspected. It breeds in Iceland, Norway, Denmark and the Baltic.

Except for some slight differences in the length of the wings and the thickness of the bill, it is identical in appearance, as well as in behaviour and habits, with the British Razorbill. The length is 16 in. *See also* Razorbill.

NORTHERN TREE-CREEPER — Certhia familiaris. Found throughout all parts of eastern Europe, the Northern Tree-Creeper has been identified in Britain only seven times—twice in England and on five occasions in Scotland. It is, however, so similar in appearance to the British Tree-Creeper that it may have occurred more frequently without being recognized. Paler upper parts and pure white underparts are its distinguishing marks, but in all else—general behaviour, breeding habits and voice—it does not differ from its relative. Its length is 5 in., the tarsus 0·65 in., and the wing span about 6 in.

NOSTRILS. These vary considerably in shape, size and position. Often they are round, as in the tits, in certain birds of prey, such as the Kestrel, and in the shrikes. In the finches and the ducks they are more oval, while in some other birds, such as dippers, pigeons, storks and cormorants, they are slit-like.

The nostrils are usually situated near the base of the bill, but sometimes near the middle, as in ducks and in the Puffin. In only one bird, the Kiwi of New Zealand, do they extend right to the tip of the bill.

Generally the nostrils are simple apertures, but in many birds they are protected by a covering, or *operculum*. In the petrels and albatrosses this covering is prolonged into a hard, forwardly-directed tube. In the Nightjar, too, each nostril is prolonged into a short, narrow tube. In the plovers the operculum is leathery, while in the pigeons it is soft and swollen. In the birds of prey and in the parrots the nostrils are enveloped in a soft, wax-like area of skin at the base of the upper mandible, known as the *cere*.

In some birds (the crows and birds of prey, for example) the nostrils are protected by bristles ; in others, such as the Goldfinch, the Linnet, the tits, shrikes, buntings and sparrows, they are concealed by feathers.

In a few birds, such as the Cormorant, the nostrils are vestigial, while in the Gannet they are completely closed, the greater part of the nasal cavity being filled with bony tissue. The reason for this peculiarity may be inferred from the Gannet's habit of diving from a height into the sea to catch its prey. However, its wide inner nostrils open into its mouth, and enable it to smell its food. Nevertheless, it should be noted that in no bird is this sense at all acute. *See also* Smell, Sense of.

The nasal cavities may communicate with each other, or they may be completely separated by a septum, or division, as, for example, in the owls and certain birds of prey. The former condition is termed *nares perviae*, the latter is generally known as *nares imperviae*.

NOTAEUM. Name for the back of a bird.

NUCIFRAGA (Latin, " nutcracker "). Genus of the family *Corvidae* of the order *Passeriformes*. It contains only one Old World species, the Nutcracker (*q.v.*), which occurs in a number of different forms in Europe and Asia. A separate species occurs in north America.

Two forms of the Nutcracker (*q.v.*) occur in the British Isles ; one of these, the Slender-billed Nutcracker, is an irregular visitor, mainly to south and east England ; the other, the Thick-billed Nutcracker, has been recorded here only six times—on each occasion in England.

NUMENIUS. Genus of the family *Scolopacidae* of the order *Charadriiformes*. It contains eight species, distributed over northern Europe, northern Asia and north America, and migrating in many cases to regions far to the south for the non-breeding season. There are four species on the British list : the Curlew, Whimbrel, Eskimo Curlew and Slender-billed Curlew, the last two being extremely rare in the British Isles. They are separately described under their own headings.

The members of this genus are medium-sized to large waders. They possess long curved bills, which are blunt and slightly thickened at the tip. The wings are long and rather pointed ; the first developed primary feather is the longest. The tail is short and somewhat rounded. The tarsus is long, and is covered with hexagonal scales. There are three front toes, and a hind toe which is remarkably well-developed.

NUTCRACKER. A genus of birds of the Crow family, the members of which have a stout conical bill in which both mandibles terminate in a blunt point. They are also distinguished by their square-ended tails. Four species are known, ranging from northern Europe and Arctic Siberia to the Himalayas and China. Two subspecies occasionally seen in Britain are the Slender-Billed (*Nucifraga caryocatactes macrorhynchos*) (*q.v.*), and the Thick-Billed (*N.c. caryocatactes*) (*q.v.*), which are both very similar in appearance.

NUTHATCH — Sitta europaea. Although confined to the British Isles, the Nuthatch is not one of our most familiar birds, but it is common in suitable areas of south and central England, except the Isle of Wight, where it is unknown. It is rare in the north of England, and in Scotland, and Ireland appears only as occasional visitor. Abroad, it is represented in

W. Farnsworth

NUMENIUS. The Curlew is the only resident of this genus to be found throughout Great Britain

Europe by other subspecies which differ somewhat in coloration.

The unusual shape and climbing habits of the Nuthatch are easily recognized. Its plump and short-tailed body is clad above in greyish-blue ; the underparts are buff, and the flanks tinged with a rich chestnut. Through its eye runs a dark line extending towards the neck. Its cheeks and throat are white, its thin pointed bill grey, and its legs yellowish-brown. The sexes are alike ; but the young are duller and lack the chestnut colouring. The length is $5\frac{1}{2}$ in., the tarsus 0·8 in., the wing span 8 in. or 9 in., and the weight 1 oz.

I have had the opportunity of recording the Nuthatch's call notes and song, and was astonished at their extraordinary variety. My records were obtained during the best part of a week from a pair of nuthatches busily preparing their nest about 40 ft. from the ground in a high tree. The microphone, placed quite near the nest, interrupted their activities for a day or two, but the birds finally got used to the strange object, and I was able to record their complete vocabulary.

The typical call notes are extremely varied, sweet and musical ; one is very like a boy's whistle, and another—quite different from them all, and even sweeter and more musical—is uttered just before coition. The song is totally different from these mating calls, and with a little imagination could be described as the sound of bubbling water.

The Nuthatch begins to call in January while snow may still be on the ground, but the real song period starts in March and continues into May or early June.—EDITOR.

The undulating flight of the Nuthatch lasts no great distance, and it prefers to keep near its tree, where it clambers among the branches ; climbing with short jerky movements along the tree trunk, it can move with equal agility, upwards, head downwards, or sideways. Although it shows some affinity to the Tree-Creeper, its movements differ from the latter's mouselike progress. The Nuthatch never uses its tail in climbing and is the only bird which habitually descends trunks head downwards.

Although not gregarious, the Nuthatch nevertheless winters in company with tits and joins their foraging parties. It roosts in a hole in a large tree, sometimes in a nesting box.

The Nuthatch, as its name indicates, is an accomplished " hacker-open " of nuts. Its presence is often proclaimed by a loud tapping, not unlike that of the woodpecker, as it goes about the business of cracking nuts for food.

A woodland dweller, the Nuthatch frequents woods, parks and gardens with old trees, and will, if encouraged, occupy a nesting box. A hole or crevice, blocked with dried clay or mud and made just sufficiently wide for the entry and exit of the birds, and lined with bits of bark and dried leaves, houses the 6-11 eggs, which are white, spotted with reddish-brown. These are laid in April or May. The incubation, lasting 13-17 days, is done by the hen alone, but both parents share in the rearing of the one brood. The chicks are independent after about three weeks.

Nuts of many kinds—beechmast, acorns and yew seeds—berries and insects are the Nuthatch's food, but the young are fed on insects.

NYCTEA. Genus of owls of the family *Strigidae* of the order *Strigiformes*. It contains only one species, the Snowy Owl (*q.v.*), which is mainly distributed over the northern parts of the Northern Hemisphere and occurs in Britain only as an irregular winter visitor.

NYCTICORAX. Genus of herons of the family *Ardeidae* of the order *Ardeiformes*. Its members are mainly distributed over Europe, Asia, Africa, and north and south America. One member of this genus, the Night Heron (*q.v.*), occurs here as an irregular summer visitor.

NUTHATCH. *The Nuthatch occurs only in the British Isles, though it is rare in Scotland and Ireland. The subspecies of Nuthatch abroad are of different coloration*

W. Farnsworth

OYSTERCATCHER

OBSERVATORY. A bird observatory is a study centre primarily designed for research into problems of bird migration (*q.v.*). This work can be broadly subdivided into observational study and laboratory research. The first demands the watching and recording of " visible migration "—i.e. bird movements actually in progress—and the daily computation of numbers of the various species present in the sampling area. The second includes the examination and marking of migratory birds caught in specially constructed traps (*q.v.*).

Both phases of this work are essentially co-operative, and the Bird Observatories' Committee of the British Trust for Ornithology demands as a requisite of " official " recognition the provision of accommodation so that amateur bird watchers and students may visit the observatories and take part in the work. The help of such voluntary workers is invaluable where much ground has to be covered. At most observatories a Director or Warden is responsible for organizing this field study, maintaining the records and analysing the results obtained in the course of this work.

To study migration, it is obviously important to go where there is fair certainty of finding large numbers of migratory birds concentrated in a small area. Where such heavy concentrations occur, one can study the phenomenon of migration actually in progress, correlate observations with prevailing meteorological conditions, and obtain sufficiently large samples of the various species for laboratory investigation and the statistical treatment of the results. Apart from this, such places are haunts of many of the very rare species seldom seen elsewhere. So it is to the small offshore islands and prominent coastal headlands (and in particular those with lighthouses to guide night migrants to a landfall) that we must go for the best sites for bird observatories. Some of these sites have been well known by reputation for many years, as for instance Cley and Blakeney on the Norfolk coast ; Fair Isle, made famous by the studies of Dr. William Eagle Clarke and Surgeon Rear-Admiral J. H. Stenhouse ; and the Isle of May, where the Misses E. V. Baxter and L. J. Rintoul did stimulating work before the First World War.

The development of bird observatories has been one of the outstanding achievements in British ornithology since the Second World War, and one for which amateur effort is largely responsible. Before 1939 there were only two such places, at Skokholm and the Isle of May, though some European migration study centres—such as Heligoland in the North Sea, and Rositten in the Baltic—were already justly famous. Since the war, stations have been set up at Ottenby,

Paul Popper

OBSERVATORY. *A bird is removed from the catching-box of a Heligoland Trap to be carried in the holding-box (foreground) to the laboratories*

the southern tip of Oland, and Falsterbö in Sweden ; re-established at Texel and other points in Holland ; and started in south-west Norway and elsewhere.

In the British Isles the number of bird observatories has grown rapidly. From north to south round the coast these are :

Fair Isle. This island lies midway between Orkney and Shetland, 25 miles from each. The observatory, originally the idea of a Scottish ornithologist, George Waterston, was established in June 1948 by the Fair Isle Bird Observatory Trust, with Kenneth Williamson as Director. The island was acquired by the National Trust for Scotland in 1954. In the same year a sub-station under C. K. Mylne was set up on the Shetland isle of Foula, 45 miles to the north.

Isle of May. A much smaller island in the entrance to the Firth of Forth, this is governed by a committee representing the Scottish Universities and the Midlothian Ornithological Club.

Monk's House, near Seahouses, Northumberland. A coastal study-centre privately run by Dr. E. A. R. Ennion, its work extends to the Farne Islands.

Spurn Point, Kilnsea, Yorkshire. Commanding the mouth of the Humber ; administered by the Yorkshire Naturalists' Union.

Gibraltar Point, near Skegness, Lincolnshire. A coastal station covering the southern approach to the Humber and the northern approach to the Wash. It is part of the Lindsey County Council Nature Reserve, and is administered by the Lincolnshire Naturalists' Trust.

Blakeney, Norfolk. The successor in 1954 of a bird observatory sited at Cley and destroyed in the severe coastal flooding of January 1953, it was established by the Norfolk Naturalists' Trust, with R. A. Richardson as Warden.

Dungeness, Kent. An important coastal site well placed for the study of bird movements in the Channel region, this observatory is run jointly by the Kent Ornithological Society, London Natural History Society, and Hastings Natural History Society, with H. E. Axell as Warden.

Jersey, Channel Islands. Situated in the St. Ouen's Nature Reserve, and organized by the ornithological section of the Société Jersiaise.

Lundy, North Devon. An important island covering the southern approach to the Bristol Channel, run by the Lundy Field Society, with Miss Barbara Whitaker as Warden.

Skokholm, Pembrokeshire. Begun as a private venture by R. M. Lockley, this island observatory is now run jointly by the West Wales Field Society and the Council for the Promotion of Field Studies (*q.v.*), in association with Dale Fort Field Centre at Haverfordwest. The Warden is Peter Davis, formerly of Lundy.

Great Saltee, Co. Wexford. This excellently situated island observatory, off south-east Ireland, owes its existence to the zeal and initiative of an Irish ornithologist, R. F. Ruttledge.

Bardsey, North Wales. An island off the Lleyn Peninsula, where the West Wales Field Society and Birmingham and West Midland Bird Club founded a station in 1953, with Alan Till acting as Honorary Warden.

Organized along quite different lines from the foregoing, but conducting invaluable research into duck and goose migration, is the

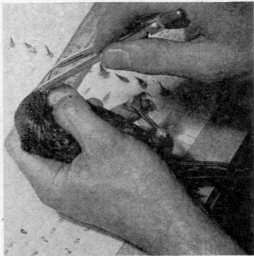

Eric Hosking

OBSERVATORY. *Among routine investigations are precise measurements of the bill, wings, etc.*

Wildfowl Trust (*q.v.*) at Slimbridge, Gloucestershire, whose Director is Peter Scott.

Close liaison between the observatories is maintained through the Bird Observatories' Committee of the British Trust for Ornithology, through the circulation of annual reports, and through the publication of results from several of the stations in this country and abroad in the *Fair Isle Bird Observatory Bulletin*, which is issued three or four times a year. Contributions based on the work of the bird observatories appear regularly in the journals *British Birds*, the *Scottish Naturalist* and *Bird Study*.

Trapping and Ringing. It is difficult to catch enough birds to build up a potential source of ringing returns and provide the raw material for other studies, and an important part of bird observatory work is to design and develop new catching methods. Of the different traps, the Heligoland Trap (*q.v.*), named after the German island where it was first developed, is the most popular and widely used. It is really a huge cage with sides and roof of wire netting, open at the front and narrowing at the rear to an angled " funnel " down which the birds are driven into a wooden catching box. This has a glass window through which they try to escape, only to fall into a holding chamber below. Ideally these Heligoland Traps have bushes and other cover planted in the entrance as an attraction to the birds ; but on some remote wind-swept islands, where such cover is difficult to grow, the plan has had to be adapted to suit the terrain. At Fair Isle, for example, the best traps have been made by roofing over narrow gullies with wire netting, and by constructing two-way traps (shaped rather like an hour glass) over the dry-stone walls along which many migrants move.

The procedure with captured birds varies from one observatory to another, according to what studies are in progress, but at all stations the birds are ringed before they are released (*see* Ringing). Subsequent recoveries of these marked birds, in this country or abroad, help us to build up our knowledge of the pattern of migration in the various species. At most observatories the birds are closely examined for aberrations in plumage or structure, for evidence of moult, and for ectoparasites ; weight and measurements of wing, tail, etc., are also taken. Knowledge of bird weights and the factors involved in their individual and specific variation was negligible until the bird observatories used their unique opportunities to make this a routine investigation.

Much interesting information with a direct bearing on the physiology of migration has been accumulated. It is well known from the work at Fair Isle, for instance, that migrants crossing the North Sea may lose up to 20 per cent of their body weight in the course of a night's flight, and often remain for some time " off-passage " at the island until this loss has been made good. The real importance of ringing at this and other observatories engaged in similar studies has shifted from the chance recovery of a ringed individual at some distant point to the local " repeat " or re-capture, which provides evidence of the rate of recuperation. A new development at Fair Isle, co-related with this study in weight variation, is the taking of blood smears, for it has been discovered that the condition of the blood also provides a valuable clue to the bird's migrational history.

Lastly, mention should be made of the great strides made in the study of the fleas and blood-sucking flies parasitic upon birds since the bird observatories took up work in this field. An apparatus designed by Dr. W. A. Timperley at Fair Isle is now becoming widely used at other stations, and for the first time it is possible to undertake quantitative studies of infestation at different seasons and in different species.

K. WILLIAMSON.

OCEANITES. Genus of marine birds of the family *Procellariidae* of the order *Procellariiformes*. It contains two or three species, mainly distributed over the seas of the Southern Hemisphere, particularly the Antarctic regions. They also occur over parts of the north Atlantic, over the Persian Gulf and over the seas of Australasia outside the breeding season. The only species on the British list, Wilson's Petrel (*q.v.*), has been recorded here a dozen times.

OCEANODROMA. Genus of marine birds of the family *Procellariidae* of the order *Procellariiformes*. It contains about a dozen species, which are mainly distributed over the north Atlantic and north Pacific. The only species on the British list are Leach's Petrel (*q.v.*) and the Madeiran Petrel (*q.v.*).

These birds have a slightly hooked bill. The wings are long and the tail, which is forked, is more than half the total length of the wing.

OBSERVATORY. *A Swift, carefully wrapped up to prevent any possible injury to its feathers, is weighed to check on loss of body-weight during its long migratory journey*
Eric Hosking

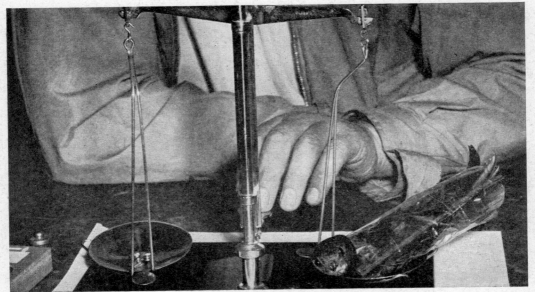

OENANTHE. Genus of the family *Turdidae* of the order *Passeriformes*. It contains many species, distributed over Europe, Africa, Asia, the north-eastern and north-western parts of north America, and Greenland. The six species on the British list are: Wheatear, Desert-Wheatear, Black-eared Wheatear, Pied Wheatear, Isabelline Wheatear, and Black Wheatear. (These are separately described under their own names.) Only the Wheatear (a breeding visitor and passage migrant) is at all common in Great Britain.

These small members of the Thrush family may be distinguished by their conspicuously white rump and tail, the latter being square-shaped. They have longish wings. The bill is slender and is black in colour. The front of the tarsus is covered with an unbroken thin horny plate, except at the base. The males and females are mostly different in plumage (except in the Isabelline Wheatear).

OIL-GLAND. Situated at the base of the tail, this is the bird's only external gland, apart from some small organs sometimes found near the ear-openings. Popularly believed to be used for anointing the feathers, the true function of this gland, also known as the preen gland (*q.v.*), has yet to be finally determined. It does not seem to be an essential organ, for it is absent from several species.

In most birds, however, the oil-gland is well-developed, and particularly so in the aquatic species, thus indicating that its main function *may* be to waterproof the plumage. Another theory is that the oil stimulates the secretion of the salivary juice used by the bird in preening. A third, but more unlikely, theory is that it is really a scent-gland, which helps the bird to recognize its relatives. However, although there is an odour attached to the gland's

Fischer-Wahrenholz
OENANTHE. *The only member of this genus at all likely to be seen in this country is the Wheatear*

secretion, and a strong and unpleasant odour it is in some cases, it must be remembered that most birds possess a poor sense of smell.

Another peculiarity about this gland is that in most birds there is a tuft of feathers on the tip of the gland, the remainder of the skin covering being naked; but in others the tip is naked, while the remaining surface is feathered.

Structurally this gland resembles the odoriferous glands of several reptiles. It consists of a two-lobed mass of secretory tubes, which unite in a common cavity opening on the surface of the skin through a variable number of orifices, often prolonged in the form of a nipple. The secretory tubes are surrounded by connective tissue, and are supplied by blood-vessels and nerves. In composition, the secretion resembles that of the sebaceous product of mammals.

OIL POLLUTION. Oil pollution of the sea brings a terrible death to countless numbers of sea-birds. If they unsuspectingly come in contact with a patch of waste oil, this adheres to their feathers and sticks them together so that the birds become water-logged and have difficulty in keeping afloat. Further, the down next to their bodies becomes glued up, so that the protecting layer between this and the body is destroyed and the bird is deprived of its natural means of warmth. Diving birds, which are liable to come up in the middle of a patch of oil after diving into clear water, seem to be the worst affected. The birds do their utmost to rid themselves of the clinging oil by shaking their wings, preening, diving, or throwing water over themselves, again and again in a frantic effort to clean themselves, but their efforts are in vain. Those which are so badly oiled that they cannot swim are dashed about by the waves until they die, or are washed up helpless on the shore, resembling, as H. de Vere Stacpoole wrote as long ago as 1920, " a mass of black filth, terrible because alive ".

When oiled birds preen themselves to rid their feathers of the clinging oil, they inevitably swallow some oil which poisons them. Post-mortem examinations of oiled birds have shown that the intestines are very hard, and much inflamed and enlarged, so that death must have been agonizing or a relief. Oiled red-throated divers and great crested grebes have been found with their legs completely raw, as if the scales and skin had been burnt off.

Thousands upon thousands of birds, dead or dying from the effects of waste oil, have been found round the coasts of European countries. From a survey of the numbers of oiled birds found round the British coasts during the Winter of 1951-52 it was estimated that between 50,000 and a quarter of a million birds were affected; at least 54 different species were represented,

Eric Hosking

OIL POLLUTION. Since 1919, when oil-burning ships came into use, thousands of dying sea-birds are washed up every year, their feathers clogged with waste oil

but the majority were gulls, guillemots, divers and grebes. In the Spring of 1952 in one month 30,000 birds were washed up on the coast of Gotland, Sweden. Off the coasts of south Africa oil-stained penguins were seen dead on the beaches or lingering on the islands to perish of hunger ; and even in the Antarctic penguins have been seen fatally clogged with oil.

In addition to the birds which are washed up on, or struggle to, the beaches, many more perish at sea. The Director of the Danish Fisheries and Marine Research Institute reported that he had seen razorbills and guillemots far out to sea so soaked with water that they could hardly keep their heads and necks above the surface, and stated that without doubt masses of birds had sunk to the bottom unseen. Those which reach land are thus probably only a fractional part of the number that have perished. Very little oil on the plumage is sufficient to drown a bird unless it comes into the hands of a human rescuer at a very early stage. For the treatment of oiled birds *see* the article on First Aid.

Destruction of sea-birds by waste oil has been continuing ever since 1919, when the advent of oil-burning ships and the consequent discharge of waste oil into the sea began to show its effects. In the early 1920s Great Britain and many other nations protected their shores as far as possible by prohibiting the discharge of waste oil in their territorial waters. But this did not solve the problem, since oil floats many hundreds of miles. In 1926 an international conference was held in Washington D.C., and a Convention was framed, the main provisions of which were the establishment of zones in which the discharge of oil was prohibited. This Convention was, however, never brought into

effect. In 1934 the British representative raised the matter at the League of Nations, but again no practical progress was made, though a large number of shipowners voluntarily undertook not to discharge oil within 50 miles of any coast.

After the Second World War oil pollution and the destruction of sea-birds became increasingly serious. One of the chief reasons for this was that, instead of being refined in the country of origin, crude oil was shipped to European countries where refineries were installed, and the cleaning out of bunkers on oil-tankers contributed largely to the increase in pollution. In 1952, on the initiative of the British Section of the International Committee for Bird Preservation, a Committee of representatives of the interests affected by oil pollution was set up to press for action, and the efforts of many organizations which had for years been working individually to secure a solution of the problem were co-ordinated. Later in the same year the Minister of Transport set up a special Committee to investigate the matter, and a valuable report, with recommendations for dealing with the problem, was issued ; the chief conclusion was that no oil should be discharged into the sea at all.

In 1954, on the invitation of the United Kingdom Government, an international conference was held in London to discuss the matter. To this conference, 33 countries sent delegations, ten more being represented by observers. Although the other nations were not prepared to accept the recommendations made in the British report, an international convention was drawn up. Within three months, 20 of the participating countries had signed the convention.—P. BARCLAY-SMITH.

OLD SQUAW. Local name for Long-tailed Duck (*q.v.*).

OLIVACEOUS WARBLER — **Hippolais pallida.** This warbler, which is a native of the Balkan countries and south-west Asia, has paid three recorded visits to the British Isles—all to Sussex. About the size of a Sedge-Warbler, it is distinguished by its pale brown upper parts, darker on wings and tail, and its whitish-buff underparts. The length is 5 in., the tarsus 0·83 in., and the wing span about 6 in.

A restless, tree-haunting bird, the Olivaceous Warbler breeds in gardens, plantations, orchards and olive groves. It is said by one observer to have a simple song, " soft and pleasing ", uttered from some thick cover. Its nest, composed of vegetable down and grasses, is placed some 3 ft. from the ground. Three or four greyish-white eggs, streaked in black, are laid in late May or June ; the hen incubates them alone for 13 days. The young are ready to fly in approximately 15 days. Insects are presumed to be this warbler's main food.

ORDER. Grouping of families (*q.v.*) considered to possess certain *general* affinities. It is the largest subdivision of the class *Aves* (*q.v.*) which contains all the birds. Order is a *systematic* term (*see* Classification), meaning that it was created by Man for his convenience and has little foundation in biological reality. However, the mere fact of long usage has given " order " a certain reality, for there is by now a large measure of agreement among the world's scientists on what is meant by this term.

The difficulty lies in applying it, for the various classifiers of birds are by no means agreed as to what particular order a certain bird should belong to, nor about the arrangement of the different orders as a whole. Thus, even in

Eric Hosking

ORIOLIDAE. *Only one bird of this family, the Golden Oriole, has been known to visit our shores*

the 20th century, Wetmore's classification (adopted in the United States and endorsed by the International Ornithological Congresses of 1950 and 1954) differs in detail from the British list, used throughout this work.

Wetmore, for instance, places the flamingoes as a suborder of the Heron-Stork order (called *Ciconiiformes*—Latin, " stork-like "—by him, and *Ardeiformes*—Latin, " heron-like "—by the British list), whereas the British list and others place the flamingoes in an order of their own, the *Phoenicopteriformes*. Then again, Wetmore arranges the orders from the lowest or most primitive birds to the highest, whereas many Continental and British ornithologists— although *not* the British list—adopt the high-to-low principle of arrangement.

But all of these differ markedly from the Russian ornithologists in their arrangements of orders and families. *See also* Classification ; Family ; Genus ; Race ; Species.

ORBITAL RING (or Circumnocular). A ring of distinctive colour round a bird's eye.

ORIOLE, GOLDEN. *See* Golden Oriole.

ORIOLIDAE. Family of the order *Passeriformes*, comprising the orioles. It contains many species, mainly distributed over tropical Africa, Asia, the Malay Archipelago and Australia. The single genus, *Oriolus*, is on the British list. This genus contains the Golden Oriole (*q.v.*).

ORNITHOLOGICAL ORGANIZATIONS. Apart from many local bird-watching societies and the like, there are five important societies dealing exclusively with ornithological matters.

The British Ornithologists' Union (B.O.U.) has existed since 1859. It has its own scientific quarterly, the *Ibis*, which deals with all connected subjects and literature. The Union's address is : c/o The Bird Room, British Museum (Natural History), London, S.W.7.

The British Trust for Ornithology (B.T.O.) centralizes field work and is responsible, with Oxford University, for the upkeep of an ornithological library at the Alexander Library. It publishes its own quarterly, *Bird Study*. The address is : 2, King Edward Street, Oxford.

The British Ornithologists' Club is closely connected with the B.O.U. Its Bulletin is published monthly, apart from July–September. The address is : 14, Elm Place, London, S.W.7.

The Royal Society for the Protection of Birds (R.S.P.B.) is mainly concerned with educating the public in bird protection and with the creation and upkeep of bird sanctuaries. It publishes an illustrated quarterly, *Bird Notes*. Its address is: 25, Eccleston Square, London, S.W.1.

The Wildfowl Trust at Slimbridge, Glos, collects and maintains a large number of water fowl, especially foreign ducks, geese and swans.

ORPHEAN WARBLER—Sylvia hortenis.
This warbler of Europe and north-west Africa
has visited the British Isles three or four times.
It is not unlike our Blackcap, but is greyer on
the mantle, and its dark cap extends below the
eye. Its throat is white, and the outer tail
feathers also have some
conspicuous white. The
cap is less dark in the
female ; otherwise both
birds are alike. The
length is 6 in., the tarsus
0·9 in., and the wing
span about 7 in.

Woods, plantations,
olive groves, orchards
and gardens are the Or-
phean Warbler's breed-
ing places, and much of
its time is spent flitting
among the branches.
Its song, which is de-
livered from this cover,
is described as being
" a loud, vigorous and
pleasant warble ".

Its nest, placed some
5–8 ft. from the ground,
is built of grasses and roots. Four to six
greenish-white eggs, with brown spots, are laid
in early May in south Europe, and late April
in north Africa.

As far as is known, both male and female
take part in hatching and rearing the young.
Insects are the main food of this warbler.

ORTOLAN BUNTING—Emberiza hortulana.
Although purely a bird of passage in Britain, the
Ortolan Bunting puts in a regular appearance in
small parties on the south and east coasts of
England and Wales in Spring and Autumn. It is
also seen regularly in Scotland, mainly at coastal
migration stations. It breeds in Europe, north
Africa and western Asia.

Among the buntings the Ortolan can easily be
overlooked, since its only distinguishing mark is
a pale yellow ring round the eye, sometimes
called the "spectacle", which can be seen clearly
only at close range. For the rest, it has the
shape of the Corn-Bunting, and has a brown
mantle, pinkish-buff underparts, and the usual
white marks in its dark tail. The female is similar, but duller. The length is about 6½ in., and
the wing span 7 in.

In flight and movements the Ortolan is similar
to others of its kind. In nature, however, it
tends to be quieter and more secretive, and frequents more varied districts. Breeding ortolans
are to be found both in hilly and mountainous
places and in low ground near water. They
usually nest in cultivated fields, vineyards and
gardens. In Winter they are found in flocks in
cultivated fields. On their migration passage,
many rest in Egypt on dry sandy fields on the
edge of the desert.

This bunting has several, varied calls in the
breeding season. Its song is reminiscent of the

Arthur Christiansen

OSPREY. The Fish-Hawk, as it is also called, no longer breeds here,
though from time to time rumour has it that a bird is nesting in Scotland

Yellow Hammer's, but somewhat more musical.

The nest, placed on the ground, usually among
dense and growing vegetation, is made with
dead grasses and roots, and lined with hair.
Four to six bluish-white eggs are laid, the date
varying according to the country, but most frequently being in May or June. The hatching
is done chiefly by the hen ; two broods are
usually reared.

The food consists of various seeds and insects.
On migration ortolans eat young locusts.

The Ortolan is greatly favoured in southern
Europe as a delicacy for the table.

OSCINES. Name formerly applied to a
suborder of *Passerines,* or perching birds, particularly those which are noted for their singing,
although this group also includes a large number
which do not sing. The name, which is still
found in literature, is derived from the Latin
oscen, " singing (or divining) bird ".

OSPREY—Pandion haliaetus. Once one of
the finest ornaments of Scottish Highland lochs,
the Osprey—or Fish-Hawk, as it is also called—
is now extinct as a British bird. During the 18th
and 19th centuries it was the victim of constant
persecution, a fate shared with many other birds
of prey because of their interference with the
sports of shooting and fishing. Valiant but vain
efforts were made by the bird protectionists of
the day to stay the disappearance of this beautiful bird from the Scottish Highlands, but the

Eric Hosking

OUZEL. The Ring-Ouzel, also called Mountain-Ouzel or Mountain-Blackbird, is a relative of the Blackbird—who is also known as the Ouzel Cock!

pation is fishing. This is an astounding performance to watch. On sighting its prey, the Osprey hovers at a height of 50 ft. or more; then, swooping down feet foremost and with wings almost closed, it plunges into the depths to seize its victim in its powerful talons, the toes of which are fitted underneath with sharp spiny scales, the better to hold the fish. Rising with its fish carried lengthwise, it flies to some selected perch to devour it.

In courtship, the Osprey indulges in wonderful aerial acrobatics, rising to great heights with wings rapidly beating, and wheeling and turning with complete abandon. The call note is a loud, short and shrill scream, and various alarm notes are employed if danger should threaten.

egg collector finished the task the sportsmen had begun. It is worthy of mention that two of the chief Highland landowners of the day did their utmost to protect the Osprey on their estates, and were awarded the Gold Medal of the Zoological Society for their efforts.

From time to time rumours are current that the Osprey is again breeding, but there is no direct evidence of this. There is no record of the Osprey's ever having bred in England. To-day it is only a rare but regular passage migrant in the Spring and Summer to the British Isles, both on the coast and inland. Abroad, the Osprey is found all over Europe, Asia and Africa, and closely related forms breed in Australasia and north and south America.

The Osprey is dressed in deep brown above, tinged here and there with white; its underparts are pure white, except for a brown patch on its breast; from the eye runs a dark line to the back of its neck. Its dark wings are long and narrow; its powerful legs and feet are greenish, and its black beak hooked. Its eye is yellow. The female is larger than the male, as is common in birds of prey, but she has similar plumage. The length of the male is 20-23 in.; the tarsus is 2·4 in.; and the wing span is 4½-6 ft. The weight is 4 lb.

The European Osprey is not particularly gregarious, but the American race is extremely sociable, and, where it is common, hundreds can be seen nesting together.

Never far distant from water, the Osprey, especially when hunting, glides slowly over the surface with leisurely flapping wings—a flight not unlike that of the Kestrel. Its most outstanding accomplishment and favourite occu-

The nesting places of the Osprey in Scotland were on rocky islands and loch sides, but in other countries the sites vary considerably; meres, lakes, rivers near woods, and coasts are all favoured. The Osprey mates for life, and will return year after year to the same home. One of the most famous nesting sites was an island in Loch-an-Eilean, in Invernesshire.

Even when first built, the nest is a huge structure of sticks, roots, heather, seaweed or any other useful matter; and as it may be used for generations, it reaches in time fantastic proportions. Both male and female share the work of building. Two or three white eggs, blotched and spotted in reddish-brown, are laid. The month of laying varies according to the different countries—from January or February in the Red Sea to early June in Lapland. In Scotland the eggs used to be laid in late April or early May. The incubation begins with the first or second egg and falls mainly to the hen, though the male occasionally relieves her; the period is about 35 days. The male carries the food to the nest in his talons. The mother feeds the chicks for six weeks, and they then feed themselves with the food brought by the cock for a few more weeks until they can fly. One brood is reared. Fish form the staple food of the Osprey.

The Osprey has no connection with the misnamed " osprey plumes " of the millinery trade, which are really the feathers of egrets.

OTIDIDAE. Family of the order *Ralliformes*, comprising the bustards. It contains about two dozen species, mainly distributed over Africa, eastern and southern Europe, Asia and Australia. Two of the genera are on the British list—*Otis* and *Chlamydotis*.

The members of *Otididae* are large or medium-sized terrestrial birds, frequenting mainly open country. They have a short, curved and rather blunt bill, flattish head and a rather thick neck. The wings are broad and rounded. The tail is of medium length ; the legs stout, and the tarsus and the bare part of the tibia covered with small, irregularly-shaped scales. There are three stout front toes with flattish nails ; the soles of the feet are also flat.

OTIS. Genus of the family *Otididae* of the order *Ralliformes*. Its members are mainly distributed over eastern and southern Europe, northern and western Asia, and northern parts of Africa. The two species on the British list—the Great Bustard (*q.v.*) and the Little Bustard (*q.v.*)—are both rare and irregular visitors to Britain, mainly during the winter months.

OTUS. Genus of small owls of the family *Strigidae* of the order *Strigiformes*. Its members are found in southern Europe, western Asia and north Africa, also in tropical Africa outside the breeding season. The only species occurring in Europe, Scops Owl (*q.v.*), is an irregular visitor to Great Britain, mainly in the Spring and early Summer.

OUZEL COCK. Alternative name for the Blackbird (*q.v.*).

OUZEL, RING-. *See* Ring-Ouzel.

OWL. Mostly nocturnal birds of prey with large heads and flattened faces (facial discs), surrounded by ruffs which may be with or without ear-tufts (*see* Ear). The bill is typical of birds of prey—sharp and hooked, enabling the bird to strike down its prey and tear it apart.

Their feet are unique, for owls can turn the outer of their three front toes back until it meets the single hind-toe and can thus hold and crush their prey in a vice-like grip.

In flight, owls are generally noiseless, with only their uncanny voices giving away their presence—the more so, as most of them hunt at night and sleep during the day (unless their whereabouts become known to other birds who will band together and mob any unfortunate owl).

Depending on their size, owls feed on mammals, including many rodents, birds, fish, insects and suchlike. Indigestible matter is ejected in the form of pellets (*q.v.*). Owls make little attempt at nest-building and usually nest in hollow trees or among rocks on the ground, though they may occasionally take over the nest of another bird of prey or a woodpecker's hole. Their white eggs are almost spherical.

Of the ten species on the British list (*see* separate entries), the Eagle-Owl, an irregular visitor, is the largest and fiercest. Next in size is the Snowy Owl, also an irregular visitor, which has the peculiarity of irrupting from its Arctic home at roughly four-year intervals.

Four of the five medium-sized owls breed freely in this country—the Barn-Owl, Tawny Owl, Long-eared Owl and Short-eared Owl, though the latter occurs only in certain districts. The Hawk-Owl (and its American variant) have been recorded only as rare stragglers.

Only one small owl—the Little Owl—is at all common in Britain and even this bird was introduced artificially. The Scops Owl is an irregular visitor, and so is Tengmalm's Owl.

OX-BIRD. Local name for the Dunlin (*q.v.*).

OYSTERCATCHER—Haematopus ostralegus. The attractive and distinctive Oystercatcher is a familiar figure at all seasons of the year on all the sea-shores, both rocky and shingly, of Scotland, Wales and Ireland ; it is somewhat less common in England. In Scotland it is also found inland on agricultural land, consorting with gulls and accompanying them in the wake of the plough. Many non-breeding visitors and passage migrants arrive in the Spring and Autumn to augment the

G. E. Kirkpatrick

OWL. Occasionally the Long-eared Owl may flatten its ear-tufts, as is happening in this photograph

British birds. Abroad, the Oystercatcher occurs in Europe, Asia, Australasia and north and south America.

Easily recognized at first glance, the Oystercatcher is the only wader boldly dressed in black and white with a long, straight and bright red bill and pink legs. The mantle is completely black, the white underparts and rump showing in vivid contrast. The tail, also white, ends in a broad black band. In winter plumage, a white collar runs across the neck. The sexes are alike. The upper parts of the young are mottled brown. The length is 17 in., and the tarsus 1·8 in. The wing span is 18-20 in. and the weight 1 lb.

Outside the breeding season, oystercatchers are very gregarious and large flocks assemble on their favourite shores in Autumn and Winter. Noisy and excited, they swim easily and, if wounded, will dive. On the ground they walk and run gracefully, and are fond of perching on walls, posts, sheds and so on. The flight, usually low over shore or water, is fast and direct with regular wing beats, but the Oystercatcher can and does fly high.

It can open oysters, and its attack on mussels, which form its main food, has been brought to a fine art. It drags them from the rocks, and prises them open with its powerful bill.

As Spring approaches, the Oystercatcher commences a most unusual and individual display, accompanied by an extraordinary "piping". Two or three—usually a pair and another male—but often more, form a group and perform endless "piping" competitions. With heads close together, bills pointed downwards and wide open, they run or dance excitely in a curving line with quick steps, uttering the while their mating "trill"—their real song—in a succession of notes rising to a climax and then falling away ; the performance ends in a duet between the two birds. The "piping" is so loud and piercing that it can be heard a quarter of a mile away. (For an illustration, see Behaviour, page 49.) A special display-flight, called the "butterfly flight", is also indulged in. The performance still takes place long after the breeding season, but the "piping" is best heard during March, April, May, June and July.

Apart from the spring song, the Oystercatcher's ordinary note is a rapid, loud and clear pipe. It has many other calls, less often heard.

Many different nesting sites—shingle banks, rocks, sand dunes—are favoured. In Scotland, the Oystercatcher often nests inland beside rivers and lochs. The three eggs, yellowish to buff and blotched and streaked in brown, are laid in or about May in a depression in the shingle, sand or rocks. Very little material, if any, is used for housing them. Both male and female incubate, the hen taking the larger share, for 24-27 days. The chicks, which are clad in grey and brown striped down, stay in the nest for the first day or two ; they are tended for a month by the parents. One brood is reared.

Besides mussels, cockles and suchlike some vegetable matter is eaten by the Oystercatcher.

OYSTERCATCHER. This is the only black and white wader to possess a straight red bill. It has been named after its expert way of opening oysters and other shellfish

John Markham

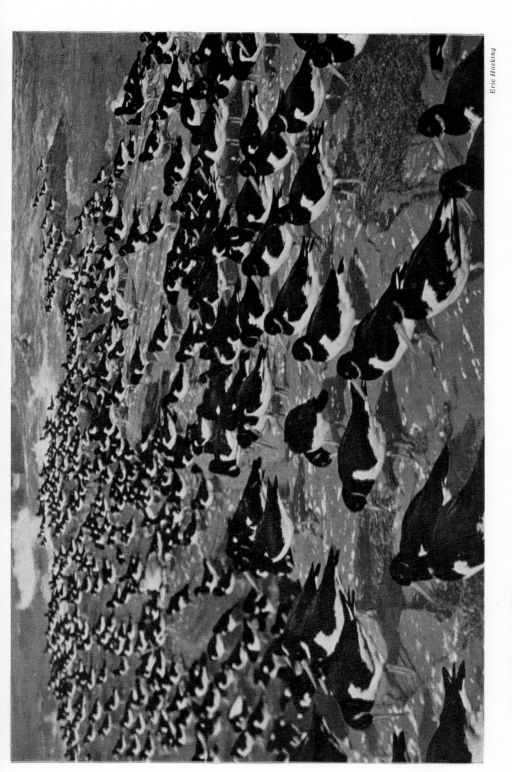

OYSTERCATCHER, *the only wader dressed in black and white, with straight bill and pink legs*

To face page 400

PHEASANT

PADDY-FIELD WARBLER—Acrocephalus agricola. The inclusion of this warbler, a native of central Asia, on the list of British birds is due to one visit it paid in October 1925, to Fair Isle. It resembles a small Reed-Warbler, in appearance, behaviour and breeding habits. The length of the Paddy-Field Warbler is 5 in.

PAD. Underpart of toe (q.v.).

PAGOPHILA. Genus of gulls of the family *Laridae* of the order *Charadriiformes*. It contains only one species, the Ivory Gull (q.v.), a rare winter visitor to the British Isles.

PAIRING. This term may be used as a synonym for mating (q.v.) or for the occasion when pairs are formed and the *female* selects her mate. Time and method vary with different species and their social habits.

Some birds live in colonies all the year round and little is known about the way in which they form pairs. Others live together in flocks during the winter months and split up into pairs for the breeding season. Again, there are birds, like the Robin, which hold their territories the whole year, that behave in a similar, if modified, way. Out of the breeding season the two sexes live apart, maintaining separate territories (some hens *may* migrate).

As explained under Mating (q.v.), the reason why a hen selects a particular mate is still a mystery, as is also in many cases the way in which a male recognizes a female. With robins, the male at first displays aggressively to the female who has selected him as her mate, apparently mistaking her for another male. It is only because she refuses to be cowed by rebuffs that he eventually accepts her. The same applies in certain other species (e.g. the common Heron and the American Red-winged Blackbird), but in some species the problem

PAIRING. Nobody yet knows why a hen will choose one particular mate and reject another

of recognition is much simpler ; either there are marked differences in plumage or the call notes are different. Whereas the male of some territorial species may find difficulty in determining the sex of a visitor to his territory, the female has no such difficulty, because the male claims an isolated area and sings and displays.

With some species of territorial birds the procedure is quite different. For example, with the Reed-Bunting, the males will " fight " any other male buntings entering their territory but will feed amicably together on neutral ground. If a female in condition to attract appears in their midst, all the males in the area are stimulated, but in different ways— one may cease to sing, another flutter from bush to bush like a moth, and yet a third fight another male. A male will then set off in pursuit of the female.

Association in pairs is quite distinct from courtship proper, which does not occur until just before nesting begins. Blackbirds form pairs in the late Autumn ; starlings in late Autumn or early Spring ; but summer migrants, on the other hand, do not form pairs until April or May, frequently only a few days before nesting proper starts.

PALE-BREASTED BRENT GOOSE. One of the two varieties of Brent Goose (q.v.).

PALLAS'S GRASSHOPPER-WARBLER— Locustella certhiola. A bird of western Siberia, this warbler has been identified once in the British Isles ; this was at Rockbill Light, Dublin, in September 1908. Its plumage has a general similarity to the Reed-Warbler's, but the eye stripe is less clearly defined and the mantle darker ; the underparts are whiter and the tips of its graduated tail greyish-white. The length is 5¼ in. This bird's behaviour much resembles that of the British Grasshopper-Warbler.

PALLAS'S SAND-GROUSE — Syrrhaptes paradoxus. No one knows why this inhabitant of the desolate desert steppes of central Asia should, from time to time, invade Europe, including the British Isles, in large numbers. The impulse which compels it to set out into the unknown may arise from a scarcity of food or some other upheaval in its normal haunts ; but it cannot be assigned to any certain cause. During the 19th and 20th centuries, there have been several invasions of Europe by the Sand-Grouse, the greatest being in 1863, 1888 and 1908, when they appeared in small flocks all over the British Isles. In the Springs of 1888 and 1889 attempts were even made to breed in Yorkshire and on a stretch of desolate sand in Morayshire, but it is doubtful whether any of the young hatched in Great Britain would survive for long.

In appearance the Sand-Grouse seems to be a cross between a pigeon and a partridge, for it

R. P. Bagnall-Oakeley

PALLAS'S SAND-GROUSE. This grouse now and then irrupts from Asia to more temperate countries

has the head of the former and the body of the latter. A light sandy brown, covered with dark mottling, is its general colour. Its wings and tail are long and pointed, its legs short, its feet feathered, and its bill short. The female is smaller, duller in appearance and more spotted. The length is 13 to 16 in., the long central tail feathers accounting for about 3 in., the tarsus is 1 in., and the wing span about 18 in.

The Sand-Grouse has an awkward gait on the ground, experiences difficulty in rising, and is said never to perch. Its remarkably rapid flight recalls that of the Golden Plover. Its voice is described as a soft guttural cluck.

The Sand-Grouse is very gregarious and, in its natural home, nests in small colonies. Outside the breeding season the flocks number thousands. The normal nesting haunts are

sandy steppe and desert country. On their European invasions, birds frequent sand dunes, sandy flats and stubble fields, sandy shores at low tide, marshes and grasslands. The nest is only an unlined scrape in the sand, and the three buff or yellowish-brown eggs, blotched in purplish-brown, are laid on the bare ground. The nesting season varies according to the country ; in Great Britain it was in June or July. Two or three broods are reared a year. The Sand-Grouse eats grain, grasses and weeds.

PALLAS'S WARBLER—Phylloscopus proregulus. The only recorded visit of this warbler to Great Britain (Norfolk) occurred in 1896. A native of the southern Siberian forests, the bird is not unlike the Goldcrest in size and coloration, for it also has a yellow stripe down the centre of its crown and a conspicuous yellow rump. Its upper parts are bright green. The bird's length is $3\frac{1}{2}$ in.

PALLID HARRIER — Circus macrourus. Breeding in Russia and south-west Asia, and wintering in Africa and south Asia, the Pallid Harrier has appeared in the British Isles only on three occasions ; once in England, and twice in Scotland. It is almost indistinguishable from the Hen-Harrier, but at close range is seen to be rather paler in plumage ; its breast and the sides of its head are white, and, instead of the pure white rump patch on the Hen-Harrier, that on the Pallid is barred in grey. The female, which is the larger bird, and the young are identical with those of Montagu's Harrier. The length of the male is 17 to 19 ins.

PANDION. Genus of the family *Falconidae* of the order *Falconiformes*. It contains only one species, the Osprey (*q.v.*), which occurs in three forms or subspecies in Europe, Asia, north Africa, Australasia and north America, as well as in tropical parts of Africa outside the breeding season. It formerly bred in the British Isles, but is now only a rare passage migrant.

PANURUS. Genus of the family *Paridae* of the order *Passeriformes*. It contains only one species, the Bearded Tit (*q.v.*), which occurs in two forms, mainly distributed over Europe and the more temperate parts of northern Asia as far east as China. One form occurs here as a local resident, mainly in eastern England.

PARASITES (BIRD). The word " parasite ", derived from the Greek *para* (besides) and *sitos* (food), originally meant merely one which eats beside another. Today it has acquired the meaning of one which feeds on another. The latter definition is too exclusive, however, for there are many different kinds of parasitism. Two are worth mentioning here : the first is *commensalism*, in which two organisms live

Eric Hosking

PARASITES. *Upside down Whitethroat is busily removing some parasites from the depth of its nest*

intimately and harmlessly together, but only one partner derives benefit. The second is *symbiosis*, where two different species live in close association from which they both derive benefit.

The modern view is that all organisms are " hosts " to parasites both internal and external. Birds are infested with innumerable species of fleas, flukes, lice, mites, worms, and so forth. Ten thousand nematode worms have been found in one grouse's intestine, and one thousand feather lice have been taken from the plumage of one Curlew. Birds of prey are frequently affected with fleas from the rats and rabbits they catch for food, in addition to the natural bird parasites. The Starling, to be seen perching on the backs of sheep searching for ticks parasitic on the sheep, is itself " host " to a species of parasite which is preyed on in its turn by other minute organisms. House-sparrows taking a dust-bath in the garden bed are trying to rid their bodies of parasites.

Parasitologists collect fleas and mites by putting a discarded nest into a paper bag and damping it from time to time ; in due course a hatch of larvae occurs, and microscopy can begin. Other sources of supply, which have arisen in late years, are the bird-ringing stations where, each year, thousands of migrants are trapped, weighed, marked and " de-loused " before release, the parasites dropping dead out of the plumage when this is carefully treated with a volatile spirit vapour. Most, but not all, bird parasites are harmless to Man ; but one species of flea occasionally encountered when searching blue tits' nesting boxes for infertile eggs after the young have flown, can bring up enormous weals on one's arm.

Often people who keep cage birds have to concern themselves with the destruction of parasites. The chief enemy of such cage birds as the Budgerigar and Canary is a tiny but very active bloodsucker, called the red mite. This is naturally grey in colour, but appears red when full of blood. As this parasite is nocturnal in habit, infested birds should be turned out during daylight into insect-free cages, while their nesting boxes, etc., are immersed in boiling water. With aviaries, a blow-lamp should be used in all cracks and other places where red mites are likely to be hidden. If creosote be dabbed in, no bird should be allowed back until this is completely dried. *See also* Aviary ; Captive Birds.

Another less deadly visitor is the feather-louse. This can be eradicated by destroying all discarded feathers daily, and dusting the affected bird's plumage with flowers of sulphur.

PARASITIC JAEGER. American name for Arctic Skua (*q.v.*), from German for " hunter ".

PARIDAE. Family of the order *Passeriformes*, containing the tits. This family, whose members are distributed over much of the globe (except south America, New Guinea, and the Pacific Islands), contains three genera on the British list : *Parus, Aegithalos* and *Panurus*.

Its members are all small or very small insectivorous birds, with a short, stout, and somewhat rounded bill. They have short, thick necks, and long rounded wings. The tail, which has twelve quill-feathers, varies in shape and length. The plumage is soft and plentiful. The tarsus (*which see*) is covered with scutes (horny scales).

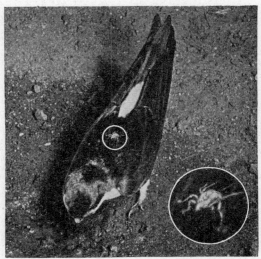

Eric Hosking

PARASITES. *The presence of a parasite on its back does not seem to worry the House-Martin much*

PARROT-CROSSBILL — **Loxia pytyopsittacus.** Of all the family of crossbills, this is the one most resembling the Parrot. It breeds in Scandinavia, Russia, Finland and other countries, and is a rare visitor to Britain.

In appearance it is not unlike the Scottish Crossbill, but is somewhat larger in size and its bill is broader and longer than the common Crossbill's. Its voice is louder and clearer than those of others of the family. In all other ways, it follows the normal breeding and nesting habits of crossbills. Its food is chiefly the seeds of pine and larch cones, but in Winter it eats berries.

PARTRIDGE — **Perdix perdix.** This game bird, well known and familiar to all, is essentially a bird of cultivated country, and breeds generally throughout the British Isles. It is abundant and widely preserved in England, but less so in Scotland, Wales and Ireland. It frequents all kinds of farmland, especially if provided with some cover of bushes and hedges ; it is also found, but less frequently, on hillsides, moors, heaths, etc. Abroad, it breeds throughout Europe and Asia.

The Partridge is easily recognized by its round body and brown plumage, streaked all over with dark and light markings. Its head, tail and the bars on the flanks are chestnut ; its breast is grey, and is decorated with a distinctive horseshoe-shaped chestnut patch, specially prominent in the male. In the female the chestnut colour is paler, and the horseshoe patch less evident—or, in some birds, absent altogether. The bill and legs are grey-blue ; behind the eye is a small patch of red. The juveniles have no chestnut colouring or horseshoe on the breast. The length is 12 in. and

John Markham

PARTRIDGE. One clutch may contain as many as 20 eggs, all to be incubated by the female alone

the tarsus 1·4 in. The wing span is between 12 and 14 in., and the weight 14 oz.

The Partridge rises with a whirr of wings and flies with the typical swift, strong and low, but not long sustained, flight of game birds. Like the Pheasant, it is a ground bird, and walks and runs with ease. If startled, it will often crouch close to the ground rather than fly ; its protective coloration then makes it very difficult to detect among the growth. The Partridge does not, like the Pheasant, perch in trees. It feeds during the morning and evening, the day as a rule being spent concealed and resting in the grass or under a hedge. It delights in " dusting ", and can swim if necessary.

The Partridge is sociable in its habits, and, after the breeding season, parents and young keep together in coveys during the Winter, and will even join up with the others until the call of the Spring. But they do not mix with quails or red-legged partridges.

The voice of the Partridge is heard mostly in the evening. Its main note is a curious high-pitched creaking sound, chiefly used by the male in the breeding season, but also when flushed. The female has a low chuckling note to the chicks. Rarely, and only when in danger, the Partridge utters a very loud, long drawn-out alarm call, and there is a similar call to protect the young.

Partridges begin to pair early in February, and for some weeks indulge in constant fights, the males challenging one another while the excited female runs round with flapping wings.

The Partridge nests in the growth at the foot of a hedgerow, in a plantation or field of corn, clover and grass, or sometimes even among roadside herbage. The nest is well concealed in a sheltered hollow scraped by the hen, and lined with dry grass and leaves. The olive-brown eggs, varying in number from 9 to 20, are laid at the end of April or early May. The female hatches them alone for 22 to 25 days. The young, clad in greyish-buff down, leave the nest soon after hatching, and, tended by both parents, are able to fly in 16 days. One brood is reared in a season.

The Partridge feeds mainly on vegetable food—leaves, fruit and seeds—but many kinds of insects are also devoured.

PARUS. Genus of the family *Paridae* of the order *Passeriformes*. It contains all the British tits, apart from the Long-tailed Tit and the Bearded Tit. There are nearly fifty species— with a number of subspecies—in this genus, widely distributed (*see* Paridae). The British species—the Great Tit, Blue Tit, Coal-Tit, Crested Tit, Marsh-Tit, and Willow-Tit—are separately described under their own headings.

Ronald Thompson

PASSERIFORMES. *The sparrow has given its name to the huge order of perching birds—the only birds that can grip an object such as a twig firmly in their claws*

PASSER (Latin " sparrow "). Genus of the family *Passeridae*, of the order *Passeriformes*. Its members are mainly distributed over Europe, Africa and Asia, and have also been introduced into many other parts of the world, including America, Australia and New Zealand. There are two species of this genus on the British list, the well known and very common House-Sparrow (*q.v.*), and the Tree-Sparrow (*q.v.*).

The members of this genus have a rather heavy, conical, finch-like bill, which is shorter than the head. The nostrils are large and close to the feathers, which almost conceal them. The wings are broad and the tail, which is three-quarters as long as the wing, is square-shaped.

PASSERIDAE (Latin, " sparrows "). Family of the order *Passeriformes*. It includes the sparrows, and its members are found over a large area of the globe. Its two genera on the British list are *Passer* and *Montifringilla*.

PASSERIFORMES (Latin, " sparrow-like "). This huge order of birds contains between 5,000 and 6,000 species, about half the total number of bird species.

Birds in this order have been grouped in some 65 families, but they are so closely inter-related and exhibit such slight differences in terms of anatomical and osteological structure that they are extremely difficult to define satisfactorily. The members of the order are found in all parts of the world, except the Antarctic, but there are no marine birds amongst them.

No fewer than 20 of the families contain birds which are on the British list. These families are : *Alaudidae, Bombycillidae, Certhiidae, Cinclidae, Corvidae, Fringillidae, Hirundinidae, Laniidae, Motacillidae, Muscicapidae, Oriolidae,*

Paridae, Passeridae, Prunellidae, Regulidae, Sittidae, Sturnidae, Sylviidae, Troglodytidae, Turdidae. They include such familiar species as the thrushes, larks, tits, warblers, swallows, finches and crows.

For the most part the birds of this order are small or medium-sized (the largest are the ravens and lyre-birds), and their chief external characteristic is the form of the foot. This has three toes directed forwards, and one behind. The latter is always inserted at the same level, and is not reversible ; it is well-developed, and is generally at least as long as the middle front toe. The three front toes are free, and all four toes can be bent downwards to obtain a firm grip on objects such as branches or twigs. A muscular arrangement in the legs, controlling the toes, causes the toes automatically to " curl " tightly round an object such as a twig, as the bird bends its legs to sit. From this characteristic the members of this order have come to be known as the " perching-birds ".

The vocal organs of many of the birds in this order are well developed for the production of song, and all the " oscines " or " song-birds " belong to *Passeriformes*. The wings of members of this order have nine or ten developed primary feathers. Mostly there are 12 tail-feathers, but in some species there are only ten. The young are hatched naked and helpless, and are completely dependent on their parents for days, or in some cases weeks, until fully fledged.

The great majority of these birds live in trees or undergrowth, and build more or less elaborate nests. Except in a few cases (the crows, larks, wagtails, for example), they hop on the ground.

PASSERINES. Descriptive title applied to birds belonging to the order *Passeriformes* (*q.v.*).

PROTECTIVE and OTHER COLORATION

JULIAN HUXLEY, F.R.S., D.Sc.

The author discusses the importance of pattern and colour in bird life, and shows that it has many functions, varying from concealment from foes to recognition of the sexes and courtship and display. See also *Camouflage ; Display ; Egg ; Feather ; Research*

PATTERN AND COLOUR. The colour and pattern of birds will here be treated in respect of their *allesthetic* functions : that is to say, the biological effects which they exert on the behaviour of other individuals, whether of the same or other species, via their senses. They can also be exerted through other than the visual sense, and we shall have occasion to mention some auditory allesthetic characters in addition to visual ones. Most of the externally visible characters of birds can have an adaptive allesthetic function assigned to them, many with certainty, others with much probability.

Visual allesthetic characters fall into two main categories—*cryptic* (concealing) characters, whose function is to hide their owner; and *sematic* (signalling) characters, whose function is to make him or her conspicuous, and to provide means of signalling to other individuals.

Cryptic characters include everything popularly known as animal camouflage (*q.v.*) ; their function is to enable an animal to escape detection through its resemblance to its surroundings. The resemblance may merely mean a lack of contrast, such as is achieved by the familiar counter-shading of those numerous birds in which the darkness of the upper parts and the lightness of the under-surface compensate for the play of light and shadow. Or it may be a general resemblance, as in that of brooding nightjars or female ducks or grouse to the surroundings of their nest-sites. Or it may be a special or specific one, to a particular object : this type of crypticity is rare in birds, though the resemblance of the Nightjar to a broken branch provides an outstanding example, and also illustrates the general association between coloration and behaviour (*q.v.*).

The Bittern's resemblance to reeds, in which if the intruder moves, it will even turn round so as always to present its striped under-surface to his view, is halfway between general and special—it resembles its general surroundings, but does so by means of the special resemblance of its pattern of stripes to vertical reed-stems. A similar mixed resemblance is that of the snipe, in whose general cryptic coloration pale stripes simulate dead grasses.

The selective effect of the prevailing colour of the habitat on cryptic coloration is well seen in warblers. The leaf-warblers, spending most of their time among green foliage, are predominantly green, while species inhabiting low bushes, reed-beds, and other places where stems and dead leaves preponderate, are predominantly brown.

Eggs too may show cryptic coloration. This is especially striking in species which nest on the ground. The close resemblance of lapwings' eggs to brown soil or of ringed plovers' eggs to pebbles is notorious. In most Passerines, the conspicuousness of eggs is merely reduced, by various types of blotching or spotting. When there is no need for visual protection, as in the case of hole-nesters, there has often been a degeneration in coloration, leading to white eggs, as in kingfishers, owls, and rock- and stock-doves. The whiteness of wood-pigeons' eggs may be regarded as an indication that the birds are descended from hole-nesting ancestors.

Eric Hosking

PATTERN AND COLOUR. *Some eggs may be so well camouflaged as to be hard to discover*

The behaviour needed to render cryptic coloration effective often involves the obliteration of outline and shadow by crouching close to the surface. This is well seen in the instinctive crouching of the chicks of many birds in response to the mother's alarm-note, or of the adults of many species in response to the sight of a hawk overhead.

Disruptive Patterns. Some cryptic patterns achieve their effect by their ruptive or disruptive qualities, by breaking up the animal's silhouette, and so impeding its recognition by its enemies; or by breaking down the conspicuousness of the eye.

Excellent examples of disruptive cryptic coloration are seen in waders like the Ringed

Plover and other species of *Charadrius*, and the Turnstone. Their general ruptive pattern includes dark markings involving the eye and reducing its conspicuousness. Such ruptive eye-markings are also found in association with general cryptic resemblance, as in snipes and woodcocks, various partridges, and so on.

We next come to sematic coloration. This is best clarified in relation to the type of situation in which the signals operate and the kind of information they are designed to convey. We can distinguish group-recognition, sex-recognition, parent-offspring recognition, deflection, advertisement, warning, threat, and courtship or readiness to mate.

Characters concerned with *group-recognition* include the so-called recognition marks of so many species. In many cases these are invisible when the bird is at rest or feeding, thus permitting protection by cryptic coloration, but are prominently displayed in flight—e.g. the white or otherwise distinctive outer tail-feathers of so many species, and the conspicuous rump-patches or wing-bars of so many others. The sudden display of such recognition marks serves to alert other birds of the same species of some danger which has alarmed the bird that has flown up; and their visibility in flight serves to keep flocks together and to permit stragglers to recognize and join their fellows.

The combination of invisibility when at rest with visibility in flight will only be evolved in birds requiring cryptic protection from active enemies ; in powerful species not requiring such protection, cryptic concealment will not be evolved, and the entire coloration may then be permanently recognitional. This appears to be the case in rooks, crows and other all-black corvids, in cormorants, in all-white herons, spoonbills, gannets, pelicans and swans, and in brightly-patterned species

like sheld duck, various gulls and terns, avocets, kingfishers and suchlike. In such cases, the bird's conspicuousness may also have a warning function (*see* below).

Recognizing the Sexes. Sex-recognitional coloration enables one sex to recognize the other. One of the best examples is that of the American woodpecker, the Flicker, in which only the male possesses a black " moustache ". When Dr. Noble fixed an artificial black moustache on to a captured female, she was promptly attacked by her own mate, but again accepted as a mate as soon as the moustache was removed. The black moustache is thus a sign-stimulus causing a Flicker to be recognized as a male, and automatically releasing hostility on the part of other males.

Sex-recognition in many birds is not effected in this way, but by means of differential behaviour on the part of the two sexes. If an individual reacts with an aggressive pose to the approach of another, it is recognized and treated as a male, if with a non-aggressive pose, it is recognized and treated as female. This differential behaviour may be designed to display certain patterns of coloration ; thus in Night Herons, females are recognized as such by approaching males by adopting the so-called appeasement or greeting attitude, in which the black head and white nape-plumes are prominently displayed, in a deep bow.

" Recognition " of offspring by parents or of parents by offspring is often mediated by special coloration (always in association with appropriate patterns of behaviour). Parent-recognition by very young birds demands special mechanisms. The best-investigated example is that of the new-hatched young of herring-gulls—and doubtless of other species of gull also. The biological significance of the bill-coloration of the Herring-Gull—yellow with a light red spot towards the tip of the lower mandible—had long been a puzzle to naturalists. Tinbergen, by a brilliant series of experiments on newly-hatched wild chicks, showed that it was a sign-stimulus releasing the chick's pecking response. In nature the chick pecks in the direction of the red spot on the parent's bill, and this is followed by the parent's regurgitating food into the chick's bill. By using painted cardboard

Ronald Thompson

PATTERN AND COLOUR. The Nightjar's likeness to its surrounding nest is a good example of cryptic, or concealing, coloration of birds

Eric Hosking; John Markham

PATTERN AND COLOUR. Differences in pattern between related species, like the Stonechat (left) and Whinchat (right), help to prevent inter-breeding among these birds

models, Tinbergen quantitatively evaluated the importance of shape, of ground-colour, and of presence, colour, and position of spot, in eliciting the response ; and was eventually able to construct an artificial " bill " which was considerably more effective than the natural bill, even though it was quite un-bill-like.

In young Passerines, the gape is usually brightly coloured, and often also strikingly patterned. This acts as a sign-stimulus releasing the parent's feeding reaction : in hole-nests and shady situations it also helps to indicate the position of the hungry nestling's mouth. The automatic (instinctive) nature of the reaction has been experimentally demonstrated by constructing an artificial model " nestling ". Provided that this has the right coloured " gape " and can grip the food with its artificial " tongue ", it is " fed " by the parent even in the presence of the rest of the brood.

Diverting Aggressors. Deflection is the function of patterns and colours which serve to deflect the attacks of predators from more vital to less vital parts of the body. The eye-spots and false heads of certain butterflies are the best-known examples. This type of character appears to be unknown in birds. But coloration (and behaviour) may also serve to deflect predators from more to less vulnerable stages of a species, and birds present the best example of this, in so-called injury-feigning (*q.v.*).

Deflection may also be from more to less biologically valuable members of the species : thus the bright coloration of many male ducks, by ensuring that most individuals taken by falcons shall be drakes, who do not incubate or care for the young, almost certainly serves as an extra (deflective) protection for the cryptic brooding females. In some species of

Ptarmigan (*Lagopus*) the males' moult from white winter to brown summer plumage is delayed, so that they are extremely conspicuous while the hens are safely incubating in their brown cryptic summer plumage. This must serve to deflect the attacks of predators, such as eagles, preponderantly to males, during this period while the next generation depends solely on the females.

Advertisement. This is the function of many allesthetic characters, especially those restricted to the male sex. Much of the brilliant colouring of the males of territorial birds appears to be concerned with advertisement, as does their song. When the need for visual concealment is paramount, as in most warblers, visual advertisement characters are not evolved, but the songs are distinctive and far-carrying.

It is clearly important that advertisement characters should be specifically distinctive, so that females should not attempt to pair up with males of another species, and males of one species should not be warned off the territories of another. As a result we find great variation in such characters as between closely related species in the same geographical area. Examples are the male coloration of Stonechat and Whinchat, and the songs of Chiffchaff, Willow-Warbler and Wood-Warbler.

Colour as Deterrent. Warning coloration constitutes a special type of advertisement, advertising to predators the possession of nauseous or dangerous properties. The most familiar examples come from insects, for instance the black-and-yellow pattern of wasps and Cinnabar moth caterpillars.

Warning characters were usually thought to be absent in birds, but H. B. Cott has recently carried out a large number of experiments

John Markham

PATTERN *of Corncrake's plumage is an aid to camouflage*

For text see pages 111, 155 and 408

which have conclusively demonstrated a co-relation between unpalatability and conspicuousness of plumage and eggs. The conspicuousness of drongos and the brilliance of the Kingfisher, for instance, appear to be in part a warning of distastefulness, though they doubtless also subserve recognition.

A special type of mimicry is seen in cuckoos' eggs, which in many species are closely similar in size and markings to those of the host in whose nest they are laid. This undoubtedly reduces the risk of their ejection by the host. In our own Cuckoo, the mimicry is polymorphic, different strains laying eggs of different types each adapted to a particular host. A detailed analysis of this complex problem has recently been made by Southern (1954).

Threat-characters, including of course threat-behaviour, are employed to denote readiness to fight, or to increase the animal's intimidating appearance, or both. In birds, they are often confined to the male sex, but occur in females also where both sexes show territorial behaviour, as in the Robin, or where both share the duties of incubation equally and both possess the same courtship characters, as in grebes (*see* below). They may be employed either against enemies (e.g. the aerial swoops of the Night-Hawk (American Nightjar) against human or animal intruders near its nest, or the formidable threat-displays of cornered herons or bitterns, or of the Amazon Parrot mentioned by Cott ; or, more commonly, against rivals of the same species. Many examples of this latter type occur in birds, including most of the striking head and breast patterns of males, e.g. in tits, Ringed Plover, Robin, Redstart and so on.

Robin's Red Breast. The Robin is of particular interest in several respects. For one thing, the threat character—here the red breast—is developed in both sexes, in correlation with the fact that in the Winter both females and males hold and defend individual territories. For another, experiment has shown that here again there is a built-in instinctive reaction to a specific sign-stimulus, namely the red breast. A male Robin in possession of breeding territory will not attack a stuffed immature Robin, which lacks red on the breast ; but it will attack a stuffed adult Robin, whether intact, or headless and tailless, or even when reduced to nothing but the red breast. In normal

threat, the Robin assumes an erect posture which renders the red breast especially conspicuous.

The red breast of the Robin is also an example of the general rule that visual sign-stimuli consist of simple but striking and distinctive patterns. This is illustrated by many other examples, such as the black-and-yellow breast of the Great Tit, the red breast and black head and bill of the Bullfinch, the black crown of the Blackcap, the black underparts of the Golden Plover, the white breast of the otherwise brown-black Dipper, and the black-bordered, yellow crown-stripe of the Goldcrest. This last threat character only becomes conspicuous when erected ; similar special behaviour " making the best of " threat-coloration is also seen in the Great Crested Grebe, Ruff, Hoopoe, and many other species.

Epigamic coloration is concerned with courtship and mating. That of the Ruff is unique in being polymorphic—i.e. in showing an enormous range of distinctive variations. In fact, no two breeding males on a " hill " or display-ground are alike : they differ in the colour and markings of their ruffs and eartufts, both of which, or either independently, may be white, dark brown, black, purple, chestnut or buff, and either unbarred or barred. It is probable, as E. B. Ford has suggested, that this variety of allesthetic epigamic coloration may further enhance the stimulating effect of communal display.

It should be mentioned that some species of bird may utilise parts of the environment in advertisement and epigamic display. Thus woodpeckers " sing " by drumming on wood, and snipe by the vibration of specially modified tail-feathers. Some male ducks enhance their display by splashing up fountains of water, and grebes by emerging suddenly from below the surface in striking attitudes. The ritual presentation of food is a constant element in the display of many birds, such as terns ; and of nest-material in that of many others, such as grebes and herons. Finally, the bower-

Eric Hosking

PATTERN AND COLOUR. The Bullfinch's red breast and black head form a striking and effective contrast to attract the female's attention

Arthur Christiansen

PATTERN AND COLOUR. *The polygamous Ruff shows great variations in epigamic male pattern : this enhances the effect of communal displaying*

feeding, and sematic characters only are visible when needed— recognition marks in flight (see above), epigamic characters during actual display ceremonies, as in the male Prairie Chicken or both sexes of the Great Crested Grebe. In the Little Grebe, which is smaller and apparently more in need of cryptic protection, the visual epigamic characters are much less conspicuous, but a mutual vocal display occurs.

Even when epigamic characters are visible while the bird is at rest, they are rarely shown off to their full extent except by means of appropriate display ceremonies, as in the Ruff, Peacock, or Argus Pheasant : in other words, they act as enhancers of the effect of a special type of behaviour. In many species, epigamic characters are further restricted by appearing only in the breeding season : thus the ruffs and ear-tufts of the male Ruff disappear entirely, and those of both sexes of the Great Crested Grebe very largely, at the autumn moult.

In polygamous and promiscuous species, one male may secure a large number of mates, another a smaller number, and still another none at all. This must clearly be so on theoretical grounds ; but it has also been established by observation in various grouse and especially in ruffs, where males can be individually distinguished by their coloration. (In passing, it may be noted that the most successful male ruffs were usually those whose epigamic characters appeared most striking to the human observer.) Since the arrival of a female on the display ground initiated epigamic (as opposed to threat) display by the males, and since a female can be seen to pass some males and to allow or solicit another to mate with her, sexual selection in Darwin's sense is here operative. Furthermore, the reproductive advantage of successful display in such species is a *multiple* one.

The consequences of these differences in reproductive advantage or selective value of display are obvious and striking. Any sematic characters, including those of display, will tend to make the animal more conspicuous to predators as well as to its potential or actual mates. When display has only a *fractional* advantage,

birds have the unique habit of constructing special display structures, either cleared areas on the forest floor, or " bowers " of overarching twigs, with a passage between, on or by which they collect various bright objects like shells, bones, flowers, leaves with white underside, etc. Some species show very definite colour-preferences : thus the male Satin Bowerbird, if a selection of bits of blue and red paper or ribbon is placed near his bower, will remove the red and bring in the blue. Finally, many ' species actually colour their bowers artificially, using their saliva mixed with charcoal or coloured plant-juices as paint. The bower or playground with its associated collection of unusual objects appears to act as an extra stimulus to the female.

Nature's Dilemma. The biological or selective value of conspicuousness has always to be balanced against that of inconspicuousness : in other words, the development of striking sematic visual characters, such as epigamic plumage and elaborate display, is always being opposed by the need for the development of cryptic characters, such as concealing coloration and immobility or skulking habits.

Sometimes the need for concealment preponderates to such an extent that no visual sematic coloration can be evolved. This happens, e.g. in most warblers, where recognition and advertisement are vocal, and epigamic display consists merely in wing-waving, tailspreading and other attitudes, and is not enhanced by epigamic colours or patterns or special plumage.

In a number of other species, cryptic coloration dominates when the bird is at rest or

this will not outweigh the dangers of conspicuousness and the need for concealment.

The displays of such forms are thus mostly confined to certain attitudes and types of behaviour acting as sign-stimuli, but are not enhanced by the evolution of bright colours, striking patterns, or special developments of plumage. When the fractional advantage is larger, however, as in birds where the sexes share equally in the care of eggs and young, conspicuous mutual epigamic displays may result, often enhanced by bright coloration and sometimes by special plumage (e.g. in the Great Crested Grebe). On the other hand, the selective value of concealment is still usually high enough to ensure that conspicuousness lasts only while display is in progress.

Unit advantage accrues from advertisement displays which secure the possession of a mate and territory, thus tilting the balance in favour of conspicuousness. This may often result in striking coloration, but it is not usually further enhanced by the high development of special plumage characters, though small and moderate crests serving this purpose are not infrequent. Highly developed advertisement plumage-characters are to be seen, however, in a few species, notably those in which advertisement flight-displays occur, like the pennant-winged nightjars of Africa. In these the second primaries of the males have greatly elongated shafts with a pennant or racket at the tip, and give the animal a very striking appearance during its crepuscular display-flights.

Finally, when multiple reproductive advantage is involved, the risks of conspicuousness become relatively negligible, the need for cryptic concealment may be largely or entirely overridden, and the most extravagant special display patterns may be evolved. Sometimes indeed, as in the Peacock and Argus Pheasant, the male's special epigamic plumage may be so over-developed as to handicap the animal in the daily struggle for existence : but even this is outweighed by the selective advantages of potential multiple paternity. Even with multiple reproductive advantage, however, the need for concealment

may be so great as to prevent the appearance of visual epigamic characters except during display ; this occurs in plains-living birds exposed to predators, like the Prairie Chicken.

Evolutionary Meaning. There is one further interesting point concerning visual sematic characters. Whereas warning, threat and advertisement coloration are almost always a matter of simple but effective patterns, epigamic coloration is often elaborate and detailed. The human observer tends to describe such epigamic characters as those of the Peacock, Argus Pheasant, or Amherst Pheasant as *beautiful*, while the adjective *striking* seems more appropriate to other types.

The reason, I think, is clear. The patterns of warning, threat and advertisement are designed to be effective at a distance and to act as sign-stimuli automatically releasing specific instinctive reactions in the percipient. Those of courtship-display, on the other hand, are designed to be effective at close quarters and to act so as to increase the intensity of sexual feeling and to raise and modify the female's emotional level : only when the required threshold has been reached can sign-stimuli be called into action to release actual mating behaviour. It is in any case true that highly developed epigamic displays have resulted in the first appearance of elaborate beauty as a factor in evolution.

The coloration of birds has an obvious attraction for everyone. But its interest is enhanced as we begin to grasp the way in which coloration is related to other allesthetic characters, to behaviour, and to habitat and

Fox

PATTERN AND COLOUR. The Peacock is among the few birds to possess special plumage characters to enhance the effectiveness of its display

way of life, and as we discover its varied biological and evolutionary significance. Take a couple of dozen common species of bird, like Chaffinch and Goldfinch, Yellow Hammer and Reed-Bunting, Blackbird and thrushes, Willow-Warbler and Whitethroat, Great and Coal-Tit, Pied Wagtail and Skylark, Mallard and Mute Swan, Green Woodpecker and Nuthatch, Swallow and House-Martin, Cuckoo and Sparrow-Hawk, Moorhen and Dabchick, Wood-Pigeon and Turtle-Dove, Partridge and Pheasant. You might easily see all of these on a single country walk. Yet if you once begin to try to understand the significance of their coloration, you will find yourself exploring the most varied fields—natural and sexual selection, animal senses and methods of communication, the relations between predator and prey, between male and female, between parent and offspring, between organism and habitat. In fact, the study of bird coloration opens up a large part of the whole field of evolutionary biology.

Consult : Adaptive Coloration in Animals, H. B. Cott (Methuen), 1940 ; Bird Display, E. A. Armstrong (Cambridge University Press), 1942 ; The Courtship of Animals, W. P. Pycraft (Hutchinson), 1913.

The Herring Gull's World, N. Tinbergen (Collins), 1953 ; The Life of the Robin, D. Lack (Witherby), 1943 ; Social Behaviour in Animals, N. Tinbergen (Methuen), 1953 ; The Study of Instinct, N. Tinbergen (Clarendon Press), 1951.

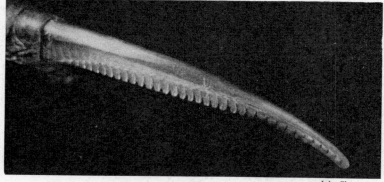

John Clegg

PECTINATED CLAW. *The Bittern's claw-comb is outstanding both for its perfect regularity and because its use has been observed and filmed*

PECTINATED CLAW. In several species the middle toes of both feet bear claws with serrated edges on the inner-facing side. Claws bearing toes serrated in this way are said to be pectinated and the combs themselves are colloquially called "claw-combs". The development of the " comb " varies greatly among the different species possessing them. In the Gannet, for instance, the pectination consists of little more than a series of cracks in the nail, whereas the Bittern has a perfect comb made up of 36 well-formed teeth. In between

these two extremes a series showing increasing complexity can be traced.

The structures are not confined to any one group of birds as will be seen from the following list of British species with pectinated claws :

Nightjar, Barn-Owl, Glossy Ibis, the herons, the bitterns, Cormorant, Shag, Gannet, Cream-coloured Courser, Collared Pratincole and Black-tailed Godwit.

There seems little doubt that the structural modification of a claw-comb arose independently among birds of widely differing relationship, but it seems strange that whereas, for instance, the Black-tailed Godwit possesses one, the closely-related Bar-tailed Godwit, with similar habits, does not. Nor is it easy to understand why the Barn-Owl is alone among our British owls in possessing a comb.

That the combs are used for cleaning purposes there is little doubt ; and it is significant that most of the birds possessing them feed largely on fish or other slimy foods. and must in consequence often get their plumage soiled, particularly on the head and neck region where cleaning by the beak is difficult, if not impossible. That the comb is used for this purpose in the Bittern at least has been observed, and filmed by Lord William Percy and others. In the toilet of this bird the feathers of the neck and head region are rubbed on the powder-down (*q.v.*) patches of the breast and the upper thighs, which breaks down the slime, and the plumage is then combed out by the claws.

As an example of a bird which does not feed on slimy food, the Nightjar may be cited. Here the purpose of the comb seems to be the cleaning of the stiff bristles, which fringe the mouth, of the scales of moths on which the bird feeds largely. The use of the claw-comb in flight, in this way, was observed by Gilbert White, but he attributed the action to the capture of the prey. The Gannet, too, was seen to use its claw-comb while flying.

PECTORAL SANDPIPER—Calidris melanotos. A considerable number of these birds, whose home is in Arctic north America, have come as winter visitors to Britain. The Pectoral Sandpiper's appearance has something in common with the Dunlin's, but it is a larger bird, and has longer, yellowish legs and a shorter bill. Its mantle plumage is speckled dark brown, its head much lighter, shading to

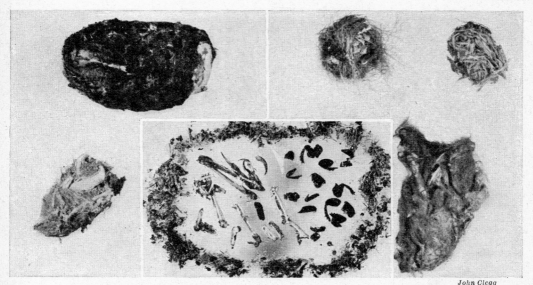

John Clegg

PELLET. The following bird's pellets are shown : top—left, Barn-Owl, right, Herring-Gull ; bottom—left, Long-eared Owl, right, Greater Black-backed Gull. The inset depicts a broken-up casting of the Tawny Owl, showing indigestible food remnants

dark on back and wings. Its underparts are white, and there is a distinct line separating the speckled breast from the white belly. The length is 7–8 in., and the tarsus is 1 in. The wing span is about 1 ft. and the bird weighs approximately 2 oz.

This sandpiper (*q.v.*) moves like a Dunlin and flies with regular wing beats. Its call, heard when it rises from the ground, is reminiscent of both the Curlew-Sandpiper's and the Dunlin's. It will stand motionless for a long time, a habit of the snipes, and then move slowly on, probing for food with its long bill.

PECTUS. The breast of a bird. *See* illustration facing page 1. *See also* Anatomy.

PEEWIT. Local name for Lapwing (*q.v.*).

PEEWIT GULL. *See* Black-headed Gull (*q.v.*), so called because of its shrill feeding-note.

PELECANIFORMES. Order of large fish-eating birds, including cormorants, gannets, frigate-birds, and pelicans. Its members are distributed over the coasts and inland waters in most parts of the world, except the central Pacific. Two of its five families — *Sulidae* (gannets) and *Phalacrocoracidae* (cormorants) —are on the British list.

The birds belonging to this order are unusual in having all four toes joined by webs, the " hind " toe being turned forward for this purpose and joined by a web with the second toe. They share the following characteristics :

The tongue is almost absent. The nostrils are rather large, slit-like, and, in most cases,

more or less blocked up. The wings are fairly long. The tail usually has between 12 and 16 quill-feathers, but in the Pelican there are between 20 and 24. The featherless tracts are reduced, the feather-tracts being broad. There is down on both the feather-tracts and the featherless tracts. The oil-gland is tufted.

PELAGODROMA (Latin, " a bird of the ocean "). Genus of marine birds of the family *Procellariidae* of the order *Procellariiformes*. It contains only one species, the Frigate-Petrel (*q.v.*), which has been recorded in the British Isles two or three times. The members of this genus are mainly distributed over the Atlantic isles and Australasia.

PELLET. Pellets or " castings ", consisting of the indigestible parts of a bird's diet, are ejected from the mouth, not only by owls, hawks and other birds of prey, but also by a variety of other species, including rooks, shrikes, gulls, herons, kingfishers, curlews and even warblers and robins. The Curlew, in fact, ejects not merely pellets, but also the lining of its gizzard.

Pellets are found most abundantly near nesting and roosting sites and, although they may vary somewhat in size and shape between individual bird's they are usually sufficiently characteristic of each species as to make it possible to determine, from an examination of pellets, the site of a particular bird's haunt.

Dissection of a pellet will reveal the bones, claws, beaks, or other hard parts of a bird's prey, often surrounded by a softer layer of

Eric Hosking

PEREGRINE FALCON. No other British bird of prey rivals the Peregrine's swiftness and grace

the fur or feather. Newly disgorged pellets frequently have a shiny appearance, derived from a mucous secretion which, no doubt, serves as an aid to ejection.

Although the dissection of pellets can be very useful in eliciting information about a bird's diet, care should be taken not to form hasty generalisations from an examination of a few pellets. In the first place, they contain only the *indigestible* part of the food and the easily digested worms, grubs, etc., may leave no trace. With some birds, such as herons, even fish bones seem to be digested and the castings are often composed of vegetable remains only. Pellets, too, can only reveal what a particular bird has been eating at one specified time and this may not be representative of the diet throughout the year. Thus one of the Herring-Gull pellets shown on page 413 consisted entirely of the husks of oats, but no one would be so rash as to deduce from this that the Herring-Gull fed entirely, or even mainly, on oats.

Nevertheless, the examination of pellets in quantity and throughout the year can reveal interesting, and sometimes spectacular, information on the food taken by particular birds. Some years ago a systematic investigation of 700 pellets of the Barn-Owl revealed the remains of 239 house mice, 93 voles, 1,590 shrews, 3 rats, 16 bats and 19 sparrows.

PERDIX (Latin, " partridge "). Genus of the family *Phasianidae* of the order *Galliformes*. It contains three species, only one of which occurs in Europe, the other two in northern Asia. The European species is the Partridge (*q.v.*), one of the most common of all the British game birds.

PEREGRINE FALCON—Falco peregrinus. The largest of British falcons—it is the " Duck Hawk " of America—the Peregrine is unmatched among them for its magnificent mastery of the air. No other bird has such perfect equipment for speed and accuracy of aim. The favourite of falconers through the ages, it rivals even the Goshawk in its swiftness and dash.

As a British resident, the Peregrine breeds both on the coast and inland in northern England, Wales, Scotland and Ireland; it is much rarer in the south of England. It is also a passage migrant. Abroad, it occurs in Europe, Asia, Africa, Greenland, Australasia and north and south America.

The mantle is slate-grey, and the underparts are buff, boldly barred in black. The crown and sides of the head are black, and on the side of the neck appears a whitish patch. The very distinct black moustachial stripe sets it apart from all other birds of prey, except the Hobby. The wings are long and pointed, the tail rather short and tapering. The cere, legs, and skin round the eye are yellow, and the bill is bluish-grey and hooked. As is usual among falcons, the female is larger; she is rather darker above and more heavily barred below. The length of the male is 15 in. and the tarsus 2 in. ; the wing span is about 2 ft. ; the weight 2 lb. The length of the female is 18 in., and the tarsus 2·3 in. ; the wing span is about 2½ ft. ; the weight 3 lb.

In flight, the Peregrine has no rival among our birds of prey in beauty and grace of movement as it soars, glides and circles in the air. But even more wonderful is the swift suddenness and incredible speed of its " stoop " —estimated at more than 180 miles an hour. For hours it will perch upright on some rock or point of vantage, its head sunk between its shoulders. Then, sighting its quarry, it swoops down, strikes it with its powerful talons and hurls it to the ground, where it is retrieved and then carried to some special hide-out near the falcon's eyrie on a cliff top or ledge. The Peregrine, which rarely strikes its victim on the ground, can carry a weight almost equal to its own. The sound of the " stoop " has been likened to that of the passing of a rocket.

In courtship, male and female join together in wonderful aerial manoeuvres, tumbling and twisting, chasing each other and frequently " looping the loop ".

Usually a silent bird, the Peregrine is noisy at its breeding site, especially at the approach of an intruder. Its main calls are a hoarse and shrill chattering, and a long drawn-out plaintive cry. The female has a piercing scream.

In Great Britain, treeless country is usually frequented by the Peregrine Falcon. It nests on coastal and inland cliffs, moors, fells, mountain sides, and, occasionally, in some high building, such as a church tower. On the Continent, it breeds regularly in wooded country in the plains and mountains. It is thought to mate for life. If the Peregrine does not annex an old nest of a Raven, crow or some other bird, it will not build one, and the three or four whitish eggs, with reddish-brown markings, are placed in a scrape on a ledge or a hole in a cliff. They are laid in April or May, at two-day intervals. Both male and female take part in hatching the eggs, but the female seems to take the greater share ; the male brings her food which, at his call, she leaves the nest to receive in the air. Each egg takes 28 or 29 days to hatch, and as a rule only two of the chicks survive. Clad in greyish down, they are tended for as long as six weeks and fed for some time longer. One brood is reared.

The Peregrine has a wide choice of food. Pigeons, both domestic and wild, are a favourite item ; indeed, during the 1939–1945 war, its depredations among the carrier-pigeons used by the military were so great than an Order in Council was passed depriving the Peregrine of any legal protection which it had hitherto possessed ; the Order was later rescinded, and it is once more legally protected. The list of birds which become its victims is too long to detail. Some mammals are also eaten.

PERNIS. Genus of the family *Falconidae* of the order *Falconiformes*. Its members are mainly distributed over Europe and much of Asia, and also occur outside the breeding season in southern Africa. The only species of this genus on the British list is the Honey-Buzzard (*q.v.*).

PETCHORA PIPIT—Anthus gustavi. Nine or ten visits of the Petchora Pipit have been recorded at Fair Isle in the Shetlands. The bird takes its name from the river Petchora in north Russia, and also occurs in north-east Russia and north Siberia. It closely resembles the Tree-Pipit, except that it has two pale streaks down its back. The length is 5¾ in.

Its song appears to be quite individual ; it is described by those who have heard it in Shetland as rather like the song of the Meadow-Pipit, but softer and lower-toned. It is often delivered while the bird is hovering high in the sky.

PETREL. Common name of a group of seabirds, comprising 18 widely distributed species, all belonging to the family *Procellariidae* (*q.v.*). The following petrels, separately described under their own headings, appear in the British list : Wilson's Petrel, Leach's Petrel, Madeiran Petrel, Storm-Petrel, Frigate-Petrel, Bulwer's Petrel, Kermadec Petrel, White-winged Petrel, Black-capped Petrel, Fulmar Petrel. The best known among them is the Storm-Petrel, or Mother Carey's Chicken, scarcely larger than a lark, and the smallest sea-bird known.

True petrels are small to smallish, dark compact birds, most of which have a white or greyish rump. They have long wings, broad, moderately long tails, narrow and pointed claws, and short, slender bills, with the nostrils enclosed in a pair of horny tubes. They are truly oceanic birds, and are but rarely seen in coastal waters outside the breeding season.

The name petrel—a diminutive of Peter— refers to the way in which these birds appear to "walk on the water", when they indulge in their favourite habit of skimming the waves, with only enough motion of the wings to keep the feet from sinking under the surface ; or, as Gibson-Hill describes it, " fluttering over an erratic, wandering course, like large-winged butterflies crossing a wind-swept meadow . . ."

PHALACROCORAX. Genus of aquatic birds of the family *Phalacrocoracidae* of the order *Pelecaniformes*. The only genus in its family, it contains nearly 30 species, distributed over the coasts and inland waters in almost all parts of the world (particularly in the tropical regions), but absent from the islands of the central Pacific. There are only two British species, the Cormorant (*q.v.*) and the Shag (*q.v.*).

The members of this genus have a long, rather slender bill, laterally compressed and terminating in a sharp hook ; there is a linear groove along the sides of the bill. In the adult birds the nostrils are closed. The neck is rather long. The wings are of medium length, and the tail is also of medium length or rather long. The legs are short and set fairly far back. The feet are large, and all the four toes are united by webs.

John Markham

ↃHALACROCORAX. *The Shag is one of the two representatives of this genus on the British list*

PHALAROPE. Family of wading birds (*Phalaropodidae*), related to the sandpipers, dunlins, redshanks, and the like. There are two species on the British list ; the Grey Phalarope (called in America the Red Phalarope) and the Red-necked Phalarope (American name, Northern Phalarope), both of which are described under their own headings. They are dainty little birds, closely resembling sandpipers, with slender bills and longer necks than most waders. They are characterised not only by their coot-like toes with lobed webs (suited for both swimming and running) but also by the fact that the *females*, who are larger and brighter than the males, *take the initiative in courtship,* and during incubation allow the male to carry out most of the duties normally performed by the female.

The Grey Phalarope is an irregular and scarce passage migrant from August to November, and March to June. It is very tame, and swims buoyantly, often far out to sea, but on passage is found occasionally on coasts and inland waters. When feeding on shallow waters it " spins " characteristically.

The Red-necked Phalarope is similar in habits and voice to the Grey Phalarope, but is smaller and differently marked. It is a breeding visitor from May to August to Scotland and Ireland.

PHALAROPODIDAE. Family of small aquatic birds of the order *Charadriiformes*. It comprises the phalaropes, and contains three species which are distributed over most of the seas of the world, except during the breeding season, when they are to be found in the northern parts of the Northern Hemisphere.

PHALAROPUS. Genus of aquatic birds of the family *Phalaropodidae* of the order *Charadriiformes*. It contains three species, of which two, the Grey Phalarope (*q.v.*) and the Red-necked Phalarope (*q.v.*) occur in the British Isles.

The members of this genus have wings of medium length, while their tail is shortish and well rounded. The legs are very compressed.

PHASE. Certain variations in colour of plumage, regularly found in successive generations of a single species, and which are not due to sex, age, or season. Thus, the Arctic, Skua exhibits two very distinct plumages—one form being darkish brown all over, and the other showing white underparts—which are known respectively as the dark and light phases of the Arctic Skua. The two phases cross-breed, and thus every gradation of colour between them may be found.

Although with Arctic skuas there may be an admixture of light and dark phases in various proportions independent of geographical position (both light and dark phases may be found in the same colony), with some other species a particular phase may be roughly confined to one or more regions. For example, the Fulmar, which exhibits several colour phases, may show every gradation from white on the head and underparts to deep, smoky grey all over. In Britain, Faeroe, Norway and Iceland, most breeding fulmars are light-coloured, whereas at Bear Island, off east Greenland, about half are light and half dark, and, farther north, in north-east Greenland, Spitzbergen, and Franz Josef Land, nearly all are dark.

Although, as stated in the definition, the term phase is not, in general, applied to differences of plumage such as frequently exist between juvenile and mature birds, it *is* used in connection with birds, such as gulls, which do not reach full adult plumage until their third, fourth or even fifth year, and whose adult plumage is said to pass through several phases before reaching maturity.

It is sometimes difficult, both in theory and practice, to draw a line between phases of a species, and subspecies, particularly as the difference in appearance between two phases of the same species is frequently greater than that between two subspecies. It has happened several times that a particular group of birds has been accorded the status of a subspecies, and has later been found to be a phase of a recognized species. But it will be seen from the definition on page 133 that, to rate as a subspecies, certain regional qualifications are required, in addition to distinctive characteristics—a random distribution is not sufficient.

Finally, the term phase is not applied to individual " sports " who show variations like albinism, melanism and erythrism (*qq.v.*).

R. P. Bagnall-Oakeley

PHALAROPE. *The waders of this family are characterised by the fact that the females are more colourful than the males and—make all the advances*

John Markham

PHEASANT. *Classical legend tells that the Argonauts introduced this bird into Europe ; probably it was already known in Roman Britain, certainly the Normans knew of it*

PHASIANIDAE. Family of game-birds of the order *Galliformes*. It contains the pheasants, partridges and quails, and its members are distributed over all parts of the globe, except southern south America and the Pacific islands. Four genera are on the British list : *Alectoris*, *Perdix*, *Coturnix* and *Phasianus*.

The members of this family are medium- or large-sized, four-toed land-birds. They have a stout, arched bill. Their wings are broad, with ten primary feathers. Both tarsus and toes are bare of feathers. In the male birds, the tarsus often has spurs, and an elevated hind toe.

PHASIANUS. Genus of game-birds of the family *Phasianidae* of the order *Galliformes*. It contains one species, the Pheasant (*q.v.*), which occurs in a number of forms or subspecies in much of Europe and Asia.

PHEASANT — **Phasianus colchicus.** The Pheasant is reputed to have been brought from the banks of Phasis, in Colchis, to southern Europe at a very remote period, its introduction being ascribed in classic legend to the Argonauts. Its supposed place of origin is perpetuated in its Latin name. The date of its introduction into England is not known, but it is thought to have been during Roman times. It was certainly before 1199, when King John granted William Brewer a licence " to have free Warren throughout all his own lands for hares, *pheasants* and partridges ".

Various races have since been introduced, and all have interbred, with the result that the Pheasant of today is somewhat of a mongrel. It takes its place among our native birds only by reason of its long residence, for it can hardly be regarded as a wild bird since in so many areas it is preserved for game. Some characteristics of

the early stock still survive ; the white ring at the base of the neck of some pheasants, for instance, owes its presence to the introduction of the Chinese Pheasant (*P. torquatus*) some 200 years ago. *See also* Introduced Birds.

The Pheasant was introduced into Scotland and Ireland about 500 years later than into England. It is found in the Orkneys but not in the Shetlands, nor the Outer Hebrides. It has been introduced into almost every European country, and is found in a truly wild state only in some parts of Russia and Asia Minor.

Most people are familiar with the appearance of the Pheasant, if only from having seen it hanging in poulterers' shops. The variegated plumage of the gorgeous male shades from rich burnished copper to golden red, copiously mottled in black. Dark purple crescent markings cover his breast and flanks. His head and neck are a glossy dark green, and behind his crown are small ear tufts. Prominent red wattles surround his eyes. But his most conspicuous feature is his beautiful long tail, with its black bars. Compared with her colourful partner, the female is sober-looking, but she too has a fine long tail. Her protective coloration is so excellent that when sitting on the nest she completely merges into her surroundings. The legs of both sexes are grey, and the bill pale green. The size and length of tail vary according to the different breeds. The length of the average male, including the tail, is 30–35 in., and the tarsus is 2½ in., the wing span is from 1 ft. 6 in.–2 ft., and the weight 3 lb. The female is smaller ; her length, including tail, is 21–25 in., with the other measurements in proportion.

Still a shy and wary bird, in spite of its long history of preservation, the Pheasant is essentially a woodland species. It is happiest on the

1 F

ground, where it both walks and runs, but it roosts in trees to be out of harm's way. If disturbed, it will run for shelter rather than fly, but, when forced to do so, it rises with a flurry of its round wings. Its flight is then swift and strong, but never long sustained. When necessary, it can swim.

In his fine spring courtship display, the male parades in front of his mate, and runs round her with his feathers fluffed out and ear tufts erected. He readily fights any opponent, striking effectively with the spurs on his feet.

The familiar crowing of the Pheasant is first and foremost a mating call. It is a far-carrying sound, which can be heard as a background to many sound recordings of other birds. This principal call is also used for other purposes—as an alarm note, for instance.

As the Pheasant is of a quarrelsome nature, a variety of more or less high-pitched sounds, hastily uttered, can be heard between male and female. Other notes include the three- and four-syllabled crowing of the male, the whistling of the female, and call notes that remind one of the domestic fowl.

Pheasants nest in woods, copses, hedgerows, wooded heaths and commons, and reed beds. The nest is a hollow in the ground, usually with some sort of cover, scraped by the female, and lined with grass and dead leaves. The number of eggs varies from 8–15, but since the Pheasant is generally polygamous as many as 22 eggs have been recorded in one nest ; olive-brown in colour, they are laid in April. The female incubates alone, for 22–24 days, beginning when the clutch is complete. If the clutch has been produced by two "wives", they incubate

together quite amicably. The chicks are buff-coloured, with darker stripes. They are fed and tended by the hen, and can fly in about a fortnight. One brood is reared in a season.

The Pheasant is an omnivorous eater of both animal and vegetable food. Ants' eggs and the spangle gall of the oak tree are favourite items.

PHILOMACHUS. Genus of the family *Scolopacidae* of the order *Charadriiformes*, containing only one species, the Ruff (*q.v.*).

PHOENICOPTERIDAE. The only family in the order *Phoenicopteriformes*, containing the flamingoes. It is divided into three genera, the members of which are found in southern Europe, Africa, Asia, and north and south America.

The only genus on the British list is *Phoenicopterus*. This contains only one species, the Flamingo (*q.v.*), which occasionally wanders to Britain from southern Europe and elsewhere.

PHOENICURUS. Genus of the family *Turdidae* of the order *Passeriformes*. Its members are distributed over Europe, northern Asia and north-west Africa, and, outside the breeding season, occur in parts of tropical Asia and tropical Africa. Two members of this genus, the Redstart (*q.v.*) and Black Redstart (*q.v.*), occur in the British Isles.

The members of this genus have a slender, pointed bill, with distinct bristly hairs on each side of the gape. Their wings are of medium length, and the primary feathers are considerably longer than the secondaries. The tail, which is of medium length, is slightly rounded and is reddish-brown in colour. The females have much duller plumage than the males, and the young birds are mostly spotted.

PHOENICURUS. *The only member of its genus to be at all common in the British Isles is the Redstart (shown here), which is a breeding visitor from April to October*

Eric Hosking

SECRETS OF BIRD PHOTOGRAPHY

ERIC HOSKING, F.R.P.S., M.B.O.U., and STUART SMITH, Ph.D., M.B.O.U.

After a brief, but informative, historical survey, this article discusses the special technique of successful bird photography and stresses the importance of careful preparatory work. It also gives practical information on hides, cameras and plates

PHOTOGRAPHY. The photography of birds dates back to an early but important advance in photographic technique, namely the invention of the dry plate. Until then the impedimenta that surrounded the photographer were so numerous and cumbersome that working on natural history subjects was out of the question. This invention enabled the photographer to carry sensitised plates about with him and bring them home for processing. The flexibility thus given to the photographic art greatly widened its scope, and almost immediately the possibility of its application to natural history subjects was recognized by a few pioneers.

Who actually took the first photograph direct from wild nature must inevitably remain in dispute, but there is no doubt about the first *published* photograph of this kind. This was a photograph of a Song-Thrush's *nest and eggs* taken on April 11, 1892, by the Kearton brothers, Richard and Cherry, who were certainly the greatest and best-known of the early bird photographers. The first photograph of a wild *bird* was that of a Lapwing on its nest, taken in 1895 by R. B. Lodge, of Enfield, who used an ingenious electric trip-wire whereby the bird " took its own photograph ". To Richard Kearton must go the credit for the fundamental invention of the hide as the means of obtaining close-up photographs of birds. After experimenting with a number of curious structures, the Kearton brothers finally evolved the hide tent, worked out the best method of using it, and established a technique that has scarcely changed with the years.

The success achieved by the Keartons became known throughout the country through their books and lectures, and it was inevitable that many others should follow their lead. As early as 1899 a club, known as the Zoological Photographic Club, was founded to further the art of natural history photography in the zoological field. This club, which is still flourishing, has counted in its membership practically all the greatest bird photographers of this country, and no society has done more to further the art of bird photography.

Although each worker has his own methods, a fairly standard technique is adopted by most bird photographers. The first point to notice is that the preparatory field work is usually three-quarters of the battle. By this is meant the stages up to the erection of the hide in its final position.

Hides. The hide itself is a most important factor. It should not be too large, yet must be large enough for the photographer to be able to sit inside it in comfort, and operate his camera and change his plates without moving the sides of the tent. A good cotton twill or gaberdine fabric, dyed khaki or dark green (as camouflage) and rot-proofed, is ideal for the hide. It should be placed on a rigid frame about a yard square. In the design of hides individuality can have full play, but a useful and simple model is given in Hosking's and Newberry's *The Art of Bird Photography*.

There are three golden rules concerning the erection of hides. The first is that a hide should never be erected in a place where its presence will endanger the bird or its brood ; if the nest is in so public a place that a hide would invite attention, the nest must be left undisturbed. Secondly, no hide should be erected directly in front of a nest in the final position it is to

Eric Hosking

PHOTOGRAPHY. This tubular steel hide was specially built to photograph the Hobby (inset)

Eric Hosking

PHOTOGRAPHY. Another pylon hide—this one was built to get close enough to a shy woodpecker

occupy, for this invites desertion of the nest. The hide should be carefully erected, preferably at half height, some distance from the nest, and gradually moved into position over a period of several days. Thirdly, a hide must never be put up to the nest of a Passerine bird before the young are hatched ; it is necessary to wait until they are several days old.

When it is certain that the bird has accepted the hide, photography can be contemplated, but before this is possible it is usually necessary to arrange the foliage round the nest to open up the site somewhat and make an artistic setting for the picture. This is known to bird photographers as " gardening ", and must be expertly and carefully carried out. Nothing should be done in removing herbage, branches, and so on, that is likely in any way to endanger the bird and its brood. When photography is over, at least as much time must be spent in replacing the site as was given to arranging it, so that it looks as little disturbed as possible.

The Camera. For bird photography, the camera generally used is large by modern standards. Richard Kearton used to say that the ideal was a 5 in. × 4 in. field camera, with a lens of focal length about 9 in. ; in spite of the passage of half a century, his words remain substantially true today. Most of the best modern workers employ a field type of camera

of ¼-plate or 5 in. × 4 in. size, with a lens of about 8 in. focal length

The camera stand must be absolutely rigid, since, contrary to general belief, the bird photographer (except for flight pictures) gives a comparatively long exposure. He is usually working within a few feet of his subject and consequently, in order to get it and a reasonable part of its surroundings in sharp focus, must make use of a fairly small stop, especially since he is using a long-focus lens. Thus with an 8-in. lens at 5 ft. from the subject it is frequently necessary to stop down to f/11 or f/16 to cover a depth of 6 in., such as would be necessary to bring both the front and the back of a thrush's nest into sharp focus. In the lighting conditions frequently prevailing, an exposure of at least ⅕ sec., at a stop of f/16 is necessary. Since the bird must be still for ⅕ sec., or even longer, if a clear sharp image is to be obtained, the skill of the photographer consists largely in choosing the right moment to release his shutter.

The need for a small stop to give a sufficient depth of field means that the extra expense of a lens of large aperture is rarely justified, and the would-be bird photographer should content himself with a first-class lens of f/6.3, or even f/8, aperture. The lens should be fitted with a deep lens hood that screws rigidly on to the lens flange. The shutter, which must be fitted behind the lens, must be of a type that works quietly, or gives its " click " as it closes and not as it opens. There are several such shutters on the market, the one in most common use by bird photographers being the " Luc " type.

Taking the Photograph. It is often necessary to tilt the camera downwards, especially when photographing nests on or near the ground ; a tilting head, composed simply of two hinged boards that can be fixed rigidly at various angles, should be fixed to the top of the stand. Choice of a correct view-point is important. If it is too high the picture will show too much of the back of the bird and give it a " squat " appearance. If it is too low, out-of-focus foreground will appear and spoil the picture.

A bird photographer must have an assistant to help him into the hide, tuck him in, help with the focusing, and remain in the area (though not in the near vicinity of the nest) while he is photographing. Unless someone comes with the photographer to the nest, and then goes away again, the bird will not return. Most birds cannot count and, when the bird sees the assistant go away from the hide, it will assume that all danger has departed. If the bird has not returned within about half-an-hour, the assistant must let the photographer out of the hide. 'A photographer must never keep a bird from its eggs or young by pitting his patience and endurance against the bird's.

For the photography of birds in flight, the new electronic flash technique has made possible some fine work, but the apparatus required is heavy and expensive. Good photographs of birds in flight can be obtained with miniature cameras fitted with lenses of long focal length, but this requires long practice and clever timing for successful results.

Dark-room Technique. Finally, a good dark-room technique is essential for first-class results. Ornithological subjects are frequently high-contrast subjects, with strong high-lights in the foreground and heavy shadows in the background. Consequently a full exposure should be followed by careful development to a low degree of contrast to produce a thin negative of good gradation and very fine grain. This will make possible a high degree of enlargement on normal grade papers.

The tools of bird photography may be summarised as follows :

1. *Hide Tent.* A stout cloth covering a jointed frame, about 1 yard square and 5 ft.–6 ft. high. Holes for lens and observation. Must be rigid and taut when erected.

2. *Camera and Stand.* A ¼-plate field camera of robust construction, with quiet shutter fitted behind lens. Stand capable of wide range of extension. Tilting head on stand.

3. *Lens.* First-quality anastigmat lens of focal length about 8 in. Aperture about f/6.3. Rigid, screw-in lens hood.

4. *Negative Material.* Fast panchromatic plates, must be developed with fine grain developer.

PHOTOGRAPHY. The hide (below) was used to get the photograph of the Oystercatcher shown in the inset. The camera (right) is of the type used inside the hide—and can be seen protruding from one wall

Eric Hosking

PHYLLOSCOPUS. Genus of warblers of the family *Sylviidae* of the order *Passeriformes.* The genus contains species distributed over Europe, Asia, and northern Africa (south of the Atlas Mountains in the winter months only). There are ten species on the British list : the Willow-Warbler, Chiffchaff, Wood-Warbler, Greenish Warbler, Bonelli's Warbler, Arctic Warbler, Yellow-browed Warbler, Pallas's Warbler, Dusky Warbler and Radde's Bush-Warbler. These are separately described under their own headings.

The bill of these birds is in some cases slender and pointed, but in others somewhat flatter and wider ; it is shorter than the head, and is always surrounded by bristles, which may be very small. The wings are shortish and rather pointed. The tail, which has 12 quill-feathers,

Eric Hosking

PHYLLOSCOPUS. *The little Chiffchaff is one of the more common members of its genus in Britain*

is squarish in shape. The plumage is greenish-brown on the upper parts, while the under-parts are pale. Different species are so alike, that identification would be almost impossible, were it not for their individual songs.

PICA (Latin, " magpie "). Genus of the family *Corvidae* of the order *Passeriformes*. It contains the Magpie (*q.v.*), which is distributed over Europe, northern and central Asia, north-west Africa, and parts of north America. The Magpie is a resident British species, fairly common in most regions, but rather scarce in parts of Scotland and Ireland.

PICIDAE (Latin, " woodpecker "). Family of the order *Piciformes*, mainly including the woodpeckers. Its genera contain more than 400 species, distributed over all parts of the world, except Australia, New Zealand, the Pacific Islands, New Guinea, the eastern Malay Islands, and Madagascar.

The members of this family are mostly adapted for climbing about the trunks and boughs of trees, and are equipped for wood-boring with a strong, hard, chisel-like bill, a large head, and a very strong muscular neck. In addition, they possess an exceptionally long and mobile tongue. This is often barbed at the tip and rendered sticky by a secretion from the salivary glands ; it can be protruded far beyond the bill, and with its aid these birds can drag insects from deep holes.

The tarsus is short, with a row of scutes (horny scales) in front. The feet are strong ; they generally have two toes directed forwards (the second and third toes) and two backwards. This arrangement provides additional support for the back of the foot when the bird is climbing. The toes are equipped with strong claws. The tail, which is wedge-shaped, has

12 feathers with stiff, spiny shafts which, when pressed against a tree-trunk, help the bird to support itself. During the moult the central pair of the tail-feathers is the last to be shed instead of the first as in most birds, and thus the tail preserves much of its supporting function during the period of the moult.

PICIFORMES (Latin, " woodpeckers "). Large order of birds (mostly arborial), including the woodpeckers. It contains six families consisting of several hundred species, occurring everywhere, except New Guinea and many oceanic islands. The order contains only one family which is on the British list, *Picidae*.

PICUS (Latin, " woodpecker "). Genus of woodpeckers of the family *Picidae* of the order *Piciformes*. It contains many different forms distributed over Europe and Asia, but only one of these, the Green Woodpecker (*q.v.*), occurs in the British Isles.

PIED FLYCATCHER—Muscicapa hypoleuca. This bird, a summer breeding visitor and passage migrant to the British Isles, is extremely restricted in its distribution. It is found only in central and northern Wales ; the Welsh border countries ; the dales of Lakeland ; and the north-eastern corner of Yorkshire. The southern counties of Scotland attract it, but in Ireland it is known only as a rare vagrant. Abroad, the Pied Flycatcher breeds throughout Europe, temperate Asia and west Africa and winters in tropical Africa.

More rotund in build than its commoner relative, the Spotted Flycatcher, the male Pied is easily recognized. In summer dress he is markedly pied, black above and white below. His forehead is white, and a broad white wing bar contrasts vividly with his black mantle. The female is much less spectacular ; brown replaces the black in her plumage, she has no white on her forehead, and the white patch on her wing is smaller. In Autumn both male and female are alike. The length is 5 in., and the tarsus 0·6 in., the wing span is about 10 in. and the weight just under ½ oz.

Although the general behaviour and most of the habits of the Pied Flycatcher are like those of the Spotted, there are a few differences. The flight of the Pied is equally undulating and erratic, but the bird does not return to the same branch after darting out to catch an insect, as the Spotted always does, but alights on a different branch, on another tree, or on the ground. It is tit-like in its habit of clinging to a branch, and will feed on the ground. When settling, it moves its tail constantly up and down, and flicks its wings. On the ground it hops.

In his spring display the male draws himself upright, making much of his white breast. But unlike the Spotted Flycatcher, which is more or less a silent bird, the Pied has a pleasing and varied little song, frequently repeated and usually delivered from a perch. The call notes are described as not unlike those of the Redstart and Chaffinch. May is the best month to hear the song, which is seldom heard after June.

Although it is not in reality a mountain bird, the Pied Flycatcher has some preference for the valleys and slopes of hilly country. Oak and birch woods, wooded parks, large gardens—nesting boxes attract it—are all favourite breeding sites ; a stream or other source of water is usually never far away.

A hole in a wall, tree or building suffices for the nest, and often the old nest of a woodpecker is utilised. The cock arrives before his partner to choose the site, but the hen prepares the nest, which is loosely put together with grass, moss, leaves and hair. Four to seven pale blue eggs are laid in May. Incubation begins with the last egg laid, and takes 12 or 13 days ; the hen, fed on the nest by the cock, hatches alone. The young are fed and reared by both parents for nearly another fortnight.

Insects caught on the wing form the chief food of the Pied Flycatcher, but during the autumn months, berries will also be devoured.

its place is taken by the White Wagtail (*Motacilla alba alba*), a very similar subspecies (race).

The Pied Wagtail is one of the most attractive of our small birds, and is readily identified by both movements and appearance. Though it is never far from water, and delights in frequenting the banks of rivers and streams, it is by no means absent from grassland and seems to like the company of cattle ; it also favours lawns and playing fields. It is an interesting bird to watch, as it darts hither and thither, its long tail constantly moving up and down. —clearly indicating the origin of its names.

The Pied Wagtail's usual call note is short and pleasant ; it is uttered when the bird is rising from the ground. The sound seems shriller if heard from very close at hand. The birds can be heard throughout the year. They are very aggressive when nesting, and will greet any intruder with an abrupt, short call.

The sweet, not far-carrying, song, often uttered from the ground, is at its height in March and April. It can also be heard in September and October. While "digging for victory" in 1941, I was facing a Pied Wagtail singing continuously for half an hour, about three yards away from me. The bird was quite undisturbed by my presence and only flew away when I left.—EDITOR.

The Pied Wagtail is a small black and white bird. The forehead, cheeks and underparts are white ; the crown, breast, mantle and tail are black, the latter with outer feathers of white. The wings have a double wing bar. The thin bill is black, as are the legs. The female is greyer on her back, and less black on her crown and breast. The length is 7 in., the long tail accounting for about half ; the tarsus is 1 in., the wing span 7 to 8 in., and the bird's weight is very small, being only a fraction of an ounce.

The undulating flight of the Pied is typical of the wagtails. After a series of rapid wing beats, it rises and sinks with closed wings in a

Arthur Park

PIED FLYCATCHER. *The male (left) is a handsome little fellow in his black and white plumage, whereas the female (right) looks far more drab*

PIED WAGTAIL—Motacilla alba yarrelli. The most familiar of our wagtails, the Pied or Water-Wagtail, as it is also called—is a resident almost everywhere in the British Isles, except in Shetland, where it is less common and does not usually breed. In the Autumn many of the more northerly birds migrate to the southern counties, and some cross the Channel. Abroad,

long curve ; then there is another series of wing beats, and so on. Larks and finches fly with much the same undulations.

Pied wagtails are gregarious, and outside the breeding season roost, often in hundreds, in some place near water. Their courtship is more elaborate than that of many of our small birds ; one female is chased by several males in a dancing and erratic flight which displays their black throats.

The Pied Wagtail has a variety of nesting sites. The bank of a stream with hanging vegetation is among the most favoured, but a hole in a wall, rock, or building is also used, and sometimes the bird lays even under a clod on ploughland. The nest, built by the hen, of moss, dried leaves, twigs and roots, is lined with hair, feathers and wool. The five or six bluish- or greyish-white eggs, speckled in brown and grey, are laid at the end of April. The hen incubates alone, but her mate sometimes relieves her during the 14 days' sitting. The young are fed by both parents for a fortnight. Two broods are normal, often there are three. Insects of many varieties form the main food.

John Markham

PIED WAGTAIL. This bird's movement is quite typical as it darts about, its tail always bobbing

PIED WHEATEAR—Oenanthe leucomela. A native of east Europe and central Asia, the Pied Wheatear has twice been recorded in the British Isles : in the Isle of Man in 1909, and in the Orkneys in 1916. Its black back distinguishes it from its near relative, the black-throated phase of the Black-eared Wheatear, which it resembles in habits and behaviour. The length is $5\frac{3}{4}$ in., the tarsus 0·9 in., the wing span 7 in.

The Pied Wheatear frequents stony banks, rough hilly country and ground with little vegetation. Its song, described as very variable and imitative, is delivered from some high perch, or in its song flight, from May to July, and is also heard during August.

PIGEON. The terms " pigeon " and " dove " are used loosely, and often interchangeably for members of the family Columbidae (q.v.), of which the following five species appear on the British list : Stock-Dove, Rock-Dove, Wood-Pigeon, Turtle-Dove and Eastern Turtle-Dove. These are all described under their own headings. Also found in Britain are the London Pigeon, which may be semi-domesticated or feral (wild),

and which originated from escaped domestic stock, and the many different " fancy " and " sporting " breeds.

The largest of pigeons found in the wild is the Wood-Pigeon, a common resident and winter visitor. The Stock-Dove, another common resident, is somewhat similar, but smaller. The Turtle-Dove and Eastern Turtle-Dove, two almost identical birds belonging to the genus Streptopelia, are smaller and more slender than other members of the family. The former is a common breeding visitor, whereas the latter has been recorded only twice in this country.

The Rock-Dove has been left until last because it is in rather a special position ; many authorities believe that from it are descended all domesticated pigeons, including the numerous varieties of fancy pigeon, the Racing Pigeon, and the Homing Pigeon ; furthermore, that it is the forbear of the London Pigeon, which is considered to have originated from domesticated stock returned to the feral state.

Darwin was the first to suggest that all varieties of domesticated pigeon could be traced back to the Rock-Dove (Columbia livia) and stated that if any domesticated pigeons were cross-bred without careful selection, distinct features of Columbia livia were to be found in future generations. That there is now any division of opinion on this question is due to the almost infinite variety of colour and form to be found among domesticated pigeons compared with the uniformity in size, form and colour of the Rock-Dove, in which the prevailing colour is bluish-grey with black-barred wings, or, as an occasional variant, a blue chequered pattern. The fact that in the genetics of the Pigeon the colour red is dominant to black or blue, adds to the puzzle.

The domestication of the Rock-Dove appears to have begun in pre-historic times. Darwin gives the earliest known record of the domestic pigeon as 3,000 B.C. in Egypt, but it is reasonably certain that the Dove of the Ark was the Homing Pigeon of its time. From these early beginnings pigeon breeding has for many centuries past been a favourite pursuit in many countries of the world ; outside Europe it has long had its enthusiasts in India, Iran, north Africa, Turkey and the Middle East. It seems therefore not unlikely that at some stage in producing the domesticated pigeon, the Rock-Dove has been crossed with members of other species ; and that in breeding some of the present British varieties, it has been necessary to obtain progenitors from foreign sources.

There are now several hundred distinct breeds of fancy pigeon ; such as the Carrier, Dragoon, Barb, Antwerp, Pouter, Norwich Cropper, Owl, African Owl, Jacobean and

John Markham

PIGEON, *the largest of the British species—*
the Wood-Pigeon or 'Cushat', also called the 'Cushie Doo'

                    For text see pages 424 *and* 585

Tumbler—to name but a few. But interesting though these are, a detailed description of them has no place in a work concerned mainly with wild birds. The Carrier, which has been described as the " King of Pigeons ", must not be confused with such sporting birds as the Racer and the Homer. It was at one time used for carrying both commercial and private messages, but it only had an effective range of about 30 miles. Now, having been bred for show for generations, it has not only lost its homing instinct, but has become too heavy and cumbersome to fly. Moreover, a prize Carrier would now be too valuable to risk on the road.

According to Moore (1735), the English Carrier had been in existence as a recognized breed for many years before his time. It originated from birds imported from Baxora, Persia, and was sometimes called a " Bagadet " or " Bagdad ". Moore adds that, in Turkey, the same breed were called bagatins or couriers. The modern Racing Pigeon, as used in the British Commonwealth and the United States, derives almost entirely from the Belgian bird, which, in its turn, was based upon descendant varieties of the Eastern Carrier, the high-flying Cumulet, the Owl, and the resultant cross, the Smerell. Compared with the poor flying capabilities of the Carrier, long-distance racers can cover some hundreds of miles, the record being held by a former R.A.F. pigeon which homed from Gibraltar to Gillingham, in Kent, a distance of 1,096 miles in 12 days.

London Pigeon. The Rock-Pigeon is distinguished from all others by its white rump ; from the Stock-Dove, by the absence of black on the wing tips ; and from wood-pigeons, by its shorter tail and lack of white on neck and wings. The plumage of the London Pigeon is more variable—there are " blue-chequer," " red-chequer " and " mealy " forms. The blue-chequered plumage of some forms of London Pigeon may also occur as a genuine wild variant in some colonies of Rock-Dove.

The Rock is a resident, breeding on most parts of the *Scottish* and *Irish* coasts, especially in the north and north-west, and in the isles ; and locally in the Isle of Man. Its habitat is mainly confined to the maritime cliffs, although it will feed on cultivated land up to a mile inland ; whereas, the London occurs mainly in built-up areas, some cliffs, occasionally in quarries and on the banks of tidal waters. Most of the colonies of wild pigeons on coasts of *England* and *Wales* are London pigeons, but on some, e.g. Pembrokeshire and Flamborough Head, there appears to be a substantial element of the original wild stock, and even in Scotland and Ireland some semi-domesticated pigeons have found their way into a few wild colonies.

PIGEON'S " MILK ". *See* " Milk " of Birds.

PIGMY CURLEW. Local name for Curlew-Sandpiper (*q.v.*), a passage migrant.

PINE-BUNTING — Emberiza leucocephalos. An extremely rare visitor to Britain which has, in fact, been recorded only twice—once on Fair Isle, Shetland, in 1911, and once in the Orkneys. The bird breeds in east Russia and Siberia, and winters as far south as Kashmir.

In form and plumage it resembles the Yellow Hammer, except that the yellow on head, throat, and upper parts is replaced by white. The female is similar to the female Yellow Hammer, also with white replacing yellow. The length is 6 in., and the wing span 8 in.

In the breeding season, the Pine-Bunting frequents bushy open ground near birch and coniferous forests, and often near rivers and lakes. In Winter it goes about in flocks. The nests and nesting habits, so far as is known, are similar to those of the Yellow Hammer. The four to six eggs are laid from the end of May to July, and are hatched by the hen for an unknown length of time. There are two broods in a season. The food consists of seeds of grasses and mountain plants.

Accounts of the song of the Pine-Bunting do not agree, but observers say the call is very like that of the Yellow Hammer.

PINE GROSBEAK—Pinicola enucleator. A member of the Finch family, the Pine Grosbeak breeds in north Europe, north Africa and north America. It has been seen in the wild only four times in the British Isles. It is, however, often found in captivity. It looks very like a large common Crossbill in colouring and shape, but the beak is typically finch-like. The mantle and breast are rose-pink, shading darker towards

PIGEON. *Word must have gone out among London's pigeons that our Editor was to pay them a visit*

the wings, which have a double white wing-bar ; the underparts are grey, and the tail rather long and dark. The female's plumage is bronze-coloured instead of rose-pink. The length is 8 in., and the tarsus 0·9 in. The wing span is about 10 in., and the weight 2 oz.

The behaviour, flight and breeding habits of the Pine Grosbeak largely resemble those of the Crossbill. Its favourite trees are conifers, birches and junipers, in which it spends its time hopping from branch to branch. It is extraordinarily tame. The song is described as a mixture of harsh and musical calls.

The nest, built by the hen, is composed of twigs of birch and pine, and lined with roots, grass and moss. Late in May or June, four eggs, deep green blotched in brownish-purple, are laid. Both male and female rear the young.

The Pine Grosbeak feeds chiefly on wild berries and seeds, but some insects are also taken. It is often called the " Pinefinch ".

PINICOLA. Genus of the family *Fringillidae* of the order *Passeriformes*. It contains only one species, the Pine Grosbeak (*q.v.*).

PINK-FOOTED GOOSE—Anser arvensis brachyrhynchus. During recent years the Pink-footed Goose has greatly increased in the British Isles, and it is now probably the most abundant, as well as the best known, of our wild geese. It is so like a smaller edition of the Bean-Goose that for a long time the two birds were confused. Recent investigation, however, has thrown much light on the history of the Pink-footed, and it is now established as the subspecies of the Bean-Goose, breeding in Iceland, Spitzbergen and parts of Greenland.

Two expeditions, one in 1951 and another in 1953, were made by a party of British ornitho-logists to study the habits of the Pink-footed Goose. They penetrated far into the centre of Iceland and, amid the mountains, glaciers and ice-caps, found a plateau of rich Arctic vegetation which was the breeding place of thousands of these birds.

A winter visitor to Great Britain, the Pink-footed Goose chiefly favours the eastern coasts, but also visits the Severn Valley, Solway Firth and some other parts. It is rarer in the west, in Ireland, and in the north and north-west of Scotland. The birds begin to arrive in September, and all that are coming are here by the end of October. They leave in March and April.

As well as by its smaller size, the Pink-footed can be distinguished from the Bean-Goose by its brownish-grey plumage, the neck and head being in dark contrast to the body. The underparts are grey shading to white, the fore-wing is conspicuously grey, and the rump paler. The under tail coverts are white, and the white tail has a broad dark band. The short bill, finer than that of the Bean-Goose, is black, with a pink band. The legs are pink, as the name indicates ; no other grey goose has pink legs and bill. The length is 2 ft. to 2 ft. 6 in., the tarsus is 2·8 in. The wing span is between 3 ft. and 3 ft. 6 in., and the average weight 6½ lb.

The habits and behaviour of the Pink-footed Goose are similar to those of other grey geese. It is highly gregarious. The large skeins fly in lines or in V-formation, the sound of their continuous calling carrying a great distance. They roost chiefly on the sandbanks of coasts and estuaries ; by day they feed in meadows, fields and arable land.

The Pink-foot has a variety of high-pitched calls. The alarm note is a short, high squeak, and the bird has the typical angry hiss of all geese.

The spring display closely resembles that of the Grey Lag-Goose.

The ledges of cliffs and the rocky sides of desolate Arctic valleys are the favourite sites of the large breeding colonies. The nest is a hollow in the ground, well lined with grasses, moss and Arctic plants, mixed together with down and earth. The four or five eggs, dull white in colour, are usually laid in mid-June. Incubation by the female alone begins when the clutch is complete ; the gander keeps

Eric Hosking

PINK-FOOTED GOOSE. *This bird looks exactly like a smaller edition of the Bean-Goose, and, as a result, the two geese have often been confused*

Erica

PINTAIL. Also called " Sea-Pheasant," the distinctive Pintail is one of the most widely distributed ducks in the world, though it breeds somewhat locally in the British Isles

guard near by. The incubation period is 25–28 days. Both parents tend and rear the goslings, which are very active, leaving the nest for the water as soon as they are dry. The single brood are fully fledged in about two months.

Arctic plants are the main food of the Pink-footed Goose at its breeding places ; on migration, and in Winter, it feeds on grain picked up on the stubble fields, potatoes and various plants. *See also* Goose.

PINTADO PETREL. *See* Cape Sea-Pigeon.

PINTAIL—Anas acuta. Although breeding regularly, if somewhat locally, in several counties of Scotland, the Orkney and Shetland Islands, and occasionally in England, this sur-face-feeding duck is mainly a winter visitor and passage migrant. It also breeds in some Irish counties. The Pintail is one of the most widely distributed ducks, and is found in Europe, Asia, many parts of Africa and north America.

It is easily identified, especially in flight, by its long tail feathers. Its neck is long and slender, and its wings long, narrow and pointed. The general colour is grey, but the head, throat and back of the neck are dark chocolate brown. The breast and underparts are white, and a white stripe runs up the side of the neck to the nape. The back and sides are grey, with fine mottlings. The speculum (*q.v.*), less prominent than in some other ducks, is bronze-green, tinged with dull pink ; behind it is a white bar, in front a brownish one. The under tail coverts are black, contrasting with some yellowish patches below.

The duck is not unlike the female Mallard in plumage, but has a more slender body and a pointed tail. Her brownish speculum is even

less prominent than that of the drake. The bill and legs are grey. The length, including the tail feathers, is 25–29 in. ; without them, it is 21–23 in. The tarsus is $1\frac{3}{4}$ in., the wing span about 18–24 in., and the weight $1\frac{1}{2}$ lb.

The Pintail keeps company with many other species of surface-feeding ducks, especially the Wigeon. In inland waters, it is not abundant and is usually seen singly, in pairs, or in small parties ; at sea large numbers collect, and flocks of as many as 1,100 have been recorded.

Its flight resembles that of the Wigeon, but is even more rapid, and the quickly beating wings produce a humming sound. The Pintail has grace and elegance on both land and water, for it swims with buoyancy and walks on the ground with ease. It will " upend ", but it does not dive readily unless wounded.

The courtship display of the Pintail is very similar to the Mallards. A characteristic pur-suit flight is also recorded. Usually a silent bird, the Pintail is not heard except in the breeding season. The drake has then a low musical croak ; the duck a low quack.

Islands in lakes and woodland, dunes and cultivated country near lakes are the favourite nesting haunts of pintails. The nest, a mere hollow on dry land, is lined with down. In Scotland, seven to nine eggs, varying in colour from yellowish-green to cream, are laid in May. On completion of the clutch, the duck hatches them alone for 23 days, the drake keeping guard near by. The chicks, clad in brownish down, are tended by both parents for five to seven weeks. One brood is reared in a season.

Usually described as nocturnal, the Pintail often feeds by day. Its main diet is vegetable.

Arthur Christiansen

PLATALEA. *Only the Spoonbill, with its unique beak, represents this genus in the British Isles*

PIPIT. Genus of small ground birds forming, with the wagtails, the family *Motacillidae* (*q.v.*). Pipits (the name is ultimately derived from the imitative *popio*, " to chirrup "), are relatively small, brown-streaked birds, with white or whitish outer tail feathers and long hind claws. Less slender than the wagtails, they are otherwise very similar.

The following species are on the British list : Meadow-Pipit ; Richard's Pipit ; Tawny Pipit ; Tree-Pipit ; Petchora Pipit ; Red-throated Pipit ; Rock-Pipit ; Water-Pipit ; American Pipit—each is fully described under its own heading. In addition, several subspecies have appeared in Britain as irregular visitors.

PIT-SPARROW. Alternative name for Reed-Bunting (*q.v.*), a common resident.

PLATALEA. Genus of the family *Plataleidae* of the order *Ardeiformes*. One species, the Spoonbill (*q.v.*), is a fairly regular visitor to East Anglia (and, to a lesser extent, to other parts of the east and south coasts) on migration.

PLATALEIDAE. Family of the order *Ardeiformes*. Its members are distributed throughout the globe. There are two genera on the British list, *Platalea* and *Plegadis*, containing the Spoonbill and the Glossy Ibis (*qq.v.*).

PLAUTUS. Genus of marine birds of the family *Alcidae* of the order *Charadriiformes*. It contains the Little Auk (*q.v.*), which is mainly distributed over the Arctic region, from Greenland east to Franz Josef Land. This bird is an irregular winter visitor to the British Isles.

PLAY. *See* Behaviour, Display.

PLECTROPHENAX. Genus of the family *Fringillidae* of the order *Passeriformes*. Only one species, the Snow-Bunting (*q.v.*), occurs in the British Isles, mainly as a winter visitor, although a few do breed in parts of Scotland.

PLEGADIS. Genus of the family *Plataleidae* of the order *Ardeiformes*. Its members are mainly distributed over southern Europe, Asia, Africa, Australasia and north America. One species of this genus, the Glossy Ibis (*q.v.*), is an irregular autumn visitor to England.

PLOVER. Name given to numerous, widely distributed, species of small wading birds belonging to several genera of the family *Charadriidae* (Gr. *Kharadrios*, " water-bird ").

Many reasons have been advanced to account for the name plover, which is a corruption of the old French *plovier* (" to rain "). One suggestion is that these birds foretell rain by their restlessness ; another, that they sing in the rain ; and yet a third " authority " suggests that it is because some kinds of plover have markings like raindrops on their upper plumage. Whatever the explanation, there is no doubt that a connection is often thought to exist between plovers and rain. A local name for the Golden Plover is " rain-bird ".

The following species belonging to the genus *Charadrius* (*q.v.*) appear on the British list : Ringed Plover ; Little Ringed Plover ; Kentish Plover ; Killdeer Plover ; Caspian Plover ; Grey Plover ; Golden Plover ; American Golden Plover ; Dotterel. In addition, there are several subspecies. The Sociable Plover and Lapwing each belong to a separate genus of their own, as does the Turnstone, which lies somewhere between the true plovers and the sandpipers. All these species are fully described under their own headings.

PLOVERSPAGE. *See* Stonehatch.

PLUMAGE. Collective term for the covering of feathers with which a bird is clothed. The plumage of an adult bird may be divided into three main groups : body, wing (*q.v.*), and tail feathers. These groups may be further subdivided according to the position and function of the feathers composing them (*see* Plate f. p.1). There are also three main classes of feather (*q.v.*): contour, down and *filoplumes*. In reaching maturity a bird may pass through several distinct phases of plumage.

In general, the nestling begins life with one or two coats of small immature feathers (or " down "), known as *nestling plumage* or nestling down. This is succeeded, usually after about 10–14 days but sometimes not for many months, by the first plumage of true feathers, called *juvenile plumage*. This is worn until about the first autumn moult (*q.v.*) of the parents, or sometimes to the following Summer, when the young bird acquires its *adult (or mature) plumage*. This is thereafter renewed once or twice a year, but, apart from possible seasonal changes (*see* below) and deterioration due to old age, it remains substantially the same year after year. This is the general picture, but there are many individual variations from it.

Although most birds when hatched have at least a scant covering of down on the top of the head and back, some, e.g. kingfishers and swifts, sparrows and crows, are at first completely naked. Young thrushes have a little down, but not much ; young larks and wagtails still more, but never fully developed, except in a few restricted areas. So instead of every contour feather being preceded by a down feather, as in nidifugous (*q.v.*) birds, only a few have these fore-runners. Thus, a row of down feathers occurs over each eye, and a few round the back of the head, and there are rows of downy tufts over the " shoulder blades " and down the spine, but the under surface of nidiculous (*q.v.*) birds is always bare.

Most modern birds have only one plumage of nestling down, but some species have two distinct and successive " generations " of nestling plumage ; for example, penguins, the Tawny Owl and some primitive species of geese. In penguins, the first barely covers the body, and resembles hair rather than feathers, whereas, the second is longer and has a peculiarly " woolly " texture. The purpose of the downy feathers may be to restrict the power of flight, which, if acquired too early, would be dangerous to some species. Sometimes the change from down to true feathers is quite rapid ; the majority of passerines are entirely covered with feathers within a week to ten days, and within a further

ten days to a fortnight are able to fly. On the other hand, the change may be very gradual, as with game birds, where the head and neck, the middle of the breast and lower part of the back retain their down until the rest of the body has been clothed with feathers. Some species may remain nestlings for many months ; thus the King Penguin remains in the downy stage for as long as twelve months ; the Albatross for nearly as long ; and the Secretary-Bird does not leave its nest until six months old.

The juvenile dress worn from fledging to the first Autumn may resemble the mature dress of either parent or neither. Where the adult plumage of the two sexes differs, the juvenile usually resembles the female, if only approximately, but there are instances, not among British birds, where the juvenile is like the male. Where the adults of both sexes are alike, the plumage of the juveniles may differ from that of their parents (e.g. starlings, gulls, gannets, coots, water-rails, goshawks) ; be similar to that of the parents, but less brilliant (crows, rooks, kingfishers), and in a few cases be brighter than that of the parents, as with some warblers. In the second case, where both parents have a second moult, or brightening up, in the Spring, the plumage of the juveniles usually resembles the winter plumage of the adults, but sometimes it is like the summer plumage (e.g. Ptarmigan).

Although the assumption of the full characteristic plumage is a sign of maturity, some gulls take at least three years, and some species as many as five, to attain their full dress, reaching it by almost insensible changes. Similarly, birds of prey take several years to reach maturity. After reaching maturity, many species have two very distinct liveries each year, often called, respectively, winter and summer plumage —although nuptial dress is a better name for the latter, because it is assumed just before, and

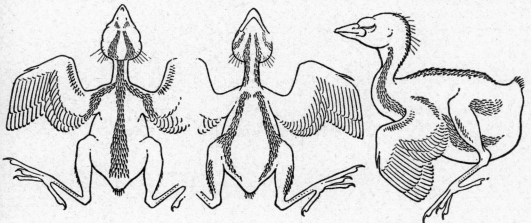

PLUMAGE. *Feathers grow along well-defined paths, the feather-tracts. These can be seen in our diagrams of a nestling sparrow, showing (left) the bird's back, (centre) its front, and (right) the side view*

worn during, the breeding season. When it occurs, it is usually adopted by both sexes (e.g. plovers, dunlins, knots, guillemots and auks), although in most cases, the nuptial dress of the male is the more brilliant of the two. In some species (e.g. Ruff, Brambling, Pied Flycatcher and Wheatear) only the male acquires this distinctive dress ; with many species (e.g. swans, geese, kingfishers, birds of prey), there is no special change. All species renew their plumage at least once a year, at the autumn moult (*q.v.*), and some, as indicated, moult twice a year (*see* Moult). Others, again, may freshen their feathers in the Spring by shedding the tips of the barbs (*see* Moult).

Plumage serves many purposes. It keeps a bird warm and provides the flight mechanism of flying birds (*see* Flight and Wing) ; often it serves for camouflage, in attack or defence (*see* Camouflage ; Pattern and Colour). The brilliant plumage of some males serves either to attract females or to warn off interlopers. In some instances plumage enables the sexes to tell one another apart (even the presence of a moustachial streak may be sufficient indication) and to recognize their own species (*see* Recognition), and, although not necessarily intended by Nature, it helps bird watchers to identify the various species (*see* Identification).

PLUMULE. Feather having the barbs soft and free from one another, for example, the down feathers. *See* Feather.

POCHARD — Aythya ferina. A British resident of restricted distribution and decreasing numbers, the Pochard breeds in several northern and eastern counties of England, in most counties of Scotland except the north-west, and sparingly in a few Irish counties. It is probably better known as a winter visitor, for many will congregate on inland waters. This duck is rarely seen at sea except during stormy weather. Abroad, it occurs in most countries of Europe, northern Asia and also in the north-west of Africa.

The handsome drake is easily recognized by his rich chestnut head and neck. He is distinguished from the male of the Red-Crested Pochard (red bill, white on wing) by his black bill with pale blue band, grey wing band and absence of white on

wings, black breast and grey vermiculated back and flanks. His underparts are whitish, and the upper and under tail coverts are black.

The less colourful duck is dressed in various shades of brownish grey, paler underneath, and has whitish cheeks and throat. The speculum is grey, and does not show very distinctly against the grey wings ; it is similar in the duck, but darker. The bill is greyish-blue, and the legs grey. The length is 1 ft. 6 in., and the wing span is about the same ; the tarsus is 1½ in., and the weight 2 lb.

The Pochard is found in company with other ducks, especially the Tufted Duck. An excellent swimmer and diver, it has a curious habit of splashing the water about with its wings as it slips down. Its manner of diving varies with the depth of the water ; it prefers shallow water, and 3 ft. is the usual depth of its dive, although 8 ft. has been recorded ; the longest recorded dive lasted 30 seconds.

As is common among diving ducks, the Pochard's manner of rising from the surface is very laboured, and it has to patter along for some distance before getting clear. It has a straight and rapid flight, its short wings making a rustling sound. It walks awkwardly.

The spring courtship takes place on the water. Several drakes display round one duck, dipping their bills, raising and expanding their necks, and twisting their heads round.

The Pochard spends most of the day resting on the water, and feeds in the morning and evening (also to some extent at night). It is on the whole a silent bird, and the voices of both drake and duck are heard only in the breeding season. The drake has a moaning wheeze, and the duck a harsh croak.

Pochards nest on such ponds and lakes— including those in city and town parks—as

Arthur Christiansen

POCHARD. *Although decreasing as a resident, this diving duck still breeds in some northern and eastern English counties and parts of Scotland*

PODICEPS. Head of the Great Crested Grebe—probably the most beautiful member of its genus

afford plenty of cover of reeds, flags and rushes. Unlike many ducks nests, the nest is built very near water, and often actually in it. It is a bulky structure, especially if above the water, made of dead flags, reeds and rushes ; the amount of down with which it is lined varies considerably. Six to eleven—frequently more —large greenish-grey eggs, with very little gloss, are laid in late April and May. The duck hatches these alone, rarely leaving the nest, for 24–26 days. The young, clad in brownish down, leave the nest immediately they are hatched out. They are tended and fed by the duck ; the drake takes no part in the parental duties. The young fly in seven or eight weeks ; and attain adult plumage after a year.

The Pochard feeds almost exclusively on marine plants dragged up from the bottom of lake or pond, but some molluscs and water insects are also eaten. *See also* Red-crested Pochard ; White-eyed Pochard.

PODICEPS. Only European genus of the family *Podicipidae*, which is the only family in the order *Podicipidiformes*, containing the grebes (*q.v.*). *Podiceps* contains about 15 species, distributed over much of the globe, mainly on fresh water. The following five species are on the British list : the Great Crested Grebe, Red-necked Grebe, Slavonian Grebe, Black-necked Grebe, and Little Grebe. All are described under their own names.

POLYSTICTA. Genus of ducks of the family *Anatidae* of the order *Anseriformes*. It contains only one species, Steller's Eider (*q.v.*), mainly distributed over the Arctic regions of the Northern Hemisphere. This bird has been recorded four times in the British Isles.

POMARINE JAEGER. American name for Pomatorhine Skua (*q.v.*), a winter visitor.

POMATORHINE SKUA—Stercorarius pomarinus. Known in the British Isles as only an unusual winter visitor and spring and autumn passage migrant, this Skua is an inhabitant of the Arctic regions. It breeds in the northern countries of Europe, Asia, north America and Greenland, and winters chiefly in Africa, Australia and south America. British observers see it as a rule far out to sea off the east and south coasts of England, but after a storm it may occasionally occur even inland.

Midway in size between the Arctic and Great Skua, the Pomatorhine differs from the others in its characteristic, curiously shaped tail. The broad central feathers with rounded tips project some inches beyond the rest, and are twisted so that they appear almost at right angles to the others. This bird is larger and more stoutly built than the Arctic Skua, but has much the same white and brown appearance as its relations. There is a dark and a light phase (*q.v.*), the birds of the latter being more numerous. Like the Great Skua, the adult Pomatorhine has a light wing patch, but it is smaller and less conspicuous. The slightly hooked bill is yellowish-brown, with a black tip. The legs are black. The unique tail is less well developed in the juvenile, which is very similar to the young of other skuas. The length of the Pomatorhine Skua is 20 in., the projecting tail feathers accounting for 2 or 3 in. The tarsus is 2 in., the wing span about 3 ft., and the weight 1 lb.

In general the habits and behaviour of the Pomatorhine Skua are similar to those of the Arctic Skua. Although it is a heavier bird, its flight has great speed and agility. It has the same piratical mode of life—attacking other sea-birds and forcing them to disgorge their prey—and is likewise a scavenger.

The calls of the Pomatorhine Skua vary between harsh and squeaky notes ; sometimes it whistles, and occasionally it utters a two-syllabic call similar to the Herring-Gull's. A low raucous "conversation" is heard from a crowd of these birds feeding together.

The Pomatorhine breeds in the swampy tundra of the Arctic. The nests, which are mere depressions among the moss, are widely scattered. Two olive-brown eggs, blotched and spotted in black and brown, are laid late in June or early July. Both male and female incubate for an unknown period ; little information is available regarding the tending of the one brood.

At its breeding grounds ; the Pomatorhine Skua feeds largely on lemmings and the eggs of young birds ; at sea, on fish, ships' refuse, and the food it forces other birds to disgorge. Its American name (*see adjoining column*) is derived from the German word for hunter (*Jaeger*).

BIRD NUMBERS—A Survey of Populations

JAMES FISHER, M.A., F.L.S.

The author, from a wealth of practical experience, describes how the task of conducting a census of birds is accomplished, gives figures for various species, and discusses the factors controlling population changes. A typical distribution map is shown opposite

POPULATION. Although the human race has been making censuses of its own number since Biblical times, it has become interested in enumerating wild animals only in the last 200 years, and in doing so with any plan and accuracy only in the last 50 years. Such records as were previously kept the world over were usually of the annual number of creatures killed for sport or food, and not of the population from which this number was obtained. The earliest observations on bird population, and the most recent studies at Oxford recounted by David Lack, Director of the Edward Grey Institute of Field Ornithology, in his *The Natural Regulation of Animal Numbers* (1954), have this in common: they have no economic, but only a scientific, value that extends into the most fundamental realms of the study of evolution, of natural selection and of survival.

In the 18th century inquiring naturalists, such as Thomas Pennant, occasionally noted the numbers of animals that they saw, but only when they considered such numbers exceptional. The first bird census of any value was probably a very simple observation by Gilbert White, who in 1778 reported that he constantly found from season to season that eight pairs of swifts nested in the village of Selborne. In 1896 Hudson found six pairs of swifts in Selborne, and helped to confirm the well-known stability of the numbers of this British summer visitor.

The first census of the members of a local *community* of birds was published in 1811 by the American, Alexander Wilson, who counted 51 pairs of breeding birds on 8 acres. Since the observations of these pioneers, bird census work has preserved their two approaches ; first, the study of a single species, and its enumeration throughout its range, or part of its range ; and,

secondly, the study of an area, and the enumeration of all the species in it.

Individual Species. The pioneer censuses of individual species were largely confined to social birds which nest in colonies. Of some of these species, all the colonies in a county, country, or even in the world can be found, and have been found ; so that a complete census with a considerable degree of accuracy has been made of the occupied nests in a season.

One of the first to realize the possibility of a census of this sort was probably J. H. Gurney, whose book, *The Gannet,* was published in 1913. Gurney believed that he knew of all the world's colonies of the North Atlantic Gannet at that time and suggested that in 1912 the species occupied about 55,000 nests. In fact, he had overlooked a few colonies, and subsequent investigations showed that the number of nests at that time may have been nearer 65,000. Since Gurney's time the Gannet census has been repeated several times. In 1935 V. C. Wynne-Edwards, R. M. Lockley and H. M. Salmon arrived at a figure of about 78,000 nests, and in 1939 H. G. Vevers and the writer obtained a result approximating to 83,000. In 1949 colonies were investigated again, and evidence collected that the present population is 100,000 nests or more. The increase has certainly been due largely to human protection. The number of colonies occupied in the North Atlantic in 1949 was 29.

Many similar sea-bird censuses have been made. It is possible to guess that the world population of the Fulmar, which a century ago Darwin believed to be the most numerous bird in the world, may not be more than 2 million. The Great Shearwater of Tristan da Cunha, in the South Atlantic, which nests in no other archipelago, may have had between 2 million

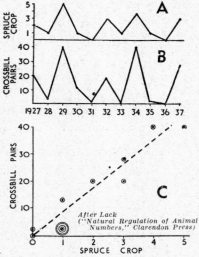

POPULATION. Fig. I : Relation between the population density of the Crossbill and the spruce cone crop in the years 1927 to 1937. Fig. 1a, relative abundance of cones, plotted to an arbitrary scale. Fig. 1b, pairs of crossbills per 120 km. (note the corresponding rise and fall). Fig. 1c, shows Crossbill pairs plotted against corresponding spruce crop (note the almost linear relationship)

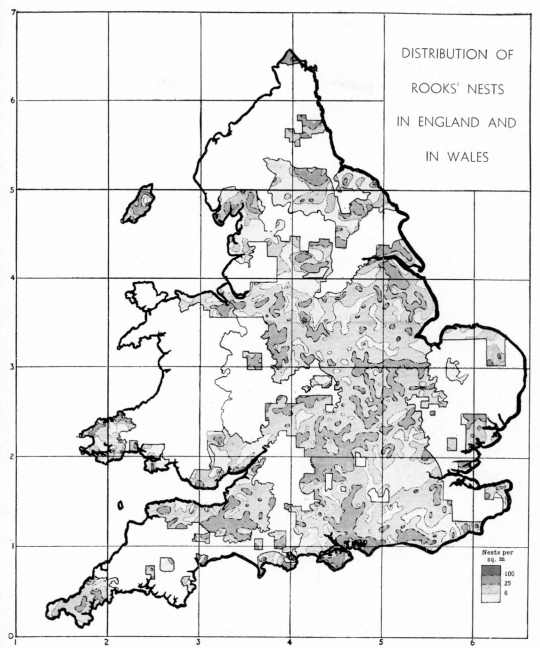

DISTRIBUTION OF
ROOKS' NESTS
IN ENGLAND AND
IN WALES

Nests per
sq. m.
100
25
6

The above map, drawn by R. G. Newton, is indicative of the painstaking work underlying the study of bird numbers. It shows the density of rooks' nests in certain areas of England and Wales; and it is based on a survey undertaken by the British Trust for Ornithology in 1944-46, from which the figures were calculated by James Fisher and R. G. Newton. In England the average density was about 18, in Wales and Monmouth about 12 nests to the square mile. South of the Scottish Border only two areas had densities of over 100 nests to the square mile, though such areas are found in all east Highland coastal counties of Scotland

and 2½ million nests in 1949–50. The Guanay Cormorant of the Guano Islands off western south America may number between 4½ million and 6 million birds. Of Antipodean gannets nesting in New Zealand, there are probably over 40,000 individuals, but the population of the same species nesting in Australia is unknown. It was suggested in 1932 that the world population of the American White Pelican, which nests on inland waters, was about 30,000. The Cahow, the rare petrel of Bermuda, long ago thought to be extinct, may have a population of about 100 adult birds. Abbott's Booby of Christmas Island in the Indian Ocean (it nests nowhere else) had 500–750 nests in 1941.

One of the early research results of the British Trust for Ornithology (*q.v.*) was a census of an inland colonial species whose colonies could be easily discovered—indeed, were very well known —the Heron. In 1928 the magazine *British Birds* had invited E. M. Nicholson to organize the discovery and nest census of every heronry in England and Wales. From the formation of the Trust in 1933 an annual recount of at least a substantial part of the Heron colonies was conducted until the Second World War by Nicholson, and subsequently by W. B. Alexander and others. The " normal " population of herons' nests in " good " years in England and Wales was about 4,000, but it was discovered that it may fall after hard Winters to under 3,000, or sometimes to little over 2,000.

Much earlier, attention had been given to counting another inland colonial nester of the British Isles : the Rook, Britain's most common large passerine bird. A complete census of the rookeries of a British county was attempted as long ago as 1875 in Caithness, and since then rookery censuses have been conducted with increasing accuracy over an increasing area. All culminated in the wartime survey organized by the writer, in which rookery nest counts were made over two-thirds of the area of England, Wales and Scotland. Nearly one million nests were counted. *See* map facing page 432.

The present population of rooks in England and Wales is about two million individuals.

If a bird is conspicuous, or always nests in accessible places like lakes, it does not have to be colonial to be counted. Successful censuses have been taken of several conspicuous birds. In 1934 there was an almost complete census of the White Stork in Europe and north Africa ; and the Great Crested Grebe was found to be occupying about 1,240 nests in England, Wales and Scotland in 1931, when T. H. Harrisson and P. A. D. Hollom organized a census. If a bird is rare, it can be counted more easily than if it is common. The Cahow of Bermuda has already been mentioned ; the Condor of California, the Ivory-billed Woodpecker of Louisiana, Florida and Cuba, the Kite in Wales, and many birds living uniquely on small islands are other examples.

Census by Relative Numbers. The technique of assessing the population of birds in an area is based on a count of the number of breeding pairs of all the different species. For a breeding-season census the standard of measurement is usually the number of adult breeding birds per 100 acres. The figure may run from nil (in deserts) to as many as 1,700 (in gardens, at wood edges, certain kinds of well-planted parkland and in tropical grassland). There are many habitats, besides desert, with less than one bird per acre. Seldom are there more than 30 birds to 100 acres on the most lush Arctic tundra, and not often as many in pure mountain pinewoods. Heathland, moorland and virgin temperate forest scarcely ever support a bird to an acre.

Population becomes high where one habitat abuts on another. A wood edge will add many

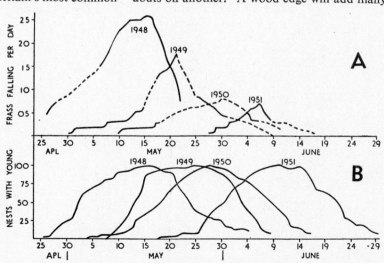

After John Gibb from Lack's "Natural Regulation of Animal Numbers", Clarendon Press

POPULATION. *Fig. 2 : Relation between abundance of food, determined by caterpillar droppings (o frass) per day and nests of great and blue tits in the same area. (Broken lines show incomplete frass records.) Greatest number of nests in any one year shown as 100, other figures scaled down. Note correspondence between peak number of nests and peak in the food supply*

species to the list of birds at the wood centre. Most fairly mixed woodland—even coniferous—can raise 200 birds to the 100 acres, and agricultural land between 200 and 400 ; mixed deciduous woodland with plenty of rides and fringes, or a mixture of deciduous and coniferous woodland, can support between 300 and 600 birds to the 100 acres and an orchard or any well-planted park or garden can often raise 700. The record density comes from City Park in California, where Miss M. T. Cooke records that in one of the five years of study the density in the 40-acre study area reached just over 2,000 adults per 100 acres.

Populations of British Species. From a study of censuses of individual species and of different habitats, generalised approximate figures can be obtained for the density of birds over large areas, and of the share of this population between different species. In 1932, E. M. Nicholson suggested a figure for the total land bird population of England and Wales in May, based on this kind of analysis. Subsequent work on the density of different British habitats has led to no serious modification of his estimate.

At least 162 species of inland birds have nested in England and Wales ; but about 97½ per cent. of the May breeding population of 60 million individuals is accounted for by the 30 commonest species, and 10 per cent. of the 162 species account for over 90 per cent. of the population. The estimate of the total bird population of England and Wales at 60 million is only approximate, and the fluctuation between one season and another is considerable.

It is probable that in this total two species alone, the Chaffinch and the Blackbird, number over 10 million individuals each. Probably the British breeding starlings and robins come next, with about 7 million ; House-Sparrow, Hedge-Sparrow, Song-Thrush and Meadow-Pipit with about 3 million ; Rook, by direct count of a very large sample of rookeries, a little over 2 million ; Yellow Hammer, Wren, White-throat, Willow-Warbler and Wood-Pigeon at between 1 million and 1½ million.

About 16 species probably have over 100,000 but under one million breeding individuals in England and Wales in May ; the most abundant of these are probably Jackdaw, Skylark, Blue Tit, Swallow, House-Martin and Linnet. Figures in this category must be tentative, and in the next lower category even more so : there are probably 34 species in the latter category (with over 10,000 but under 100,000 individuals) ; and probably 41 species in the next (with over 1,000 and under 10,000). Of the species with over 100 and under 1,000 individuals, there are, it is believed, 22 ; one of these, the Peregrine Falcon, has been directly counted by mapping all eyries, and in the period 1947-49 the breeding birds in occupation of those in England and Wales were about 320.

Coming to the rare (probably about nine) species with under 100 individuals but over ten, some, like the Kite, Bearded Tit, Montagu's Harrier and Quail, have excited so much interest that attempts have been made to enumerate them by direct counting, though undoubtedly breeding records of all of them must be fairly often overlooked. There are several species, of which in England and Wales there is at least one breeding pair but not often more than five, and 20 more which have bred intermittently and irregularly in the last 50 years.

It is not possible seriously to extend the results of sample densities to approach a figure of the total number of birds in the world ; but it seems clear that it must be something of the order of 100,000 million. This population is distributed over 8,600 species.

Censuses and Evolution. Sea-birds, which are comparatively easy to count (though not so easy to count as was at first thought by ornithologists) have provided material for examining the problems of relationship between bird numbers and food supply.

For instance, it seems probable that the Gannet's numbers were, towards the end of the last century, a little over half of what they are in the North Atlantic today, and that this was due to the depredations of Man. Increase of the Gannet has been steady, and there is no evidence that it is yet even straining the existing food supply, far less that it is dependent on any change in food supply. On the other hand, the remarkable increase of the Fulmar during the last 200 years is probably due to a change in the food supply ; whaling in the North Atlantic and neighbouring parts of the Arctic long provided much waste blubber for the birds, and, when it ceased, it was followed by the development of trawling, which provides a continuous supply of fish offal. Thus the Fulmar's spread may be dependent upon Man.

To turn to a quite different example : the research team at the Edward Grey Institute at Oxford have for many years studied the population of tits in local woodland. By providing the birds with nesting boxes (*q.v.*), they have been able to remove any limitations on population due to shortage of nesting-site (limitations which can be quite considerable in young woodland). Moreover, nesting tits are easily counted. They live in, or primarily in, nesting boxes when these are provided, and it is simple to determine, without undue disturbance, their output of eggs and young. To link these figures with food supply has been the task of the Oxford researchers, who have been able to correlate the fortunes of the tits with the annual crop of defoliating caterpillars in the woodlands (*see* illustration in page 433).

Results have shown conclusively that the reproductive output of tits is closely linked with this food supply, and that the number of eggs they lay is closely adapted by natural selection to the caterpillar crop likely to be ready at the time when the eggs hatch. By these population studies Lack, his colleagues Hartley and Gibb, and others have been able to show that the view that the reproductive rate of birds is adapted to mortality is mistaken, and that it is in fact adapted in most circumstances to food supply. By population studies they have discovered that food shortage is probably the chief factor in limiting the numbers of many animals. This may not, however, always be the case, for some population studies of game-birds in the U.S.A. have shown that their numbers may to a large extent be controlled by their predators, and that Man is the predator who can most easily control the numbers of his prey.

Cyclic Changes. Bird population studies are beginning to be of primary importance in the study of those special changes in animal populations which are known as cycles ; that is, the changes which take place with a regularity which cannot be overlooked. Especially is this true of game-bird studies. In Europe, for instance, the numbers of the Willow-Grouse fluctuate with marked regularity in a four-year cycle. In Britain the numbers of Red Grouse also fluctuate, though with less regularity, the period of their cycle (if cycle it be) being on an average about 5·3 years. In north America the grouse cycles may be about 10 years for at least four species ; and the Bob-white Quail may have the same sort of cycle. Cycles of a sort have also been described in Europe for partridges and Woodcock.

Whether these cycles depend on food supply, on weather, on the see-saw of balance between the birds and other animals which prey upon them, or on a combination of some or all of these factors, is as yet by no means certain. There may be other factors involved, such as disease and the aggressive nature of the birds' own behaviour in the breeding season, which may limit their reproduction when their population is high. It is possible that weather conditions (in which cycles have been often observed and described) may act as a kind of "governor" to cycles fundamentally due to quite different causes. The reader is referred to discussions on cycles in Elton (1942), Fisher (1954), Lack (1954), and G. R. Williams (1954).

Population studies are of first importance to understand the evolution (*q.v.*) of birds and of their status in the animal communities to which

Maslowski & Goodpaster

PORZANA. *The Sora Rail, or Carolina Crake, is among the American representatives of this genus*

they belong. These studies are also proving of primary importance in the question of bird protection (*q.v.*). Indeed, in the world of today, where Man's activities extend to every corner, the preservation of our wild life, including its bird element, which is of such importance to most of us, depends fundamentally on our understanding of the principles governing the changes in animal populations.

> *Consult :* Voles, Mice and Lemmings, C. Elton (Clarendon Press), 1942 ; A History of Birds, J. Fisher (Hutchinson), 1954 ; Measurement of Bird Populations, S. C. Kendeigh, *Ecological Monographs*, 14, 1944 ; The Natural Regulation of Animal Numbers, D. Lack (Clarendon Press), 1954.

PORZANA. Genus of the family *Rallidae* of the order *Ralliformes*. It contains a number of species, found in all parts of the world. The four on the British list—the Spotted Crake, Baillon's Crake, Little Crake and Sora Rail— are described under their own names.

POWDER-DOWN. Matted feathers so friable that they continually disintegrate into a fine powder resembling fuller's earth. Herons possess conspicuous powder down forming large patches over the breasts and thighs. It is found also in many other birds, notably parrots and cockatoos ; the bloom covering the beak and face of the African Parrot and the face and plumage of cockatoos is due to this powder. Its actual significance is not known.

PRATINCOLE. Genus of birds (*Glareola*) related to coursers, and resembling terns in appearance. Two species are included in the British list : Collared Pratincole and Black-winged Pratincole—both fully described under their own headings.

The former is an irregular visitor, chiefly from May to August, and the latter a straggler that has been recorded in England only eight times, and only once each in Scotland and in Ireland.

PREEN-GLAND. A gland possessed by many species, but particularly well developed in aquatic and sea-birds. It secretes an oily substance, the purpose of which is not understood, although many theories have been advanced as to its possible function. At one time it was widely believed that the preen-gland performed the same service in birds as the glands at the roots of the hair in mammals, whose secretion helps to keep the fur sleek and

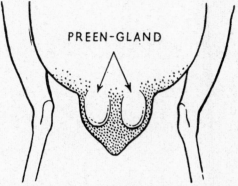

PREEN-GLAND

PREEN-GLAND. *The purpose of this gland, also known as the Oil Gland, is not yet fully known*

in good condition—no corresponding gland exists at the base of birds' feathers. It was thought that, during preening (hence the name), the bird reached back, extracted the drops of oil from the gland with its beak, and spread them over the feathers. But not only is it quite impossible, because of their anatomical structure, for some species to behave in this way, but birds that do not possess a preen-gland keep their feathers in as good a condition as those that do. Experimental removal of the gland has been shown to have no effect on the feathers, or on the health of the bird.

It has also been suggested that as the oil has a characteristic scent, at least for human beings, its purpose might be to enable birds of the same species to recognize one another, or even to distinguish between the sexes. The fact that no birds seem to have a pronounced sense of smell, and in most birds the sense appears to be almost, if not entirely, absent, seems to negative this. *See also* Oil Gland.

PRIMARIES. These are the large quill-feathers of the wing which are attached to those bones corresponding to the hand (*see Plate facing* p. 1). The large quill-feathers attached to the forearm are known as Secondaries (*q.v.*).

There is little variation in the number of primaries, most birds possessing ten or eleven. However, some birds, such as the grebes, have one or two more than usual. On the other hand, flightless birds generally have fewer primaries. The primary feathers are much more closely

"packed" together than are the secondaries. In the more "aerial" species, such as the Swift, the outer primaries are very long, thus giving the wing a pointed shape. But in those birds which fly comparatively little, the outer primaries are short, so that the wings are rounded. *See also* Anatomy ; Feather ; Wing.

PROCELLARIA. Genus of marine birds of the family *Procellariidae* of the order *Procellariiformes*. It contains more than twenty species, distributed over all the oceans of the world. Six are on the British bird-list : the Manx Shearwater, Little Shearwater, Audubon's Shearwater, Great Shearwater, Sooty Shearwater, Mediterranean Shearwater and North Atlantic Shearwater. These are separately described under their own headings.

PROCELLARIIDAE. Large family of marine birds of the order *Procellariiformes*. It comprises the shearwaters, petrels and albatrosses, and contains a total of more than fifty species. The following seven genera are on the British list : *Oceanites, Oceanodroma, Hydrobates, Pelagodroma, Procellaria, Bulweria* and *Fulmarus*.

PROCELLARIIFORMES. Order of oceanic birds, containing the petrels, shearwaters, and albatrosses. Two families in this order, *Diomedeidae* (*q.v.*) and *Procellariidae* (*q.v.*), contain birds which visit the British coasts.

PROTECTION of BIRDS. Great Britain's first legislation for the protection of birds dates from 1869 when, thanks very largely to the efforts of Professor Alfred Newton, a Bill reached the Statute Book giving limited protection to certain sea-birds. In 1880, an Act was passed which formed the basis of all legal protection until as recently as 1954. Many amendments to the early Act were passed, which tended to confuse matters hopelessly.

In the 1930s public opinion began to make itself felt and the Government set up a Committee to consider new legislation for the protection of birds ; unfortunately the outbreak of the Second World War caused this Committee's proposals to be shelved *sine die*. But it was at this time that the Royal Society for the Protection of Birds (*q.v.*) produced a draft Bill, which was essentially similar to the Protection of Birds Act, 1954.

In 1947 the Home Secretary set up a new Committee, under the chairmanship of Lord Ilchester, to make recommendations on revised legislation. The Committee made its report in 1951, but the Government stated that they could not introduce new legislation for some time. The fact that a new Act—the Protection of Birds Act, 1954—is now in force is due largely to the efforts of Lady Tweedsmuir, who introduced it as a Private Members' Bill in

November 1953, and steered it through the Commons with great patience and skill, her husband handling it in the Lords.

Protection of Birds Act, 1954. This Act completely revolutionises bird protection in Great Britain because it lays down at the outset the principle that *all* birds, their eggs and their nests are *fully protected at all times.*

Certain birds which are harmful or alleged to be harmful are listed in the Second Schedule to the Act. These birds may be killed or taken at any time by authorised persons, and so may their eggs. This Second Schedule at present includes some 20 species, of which the Wood-Pigeon, Stock-Dove, Carrion-Crow, Hooded Crow, Rook, Greater and Lesser Black-backed Gull and the Herring-Gull are examples.

The only other birds which are not wholly protected are included in the Third Schedule and Part Two of the First Schedule to the Act. These are sporting or quasi-sporting birds, including certain species of duck and geese, Common Snipe, Curlew, Capercaillie, Woodcock and certain other birds. They may be killed or taken outside the close-seasons laid down in the Act. These are :

   (i) Capercaillie and (except in Scotland) Woodcock, from February 1 until September 30 ;
   (ii) Common Snipe from February 1 until August 11 ;
   (iii) wild duck or wild geese in or over any area below high-water mark from February 21 until August 31 ;
   (iv) in any other case from February 1 until August 31.

It should be noted that the Home Secretary has power to extend these close-seasons (but not to shorten them). It may also be mentioned that the Act does not cover Partridge, Pheasant, Grouse, Black Game and Ptarmigan.

It cannot be too strongly emphasised that the method of killing or taking those birds which can be legitimately killed or taken are very strictly limited, many methods being forbidden under Section Five of the Act. Springes, traps, gins, snares, hook and line, poisoned or stupefying bait, floating container holding explosives, net, baited board, birdlime or any similar substance are all illegal.

A number of uncommon or rare species are listed in the First Schedule to the Act, including birds like the Osprey, Hobby, Avocet, Bearded Tit, Dartford

Warbler and Bittern. All these are protected by especially heavy penalties : up to £25 *for each bird or egg*, together with a month's imprisonment for a first offence or three months' imprisonment for subsequent offence. In other cases the penalty is £5 *per bird or egg.*

With certain minor exceptions, it is illegal to sell or offer for sale the eggs of any species which has nested in the British Isles, and this provision covers blown eggs. Barter and exchange are construed as sale for the purposes of this provision. Lapwings' eggs can be taken and sold up to but not after April 14, and the eggs of five species of gull for human consumption or as food for poultry, i.e. Greater and Lesser Black-backed Gull, Herring-Gull, Common Gull and Black-headed Gull.

Only the basic principles of the Act can be given in this short summary. For fuller details the Act itself can be consulted and copies can be obtained from Her Majesty's Stationery Office. The Royal Society for the Protection of Birds has also produced a summary of the Act, together with an up-to-date list of the birds included in the various schedules to it, and a copy can be obtained free of charge on application to the Secretary, R.S.P.B., 25, Eccleston Square, London, S.W.1.

PROTECTIVE COLORATION. *See* Pattern and Colour ; *also* Camouflage.

PRUNELLA. Sole genus of the family *Prunellidae* of the order *Passeriformes*, containing the accentors. About a dozen species occur in several forms in Europe, Asia and north Africa but only two—the Hedge-Sparrow and the Alpine Accentor (*qq.v.*) are seen in the British Isles.

PTARMIGAN—Lagopus mutus millaisi. A resident in Scotland only, this close relative of the Red Grouse breeds in the Highlands, and in a few islands of the Inner Hebrides. Once it bred—but is now extinct—in Galloway, the Orkneys, Peebles and the Isle of Arran ;

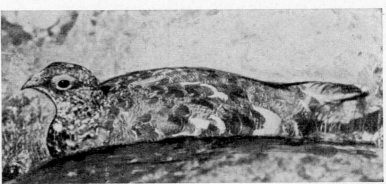

Arthur Christiansen

PTARMIGAN. *Grouse-like in build, the appearance of this game-bird, confined to parts of Scotland, is unique both in its summer and winter dress*

unsuccessful attempts were made to introduce it into Ireland. Five subspecies occur in Europe (the Alps, Spitzbergen, Franz Josef Land, Iceland) and in Greenland.

The appearance is unique. In Winter, the whole plumage is almost pure white, except for the rather inconspicuous black tail tipped with white and the male's black lores (the female's are white). In Summer, the male plumage is pale brown—grey for a short period during the autumn moult—darkish above and finely mottled on mantle and breast. The wing tips and belly remain white. The female at this time is more tawny, with black barrings. Over the eye of both male and female there is at all times a red patch, rather less conspicuous in the female. The bill is black, and the legs feathered. The length is 15 in. and the tarsus $1\frac{1}{2}$ in. ; the wing span is 14–16 in., and the weight 1 lb.

In flight the Ptarmigan is swifter and more buoyant than the Red Grouse, gliding in and out of the mountain corries and rocks with astonishing ease. Swift on the ground, it is adept at hiding, rising only when danger is near. Often it is quite tame, at other times very shy. The Ptarmigan produces various sounds, including a continuous hoarse " automatic " croaking and a cackle like the domestic hen's.

As Autumn approaches, ptarmigans form themselves into packs, and in Winter they usually descend to lower altitudes. In the Spring the pack breaks up to prepare for the breeding season. The nest is only a scrape on the stony ground among the heather, sometimes lined with grass, where six to nine yellowish-white eggs, with blotches of dark brown, are laid at intervals of 24–48 hours during May. The hen hatches these alone for 24-26 days, with the male keeping watch near by. The chicks, clad in buff-coloured down with a dark stripe down the back, are tended and reared by both parents ; they are soon able to fend for themselves, and can fly after ten days. One brood is reared.

The food of the Ptarmigan is almost entirely composed of Alpine plants and berries.

PTEROCLIDAE. Family of terrestrial birds of the order *Columbiformes*. It contains two or three genera, having altogether some 16 species, mainly distributed over the plains and deserts of southern Europe, Africa, and Asia. One genus, *Syrrhaptes*, is on the British list.

PUFFIN—Fratercula arctica grabae. Among the various sea-birds, none looks more quaint and comical than the Puffin ; and this, together with its sociable and friendly nature, makes it one of the most attractive and amusing birds to watch. It is impossible not to smile at their almost human mannerisms, as they sit in rows on the cliffs and islands, solemnly gazing around with their curiously placed eyes.

The Puffin is a locally common resident in the British Isles, colonies being scattered round the coasts on all suitable cliffs and islands ; Scotland, Wales and Ireland have colonies where thousands breed each year, but the Puffin is scarcer on the east and south coasts of England. Abroad, it breeds in north-west Europe, north America and Greenland.

Smaller than the Guillemot and Razorbill, the Puffin has the general build and colouring of the auks, to which family it belongs. It is a glossy black above, with white underparts. The legs and feet are bright red, and round each eye is a crimson ring. But it is the extraordinary shape of its huge parrot-like, many-coloured beak which gives the bird its unique appearance. In Summer the beak is adorned with a horny

James Gibson

PUFFIN. *A comical bird with its heavy bill and nautical gait, the Puffin is fascinating to watch*

sheath, the basal part of which is blue-grey and the front bright red, with a yellow line separating them ; another yellow rim encircles the base of the bill, and each corner of the mouth is decorated with a yellow rosette of skin. The horny sheath is lost in Winter, and the beak becomes smaller and almost colourless. Male and female are alike. The length is 1 ft., and the tarsus 1 in., the wing span is 12–14 in., and the weight $\frac{3}{4}$ lb. *See* plate f. p. 8.

The Puffin flies much as other auks, with rapid wing beats described as " vibrating rather than flapping ". It settles awkwardly on the water, and patters along on the surface for some distance before taking off. But it dives easily, and can swim under water, propelled by its wings, for half a minute or more. It carries itself erect, and its progress was described by T. A. Coward as " a nautical roll ". Often it stands for hours, only turning its head from side to side to survey the surroundings.

The Puffin's only sound is a comic, rather low growl, uttered at the nesting burrow; during the seven months of the year, spent some 200 miles or more out at sea, it is silent. Very few have heard this growl. On one occasion I spent a long time watching an islet, where I knew there was a colony of several thousand, but could hear nothing for the raucous din made by the neighbouring gulls, razorbills, guillemots, cormorants and other sea birds—and, indeed, never even saw a Puffin. One day, after an eight-hour wait, a swarm of about 600 Puffins flew in from the sea, but they disappeared immediately into their burrows in complete silence.

I almost lost hope of recording the puffin's voice, but determined to persevere a little longer. With the recording gear ready to start at a moment's notice and the microphone in the hand of a local fisherman, we watched a number of burrows intensively until we heard noises inside. Finally, one adult bird came out, undisturbed by our presence, and his comic growling induced a female with young to appear from a neighbouring burrow. The latter made somewhat different sounds. The fishermen told me that they had never before heard a Puffin's voice.—EDITOR.

The Puffin's courtship display is a simple ceremony, consisting of much bill-shaking by the two birds facing each other, breast to breast.

Breeding colonies of puffins are on grassy slopes of coastal cliffs, hillsides and islands. The birds arrive during March from their winter sojourn at sea, but do not usually begin nesting until April ; like other auks, they first assemble on the water and disperse several times to feed before finally settling to nest. The burrow is usually excavated by the combined efforts of both male and female, but often one made by a rabbit or shearwater is appropriated. Apart from a rough lining of a few bits of grass no attempt is made to protect the one white egg, with purple and brown markings, which is laid in May in a hollow some feet from the entrance of the burrow. As far as is known, both male and female take part in the incubation, which takes as long as 40–43 days. The chick, clad in very thick, soft, brown down, is carefully tended and fed with fish by both parents for about the same period. It is then ruthlessly abandoned. Left in the burrow to starve for some days, it finally makes, as night falls, its arduous journey to the sea, and is soon able to fend for itself. In a year's time it will appear with its fellows to breed. The nesting sites are deserted in August, when the Puffins scatter over the sea. Little is known of their movements there.

The Puffin was at one time much appreciated as food ; indeed, in the 14th century the rent of the Scillies was partly paid in puffins. Scavenging gulls and rats are their principal enemies.

It is not surprising that such an unusual looking and attractive bird should have gathered to itself several local—and some humorous—

G. K. Yeates

PURPLE HERON. This beautiful bird is a rare visitor, seen here mostly in its immature plumage

names, including Sea-Parrot, Coulterneb, Bottle-Nose, Pope, and Tommy Noddie. In the Shetlands the last becomes " Tammy Norie " ; and Saxby remarks in his *Birds of Shetland* that, whenever "compliments" were flying, the phrase " for a' the world like a Tammy Norie " was often used. The Welsh name for the Puffin is " Pal," but an island off Anglesey, where the bird was once abundant, is named Puffin Island. The Puffin's Anglo-Saxon name, " Lunde ", survives to this day in the name of Lundy Island.

PURPLE HERON—Ardea purpurea. This heron is occasionally seen in eastern England on its spring and autumn migration, and one has been sighted off the west coast of Ireland. It breeds in many parts of Europe, apparently quite abundantly in the Camargue (France), and in Asia and Africa. Smaller and darker than the common Heron, the Purple is a beautiful bird, with mantle and wings of dark slate-grey, and long chestnut plumes on the back. Its crown and crest are purplish-black ; its breast reddish with some black at the sides ; and its neck reddish and black-striped. The majority of the visitors to Britain are in immature plumage, and lack the long, colourful plumes. The bird's length is 31 in., the body being 15 in. ; the tarsus is 6·2 in., the wing span about 2 ft. 6 in., and the weight 2 or 2½ lb.

The movements, flight, walk and bearing are similar to those of the common Heron, but the Purple species is more secretive and even more silent than its relatives. Its voice is higher pitched and softer than the common Heron's.

PURPLE SANDPIPER—Calidris maritima.

An inhabitant of the Far North, breeding in north Europe, north Asia, north America and Greenland, the Purple Sandpiper comes to the British Isles as a winter visitor and passage migrant. A few non-breeders may stay all Summer. This attractive little wader is widely distributed on all our coasts, but is seldom seen inland. In the Shetlands, it is said to be the commonest of the sandpipers occurring as a passage migrant.

Rather larger than the Dunlin, the Purple Sandpiper is a sturdily built and robust-looking bird, with short, dull yellow legs. In Winter the plumage is very dark, almost black, above, but tinged with a purple gloss and relieved with grey edgings to the feathers. The head, neck and breast are dark brown, and the throat and underparts white. A white bar on the wing is most conspicuous in flight. The bill is dark, with a yellow base. The length of the Purple Sandpiper is 8¼ in. and the tarsus 0·9 in. ; the wing span is 9 or 10 in., and the weight 2 oz.

These birds are so tame that they almost seem oblivious to the presence of Man. Saxby in his *Birds of Shetland* remarks that " so little fear of Man do they show, that occasionally it is difficult to alarm them " ; when sportsmen go out shooting, he says " the little monkeys sometimes turn the tables on you altogether, for you *can't* shoot a bird when it is pleased to see you ".

More or less silent during the Winter—even when flushed—the Purple Sandpiper has a low whistle and a piping note ; at its breeding sites, however, it utters a variety of twittering and trilling calls.

PYRRHULA. Genus of the family *Fringillidae*

of the order *Passeriformes*. Its members are distributed over Europe, northern Asia and the Azores, and also occur in northern India, the Malay Peninsula, Formosa and the Philippines. The only British species is the Bullfinch (*q.v.*).

Arthur Christiansen

PURPLE SANDPIPER. *A winter visitor and a passage migrant, this wader is extremely friendly*

QUAIL—Coturnix coturnix.

Once a common summer resident throughout the British Isles, the Quail must now be included among our rarities. Its disappearance has not been due to either the sportsman or the egg collector, but to its use as a table delicacy. Unlike our other game birds, the Quail is migratory, and of the vast numbers which congregate in the countries bordering the Mediterranean on their journey from Africa to the north, large quantities are netted and snared, for the markets. Over a million birds, it is said, have been taken on the Isle of Capri during the spring migration, to supply the tables of epicures all over the world.

The Quail still breeds sometimes in the west Midlands and south of England, but elsewhere is scarce as a breeding bird—although it has bred far as north as the Orkney and Shetland Islands. Once resident and plentiful in Ireland, the Quail is now a rare summer visitor there, chiefly in the east. Abroad, it occurs throughout Europe, Asia and Africa.

The Quail arrives in England in May and leaves again in October ; some may remain through the Winter. The smallest of our game birds, it is like a tiny edition of the Partridge. Its general appearance is a sandy-buff, its mantle variegated in dark and light brown. The flanks are reddish buff with broad pale streaks ; the rest of the underparts are light buff. The male has a dark double collar, running back to the dark ear coverts, a buff streak on the head, and a buff eye stripe. The female's throat is buff without the dark collar, and her breast is more speckled than the male's. The juvenile resembles the hen. The bill and legs are brown. The length is 7 in., and the tarsus 1 in. ; the wing span is about 8 in., and the weight 4 or 5 oz. *See plate f. p. 276.*

In habits, behaviour and walk, the Quail resembles the Partridge. It does not perch, but lies concealed under cover of the vegetation, rising only when forced to do so. It then flies low, and only for a short distance. If disturbed, it may not take to the air at all, but run away at full speed.

The Quail proclaims its presence with its unique trisyllabic call ; this comprises first a long crowing whistle, then two shorter notes. The call can be translated into human language as " wet-my-lips ". This is the call of the male, but there is also a faint hoarse note common to both sexes, and a variation of the common call notes, that are only to be heard at close range.

Eric Hosking

RALLIDAE, *a member of the family—a ' bald-headed ' Coot*

ROBIN

R

RACE or Subspecies. By modern practice, this is now defined as a population of birds of a particular species in which 75 per cent. differ in one or more characteristics (such as wing length, colour, size, and so on) from 98 per cent. of those of the same species from another area. The differences may be due to geographical, environmental or other causes.

The name of a race is now given as a combination of three names ; the first of which is that of the genus, the second of the species and the third of the race. Thus, the Crossbill genus is *Loxia*, its species is *Loxia curvirostra*, of which *Loxia curvirostra curvirostra* is the common Crossbill race and *Loxia curvirostra scotica* the Scottish race, resident, as its name implies, only in Scotland. In other words, by definition, the specific name is always repeated in the nominate race, which is not necessarily the most important, but the first to be described.

RADDE'S BUSH-WARBLER—Phylloscopus schwarzi. Little is known concerning this unusual visitor, one of which was identified in Lincolnshire in 1898. Its home is in eastern Siberia. It resembles the Dusky Warbler, another rare visitor from Siberia, but its whole appearance is duller. The best distinguishing marks are its stouter bill, yellower legs and very prominent eye stripe. Its length is 5 in., and its tarsus 0·9 in. ; its wing span is about 6 in., and its weight a fraction of an ounce.

RADIO. One of the popular features of the 1951 Festival of Britain Exhibition on the South Bank, in London, was a device which performed the songs of wild birds and signalled the identity of each bird as its song was heard. Occasionally, from some defect of synchronisation, the wrong identification was given, and immediately there were derisive comments from the listening crowds. A surprisingly large number could instantly recognize and name a Curlew by its call, although the bulk of them had probably never seen this bird.

This was a proof of the way in which broadcasting has broadened and enriched our national love of wild birds. Since the War, particularly, nature programmes of various kinds have come to occupy quite an important place in British broadcasting; and to many thousands of city-dwellers " the wireless " has brought an intimate sense of the sounds and atmosphere of scenes far remote from anything they can experience in their daily life.

Of all living creatures birds are the most attractive of Man's neighbours, and I believe the main reason for this is that they make pleasant and varied sounds. Admittedly they appeal to us in other ways also, but it is their vocal powers which are unique. Some birds are gaily coloured, but so are butterflies. Most birds move gracefully—but are they more graceful than fishes ? Imagine, however, a world in which all birds are silent, and then you have the key to the fascination they hold for us. No other group of living things can begin to compete with the lavish variety that ranges from the vocal buffoonery of puffins and the eeriness of shearwaters to the romantic wildness of Curlew and diver and the melodious

Erica

RADIO. *A shy goose is bashfully repulsing the Editor's tentative advances with his microphone*

sweetness of Nightingale and Blackbird and Garden-Warbler. Ever since Man discovered that his ears had other uses besides keeping the flies off, the music of birds has been a source of wonder and delight.

Yet how many of our ancestors could ever claim to have heard more than a fragment of this wonderful symphony, and who could describe it ? It cannot be conveyed in print, musical notation or phonetics, and so it remained outside the possibility of either serious study or popular dissemination, until the present century brought two inventions—the gramophone record and the radio. These technical achievements in the medium of sound gave an altogether new significance to the songs of birds. What had always been a fugitive and seasonal joy, became a subject of controlled reference. Ours is the first generation able to hear a Nightjar, a Fieldfare, a Fulmar and a Golden Oriole in the space of a minute—and to do so while sitting in an armchair at home.

No radio listener will need to be reminded that the pioneer in this field was Ludwig Koch. There must be millions of bird-lovers who owe a great deal to the skill and enthusiasm with which he has taught us to appreciate bird-song. Gifted with the temperament and personality of an artist, he has created something more than mechanical reproductions of sounds : his recordings are, in their own way, miniature works of art. And in the history of broadcasting they are an important landmark.

Thanks to them, radio could offer a distinctive contribution to ornithology. When *The Naturalist* programme was first broadcast, I chose the call of the curlew as its signature tune, and in *Bird Song of the Month* we sought to accomplish in sound what a bird-book does with pictures. One by one the birds of Britain were " illustrated " with recordings, so that listeners could learn to identify them by ear.

Ludwig Koch's collection formed the basis of the B.B.C.'s Library of Wild Life Recordings, which continues to expand and is unquestionably the best in the world. The Library is available to scientific bodies for research purposes, and provides a wealth of material for the many broadcasts that are now available to the bird-

lover. James Fisher has described how, as a child, he was fascinated by a picture of a Great Northern Diver in one of his father's books and dreamed of the day when he would see the bird itself. Nowadays there must be many children who have been fascinated in the same way by the wonderful calls of the diver heard on the radio. To millions of listeners these sound pictures have given the first real acquaintance with some of our rarer birds in their natural living characters.

I stress the importance of sound pictures because they are the very essence of broadcasting, but they are not by any means the whole story. Where the popular Press has been niggardly of space for bird topics, the B.B.C. in contrast has developed a comparatively full service of ornithological news, information and discussion; and some of the most successful broadcasters of the present time are naturalists like Peter Scott and James Fisher, who have won a wide audience without making any concessions to the allegedly simple-minded masses. The truth is that public demand

Maslowski & Goodpaster

RALLIDAE. The Moorhen's frontal shield, although not so conspicuous as its relative's, the Coot's (q.v.), can be seen clearly in this photograph

requires a strikingly high standard in the presentation of the various bird topics.

The value of this kind of broadcasting is that it supplements the one or two reference books, mainly books of identification, that the average bird-lover has in his home. The study of birds, like the study of any other subject, is constantly changing as new facts are brought to light, new theories are propounded, new events take place. Let me give some examples of this kind of specialist news-reporting in such programmes as *The Naturalist* and *Birds in Britain*. Large-scale wrecks of sea-birds on our coasts; the return of breeding avocets to England, and later the effects of the east coast floods on their breeding grounds; the sighting of a species never before reported in Britain; the establishment of a new bird observatory; seasonal reports of Peter Scott's ringing of wild geese; an invasion of crossbills—items of this kind are of the greatest interest to bird-lovers, and the B.B.C. has now established itself as the one national medium of information which is prepared to undertake this task.

In addition to straightforward news items, there are matters of controversy and fresh projects of scientific research to be presented—such as the influence of Starling migration on foot-and-mouth disease, the value of flight calls as a kind of bird " radar ", the economic relation of rooks to agriculture. In this field it is important to bring to the microphone the men and women actively engaged in the investigation of each subject.

In too many branches of modern science the expert speaks a language which is incomprehensible to the layman. Radio does a service to ornithology by introducing eminent men of science to an audience which is counted in millions. There are times when the radio audience can make a positive contribution : broadcast request for reports of paper-tearing by tits brought in a total of 758 letters and postcards in 24 hours. Perhaps that is as strong evidence as any of the popularity of birds in British broadcasting.

DESMOND HAWKINS.

RADIUS (pl. radii). Technical name for barbule (*q.v.*) of feather (*q.v.*).

RAIL. Genus of marsh birds related to the crakes, coots and moorhens. Rails are shaped rather like domestic fowls and are shy and secretive, more often heard than seen. Only one species appears on the British list, the Water-Rail (*q.v.*), a resident and passage migrant ; while the Sora Rail (*q.v.*) or Carolina Crake is a member of the genus *Porzana*, to which the marsh-crakes belong (*see* Crake). For Landrail, *see* Corncrake.

The name " Rail " may also be loosely applied to all members of the family *Rallidae*.

RAINBIRD. Local name for several birds, especially the Green Woodpecker (*q.v.*).

RAIN-GOOSE. Alternative name for Red-throated Diver (*q.v.*).

RALLIDAE. Family of the order *Ralliformes*, containing rails, crakes and coots. Its members occur in all parts of the world. It includes five genera on the British list : *Rallus*, *Porzana*, *Crex*, *Gallinula*, and *Fulica*.

The members of this family are small or medium-sized marsh- and water-birds. Their bodies are much compressed laterally, a

Eric Hosking

RAVEN. Once a common bird in this country, the Raven now breeds only in the less populated spots

peculiarity which enables them to make their way without difficulty through reed-beds and dense vegetation. The bill is rather stout and of varying length; there is often a horny " shield " extending from the forehead down to the base of the upper mandible. The wings are rather short, and rounded, as is the tail. The legs are fairly long. The toes are long and slender, and in a few species are lobed.

RALLUS. Genus of the family *Rallidae* of the order *Ralliformes*. Its species are distributed over Europe, Asia, Africa, Australasia and America. Only one, in a number of forms, occurs in Europe; this is the Water-Rail (*q.v.*).

RAMUS. Another name for the barb or lateral branch from the shaft of a feather (*q.v.*).

RATTLEWING. Local name for the Golden-Eye (*q.v.*), from the loud noise of its wings.

RAVEN—Corvus corax. The largest of the *Corvidae*, the Raven was in medieval times as common as the Kite in London and in other cities, and was at that time even protected for its usefulness as a scavenger. Today, although it has managed to survive and combat changing conditions with more success than the Kite, it is banished to the solitudes of wild mountainous country or the desolate cliffs and islands of the coasts. The last pair of ravens to nest in London built in Hyde Park in 1826.

The Raven is still a resident more or less abundant in all suitable parts of England, especially round the coasts of Cornwall, north Devon, Somerset and the Isle of Wight—now probably its nearest breeding place to London. Inland, it is found in the quarries and trees of

Devon and Somerset. It is still numerous in Cumberland and the Isle of Man, but rarer in the Midlands and eastern counties. Of recent years Wales has seen a considerable increase, and the Raven is comparatively common in the Highlands and islands of Scotland, especially in the Hebrides and Shetland, though less in Orkney. In Ireland, it breeds in all suitable wild country, especially in the west. Abroad, the Raven occurs in Europe, parts of Asia, north Africa and north America.

The Raven is a handsome, fierce-looking bird, clad entirely in black, its lustrous mantle shimmering with a blue and green gloss. Its legs and bill are also black. It can be distinguished from the Carrion-Crow by its larger size and stouter bill. The sexes are alike. The length is 25 in., and the tarsus 3 in.; the wing span is 4 ft. 4 in., and the weight 2½ to 3 lb.

The Raven is most fascinating to watch in the air where, from a great height, it performs magnificent aerial evolutions, wheeling, tumbling upside-down and soaring with apparent delight in its mastery of the elements. The flight is at its best in the mating season, when both male and female take part, but the aerial display takes place, though less energetically, at other times of the year. On the ground, the Raven has a sedate and dignified walk; if alarmed, it will break into an awkward and clumsy hop. It perches on crags, cliffs and trees, where these are available. Fierce, predatory and wary of the human race, it has always had the reputation, especially in the north, of a bird of evil omen. It may live to a great age, perhaps for 60 or 70 years.

In districts where they are numerous, ravens will congregate in large flocks, if carrion becomes abundant, and roost together. Saxby relates in his *Birds of Shetland* how a number of carcases of whales were lying on a beach, and as many as 800 ravens were attracted to the spot. This was during the nesting season, and Saxby says many of the birds " must have been sitting on their eggs at the time and it appears rather unaccountable that as night approached a considerable number of the gorged birds would fly across the island, where they would remain in safety until daylight enabled them to return ".

Eric Hosking

RAVEN. *Intelligent and endowed with a gift for mimicry, the Raven may be taught to speak*

The vocal production of the Raven has more variety than is generally believed. The honking of the male—differently pitched in each individual—can be heard on the ground as well as in flight. The female has a short call rather reminiscent of the Hooded Crow's. Both male and female utter surprisingly high-pitched sounds when angry. The Raven possesses a highly developed faculty for imitation, and some have been trained to speak short words.

In the days when ravens were more common, their nests were usually built in ancient trees, and in many districts the name " raven trees" is still attached to their former habitats. Now ravens build on inaccessible sea-cliffs and in hilly and mountainous districts, with or without trees. Watching the Raven therefore presents many difficulties. The Editor once had the good fortune, however, to be able to watch a pair in the early mornings over a period of several months. Each day he saw the same bird and its mate fly out to forage for food, and observed the aggressiveness with which they met any competition for their booty.

Their bulky nest is built by both male and female of sticks, heather stems and roots, mixed with earth and cosily lined with soft hair and wool. In late February and March, four to six bluish-green eggs, blotched and spotted in brown, are laid. They are hatched almost entirely by the female for 20 or 21 days, but she is fed by the male during that period. The young are fed by both parents for five or six weeks. One brood is reared in a season.

The Raven's food is extremely varied, and includes all kinds of carrion—animal, fish or bird. Some vegetable matter is also taken.

Six handsome " pinioned " ravens strut on the lawns of the Tower of London, and form a great attraction for visitors. Tradition has it that ravens have lived by the Tower since 1078, and a legend handed down from the time of Charles II relates that should these birds leave the Tower, the " White Tower " will crumble and fall and with it the whole British Empire ! Great care is therefore taken to maintain this small colony of ravens, whose wings are clipped at intervals ; one of the Warders has them in his charge, and they are provided with their food.

RAVENGLASS. Local Nature Reserve in Cumberland, near the mouth of the river Esk and not far from Muncaster Castle. It has long been noted for its gullery and ternery and was declared a Local Reserve by Cumberland County Council in 1954. *See also* Sanctuary.

RAZORBILL—Alca torda islandica. A typical member of the Auk family and a descendant of the extinct Great Auk, the Razorbill is related to the common and black guillemots and the Puffin. It resembles the Great Auk more closely than any other bird now living, and, as a result, used to be known as the " Razorbill Auk ". The Razorbill is a resident from the end of March until August, it breeds in company with its relatives on suitable coastal cliffs and marine islands. In Winter, it roams the wide oceans both day and night, and is only driven inland by storms at sea. Abroad, it breeds in northern Europe, north America and Greenland.

The Razorbill has a neat and compact body rather heavier and more thick-set than other auks', and a larger head than they. In summer dress, its head, neck and upper parts are a glossy black. A narrow white line runs from its massive bill to its eye, and its secondaries are tipped with white, forming a kind of white wing bar. Its underparts are snowy white. In Winter, its plumage does not differ greatly, except that its face, chin and throat are white (the white line on the face therefore scarcely shows), and its glossy back becomes tinged with sooty brown. The large compressed bill which gives it its-name —formerly it was called the Razorbill Auk—is quite different from that of either the Guillemot or the Puffin, being grooved and black, crossed with a vivid white line. The inside of the mouth is yellowish, and the legs and feet black. The sexes are alike. In their first Winter the young are like the adults, but their bills are less conspicuous. The length of the Razorbill is 16 in., and the tarsus 1¼ in. ; the wing span is 25 in., and the weight is approximately 1½ lb.

In its flight, which, like that of all auks, is laboured and short, the Razorbill's wings make a whirring sound. It flies round several times before settling, which it does awkwardly. It swims buoyantly and high, but makes faster progress submerged than on the surface ; under the water its wings propel it forward, and its

feet act as a rudder. It is an excellent diver, its normal dive being to a depth of 7 ft. and for 22 secs. On land, the Razorbill has an upright stance and walks with an ungainly shuffle.

During their spring mating, these birds indulge in all kinds of games on the water, and affectionately touch and rub each other's bills. In a special " ecstatic " posture, in which both male and female take part, they rattle their mandibles like castanets and vibrate their wings.

The Razorbill's voice, heard only at its breeding colonies, is a grating growl. The young have a soft, plaintive note.

Razorbills are gregarious and are usually seen in small groups or scattered parties. Outside the breeding season, they roost on the water. They drift in from the sea near their breeding sites on the cliffs and shores in February, but it is March—or in Shetland even May—before they finally settle to their domestic duties. No nest is built, the one whitish egg, blotched and spotted in brown and black, being laid on the bare rock, or in a hole under a rock. Both male and female incubate for about a month, and the chick, clad in white silky down, is fed and looked after there for a fortnight. It leaves the nest at dusk one night, and makes its arduous way alone, but urged on by its parents, down to the sea. Arrived there, it falls into the water, and swims beneath the surface until it reaches a calm spot, where it quenches its thirst. One authority has suggested that thirst may be the force that impels it to leave the nest.

Razorbills begin to desert their breeding sites in July, and by the end of August nearly all have departed to wander the sea once more. Small fish, caught under the water, crustacea and marine worms form their staple food. To feed the chick, a Razorbill will carry small fish across its bill ; and as many as 12 have been recorded.

H. N. Southern

RAZORBILL. On land this member of the Auk family walks with an ungainly shuffle, but it is an expert diver, usually diving to a depth of 7 feet

HOW BIRDS RECOGNIZE EACH OTHER

B. VESEY-FITZGERALD

How one bird recognizes his mate, or that another bird belongs to a different species, will probably remain a matter for conjecture ; but birds seem to rely on much the same aids as humans. For some tests of the theories advanced below see Research

RECOGNITION. Birds recognize one another by sight and by sound. So much is obvious to anybody who has observed birds even casually. Recognition by sight includes, of course, colour and shape and size. One Blackbird recognizes another by colour, and cannot confuse a member of its own species with a Rook or Carrion-Crow, since (apart from the yellow bill) both shape and size differ. But a Blackbird dyed canary-yellow will not be recognized at sight as a Blackbird by other blackbirds, and equally will not be recognized as a Canary by canaries because of the difference in shape and size. It will, however, be recognized as a Blackbird by blackbirds because of its voice.

Sound plays a very important part in bird recognition. Each species has its own " language ", which we describe as " song ", " call notes " and " alarm notes ". All blackbirds have the same timbre in their song, all chaffinches, all nightingales, all mistle-thrushes. Some may be, from our point of view, better songsters than others and there may be slight regional differences—Belgian chaffinches do not sing exactly the song of British chaffinches, for example, and I have sometimes thought that I have been able to detect a slight dialectal difference between the songs of Somerset chaffinches and Kent chaffinches— but the song is the song of the species, and recognizable as such not only by ourselves but also by all the members of the species. This applies to the call notes and the alarm notes.

We do not know if the song of a Blackbird means anything to a Chaffinch, nor if the call notes of a Chaffinch mean anything to a Blue Tit. The fact that a bird does not apparently take the least notice of the songs and call notes of birds of other species does not necessarily indicate that it has no understanding of them. With alarm notes, however, the position is different. Certain alarm notes are well understood by birds of many species. The alarm of a Jay will warn every bird in the wood, that of a Redshank every bird on the marsh, that of the Curlew every bird on the shore, that of the Blackbird every bird in the garden or hedgerow.

Within the language of birds there are nuances which we do not fully understand, and perhaps do not even notice. There can be no doubt that the call notes of a mother to her chicks, though they may all seem alike and characteristic of the species to our ears, do differ with the individual. The farmyard hen calls her own chicks, and not the chicks of the hen in the next coop. The chicks may occasionally go to the wrong hen, but only rarely.

Birds are, so to speak, born with the language of their own species ; they do not have to learn it. But some have the ability to learn, if only in part, the essentials of the language of other species. A Pheasant hatched beneath a domestic hen and brought up by her understands the sounds made by that hen, and can distinguish them from the sounds made by neighbouring hens, for it will rarely run to the wrong foster-mother. Yet, as soon as the Pheasant is released to a wild life in the woods, it forgets the speech of the rearing-field and understands the calls and alarms of wild pheasants, although it has never heard them before.

Individual recognition is more difficult to understand than species recognition. While colour, shape and size play an obvious part in the broad recognition of species, for the direct recognition of individuals within the species they must possess more significance than human eyes can appreciate. All cock blackbirds look alike to our eyes when seen in the field ; it may be regarded as certain that they do not all look alike to blackbirds. Precisely how they differ is not known. Birds have exceptionally acute sight, but we know no more than that.

In the breeding-season many outside factors *may* operate to aid recognition—the site of the nest, the features of the territory, and so forth— but I doubt if they do : we do not recognize our wives by the houses we live in. In any case, these factors cannot operate among the huge nomadic flocks of Winter. Yet one has only to watch a flock of rooks or starlings at work in a field, or a mixed flock of finches in a stackyard, to realize that many of the birds (although they are at this season sexless) are " paired ", have particular friendships, and are able to pick out their partners without difficulty from a crowd of apparently similar birds. Birds, to birds' eyes, probably differ as much and as strikingly as do sheep to their shepherd, or as one human does from another.

It is probable that birds make many sounds which we do not hear at all because they are uttered at too high a frequency for our ears. Some of these ultrasonic sounds may occur in song, and there may well be many in the call notes. If they do occur they aid recognition.

RECORDING the SONGS of WILD BIRDS

LUDWIG KOCH

The Editor made his first recording of bird song at the age of eight, before the gramophone had been invented and when broadcasting had not been thought of. After telling of his experiences, he gives a few practical hints to would-be recorders

RECORDING. The story of human efforts to capture and record sounds is as old as humanity itself. The Chinese claim to have solved the problem some 6,000 years ago, when —according to their legend—they sent spoken messages in a sealed tube, to be heard by the recipient hundreds of miles away. What method they applied to sound preservation nobody knows; but we know that other attempts have been made ever since the 16th century—including fakes, such as the tube into which, as children, we spoke a few words, to hear them repeated from another tube at a considerable distance . . . by a second person hidden away.

The first instrument really to record sound was the French "Phonoautograph", which, however, failed to reproduce what it had recorded. That was about 1860. Only 17 years later Thomas Alvar Edison constructed the "Phonograph" (so named by him in 1878), which recorded sound first on tinfoil and soon afterwards on wax cylinders, and could reproduce it audibly with the help of a largish tin horn. It was

Edison's Phonograph

such an instrument that my father brought home from the 1889 Leipzig Fair; and with it began the history of bird-song recording. For with it, as a boy of eight, I recorded in my own little private "Zoo" the voice of a Shama, an Indian bird—the first bird-song ever to be thus preserved. Primitive as this first of all such records was, it still exists. Many other early records—of famous men whom I approached with my Phonograph, and possibly of historical interest—were destroyed by the Nazis in the Second World War. The song of the Shama escaped that fate by having been left in Switzerland, and it was once more heard on the B.B.C. in 1951.

The gramophone also goes back to the late 'eighties. It progressed *via* glass

Berliner's Gramophone

disks to wax disks, and extant records, e.g. those made by Caruso in 1902, bear witness to its good qualities. Outdoor recording became possible only when, in 1906, the Lindstrom Co. in Germany presented me with a portable disk recorder and a number of waxes. With this I subsequently recorded some 50 different birds, as well as many other voices, human and animal. Since there was no commercial interest, nobody thought of preserving those records for pos-

RECORDING. *The Editor listening intently to the sounds that are coming over his disk-recorder*

terity, as could have been done by making shellac disks from the original wax.

Though Edison had foreseen it as far back as 1877, we had to wait until 1926 for electric recording—the procedure in use today—with its microphone, amplifier, volume control, loudspeaker, electrically operated cutter, monitoring and all the rest. Two years later I had at my disposal a first class aggregate of that kind, and a car to carry it in.

It was hard pioneering work at first. The technique of electric recording differs greatly from that of the old purely acoustic recording and, since there were as yet no specially trained engineers, any electrician had to do. I had to drag with me long cables that were sadly subject to short circuits in rain or snow, and most repairs could be done only in the Odeon or

Erica

RECORDING. *Despite the advent of the lighter and more portable tape-recorder (opposite), the Editor prefers, when possible, to record on disks*

bird's song in the sensitive microphone, a gale puts the gear completely out of action, and even the rustling of leaves may spoil an otherwise good recording. It needs endless patience—and luck !—to record a bird's voice, for, when at long last you are near enough, and the bird begins to favour you with its song, the whims of either Nature or Man usually interfere. As when, for instance, after nights of watching and failing to capture its voice unspoiled by rustling reed, I had the Bittern booming perfectly, and, at the precise moment when I started my recording gear, a squadron of bombers began wheeling and droning overhead for half an hour . . .

Parlophone factories. The first bird-song I thus " captured " was that of a Siskin ; I brought it back, after another short circuit, with 30 wasted waxes. Such rare and difficult recordings—every one a gamble—during the following five or six years of experiment and development, gave me the inspiration for my series of *Tönendes Buch* (" Sound Book "), combining text and pictures with sound on gramophone disks attached to the book, of which, in the few years before I emigrated to Britain, 11 different volumes were published.

By then my own collection of bird-song records comprised about 75 species, among them such rarities as the Great Bustard (extinct in this country), the Thrush-Nightingale and the Stone-Curlew, which I had been watching unceasingly for three years. These were lost with the earlier recordings, however, and it was only in the Spring of 1936 that I was able to start a new bird-song collection in this country, using much the same methods as I had in Germany. The difference between British and Continental voices of the same species provided me with an added interest, and soon, as war approached, the noise of aeroplanes overhead created an added difficulty. Even so, I had about 50 species on record when war broke out in 1939. After working for over a year with the B.B.C., I acquired my own gear and made recordings all over the country, using such improved equipment as cellulose acetate records, which can safely be played back immediately.

Even so, the difficulties of the British climate persists. Snow, hail and rain will drown a

The disk recorder, still my preference whenever it is possible to approach my hunting ground by car, has had to endure competition in recent years. The invention of magnetic steel tape recording goes back to 1911, although it was not exploited for many years ; and in the 'twenties, at the Berlin Telefunken laboratories, I watched research work on what later became known as the Magnetophone. Yet a really practical result was not obtained until the end of the Second World War, when tape recording by handy, comparatively light and mobile machines made its appearance. These machines have the great advantage for bird-song recording that, with a weight of only about 14 or 15 lb., inclusive of batteries, they can be used in spots to which the heavy and bulky disk recorder cannot be carried. I used one in 1953 in almost inaccessible spots in Iceland, though the hum of its vibrator gave me some trouble.

Perfected, and produced at a low price, the tape recorder should make a great contribution towards popularising among young people the rewarding sport of collecting bird-songs, for it spares one the long and arduous training needed for disk-recording.

Anyone should be able to learn how to operate a tape-recorder satisfactorily in a few days at the most. But this is only the beginning, because recording bird song not only demands technical skill but also a good knowledge of birds, and particularly of their songs and call notes. To make a true record requires a musical ear and a sensitive appreciation of atmosphere—in fact, one must learn to " paint " in sound in the same way as an artist does in colour. Furthermore, for successful recording, one must possess almost unlimited patience and the ability to rise above any setbacks.

The first thing to do is to locate the " singing spot " of the bird whose song one wishes to record. In general, the best time for recording is at or before dawn, though some species must be recorded in the evening or at night.

Assume that one wishes to start with a well-known songster that is easy to track down, and decides to record the flute-like notes of the Blackbird. Reference to the Calendar of Song, *facing page* 518, shows that the Blackbird is in full song from the end of February to the middle of July. Mark down the particular bird it is intended to record as early as possible in the year—preferably in some convenient spot in quiet surroundings. Visit this place for a week or so beforehand, and watch where the bird is singing, timing the visits a little earlier each day—between 5 a.m. and 6 a.m. in April, 4 a.m. in May and 3 a.m. in June. When you know the bird's favourite spot for singing, place the microphone a few yards away from it—this must be done while the bird is roosting, between 11 p.m. and 2 a.m.—and the recorder well out of sight of the bird.

When you are ready, and if your set provides for monitoring, put on the headphones (altern-atively, a loudspeaker may be used), set the control switch at monitoring, and when the bird can be heard satisfactorily, switch to recording. One must be prepared to make continuous further adjustment to the volume control to maintain the volume of sound at a constant level, as judged by ear or by the volume control meter (if one is provided). If the bird moves out of recording range or there are any extraneous disturbances, stop recording and continue monitoring until conditions are favourable again.

With a little practice, you will be able to provide yourself with a series of home-made recordings, from which—even if they are not up to professional standards—you will, never-theless, obtain a great deal of pleasure when they are played back, in the knowledge that you have made them yourself.

RECTRIX (pl. rectrices). One of the large tail feathers. *See Plate f.p.*1.

RECURVIROSTRIDAE (Latin, " curved bill "). Family of wading birds of the order *Charadriiformes.* Two genera are on the British list—*Recurvirostra*, containing the Avocet (*q.v.*) and *Himantopus*, containing the Stilt (*q.v.*).

The members of this family occur in coastal and marshy areas in many parts of the world.

The bill is very long and slender, and either curves upwards (as in the Avocet) or is straight (as in the Stilt) ; it tapers to a very thin point, and is fairly flexible. The neck is rather long, and the wings are long and pointed. The tail is comparatively short and is squarish in shape. The legs are very long, particularly in the Stilt.

RED-BACKED SHRIKE—Lanius collurio. This is the only summer visitor among the shrikes that come to the British Isles. Its breeding is confined mainly to England south of the Mersey and Humber ; elsewhere it is local. It is also a bird of passage in England, and a rare visitor to Scotland and Ireland. Abroad, it occurs throughout Europe, temperate Asia and Africa.

A striking and handsome bird, the male Red-backed Shrike has a blue-grey head and rump, and a rich reddish mantle. A con-spicuous dark mark runs back through his eye to his ear coverts. His underparts are a creamy colour, tinged with pinkish-grey. His long, graduated tail is black, with white sides and base. The female is duller, her plumage is very variable, and she has no facial stripe. The slightly hooked bill is black in the male, brownish in female and juvenile. The legs are grey. The length is 6¾ in., and the tarsus 0·95 in. ; the wing span is 8-10 in., and the weight 2 oz.

The name " Butcher Bird," given to the Red-backed as to other shrikes, derives from its habit of keeping a " larder " of its dead victims impaled on a thorn or on barbed wire.

In the air the Red-backed Shrike has an undulating flight, and occasionally hovers over

Erica

RECORDING. A tape-recorder came into its own during the Editor's now famous visit to Iceland

C. W. Teager

RED-BACKED SHRIKE. " Handsome, but cruel "
might well be the description given of this bird

its prey. On the ground it hops, but does not often settle. In common with its relations, it has a characteristic action of its long tail, which is expanded, moved up and down, or swung from side to side, partly to maintain balance but also as an expression of excitement, curiosity or anger.

Red-backed shrikes are not particularly gregarious, but on passage are sometimes seen in numbers. In courtship display, the cock makes great play with his striking black and white tail, rosy breast and rich red mantle.

A wide variety of harsh discordant notes are produced when the bird is angry or alarmed. The song, best heard during May, June and early July, is a pleasant, low, warbling sub-song, uttered for some minutes on end, but audible at a short distance only. Its most noticeable feature is mimicry of the songs and notes of other birds, such as the Reed-Warbler, Sedge-Warbler, Robin, Linnet and Greenfinch.

The Red-backed Shrike arrives in Britain in early May, and leaves again in August. Hedgerows, thickets and bushy places are its breeding sites, and the same place is often used year after year. The rather large nest, placed in a clump of brambles, a bush or a thick hedge, is put together almost entirely by the male, though the female is said to help occasionally. It is composed of green moss, roots and wool, and lined with fine roots and hair. Four to six variously tinted eggs—some with a creamy ground, others with green, grey or pink—blotched and spotted with yellowish-brown and

grey, are laid at the end of May or in early June. The hen hatches them for a fortnight, and the chicks are fed and reared by both parents, for much the same period. By then they are usually able to fly from the nest. One brood is normal, but should the nest or eggs be destroyed other clutches—even as many as four—will be laid.

The food is very varied : mice, voles, shrews, frogs and lizards being some of the items devoured ; also the young of many species of small birds and many large insects.

RED-BREASTED FLYCATCHER— Muscicapa parva. This attractive little flycatcher occurs in fluctuating numbers in the British Isles on its autumn migration, but is rarely seen in the Spring. It is observed as a rule on the east coast and islands of England. Its breeding quarters are in Europe and Asia, and it winters in India.

The Red-Breasted Flycatcher is very like a small Robin. Its plumage is brown above and whitish below ; on each side of the underpart of its tail appear two patches of white. Very conspicuous in flight, these are also made visible, when the bird is at rest, by the constant upward flicking movement of its tail. Only the male has a red breast. The length is $4\frac{1}{2}$ in., and the tarsus 0·68 in., the wing span is about 6 in., and the weight a fraction of an ounce.

In its native haunts, this small flycatcher is shy and secretive, and flits out of the foliage only to catch a passing insect. It is not gregarious, and appears only at night in its winter quarters. Its voice has a chattering note and is described as reminiscent of the Wren's and Mistle-Thrush's ; its call note resembles that of the Redstart. Its rich and musical song is usually uttered from a perch high in a tree.

RED-BREASTED GOOSE—Branta ruficollis. This bird has paid nine or ten authentic visits to the British Isles, all during the Winter. It breeds on the Arctic rivers of Siberia, and outside the breeding season haunts the grasslands bordering the Caspian Sea.

The appearance of this goose is unique. Its chief colours—black, white and chestnut—are distributed over its body in a curious pattern. The crown, back of neck and sides of face—including eye—are black. The cheeks are chestnut, bordered by a line of white running down to meet the circle of white which borders the chestnut breast. A patch of white appears between the eye and bill. The upper parts are black, and underneath, beyond the breast, is black. The dark wing coverts have white edgings, and the flanks are barred in white. The upper and under tail coverts and the rump are white. The tail is black, as are the bill and legs. The sexes are alike, but the young are less colourful and less prominently patterned. The length is 21 or 22 ins., and the tarsus 2 in. ; the wing span is approximately 2½ ft., and the weight 3 lb.

Its habits and behaviour much resemble those of other grey geese. Both in winter quarters and on migration huge numbers are to be seen.

All the movements of the Red-breasted-Goose are quick, especially those of its head when the bird is feeding. Its call has been described as a curious double screech, quite impossible to imitate, and it hisses when angry. When red-breasted geese are feeding *en masse*, a concert of high-pitched squeals is heard.

RED-BREASTED MERGANSER — Mergus serrator.

A breeding resident in Scotland and Ireland, this merganser is said to have increased its range considerably of late. Every county in Scotland, except those of the south-east, now has its complement of this handsome duck ; in Ireland, it is also abundant and widely distributed. England and Wales see it only as a frequent winter visitor and passage migrant off the coasts and estuaries ; as a rule it does not penetrate inland. Abroad, the Red-Breasted Merganser frequents the northern parts of Europe, Asia, north America and Greenland ; it winters in countries bordering the Mediterranean.

The Red-Breasted Merganser is probably the best known of the saw-billed ducks. Rather smaller than the Goosander, to which it is closely related, it is very similar to that bird. The drake is extremely beautiful ; his dark-green head is decorated with a double crest of long feathers hanging down on each side (the Goosander does not have these). A broad white collar encircles his neck, and a white line runs down his nape to join his dark upper back ; his lower back and flanks are delicately streaked in grey. His wings are black and white, crossed with two black bars, and on his shoulder more white appears. Beyond his chestnut breast the underparts are white, including the rump and tail.

The duck has a smaller crest and a brown head and neck ; her back is greyish-brown, and her underparts are white. The white on her wings is much less evident. In his eclipse plumage the drake resembles the duck, as do the young. The bill and legs are red. The length of the drake is 23 in., the body being 14 in. ; the tarsus is 1½ in. The wing span is 20—22 in., the weight 2 lb. The female is smaller.

The Red-Breasted Merganser is more inclined than the Goosander to frequent salt water. Its flight is similar to the Goosander's—low, straight and fast—it patters along the surface before taking off, and its wings make the same humming sound, though rather softer. It is a fine swimmer, swimming for the most part with its head submerged, but at other times it moves its head backwards and forwards as it goes along, in the manner of the Moorhen.

A constant, graceful and expert diver, it seeks its food well below the surface of the water. This it brings to the surface, and after swallowing it raises its body from the water, makes a great flapping of its wings, and drinks some salt water. The deepest dive recorded is 18½ ft., and the longest two minutes ; its normal dive is 6—12 ft., and the normal time 22 sec.

The spring display resembles that of the Goosander, but it is said to be even more violent than most ducks' ; there is the same stretching of the neck, rising in the water with head on breast, and gaping.

The Merganser is gregarious, but is seen in small parties rather than flocks. It is a silent bird ; its voice being rarely heard outside the breeding season. It then produces a harsh " churring " with a double note.

The nest, merely a collection of grey down and grass, is placed on ground sheltered by rocks and boulders, or among vegetation. The 7-12 greenish-buff eggs are laid daily during May or early June, and for 29 days the duck hatches them alone ; the drake does not even remain near by. The numerous chicks, clad in reddish-brown down and very like those of the Goosander's, are tended and reared by the hen alone. They attain their adult dress in the second Spring after that in which they were hatched.

Fish of various kinds, hunted and caught during its long dives, are the main food of the merganser. It likes to feed in shallow water, where it swims with head submerged, picking up small fish and molluscs. Some insects are taken, but very little, if any, vegetable matter.

R. P. Bagnall-Oakeley

RED-BREASTED GOOSE. *This beautiful bird in its striking plumage is seen here only rarely*

RED-BREASTED SNIPE — Limnodromus griseus. A native of north America—formerly called the Red-breasted Sandpiper and known to the American list as the Eastern Dowitcher—the Red-breasted Snipe has been identified in the British Isles some 20 or 30 times on its autumn migration. In form and plumage, it is rather like the godwits, but it has the typical long bill of the snipes. Its chief identification mark is the narrow white stripe which runs down the centre of its back and is especially conspicuous in flight. Its body is plump and stocky. In summer plumage, the mantle is dark, with reddish mottlings ; the face and underparts are chestnut streaked in black ; the wings are grey ; and the lower back and tail are white, with black and buff. In winter plumage, the bird is grey above, the underparts white and the breast tinged with grey. The bill and legs are olive. The sexes are alike. The length is 10 in., the bill being 2½ in. and the tarsus 1½ in. The wing span is 11 or 12 in., and the weight about 7 oz.

The flight note is described as rather similar to the whistle of the yellow-legs, and the Red-breasted Snipe has variations of snipe-like calls.

RED-CRESTED POCHARD—Netta rufina. This pochard is an uncommon visitor from its home in southern Europe, temperate Asia and north-west Africa, from September to March ; but it is also a favourite occupant of many private ornamental waters.

A handsome and elegant diving bird, rather larger than the common Pochard, the drake is distinguished by his crimson bill and rich chestnut head, decorated with a golden top forming a kind of crest. The whole of his underparts, neck and breast are black. A large area of white covers nearly the whole of the outstretched flight wing ; white patches also appear on the shoulders and the ends of the wings. The mantle is yellowish-brown, the flanks greyish, and the legs orange. The duck is dressed in a uniform pale brown, and her underparts are grey. Her dark head shows no crest. Her white wing patch resembles that of the drake, but is duller. Her blackish bill has a yellow tip, and her legs are pale yellow. The length of the Red-crested Pochard is 22 in., and the tarsus 1½ in. ; the wing span is from 16 in. to 2 ft.

" Extremely disagreeable and unmusical " is one description of the drake's voice. He also utters a low groaning note in display. The duck has the same call as other diving ducks.

RED CROSSBILL. American name for (common) Crossbill (*q.v.*).

RED-FOOTED FALCON—Falco vespertinus. Very like the Kestrel in size, shape and flight, but more gregarious, this falcon is an occasional visitor to the British Isles, usually on its spring migration from its home in eastern and south-eastern Europe. Its appearance is distinctive. The whole of the upper plumage of the male is slate-grey, darkest on the head ; the thighs, underparts and under tail-coverts are chestnut ; the legs, cere and eyes are orange-red. In the less colourful female the chestnut of the male is replaced by rufous-buff, and her back, though grey, is barred in black. The sexes do not differ much in size. The length is 11 or 12 in., and the tarsus 1½ in., the wing span is from 18 to 20 in., and the weight about 9 oz.

RED GROUSE—Lagopus scoticus. This game bird was at one time confined exclusively to Great Britain, but now also breeds as an introduced bird in those parts of the Continent where it has become acclimatised. A moorland bird, it is common and widely distributed in Scotland, in suitable parts of Wales and the Welsh border counties, and in England, northwards from Derbyshire. Elsewhere, it is known only on Exmoor, where it has been introduced.

Sometimes called the Moorfowl, the Red Grouse owes its latter name to its general dark red colour, although its many all-over dark markings give it an almost black appearance. Its tail and wing tips are black. Its feet are whitish and feathered,

Arthur Christiansen

RED-CRESTED POCHARD. *This is a larger and more beautiful duck than the common Pochard ; and the drake (left) is a specially handsome bird*

and its bill is black. The red wattle over the eye of the cock is more prominent than in other game birds. The plumage of both sexes varies considerably, but generally the hen's markings are lighter and her wattle less prominent. The length of the male is 14-15½ in., and his tarsus is 1·8 in. ; his wing span is between 18 and 20 in., and his weight 1 lb. 3 oz. The hen is smaller ; her length is 13 or 14 in., and her other measurements in proportion.

Eric Hosking

RED GROUSE. *At one time this bird, a close relative of the Ptarmigan, was exclusively confined to Great Britain and, in particular, to Scotland*

The habits, behaviour and movements of the Red Grouse have much in common with those of the Partridge. Rising from the heather with a whirr of wings, the Red Grouse travels close to the ground with rapid wing beats. Its flight is sustained usually for about half a mile, but much longer distances have been recorded. It will occasionally perch on trees, but generally roosts among the heather. Red Grouse are gregarious and Autumn and Winter find them collected into packs.

Although the Red Grouse cock has as a rule only one mate, he carries out some half-hearted sparring with other males, even after he is paired. Like that of others of his species, his spring display includes some curious postures ; in one manoeuvre he springs upright into the air, frequently from perch to perch, with his wings outspread, and sinks to earth again with rapidly beating wings, while uttering his characteristic courtship crow. His alarm is a clear, loud call, by which the bird can be unmistakably recognized, as he hastens to safety among the heather. The male has a large vocabulary of calls ; that of the female is less extensive, and she usually contents herself with uttering a low, short croak.

The nest is a mere hollow with some shelter of ling, scraped by the female, among the peat bogs and heather, with the cock supervising the operation. The eggs, 6-11 in number, are a yellowish-white, blotched over with dark chocolate or reddish-brown. They are laid in April or May and hatched by the hen, with the cock never far away, for some three weeks. All hatched in a few hours, the chicks, clad in yellowish-buff down, are led away and brooded by the hen, while the male keeps guard ; they can fly in about a fortnight.

The Red Grouse feeds usually in the evening and early morning, and is said to be very fond of grit for which it repairs to roads and railway tracks. Its food is mainly vegetable, and comprises chiefly the shoots, flowers and seeds of heather and ling. In the Autumn, some cereals (mostly oats) and the berries of brambles, hawthorn and rowan are taken. The chicks are generally fed on insects.

The **Irish Red Grouse** (*Lagopus scoticus hibernicus*) is confined to Ireland and the Outer Hebrides. It is well distributed in Ireland, but is said to have been decreasing of recent years in the Outer Hebrides.

RED-HEADED BUNTING—Emberiza bruniceps. This is an extremely rare visitor to Great Britain. Indeed, only one, an adult male bird, has been recorded ; this was in 1931, in the Orkney Islands. This bunting's breeding places are in Russia and Asia, where it is abundant in some districts ; it winters in India.

The male has a bright chestnut head and throat, yellow underparts and a greenish mantle. There is no white in its tail—a distinguishing feature when comparing it with the other buntings and one which it shares with the Black-headed Bunting. The female is almost identical with the latter bird. The length is about 6 in., the tarsus is 0·75 in. ; the wing span is approximately 7 in., and it weighs ¼ oz.

Its song and its harsh call-notes are similar to those of the Yellow-breasted Bunting. But it has a song-flight, which can be observed during the display, similar to that of the Tree-Pipit, though different from it in its sound.

Little information is otherwise available about this bird. Its habits are said to resemble those of the Corn- and Black-headed buntings.

RED KITE. Alternative name for the Kite (*q.v.*), to distinguish it from the Black Kite (*q.v.*)

RED-LEGGED DAW. Local name for the Chough (*q.v.*). This bird is also variously called the Cornish Chough and the Sea-Crow.

RED-LEGGED PARTRIDGE — Alectoris rufa. The Red-Legged Partridge—also called the French Partridge—was introduced from the Continent for the purpose of sport as the 18th century was drawing to its close (i.e. a good deal later than the Pheasant). It is widely distributed, although never abundant, throughout England, except in the south-west counties. It also breeds in some parts of Wales but is not found in Scotland or Ireland. Abroad, the

John Markham

RED-LEGGED PARTRIDGE. *Larger than the common Partridge, this game bird was introduced from the Continent near the end of the 18th century*

Red-legged Partridge occurs in south-west Europe and some Atlantic islands.

At a distance the Red-legged Partridge can easily be confused with the common Partridge, but it is larger and heavier, and closer inspection reveals some differences in plumage. There is, for instance, no dark horseshoe on its breast, and its bluish-grey flanks show much more conspicuous barring in black and chestnut. Its cheeks and throat are white, the latter encircled with a black band which merges into the grey speckled breast. The underparts are chestnut. Bill and legs are red. The young birds, lacking these distinctive colours, are very like those of the common Partridge. The length of the Red-legged species is 13½ in., and the tarsus 1·7 in., the wing span is approximately 15 in., and the weight 13 oz.

Although very similar even in behaviour and habits to its close relation, the Red-legged chooses rather wilder country ; stony and sandy wastes, chalky downs and heaths, as well as arable land and coastal shingle are all frequented. Restless and shy, it runs more quickly on the ground, and is even more reluctant to fly, than the common Partridge. Unlike the latter, it will perch on fences, walls,

etc., and even on trees. It delights in "dusting" in the sunshine.

Its voice is very different from its close relation's ; the call-note, a loud and challenging " chuck ", has been likened to a " labouring steam engine " or the " whetting of a scythe ".

Red-legged partridges nest in hedgerows, plantations, among growing crops and waste lands. A hollow scraped in the ground, lined with dead leaves and grass, houses 10 to 16 yellowish-white eggs laid at the end of April or in May. These are laid at intervals of 36 hours, and are often left uncovered for long intervals. The period of hatching is 23-24 days. The one brood is sometimes reared by one parent only, at other times by both, for an unknown period. A footnote in the *Handbook of British Birds* says : " There is some evidence, but no proof, that the hen lays clutches in two nests and that she incubates one and the cock the other and that the broods are kept separate, each attended by one parent, but are sometimes amalgamated and tended by both parents." The food preferred is mainly vegetable.

RED-NECKED GREBE — Podiceps grisegena. A regular winter visitor to the British Isles, the Red-Necked Grebe arrives chiefly from October to March, on the east coast of England, in the north and west of Scotland and in Ireland. Severe weather occasionally brings an exceptional influx. A salt-water bird, it haunts the coast and tidal estuaries ; of the five British grebes it is the one least seen inland. The Red-necked Grebe breeds in eastern Europe, Asia and north America.

In winter plumage, when it is likely to be seen here, the Red-Necked Grebe is very like the Great Crested Grebe, but at close range it is seen to be rather smaller and to have a sturdier body and less graceful movements ; it also lacks the Great Crested Grebe's white stripe over the eye. It is grey-brown above, with white cheeks, wing bar and underparts. In its rather darker breeding plumage, it has a rich chestnut neck. A conspicuous feature is the yellow base of the black bill. The head decoration of the Red-necked is much less prominent than that of the Great Crested

Grebe, but in its summer dress it has some inconspicuous ear-tufts. The legs are black. The sexes are alike ; the young birds are duller, with broad stripes on the sides of their whitish cheeks. The length and wing span are both 1 ft. 5 in., the body being 10 in. long, the tarsus is 2 in., and the weight 1 lb. 6 oz.–2 lb.

The habits and behaviour of the Red-Necked Grebe do not materially differ from those of its close relative. It is said, however, to be even more secretive, and it has a less awkward walk on the ground than other grebes. The spring display includes the peculiar " penguin dance " common to the grebes. The voice of the Red-Necked, seldom or never heard in Great Britain, is said to resemble that of the Great Crested, but higher-pitched.

The Red-Necked Grebe feeds on small fish and water insects, together with feathers and some vegetable matter.

RED-NECKED NIGHTJAR. *See* Algerian Red-Necked Nightjar.

RED-NECKED PHALAROPE — Phalaropus lobatus. This attractive little Arctic wader breeds sparingly in the Orkney and Shetland Islands, the Outer Hebrides, and one district in Ireland : but on the south and east coasts of England it is only an uncommon passage migrant and a rare winter visitor. Abroad, it occurs in the northern countries of Europe and Asia, north America and Greenland.

In both the Red-necked and the Grey Phalarope, the normal breeding habits and behaviour are reversed ; the female sports the bright plumage and is the more active in courtship, while the male takes on almost all the domestic duties. He is, indeed, one of the few hen-pecked husbands among birds.

The Red-necked is rather smaller than the Grey Phalarope. In her summer plumage the hen is distinguished by her black bill—the Grey's is yellow—and by an orange patch on the side of the cheek ; her head and upper parts are grey, and underparts and throat white. Occasionally a white spot appears over the eye. The male is rather smaller and less colourful ; his upper parts have more buff streaks, and his orange patch is either duller or lacking altogether. In Winter both sexes of the Red-necked and Grey Phalarope are alike, but at close range the smaller size as well as the darker back and longer and more slender bill, of the Red-necked are apparent. The legs are blue-grey and the toes lobed, as in the Coot. The length is 6½ in., and the tarsus 0·8 in. ; the wing span is between 7–8 in., and the weight 1¼ oz.

The voice of the Red-necked Phalarope is similar in timbre to that of the Grey, but is lower-pitched. It utters a variety of long and short whistling and scraping calls.

The Red-necked species shows little difference in behaviour and habits from its close relative. One of the tamest of birds, it pays little heed to the presence of Man, often alighting without fear on a wayside pool to feed. Its flight is swift and erratic. Waders do not normally swim, but swimming is the delight— especially in Winter—of the Red-necked Phalarope, which sails along, looking like a small gull. Like the Grey, the Red-necked Phalarope will " upend ", and it also indulges in the well-known and curious " spinning trick ", turning round and round on the surface of the water, perhaps to churn up bottom-living organisms for food. It walks and runs on land, but does not perch.

In Winter, and on passage, red-necked phalaropes are usually seen at sea in large or small flocks which perform amazing evolutions in the air. They often accompany whales and will rest on their backs ; they also follow shoals of fish.

In her ceremonial courtship-flight in Spring, the hen rises from the water, uttering her mating call, and her rapidly beating wings make a humming sound as she pursues her selected mate. Several females may chase one male.

Red-necked phalaropes arrive at their breeding haunts early in June, and remain until August. They nest in colonies in swampy ground near water. The nest is a hollow " scraped " in the ground among tussocks of grass by both parents. Sometimes the female starts " scraping " before pairing takes place, adopting the attitude characteristic of waders, i.e. with the breast to the ground and body nearly vertical. After pairing, both sexes

G. K. Yeates

RED-NECKED PHALAROPE. *This small Arctic bird occasionally breeds in the north of Scotland*

scrape, either separately or together. If the latter, the pair indulge in ceremonial behaviour in which the female turns her head backwards and pecks at the bottom of the scrape, while the male, standing behind her, does likewise, occasionally throwing grass or other vegetation over his shoulder or building it into the nest.

Preparatory to egg-laying, the female performs one or two ceremonial flights, calling her mate to follow her. Then the eggs, which have dark spots on a buff ground, are laid, usually as a clutch of four, after which the scraping ceremonial is renewed.

The eggs, which take about 20 days to incubate, are hatched by the male, who also cares for the young for about the same period. The chicks are at first clad in golden brown down, but later become buff-coloured and have two white stripes down their backs. One brood is usual.

RED PHALAROPE. American name for the Grey Phalarope (*q.v.*).

REDPOLL. Only two species of Redpoll—members of the Finch family—are on the British list, but each of these has various subspecies.

The Redpoll species proper (*Carduelis flammea*) thus has three subspecies listed : the Lesser Redpoll, a fairly common resident and winter visitor ; the Mealy Redpoll (known as Common Redpoll in the American list) which is an irregular winter visitor ; and the Greater Redpoll, an autumn passage migrant.

The Arctic Redpoll species (*Carduelis hornemanni*) is represented by Hornemann's Redpoll and Coues's Redpoll (also known as Hoary Redpoll). Both are rare stragglers from the Arctic, each having been recorded about a dozen times. *See also* under separate entries.

RED-RUMPED SWALLOW—Hirundo daurica rufula. This is a native of the Mediterranean, temperate Asia and north Africa. It is very like our Swallow—especially on the wing—except that is underparts are buff, and its white rump shades into chestnut red. No white appears on its tail. Its nape and eye-stripe are chestnut. The sexes are alike. The length is 7 in., the tarsus $\frac{1}{2}$ in., the wing span 8–10 in.

REDSHANK—Tringa totanus britannica. Always a British resident, the Redshank has of recent years greatly increased in numbers, and now breeds throughout the British Isles, except in Cornwall, Pembrokeshire and some parts of southern Ireland. As an abundant passage migrant it is a common occupant of marshes, reservoirs, sewage farms and lakes. Some remain inland all the Winter, but the majority are to be found frequenting tidal estuaries and mud flats. Some British birds cross the Channel, but many more arrive on our coasts from the Continent and Iceland.

An elegant bird, the Redshank is distinguishable from other waders by its long red legs and its long bill with a red base. The general colouring is grey-brown, speckled darker on the mantle ; the neck and breast are paler, but, like the flanks, are boldly streaked in black ; the underparts and rump are white. The upper tail coverts are white and on the hind wing appears a broad white crescent. The tail is white, barred in black. In Winter the general colouring is paler, and the underparts whiter. Male and female are alike. The length is 11 in., and the tarsus 1·9 in. ; the wing span is approx. 14 in., and the weight $5\frac{1}{2}$ oz.

In flight, the Redshank's white rear parts are conspicuous and distinctive. Its movement is swift and strong, with regular wing beats, and it calls noisily as it flies. On the ground, its progress is quick and restless ; it constantly bobs its head if uneasy or suspicious—an action common to many sandpipers, but even more noticeable in the Redshank. It perches on fences and posts, sometimes even on buildings, and tends to alight very gracefully.

Redshanks are gregarious, especially on passage, and are seen in hundreds with other waders on the shore. Inland they are usually

G. K. Yeates

REDSHANK. *A common resident in Britain, this member of the Sandpiper family sports red legs, which are much displayed in the courtship ceremony*

seen in small flocks, and will follow the plough in company with black-headed gulls and lapwings.

The Redshank, which swims easily, spends much time feeding on the shore, wading up to its belly and probing the mud for food, especially as the tide ebbs. When occupied with its toilet, it will now and then dip its bill in the water, presumably to clean it.

The courtship display of the Redshank is particularly engaging to watch. Both male and female take part. Dr. Julian Huxley, who has made a special study of the Redshank's display, has described it as follows :

> " I spent some time watching them, and soon saw the redshanks courting. It was one of the most entrancing of spectacles. Redshanks, cock as well as hen, are sober-coloured enough as you see their trim brown bodies slipping through the herbage. But during the courtship all is changed. The cockbird advances towards the hen with his graceful, pointed wings raised above his back, showing their pure-white under-surface. He lifts his scarlet legs alternately in a deliberate way—a sort of graceful goosestep— and utters all the while a clear, far-carrying trill, full of wildness, charged with desire, piercing, and exciting. Sometimes, as he nears the hen, he begins to fan his wings a little, just lifting himself off the ground, so that he is walking on air. The hen will often suffer his approach till he is quite close, then shy away like a startled horse, and begin running, upon which he folds his wings and runs after. She generally runs in circles, as if the pursuit was not wholly disagreeable to her, and so they turn and loop over the gleaming mud."

The noisy Redshank continually gives evidence of its presence, especially in the breeding season. One of its local names is " Teuke ", which gives some indication of its flute-like sound. Its musical bubbling song is uttered in the air, on the ground or from a perch.

> Whenever one approaches to within 100 yards of a Redshank's nest, the typical alarm call begins. Leaving the nest, the hen sits on a fence repeatedly uttering her very rhythmical disyllabic call. Very often the male joins in to make a duet of it. If the birds are not excited, the calls are softer. These same soft musical calls, of which the actual song, too, is composed, are also uttered in flight. On one occasion I had the good luck to observe six redshanks, 100 feet up in the air, uttering most excited calls as they mobbed a Magpie.—EDITOR.

Redshanks breed in any kind of damp neighbourhood—a marsh, a meadow near a river, rough pasture, or on the edge of a moor, up to about 1,500 ft. in the central highlands. The nest is well concealed amid the long grass ; the cosy hollow is lined with grasses, and an opening is left at the side. The arrangement is done by the hen, with the cock supervising operations. The normal number of eggs is four ; they vary widely, from bluish-white to yellowish-brown, spotted and blotched in brown

and grey. They are laid at the end of April in England, in May in the north. Both male and female hatch them for 24 days, beginning on the completion of the clutch. The chicks, clad in brown and buff down on top and white underneath, soon leave the nest, and are tended by both parents for about a month. There is one authentic instance of a parent carrying a chick while flying. The Redshank is single-brooded.

Insects, molluscs, and crustaceans probed from the mud are the Redshank's chief food, but some vegetable matter is also eaten.

H. N. Southern

RED-SPOTTED BLUETHROAT. This Robin-like bird is also often called the Swedish Nightingale

RED-SPOTTED BLUETHROAT — Cyano-sylvia svecica. Among our most regular and frequent passage-migrants, red-spotted bluethroats travel in considerable numbers along the east coast in the Autumn, and are to be found lurking in scrubland, gardens and bushes near the coast. They have also been recorded in Spring, but much less frequently.

This robin-like bird breeds in the mountain bogs of northern Europe and Asia, and spends the Winter in India. Its plumage is chiefly dark brown and reddish chestnut, much lighter underneath ; but its most striking feature is the beautiful blue, surrounded by rich chestnut, of its throat. The hen is lighter both on the mantle and underneath, and shows very little or no blue. The length is about 5 in., and the tarsus 1·1 in. ; the wing span is about 6 in., and the weight approximately ½ oz.

The Bluethroat is rarely observed, for it mostly remains hidden among swampy vegetation. It is a hopping bird, and has a flitting flight. It is a lovely songster, the clear, sweet notes of its varied song resembling the White-spotted Bluethroat's and—to a certain extent— the Nightingale's. It sings from a low perch.

REDSTART—Phoenicurus phoenicurus. One of the most attractive and striking of our summer resident members of the *Turdidae* family, the Redstart occurs throughout the British Isles. Its distribution, though wide, is extremely localised ; it breeds, for instance, in one county and is missing from the next, e.g. in Devon, but not in Cornwall. This is true also of Scotland. Ireland had it once as a nester, but it is doubtful whether any redstarts breed there now. Abroad, the species occurs throughout Europe, temperate Asia and north Africa.

No difficulty is experienced in recognizing the Redstart, or Firetail as it is often called ; no British bird has such a brilliant red tail except its close relative, the Black Redstart, and from that bird it can be told by their very different plumages. In his summer dress, the male Redstart is a lovely bird, with his blue-grey head and mantle, black throat and cheeks, and white forehead. His breast and underparts are the same colour as his tail. In Winter, he is like the hen, duller with browner underparts and a paler throat. The young are more mottled on their upper and lower parts, but have the characteristic tail. The legs and bill are black. The length is 5½ in., and the tarsus 0·9 in. ; the wing span is 7 or 8 in., and the weight ½ oz.

In April the Redstart arrives to add its attractive presence and song to the ever-growing number of summer visitors. Woods, parklands, heaths and commons, gardens and orchards— any places that afford old timber for nesting holes—are its favourite haunts ; the sides of ditches and streams with pollard willows also attract it.

The Redstart's similarity to the Robin in many of its movements is at once noticeable in its flight, walk and carriage ; it has the same bobbing action of its body, and the same inquisitiveness regarding the human race. But it is less often seen on the ground. Among trees it moves with restless activity in the branches, darting in and out after some passing insect. It perches, often at some height, on a bush, wall, or building. The Redstart is not gregarious, but on migration may often be found in the company of the Pied Flycatcher. It roosts in a hole in a tree or building.

Both cock and hen take part in the spring courtship, when they chase each other from branch to branch, constantly displaying and flirting their colourful tails.

The Redstart has a variety of chat-like call notes. The song is a brief musical warble not without some resemblance to the song of the Robin, but never attaining to that bird's cheery and continuous song ; always there is a characteristic, short, rather metallic ending. Individual redstarts, however, vary greatly in performance, and some are comparable with our best songsters. The Redstart frequently mimics the songs of other birds, and sometimes sings at night. Its song is usually delivered from a high tree, but rarely for long in one spot ; it is best heard from April until mid-June.

In choice of nesting site, redstarts are almost as catholic as robins ; holes in rocks, quarries, rotten tree stumps, walls of ruins, are usual, but the holes discarded by woodpeckers, swallows' old nests, old tins, etc., are all used, and they are easily attracted to nesting boxes. The same hole is often used year after year. The nest is built by the hen, of grasses, moss and roots, and lined with hair and feathers ; five or six—sometimes more—pale blue eggs are laid in May. The hatching takes a fortnight. Both parents rear the young for much the same period. The Redstart feeds entirely on insects, the young are fed chiefly on caterpillars.

RED-THROATED DIVER—Colymbus stellatus. The smallest, best known, and the most easily identified of our divers, the Red-throated Diver is a British resident, breeding in the Scottish Highlands and islands and in one district of Northern Ireland. It is also a common winter visitor and passage-migrant, especially on the east coast ; abroad, it breeds in the same northern countries of Europe and America as other divers.

Its appearance is distinctive ; besides its smaller size and different plumage, it can at all seasons be identified by the shape of its bone-coloured bill which, in contrast to those of both the Great Northern and Black-throated Diver, has a marked curve. In its summer plumage, its throat is a rich, dark red ; its head and the sides of its throat are grey, and even lines of grey and white run down the back of its neck. Its upper parts are brownish-grey, without the conspicuous white speckles of the other divers. Underneath it is white. In Winter, the grey of

John Markham

RED-THROATED DIVER. *Not only its red throat-patch, but its curved bill are unique* the upper parts is slightly speckled in white, and the throat and underparts are white. The legs are grey and black, and the eye red. The total length of the Red-throated Diver is 21-32 in., the body being 14 or 15 in., and its tarsus is 2·6 in. ; its weight ranges from 3 to 4 lb. The wing span is 1½-2 ft. *See* plate f. p. 182.

The Red-throated has some similarity to the Black-throated Diver, and in a bad light, or at a distance, it might be mistaken for that bird. The watcher will note, however, how much more easily it takes to its wings than its relatives. Its flight is fast and powerful. It owes its local Northern name of " Rain Goose " to a superstitution that its call presages rain, and it is a curious fact that during rain it likes to circle at a considerable height, uttering its curious call.

I had the opportunity to watch a pair of red-throated divers in a wild and remote, crater-like district on a fairly large loch. Day and night observation only gives an idea of their vocal production ; my recording gear in a tent was about 300 yards from the nest in which the female was sitting on the two eggs. The male was swimming around when suddenly the female joined it and the air vibrated from the eerie loon call of both, going on for many minutes. Another time, after midnight, the female was sitting and the birds were calling to each other. This call or song was very different from the first one : much harsher, but also carrying far and repeated about 20 times. I heard, furthermore, the characteristic croak-like alarm note uttered on the ground and in flight, and finally the flight note, which I tried to record when the bird was flying very high and far from my microphone.

These recordings were made before the birth of the young. When the young are hatched the vocabulary of calls is enlarged but the young themselves can only be heard at close quarters.—EDITOR.

The Red-throated Diver is, of course, an excellent diver ; its longest recorded dive lasted 69 seconds, and its greatest recorded depth is 29 ft. Although awkward and clumsy on the ground, it is a graceful and playful bird on the water, frisking about, flapping its wings, and at times turning complete somersaults and lying on its back. These gambols are no doubt connected with its spring displays, but are not confined to that season.

The Red-throated Diver, although shy, is more socially inclined than the other divers, and will breed in company with its fellows. Small tarns and pools among the hills, rather than large lakes or lochs, attract it in the nesting season, which is usually late May or June. The nest, typical of the divers, is merely a flattened bit of earth hastily chosen on a hummock near the water, or on a small islet. In a rainy season it is often in danger of being submerged by the rising water. Normally two eggs make a clutch ; they are ovate, and variable in colouring, sometimes olive or green and some-

G. K. Yeates

REDWING. Unlike the Song-Thrush, its very near relative, a Redwing is extremely fond of company

times dark brown, with blackish-brown spots and blotches. Both birds are thought to take a share in the hatching, but the hen probably does the major part; the period is three or four weeks. Red-throated divers are devoted parents, and tend their chicks for as long as two months. One brood is reared in a season.

The food is principally fish of all kinds, which are sought on larger lakes, in lochs, and at sea.

RED-THROATED PIPIT—Anthus cervinus. The Red-throated Pipit occasionally wanders to Great Britain on its spring and autumn migrations from and to northern Europe and Asia; there are about 20 records chiefly from south-east England and from the lighthouses.

In general appearance, and when it is likely to be seen here, it closely resembles the Tree-Pipit; it is only in its summer dress that the Red-throated Pipit has the reddish throat and breast from which it gets its name. The length is 5¾ in., and the tarsus 0·9 in.; the wing span is 7 in., and the weight about ¼ oz.

Only the song is characteristic. This is described as quite different in the breeding season from those of other pipits and in particular as more musical and fuller in tone than the Meadow-Pipit's.

RED-THROATED THRUSH. Alternative name for Black-throated Thrush (*q.v.*).

REDWING—Turdus musicus. A regular and common winter visitor to the British Isles, this beautiful northern thrush arrives—sometimes in large numbers—in September and October, and leaves again in March or April. One or two pairs of redwings have nested successfully in north Scotland. The Redwing breeds in Norway, north Sweden, Russia, Siberia and even in Germany, in country where birch trees and

Eric Hosking

REED-BUNTING. The most conspicuous identification mark of this bunting is its wide white collar that gives the bird a somewhat pontifical air

black head and throat, and distinctive clean white collar. Its underparts vary from white to a pale buff brown The hen is duller and lacks the black on head and throat. Both birds have the outer white tail - feathers common to the majority of buntings. The Reed-Bunting has rather a jerky and undulating flight, and on the ground it walks, hops and runs. Its length is about 6 in., and its tarsus 0·8 in. Its wing span is 9 in. and its weight ¾ oz.

Bird watchers find the behaviour of the Reed-Bunting in its breeding season of great interest, for its whole life is devoted to staking its claim to nesting territory, mating and rearing young. Once his mate is chosen, the male performs his " sexual chase ", pursuing the female with frantic twistings and tumblings among the branches of the trees. Injury-feigning (*q.v.*) is very common in these birds during the breeding and nesting season.

The Reed-Bunting's song consists of a monotonous repetition of notes uttered from a perch on a reed stem, bush, a stump or low tree, but patient watching has shown that this song has variations which the Editor was able to record. Its song begins at the end of March and lasts well into July.

The breeding season begins in late April. The nest is placed usually on marshy ground, not actually among the reeds but in herbage, as is the habit with buntings. It is built by the hen alone and is composed chiefly of leaves, moss and fine grasses, and lined with hair. Four or five pale brown eggs, with the usual blotches and scrawlings of bunting eggs, are laid. The hatching is done chiefly by the hen, with the cock taking an occasional part ; the period is about a fortnight. The young are fed by both parents, and at least two broods— sometimes even three—are reared in a season.

The Reed-Bunting's food, like that of other buntings, consists chiefly of seeds, but insects are also taken. This bird is also known as Reed-Sparrow and Pit-Sparrow.

REED-PHEASANT. Local name for Bearded Titmouse (*q.v.*).

REED-SPARROW. Alternative name for the Reed-Bunting (*q.v.*) also called Pit-Sparrow.

scrubland abound. The Iceland Redwing (*q.v.*) is an allied race, breeding in Iceland.

In size, build and plumage the Redwing is very similar to the Song-Thrush, but its broad and conspicuous white eye-stripe, and chestnut flanks and under wing, are sufficient to distinguish it. It is olive-brown above, but much paler below, with spotted neck, breast and flanks. It has a blackish bill and yellowish-brown legs. The sexes are alike. The length is 8¼ in., and the tarsus 1·2 in.; the wing span is about 10 in., and the weight 2½ oz.

The Redwing resembles the Song-Thrush in flight, walk and behaviour, but, unlike the latter, is one of the most gregarious of our winter visitors, roaming the countryside in flocks, often in the company of the Fieldfare.

The true song of the Redwing is unknown in Britain, where only its harsh alarm call and a low, warbling chorus from a flock preparing to depart are heard. As the birds pass over on migration, through the night, a soft but penetrating sub-song is audible for some distance. At its breeding quarters its simple song, typical of the Thrush family, consists of three or four clear, flute-like notes.

REED-BUNTING—Emberiza schoeniclus. In the breeding season this is a resident of reed and osier beds, fens and river banks all over Britain. In Winter many birds leave the marshy places and, in company with finches and other buntings, seek their food in the open fields. Others cross the Channel but return again in the Spring. On the other hand, many reed-buntings arrive from the Continent to winter in Britain and leave again in the Spring.

The Reed-Bunting is an attractive and handsome bird, with its brown streaked dress,

REED-WARBLER—Acrocephalus scirpaceus.
Summer visitors only, reed-warblers arrive in
England at the end of April and leave again in
August and September for their winter quarters
in the tropics. During their stay, the reed beds
of the south and Midlands give the majority
cover to nest and rear their young. A few will
venture to breed in the west and even further
north, but reed-warblers rarely wander to
Scotland and Ireland, although there is a
known record of a nest and young in Ireland in
1935. Abroad, reed-warblers breed in many
parts of central and south Europe, temperate
Asia and north-west Africa.

The Reed-Warbler is a sober-looking little
bird, and its dress of brown is in keeping with
its surroundings. Closely allied to both the
Sedge- and Marsh-Warbler—two other summer
visitors—and very like them in general colouring,
the Reed-Warbler lacks both the conspicuous
eye stripe and the dark markings on the head
and mantle of the Sedge-Warbler, and can be
distinguished from the Marsh-Warbler—though
with greater difficulty—by its slightly darker
colouring and reddish tints, especially on the
rump. Its dark legs and thin bill are brown.
The sexes are alike. The length is 5 in., and
the tarsus 0·9 in. ; the wing span is about
6 in., and the weight less than ¼ oz.

The Reed-Warbler is not really gregarious,
but a shortage of nesting sites may bring
several pairs to the same reed bed. A skilful
acrobat, it climbs and hops restlessly among the
reeds, with one foot clinging to the stem and
the other drawn close up to its body.

The Reed-Warbler's nest is a wonderful work
of art. Slung among the swaying reeds, or
occasionally placed in
a bush or hedge some
distance from water, it
is a deep cup-shaped
construction made by
the little hen alone from
moss and reed flowers,
woven round one or
two stems so firmly that
it will stand the strain
of any winds that blow.
The lining is of grass,
feathers, wool and hair.
The four eggs, greenish-
blue and spotted, are
laid in late May or early
June. Both birds share
the hatching for 11 or
12 days, and tend the
chicks for much the
same period. Two
broods are often reared
in a season. The Reed-

Warbler is one of the birds upon which the
Cuckoo most commonly foists its offspring.

The courtship is of the simplest ; there is
little display or posturing, the male merely
fluffing out his feathers and spreading his tail
while he utters his little love song.

In the mating season the Reed-Warbler is
the noisiest of the birds that nest in reed and
osier beds. The timbre of its song is unmistakable, and cannot be confused with that of the
Sedge-Warbler. But the chief feature of the
song is its length ; in the early morning and late
evening the Reed-Warbler will, if undisturbed,
sing for hours on end. Sometimes, after a
hurried phrase in the song, I have been delighted
to catch the rarely heard but typical " chuckling ", which is more musical than the ordinary
song. The song is at its best from the bird's
arrival until the end of April or May ; it declines
from June onwards. Like the Sedge-Warbler,
the Reed-Warbler is inclined to mimic other
birds, but in this neither of them can compare
with that master mimic, the Marsh-Warbler.
The Reed Warbler's brawling alarm call is
lower and louder than its song.—EDITOR.

Marsh insects and their larvae are its principal
food, but spiders, worms and suchlike and
some autumn berries are also taken.

REEVE. Female of Ruff (*q.v.*).

REGULUS. The only genus in the family
Regulidae (the Goldcrest family) of the order
Passeriformes. The genus contains four species,
various forms of which occur in Europe,
northern and western Asia, Formosa, northern
Africa, and north and south America. There
are two species on the British list : the Goldcrest
(*q.v.*) and the Firecrest (*q.v.*).

REMEX (pl. Remiges). Quill feathers of the
wing (*q.v.*). *See also Plate f.p.* 1 ; Feather.

W. Farnsworth

REED-WARBLER. *The nest is a wonderful work of art. Shaped like a cup,
it is woven round a couple of reeds and will withstand any stormy blast*

REPRODUCTION AND DEVELOPMENT

R. WAGSTAFFE, M.B.O.U.

The author discusses the processes leading up to the laying of the egg and the subsequent development of the embryo (q.v.). Various stages of development are shown in the diagrams and in the unique photographic series on the Plate f.p. 464

REPRODUCTION. In birds, the sexual act is normally preceded by courtship displays and other stimuli (*see* Breeding Season), which vary considerably from one species to another (*see* Behaviour ; Display). Such displays serve, amongst other things, to excite the sexual urge, particularly in the female who must be suitably conditioned before the male can " tread " her.

Apart from the *Ratites* (Cassowary, Emu, etc.), *Anseriformes* (ducks, geese and swans), and a few other species, birds do not possess a definite penis, and sperm is ejaculated directly from the cloaca of the male into that of the female. The spermatozoa of birds are quite typical ; each spermatozoan consisting of a head, an infinitely small middle piece, and a locomotive tail (*flagellum*). The ripe egg (*ovum*), shed from the ovary and caught up by the trumpet-shaped mouth of the oviduct, is a large globular, yellow body (in fact, the largest single cell known), consisting mainly of concentric layers of yellow and white yolk with a small cap of formative protoplasm known as the germinal disc, the whole being invested in a thin, strong vitelline membrane.

Insemination having been effected, spermatozoa find their way to the upper portion of the oviduct, where one penetrates and fuses with the ovum. This fusion is the initiation of a new individual carrying hereditary characters from both parents.

The fertilized egg now proceeds to rotate down the oviduct, from the inner walls of which it receives important additions. The albumen (white of the egg), which is first added, is twisted at both ends by the rotary movement of the egg into chords (*chalazae*), which suspend and keep the yolk in position. This

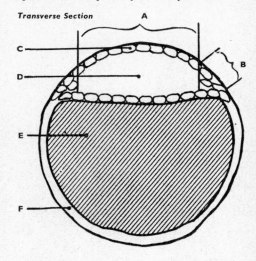

Transverse Section

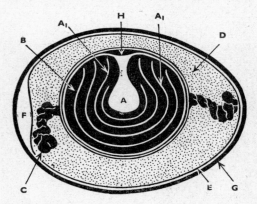

REPRODUCTION. *Fig. 1 : Structure of bird's egg, showing layers of white yolk, A₁, disposed round central portion of white yolk, A. Yellow yolk, B, lies around this, and the whole yolk is kept in place by the chalazae, C. The vitelline membrane encloses the yolk, all of which is surrounded by the white of egg or albumen, D. E is the double membrane around the egg, which forms the air-chamber, F, at the broad end. The whole egg is enclosed in a two-layered calcareous shell, G. The germinal disc, H, lies on the white yolk*

Fig. 2 : Early stage in development. Germinal disc divides into a layer of cells (blastoderm), separated from the yolk, except at the edges, by a fluid-filled cavity (blastocoel). A is area pellucida ; B, area opaca ; C, blastoderm ; D, blastocoel ; E, yolk ; and F, vitelline membrane

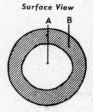

Surface View

is followed by a shell membrane and then by a calcareous shell, together with background colour (*see* Fig. 1). The membrane is double, but is separated at the blunt end of the egg to form an air cavity. Lower down the oviduct the spots of red-brown, etc., derived probably from bile pigments, are added. Finally, in the lowest portion of the ovary, mucus is secreted to assist the expulsion of the egg, the blunt end of which emerges first.

During the descent of the fertilized egg down the oviduct the early stages of division and development take place. Here it is important to emphasise that in birds, because of the immense amount of yolk, division is entirely confined to the germinal disc, in contrast with mammals in which, since there is little yolk, the whole material of the egg becomes segmented. With repeated divisions the germinal disc comes to consist of a layer of cells (*blastoderm*) separated from the yolk below by a fluid-filled cavity (*blastocoel*) except at the edges, where the cells are in direct contact with the yolk. In surface view the blastocoel appears as a relatively clear area (*area pellucida*), with the marginal cells showing as a narrower, denser area (*area opaca*), as shown in Fig. 2 b. From the underside of the blastoderm a sheet of cells s split off and comes to lie directly over the yolk (*see* Fig. 2a). It is approximately at this stage that the egg is laid and all development ceases until reactivated by the warmth of a parent or foster-parent, or, as in the case of Mound Birds (*Megapodiidae*) by the heat of decaying vegetation or of the sun.

Incubation brings about a series of further changes. In the centre of the area pellucida appears a straight raised ridge (the primitive streak), which is grooved along its length and passes into a distinct swelling at one end (the primitive knot), as shown in Fig 3a. Orientated at right angles to the longitudinal axis of the egg, it is the first indication of the embryo, which will be developed along its axis. Cells on each side of the primitive streak migrate outwards into the blastocoel cavity to form a continuous sheet of cells known as the *mesoderm*.

The original blastoderm has now formed three fundamental cell-layers—an upper layer, the *ectoderm* ; a lower layer, the *endoderm* overlying the yolk ; and a *mesoderm* layer between.

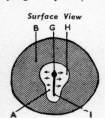

Surface View

These three layers are found in all but the lowest forms of animals. In birds, the ectoderm gives rise to the skin and its appendages such as feathers, the whole of the nervous system, and parts of the sense organs. The mesoderm gives rise to

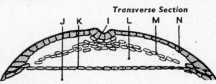

Transverse Section

REPRODUCTION. *Fig. 3: First stage in the development of embryo proper. Straight, grooved, raised ridge appears (the primitive streak), with a swelling at one end (the primitive knot). Cells migrate outwards to form a continuous layer, the mesoderm, eventually giving rise to blood system, muscles and skeleton. A, area pellucida ; B, area opaca ; G, primitive knot ; H, cells moving outwards ; I, primitive streak ; J, yolk ; K, endoderm ; L, blastocoel ; M, mesoderm ; N, ectoderm*

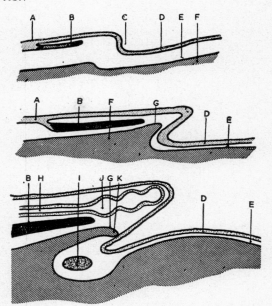

Fig. 4 : *Three stages in the development of the head of the embryo. A is the primitive knot ; B, head process ; C, origin of head-fold ; D, ectoderm ; E, endoderm ; F, yolk ; G, fore-gut ; H, spinal cord ; I, heart ; J, brain ; K, mouth*

the blood system, muscles and skeleton, connective tissue of all parts of the body, and the excretory and reproductive organs. The endoderm forms the whole of the lining of the gut (and its outgrowths, such as the liver), except for the mouth and anus which are formed as inpushings of ectoderm.

With repeated divisions, the blastoderm gradually spreads further over the yolk, and soon indications of the head of the embryo appear. Cells from the primitive knot move forward to form a notochord or head-process (*see* Fig. 4), and a wide crescentic fold—the head-fold—appears in front of this, lifting up a portion of the blastoderm above the yolk. The pocket formed within this " head " is the first indication of the fore-gut, and is lined with endoderm. (If an egg is held with the blunt end to the right hand of the observer, then the head will invariably be facing away from him.) Later in development a similar, but shallower, tail-fold appears at the hind end, and lifts up the " tail "—the endoderm lining—of the embryo (*see* Fig. 5) ; this forms the hind-gut. Eventually the head and tail folds are joined up by lateral folds, and the whole of the embryo becomes pinched off from the yolk, except at one point where it remains attached by a stalk (the yolk-plug), through which yolk passes to the developing embryo.

Concurrently with the formation of the head-fold other changes are taking place in the centre part of the area pellucida, which alone forms the embryo proper. (The blastoderm area beyond this is known as the extra-embryonic area.) The ectoderm along the middle line sinks to form a groove ; folds arise on

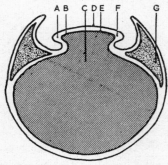

REPRODUCTION. Fig. 5 : Longitudinal section showing formation of head- and tail-fold. A, head-fold ; B, beginning of fore-gut ; C, yolk-plug ; D, ectoderm ; E, endoderm ; F, tail-fold

either side of this groove and meet in the centre to cut off a tube—the neural tube (see Fig. 6)—enclosing as they do so the primitive streak posteriorly. The anterior end of this neural tube becomes constricted into three regions—the fore-brain, the mid-brain and the hind-brain—whilst posteriorly it is prolonged into the spinal chord (see Fig. 7). With further development of the brain the head of the embryo becomes heavy and bends downwards on to the yolk. Eventually, owing to the twisting of its axis, the embryo comes to lie on its left side.

The mesoderm on either side of the middle line becomes divided into a number of cube-shaped blocks called somites (see Fig. 7). From each somite a lower portion (myotome)

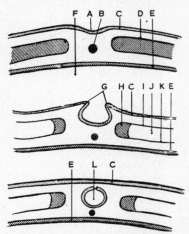

Fig. 6 : Transverse sections showing formation of the neural tube. A, is neural groove ; B, noto-cord ; C, ectoderm ; D, mesoderm ; E, endoderm ; F, yolk ; G, neural folds ; H, somite ; I and K, mesoderm layers ; J, coelom ; K, neural tube

gives rise to the body muscles ; a middle portion (sclerotome) to the skeleton ; and an upper portion (dermatome) to the lower layers of the skin. Just outside the base of each somite is a nephrotome (also formed from mesoderm), which gives rise to the excretory system. Farther out, laterally (see Fig. 6), the mesoderm splits into an upper layer adjacent to the ectoderm and a lower layer adjacent to the endoderm, with a space between known as the coelom. The coelom which spreads out beneath the extra-embryonic area is known as extra-embryonic coelom (see Fig. 8). Blood islands, formed in the mesoderm of the area opaca, coalesce to form tiny blood vessels, which in their turn unite into a pair of large veins—the vitelline veins—which carry nutriment to the embryo from each side (see Fig. 7). These veins join together and lead to the heart, which is at first a single straight tube (formed

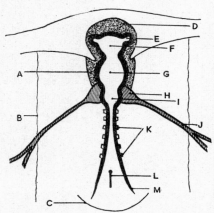

Fig. 7 : The embryo takes form. A, fore-gut ; B, amniotic fold ; C, tail-fold ; D, head-fold ; E, optic vesicle ; F, fore-brain ; G, mid-brain ; H, heart ; I, hind-brain ; J, one of vitelline veins ; K, somites ; L, primitive streak ; M, neural fold

in the coelom from mesoderm), lying directly beneath the fore-gut. From the heart a blood vessel divides to pass on either side of the gut and joins over it to form a vitelline artery, which leads back to the area opaca.

The endoderm which is pinched off into the embryo proper as the head, tail and lateral folds arise, forms the fore-gut at the head end and the hind-gut at the tail end, but remains in direct contact with the yolk until a much later stage.

As the embryo develops, it becomes enclosed in a number of foetal membranes. The blastoderm outside the embryo grows up on all sides round the embryo and fuses over it to form a double-layered dome. The inner layer, the amnion (see Fig. 8), encloses the embryo in a fluid-filled cavity. The outer layer, the chorion, is in direct contact with the shell membranes. A

DEVELOPMENT OF THE EMBRYO

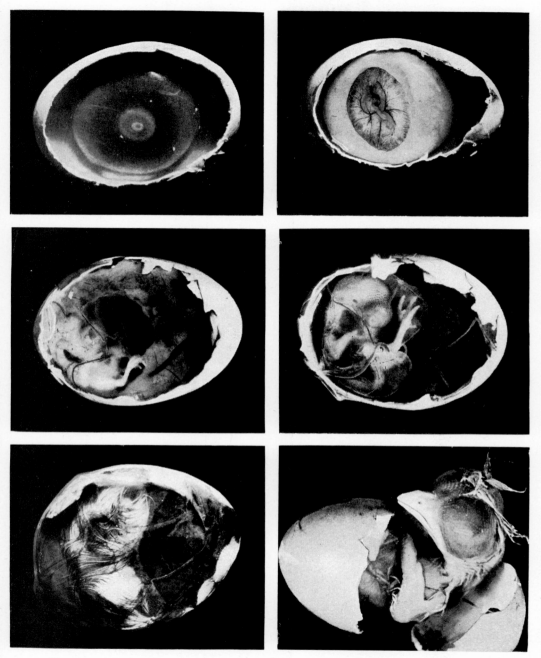

These pictures, reading from top left to bottom right, indicate the development of the embryo once incubation has started. They were, except for the last one by Lynwood M. Chace, which shows a Robin breaking the egg-shell, taken by our own photographer and depict the domestic fowl's egg. The first photograph shows what development has occurred 12 hours after incubation began; the second, taken 2½ days later, clearly shows the major blood-vessels; some parts of the future chick are already recognizable in the third photograph, taken on the 11th day; and in the next picture the changes occurring in the next four days are quite evident; while in the fifth picture the chick is almost ready to emerge after 21 days of incubation

yolk-sac is also developed, enclosing the yolk and serving to transfer it to the embryo.

From the hind-gut a small sac—the *allantois* (*see* Fig. 9)—grows out into the space between the amnion and chorion. It soon increases in size and comes to surround the whole of the embryo, the yolk-sac and any unabsorbed albumen. Blood vessels from the embryo are distributed abundantly to the allantois, and

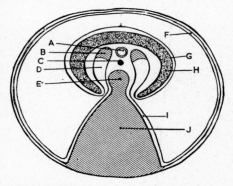

REPRODUCTION. *Fig. 8 : Developing embryo is protected by double-layered dome ; inner layer (amnion) encloses a protective " water-cushion," outer layer (chorion) is in contact with shell-membrane. A, neural tube ; B, somites ; C, noto-chord ; D, coelom ; E, gut ; F, chorion ; G, am-nion ; H, amniotic cavity ; I, yolk-sac ; J, yolk*

serve to capture the oxygen which diffuses through the shell. It is, in fact, the respiratory organ of the embryo. Moreover, as excretory products are discharged into its cavity from the kidneys, it also functions as a urinary bladder.

The origin of the main parts of the body having been determined, development continues and the embryo be-comes more and more complex. Nerves grow out from the brain and spinal cord to all parts of the body. The heart, from a simple straight tube, develops into a four-chambered structure, and its associated veins and arteries multiply and ramify throughout the body. Kid-neys and reproductive organs develop. The gut gradually becomes differ-entiated into oesophagus, stomach, duodenum and intestine, but still remains attached by the yolk-plug to the yolk-sac. Before hatching, these are drawn up into the abdomen and the body cavity is

completely closed. Outgrowths of the duo-denum form the liver and pancreas, and the lungs also arise as outgrowths from the gut. Limbs bud out from the body ; they are at first similar to each other in shape and form, but gradually begin to show typical avian characters, the fore-limbs becoming wing-like and the hind-limbs developing feet and claws. Feathers protrude as papillae from the surface of the skin and become arranged (in most birds) in clearly defined feather-tracts (*pterylae*). The skeleton which is at first cartilaginous, becomes more and more bony, but is not completely ossified until some time after the chick is hatched. On the head the ears, jaws and nose become distinct, the last developing into a beak provided with a horny knob (shed later), the " egg tooth ", which assists the young bird in breaking the shell on hatching. In the domestic fowl incubation is completed in 21 days, but in some species, it may last as long as 40 or 50 days, or as little as 10 or 11 days in small Passerine birds (*see* Breeding Tables). In the process of hatching, the young bird thrusts its beak through the inner shell membrane to the air cavity at the blunt end, whence it takes its first breath of air before proceeding to break the shell.

In ducks, geese and swans and some other birds (including the domestic fowl) the young emerge from the shell completely covered with down, and are soon able to run about and feed themselves ; such birds are called *Nidifugae*. In the perching birds and others, the young are at first helpless and naked, or covered with only patches of down, and must be kept fed and warm by the parents until they can fend for themselves ; these birds are called *Nidicolae*.

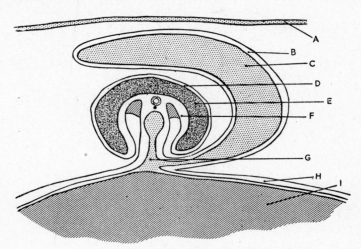

Fig. 9 : Embryo, yolk-sac and remaining albumen are finally surrounded by the allantois, which is both the respiratory and the excretory organ of the embryo. A, chorion ; B, allantois ; C, allantoic cavity ; D, amnion ; E, amniotic cavity ; F, embryo ; G, yolk-plug ; H, yolk-sac ; and I, the yolk

RESEARCH and EXPERIMENTAL WORK

STUART SMITH, Ph.D., M.B.O.U.

After showing how, during the past 25 years, the centre of interest in this work has shifted from the museum and aviary to the " field," the author describes a few of the experiments he has made to discover some of the reasons underlying bird behaviour

RESEARCH. Until the end of the First World War almost all the research and experimental work on birds was confined to the museum and the aviary. The last 25 years, however, have seen a tremendous advance in the scope of field ornithology, one result of which has been to raise its status to that of a scientific discipline recognized by the universities as worthy of inclusion in their schools of research. This transformation has taken place both here and on the European and American continents. In Europe, the now-famous researches of Konrad Lorenz in Austria, and of the Tinbergens in Holland, raised the study of animal behaviour, or " ethology ", as it is called, to a new level by the use of novel methods employing the living bird as experimental material.

Lorenz and N. Tinbergen were especially interested in studying the effect on bird behaviour

Eric Hosking

RESEARCH. Willow-warblers attacking dummy head of Cuckoo—especially round the eyes

of external stimuli, which, they found, were often quite simple. For instance, by means of cardboard models simulating the shapes of various birds, Lorenz demonstrated that the fear reaction could be evoked in geese by a model with a short, dumpy head and long tail. But if this was moved in the opposite direction, with the tail going first (resembling a flying goose), the geese ignored it.

Later, Tinbergen studied by means of models the stimulus that releases in young birds the begging reaction, i.e. the eager, upward-reaching action with wide-open gape that greets adults returning to the nest. With young thrushes it was shown that all that is necessary is that the object representing the parent bird should move ; it can be of any size greater than about 3 mm. in diameter, and has to be above the horizontal plane passing through the

nestling's eyes. Similar experiments showed that the red spot at the base of the Herring-Gull's lower mandible is the main factor governing the chicks' food-begging movements.

When Lorenz studied a colony of jackdaws that bred under his attic roof, he found that they reacted aggressively to any black object that he carried—for example, a black bathing costume — since they believed it to be one of their own number held captive.

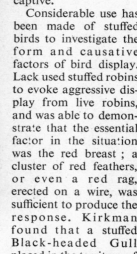

Considerable use has been made of stuffed birds to investigate the form and causative factors of bird display. Lack used stuffed robins to evoke aggressive display from live robins, and was able to demonstrate that the essential factor in the situation was the red breast ; a cluster of red feathers, or even a red rag, erected on a wire, was sufficient to produce the response. Kirkman found that a stuffed Black-headed Gull placed in the territory of a breeding pair of these birds was attacked vigorously by both birds, the point of attack being especially the black head of the mount. However, since a stuffed Black-headed Gull in winter plumage, without the black hood, was also vigorously attacked, it seems that the black hood is not an essential part of the stimulus. That the head itself is essential was proved by the fact that a decapitated dummy was not attacked by the breeding gulls.

The significance of the head in evoking attack has been studied by Edwards, Hosking and Smith in an extensive series of experiments with a stuffed Cuckoo. It was found that willow-warblers are very vigorous in their attacks against a Cuckoo whenever it appears in their breeding territories. The area attacked is always the head, nape and throat, and especially the area round the eyes. Using a wooden body to which a Cuckoo's tail, wings and head could be separately attached, these workers found that no attack occurred unless the head was present. Further experiments demonstrated that a Cuckoo's head fixed on a stick, without a body, was violently attacked.

It is probable that recognition (*q.v.*) among birds depends on similar simple but specific characters. The male of the American Woodpecker, known as the Flicker, differs from the female in having a tuft of black moustachial feathers on either side of the chin. In one experiment a female, after she had paired with the male, was provided with a pair of false feather-tufts to make her resemble a male ; and the male attacked his mate as soon as he saw the false feather-tufts. The black moustachial feathers are clearly an important sexual identification mark.

Since instantaneous recognition of a predator is of great importance in the survival of birds, simple recognition factors are an obvious advantage. Experimenting with stuffed hawks, and a stuffed Cuckoo, Edwards, Hosking and Smith showed that willow-warblers can instantly distinguish a Sparrow-Hawk from a Cuckoo, by differences between the heads. The same workers found that, when they are in the presence of a Cuckoo, birds use specific notes which are not normally used in other situations. Willow-warblers utter a harsh, " chittering " ; the Nightingale a higher-pitched, very excited screech ; and the Stonechat a swallow-like trill. Specificity of call notes appropriate to a given situation is thus proved. *See also* Call Note ; Song.

As well as stuffed birds, a mirror can be successfully used to evoke aggressive displays in some birds (though it must be remembered that many birds do not react at all before a mirror). As the attacking bird supplies, through its own mirror-image, the stimulus that provokes it, some remarkable displays are often seen. One such posture before a mirror, by a confused Oyster-catcher, was the " false-sleeping " attitude in which the bird assumed a sleeping posture, with beak tucked under its scapular feathers, and one leg raised, but with eyes wide open and body tensed. This posture, resulting from a conflict

of internal drives, is known as a " displacement reaction " (*see* Behaviour).

The fact that certain limited areas of a bird's body are specific stimuli draws attention to the colours in those areas. That most birds can see and appreciate colour is almost certain. This has been shown experimentally in various ways—for example, by colouring grains of corn used as food, or by illuminating food with varying colours. Such experiments have shown that domestic hens and pigeons are capable of discriminating colours, though over a narrower range than Man. Most owls are colour-blind, but they have very high sensitivity in conditions of low light-intensity, as befits birds that catch their prey at night.

The instinct of nest sanitation (*q.v.*), whereby birds keep their nests free from soiling by removing the faeces of the young, has been used by Smith to test the colour-awareness of yellow wagtails. By using artificial faeces made of coloured " Plasticene ", and by studying the preference shown by the birds in removing them, he was able to show that yellow wagtails have a preference for yellow as a colour. Similarly, robins find red a highly significant colour. One Robin attempted to attack, through the glass, the red side of a tomato put to ripen in a window ; another postured at the red comb of a large barn-door cockerel. It is interesting to conjecture how far specificity in colour-awareness is linked with the use of coloured adornments in the nuptial and aggressive displays of birds.

The experimental method has been applied to the study of migration (*q.v.*). Rowan demonstrated in Canada, by the use of migrant birds

Eric Hosking

RESEARCH. *Confused Oystercatcher, catching sight of itself in a mirror, assumes " false-sleeping " attitude with eyes wide open and tensed body*

(juncos) under controlled aviary conditions, that the urge to migrate was stimulated by increasingly long exposure to light. When the birds were exposed in Winter to progressively increasing doses of light from an electric lamp, their sex organs began to develop, and they reached breeding condition in spite of the fact that the temperature outside was below zero. Much work has been done since Rowan's early experiments by workers such as Wolfson and Bisonnette, who have shown that, as well as light, prolonged activity also plays its part in bringing a bird into breeding condition and thus initiating migration.

The direction finding and general homing abilities of wild birds have been studied in many countries ; in Great Britain, Lockley and Matthews especially have widened our knowledge of the homing abilities of sea-birds. For further information *see also* Navigation.

Much remains to be done, but it is evident that the methods of experimental research can find a wide application in the elucidation of the problems of ornithology.

RESERVE. *See* Nature Reserve.

RESIDENTS. *See* Status.

RESPIRATORY SYSTEM. *See* Anatomy ; *also* Air Sac.

RETICULATION. *See* Tarsus (diagram).

RHACHIS. The main shaft of a feather (*q.v.*), from which the barbs spring, which is joined at its lower end to the calamus (*q.v.*).

RHODOSTETHIA. Genus of gulls of the family *Laridae* of the order *Charadriiformes*. It contains one species—Ross's Gull (*q.v.*).

RICHARDSON'S SKUA. *See* Arctic Skua.

RICHARD'S PIPIT—Anthus richardi. A wanderer to Britain on migration from its home in central Asia and Siberia, Richard's Pipit has been recorded about a hundred times, mostly in the Autumn and chiefly in the southern and eastern counties of England, although there are one or two records for Scotland.

This pipit is a conspicuously large and long-legged member of the family. Its upper parts are dark brown and boldly speckled; its throat, underparts and outer tail feathers are white. At close range, the unusually long hind claw, much longer than that of the Tawny Pipit, is a good identification mark. The length is 7 in., the tarsus 1·2 in.; the wing span is approximately 9 in., and the weight ½ oz.

A shy and wary bird, Richard's Pipit has a strong and undulating flight and runs on the ground with an upright carriage. Its song is a monotonous repetition of five notes, uttered from the ground or a bush, or high in the air.

Grassy steppe and damp meadowland is the breeding ground of Richard's Pipit, the nest of grass and moss being placed in a sheltered hollow. In Siberia the breeding season is in June or July. Incubation of the four to six eggs is done chiefly by the hen, with the male never far away. Two broods are usually reared.

RICTAL BRISTLES. The gape bristles adhering to the bill.

RING-DOVE. Alternative name for Wood-pigeon (*q.v.*) a very common resident.

RINGED PLOVER—Charadrius hiaticula. One of our most attractive and familiar waders, the small Ringed Plover—also called the Ringed Dotterel—is found on shingle or pebbly shores, salt marshes, sandy beaches, or estuaries. It also breeds, though less abundantly, on inland sewage farms, the shingle shores of lakes and rivers, and occasionally even in cornfields. Outside the breeding season the inland sites are deserted, and the birds move to sandy or muddy shores, where their food is more plentiful. The Ringed Plover is also a passage migrant and winter visitor. Abroad, it breeds throughout Baffin Island, Greenland, Iceland,

Eric Hosking

RESEARCH. *This time a whole stuffed Cuckoo (not only a head) was used, and here is a Nightingale attacking the " foe " viciously and furiously*

Eric Hosking

RINGED PLOVER, *also called the Ringed Dotterel, one of our most attractive and familiar waders*

Eric Hosking

RINGED PLOVER. *Also called the Ringed Dotterel, this wader is found on all our shingly shores, where it lays its beautifully camouflaged eggs in a shallow hollow*

the Faeroes, Scandinavia, Spain and Portugal.

A sturdy-looking little wader, the Ringed Plover is easily picked out on the shore by its conspicuous black and white collars; the black lower collar round the breast is wide at the front and narrow at the back, while the white collar round the throat is more uniform. The upper parts are lightish brown with a white wing bar, and the underparts are white. In his breeding dress the male has black crown and cheeks that contrast with his white forehead. The female is browner on the black patches. The bill and legs are orange-red, the former tipped with black. The lack of any white wing bar on its near relative, the Little Ringed Plover, which within recent years has become established as a summer visitor, prevents confusion between the two. The length of the Ringed Plover is $7\frac{1}{2}$ in., and the tarsus is 1 in.; the wing span is approximately 11 in., and the weight 2 oz.

Active and lively, the Ringed Plover has the characteristic movement of its species on the ground, running here and there, and pausing now and then as if listening, somewhat in the manner of the thrush. It will patter in the mud, perhaps in an endeavour to bring to the surface the worms on which it feeds, but the same movement has been observed in the courtship display. Its low flight is swift and direct; when it alights, it runs a little way with raised wings before actually grounding. Outside the breeding season, a flock of ringed plovers will take wing with incredible speed, and wheel and turn high in the sky; then equally suddenly, as if at a word of command, they alight again at almost the same spot.

Although fairly tame, the Ringed Plover is nervous and suspicious, especially during the breeding season; it is particularly adept at injury feigning (*q.v.*), its perfect imitation of lameness or a broken wing being intended to draw attention from its nest and young. Protective coloration has reached the peak of perfection in this bird, as regards both the eggs and the young, but the nests are usually so exposed on the shore that the eggs must often be unintentionally destroyed by the feet of passers-by.

The Ringed Plover is highly sociable, not only with its own species, but with dunlins, redshanks, sanderlings, stints and other waders.

In the attractive spring display, the birds flit about, excitedly uttering their double trilling call notes; there is also a " scrape " ceremony, in which the male bows before his mate, scattering stones behind him or chasing her.

All plovers have a great variety of calls, especially on their breeding grounds. Apart from its trilling love song, the most characteristic call of the Ringed Plover is a liquid musical pipe, one of the most familiar and pleasant sounds of the sea-shore. The song is best heard in March, April and part of May.

A saucer-shaped hollow, scraped in the sand or shingle, protected with whatever material suits its surroundings, houses the three to five greyish dark-spotted eggs laid in May and June. Both male and female incubate for about three weeks, and rear the chicks for much the same period; these leave the nest early and are fully fledged in a month's time. Two broods—perhaps three—are normally reared, but this is difficult to ascertain.

The Ringed Plover feeds on the shore, picking up (not probing with its bill, as so many waders do) molluscs, crustaceans and worms and suchlike; some vegetable matter is also taken.

THE RINGING OF WILD BIRDS

R. M. LOCKLEY

Scientific bird-ringing began at the turn of the century—now about 100,000 birds are ringed annually in Britain alone. This has added greatly to our knowledge not only of migration but of the daily life of birds. See also *Bird Watching ; Observatory ; Trap*

RINGING. The truth of the saying that " birds of a feather flock together " was often the despair of the early ornithologists. As they could not identify the birds in their flocks they shot them, studied them in the dead flesh, and placed them acquisitively in cabinets. Today there is little excuse for collecting dead birds ; the modern way is to study them alive, by means of identification rings—first, a numbered ring with an address on it, and then, if necessary, a coloured ring.

Birds of the same species are extraordinarily difficult to distinguish individually except by some artificial mark. This is especially true where the sexes are outwardly alike ; for here exists like behaviour — mutual ceremonial, monogamy and faithfulness of male and female to each other and the home. At the other extreme, brilliantly - plumaged males are associated with polygamy, the male trying to attract several of the dowdy females, and afterwards leaving the incubation and rearing duties entirely to them. He is occupied solely with the three Ms : mating, moulting and maintenance. Yet, even to study the polygamous species, rings are needed to distinguish individuals from each other.

It is remarkable that bird-ringing should be such a new science. A search of archaeological literature might reveal that it was a Bronze Age man who placed the first metal ring on a bird—perhaps as a proprietary mark on a young Rock-Dove born in the crevices in the roof of his cave-dwelling. We know that the Romans occasionally marked a bird. In the Ligurian siege of the 3rd century B.C., the Roman garrison sent to Quintus Fabius Pictor a nesting Swallow so that it might return with news—the number of knots tied in a thread fastened to its leg was to indicate the number of days before relief would arrive. Pliny tells of one ingenious

Eric Hosking

RINGING. *Correct way of holding a bird for ringing, without causing discomfort or injury*

sportsman who took some swallows from his home at Volterra to the chariot races at Rome, and released them after painting the winning colours on their plumage !

In the 18th century the German, Johann L. Frisch tied coloured threads to the feet of swallows in order to test whether these birds hibernated under water, as the great naturalist Linnaeus (as well as Dr. Johnson and other savants of that time) believed ; when the swallows returned in the following Spring with the threads still brightly coloured, Frisch discarded the under-water theory.

Kings, courtiers and country gentlemen sometimes put a metal ring or plate around the neck or leg of a swan, goose or stork as a sign of ownership, and similarly marked any Heron that had survived being attacked and brought down by a royal falcon, as a certificate of merit ! Rarely, messages were engraved on the plates, asking for information of the bird's travels to be sent to the address on the ring.

In 1909 a devout Canadian, Jack Miner, began stamping metal rings with his address and quotations from the Bible, and placed them on the wild geese and ducks which came to his sanctuary at Kingsville, Ontario. This had a remarkable success among the superstitious and religious country people—especially Eskimo, Indian and Negro—who recovered these ringed wildfowl by shooting them elsewhere on their migrations ; many regarded the messages as personal invitations to follow the path of virtue. Jack Miner became world-famous in a few years ; his family continue to ring (or, as it is called in America, to " band ") wild fowl on a large scale at the original site.

However, the credit for the first systematic use of metal rings engraved with a serial number and an address goes to the Dane, Christian

Mortensen, who in 1899 used aluminium rings on the legs of starlings, after earlier experiments with strips of zinc. He obtained some recoveries immediately. Previous workers had merely stamped a number, or a letter, or the year and site, on their rings. Mortensen's success inspired ornithologists in Europe and America to organize bird-ringing on a national scale, for the value of this method of marking was soon obvious.

In 1904 was opened the now famous bird-marking station on the windswept North Sea island of Heligoland, where for centuries the sturdy Friesian inhabitants had trapped birds for food in their peculiar *troossel-goard* (thrush-bush) apparatus. This was made of a rectangle of imported bush- or tree-trimmings stuck upright in the ground and covered with a double net on one side ; the migrating birds, seeking a place to rest for a few hours on the island in Spring and Autumn, were attracted to this cover, and were then driven into the nets. German ornithologists copied this device in making a permanent trapping garden on Heligoland—a sanctuary surrounded with concrete walls and containing a planted copse and large funnels of wire-netting through which the birds could be concentrated into catching-boxes. In this way some 10,000 migrating birds were caught, identified, ringed and released annually.

Heligoland was made famous by Gätke, who studied birds there during the British ownership of the island in the 19th century. He listed nearly 400 species, and wrote a book in which he described the wonderful migration over the island. Some of his theories were extravagant : he estimated that waders could fly at four miles per minute, and that so small a bird as a Blue-throat could migrate at three miles per minute ! Nevertheless his *Birds of Heligoland* should be read by everyone interested in the ringing of birds. He pointed out the importance of setting up bird observatories " on the barren islands of the coasts of England ". This was a prophetic suggestion ; there are now at least twelve observatories along the coast of Britain where Heligoland-type traps are used for catching and ringing migratory birds.

Thanks to bird-ringing, we now know that migrants proceed at a much more leisurely pace, actual flight-speeds varying between 15 and 50 miles per hour ; for a bird may take many days to make its autumn migration between northern Europe and Africa, and in the reverse direction in Spring. Ringing has taught us that birds follow a traditional or hereditary route, some species preferring a westerly, some a middle, and some an easterly flight-line. There are many problems still to be solved: concerning direction-finding on migration (*q.v.*), the biological mechanism of navigation (*q.v.*) or orientation of the flocks and individuals on their long flights.

Bird-ringing is essential to all the tests needed for the answers. It has proved some very remarkable migration and homing feats. Thus ringed kittiwakes and puffins have crossed the Atlantic from Scotland to Newfoundland on a hitherto unsuspected normal migration, and Manx shearwaters from Skokholm Bird Observatory, South Wales, have been recovered in south America on what is evidently a normal migration of altogether 12,000 sea-miles. The record for a natural migration is at present held by an Arctic Tern ringed in West Greenland, which flew 11,000 miles in less than three months on its migration to winter quarters in the Indian Ocean. This speed approximates to 120 miles per day. It is easily surpassed by the Manx Shearwater which, transported by aeroplane in a homing test, returned to Skokholm from Boston, Massachusetts, in 12½ days—that is, at the rate of 244 miles per day ; allowing the bird time to feed by day and rest by night its flight-speed was probably about 25 miles per hour (this allows it no time for random searching for the way

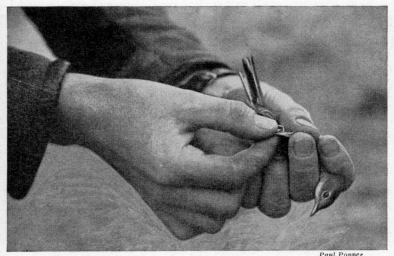

Paul Popper

RINGING. *Putting on the ring—a delicate operation requiring nimble fingers. In this country, ringers must be at least eighteen years of age*

RINGING. *If the ring was put on properly, the bird should, on release, feel no more discomfort than a lady does from her wrist-watch or bracelet*

whose pedigree and idiosyncrasies he has studied. Most wild birds have very short lives, and their genealogies build up swiftly in a few years of study. The bird-ringer is soon rewarded, although his study of one species may well last his lifetime, for there is no end to investigation of this sort, from the facts about incubation and rearing of the young to the complications of ecology (relationship of species to environment).

Close upon 100,000 birds are annually ringed in the British Isles today, the majority being caught in wire-netting traps of various kinds, and the minority ringed as young birds in the nest. In order to qualify as a ringer it is necessary to be not less than 18 years of age (Britain and U.S.A.), and to have had some experience of the technique under a qualified ringer, who will be able to vouch for the beginner's ability to identify and handle birds. The expert will handle his captures so gently that they suffer very little from the experience of being caught and ringed. He clips the ring closely around the leg of the adult bird, so that it is neither so loose as to catch in vegetation or nest-lining, nor so tight as to press on the leg's flesh or scales.

That birds are no more inconvenienced by a properly adjusted ring than a man is by a wrist-watch or a woman by a bracelet is clear from the behaviour of a bird after ringing : it will often return immediately to the trap where it was caught, to continue feeding, perhaps on the bait which first attracted it. At first a bird may peck at the ring for a moment, but it quickly forgets its existence, and will carry it lightly for the rest of its life without the slightest sign of wear—except to the ring, which may become weathered (in salt water the rings of sea-birds wear out and need to be renewed after a few years).

Provided it is properly carried out, ringing is an ideal and perfectly humane method of studying wild birds. The old way, as we have said, was to shoot the bird and place it in a cabinet. The new way is to extend protection to the bird in order that it may be studied as long as possible ; and Man has only to study an attractive creature like a bird for a short time before he begins to regard it with a lasting affection.

home over these seas which, in part at least, would be totally unfamiliar to it).

Apart from migration and homing, ringing has great significance in the study of the day-to-day life of the individual bird. Without ringing it is impossible to secure scientifically acceptable observations over the long period of years which is necessary to build up an accurate picture of the average life-history of a given species. The basis of such a study is the capture and marking of each individual forming the pairs, families and communities of one or more species in the area under survey (which may be a large island, a field, a wood, but most often is a small garden). Each bird is given a serially numbered aluminium ring which also bears an address (in the British Isles this address is the *British Museum of Natural History*, London). If it is not easy to capture the individuals at frequent intervals, a system of differently coloured rings, by which the individual can be identified at a distance, is used, in addition to the numbered ring, which is its ticket of identity should it be recovered away from the survey area. By these permanent identity marks we follow the adventures of each bird from the day of hatching throughout its growth to the adult stage, and subsequently observe its breeding behaviour, relations with others of its species, its neighbours and enemies, and eventually its death, when the length of its life can be calculated.

By ringing, patient students have built up their monographs which tell the true, fascinating story of a group of individual birds, just as the historian tells the interesting tale of some family

John Markham

ROBIN, *plump, cheeky and bold, a bird beloved by all*

For text see page 473

RING - NECKED DUCK. *See* American Ring-Necked Duck.

RING-OUZEL—Turdus torquatus. " The blackbird of the mountains ", the Ring-Ouzel comes to the British Isles as a Summer resident, haunting hilly and mountainous country, except in the south and Midlands of England ; it is very local in the west of Scotland and in Ireland. Ring-ouzels reported to have bred at lower altitudes are usually discovered to be albino (*q.v.*) blackbirds.

One of the earliest spring visitors, it arrives in the middle of March, and leaves again in September. Occasionally some stay to spend the Winter, especially in Ireland. The Ring-Ouzel is also a bird of passage in Spring and Autumn on the east and west coasts, and occasionally wanders inland. Abroad, it occurs in northern Europe and west Asia, and winters in north Africa.

In form and appearance the male Ring-Ouzel is very like the male Blackbird. Except for his conspicuous white gorget and his paler wings with grey edgings, he is dressed wholly in black. The female is browner, the light edgings of her wings are more conspicuous, and her gorget is duller. The young birds are very

Eric Hosking

RING-OUZEL. The " Blackbird of the mountains " resembles our Blackbird, except for its white bib

similar to young blackbirds, for they lack the white throat altogether. The bill is yellowish-brown, and the legs dark brown. The length is 9½ in., and the tarsus 1·3 in. ; the wing span is 11 or 12 in., and the weight 4 oz.

Although it resembles the Blackbird in much of its behaviour and habits, the Ring-Ouzel has developed some differences arising from the environment of its desolate mountain home. It is, for instance, much more a lover of the open country, and perches freely on an exposed

bush or tree, undisturbed by a passer-by. Like the Blackbird, it immediately throws up its tail on settling. Its flight is direct, rapid and less undulating, but on the ground its movements are similar to its relative's. Bold in defence of its nest and young, it will attack any intruder, and has kept off crows and buzzards.

The Ring-Ouzel is gregarious only on its migrations ; in Winter it is usually seen in small parties foraging for food.

The song, which is uttered from a rock wall or bush and can be heard at night, varies considerably in tone and timbre, but, in keeping with the bird's lonely surroundings, is loud and clear, wilder and stronger than the Blackbird's. It is heard at its best from the end of March until early July, with an interruption in June. The call is a clear pipe, and the alarm note is the same as the Blackbird's.

The nest is usually well concealed among clumps of moorland or mountain heather, in a wooded valley or a rocky ravine ; and the male and female build it. Four eggs, very like those of the Blackbird, but more boldly marked, are laid in mid-April to June—sometimes July—and two broods are reared in a season. Both birds take their turn in the hatching, which lasts 14 days, and for the same period feed their young.

The food is similar to that of the Blackbird : in Summer, insects and worms ; in Winter, various kinds of berries.

RINGTAIL. Alternative name for female and young of Hen-Harrier (*q.v.*).

RIPARIA. Genus of the family *Hirundinidae* of the order *Passeriformes*. Its members are distributed over Europe, northern Asia, northern Africa and north America, and, outside the breeding season, over southern Asia, southern Africa and south America. The Sand-Martin (*q.v.*) is the only species on the British list.

RISSA. Genus of marine birds of the family *Laridae* of the order *Charadriiformes*. It contains two species, distributed over the seas around northern Europe, northern Asia, and northern north America, and, outside the breeding season, west Africa, Japan and Lower California. The only species on the British list is the Kittiwake (*q.v.*).

ROBIN—Erithacus rubecula melophilus. Its trust in mankind gives the Robin, among our small song birds, a place occupied by no other. It is, in fact, our best-loved bird, and its tameness provides excellent opportunities of studying its behaviour and habits. A great deal of investigation has been carried out and much written concerning the Robin's life history ; and it occurs more frequently than any other bird,

ROBIN. *An inquisitive and friendly fellow, the Robin shows little fear of Man and of his doings*

John Markham

except perhaps the Nightingale, in popular legend and poetry.

The Robin is a resident, and its engaging ways and cheerful song—heard when the majority of other birds are silent—are with us almost throughout the year. It is the fearless companion of the gardener at all seasons, and with very little encouragement will even hop into the house to accept its food, especially in Winter.

The Robin is generally distributed throughout the British Isles in practically every type of country, except in the extreme north of Scotland and the Orkneys ; it is absent altogether from the Shetlands. Autumn sees some migratory movements southwards, and some robins even cross the Channel. Abroad, various sub-species of the British Robin are found throughout Europe, western Asia and north-west Africa.

Everyone knows the Robin with its red face, throat and breast, and bright inquisitive black eyes. Its upper parts are olive-brown, its flanks bluish-grey, and its underparts whitish. Its thin bill and legs are brown. The sexes are alike, a fact which is not always recognized. Juvenile robins are spotted above and below, and do not attain the red breast until after their autumn moult. The length of the Robin is 5½ in., and the tarsus 1 in. ; the wing span is approximately 7 in., and the weight ½ oz.

The Robin is the most aggressively pugnacious of birds, not only towards other species but also to its own kind ; The Editor recalls seeing a Robin fatally injured by a knock on the head from another. Since both cock and hen are so intolerant it is unusual to see more than two or three robins together. One of the most " territorially-minded " of all birds, the Robin

spends all its life, apart from the breeding season, endeavouring to defend its ground against intruders. All its powers of song are so employed, and its red breast is used not, as one might imagine, in courtship, but as a threat display. In his *Life of the Robin* David Lack writes : " Only if this display fails to make the intruder depart, and it rarely fails to achieve this, does the owning Robin come to blows with the intruder ". When their domestic duties are over, both cock and hen claim their own winter territory, and will even fight furiously for possession of it, though the next Spring may see them resume partnership. The average size of a Robin's territory is 1½ acres.

From such records as we have, the Robin is short-lived, three years being the average span of life. (A similar observation was made by the Editor some years ago with the Continental Robin.) Despite this, the Robin remains one of our commonest birds ; 7,000,000 are believed to breed in the British Isles.

The flight of the Robin is low, flitting and, usually, for no great distance. It hops on the ground, and, when it is excited or suspicious, there is a characteristic bobbing action of the head accompanied with flirting of the wings and tail. The Robin perches anywhere, even on the gardener's spade where, with head on one side, it watches for worms.

Unlike that of most birds, the Robin's courtship is simple, with little ceremony except the bringing of food by the cock to the hen.

" From the human standpoint, the sequence of the Robin's family life is curious. First the hens go out to choose their mates, the cocks awaiting them in their domain. After what seems like a brief fight the pair become engaged, and for the rest of the next two or three months they share a territory, but otherwise almost ignore each other, and there is no courtship whatever. Then the hen, assisted by her mate, constructs the family house. About the time that this is completed mating occurs, very infrequently and with little excitement. Starting about the same time, and continuing for much longer and with much more attendant excitement, the cock courts the hen by bringing her food."—D. Lack, *Life of the Robin.*

The Robin sings almost all the year round—from January to June and again from August to December—and is only silent for a short period in July and August. As evening falls, one of the common sounds of the countryside is a little, short, quickly repeated kind of scolding note which is not always recognized as the call of a near-by Robin. It has a variety of other call notes, mostly high-pitched, including a totally different one reserved for the period after the hatching of its young.

The song, which varies with the individual, is of two kinds : the spring song, a sweet and cheerful whistle which can be heard in January or even earlier and continues until the end of

June ; and the autumn song, which starts in the later half of August. The latter is completely different from the spring song, and higher-pitched. It is believed that it is the hen that sings in the Autumn, while the cock is the chief songster of the Spring and Summer. The Robin is a late rooster and as its evening melody ends, the Nightjar takes up its churring trill.

At a joint meeting in 1949 of the British Trust for Ornithology, The Linnean Society and the British Ornithologists' Union, E. M. Nicholson, the well-known ornithologist, referred to a striking advantage they had secured by the work of Ludwig Koch in a selection of recordings of the spring and autumn songs of the Robin, which no ornithologist had previously been in a position to compare with accuracy.

> As a matter of fact, I had been trying for many years to make a comparative analysis of the spring and autumn songs of the Robin. Finally in 1948 during a long visit to some friends in Hampshire, I discovered that the frequencies of the spring song vary with the individual from 1,400 to 4,500 cycles. Another spring song varies from 1,600 to 8,000 cycles. The autumn song, however, usually varies between 5,000 and 10,000 or more cycles. Further research work by means of an oscillograph proved that much higher notes are involved, some of them being beyond the range of the human ear. These recordings of mine made accurate comparison possible for the first time.
> I recommend bird-lovers to go out armed with a portable gramophone and play the disk of the Robin's spring song ; it is quite possible that a Robin will approach within a few yards and answer with the same song.—EDITOR.

As is well known, the Robin chooses the most curious and unlikely spots for its nest. Besides a hole in a wall, a bush or a tree, it has chosen a shed, an old pan, a kettle, a letterbox, a pulpit, a human skull, and even a dead cat. All sorts of tales are told of the queer homes in which pairs of robins have brought forth their young : the parents which built in an unmade bed during breakfast, and were left there to carry on ; the gardener who hung up his coat one morning and, on taking it down for his lunch-hour, found a complete Robin's nest in one of the pockets ; the pair which built in a wagon ; and so forth.

The rather bulky nest, fashioned with leaves, grass and moss, and lined with hair and feathers, is built by both male and female. In March five or six whitish eggs, speckled in pale red, are laid. Both parents take a share in hatching for about a fortnight ; both also rear the chicks and, as three broods in a season are not uncommon, they have a busy time. The cock will look after the earlier brood while the hen is laying and hatching the next. The young fly in 15 days.

The food of the Robin consists mainly of insects—worms, flies, spiders, etc.—but some berries, seeds and fruit are also taken. In Winter, it will usually accept almost anything.

ROBIN, CONTINENTAL. *See* Continental Robin (*Erithacus rubecula rubecula*).

ROCK-BUNTING—Emberiza cia. The Rock-Bunting is a very rare visitor to England ; there are only six records of its appearance, most of them from Essex. It breeds in Spain, Portugal, Germany, Switzerland and Austria, and in Asia.

It is distinguished from all other buntings by its pale grey head and breast, and by the conspicuous black bands above and below its eyes. Its underparts are reddish-brown. For the rest, with its chestnut rump and band of white tail feathers in its tail, it resembles the Yellow Hammer.

As its name indicates, the Rock-Bunting frequents rocky ground on mountain sides, usually at an altitude of 1000 ft.–2000 ft. above sea level. It is not confined to these heights, however, and is often found (particularly in Winter) much lower on the same type of ground. Its length is 6 in., its wing span about 7 in., the tarsus 0·75 in., and it weighs under an oz.

The Rock-Bunting's call is similar to the Cirl Bunting's, but its song—with three or four notes followed by a drawling note—is sharper in tone.

The nest is placed among stones about 2 ft. above the ground, on a steep bank or in a quarry ; it is composed of grasses, bark strips and moss, and lined with roots and horsehair. From four to six eggs of a greyish-white ground colour are laid in early April, but somewhat later (in May or June) at high altitudes.

ROBIN. Fierce in defence of its own territory, a Robin is seen here threatening a rival cockbird

ROCK-DOVE—Columba livia. Originally called the "Blue Rock", this is the ancestor of all our domestic pigeons, and of the pigeons so familiar in towns and cities. The latter are, in the first instance, escapes from private domestic stocks which have reverted to what is called the "feral" state, a term applied to birds which have become wild (*see* Pigeon).

As a resident in England and Wales the Rock-Dove is decreasing, and, according to the *Handbook of British Birds*, "it is very doubtful if any pure wild rock-doves now breed anywhere in England and Wales, though in many parts feral domestic pigeons breed and are much like wild birds, while here and there (Yorkshire, Isle of Man) a mixture of wild and feral, with wild type predominating, occurs." In Scotland and Ireland, the Rock-Dove is widely distributed on the north and west coasts and islands, but no longer occurs on the east coast south of the Firth of Forth ; in many districts the wild birds have interbred with domestic pigeons. Abroad, the Rock-Dove breeds throughout Europe, Asia and north Africa.

Rocky coastal cliffs are the favourite haunts of the Rock-Dove, which can be distinguished from the Stock-Dove (also breeding on rocky cliffs) and from other doves by three characteristic features: its white rump, more conspicious white wing bars, and absence of black wing tips. The mantle is darkish grey, with a greenish-purple iridescent sheen on the sides of the neck. The head, breast and underparts are still darker grey. The bill is grey, and the legs and eye red. The sexes are alike, but the young are duller. The length is 13 in., and the tarsus 1-2 in. ; the wing span is between 16 and 18 in., and the weight 12 oz.

In behaviour, habits and flight the Rock-Dove follows the pattern of its family. It is strong, swift and agile on the wing as it dashes in and out of the rock and cliff caves. It rises with a whirr of wings, flies low over the water—its white rump well in evidence—and will sometimes alight on the surface. It rarely, if ever, settles on a tree, preferring to perch on a rock or on the ground. Like the rest of the doves, the Rock-Dove is believed to pair for life. It is gregarious and breeds in colonies, and is often in the company of the Redwing, Twite and buntings and of other species of pigeons ; interbreeding with the last-named accounts for the many variations in plumage.

The voice of the Rock-Dove is very similar to the familiar " coo " of the domestic pigeon.

The Rock-Dove's nest, placed in a hole or ledge of some rocky cave, is carelessly put together with bents, roots, seaweed and heather. At least two, and frequently three, broods are reared in a season, the eggs being laid at any

C. Reid

ROCK-DOVE. The white rump and lack of black on the wing-tips are good marks of identification

time between April and July ; they have even been recorded as late as September. Two is the normal number, and they are a smooth white. Both male and female share the hatching —the female taking the greater part—for 17 to 19 days ; the young are independent in about a month. The young are fed at first with " pigeon's milk ", a substance secreted in the parents' crop, and later, for four or five weeks, with grain softened in the crop.

Grain of all kinds seems to be the favourite food, as with all pigeons, but the Rock-Dove also has to consume the seeds of grasses and weeds. Insects are also eaten when available.

ROCK-PIPIT — Anthus spinoletta petrosus. As its name implies, this pipit is confined to the rocky stretches of the coast, and is only driven inland in Winter and in stormy weather. It is both a resident and a summer visitor, for many birds migrate to the Continent and return again in the Spring. On passage, it frequents mud flats, estuaries and sandy shores.

The largest of the British pipits, this bird is dressed in a dark olive-brown mantle, tinged with grey, with darker streaks above and below. The chin is whitish ; the underparts are buff, with the breast spotted darker. The rump is brown, and the outer tail feathers are smoky-grey. The thin dark bill is longer than is usual in pipits ; the legs are flesh-brown. The sexes are alike. The length is 6¼ in., and the tarsus 1 in. ; the wing span is 7 or 8 in., and the weight a little less than ½ oz.

Many of the Rock-Pipit's movements and much of its behaviour resemble those of the Tree-Pipit. It has the same erratic flight, as it flits in and out of the rocks and along the shore. It generally walks, but sometimes runs on the ground, and perches on rocks but rarely on trees. It roosts in a hole or crevice in a rock. It is not really gregarious except on migration.

The type of country frequented by pipits has some influence on their song-flight; if it is to be heard amid the various noises of the seashore, that of the Rock-Pipit must naturally be louder and more vigorous than the songs of its close relatives. The melody, which lasts from 5 secs. to 25 secs., is voiced as the bird rises and descends with wide-spread wings; it is also often uttered, but with less intensity, from a perch on the rocks. The song is best heard from March until early July.

Holes and crevices in the cliffs are the favourite breeding sites. The nest is built of dead grasses and lined with bents, horsehair; and sometimes seaweed. The four or five greyish-white eggs, spotted in brown and deeper grey, are laid in April, and again in June, for there are usually two broods. The hen hatches them for almost

ROCK-PIPIT. This is the largest of British pipits and is—as its name implies—found on rocky shores, although Winter may drive it inland

Arthur Christiansen

two weeks, and both parents rear the chicks for about the same period.

Insects, animal and vegetable matter all provide food for the Rock-Pipit.

The Hebridean Rock-Pipit (*Anthus spinoletta meinertzhageni*), a darker edition of the Rock-Pipit, is confined to the Outer Hebrides.

ROCK-THRUSH — Monticola saxatilis. This beautiful thrush of central Europe and southern Asia is an occasional visitor to the British Isles; it has been seen and recorded at least eight times in England and Scotland; its last appearance was at Dungeness, Kent, in 1938.

Its vivid orange colouring makes recognition immediate. A plump-looking bird, in its breeding plumage it has a blue head, short orange tail and underparts, and black wings; in the centre of the back is a prominent white patch. The female is browner, with barring in black and white, and has a white throat. The length is 7½ in., and the tarsus 1 in.; the wing span is 7 or 8 in., and the weight 3 oz.

ROLLER—Coracias garrulus. A very beautiful and conspicuous bird, the Roller wanders occasionally to the British Isles on its migration journeys. It generally visits the south and east coasts of England in Summer and Autumn—less frequently in Spring—but has been seen in most parts of the country at some time or other. Abroad, it nests in eastern and southern Europe, wintering in tropical and south Africa.

The Roller is closely allied to the Kingfisher and Bee-Eater, both brightly coloured birds, and has some superficial similarity to the Crow family. Recognition is easy, and the appearance of this brilliantly coloured bird at once attracts attention. The plumage is in bright blue-green, except for the chestnut mantle. The central tail feathers and wing coverts are a darker blue, and the outer tail feathers are tipped in black (the only other British bird with a brilliant blue wing patch is the Jay). The Roller's black bill is thick and slightly hooked; its legs are yellowish-brown. The sexes are alike, the young are duller. The length is 12 in., the tarsus 0·95 in., the wing span 14–16 in., the weight 6 oz.

The Roller's easy and buoyant flight has been compared with that of the Wood-Pigeon, but its outline in the air is more reminiscent of the crows.

It is the curious spring display of the Roller that gives it its name, for the male, rising to a considerable height, tumbles and somersaults.

A noisy bird, which proclaims its presence by its call, the Roller has a loud, harsh chattering call, not unlike the crows' in timbre.

ROOK—Corvus frugilegus. This is the commonest and best known member of the Crow family in Britain. It has been estimated that there are about two million in the country, and even more when the migrants from the Continent arrive in the Winter. There is no doubt that, where their numbers have outrun the natural food supply, rooks do harm in agricultural districts by consuming corn ; others claim that the good offices they perform in feeding on insects and weed-seeds balance this. It is generally agreed that some of the methods employed to exterminate rookeries in the Spring, when the young birds are in the nest, are both cruel and illegal. The Ministry of Agriculture has put out much good advice on the use of more humane methods.

The Rook is the most gregarious British resident bird, and is hardly ever seen alone. This fact is humorously referred to in the popular rule for distinguishing rooks from crows at a distance : " If you see a rook alone in a field, it is a crow ; if you see a crowd of crows, they are rooks ". Rookeries are to be found all over the country, wherever suitable clumps of trees are available for the numerous nests ; but, although they are, as a rule, near human habitations, this bird is rarely, if ever, seen in the towns. The northernmost rookery is sited in the most northerly clump of trees in the British Isles—near a church in the Orkneys. In Shetland where there are no trees, there is only one lone Rook ; blown there in a storm, it was adopted by a crofter. Besides our numerous resident rooks, some of which cross the Channel in the Autumn, thousands arrive on the east coast from Europe and Scandinavia in September and November.

The Rook's bare grey face is very evident whether the bird is in flight or at rest. Its plumage is all black, with a green sheen. The sexes are alike, and the young birds are similar to those of the Carrion-Crow. The length of the Rook is about 19 in., and its tarsus is 2 in. ; its wing span is 2½ ft., and its weight up to 2½ lb.

The Rook will be found feeding in company with jackdaws and other members of the Crow family. On the ground, it walks along with a most sedate air, and in flight it has a slow, gliding and heavy movement. The leisurely evening flight of rooks on their way home to the rookeries is a familiar sight in the country.

The Rook's " caw " is also a familar country sound. It is not quite so harsh as that of the Carrion-Crow, and has many variations, among them some musical and very high-pitched notes. Some of the calls are similar to those of the Black-headed Gull.

The spring display and courtship takes place on the ground or in trees ; the birds bow to each other with tails fanned, cawing all the time, and the ceremony usually ends with the male bird's presentation of food to his mate. In the Autumn, rooks are often seen indulging in astonishing aerial evolutions.

The Rook's nest, placed among the higher branches of a tree, is built of sticks mixed with earth, and lined with grass, dead leaves, moss, roots and straw ; very little hair or wool is found. Both birds contribute to the contruction, and often an old nest is used again. The number of eggs varies, but is usually three, four or five ; they are a bluish-green, with some grey and brown. The breeding season starts late in March or early in April, but the Rook has been known to attempt breeding in the Autumn. The hen sits on the eggs alone, her mate feeding her, for about 18 days ; the young, brought up by both parents, are on the wing in about 30 days. One clutch is laid in a season.

Among the superstitions about the Rook is the belief that a rookery near a " stately home " will be deserted shortly before the departure of the family for good. In Shropshire, it is commonly believed that rooks will never do any " work " during Ascension Day.

ROOK. *Probably the best-known member of the Crow family in Britain. Controversy still rages unabated as to whether it does more harm than good in field and garden*

Eric Hosking

SETTLING DOWN FOR THE NIGHT

BRUCE CAMPBELL, Ph.D.

The roosting behaviour of birds which flock interested bird watchers for years, but less is known about birds which roost singly or in small numbers. The author describes both aspects of an activity which occupies at least half of a bird's life

ROOSTING. Since most birds, like men, regulate their lives by the sun, their roosting or sleeping period is less easy to investigate than the active part of their day. People do not understand where the thousands of birds seen by day disappear to at night. They can be found, however, by diligent searchers : in evergreens and thick cover, in holes and crevices, in old nests and in little shelters on the ground. But the whereabouts of those that perch at a height can only be spotted by careful watching as they go to roost.

Social Roosting. The inhabitants of many big cities have become familiar in recent years with the nightly concourses of starlings on buildings. But starlings are not the only urban roosters : the famous roost of pied wagtails in O'Connell Street, Dublin, has been known for at least 25 years, and was estimated in 1950 to contain 3,600 birds.

The mass roosting of other common birds, such as rooks, jackdaws, house-sparrows and gulls, has also attracted the attention of ornithologists.

Social roosting is often characterised by a preliminary " build-up ", a period during which the birds gather in parties of increasing size on fields or in trees, at some distance—even up to several miles—from the final roost. This phase is usually marked by a good deal of noise, by striking aerial evolutions, and by violent feeding movements, although how much food is actually taken it is hard to say.

It seems as though the build-up has been evolved to overcome the birds' resistance to settling down for the night. This may be comparable to the reluctance of some sea-birds to come to land at the start of their nesting season. There is, of course, a risk in either of these situations that an enemy may be lying in wait, and it is not uncommon for sparrow-hawks and other birds of prey to take a toll of starlings and redwings coming

John Barlee

ROOSTING. *Gannet, tucking its head under its wing, in preparation for going to sleep*

in to roost. But once the landing at the roost, at any time up to an hour after the build-up, has been made, the birds are relatively safe.

Starlings spend minutes circling dizzily above the roost before the first birds peel off into cover. Immediately they land, they set up their bedlam, and it is not far-fetched to compare this to the noises made by savages to scare off predatory animals. A Starling roost is never silent throughout the night. House-sparrows, on the other hand, although they chatter for a long time before settling down, are quiet when sleeping, and can be inspected at close range with a torch. Finches, which also roost in large numbers, are silent, but wary of observers.

It has been suggested that the stages in the build-up of Rook and Jackdaw roosts can be correlated with decreases in light intensity, and some experimental work on this has been done. The morning break-up of the roosts is usually much quicker, and few birds, except house-sparrows, linger gossiping on their perches.

Gulls, which may roost in thousands on reservoirs, flooded fields or by the shore, come in to roost without an elaborate build-up, and often preen in the fresh water before settling down. The growth of winter roosts of gulls inland in Britain, chiefly in England and southern Scotland, has taken place since about 1900. The principal species involved are the black-headed and common gulls, but recently the Herring-Gull has begun to come inland.

Nocturnal birds, such as the owls, naturally roost in the daytime. But a number of diurnal birds, especially ducks and waders, sleep by day if their feeding is governed by the moon and the tides. Thus, at full moon, huge numbers of lapwings may be seen roosting in broad daylight after feeding by night. The flighting of ducks to the stubbles by the light of the moon has long been exploited by sportsmen ; when the ducks are seen next day like

Eric Hosking

ROOSTING. *Nightjar has settled down on its nest, and gives an enormous yawn to show that the time has arrived for getting ready for its sleep*

squat lumps on the waters of a lake, they are roosting after their fashion.

Social roosts generally break up for the breeding season, when birds roost near or on their nests. Non-breeding birds and males may continue to roost together, but little is yet known for certain about this.

Solitary Roosting. Although the kind of sites favoured by many solitary roosting birds has been known for some time, a critical study of them and of the behaviour involved in roosting is only just beginning. It appears that a roost perch is not necessarily a fixed site like a nest, but that there is a continual changing round, perhaps as the result of active competition between individual birds for the best sites.

Some species choose extremely sheltered perches ; for instance, as might be expected, tits, woodpeckers, nuthatches and wrens roost in holes. But more exposed places are chosen, and maintained, even in cold weather, by other birds. Bramble bushes are an example, and their choice suggests that their prickly cover against enemies, and the ease with which they can be quitted when danger threatens, may be more important considerations to roosting birds than protection against the elements.

Postures and Places. The traditional posture of a sleeping bird with its whole head or bill tucked under one closed wing is adopted by the majority of British birds, as far as present knowledge goes. The feathers are fluffed out, and perching birds crouch so that their legs are covered. Birds which sleep standing usually do so on one leg. The owls roost upright with head up, and some foreign birds roost upside down like bats. But birds are such light sleepers that the observer usually sees them with head up and eyes open, gazing unwinkingly into the beam of his torch. Among peculiar roosting places are

the niches hollowed in the soft bark of redwoods (*Sequoia*) by tree-creepers. Since redwoods have been planted in Britain only for about 150 years, the habit has presumably been transferred from the touchwood of dead trees. It is now widespread in both Great Britain and Ireland. The roosting of gamebirds in trees makes them vulnerable to poachers, but against natural enemies above or below it offers a measure of protection. A study of roosting may show that safety against predators is the guiding principle.

ROSEATE TERN—Sterna dougallii. Of the five graceful terns that breed in these islands, the Roseate Tern is the rarest. For this the egg-collector bears most responsibility, for after it was found nesting on some islands in the Firth of Clyde in 1812, and was recognized by the ornithologists of the day as a separate species, the Roseate Tern was at once much sought after for its skin and eggs. Other colonies were discovered on the Scottish, English and Irish coast, but its numbers gradually diminished until, as the 19th century was closing, this beautiful tern became almost extinct in the British Isles. Protective legislation saved the few surviving birds.

Today, the Roseate Tern breeds sparingly in various parts of the British Isles, which may be regarded as its breeding headquarters in Europe. For different reasons, there is at present a "security blackout" on the exact location of these breeding sites, and, in deference to this, no details have been given in this work about them. The Roseate Tern is also a scarce passage migrant. It is rarely seen inland. Abroad, it is almost a cosmopolitan species.

The Roseate Tern owes its reputation as the most beautiful of the terns to its long tail streamers, which are much longer than those of the other species. Otherwise, except that it looks much whiter than either the Arctic or Common Tern, its general appearance is very similar to theirs. In its full summer dress, a soft rosy bloom suffuses the breast—hence the name—but this distinction is not always apparent to the casual observer. The bill is wholly black in Winter, but in Summer has a red base. The legs are red. The sexes are alike, but the young birds' underparts are speckled in brown. The length is 14 or 15 in., and the tarsus is

0·87 in. ; the wing span is between 20 in. and 24 in., and the weight about 11 oz.

In habits, behaviour and spring display, the Roseate Tern differs little from the other terns. But in flight the long streamers of the tail make it appear more Swallow-like, and it rarely attacks an intruder at its nesting place.

The Roseate Tern has a distinctive call which, at its breeding site, is one of the best indications of its presence. Many other calls of great variety are heard, some characteristic of its own species and others like the calls of other terns.

Unlike arctic and common terns, roseate terns never breed inland, their favourite sites being small rocky islands ; when these are not available, the colonies will collect and nest on sandy and shingly banks on the shore. The Roseate Tern attempts no real nest, but utilises a hollow in a rock, on the pebby shore or occasionally among vegetation. Two—sometimes three—buff eggs with dark reddish spots are laid from early June onwards. Male and

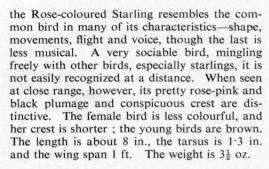

the Rose-coloured Starling resembles the common bird in many of its characteristics—shape, movements, flight and voice, though the last is less musical. A very sociable bird, mingling freely with other birds, especially starlings, it is not easily recognized at a distance. When seen at close range, however, its pretty rose-pink and black plumage and conspicuous crest are distinctive. The female bird is less colourful, and her crest is shorter ; the young birds are brown. The length is about 8 in., the tarsus is 1·3 in. and the wing span 1 ft. The weight is 3½ oz.

ROSE-FINCH. Indian name for Scarlet Grosbeak (*q.v.*).

ROSS'S GULL—Rhodostethia rosea. Very few British people have seen this Arctic bird alive, for it breeds in north-east Siberia, and, perhaps, in Greenland. Its inclusion in the British list rests on only two appearances.

Ross's Gull is rather smaller than the Black-headed Gull. Its upper parts are in grey, and in its summer dress its head, neck, underparts and rump are flushed with a delicate pink. A thin black line encircles its neck. Its long, pointed wings extend beyond the graduated tail — hence its name of Wedge-tailed Gull.

The flight of this gull has been compared with that of the terns and kittiwakes, but little is known of its behaviour and habits. Its voice is said to be higher-pitched and more musical than other gulls'.

H. N. Southern

ROSEATE TERN. The lovely, long tail-streamers, which make this the most graceful of all terns, can be clearly seen ; also the down-turned bill

female share the hatching for 21 days, and tend the young for about four weeks. The chicks are speckled buff and brown, with white underparts ; they attain adult dress in two years.

Small fish caught at sea form the principal food of the Roseate Tern.

ROSE-COLOURED PASTOR. *See* Rose-coloured Starling, also called Rosy Pastor.

ROSE-COLOURED STARLING — Sturnus roseus. This is a native bird of Russia and eastern Europe, and only a few wanderers appear in Britain each year—in Devon or Cornwall, and sometimes in Scotland and Ireland, during the summer months.

A member of the same family (*Sturnidae*) as the common Starling, but of a different genus,

Ross's Gull nests in colonies on swampy Arctic tundra, often in the company of the Arctic Tern. The nest is built of grasses and sedge, and three greenish-olive eggs are laid in June. The bird is believed to be single-brooded.

ROTCHIE. Name for the Little Auk (*q.v.*).

ROUGH-LEGGED BUZZARD—Buteo lagopus. A winter visitor of the British Isles, more regular in Scotland than in England or Ireland, this buzzard breeds in wild and barren country and in forests in many parts of the world, e.g. Norway and northern Russia. Its name refers to the fact that its legs are covered with feathers, in contrast to those of its relatives. Its tail is completely white, except for a broad black band at the tip. Apart from these distinguishing features, which are visible only at close quarters, it resembles the common Buzzard in its variable plumage and yellow feet. The female is the larger bird, being 26 in. long against his 23 in. The tarsus of both is about 3 in., the wing span over 4 ft., the weight 2½ lb.

The Rough-legged Buzzard is the wildest and fiercest of its kind. Its voice is similar to the common Buzzard's, but has a louder and more strident note. In the air it performs the same marvellous evolutions, but is more given to hovering—although this is not always a mark of difference, since both the Honey- and common Buzzard may hover.

H. N. Southern

ROUGH-LEGGED BUZZARD. This buzzard was named thus after its feather-covered legs

The breeding habits of the Rough-legged are similar to those of the common Buzzard. Its large nest, built of sticks and branches of trees, and decorated daily with fresh leaves, is placed on a ledge of a cliff or rock, or in a high tree in forests. Usually three or four eggs are laid— a larger number than either the Honey- or the common Buzzard produces. The number of eggs has apparently some relation to the bird's food supply, for, when the lemmings are on the move, for instance, the eggs are said to increase in number. The eggs are of the same colour as other buzzards' eggs. The breeding season is in April, May or June. Both the hatching and rearing of the young are chiefly done by the hen, with her watchful mate supplying the food. A single brood is reared in a season.

ROUGH-LEGGED HAWK. American name for Rough-legged Buzzard (*q.v.*).

ROYAL SOCIETY, BIRDS, for the Protection of. The R.S.P.B. is the oldest bird protection society in Europe. Its origins go back to the year 1889, when a group of women banded themselves together under a pledge to refrain from wearing the feathers of any birds not killed for the purposes of food, the Ostrich only excepted. Informal but regular meetings known as Fur, Fin and Feather afternoons were held at the house of Mrs. Edward Phillips in Croydon, until in 1891 the group joined forces with a small group of women working towards the same ends in Manchester, and calling themselves the Society for the Protection of Birds, under the Presidency of the late Duchess of Portland. In 1904 the Society became incorporated under Royal Charter, and its present Headquarters are at 25, Eccleston Square, London, S.W.1.

Whilst it is freely acknowledged that the aims and scope of the Society have long since outgrown the bounds conceived by its founders, the debt owed to these early pioneers who carried on a protracted struggle against plume hunters, traders, wholesale and retail milliners and "feather-bedecked" women, until the passing of the Importation of Plumage (Prohibition) Act came into force in 1922, is an enormous one.

The Society believes that in the long run the best protection for birds lies in an educated public opinion. It therefore lays great stress on educational activities, particularly amongst young people of school age. The Bird and Tree Competition for schools receives about 10,000 entries, each child writing an essay on a chosen tree or bird studied through the previous year. Shields are awarded on a county basis and medals and prizes on merit to individual competitors. The Junior Bird Recorders' Club, open to young bird-watchers between the ages of 11 and 18 years, encourages youngsters to a proper appreciation of the aesthetic and scientific value of wild birds. Though only formed in 1943, this Club now has a membership of over 2,000. *See also* Education.

Conservation and Protection. On the side of direct conservation (*q.v.*), the R.S.P.B. is actively engaged in efforts to secure certain areas either as complete sanctuaries or as areas in which the breeding-birds shall be left unmolested. They fall into two fairly distinct groups : first, those which contain a variety of bird-life, none particularly rare or even uncommon, but where steps are taken to encourage the widest possible variety coupled with a high density. The second type of reserve is that which is preserved specifically for rare species. In this case it may obviously be necessary to control public access by means of permits, and furthermore it may be necessary to exercise some sort of control on the animal species inhabiting the area. Examples of this type of reserve are Havergate Island, where the Avocet breeds, and Minsmere, where such rare species as the Bearded Tit and the Bittern breed. On these reserves hides have been erected from which it is possible to observe without the least disturbance to the birds themselves. *See also* Nature Conservancy ; Nature Reserve ; Sanctuary.

For some birds it is possible to do much through a system of rewards ; i.e. substantial premiums are offered to keepers and others who safeguard the nests of certain rare species until the young reach the free-flying stage. Examples of species for which rewards are paid are Kite, Golden Eagle, and Marsh-Harrier.

The Society has a quarterly illustrated magazine, *Bird Notes*, which has a larger circulation than any other magazine published in Britain devoted only to wild birds. Contributors have included Bruce Campbell, James Fisher, P. H. T. Hartley, Eric Hosking, David Lack, Peter Scott and G. K. Yeates. In addition, the Society publishes many leaflets and booklets, including a County bird-watching series of leaflets, each written by an ornithologist who is an authority on the particular area.

In the last two years, the Society has set up its own film unit, which has produced some very fine colour films of birds. Films can be hired at a nominal sum.

Under its Royal Charter, the Society is not opposed to legitimate sporting interests, but it sees the threat to bird-life from the man with the gun who blazes away at anything which flies, and who does in fact bring into disrepute the true sportsman from whom he is not always separated. A further danger comes from those gamekeepers (by no means all) and country-men who regard all hawks and owls as ver-min, although in the light of present know-ledge there is no proof to show that any hawks or owls have harmful effects on the numbers of game birds. Many landowners and sports-men are co-operating with the R.S.P.B. in its efforts to ensure that gamekeepers realize how harmless and im-portant these birds are.

As far as legislation goes, the R.S.P.B. has for many years striven to secure a more com-prehensive and simpler law for the protection of wild birds and did itself put forward a comprehensive Bill in 1939, which in essentials is very similar to the new Protection of Birds Act, which came into force on December 1, 1954, and which represents a great step forward.

The Society is one of the eight constituent Societies of the International Committee for Bird Preservation (British Section), and has always worked in close liaison with other bodies interested in the preservation of Nature.

ROYSTON CROW. Alternative name for Hooded Crow (*q.v.*).

RUDDY SHELD-DUCK — Casarca ferruginea. From its home in southern Europe, north Africa and Asia (where it is known as the Brahminy Duck) the Ruddy Sheld-Duck visits the British Isles only irregularly ; but it is a popular occupant of ornamental waters in public and private collections, and it is difficult to distinguish between the wild visitors and the "escapes". The drake is readily recognized by its wholly orange-brown dress, relieved only by the conspicuous white wing coverts, and black tail and quill feathers. The head is a paler shade of brown, and round the neck is a narrow dark collar. The speculum is bronze-green. The duck's plumage is very similar to the drake's, but her head is even lighter, and neither she nor the young have neck collars. The bill is black, and the legs dark grey. The length of this sheld-duck is 25 in., and the tarsus $2\frac{1}{4}$ in. ; the wing span is approximately $2\frac{1}{2}$ ft., and the weight about 2 lb.

Arthur Christiansen

RUDDY SHELD-DUCK. This duck rarely visits Britain in the wild, but is fairly well known as a popular addition to ornamental lakes in parks

RUFF — Philomachus pugnax. This is yet another bird to be added to the list of lost British Fenland birds. Common enough in suitable districts of England during the 19th century, the Ruff had more or less ceased to be a breeding species by 1900, though records exist of a few pairs breeding since then, the last being in 1922 in Norfolk. As a passage migrant, the Ruff still occurs regularly both in Spring and Autumn, usually on the east side of Great Britain ; but is rarely seen in Ireland. Abroad, it occurs in many countries of Europe and Asia.

In his summer dress, rarely seen here now, the Ruff presents an extraordinary appearance, his chief adornment being the wonderful " Elizabethan " ruff and projecting ear tufts, which surround his head, and from which he takes his name. The ear tufts and ruff have a great variety of patterns and colours, but the ruff is usually different from the ear tufts. The upper parts may be either black, brown, chestnut, and streaked with another colour. On either side of the dark tail a conspicuous white patch appears, and the breast and flanks have a good deal of black.

The Reeve, as the female is called, is smaller ; her plumage is greyish-brown, with black spots at the side of the breast, and grey-edged spots on the mantle. Her underparts are white, and she has also white patches at the sides of her tail. The winter plumage of both Ruff and Reeve is similar. Like the rest of the bird, the legs are also greatly varied, and may be in shades of green, orange, yellow, brown or grey. The blackish-brown bill is

Arthur Christiansen

RUFF. The colour-differences ruffs present in breeding plumage, are bewildering in their variety

straight or slightly curved. The length of the Ruff is 11-12 in., and the tarsus 2 in. ; his wing span is 15 or 16 in., and his weight 5 oz. The length of the Reeve is 8½-10 in., and her tarsus 1¾ in. ; her wing span is approximately 12 in., and her weight 3½ oz.

The Ruff's flight is somewhat similar to the Redshank's, but the Ruff does not perform aerial evolutions. In Winter the flocks are usually small, but in Spring as many as 400-500 birds have been seen together.

The spectacular spring display of the Ruff shows off his wonderful ruff and ear tufts at their best. The males assemble each morning at their " ruff hills "—usually selected hillocks on a marshy flat—and the reeves watch their display and their fighting bouts. These are never particularly fierce, and it is seldom that feathers fly or blood is spilt ; the protagonists merely crouch and face each other, beak to beak, and chase one another from their own special parts of the hill.

RUFOUS TURTLE-DOVE. *See* Eastern Turtle-Dove.

RUFOUS WARBLER—Agrobates galactotes. A rare autumn visitor from its homes in southern Europe, north Africa and Asia, the Rufous Warbler has been recorded four times in England and once in Ireland. It is larger than most of our other warblers. Its upper parts are reddish-brown and its underparts much paler ; there is a white stripe above the eye. The tail is long and fan-shaped ; the central feathers are chestnut, with broad black and white tips. The sexes are alike. The length is 6 in., and the tarsus 1 in. ; the wing span is 7 or 8 in., and the weight about ¼ oz.

RÜPPELL'S WARBLER—Sylvia rüppellis. A rare visitor to the British Isles, Rüppell's Warbler was twice recorded in Sussex in 1914. Its home is in Asia Minor and the surrounding islands. A large, handsome warbler, the male is bluish-grey, with a conspicuous black throat and white moustachial streak. The hen has a whitish throat, and grey-brown cap. The outer tail feathers are white. The length is 5½ in., the tarsus 0·8 in., the wing span 7 or 8 in., and the weight about ¼ oz.

RUSTIC BUNTING—Emberiza rustica. Some eight visits to England and twelve to Scotland have been recorded of this bird, which breeds in northern Europe and Asia.

About the size of a Linnet, the Rustic Bunting is easily recognized by its warm rust-coloured breast band, its black crown, and the white stripes at the sides of its head. The bird is a little over 5 in. long, its wing span about 8 in., its tarsus 0·75 in., and its weight under an oz.

STORK

SABINE'S GULL—Xema sabini. A graceful tern-like bird, breeding in Arctic America, Greenland, Siberia and Spitzbergen, this gull occurs at rare, but regular, intervals.

A slightly larger bird than the Little Gull, the adult is distinguished from all other British gulls by its conspicuously forked tail and the beautifully marked black-and-white barred pattern of its wings. In Summer, its head is grey, and a narrow black collar encircles its neck where the grey meets the white of the underparts. Its mantle is grey. Its stout bill is black with a yellow tip, and its legs are brownish black. In Winter, the grey hood is streaked with white. In the young birds likely to be seen here, the head is greyish-brown, and the forked tail is bordered in dark brown. The back and wings are ashy-grey, with brown bars. The sexes are alike. The length is 13 in., and the tarsus 1·3 in. ; the wing span is approximately 1½ ft., and the weigh is 4 oz.

Sabine's gulls have a light and graceful tern-like flight. Except in the breeding season, they are not inclined to be sociable with their own kind, and are met with only in twos and threes. Sabine's Gull breeds in the swampy Arctic tundra—often near an icefield—in company with Arctic terns In the scanty nest, made of vegetable matter, three brownish or olive-green eggs are laid at the end of May or in June—often July, in very high altitudes. For 23-26 days both male and female incubate. One brood is produced, but few details are available regarding its rearing. Insects and their larvae, small fish and scraps from the surface of the sea make up the food of Sabine's Gull.

ST. KILDA. Lonely, uninhabited island in the Atlantic, about 40 miles west of North Uist, in the Outer Hebrides. It is a natural sanctuary (*q.v.*) for sea-birds, and is particularly noted for its gannetry (*q.v.*). Fulmars, which have only in comparatively recent years established breeding colonies in the rest of the British Isles, have bred in St. Kilda since at least 1697.

The island is also noted as being one of those which has its own particular subspecies of Wren.

ST. KILDA WREN—Troglodytes troglodytes hirtensis. The island sanctuary of St. Kilda is the only place in the world where this Wren is to be found. When it was first identified as a separate subspecies, collectors from all over the country, in their desire to obtain a specimen, nearly brought the bird to extinction, and to save it a special Act of Parliament was passed in 1904. The last investigation into the status of the St. Kilda Wren put the numbers breeding there at 68 pairs.

The St. Kilda Wren is slightly larger than the common Wren, its underparts are paler, and, moreover, its plumage is greyish-brown rather than brown. On its mantle the dark bars are bolder and cover a larger area. The sexes are alike. The length is 3½ in., and the tarsus ¾ in. ; the wing span is about 5 in., and the weight a small fraction of an ounce.

Cliffs on the island, with thick vegetation, are its favourite haunts. Its habits and behaviour follow the pattern of the common Wren. The song has been said to be even louder and also more penetrating than that of the mainland bird.

G. K. Yeates

ST. KILDA WREN. *This is a larger and also a greyer bird than the common Wren, shown above*

485

CORNWALL
1. Walmsley Sanctuary

DEVON
2. Lundy
3. Braunton Burrows
4. Chapel Wood, Spreacombe
5. Wembury
6. Wistman's Wood
7. Yarner Wood
8. Axmouth—Lyme Regis Landslip

SOMERSET
9. Steep Holm
10. Brean Down
11. Bridgwater Bay
12. Shapwick Heath

WILTSHIRE
13. Fyfield Down and Walkers Hill

DORSET
14. Hod Hill
15. Abbotsbury Swannery
16. Studland Heath, Furzebrook, and Poole Harbour

HAMPSHIRE
17. Winchester
18. Old Winchester Hill
19. Selborne

SUSSEX
20. Kingley Vale

KENT
21. Dungeness—Dengemarsh
22. Ham Street Woods
23. Blean Woods
24. High Halstow

SURREY
25. Selsdon Wood

ESSEX
26. Belfairs Great Wood

HERTFORDSHIRE
27. Dancer's End and Tring Reservoirs

LONDON
28. Royal Parks

BERKSHIRE
29. Bagley Wood
30. Wytham Wood

OXFORDSHIRE
31. Waterperry Wood
32. Wychwood Forest

BUCKINGHAMSHIRE
33. Eton

SUFFOLK
34. Staverton Park
35. Orfordness—Havergate
36. Minsmere
37. Walberswick
38. Westleton Heath
39. Cavenham Heath

NORFOLK
40. Hickling Broad and Horsey Mere
41. Calthorpe Broad
42. Cley and Salthouse
43. Blakeney Point
44. Scolt Head
45. Weeting

CAMBRIDGESHIRE
46. Chippenham Fen
47. Wicken Fen

BEDFORDSHIRE
48. Whipsnade

HUNTINGDONSHIRE
49. Monks' Wood
50. Woodwalton Fen

SOKE OF PETERBOROUGH
51. Holme Fen

GLOUCESTERSHIRE
52. Birdlip Woods
53. New Grounds

WARWICKSHIRE
54. Earlswood Lakes

STAFFORDSHIRE
55. Hawksmoor
56. Dovedale

GLAMORGAN
57. Worms Head

RADNOR
58. Llangorse

PEMBROKESHIRE
59. Skokholm
60. Skomer
61. Grassholm

CARDIGAN
62. Tregaron Bog

CAERNARVON
63. St. Tudwal's Islands
64. Bardsey
65. Cwm Idwal

ANGLESEY
66. Llandwyn Island and Newborough Warren
67. Puffin Island

LINCOLNSHIRE
68. Reed's Island
69. Gibraltar Point

LEICESTERSHIRE
70. Leighfield Forest

NOTTINGHAMSHIRE
71. Nottingham Sewage Farm

DERBYSHIRE
72. Creswell Crags

CHESHIRE
73. Eastwood
74. Cotterill Clough
75. Marbury Reed-Bed

LANCASHIRE
76. Ainsdale
77. Walney Island
78. Merlewood

WESTMORLAND
79. Meathop Moss
80. Glencoyne
81. Moor House

CUMBERLAND
82. Ravenglass Gullery

ISLE OF MAN
83. Calf of Man

YORKSHIRE
84. Spurn Head
85. Askham Bog
86. Skipwith Common

NORTHUMBERLAND
87. Farne Islands

WIGTOWNSHIRE
88. Scaur Rocks

AYRSHIRE
89. Ailsa Craig
90. Lady Isle

EAST LOTHIAN
91. Aberlady Bay

FIFE
92. Isle of May
93. Loch Leven
94. Morton Lochs
95. Tents Muir

ABERDEENSHIRE
96. Newburgh

INVERNESS-SHIRE
97. Cairngorms

ROSS-SHIRE
98. Beinn Eighe
99. Isle Ristol

OUTER HEBRIDES
100. St. Kilda

ORKNEY
101. Eynhallow

SHETLAND
102. Fair Isle
103. Noss
104. Mid-Yell
105. Hascosay
106. Fetlar
107. Hermaness

BIRD SANCTUARIES OF THE BRITISH ISLES

SANCTUARY. A bird sanctuary is an area managed for the benefit of birds. Not all sanctuaries in Great Britain are maintained primarily for the benefit of wild species ; for instance some private collections of exotic birds in semi-captivity have become sanctuaries for wild birds as a secondary consequence of their management for a different purpose. But the majority of British sanctuaries are specifically designed for the safety of wild birds. Nearly all have, as their purpose, the maintenance of breeding populations of birds which are rare, or which lack their natural habitat (particularly marshland), or which are in danger of molestation by expanding human habitation, industry and agriculture. A few sanctuaries, especially local ones, are devoted to common species which are in no danger of extinction.

In Great Britain sanctuary policy has only recently been extended to cater for migratory birds, or for birds in their winter quarters. The chain of migration observation stations which has grown up since the Second World War undoubtedly protects wild birds ; for, although multitudes of birds are trapped for marking purposes, each station provides by its very existence a guarantee that the birds are not molested by people with less benign purposes. Refuges for winter birds are very few in Great Britain ; but active steps have recently been taken to schedule certain areas of our coast as Wildfowl Refuges, in an attempt to improve our stocks of ducks and geese.

It is only about two-thirds of a century since the serious bird-protection movement began privately in Britain, with the formation of the Breydon Society in Norfolk, in 1888. The Royal Society for the Protection of Birds (q.v.) was founded a little later ; and Great Britain is now covered by a network of local and national protection organizations. Norfolk was the cradle of bird protection, and of the earliest successful sanctuaries, such as Scolt Head, Blakeney Point and Hickling Broad ; these have been provided for many years with watchers and wardens throughout the season. By the middle of the present century the maintenance of sanctuaries had had a measurable effect on Great Britain's birds—certainly on their variety, probably also on their number.

Opposite is a list and map of rather over a hundred areas in the British Isles which are at present maintained in some positive way as nature sanctuaries, and which are of special interest to bird watchers. By no means all are purely bird sanctuaries, and they vary widely in size, importance, ownership and management. Not many are accessible to ordinary members of the public, and careful enquiries should be made before a visit is contemplated. Many not unreasonably discourage visitors ; others, devoted to species of scientific interest, are accessible only to authorised investigators.

Until the coming into force of the National Parks and Access to the Countryside Act of 1949, all British bird sanctuaries were in private hands, managed by their owners, by groups of individuals, or by societies. Since then, until September 30, 1954, twenty official Nature Reserves had been declared, with a total area of 71,152 acres. Not all of these are of ornithological interest, but most are ; and though they comprise a minority of existing sanctuaries, they guard some very precious elements of our bird life. Some of them—for instance, the Havergate Sanctuary, Suffolk, of the Royal Society for the Protection of Birds—are still managed by their original owners by arrangement with the Nature Conservancy (q.v.).

There are several categories of government nature reserves, of which the most important are National Nature Reserves (such as Havergate, Scolt Head, Woodwalton Fen in Huntingdonshire, and the Cairngorms in the Central Highlands) ; Local Nature Reserves (such as Llangorse in Radnorshire, Ravenglass in Cumberland, and Aberlady Bay in East Lothian) ; and Sites of Special Scientific Interest.

Of the sanctuaries not under government management the most important are probably those of the Royal Society for the Protection of Birds—among them, Dungeness in Kent, Minsmere in Suffolk, Grassholm (the great Gannet colony off the Pembrokeshire coast), Llandwyn Island in Anglesey, and several areas in Shetland. Not all these sanctuaries are owned by the R.S.P.B., but all are administered by, or for, it.

In the forefront of local societies with a positive sanctuary policy stands the Norfolk Naturalists' Trust, with interests in at least five sanctuaries in Norfolk ; and mention should be made of the West Wales Field Society (q.v.), with interests in half-a-dozen sanctuaries in Wales.

The Society for the Promotion of Nature Reserves maintains many interesting areas, though not all of these are primarily ornithological. Similarly, the National Trust owns much land of ornithological interest.

Some of the most interesting ornithological wonders of Great Britain, such as Abbotsbury Swannery in Dorset and the great sea-bird island of St. Kilda, west of the Outer Hebrides, remain in private hands and under private management.

The present balance between private enterprise and public responsibility in Britain must inevitably tip a good deal further, in the coming years, to the side of the latter ; but it must be stressed that it is more than half a century of private effort that has brought about the present progressive sanctuary policy.—JAMES FISHER.

SANDERLING—Crocethia alba. A bird of the Far North, breeding in Arctic Asia and America, the Sanderling is a passage migrant and winter visitor to the British Isles. It is met with on all sandy coasts—as the name suggests—but also occasionally inland. Some non-breeding birds remain all the Summer.

In Summer, the plumage of this plump little wader is a rich brown chestnut, with darker streaks and mottlings. Its head, neck and breast are in a lighter chestnut shade, and it has a white wing-bar conspicuous in flight. The rest of the underparts are whitish. In Winter, it presents a much greyer appearance, the mantle being a pale grey with slight dark mottlings, and its underparts and head white. On the shoulder it has a dark patch, noticeable against the light grey. Its bill and legs are black. The Sanderling has no hind toe. The sexes are alike. The length is 8 in., and the tarsus 0·8 in. ; the wing span is 9 in. to 11 in., the weight 2 oz.

A gregarious bird, the Sanderling mingles on the sandy shores with the Ringed Plover and Dunlin. In behaviour and habits it has much in common with the latter, but is distinguished by its rapid, lightning movement along the sea shore. It seems ever in a hurry as it darts restlessly here and there in pursuit of insects. The flight of Sanderling flocks is rapid and co-ordinated, but they do not perform the aerial evolutions so remarkable in the Dunlin. If approached, the Sanderling will run away.

Its voice in flight or when flushed is a pleasant, if rather shrill, cry ; from the feeding flocks a continuous twittering conversation is heard.

SAND GROUSE. *See* Pallas' Sand-Grouse.

SAND-MARTIN—Riparia riparia. One of the earliest arrivals among our summer visitors —sometimes even preceding its relative, the Swallow—the Sand-Martin is, as its name implies, somewhat restricted in its nesting sites. It breeds throughout the British Isles, except in the chalk and limestone areas of England, and in the north of Scotland, where it is scarce and very local in appearance. Abroad, it occurs throughout Europe, Asia, Africa and north America.

The smallest, and probably the least familiar, of its aerial family, the Sand-Martin is distinguished by its general dark brown appearance. Its underparts are white, with a broad brown band cutting across its breast. Its tail is slightly forked. Its bill and legs are dark brown. The sexes are alike. The length is 4¾ in., and the tarsus 0·45 in. ; the wing span is 7 or 8 in., and the weight a fraction of an ounce.

Although the Sand-Martin is as completely a creature of the air as its allies, its flight is jerky and erratic ; it is also much lower. Sand-martins are gregarious at all times and roost in their hundreds in holes in walls and the clayey soil of sand and gravel pits. As the time of their departure approaches, in August or September, they congregate in huge numbers from all directions, wheeling and turning in the failing evening light, while their continuous twitterings fill the air. To and fro, the flock soars high above ; then, diving downwards in a wonderful spiral column, it suddenly vanishes from sight. At their nesting sites, sand-martins have the strange habit of rising in one body as if at a word of command, only to return almost at once—behaviour similar to the Starling's and that of other species.

The Sand-Martin perches on telegraph wires, low bushes and branches overhanging a stretch of water, where it skims over the surface, pursuing insects.

The song, a series of short twitterings, can usually be heard on the wing ; at the nesting site a continuous soft chirruping conversation goes on. The call note, especially when the bird is disturbed, is a high-pitched short sound. The Editor has never heard a real song, from the Sand-Martin, but only a " gossiping " similar to the House-Martin's. The Sand-Martin is

Eric Hosking

SAND-MARTIN. *Wherever there are sand or gravel pits, sand banks, railway cuttings and suchlike, this relative of the House-Martin is found*

best heard during April, May and early June.

The Sand-Martin's nest is a tunnel bored into the soft sand, as far out of reach as possible. The tunnels are usually two or three feet long, but many longer ones have been recorded. Both male and female excavate, digging out the sand with their feet. The little chamber at the end is strewn with feathers and straw to house five or six small white eggs laid in May or early June. For 12 or 14 days both parents share the

Eric Hosking

SANDPIPER. Despite its name, the Common Sandpiper (above) is by no means the most common member of the Sandpiper family in Great Britain

hatching. When the chicks appear, the colony is the scene of the greatest activity, the devoted parents spending their lives hurrying backwards and forwards to satisfy the appetites of the small white heads peeping through the tunnel. The chicks can fly in about three weeks. Two broods are usually reared in a season.

The Sand-Martin's food is made up entirely of insects, which are caught on the wing.

SAND-PIGEON. *See* Stock-Dove (*q.v.*).

SANDPIPER. Common English name of a group of birds—most of which are small waders—belonging to the family *Scolopacidae* (*q.v.*), which, in addition to the *typical* sandpipers, includes the Snipe, Knot, Sanderling, Ruff, curlews, Dunlin, stints and godwits. At one time it also included the phalaropes, which now have a family of their own (*Phalaropodidae*).

Species having the word " sandpiper " as part of their English name are distributed between six genera, as follows :

Bartramia. Bartram's Sandpiper.
Tringa. Green Sandpiper; Wood-Sandpiper; Solitary Sandpiper; Common Sandpiper; Spotted Sandpiper; Redshank; Spotted Redshank; Greater Yellow-Legs; Lesser Yellow-Legs; Greenshank; Marsh-Sandpiper; Grey-rumped Sandpiper.
Xenus. Terek Sandpiper.
Calidris. Knot; Purple Sandpiper; Baird's Sandpiper; Bonaparte's Sandpiper; Little Stint; American Stint; Temminck's Stint; Pectoral Sandpiper; Siberian Pectoral Sandpiper; Dunlin; Curlew-Sandpiper; Semipalmated Sandpiper.
Tryngites. Buff-breasted Sandpiper.
Limicola. Broad-billed Sandpiper.

All of the above species are fully described under their own headings. In character, habits and general appearance they are all very similar, although there are individual differences, particularly in relation to the colour of plumage,

which also frequently differs in Summer and Winter, and in juveniles.

Sandpipers are characterised by their long, spindly legs, in which the lower part of the tibia is naked, and by a long, or rather long, slender bill, grooved throughout the whole, or most, of its length—straight in some species and slightly curved or de-curved in others.

In many of their mannerisms, typical sandpipers are very similar to the stints (*q.v.*), but outside the breeding season they have a much wider range of habitats and their feeding habits are different. They are inclined to be less gregarious, and, although associating in flocks with other small birds, seldom consort in groups of more than a dozen themselves. They are usually found in estuaries, sandy and muddy beaches and sea-shores, but also frequent inland waters and marshes. They may seek their food by probing the ground, but usually take it from the surface of pools or within the margin of the sea itself. Their movements on land are active and graceful. Although not keen swimmers, they are much less reluctant to enter the water than are the stints, and can swim well.

SANDWICH TERN—Sterna sandvicensis. The largest of the terns that occur in the British Isles as summer residents, the Sandwich Tern is more restricted than the others in its breeding sites, but occupies some large colonies in suitable coastal areas. England has five main colonies ; at Farne Islands, Ravenglass (Cumberland). Walney (Lancs), and two in Norfolk between Scolthead Island and Salthouse. Wales has one in Anglesey. Scotland has its main colonies on the coasts of Ayrshire, Fife and the Moray Firth. Ireland has several, mainly in the north and west. Elsewhere the Sandwich Tern is a passage migrant. Abroad, the Sandwich Tern breeds throughout Europe, north-west Africa, north and south America and the West Indies, and winters in south Africa, India and south America.

Its larger size and bulkier body make this tern easily distinguishable from others. Other distinctive features are its less deeply forked tail, its yellow-tipped bill, and its crest of long black nape feathers—but this last is not always apparent unless the bird is excited. Its mantle is pearl-grey, and its underparts white ; like the Roseate Tern, it is sometimes tinged with salmon pink. In Summer, its forehead, crown and nape are black ; in Winter, its forehead is white, and its crown and nape speckled with grey. Its dark grey wings are long and narrow ; its black legs are longer than those of other terns ; and its black feet have yellow soles. The sexes are alike. The juvenile's mantle and wings are boldly speckled and barred in blackish-brown, its crown and nape brown, and the rest whitish. The length of the Sandwich Tern is 15 to 17 in., and its tarsus is 1·2 in. ; the wing span is 2 ft.–2½ ft., and its weight is approximately 12 oz.

The Sandwich Tern is gregarious, and is often found in the company of other terns. Although retaining much of the aerial beauty of its family, its flight appears heavier, less buoyant and more gull-like in movement. It plunges in pursuit of its prey direct to the sea from a greater height than is usual among terns, and submerges wholly under the water. The Sandwich Tern is said to be less aggressive than its relatives, and, although it may swoop down on an intruder, it seldom, if ever, strikes.

Otherwise in habits and behaviour it follows the pattern of the Common Tern. The spring display is marked by the same attractive ceremonies. Both male and female take part in the "fish" and courtship flights, which often take place at a great height, and their gliding performance is even more spectacular than that of other members of the family. On the ground both male and female bow and scrape, and scissor their bills (see Behaviour).

The Sandwich Tern has a characteristic voice ; the call note is a loud harsh cry with many variations. The tremendous clamour which issues from their colonies can be heard over half a mile away.

This tern is erratic in its choice of nesting site, and a site used for years will suddenly become deserted for some unknown reason. The Sandwich is the first of the terns to arrive ; some come in as early as March, and the main body takes up its quarters in the second week in April. Sandy, shingly and stony sea-shores, as well as low-lying and rocky islands—and occasionally inland lakes—are the favourite nesting sites. A mere hollow scraped in the sand or stones, sometimes not even lined with sea grass, suffices for the nest. Here one—or more normally two—eggs are laid in May. The eggs vary from creamy-white to brownish-buff, and are spotted and blotched in reddish-brown. Both male and female take their share in the hatching for a period of 20 days. The nestlings—"hairy" in their dress of mottled black down, white underneath—are soon guided to join the community in the water. Their parents are then no longer concerned exclusively with their own progeny, and will feed any of the clamorous youngsters. The young can fly in about five weeks, and attain adult dress in their third summer. One brood is reared.

The Sandwich Tern lives entirely on animal food—sand-eels and other fish form a large part of the diet ; but also worms and molluscs.

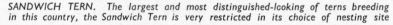
SANDWICH TERN. *The largest and most distinguished-looking of terns breeding in this country, the Sandwich Tern is very restricted in its choice of nesting site*

Stuart Smith

HOW BIRDS KEEP THE NEST CLEAN

R. H. BLAIR

The present article shows that with few notable exceptions the old adage that " no bird fouls its own nest " is strictly accurate. It describes the painstaking way in which the excrement of the nestlings is removed and how the young are taught cleanly habits

SANITATION. The problem of nest sanitation is a formidable one. From hatching until they leave the nest, the baby birds have to be kept clean in spite of their crowded and cramped quarters, while the nest must not become foul or be rendered conspicuous by droppings. The sight of a brood of young fledglings just out of the nest, every baby spick and span, is proof that the problem is successfully solved.

Although birds are notoriously impossible to house-train, some instinct induces the parents to co-operate with their young (which will become neglectful of this matter as soon as they leave the nest) in a rigid discipline of sanitation.

An early observer of this subject was Gilbert White who, in his sixteenth letter to the Hon. Davies Barrington, dated Nov. 20, 1773, wrote of the House-Martin :

> " At first when the young are hatched and are in a naked and helpless condition, the parent birds with tender assiduity carry out what comes away from their young . . . In the quadruped creation the same neat precaution is made use of, particularly among dogs and cats, where the dams lick away what proceeds from their young. But in birds there seems to be a particular provision, that the dung of nestlings is enveloped in a tough kind of jelly, and therefore is the easier conveyed off without soiling or daubing. Yet, as Nature is cleanly in all her ways, the young perform this office for themselves in a little time by thrusting their tails out at the aperture of their nest."

For 150 years after this accurate description there are found only scattered observations, but in recent years the methods of nest sanitation adopted by many species have been studied. It has been found that the nestling co-operates from a very early age, having a powerful instinct to keep inviolate the " cup " of the nest, though in many species the " rim " is used as a collecting place. In the majority of species—as in Gilbert White's house-martins—more than one type of sanitation is employed, one method succeeding another as the nestling grows.

Not all species of birds have a sanitation problem, for many ground-nesting birds such as waders, ducks, many gulls, terns and skuas leave the nest soon after hatching. In almost all the numerous species which remain in the nest until fledged, from the Raven to the Goldcrest, the droppings are swallowed by the parents in the early stages. This may continue for a week or more in some species, e.g. the Bullfinch and Mistle-Thrush. More commonly in Passerines

the droppings, which are voided surrounded by an elastic pellicle of tough mucus (like little " Cellophane "-wrapped parcels), are carried away by the parents after feeding.

As the nestlings become more active some co-operate by turning up their " tail-ends " to deliver the dropping to a parent on a feeding visit. The parent will watch for this, and give a prodding reminder with its beak to induce the baby to produce a dropping. Other nestlings

G. K. Yeates

SANITATION. Droppings, enclosed in a special membrane, are removed from the nest by a warbler

deposit their droppings at a convenient spot on the rim of the nest, so that the parent can carry them off on its feeding visits without change of foothold. Baby willow-warblers use a spot to one side of the opening for a similar purpose : the parent feeds them, then turns a little aside to pick up the dropping before flying off.

At a late stage wheatears and sand-martins come to the entrance of their nest-holes for sanitation. Young swallows have been seen to jostle each other as they take turns at the particular corner of the nest set apart for sanitation, and some parent swallows build mud runways, when the young are old enough to use them, to give them access to a point with a clear drop to the ground.

Well-grown Dipper nestlings project their droppings from the opening of the nest clear into the water below. Any dropping which fails to fall into the water is retrieved by a parent and placed in the stream.

In both Greater and Lesser spotted wood-peckers the early droppings are white capsules, which are carried away by the parents. Later droppings are brown, owing to admixture with " sawdust " made by the parents' hammering inside the nest-hole. In the last few days much hammering occurs, but no carrying, and it is believed that the plumage of the young is pro-tected from being fouled by this sawdust " indoor sanitation ".

In the larger species, such as birds of prey and certain sea-birds—for example, kittiwakes and fulmars—the young have powerful ejaculatory muscles with which they project their droppings clear of the nest, taking care not to foul it.

The Montagu's Harrier has even runways leading to latrines to which the nestlings repair.

These examples serve to show how instinct, while varying in different species, impels parent birds and nestlings to co-operate in keeping their plumage and their surroundings spotless.

SARDINIAN WARBLER — Sylvia melano-cephala.
One visit to Sussex in 1907 is the only recorded appearance in Great Britain of this warbler, a typical bird of the Mediter-ranean woodlands. The male is not unlike our Blackcap, for he has a black cap and cheeks ; the throat is pure white, the upper parts slate-grey, and the underparts a paler grey. The dark tail is graduated at the sides with white, which is conspicuous in flight. The length is 5¼ in., the tarsus 0·82 in., the wing span 7 in.

In behaviour and habits, the Sardinian Warbler differs little from the Whitethroat ; it has a similar dancing song-flight, and the song is said to be similar but more sustained and of better quality. Insects form the sole food of both young and adults.

SAVI'S WARBLER — Locustella luscinioides.
Once a summer resident, though never abund-ant, in Norfolk, Cambridgeshire and Hunting-don, this Warbler must now be added to the list of lost British birds. It began to decrease some two centuries ago, and the drainage of the Fens during the 19th century gradually but inevitably destroyed the type of country necessary for its survival as a breeding bird. Its last appearance was in 1885. It is doubtful whether the small area of Fen now remaining in Britain, will ever again become its breeding place, even under legal protection. It still occasionally visits us as a summer migrant,

Fischer-Wahrenholz

SAXICOLA. The little Whinchat is one of the two members of this genus found in Great Britain

however, from its homes in central Europe, the Mediterranean countries, and, rarely, Belgium and France ; it winters in Africa.

Savi's Warbler is a very close relation of the Grasshopper-Warbler, with which it could be confused were it not for its unmottled and un-streaked rich brown mantle. The underparts are whitish, palish on the throat. The gradu-ated and fan-shaped tail is another feature. The sexes are alike. The length is 3½ in., and the tarsus 0·9 in. ; the wing span is between 6 and 7 in., and the weight a fraction of an ounce.

In behaviour and habits this warbler follows the pattern of the Grasshopper-Warbler. A restless bird, it darts so swiftly among the dense growth of reed beds, swamps and Fens that it is difficult to observe.

The song of Savi's Warbler is the most outstanding feature. It is different from the trill of the Grasshopper-Warbler, more " rat-tling ", fuller, lower-pitched and less prolonged, although a duration of three minutes has been recorded. The song is uttered with quivering body and open beak from the top of a reed, the bird's head turning from side to side.

The songs of the three main warblers of the genus *Locustella* can be summed up as follows : the Grasshopper-Warbler (*naevia*) makes a clattering, Savi's Warbler (*luscinioides*) a rattling, and the non-British River-Warbler (*fluviatilis*) a grinding sound. The rattling of Savi's Warbler and its relationship to the Nightingale, are both shown in its German name *Nachtigallschwirl* (" rattling nightingale "). The hen also sings. The alarm and call notes, often uttered before the " song ", are short and very low, and can be heard only at close range.—EDITOR.

The tiny nest, built by the hen alone, is well concealed among the reeds ; it is com-posed of dried leaves, etc., and lined with fine marsh grasses. From April to May four or five greyish-white speckled eggs are laid ; for 12 days the hen hatches them alone, with the male occasionally relieving her. Both parents tend the nestlings for another 15 days. Two broods are usually reared in a season.

Marsh insects and their larvae form the main food of this warbler.

SAW-BILL. Colloquial name for the mergansers (*q.v.*), especially the Red-breasted.

SAXICOLA. Genus of the family *Turdidae* of the order *Passeriformes*. Its members seem to be closely allied to those of the genus *Oenanthe* (wheatears). They are distributed over Europe, Asia, and Africa. The genus contains two species which are on the British list, the Stonechat (*q.v.*) and the Whinchat (*q.v.*).

SCANDINAVIAN CHIFFCHAFF — Phylloscopus collybita abietinus. A breeding bird of Scandinavia, this is a very rare visitor to Britain. It differs so little from the British Chiffchaff that its identification is difficult ; at close range it sometimes looks greyer, with paler underparts. In courtship, breeding and nesting habits, food and song, it is very similar to the British species.

SCANDINAVIAN HERRING-GULL — Larus argentatus omissus. This native of Scandinavia differs from the British Herring-Gull only in some small details of plumage and leg colouring, which can be distinguished only by an expert familiar with both birds. One or two definite identifications have been made in Britain, but in all probability many of this species mingle from time to time with British herring-gulls without being picked out.

SCANDINAVIAN JACKDAW — Corvus monedula. This bird of Sweden, Norway and Denmark has seldom appeared in the British Isles. One bird was observed in England in 1911, and in 1936 another was shot in Scotland and a third was seen on Fair Isle, Shetland.

Its appearance is very similar to that of the British Jackdaw, but its " collar " is a much paler grey, turning almost to white lower down. The nest, nesting habits, voice and courtship are similar to those of other jackdaws.

SCANDINAVIAN LESSER BLACK-BACKED GULL — Larus fuscus. A passage migrant and winter visitor to the British Isles from Scandinavian countries, this typical form of the Lesser Black-backed Gull has been recorded often, usually on the east coast in Spring and Autumn. As it mingles with the British birds, it can be picked out by its darker mantle. In its behaviour and habits it does not differ at all from the British Lesser Black-backed Gull. The length is about 21 in.

SCANDINAVIAN ROCK-PIPIT.—Anthus spinoletta littoralis. The Rock-Pipit of north Russia, the Danish islands and the coasts of Sweden and north Finland, this subspecies visits the British Isles on its migration. It differs so little in plumage from the British Rock-Pipit that identification, except at very close range, is difficult. The length is 6¼ in.

As far as is known, its song, behaviour and nesting habits are also similar to those of the British species.

SCAPULARS. Name given to the feathers covering the shoulder blades.

SCARLET GROSBEAK—Carpodacus erythrinus. A breeding bird of eastern Europe and Asia, wintering in India, where it is quite common, this is a rare visitor to the Scottish islands, especially Fair Isle in the Shetlands. Of much the same size as the Bullfinch, but with a less stout appearance, the Scarlet Grosbeak has a carmine head, breast and rump, shading to brown on the wings and tail. Its stout beak is typically finch-like. The female, though much less colourful, is distinguished by a conspicuous double white wing bar. The length is 6 in., the tarsus 0·8 in. and the wing span about 8 in.

In flight, the Scarlet Grosbeak is typically finch-like. Its call in the breeding season has something of the sweetness of the caged Canary; its song reminds one of that of the Golden Oriole, though lacking that bird's fluent sweetness. Grosbeaks are usually silent in the winter months, when large flocks roam the countryside feeding on bushes and undergrowth.

John Barlee

SCANDINAVIAN CHIFFCHAFF. This visitor is almost indistinguishable from the British bird

SCART. Local name for Cormorant (*q.v.*) or Shag (*q.v.*)—sometimes also called Scarf.

SCAUP—Aythya marila. Although it is known to have bred about a dozen times between 1899 and 1913 in the north of Scotland, it is as a winter visitor—often abundant—and passage migrant around our coasts that the Scaup is known in the British Isles. It is seldom seen inland. Abroad, it occurs in Iceland, northern Europe and north Siberia, wintering in southern Europe and South-west Asia.

A sturdy, compactly-built diving duck, inured to battling with the elements, the Scaup has the general appearance of the Tufted Duck, although at close range the vermiculated grey of the drake's back—that of the Tufted is black—is a sufficient distinguishing feature. His head, neck, tail and tail coverts are black; his

Erica

SCAUP. A diving duck that is mainly seen as a visitor to our shores, although it has bred here

flanks and underparts are white, and he has a white wing bar. In Winter, he is browner, but the grey is still apparent on his mantle. The duck is browner, and at the base of the bill has a large and conspicuous white patch. The bill and legs are blue-grey, and the eye yellow. The length is 19 in., and the tarsus 1½ in.; the wing span is between 16 and 20 in., and the weight 2 lb. 3 oz.

The Scaup is extremely sociable, and will congregate in large flocks in company with other diving ducks. It is almost stupidly tame, and can be easily approached. It is an excellent swimmer and diver in either fresh or salt, shallow or deep, water. Its deepest dive is recorded as being 21 ft., and its longest lasted for nearly a minute; its normal depth is 11 or 12 ft., and the normal time is half-a-minute.

Like the Tufted Duck, the Scaup is awkward on the ground and patters over the surface of

the water before taking off. Its flight is rapid, the movement of its beating wings making a rustling sound overhead as it flies along. In his spring display, the drake approaches the duck with head thrown back and neck extended to its fullest extent. As he lowers his head, he utters a cooing note.

The Scaup's voice is rarely heard outside the breeding time. The duck has then a loud harsh croak, and the drake a whistling note.

Scaups breed amicably with others of the family, in colonies situated usually on islands in lakes. The nest is only a hollow (lined with down and feathers) near the water, sometimes with some shelter but frequently with none. The 7–11 greenish- or olive-grey eggs are laid in May or June. The duck incubates for 28 days, rarely leaving the nest during that period, but the drake helps to rear the ducklings, which are led to the water as soon as they are dry. They are independent in five or six weeks. One brood is reared in a season.

The Scaup feeds on molluscs, worms, and so on, brought up from the bottom of the lake; some vegetable matter is also taken.

SCHOOL NATURE STUDY UNION. This organization, founded in 1903, was pioneered by one or two enthusiasts who saw an urgent need to change the methods of teaching the little that then was taught of Natural History, and for enlarging the whole field of study.

At the time of its foundation, the one and only school contact a child had with the natural world around him lay in the weekly " object lesson ", in which he was told facts concerning some object that might or might not be shown to him : a piece of sugar-cane from the school museum, or a sponge, familiar to him in the home. The only " bird study " he was likely to pursue, apart from birdsnesting, would be the daily sight of such museum pieces as an ostrich egg and a stuffed bird or two.

The pioneers saw the need for every child to know more of the living world in which he moved, and aimed to " bring the children into harmonious contact with the living world ". Their work has in 50 years brought about a revolution in the approach to Nature Study, including birds, in schools.

There were in the early days too few " field " books, giving the characters by which a bird might be recognized in the open. The " School Nature Study Journal ", published by the Union, featured articles by field naturalists, and later reprinted them as leaflets at a price within the reach of all. Today the Union executive arranges summer and winter programmes of meetings, many out-of-doors, for the instruction of teachers in modern methods of Nature Study. Further, regular indoor meetings and exhibitions are arranged, where members and kindred societies display work from all types of student. The emphasis is largely and increasingly upon bird studies—population numbers, ringing, migration observations, nesting and food habits. From the interest these activities arouse, may spring the highest kind of study : the research of the individual worker. Union members have enriched the world of bird-lore by the results of their research. We may instance the studies of Miss Hibbert-Ware, M.B.O.U., who gave years of enthusiastic service to the Union. Today her name is famed for the research she made into the status of the Little Owl.—FRED J. SPEAKMAN.

SCIENTIFIC NAMES. In the present work, the use of scientific names has been reduced to the bare minimum. Sometimes they are unavoidable, because there is no equivalent term in common use. At other times, they have been employed because they occur so frequently in bird literature that the reader will find it essential to become acquainted with them. Here, the practice has been to follow them, where possible, by an explanatory word or phrase, the first time they appear, and/or define them under their own heading.

They are commonly regarded as Latin names, the language from which most are derived ; but many come from the Greek, and some from the names of noted scientists or places.

In a special class are the names of orders, families, genera and so on, for which at one time it could be claimed that they formed part of an international language understood by ornithologists and others interested throughout the world. Because of the changes in nomenclature which have taken place recently and the fact that these changes have not yet been universally accepted, this claim is not at the moment entirely true. In the meantime, a knowledge of the scientific names used in, say, the *Check-List of the Birds of Great Britain and Ireland*, is useful in showing the relationship of species, where such relationship would not be suspected from their common names or from their general appearance.

SCIENTIFIC SITE. Shortened, popular name for what is officially known as a " Site of Special Scientific Interest ". This is an area considered by the Nature Conservancy (*q.v.*) worth protecting and preserving because of the special interest of its flora, fauna, or geological or physiographical features, although it is not of sufficient importance to warrant its constitution as a permanent Nature Reserve (*q.v.*).

When an area has been designated as a Scientific Site, the Nature Conservancy notifies the local planning authority by depositing a map, with the scheduled land marked on it, together with a short explanatory note. Where possible, the owner or occupier of the property is also notified. Thereafter, before the local planning authority can give consent to any development that is likely to affect the site, it must consult the Nature Conservancy. The latter has, however, no statutory authority to prevent the development, and can only state its case, when the planning authority is considering a development proposal. Where development must proceed, and no compromise is possible, the scientific interest has to take second place. No legal obligations or other restrictions are imposed on the owners or occupiers of such sites, nor does " notification " confer any rights of entry or of public access.

SCOLOPACIDAE. Family of wading birds of the order *Charadriiformes*. It contains some eighty different species, which are distributed over much of the globe. There are 41 species on the British list, contained in the following 14 genera : *Bartramia, Calidris, Capella, Crocethia, Limicola, Limnodromus, Lymnocryptes, Limosa, Numenius, Philomachus, Scolopax, Tringa, Tryngites* and *Xenus*.

The members of this family vary considerably in size, and the long and slender bill is curved in some species, straight in others. In the majority of species the wing is of medium length or rather long, with 11 primary feathers, of which the first is much reduced. There are 12 tail-feathers. The legs are generally long ; the hind-toe is very small or absent altogether. The young are covered with down, which is often beautifully coloured, and are active soon after hatching. *See also* Sandpiper ; Snipe.

R. P. Bagnall-Oakeley

SCOLOPACIDAE. The Common Snipe is among the very many members of this family of wading birds

Eric Hosking

SCOPS OWL. *Smallest owl to be seen here, it is recognized by its beautifully patterned plumage*

SCOLOPAX. Genus of the family *Scolopacidae* of the order *Charadriiformes*. It contains five species, distributed over a wide area of the globe. The only species which occurs in the British Isles is the Woodcock (*q.v.*).

SCOPS OWL—Otus scops. At rare intervals, usually in the Spring, this owl wanders to the British Isles from its home by the Mediterranean and in central Europe. The smallest owl to be seen here, it can be distinguished from the Little Owl not only by its more slender build and smaller size, but by its head decoration and beautifully patterned dress of delicate greys and browns. Its rounded wings and tail are barred. Its legs and feet are feathered. The sexes are alike. The length is 7½ in., and the tarsus 0·95 in. ; the wing span is from 10 to 12 in., and the weight about 5 oz.

In habits and behaviour this owl follows the pattern of its family, but it is said to be more nocturnal than the Little Owl. It roosts upright pressed against a tree branch, merging so completely into the background that it is very difficult to observe.

Its " song " is perhaps its best identification, for it proclaims its presence by soft and musical whistling hoots, with a short interval between them, and monotonously repeated for hours on end. This is usually delivered from a tree at dusk, but is also occasionally heard by day.

Open woodlands, parklands, gardens, olive groves, etc., are the haunts of this owl. In southern Europe it breeds regularly in the trees lining the streets of towns and villages. No nest

is built, the four or five eggs being laid in a hole in a tree, wall or ruin. On completion of the clutch, the hen hatches them for 24 days. Both parents tend the young, which quit the nest in about three weeks. One brood is reared.

Insects of various kinds form the chief food of the Scops Owl.

SCOTER. Genus of ducks which, outside the breeding season, are oceanic. They are represented on the British list by the Common Scoter, Velvet Scoter, and Surf-Scoter, described under their own headings.

The Common Scoter is resident only in Scotland and Northern Ireland, and there only locally, but it is a common winter visitor to many parts of the British coast. The male is the only duck that is entirely black (except for a bright orange patch on its bill) ; the female is dark brown, with whitish-brown cheeks and throat. The Velvet Scoter, which is a passage migrant and winter visitor, is fairly similar to the Common Scoter in form and habits, but when the wing is extended, can be distinguished by a white patch along the hind end. The male also has a small white patch below the eye. The Surf-Scoter, which is an irregular visitor from north America, is also very similar to the other scoters, but the male has white head patches and the female has light face spots and is free from white on the wing.

Arthur Christiansen

SCOTER. *Scoters are heavily built, but buoyant swimmers. The drakes are almost completely black*

John Markham

SCOLOPAX, *only British species of this genus—the Woodcock*

BIRD WATCHING IN SCOTLAND

GEORGE WATERSTON, F.R.S.E., M.B.O.U.

Because so much of Scotland remains in its natural state, unspoilt by the hand of Man, the country offers many attractions both to birds and bird watchers. The author, a noted Scottish ornithologist, here describes briefly the bird-life of his home-land

SCOTLAND, Birds in. Throughout the ages, Man has been changing the face of the whole British countryside. He has felled forests, drained swamps, cultivated and enclosed barren ground and built large cities. This has, however, been less apparent in Scotland than in England ; and it is probably this factor which makes Scotland so attractive to both birds and bird watchers. There are large tracts, too, where the density of human population is very low indeed, and there is consequently much less disturbance to breeding birds.

One has but to take a glance at a physical map of Scotland to realize how much of it is composed of mountain and high moorland— bleak and barren. As against this, the main areas of arable land are to be found on the east coast ; and where in England there are ditches and hedgerows, Scotland has stone dykes and wire fences. Although we have lost many interesting raptorial species such as the Goshawk, Kite, White-tailed Eagle and Osprey, our high moorlands and mountains still hold the Golden Eagle. The Hen-Harrier is establishing itself as a breeding species on the mainland.

At one time Scotland was covered with thick forests. These are now much restricted, and vary widely in character between north and south. In the southern parts of the country the woodlands are composed largely of deciduous trees, whereas in the north they are mainly coniferous. There are still relics of the fine old Caledonian pine forest in Rothiemurchus, where the Scottish Crossbill, Scottish Crested Tit and the Siskin breed. The planting of large-scale commercial plantations in so many parts of the Highlands is bound to effect changes in the bird population.

The west coast is intersected with numerous sea-lochs and broken up into islands of varying size and beauty. The rugged majesty of the west Highlands makes them a favourite haunt

Eric Hosking

SCOTLAND. *The Scottish Crossbill differs from the common race in its more massive bill*

of the bird watcher. These physical features of Scotland have, of course, a great influence on the composition of its avifauna.

Scotland has a wealth of interesting islands, and great fascination is always to be found in studying birds on an island. The sea which surrounds it makes a much more satisfactory demarcation than any Man-made parish or county boundaries. Our islands vary in character from the remote uninhabited group of St. Kilda, with its magnificent sea-bird colonies, to the Outer Hebrides with their myriads of lochs; the austere beauty of the Shetland Islands ; and the richly cultivated lands of Orkney. There are sea-bird colonies on the Bass Rock, Ailsa Craig, and Sula Sgeir.

The northern islands of Orkney and Shetland have many attractions to offer the bird watcher. Here the Storm-Petrel, Red-necked Phalarope, Great and Arctic Skua, Eider Duck, Black Guillemot and the Hen-Harrier are breeding.

Bird observatories (*q.v.*) have been founded on the Isle of May in the Firth of Forth, and on Fair Isle between Orkney and Shetland. Both these islands are important stations for studying drift migration, and facilities are available for bird watchers to stay on them and study migration and breeding biology.

The Nature Conservancy (*q.v.*) has established two important Nature Reserves in mountain and moorland areas. In and around the Cairngorm Reserve are many interesting breeding species— Golden Eagle, Dotterel, Ptarmigan and Snow-Bunting on the high ground, and lower down in the pine forest area, Crossbill, Siskin, Crested Tit, Greenshank, and Capercaillie. At the other Reserve at Beinn Eighe, in Wester Ross, there are fine tracts of mountain, moor, and forest, with Golden Eagle, Greenshank and several rare mammals.

The many fine estuaries around our coast are excellent places for wildfowl and waders in the

1 L

Winter. The Solway estuary has long been famous for its wildfowl, and the bird watcher who knows where to look will find big packs of white-fronted geese, grey lag-, pink-footed and barnacle geese. On the east coast, the estuaries of the northern firths—such as the Dornoch, Cromarty, and Beauly Firths—make excellent feeding grounds. Further south down the east coast there is the Ythan estuary, with its huge flocks of eider duck and waders, and the Eden estuary between Guardbridge and St. Andrews, which is a great wintering ground for Wigeon, Sheld-Duck, Pintail and Shoveler. Out to sea there are big rafts of scoters. Not far from Edinburgh there are the estuaries at Aberlady and the Tyne near Dunbar where during the spring and autumn passage many interesting waders are to be seen.

There are many fine inland wildfowl haunts. The Loch of Strathbeg, in the north-east corner of Aberdeenshire, supports a vast population of waterfowl. Spynie Loch in Morayshire is an attractive breeding loch with excellent reed beds. Loch Leven has long been famous for its wintering flocks of geese, and is also an important loch for breeding birds. The Clyde between Bothwell Bridge and Hamilton is a favourite winter bird watching haunt for Glasgow ornithologists, with its grey lag geese, whooper-swans, and a large variety of ducks. Several uncommon species have been seen in this area.

There has been a great surge of interest in birds in Scotland since the Second World War, and it is to be hoped that, under the Protection of Birds Act (1954), many birds, whose status is at present precarious, will be permitted to establish themselves as regular breeding species.

SCOTTISH CROSSBILL—Loxia curvirostra scotica. This resident bird of the Scottish Highlands, differs in appearance from the common Crossbill only in its stouter and larger beak, especially noticeable in the male bird. In habits, voice, breeding and nesting, it resembles the common species. There are some variations of sound, however, especially a threatening call.

SCOTTISH ORNITHOLOGISTS' CLUB, Founded in 1936, now has over a thousand Members. Winter meetings are held at six centres—Aberdeen, Dundee, Edinburgh, Glasgow, Perth, and St. Andrews—and in Summer excursions are organised to places of interest. Enquiries should be made to the Secretary, c/o The National Trust for Scotland, 5, Charlotte Square, Edinburgh 2.

SCOTTISH SOCIETY, WILD BIRDS, for the Protection of. This organization was founded in Glasgow early in 1927 by Mr. John McLean Crosthwaite, who, until his death in 1942, was its honorary secretary and treasurer. Membership of the Society, on payment of a small subscription, is not limited to persons living in Scotland ; and inquiries should be made to Mr. James M. MacKellar, the honorary secretary, at 125, Douglas Street, Glasgow, C.2.

Lady Isle, Troon, Ayrshire, the first bird sanctuary to be established in western Scotland, is leased by the Society. The sanctuary at Possil Marsh, Lambhill, Glasgow, is owned by the Scottish Wild Birds Sanctuaries Trust, which is controlled by the Scottish Society for the Protection of Wild Birds.

Since its inception, the society has ceaselessly advocated a law protecting wild birds, their nests and eggs throughout the year, unless

SCOTLAND. Fair Isle Observatory was established in 1948. It lies midway between Shetland and Orkney, and is particularly suited for studying migratory movements

George Waterston

there were sound and scientific reasons why certain birds should not be protected. Many years ago a Private Member's Bill was introduced by the Society in Parliament, but fell through ; but the Protection of Birds Act (1954) embodies, in the main, the society's aims.

SCOUT. Local name for Guillemot (*q.v.*) ; Black Guillemot (*q.v.*) and Razorbill (*q.v.*).

SCOUTIALLAN. Local (Scottish) name for the Arctic Skua (*q.v.*).

SCREAMER. Local name for Swift (*q.v.*).

SCREECH-MARTIN. One of several alternative names for the Swift (*q.v.*).

SCREECH-OWL. Alternative name for the Barn-Owl (*q.v.*).

SCRIBE or SCRIBBLE-CLERK. Local names for Yellow Hammer (*q.v.*), because of the dark blotches and irregular scribblings on the eggs.

SCUTE. A thin plate or large scale such as is found, for example, on the legs of some birds.

SEA. Prefix used in connection with alternative and local names of a number of species, e.g. -COBB, Common Gull (*q.v.*) ; -CROW, Chough (*q.v.*)—also called Cornish Chough and Red-Legged Daw ; -DOVE, Little Auk (*q.v.*) ; -EAGLE, White-tailed Eagle (*q.v.*)—sometimes called Gray Sea-Eagle ; -LARK, Common Sandpiper (*q.v.*) ; -MAGPIE, Oystercatcher (*q.v.*); -MEW, Common Gull (*q.v.*) ; -PARROT, Puffin (*q.v.*) ; -RAVEN, Cormorant (*q.v.*) ; -SWALLOW, various terns (*q.v.*).

SECONDARIES. Name given to the large quill feathers of the wing which are attached to the " ulna ", or forearm. The quills attached to the " hand " are known as primaries (*q.v.*). The bases of both the secondary and primary feathers are covered above and below by wing-coverts. *See Plate facing p.* 1.

The secondaries vary in number from six to 30 or more ; in the majority of birds' wings there are about a dozen, as in the pigeon. Unlike the primaries, which should properly be counted outwards from the wrist, the secondaries should be counted inwards from the wrist.

The secondaries are shorter and less closely " packed " than the primaries. They are of major importance in the wing stroke, whereas the main function of the primaries is to assist in side steering. *See also* Feather ; Wing.

SEDGE-WARBLER—Acrocephalus schoenobaenus. Remarkable for its power, of song and mimicry, the Sedge-Warbler arrives as a summer resident late in April, and breeds in all suitable areas throughout the British Isles. It is also a passage migrant on our coasts. Abroad, it breeds throughout Europe, temperate Asia and north Africa, wintering in south Africa.

The Sedge-Warbler is dressed in warm brown, its crown and mantle being streaked darker ; a prominent buff eye-stripe distinguishes it from the Reed-Warbler. Its brown rump is unstreaked and tinged with reddish. Its breast and underparts are cream-coloured, deepening at the sides and flanks. Its bill is dark, and its legs grey. The sexes are alike. The length is 5 in., and the tarsus 0·8 in. ; the wing span is about 6 in., and the weight a fraction of an ounce.

The Sedge-Warbler is seldom visible, and spends most of its life under cover of reeds and

G. K. Yeates

SEDGE-WARBLER. *Seldom visible, this little warbler is remarkable for its prowess at singing*

other vegetation, creeping up and down the stems. It flies low, and only for short distances. On migration its flight is erratic and jerky.

It has little actual courtship, but its song-flight is remarkable ; the bird rises almost vertically in the air, then turns quickly and comes back to its perch, with wings and tail outspread.

Among the Sedge-Warbler's call notes are a very soft, high-pitched call, and a deeper note not unlike one of the Blackbird's call notes. The song, a fine performance, is one of the most outstanding among warblers' songs. A loud and vigorous outpouring of a variety of notes—some musical, some harsh and jarring—uttered from its hidden perch, it lasts as long as a minute and sometimes longer. The song is frequently heard at night, and on migration it has been heard in such unusual places as town and city parks. It is best heard from April to July, and sometimes extends into August, although not with the same vehemence. The Sedge-Warbler is also an excellent mimic and produces exact imitations of other birds breeding in its area.

This bird nests in colonies, usually among the rank vegetation of reed beds, ditches, etc., but it may build in a hedgerow or bush some distance from water. The nest, usually within two feet of the ground, is larger, but less deep, than the Reed-Warbler's. It is built by the little hen (under the male's supervision) of moss, grass and stalks, and cosily lined with hair, willow-down and feathers. The five or six yellowish eggs, mottled in brown, are laid in May. The hatching, which takes a fortnight, is done mainly by the hen ; both parents feed and tend the nestlings for the same period. One brood is usual, but sometimes two are reared.

The Sedge-Warbler feeds upon insects.

SEMI-PALMATED RINGED PLOVER—Charadrius hiaticula semipalmatus.

This species of Ringed Plover is the American counterpart of the bird seen round the British coasts. It breeds on the Arctic coasts of north America, and winters in the south. One bird paid a visit to Rye, Sussex, in 1916. Very similar in appearance to the Ringed Plover, the American bird is slightly smaller and has a narrower breast band. The length is 7 in. Its habits and behaviour are identical with the British bird's.

SEMI-PALMATED SANDPIPER—Calidris pusilla.

This small sandpiper from Arctic America once wandered to the Romney marshes, Sussex, in 1907. It is so similar to the Little and American Stint that identification in the field, even by the expert, is difficult ; but it is recorded as greyer in plumage, with decidedly darker legs than the others. The male and female are alike. The length is 5¾ in. and the tarsus 0·95 in. ; the wing span is about 8¾ in. Its behaviour and habits do not differ from those of allied species.

SERIN—Serinus canarius.

A small greenish-brown finch, the ancestor of the Canary, the Serin is an irregular visitor (chiefly from November to May) and has been recorded some forty times, almost all in England. Abroad, it is on the increase, and it breeds throughout Europe, coming as near to our shores as the north of France.

Its plumage is predominantly a streaked greenish-brown. Its light yellow rump distinguishes it from the Siskin, and it also lacks the yellow at the base of the tail. The male Serin has some bright yellow on his head and breast ; the female is duller, but has the yellow rump. The tail is short and forked, the legs and short bill flesh-brown.

Gardens, vineyards and orchards, as well as wooded suburbs, are its favourite haunts, and on the Continent the Serin is a common bird in towns and villages. At all times it is sociable, and when seen here is usually in the company of other finches.

Its undulating flight has the same light and fairy-like action as that of the Goldfinch and Redpoll. The Serin hops on the ground, and perches freely on trees, telegraph wires, etc.

The song is pleasant—sometimes soft, sometimes harsh—but does not carry far. The subsong heard early in the season is soft and sweet and very finch-like. The short call note is very similar to that of the Goldfinch.

The Serin breeds in many kinds of trees and bushes. The hen, accompanied by her mate, builds a small and well-concealed nest of stalks, lichen, moss, etc., woven together with spiders' webs and well lined with hair. Four pale-blue eggs, very like those of other finches, are laid in April and May, or even in July, according to the locality. Both male and female take part in hatching and rearing the two broods. All kinds of plant seeds are eaten and enjoyed.

Maslowski & Goodpaster

SEMI-PALMATED SANDPIPER. *An Arctic bird, very similar to the Little and the American Stint, except for its greyer plumage and dark legs*

SERINUS. Genus of the family *Fringillidae* of the order *Passeriformes*. It contains a number of species, distributed over Europe, Asia, and Africa. The majority of species are African, the only European one being the Serin (*q.v.*), an occasional visitor to Britain.

SEX LIFE. *See* Breeding Season ; Courtship; Display ; Mating ; Pairing ; Reproduction.

SEX REVERSAL. This phenomenon has attracted attention from ancient times ; references to it are found in Aristotle, Terence and Livy, and the basilisk or cockatrice of legend was supposed to emerge from a cock's egg.

All vertebrates possess rudimentary organs or tissues of the opposite sex which can, in certain circumstances, develop until they equal or overcome the others. In birds, sex reversal from female to male, which is relatively common, is due to the fact that female birds generally develop only one (the left) functional ovary (*see* Anatomy, Fig. 7). If this single ovary is destroyed by disease, or removed experimentally, opportunity is given for the rudimentary male tissue to develop, and a male organ—the testis—can arise. Sometimes it develops sufficiently to produce viable spermatozoa, and the former hen can become a father.

In any case, the new male tissue will in time secrete male sex hormones (androgens) into the blood-stream. These will become dominant over the decreasing female sex hormones (oestrogens) and cause the assumption of the plumage, comb and spurs of a cock. They will also stimulate the brain centres which control male behaviour patterns involving spirited crowing, fighting and a desire to tread hens. Sex reversal in the other direction—from male to female—is of much rarer occurrence.

" Cocks' eggs " are almost always produced by hens that are in the process of changing into roosters, but in which, while the outward appearance is that of a cock, the ovarian function is still not entirely destroyed. Often the egg is merely very small, but occasionally on its journey down the now withered and constricted oviduct (*see* Anatomy, Fig. 7) it gets so twisted and attenuated that it appears deformed, twisted or serpent-like. This appearance gave rise to the legend that such monstrous-looking eggs grew into basilisks.

SHAFT. Part of the quill (*q.v.*). For further information, *see also* Feather (drawings).

SHAG—Phalacrocorax aristotelis. A close relation of the Cormorant, and itself often called the Green Cormorant, the Shag is a British resident, and breeds on all suitable rocky coasts round the north and west of Scotland and Ireland. In England, it is found only on the Farne Islands and on the Channel and Bristol

Eric Hosking

SHAG. Smaller than the Cormorant, to which it is related, the Shag is known as Green Cormorant

Channel coasts from the Isle of Wight to Lundy Island. Abroad, it breeds in suitable districts of Europe and north-west Africa. In Scotland it goes by the name of " Scart " or " Scarf ".

Although the Cormorant and Shag may both haunt the same stretches of coastline, they are seldom seen together, for whereas the former is found on sea-coasts of all kinds—sandy, muddy, or rocky—as well as on cliffs and islands, the latter is confined to rocky cliffs and islands, where it nests in crevice of a rock, a narrow ledge, or an over-hanging boulder. At a distance, the casual observer might have difficulty in distinguishing one from the other, for they are very similar both in build and plumage. Closer inspection, however, reveals the Shag's smaller size, the rich greenish gloss of its dark plumage, and its lack of the white so conspicuous on the neck of the Cormorant. Further, in nuptial dress the Shag sports an unruly tuft of crest feathers on the front of the head. Its feet are blackish ; its slightly hooked bill is blackish, yellow at the base, and also yellow on the area of skin surrounding the gape. The sexes are alike. The juvenile has a darker appearance than the juvenile of the Cormorant, and has a whitish patch at the chin. The Shag's total length is 30 in., the body being 18 in. ; the tarsus is $2\frac{1}{4}$ in., the wing span $3\frac{1}{2}$ ft., and the weight 4 lb.

The Shag is a sedentary bird, and even in Winter rarely wanders far from its breeding site. Its habits and behaviour do not differ to any

Paul Popper

SHEARWATER. *Manx Shearwater, surprised near its burrow by a photographer's flashlight. This species of shearwater is the only one of its kind to be resident here*

great extent from those of the Cormorant, but it is almost wholly marine, seldom moving inland unless driven by storms. Its movements are more graceful than the Cormorant's; and its diving ability is as great, but it has an individual habit of springing clear from the water before submerging, in contrast to the quiet gliding off of the Cormorant. The Shag also has the characteristic habit of standing upright with its wings outspread like some heraldic bird. It prefers rocks to posts or buoys as perches. As with the Cormorant, the female Shag is the principal performer in the spring display.

The Shag is a silent bird, and only at its breeding site is its voice heard. Approach to the nest of a breeding Shag is always very difficult. My recording was made from a corner of an almost inaccessible rock. I put the microphone in front of a sitting female Shag, which took little notice of human intruders, and, having climbed down again to my recording "studio", recorded the sounds she made on her nest. For the first time I noticed a very distinct "clipping" noise, followed by the raucous call note, which became more and more excited. When I returned to the nest I discovered that the "clipping" sound was made with the bill. Further recording of the Shag proved that the male utters his call note without this "clipping" of the bill. I believe this difference between the calls of the male and female Shag has rarely been noticed. The call note of the male is harsher than that of the female, and is rather reminiscent of the Cormorant's. Whether the young are with the male or the female parent, they utter barking noises.—EDITOR.

Shags breed in colonies of varying size on the narrow ledges of cliffs and rocky islands. The nest is constructed of seaweed, and any other suitable material available, by both birds, one building and the other bringing the material. The breeding season is usually in March or April, but varies considerably according to the weather, owing to the exposed nature of the sites. The normal number of eggs, which are similar to those of the Cormorant but rather smaller, is three. Both male and female incubate for four weeks, and both feed the young for about five or six weeks. One brood is reared in a season, but should disaster overtake the first clutch, another will be laid.

A voracious feeder, the Shag hunts fish in much the same manner as its relative the Cormorant. It prefers round to flat fish, and for some peculiar reason seems to have a special liking for sand-eels and sprats.

SHARP-TAILED SANDPIPER. Alternative name for Siberian Pectoral Sandpiper (*q.v.*).

SHEARWATER. Genus of oceanic birds closely related to the petrels. They are represented in all the oceans and visit land only when breeding. The name refers to their habit of skimming close to (i.e. "shearing") the waves. Shearwaters are medium-sized birds, with rather elongated, slightly hooked, slender bills (with tube-like external nostrils), long narrow wings and wedge-shaped tails.

Most shearwaters are sooty-brown or greyish above and white below. They are strong on the wing, and the flight of the larger species is characteristic—consisting of long, sweeping glides very close to the water, interrupted by short periods of quick wing beats. When turning, the birds bank very sharply.

The following species and subspecies, all of which appear under their own headings, are on the British List : Manx Shearwater ; Little Shearwater (Madeiran and Cape Verde races) ; Audubon's Shearwater ; Great Shearwater ; Mediterranean Shearwater ; North Atlantic or (Cory's) Shearwater ; and Sooty Shearwater.

SHELD-DUCK—Tadorna tadorna. The largest of all the ducks, the Sheld-Duck is a resident in Great Britain all round the year on sandy coasts and muddy estuaries, as well as some distance inland. By all accounts it is on the increase, especially in Scotland, where previously it was a rare visitor. The Sheld-Duck is subject to seasonal changes. In July, the British birds leave their young and migrate to Heligoland Bight and the Bristol Channel, returning after their moult. In Spring and late Summer, some passage movements occur along the coasts, where the birds congregate in large flocks. Abroad, the Sheld-Duck breeds in many parts of Europe and Asia.

Boldly patterned in black and white, with a broad brown band encircling its lower breast, shoulders and mantle top, the Sheld-Duck is not easily confused with any other duck. Its head and neck are black with a green gloss. Its flanks are black, and down the centre of its white underparts runs a black line. Its tail is white, bordered in black, and its wings are patterned in black and white. The speculum is in bronze-green and chestnut. The bill of the male is bright red, with a knob at the tip in Summer. The legs and feet are flesh-coloured. The sexes are alike, except that the female has no knob on her bill. In eclipse plumage, both male and female are much duller. The juveniles have dark, greyish-brown upper parts, and no chestnut band. The total length is 24 in., the body being 16 in. ; the tarsus is 2·3 in. The wing span is approximately 2 ft. or 2½ ft., and the weight is about 2 lb.

The Sheld-Duck has some characteristics, both in form and habits, of the goose. Its bulky body makes its flight slower than that of most ducks. Its movements are goose-like, and the flocks fly in the wedge-shaped formation characteristic of geese. On the ground the Sheld-Duck walks with ease, and sometimes runs. It rises gracefully, and during the breeding season perches on the ledges of cliffs and rocks. The Sheld-Duck swims buoyantly, often resting on the surface, but seems less inclined to do so than most other ducks, and rarely ventures far from land. The ebbing of the tides governs the feeding time of the Sheld-Duck, which wades in the shallow water, often with its head submerged, and sometimes even " up-ending ". Unless injured, it rarely dives. In common with many water birds, it stamps on the wet ground to try to bring up worms.

In the spring display the aggressive males indulge in short fights with rivals, and in their excitement often spring clear of the ground. Duck and drake have a mutual display with much posturing, the drake stretching and dipping his neck and walking round the duck. Bowing, whistling and clucking also occur.

Sheld-ducks are on the whole silent birds, but at their breeding sites, where many nest together, they can be very noisy by day and by night. Both duck and drake have various quaint calls. The drake's is a low whistle, and sometimes he utters what sounds remarkably

SHELD-DUCK. This is the largest of all ducks, and is thought by some to be a sort of link between the ducks proper and geese. Sheld-ducks are very handsome birds

Eric Hosking

Eric Hosking

SHELL DISPOSAL. *Bittern cleaning up its nest after the young have been hatched, by dropping the empty egg-shells neatly over the nest's edge*

in some birds at least, that a visual stimulus is primarily responsible, for light-coloured scraps of paper and similar objects will also be removed from the nest at this time.

The habit of shell-removal undoubtedly has survival value both in protecting the delicate nestlings from injury by the shells and, more important, in preventing the disclosure of the nest to predatory animals and birds. The latter applies particularly in ground-nesting birds, such as plovers, terns and gulls (*see* Camouflage; Pattern and Colour). Not all ground-nesting birds, however, remove the shells; but in such nests the two halves of the eggs are frequently fitted neatly into each other, as if to make more room in the crowded nest while the remaining chicks are being hatched.

In ordinary circumstances, if the habit of removing empty shells is to be effective, the pieces must be carried some distance from the nest, and in fact this is generally done. But the Bittern, for instance, nesting in dense reed-beds with the nest often surrounded by water, merely drops the shells over the edge of the nest.

The interval between hatching and removal of the shell fragments varies. .An Avocet has been seen to help its chick out of the shell by vigorous movements of the beak and then, almost immediately, fly away with one of the pieces in its bill. On the other hand, some birds will continue brooding the shells for some hours before removing them from the nest.

Some birds do not remove the shells, but solve the problem of disposal by crushing them and either eating the pieces or treading them into the bottom of the nest.—JOHN CLEGG.

like a raucous laugh. The duck's normal call is a harsh quack.

Normally a shore-nesting bird, the Sheld-Duck generally chooses a rabbit-hole or burrow tunnelled among the sand dunes or downs; but sometimes the nest is placed far inland near some stretch of water. The nest is a bulky structure composed almost entirely of greyish down. The 8–15 creamy-white eggs are laid in May. For a period of 28 days the duck incubates alone, with the drake in attendance near by. As soon as the ducklings appear, clad in dark-brown and white down, a procession sets out for the water, the duck leading the way and the drake bringing up the rear. For eight weeks both parents tend their numerous offspring. One brood is as a rule reared, but where many sheld-ducks nest together one pair of parents will often be found taking care of many ducklings besides their own. Two seasons elapse before the ducklings attain their adult dress.

Marine molluscs, crustaceans and suchlike form the principal food of the Sheld-Duck, but some vegetable matter is also taken.

The word " sheld " means " pied ". Local names of the Sheld-Duck include Barrow-Duck, Sheldrake, Bargander, Bargoose and Shell-Duck. *See also* Ruddy Sheld-Duck.

SHELL DISPOSAL. The methods by which parent birds dispose of shell fragments once the chicks have hatched from the eggs vary with the species, and even among individuals. Although the discomfort of sitting on the sharp-edged shells may sometimes act as a stimulus to their removal, there is evidence,

SHETLAND STARLING—Sturnus vulgaris zetlandicus. Records show that this bird has always bred in the Shetland Islands; it is also a resident in the Outer Hebrides and Faroe Islands. Most of its characteristics are similar to those of the common Starling, but it has perforce to choose a different nesting site; since there are no trees in their home islands, Shetland starlings have resorted to holes in sea cliffs, peat stacks and even rabbit warrens.

In appearance the Shetland bird is much the same as the common Starling, but it has a larger wing span and a wider bill. The young birds are much darker than those of the common species, and the Shetland Starling's voice has a sweeter timbre. The nesting season takes place a little later, in May and June. The number of eggs laid, their colour and the hatching period are the same as the common Starling's, but the male Shetland Starling takes a greater part in sitting on the eggs and in feeding the young birds. A second brood is also more often reared.

SHETLAND WREN—Troglodytes troglodytes zetlandicus. This species of Wren, a resident in the Shetlands, is confined to those islands. It is more stoutly built and darker in plumage than the mainland Wren, but its habits and behaviour are very similar. Its length is $3\frac{1}{2}$ in., and its tarsus $\frac{3}{4}$ in. ; its wing span is about 5 in., and its weight a small fraction of an ounce.

Its song is said to be lower pitched and to have a more resounding ending than other wrens'.

SHORE-LARK—Eremophila alpestris. From its home in the Arctic Circle, the Shore-Lark visits the east coast of England as a regular bird of passage, though in small numbers ; Scotland sees it occasionally, but Ireland so far has only one record. As its name implies, the Shore-Lark is essentially a bird of beaches, salt marshes and so on, and is rarely seen inland.

The male is distinguished by an all-over brown plumage, the upper parts being slightly streaked and tinged with pink, and the underparts much paler. His throat and face are strikingly decorated ; his crown, cheeks and gorget are black, and his face and throat yellow. He has also a pair of black erectile "horns", and there is some white in his tail. The female has less black. The thin bill is horn-coloured, and the legs black. The length is $6\frac{1}{2}$ in., and the tarsus 0·9 in. ; the wing span is between 8 and 9 in., and the weight $1\frac{1}{2}$ oz.

The Shore-Lark is gregarious and is usually seen in small flocks, sometimes in the company of Snow- and Lapland Buntings. Its movements in the air resemble the Skylark's, but seem more undulating. On the ground it walks and runs, sometimes also hops. It perches on rocks and buildings, but rarely on trees. It is inclined to be tame, and will visit many villages and settlements in the Far North.

This lark has a great variety of notes quite different from other larks', the commonest being a repeated shrill pipe. The song is described as a sweet low warble and, although the bird does sing in the air, the principal performance is said to take place on the ground.

The Shore-Lark breeds on, or very near, the sea-shore. The nest, placed in a sheltered hollow in peaty ground, is built with grass stalks and lined with willow down, cotton rush or reindeer hair, some outside decoration being added. In May or June four greenish-white eggs are laid. As far as is known, the incubation period is 10 to 14 days and both parents feed and tend the nestlings for a further 9 to 10 days when they are fully fledged. Two broods are, as a rule, reared in a season.

In Summer, the Shore-Lark feeds on seeds, buds and insects, and in Winter on molluscs and crustaceans of various kinds.

SHORT-BILLED GULL. American name for Common Gull (*q.v.*).

SHORT-EARED OWL — Asio flammeus. Several differences in behaviour and habits distinguish the Short-eared Owl from the rest of its family. It is, for instance, much less arboreal than other owls, and haunts open country—moors, fens, marshes, bogs, heaths and sand dunes—rather than wooded areas. It nests on the ground instead of in a hole, and it almost always hunts by day.

The Short-eared Owl is a British resident, breeding—though by no means abundantly—in the northern counties of England, and in Norfolk, Suffolk and Cambridgeshire. It breeds sparingly throughout Scotland, and Ireland has only one record of breeding. It is also a winter

H. N. Southern

SHETLAND STARLING. *Nesting in the Outer Hebrides and Faroe Islands as well as in the Shetlands, this bird closely resembles its relative*

G. K. Yeates

SHORT-EARED OWL. *Several habits distinguish this bird from other owls ; thus it prefers open to wooded country, and usually hunts by day*

Like other owls and birds of prey, it ejects pellets.

In its wonderful spring display the Short-eared Owl circles high above, soaring, gliding and flapping its wings. On uttering its "song", a low-pitched vibrating hoot, it claps its wings as it sinks to the ground. This display and "song" can be observed as early as January, and continue throughout the breeding season. Similar aerial displays, accompanied by the fall to the ground but without the "song", can be seen during the

visitor, many (known as " Woodcock-Owls ") arriving in the Autumn from abroad.

Both the breeding and the migration of the Short-eared Owl are governed by the abundance or otherwise of the destructive vole—its chief food. These rodents occur in some years in such large numbers as to constitute a plague. In a " vole year " some instinct seems to guide the Short-eared Owl, for, wherever voles are abundant, these birds will be found. The same phenomenon occurs in Europe in a " lemming year ". Short-eared owls also breed throughout the Old and New Worlds, northwards to the Arctic Circle, wintering in tropical Africa, India, and south America.

Short-eared owls vary considerably in appearance, but the general coloration is buff, the mantle being richly marbled in dark brown and the underparts in a paler shade. The ear tufts, which give the bird its name, are not as a rule very prominent unless it is excited. Its rounded wings and tail are barred, and its facial disk is buff-coloured, with a dark border surrounding the golden eyes. Its dark bill is horn-coloured, and its feet and legs are feathered. The sexes are alike in colouring, but the female is larger than the male. The length is 14 or 15 in., and the tarsus 2 in. ; the wing span is between 2 and 2½ ft., and the weight 11-14 oz.

The noiseless flight, with slow wing beats, is typical of the family, but the Short-eared Owl's wings are longer and narrower than is usual, and give an impression rather of a Buzzard or Kestrel. The bird soars, wheels and glides at a great height, but roosts on the ground under cover of grass or other vegetation ; it occasionally perches on trees or fences. Its carriage is slanting, in contrast to the uprightness of most owls.

Autumn. Outside the breeding season this owl is usually silent, but when angry or disturbed it hisses and snaps its bill.

A scrape on the ground, sheltered among vegetation, scantily lined with stems, houses the four to eight white eggs laid in late April or early May at two-day intervals. The hen incubates them alone during 3½ to 4 weeks, and for a fortnight the male brings food for the nestlings, which are clad in buff and white down. They then leave the nest, and are able to fly a month later. One brood is usually reared, but in a " vole year " two have been known.

When voles are not in plentiful supply, the Short-eared Owl feeds on field mice and other small mammals, as well as on birds and insects.

SHORT-TOED LARK—Calandrella brachydactyla. An occasional visitor to the British Isles, usually on its autumn migration, this Mediterranean bird has been recorded some thirty times, the majority of the records coming from Fair Isle and coastal lighthouses. A small sandy-looking bird, with a streaked dark brown mantle and white underparts, it nests in sandy wastes, dunes and steppe country, and has much the same habits and behaviour as other larks. Its song is delivered like the Skylark's, but generally with less vehemence and at a lower height. The length is 5½ in., the tarsus ¾ in., and the wing span about 7 in.

SHOVELER—Spatula clypeata. Although the Shoveler, a surface-feeding duck, was at one time in danger of disappearing altogether from the British scene, it is now reported to be increasing—although still not abundant—in suitable districts all over the British Isles. Its breeding sites are local, but it now nests in almost every county in England and, except those of the north-west, in Scotland. Wales has several records, and in Ireland it is widespread. The Shoveler is also a passage migrant and winter visitor. Abroad, it occurs throughout Europe, Asia, Africa and America.

The remarkable long, broad, and spoon-shaped bill of the Shoveler is, of course, its most outstanding feature and gives it both its ordinary and its scientific name. The drake possesses handsome variegated plumage. His back is dark-brown, his underparts and flanks warm chestnut. In contrast with his dark green head and neck, the breast and the sides of his mantle are white, and a white patch also shows in front of his dark under-tail coverts. The duck and juvenile are brown, with darker streaks ; in his eclipse plumage the drake is very similar to them. Both duck and drake have a pale-green forewing, and a green and white speculum. The legs of both are yellow, and the drake has yellow eyes, an unusual feature in a surface-feeding duck. The length is 20 in., the body being 12 in. ; the tarsus is 1·4 in. The wing span is between 1½ ft. and 2 ft., and the average weight is 1 lb. 6 oz.

In the air the huge bill and squat body of the Shoveler give it an unwieldy and unbalanced appearance. Although its flight is fast, with rapid wing beats, it is less speedy than the Mallard. It is an awkward walker on the ground, but an excellent and active swimmer, sailing along with its large bill resting on its neck. It does not duck, like many surface-feeders, nor is it so fond of " up-ending " or diving. It moves swiftly along, sweeping the shallow muddy water with its spoon bill ; this is specially adapted to act as a sieve, the water

and mud passing through, while the organisms and insects on which the Shoveler feeds are retained. The Shoveler is seen singly, in pairs and in small parties, but in large flocks only when on migration.

The spring display follows closely the simple and undemonstrative pattern of its relatives. This is one of the most silent of ducks. The voice of the drake is seldom heard ; it is a low, guttural croak. The duck has a deep quack.

The nest is found in a meadow near water, in an open reed-bed, or among the vegetation of a common or heath. A well-concealed hollow is selected, and lined with down and feathers. The eight to ten greenish eggs are laid in April or May ; when the last has been laid, the duck hatches them for 23-25 days. For six weeks the ducklings are tended by the duck, with the drake in attendance. One brood is reared in a season.

SHRIKE. Genus of strikingly-coloured perching birds, having a short, hook-tipped bill with a prominent tooth and forward-directed hair round its base, wings of moderate length, rather long tails, and very strong feet. The name, derived from an Icelandic word meaning "shrieker", refers to the characteristic harsh call note ; strangely enough, some species have a surprisingly pleasant song, and they delight to mimic other songsters.

Shrikes are also called " butcher-birds " from their habit of impaling their prey on thorns to form a sort of larder. The food consists chiefly of insects, but mice, frogs, lizards and small birds are also taken.

The following five species, described under their own headings, appear on the British list :

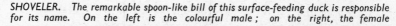
SHOVELER. The remarkable spoon-like bill of this surface-feeding duck is responsible for its name. On the left is the colourful male ; on the right, the female

Arthur Christiansen; Eric Hosking

Great Grey Shrike ; Lesser Grey Shrike ; Woodchat-Shrike ; Masked Shrike ; Red-backed Shrike.

SIBERIAN CHIFFCHAFF—Phylloscopus collybita tristis. A very rare visitor to England, but a regular autumn arrival in the Orkney and Shetland Islands, this bird breeds in various parts of Russia. Smaller than the other two races registered on the British list (*see* Chiffchaff), it is easily distinguished by its whiter underparts. Its unmistakable song is also different from that of both the other chiffchaffs. The call notes are usually softer, and rather resemble the notes of the Coal-Tit. The Editor has heard and recorded in July a two-note song, very similar to the common Chiffchaff's but sweeter and uttered much more quickly. It is said that on migration in March the Siberian species has been heard to utter the typical Chiffchaff song heard in India.

SIBERIAN LESSER WHITETHROAT— Sylvia curruca blythi. This bird has wandered from its home in Siberia to the British Isles about a dozen times ; all the records have been from Scotland, the majority from Fair Isle. Except for some slight difference in the length of its second primary, this species is identical both in behaviour and habits with the British Lesser Whitethroat. The length is 4¾ in.

SIBERIAN PECTORAL SANDPIPER— Calidris acuminata. This breeding bird of north-east Siberia has been recorded in Norfolk four times, all during the Autumn. Its appearance is very like that of the American Pectoral Sandpiper, except that its breast is almost unstreaked. Its tail is wedge-shaped. The

length is 7 to 8 in. ; the tarsus 1·1 in., and the wing span about 10 in.

Very little information is available concerning the breeding of this rare visitor, but it is presumed to follow the pattern of its American relation with which it associates. It is called " Sharptailed Sandpiper " in America.

SISKIN—Carduelis spinus. Although this beautiful and attractive little finch is a resident in some parts of the British Isles, it is probably better known as a winter visitor. Its breeding is confined to pine, larch and fir woods ; Scotland and Ireland therefore provide its principal nesting sites, but even there the Siskin is by no means abundant. From time to time records are received of nesting sites in some counties of England and Wales, but, although some of these are authentic, many are probably escaped cage-birds. But as a winter visitor from Scandinavia and the Baltic countries, the Siskin is widely distributed in suitable districts of England and Wales. The numbers fluctuate : some years see the arrival of large flocks, in others the bird is scarce or absent altogether.

The male is dressed in yellowish-green, streaked darker on the mantle. His underparts are paler, shading to white. His crown and chin are black, his rump is yellow, and his dusky wings have a yellow wing-bar. In the hen and juvenile, the yellow colouring is much duller, and the dark streaks bolder ; no black appears on crown or chin. The tail is cleft ; the short, finch-like bill and legs are dark brown. The length is 4¾ in., and the tarsus ½ in. ; the wing span is approximately 6 in., and the weight only a fraction of an ounce.

The Siskin's flight is light and airy, but it is a restless bird and spends much of its time among the trees, where it darts acrobatically in and out of the branches in the manner of the tits. Siskins are very gregarious and spend the Winter (when they are most likely to be seen here) in company with lesser redpolls, foraging and feeding among alder and birch trees, where they keep up a constant twittering.

The Siskin's gay and melodious song is one of the sweetest among the finches ; it can never be mistaken because it terminates in a

R. P. Bagnall-Oakeley

SIBERIAN PECTORAL SANDPIPER. *This rare straggler from Arctic lands is very like the American Pectoral Sandpiper, shown in the picture*

characteristic and prolonged flattish note. Unfortunately, except in its restricted nesting places, its full song is rarely heard in England, though it has been recorded in Surrey from February to April. Its winter song is a low, sweet warble. There are various call notes, varying in timbre and uttered both from a perch and on the wing.

In its graceful dancing song-flight, the little male circles over the tree tops, his feathers fluffed out and his rapidly beating wings almost meeting over his back. This display may extend beyond the courtship period, especially during sunny days, and several males are sometimes seen performing together.

The Siskin builds its nest in a pine, larch or spruce, often at a good height from the ground. It is made of moss, bents and wool, and lined with roots, feathers, down and hair ; the little hen does the work, with the male supervising her operations. In Scotland, the breeding season is in May ; in Ireland it is usually April. The three to five blue eggs are spotted and streaked reddish. Two broods are normal, the second clutch is laid in June. Hatching takes about 12 days, and both parents rear and feed the nestlings for a further 15 days.

John Markham

SISKIN. *For some reason this finch has a preference for pines, larches and spruce*

The seeds of many trees, deciduous as well as coniferous, are the main food of the Siskin.

SITTA. Genus of the family *Sittidae* of the order *Passeriformes*. It contains more than a dozen different species, distributed over Europe, Asia, north-west Africa, and north America. The only species on the British list is the Nuthatch (*q.v.*), a fairly common resident in England and Wales, but rare elsewhere.

SITTIDAE. Family of small arboreal birds of the order *Passeriformes*. Its members occur in Europe, Asia, north-west Africa, north America and Australia. This family contains two genera on the British list, *Sitta* (nuthatches) and *Tichodroma* (wall-creepers).

These birds possess a rather long, straight and stout bill. The roundish nostrils are in most cases partially concealed by feathers. The wings are rather long and pointed ; there are 10 primary feathers, of which the first is very small. The tail is short, and there are 12 tail-feathers. The tarsus is short, and is covered with scutes (horny scales). The large feet are well adapted for clinging to the bark of trees. The toes have large, laterally compressed claws ; and there is a hind-toe, equal in length to the outer front toe.

SKUA. Genus of moderately large, rather hawk-like sea-birds belonging to the same family as the gulls and terns. They have stout, hooked beaks ; powerful, thick-set bodies ; long, narrow, angled, well-developed wings ; and short, stout legs with webbed feet. In many ways they resemble the scavenging gulls, but their plumage, which is very variable and confusing, is, in general, darker, their habits more predatory, and they are more maritime.

These birds are noted pirates, obtaining most of their food by chasing other birds and making them disgorge. If necessary, however, they will pick up fresh fish from the sea, and occasionally dive for it. On land they will kill mammals and other birds, both full grown and young, and steal eggs. They breed on-shore in scattered colonies, with each nest the centre of a small territory, which the owner defends vigorously against any intruder—including Man. Outside the breeding season they disperse to pelagic and coastal waters.

Four species appear on the British list : Great Skua ; Arctic Skua ; Pomatorhine Skua ; Long-tailed Skua—all under their own headings.

SKULL. With the forelimbs used for flight, the bird's skull has, of necessity, had to take over many functions of the " hands ", and has become a very efficient substitute. By using its skull or, more strictly, its bill (*q.v.*), an integral part of the skull structure, the bird can pick up and grasp objects, capture its food or tear the flesh of its prey, build a nest, preen its feathers and, in the case of woodpeckers, bore holes in wood.

Most of the skull-bones coalesce very early (except in the running birds) to enable the skull to stand up to the strain of being used as a tool or " hand ". Yet, despite their robust qualities, the bones are remarkably light, a feature shared by the whole skeleton, and few of them are more than plates and struts. Like other parts of the skeleton, the skull-bones contain air-cavities. These, however, are in communication with the nasal chamber and auditory passage, and not with the lungs as are other air-cavities.

The absence of teeth has been very largely compensated for by the development of a horny bill, with sharp cutting edges. The bill is borne by the prolongation of the frontal bones of the skull, the *premaxillae* and the complex lower jaw (*see* illustration of Skull of White Stork under Bill, in page 56).

Unlike the structurally simple lower jaw of mammals, that of birds consists of six bones on each side, a distinctly reptilian feature. Another reptilian character is that the lower jaw articulates with the *quadrate bone*, and not with the *squamosal*, as in mammals. The loose articulation of the lower jaw with the movable *quadrate bone* is important, for it widens the gape, helping the bird to capture insects on the wing and swallow food in bulk.

As in reptiles, the bird's skull articulates with the spine by a single ball, or *condyle*, which turns on the cup of the body of the first vertebra. In mammals, on the other hand, the articulation of the skull with the spine is wholly effected by two *lateral condyles*. The skull of a bird thus has great mobility, and can be turned through more than half a circle, aided by the structure of the neck which is elongated by the multiplication of the vertebrae. The latter have articular, saddle-shaped surfaces, distinctive of birds.

Another distinctive feature of a bird's skull is the provision made for accommodating the eyes. The orbits, or eye-sockets, are very large, and are separated from one another by only a thin, and sometimes perforated, partition. The huge size of the eye-sockets is, of course, related to the great importance of vision in birds, and it results in the restriction of the greater part of the brain to the back part of the skull, which is markedly broadened out. One of the main differences between the skulls of birds and of reptiles is in the proportion between the brain-containing region and the size of the skull as a whole, the brain-case of birds being larger than that of reptiles.

The brain itself falls into five parts—the *cerebrum*, consisting of two large cerebral hemispheres, concerned with the so-called "higher senses"; a large *cerebellum*, concerned with movement and balance; the *optic lobes*, which, unlike those of reptiles, are pushed to one side; two *optic thalami*, which supply nerves to the eyes and the pineal body; and the *medulla oblongata*, from which spring most of the cranial nerves.

SKYLARK—Alauda arvensis. Who has never thrilled to the matchless melody of the Skylark poured out as it mounts into the sky until it almost disappears beyond the range of sight? One of our most familiar and popular birds, it is found usually in open country of grassland—whether fallow or cultivated—moorlands, meadows, marshes, mountain pastures and suchlike, but is absent from wooded areas. In some parts of Scotland, where it is called the Laverock, the Skylark is inclined to be local, especially in north-west districts. Many British birds emigrate in the Autumn, but large numbers arrive from the Continent on the east coast, about the same time, to replace them. Abroad, the Skylark occurs throughout Europe, Asia and north-west Africa.

The Skylark's plumage is brown, with light and dark mottlings on its head and mantle. Its underparts are whitish, with some streaks on the breast, and a buff eye-stripe shows against its dark face. It has a short crest, often quite prominent, and some white feathers appear in its tail. The sexes are alike. The Woodlark, the only bird with which the Skylark might be confused, has a shorter tail, a richer brown plumage, and also a different ascent in the air.

SKULL. *Like other parts of the bird's skeleton, the skull bones are very light and contain air cavities (illustrated). The skull performs many functions of a hand*

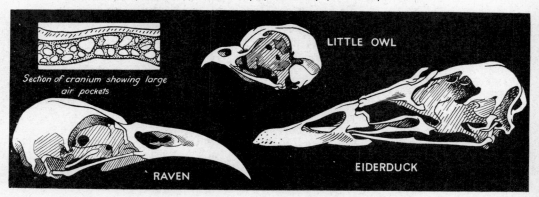

Section of cranium showing large air pockets

LITTLE OWL

RAVEN

EIDERDUCK

Arthur Christiansen

SKYLARK. The joyful song of this little brown bird, soaring into the sky, has brought pleasure to millions. Occasionally the Skylark may sing from the ground

The length of the Skylark is 7 in., and the tarsus 0·8 in. ; the wing span is approximately 8 in., and the weight 1½ oz.

The Skylark has a variety of liquid call notes, interspersed with a less common whistling note. But it is the song of its aerial flight which sets it apart from other song birds. Many other birds sing in the air, but none can compare with the masterly performance of the Skylark. Making an almost vertical ascent higher and higher into the blue, it disappears almost from human sight while uttering its continuous ecstatic and breathless melody. Although the song is heard to best advantage in the air, the Skylark sometimes sings on the ground, and occasionally on a fence or bush. It is one of the earliest songsters, and can best be heard from January to July, and again from October to December. Thanks to the Editor, an excellent recording of the Skylark's full song now exists.

Many people doubted the possibility of recording the full song of the Skylark. The difficulty is that the bird ascends in one part of the field and drops, maybe, 500 yards away. After watching for a full week one particular Skylark with a very fine song, I managed with an arrangement of several microphones to get the full song, which lasted 3½ minutes. After one minute the bird was already rising very high, and after 1¾ minutes it started to descend over another microphone several hundred yards from its point of departure. Every sound of the full song is audible, without a break.—EDITOR.

In common with all larks, the Skylark walks on the ground, and rarely, if ever, perches in trees. Over short distances its flight is un-dulating. Outside the breeding season it is very gregarious, sometimes congregating in large flocks, often in company with meadow-pipits. It always roosts on the ground, and is very fond of dust baths. Apart from its song flight, the Skylark has a ground display in which the male runs round the female with his wings dropped and crest raised. She responds with quivering wings and spread tail.

The Skylark's nest is always built on the ground in a well-concealed depression among grass or growing crops. As far as is known, the compact and cosy nest of grass and other herbage is constructed by the hen alone, under her mate's supervision. As there are always two, and sometimes three, broods, the breeding season extends from the later half of April until July. The three or four eggs of each clutch are greyish-white and excellently camouflaged with heavy brown speckling. Incubation, lasting 11 days, is done by the hen alone, and the young are fed in the nest for about the same period. They are fully fledged about ten days later. The Skylark eats vegetable and insect matter.

SLAVONIAN GREBE—Podiceps auritus. Although a resident in some parts of the north of Scotland, the Slavonian or Horned Grebe is better known as a rather uncommon winter visitor to all coasts of the British Isles. It may sometimes be seen inland, especially in severe weather. Its home is in the Arctic, and in the northern parts of Europe and Asia.

Rather larger than the familiar Little Grebe or Dabchick, the Slavonian Grebe in Winter—

when it is most likely to be seen here—is a black and white bird which may be confused with the Black-necked, or Eared, Grebe. At close range, however, the difference in the bill is apparent, for that of the Slavonian is straight and stout, in contrast to the slender and tip-tilted bill of the Black-necked ; the head patterns also differ. In summer, the Slavonian Grebe is beautifully coloured, with rich chestnut flanks and neck, black head, and decorative yellow ear tufts crossing from behind its red eyes and projecting like small horns beyond its dark head. Its mantle is black, with a white wing bar, and its underparts are white. Its bill is bluish-grey, and its legs greyish. The sexes are alike in both Summer and Winter. The length is 13 in., and the tarsus 1¾ in. ; the wing span is 12 to 14 in., and the weight 6 oz.

Outside the breeding season the Slavonian Grebe is marine in its habits. The quiet waters of sheltered bays and estuaries, inland lakes and reservoirs are its favourite haunts. It is the least timid of the grebes, and is more likely to fly than dive if disturbed. Many of its movements are similar to those of the Great Crested Grebe ; its flight is strong, with rapid wing beats, and it has the awkward pattering take-off from the surface. It swims high in the water.

It has much the same fantastic spring display as the Great Crested Grebe, including the " penguin " dance. The male may offer food to the female. A low trill is the chief breeding call, but there are many varied notes. The young have the same hunger cry as those of the Little and Great Crested Grebe.

Where it nests in Scotland, the Slavonian Grebe chooses a bay of an inland loch with some sheltering vegetation. The nest, floating on shallow water, is a mass of water weeds and vegetation, with an inside cup. Both birds help to build it. In Scotland, the breeding season is in May. Four whitish eggs are laid, and both male and female incubate for 24 or 25 days, beginning with the last egg laid. The eggs are carefully covered whenever they are left. The nestlings are carried on their parents' backs ; and they are reared and fed for over a month. One brood is usual.

The Slavonian Grebe feeds singly or in flocks by diving. Insects, crustaceans, fish, reptiles, molluscs and so on are taken.

SLEEPING. *See* Roosting.

SLENDER-BILLED CURLEW—Numenius tenuirostris. This species has wandered to Britain at very infrequent intervals from its breeding places in Siberia and west Asia ; in Winter it migrates to the Mediterranean region. It much resembles its namesake in size and appearance, but it is a paler-looking bird than either the Whimbrel or the common Curlew, its underparts being almost pure white. It is about 16 in. in length, and has a bill of 3 in.

I recall a memory of the song of a Slender-billed Curlew which some Russian friends brought to me half a century ago. It had nothing in common with either the common Curlew's or the Whimbrel's song, but rather reminded me of the high-pitched whistling note of the Common Sandpiper, except that it was louder and longer.—EDITOR.

As far as is known, the habits of the Slender-billed Curlew resemble the common Curlew's, but it is more addicted to wading.

SLENDER-BILLED NUTCRACKER— Nucifraga caryocatactes macrorhynchos. Like the Thick-billed Nutcracker, which it closely resembles, this is a very rare visitor to Great Britain. The difference between the two, visible only at close range, resides, as their names indicate, in the bill. That of the Slender-billed species is not only less broad, but also longer and less pointed.

The Slender-billed Nutcracker is a large, dark brown bird, boldly speckled in white, with conspicuous white under tail-coverts. It breeds in Siberia and north-eastern Russia. It is chiefly in Winter, when it wanders over almost

Eric Hosking

SLAVONIAN GREBE. *Larger than the familiar Dabchick, this is the least timid of the grebes : also, it will fly rather than dive to escape its foes*

the whole of Europe, that its rare visits to this country have been paid.

Very little is known of its habits, but it is assumed that they resemble those of the Thick-billed bird. The Slender-billed Nutcracker is also referred to as Clarks' Crow or Nutcracker.

Call notes and song are very similar to those of the Thick-billed species.

SMELL, Sense of. Although the evidence available is not conclusive, it would appear generally that birds have a poorly developed sense of smell. The Kiwi has the most complicated nasal organ of all birds, and, during feeding, keeps sniffing as if to compensate for its poor sight by its sense of smell. Its nostrils, unlike those of any other bird, are at the extreme tip of the beak. But experiments made on captive kiwis have not shown that their sense of smell is much, if any, better than in other birds. The petrels and south American vultures have a very large nasal cavity, yet it has been demonstrated that the first group have almost no sense of smell, and find their prey by sight.

Whether correctly or not, ducks have been credited with a keen sense of smell by which, amongst other things, they are supposed to be able to detect the presence of Man—so much so, that generations of decoymen have, when ducks were to the leeward, burnt vegetable matter to prevent any suspicion of human scent drifting towards the birds.

SMEW—Mergus albellus. The smallest of the " saw-billed " ducks, and a rather scarce winter visitor to the British Isles, the attractive black and white Smew is to be seen most frequently on inland waters in south-east England. It favours rivers, lakes, ponds and reservoirs, especially those of the Thames Valley and Essex districts ; large numbers are often to be seen on the reservoirs round London. It is rare elsewhere in England, and very rare in both Scotland and Ireland. Abroad, it breeds throughout Europe and temperate Asia, wintering in north Africa and southern Asia.

With his striking pure white dress, relieved only by a prominent black patch below his eye and the black centre of his ornamental head crest feathers, the drake is a beautiful little bird. At close range other black lines on his breast and flanks show vividly against his white body. The smaller duck is, in her own way, quite as distinctive, with her chestnut head and white cheeks, and her grey upper and paler underparts. In eclipse plumage, the drake is like the duck, but with more white on the wings. Juvenile smews are similar to the duck. The grey bill is slightly hooked, the legs grey, and the eye red. The total length of the drake is 16 in., the body accounting for 10 in.,

Arthur Christiansen

SMEW. Closely related to the Goosander and the Merganser, the Smew is only a rare winter visitor

the tarsus is 1¼ in., the wing span approximately 18 in., and the weight 2 lb.

The Smew flies in much the same manner as the Goosander, but its rapid wing beats do not produce the whistling sound common to many ducks. It is gregarious, and parties fly in oblique or V-formation. On land, where it is rarely seen in Great Britain, the Smew walks with an upright carriage and can run with ease for short distances. An excellent and agile swimmer and diver, it moves buoyantly over the water and rises without difficulty. It can stay under the water for three-quarters of a minute, but half a minute is its normal time ; under the surface it uses its feet, and occasionally its wings, to propel itself.

The Smew is a silent bird, and its voice is seldom heard here. During the breeding season the drake has a short whistling note and the duck a hoarse quack.

The breeding site is always near water—a lake, river or sheltered bay. Smews nest in the holes of trees or rocks, and no material is used except some down, feathers or moss. In Europe, six to nine creamy-white eggs are laid in May. The duck hatches them alone for, as far as is known, one month. She also tends the ducklings of the single brood.

The Smew feeds chiefly on small fish, but some vegetable matter is also taken occasionally.

SNAA FOOL (Shetland, Snowfowl). Local name for Snow-Bunting (*q.v.*)—also called Snow-Bird and Snowflake.

SNAKE-BIRD. Popular name for the Wryneck (*q.v.*), also called Cuckoo's Mate.

SNIPE. English name of a group of wading birds belonging to the family *Scolopacidae*, which also includes, among others, the curlews, godwits, sandpipers, stints and Woodcock. By common usage, the whole of this large family is sometimes called the Snipe family—in spite of the fact that its scientific name is derived from the Greek word for Woodcock. To add to the confusion, it may also occasionally be called the Sandpiper (*q.v.*) family.

Snipe are compact birds with rather long, spindly legs and a characteristic very long, straight and flexible bill, from which they derive their name, which, coming from the Icelandic, literally means "snapper". The whole bill, which is de-curved at the point, is smooth, soft and extremely sensitive; the head is compressed and the eyes large and far back. The general colouring of snipe is a rich brown, mottled with buff, giving a streaky appearance. During display (*q.v.*) the males of the Common and Jack Snipe produce a characteristic "drumming" with their wings.

Snipe are much more fond of cover than most waders and, with the exception of the Great Snipe, which prefers drier ground, they haunt marshes, water meadows, sewage farms and boggy moors.

Four snipe are included in the British list: Red-breasted Snipe; Common Snipe; Great Snipe; and Jack Snipe. Each is described under its own heading. The Common Snipe is resident over the greater part of the British Isles, with the exception of the Orkneys and Shetlands, where it is replaced by a northern race, the Faero Snipe. It breeds locally in suitable places except in southern England. The Jack Snipe is a non-breeding visitor and passage migrant; the Great Snipe is a rare passage migrant, and the Red-breasted Snipe a straggler.

SNIPPACK. Name by which the Common Snipe (*q.v.*) is known in Shetland.

SNOW-BIRD. *See* Snaa Fool; Snow-Bunting.

Eric Hosking

SNIPE. *The Common Snipe, shown here, is a resident over the larger part of this country*

SNOW-BUNTING — Plectrophenax nivalis. There is reason to believe that the small number of these little Arctic birds which breed on the high tops of the Cairngorms and other mountains of the Scottish Highlands has increased in recent years, thanks to watchful care and preservation. In addition to these residents, snow-buntings are regular autumn and winter visitors on all our coasts, especially the east coast of England. Abroad, they breed wherever Arctic conditions prevail.

About the size of a Skylark, the Snow-Bunting is recognizable by the predominating white on its wings and underparts. Its mantle is black, and there is some black in its tail. It has the stout bill of the finches. The hen has white underparts and breast, but her head and mantle are a speckled brown. In Winter, when they are most likely to be seen in England, both birds are browner, but white is still their predominating colour. The length of the Snow-Bunting is 6–7 in., and its tarsus 1 in.; its wing span is about 8 in., and its weight 1–1½ oz.

The conspicuous white plumage, which has earned them the names of Snow-Bird and Snowflake, makes these birds very attractive in flight. On the ground the Snow-Bunting normally walks but it can also hop; it spends most of its time perched on a rock, low wall or fence.

The behaviour of these birds during the breeding season is of much interest to ornithologists. During the sexual flight, both birds will rise to great heights, and cover long distances. They mate for life. After the breeding season they are very gregarious, going about in small parties or large flocks in company with other buntings, but rarely being found with other birds.

The Song of the Snow-Bunting is hardly ever heard in Great Britain, except at its breeding sites in the Scottish Highlands. The song has been described as "a fairly brief musical warble, varying a good deal in quality and at times reminiscent of the Dunnock or Black Redstart"; it is also said to be far more musical than that of any of the other buntings which breed in Britain.

The Snow-Bunting conceals its nest in a crevice in the mountain scree among loose boulders, or under a stone. It is fashioned with dead leaves, stalks, roots and moss, and lined with hair, wool and, where possible, feathers. The four or five ground-coloured eggs are covered with blotches and spots of reddish brown. The hen apparently does most of the sitting—for about ten days—but she is fed by her mate. The young are fed by both parents, for about 12 days. The breeding season starts at the end of May or beginning of June in Scotland, and later in Arctic countries. One brood is usually reared in a season.

In Summer the food consists largely of insects ; in Winter seeds of all kinds are also eaten.

SNOW-FINCH—Montifringilla nivalis. This Alpine bird, breeding in the mountain regions of central and south-east Europe at altitudes ranging from 6,000 to 7,000 ft., occasionally wanders to Great Britain in the Winter. There are three records of visits to Kent and Sussex, two being small flocks of three to five birds.

The Snow-Finch's appearance resembles that of the Snow-Bunting, but, as the two species are never found in the same type of country, confusion should not arise. The Snow-Finch is the larger and the less plump-looking of the two. In Summer, its upper parts are chocolate brown, and its underparts whitish. Its grey head and black throat are its best distinguishing marks. Its wings, which are snowy white, with black primaries, and its tail, with black central feathers and pure white at the sides, are both very conspicuous in flight. Its bill and legs are black. In Winter, when it is likely to be seen here, the white is less snowy,

and the bill orange-yellow. The female is at all times duller, with less white on wings and tail. The length is 7 in. ; the tarsus is 0·95 in. ; and the wing span is 8-10 in.

In its Alpine home the Snow-Finch is tame and is often seen near human habitations. It hops and walks, but is said to avoid trees, perching only on rocks and buildings. Outside the breeding season, these birds roam about in flocks, usually small but occasionally large.

The song, a repetition of several notes, is delivered from a perch or during the bird's beautiful and graceful song-flight, in which it descends with outspread wings and tail. The call notes are said to be many and varied.

The Snow-Finch breeds in rocks or, where there are buildings, in the holes of walls or under eaves. The large nest is built of grass, moss and feathers, and cosily lined with feathers and hair. The breeding season is from April to June, and two broods may be reared in a season. There are four or five white eggs in a clutch. As far as is known, both male and female incubate for 18 days, and both rear the young. Insects are the Snow-Finch's main food.

SNOWFLAKE. One of several local names for Snow-Bunting (*q.v.*)—also called Snaa Fool and Snow-Bird.

SNOW-GOOSE—Anser hyperboreus. A vagrant from the far north, the Snow-Goose has been recorded in the British Isles, but, since it is an occupant of many private collections of ornamental water-fowl, some of its appearances may have been " escapes ". Clad in its beautiful white dress, the Snow-Goose is a handsome

SNOW-BUNTING. This pretty visitor from the Arctic, which is also known as the Snowflake or Snow-Bird, is thought to be breeding occasionally in parts of Scotland

G. K. Yeates

Karl H. Maslowski

SNOW-GOOSE. *Its beautiful pure white dress distinguishes this bird from any other wild goose*

bird, unlike any other goose. Some black on its wings makes a vivid contrast to the white, and serves to distinguish it from the swans. The legs and bill are red. The sexes are alike. The length is 25–28 in., the body being 17 or 18 in.; the tarsus is 3 in. The wing span is between 2½ ft. and 3 ft., and the weight between 2 lb. and 3 lb.

The Snow-Goose is gregarious and keeps company with other grey geese, its behaviour and habits following their pattern. In winter quarters and when migrating, huge flocks are formed and fly in the characteristic grey-goose V-formation. The voice of the Snow-Goose is a loud and resonant single honk, and from the large flocks various curious grunting and groaning sounds issue.

On the Arctic tundra large numbers of snow-geese breed in company with other geese. A hollow among the grass, lined with grass, down and feathers, houses the five or six white eggs, laid on consecutive days in June. They are incubated by the female alone, with the male never far away, during 25 days. Both parents tend the goslings of the one brood.

Little information is available regarding the diet of the Snow-Goose, but on migration it feeds chiefly on such vegetable matter as winter wheat and sprouting grain.

The Greater Snow-Goose (*Anser hyperboreus atlanticus*) is a rare vagrant from the Arctic which only differs in size from its near relative.

SNOWY OWL—Nyctea scandiaca. A native of the Arctic regions, the Snowy Owl is a regular yearly visitor to the Orkney and Shetland Islands, and occasionally wanders to the mainland of Scotland. It has also been recorded in Ireland several times, but elsewhere is a very rare vagrant.

Recognition of the Snowy Owl presents no difficulty. Its large size and predominantly white plumage, showing some dark bars and markings—though these seem to vary in individual birds—are unmistakable. The female is considerably larger, and her plumage is more boldly barred in brown. The facial disk and breast are always white, and the legs and feet feathered. The blackish bill is hooked, and the eyes golden-yellow. The length is 21–24 in., and the tarsus 2·4 in.; the wing span is 3–3½ ft., and the weight 4–4½ lb.

The rapid flight of the Snowy Owl has more in common with the Buzzard than with other owls. A fierce and predatory bird, it hunts by day, pursuing and striking down its prey on the wing, like the falcons. Its movement on the ground, where it settles as often as on a perch, is a series of awkward jumps. Like other owls, it ejects pellets. Usually a silent bird, it will utter a loud shrieking hoot on the wing, repeated several times. It shows anger at disturbances by snapping its bill.

Breeding in the Arctic among the barren fells and wasteland, the Snowy Owl makes no nest, its four to nine white eggs being laid in a depression in the ground. The breeding season is from April to June, according to the altitude. The

John Markham

SNOWY OWL. *This owl of the north hunts like falcons, stooping down on its prey during flight*

Arthur Christiansen

SOMATERIA. The King-Eider (Somateria spectabilis) is an irregular visitor to the British Isles, but, for some obscure reason, has never yet been recorded in Wales

hen hatches the eggs alone for 33 days, but both parents feed and rear the one brood of the season. The nestlings are able to fly in about two months.

The Snowy Owl's food consists of rabbits, hares, mice, voles, lemmings, birds, and so on.

SOCIABLE PLOVER—Chettusia gregaria. A rare vagrant to the British Isles, occurring usually in the Spring, the Sociable Plover breeds in eastern Europe and temperate Asia, wintering in Africa and India. Seven or eight of this species have been identified here.

In size and plumage it is not dissimilar from the Lapwing, but lacks that bird's crest and glossy green mantle. Its wings are also more rounded. Its upper parts are greyish, tinged with mauve, and its head black ; above its eye runs a conspicuous white line from the forehead to the nape. The white feathers in its wings are most prominent in flight, and its tail is also white, with a black patch near the end. Its black legs are longer than those of the Lapwing. Its length is 11½ ins.

The Sociable Plover is said to spend more time on the wing than is common among plovers. Its movement in the air is not unlike that of the Lapwing. It gathers in flocks, some large, some small, outside the breeding season ; as many as 400 in one flock have been recorded in Russia. In Winter the Sociable Plover's voice is a shrill short whistle ; at its breeding site it utters a harsh guttural note.

The spring display includes some extraordinary postures. The males fight each other, springing as much as 2 ft. into the air and striking at their rivals with wings, feet and bill.

Tumbling displays, similar to those of the Lapwing, are also indulged in.

The Sociable Plover breeds on hilly steppes, the nest being a hollow in the ground, lined with dry grass. May is the breeding season. Its four eggs are hatched by both male and female, and both rear the single brood. As far as is known, its food consists mainly of insects.

SOLAN GOOSE. Local name for Gannet (*q.v.*) ; also called Booby.

SOLE. Back of metatarsus (*see* Tarsus).

SOLITARY SANDPIPER—Tringa solitaria. So far eight or nine visits to the British Isles have been recorded of this sandpiper, a native of the northern parts of Canada. It is about the same size as the Common Sandpiper, but in appearance is more like a small Green Sandpiper. The chief difference in plumage is its dark rump (that of the Green Sandpiper is pure white), and the white edges to its dark tail which are very conspicuous in flight. Its legs and bill are greenish. The sexes are alike. The length is 7¾ in. and the tarsus 1½ in. ; the wing span is 10 or 11 in., and the weight 2 oz.

Wooded swamps at high altitudes are its breeding haunts. Its behaviour and habits follow the pattern of the Green Sandpiper.

SOLITARY SNIPE. Alternative name for the Great Snipe (*q.v.*)

SOMATERIA. Genus of ducks of the family *Anatidae* of the order *Anseriformes*. It contains two species, mainly distributed over northern Europe, northern Asia, north America, and Greenland ; both—the Eider-Duck (*q.v.*) and the King-Eider (*q.v.*)—on the British list.

SONGS AND CALL NOTES OF BIRDS

LUDWIG KOCH

After describing how birds sing, the Editor goes on to discuss how they acquire their knowledge of the various songs and call notes, mimicry, and the importance of timbre. A Calendar of Bird Song faces this page. See also *Call Notes* ; *Recording* ; *Syrinx*

SONG. Before we discuss the songs of birds, it is important for us to know something of the manner in which they produce those sounds, which are entirely different from those uttered by any other living creature, including Man. Whereas human beings use the upper larynx, birds utter their sounds by means of the syrinx (*q.v.*). This apparatus is found at the point where the windpipe divides into two tubes leading into the lungs. It is provided with many powerful muscles ; and the true song-birds have a collection of "song-muscles" which hardly any other group of birds possesses. Oddly enough, although the male is generally the chief or only songster, the syrinx muscles of the female are equally well developed.

A bird's lung is very small, but is connected to a series of ramifying air-sacs (*q.v.*) which spread through most parts of the body ; the air returned from these is utilised in the operation of the membranes, enlarging the air cells of the lungs and the syrinx, as well as in respiration. This is one of the reasons why birds can fly with great speed over long distances without becoming breathless. For many decades I have observed the Skylark, and I have recorded the full song-flight of several species from the rise to the dropping. The average duration is from 3 to 3½ minutes, but in none of the recordings can any interruption to take breath be heard.

There is another important factor in bird song—the glands and the special hormones produced by them. As these hormones flow through the blood-stream they excite behaviour patterns, involving the use of the sound-producing organs. As soon as these glands degenerate, the urge to sing decreases.

Call Notes and Song. It is incorrect to describe song as the language of birds. The calls can be likened to a language, but not the song. The call notes of birds are inborn, but the song, with a few exceptions, has to be learnt. Many birds, such as ducks and pigeons, have an unchangeable inborn voice. The vocal apparatus may be so powerful that a bird can produce a considerable variety of songs, and become a master of the mimicry of the songs of other birds or of natural sounds, yet it will have only one limited range of call notes. However, it is always well to avoid generalisation. For instance, the claim made by foreign scientists that the Reed-Bunting's song is inborn and that,

if it is reared away from its parents, the bird still has their typical song, seems most inconclusive. When I made this experiment many years ago, the bird never produced the parental song but only short, unidentifiable, stammering sounds. On the whole, we may take it for granted that most birds learn their song from their parents.

In this connection special mention must be made of the Chaffinch, which in the early season fiercely calls up to 400 and more times within an hour. Each individual Chaffinch has its own song ; some even have two. But, as far as my observation goes, none of these is inborn. The young birds adopt the song of the adults, and preserve their geographical variations and dialects, although they may mimic other regional or Continental songs heard during migration. Thus, in the length and breadth of Great Britain one can hear hundreds of different Chaffinch songs, varying in duration from 1½ to 3 seconds. The Continental species also has numerous varying songs, including the one ending in what sounds like the German word *Würzgebühr*. When I once heard this in Essex, I wondered if it was a native bird mimicking the Continental song, or a genuine migrant. I have heard the high final note characteristic of the Flemish Chaffinch in Kew Gardens.

Many birds have the inclination to mimic, and some are specially gifted in this direction : for example, the Starling, Marsh-Warbler and Icterine Warbler. I once watched a Starling nesting near a railway station and heard it mimic the noise of an engine, and an Icterine Warbler which I had watched for many weeks finally picked up my name, having heard it frequently, and called out "Ludwig!"

Importance of Timbre. It is no more astonishing that birds of the same family should possess such a wide range of song variations than that human voices within the same family should vary widely. For instance, the brother of a talented singer may be endowed with a hoarse, unpleasant voice. The timbre is the important thing, and if the ear is tuned to this by long training, the identity of a singing bird will always be revealed. Thus it becomes impossible to be deceived by, for example, a Blackbird mimicking a Song-Thrush, for the flute-like timbre of the Blackbird is always distinguishable. An experiment of isolating a

SEASONAL CALENDAR OF BIRD SONG

Heavy black line indicates period of full song : broken lines and dots periods when singing is intermittent

	Jan.	Feb.	Mar.	Apl.	May	June	July	Aug.	Sept.	Oct.	Nov.	Dec.
BITTERN												
BLACKBIRD												
BLACKCAP												
BULLFINCH												
BUNTING, Corn-												
———, Cirl												
———, Reed-												
CHAFFINCH												
CHIFFCHAFF												
CORNCRAKE												
CROSSBILL												
CUCKOO												
CURLEW												
DIPPER												
DOVE, Stock-												
———, Turtle-												
DUNNOCK												
FLYCATCHER, Pied												
———, Spotted												
GOLDCREST												
GOLDFINCH												
GREBE, Great Crested												
———, Little												
GREENFINCH												
HAWFINCH												
KINGFISHER												
LAPWING												
LARK, Wood-												
LINNET												
MARTIN, House-												
———, Sand-												
NIGHTINGALE												
OUZEL, Ring-												
OYSTERCATCHER												
PIGEON, Wood-												
PLOVER, Golden												
———, Ringed												
REDPOLL, Lesser												

SEASONAL CALENDAR OF BIRD SONG

Heavy black line indicates period of full song : broken lines and dots periods when singing is intermittent

	Jan.	Feb.	Mar.	Apl.	May	June	July	Aug.	Sept.	Oct.	Nov.	Dec.
REDSHANK												
REDSTART												
——, Black												
ROBIN												
SANDPIPER, Common												
SKYLARK												
SNIPE, Common												
SPARROW, House-												
——, Tree-												
STARLING												
STONECHAT												
SWALLOW												
SWIFT												
THRUSH, Mistle-												
——, Song-												
TIT, Blue												
——, Coal-												
——, Marsh-												
——, Willow-												
TWITE												
WARBLER, Dartford												
——, Garden-												
——, Grasshopper-												
——, Marsh-												
——, Reed-												
——, Sedge-												
WHEATEAR												
WHINCHAT												
WHITETHROAT												
——, Lesser												
WOODPECKER, Greater Spotted												
——, Green												
——, L. Spotted												
WREN												
——, Willow-												
——, Wood-												
WRYNECK												
YELLOW HAMMER												

newborn Blackbird from its parents, and rearing it together with a Blackcap—in different cages but in the same room—revealed the decisive part played by timbre, for, whatever attempts the Blackbird made to mimic its companion, its voice was always recognizable.

The part played by timbre is one of the reasons why it is impossible to transcribe bird-song in musical notation. The world-famous violinist, Fritz Kreisler, once accompanied me in my recording van, convinced that he could write down the different notes of the Blackbird. After several hours he gave up, and fully agreed with me that the timbre of a bird's song is far more important than its pitch—and timbre cannot be transcribed.

Many composers throughout the centuries have been inspired by bird-song, and have introduced imitations of bird-song into their works—Beethoven once wrote to his friend Schindler that the Yellow Hammer, Quail, Nightingale and Cuckoo had done a lot of work for him. But their imitations are never entirely successful. The fact is that musical notation cannot be used as a means of imitating or identifying bird-song. The same applies to attempts to interpret bird-song in human language, with human vowels and consonants. Does anyone believe that *Lulalulalulalula*, etc., gives the slightest idea of the wonderful song of the Wood-Lark ? I am inclined to hold the same opinion about bird-imitators. People who could imitate bird-song may have had some use fifty or sixty years ago as teachers and demonstrators, even though the timbre of a bird can never be reproduced by a human throat. To-day, when first-class recordings of actual birds are available, the imitator should restrict himself to being a skilful and artistic entertainer, and not attempt to teach bird-song identification.

Purpose of Song. Why do birds sing ? It is a widespread misconception that their singing is a sort of pastime, perhaps meant to amuse the female. Birds sing at the beginning of the breeding season as an advertisement that they are looking for a breeding ground and a mate, and as a warning to rivals. It is the male that takes possession of a suitable site ; he seems to be singing " Charming residence offered to eligible female ". After the female has arrived, other males learn from the song that the territory is now occupied and is not to be trespassed upon without the risk of a fierce struggle. This explanation of song cannot, however, be accepted as covering all cases ; besides love and defence of territory, birds have other urges which may impel them to sing, and for many species there is no detailed information.

The parental urge to sing reaches its zenith with the hatching of the young. The singing usually ceases in the evening when the feeding of the young comes to an end. I have heard blackbirds and thrushes singing, according to the season, from 7 p.m. to 10 p.m., wonderful, unforgettable, soft tunes. The birds have finished the daily work of feeding their young ; the song becomes weaker and weaker, and then suddenly it stops. Why they make this last effort when they are surely overtired and going to roost, I do not know.

By Day and by Night. One must get up with the lark to hear the unique concert of Nature, the dawn chorus. In my experience in various parts of this country and on the Continent, this usually lasts for about 25 minutes. The time of its commencement varies with the season ; the early song-birds also vary according to the region, but mainly I have heard the Blackbird, Robin and Song-Thrush leading the chorus.

Providing the location is good, all the song-birds of these islands may be heard during the day-time. At dusk the chorus is smaller, but the Robin is then at the height of his activity. On spring and summer evenings, as the Robin ceases to sing, within a fraction of a second the Nightjar starts its jarring, while at night the Nightingale, Wood-Lark, Grasshopper-Warbler, Bittern, the Little, Tawny, Barn- Long-eared and Short-eared Owl can be heard, singing or calling. The day-songsters can occasionally be heard during the night, but nearly all the night-singing or -calling birds can be heard during the day. The reason for this is not known. Except for a break in July, the Robin sings all the year round ; the autumn song commences at the end of August and, from my first recording of this song, probably sung by the female, the difference between spring and autumn songs can be detected.

Song-Flight. An important part of the display of some birds is the song-flight. Flight in general is not chiefly a form of display, but belongs to the nature of birds. A great number of species must spend much of their lives in the air, and this has nothing at all to do with sexual activity ; it may have quite another purpose, such as feeding, as is the case with the Swallow family and the Swift. It is often the ground-living birds, such as the pipits, that excel in song-flight. The Tree-Pipit, for instance, leaves a branch, flies away to another tree several hundred yards off and then, like a boomerang, drops back to the original branch, still uttering his flight song.

Among British song-birds there are all kinds of variations in volume and pitch. Some have loud and far-carrying songs, e.g. the Blackbird, Song-Thrush, Blackcap, Chaffinch, Garden-Warbler, Marsh-Warbler, Robin, Nightingale. The Blackbird's song carries about half a mile ;

the Nightingale's a mile or more, according to its singing post. There are low and soft songs, high and low pitched, as, for instance, those of the Wood-Lark, Goldcrest, Wren, Grasshopper-Warbler, Greenfinch, Goldfinch, and Tit family. The Goldcrest's song has a carrying power of fifty yards, the Grasshopper-Warbler's five hundred and fifty yards ; the Starling's and Greenfinch's have only half this carrying power.

Apart from their ordinary loud song, many birds have a so-called sub-song, audible only at close quarters. A soft, often continuous, sweet warbling or twittering, completely at variance with the ordinary loud song and call notes, it usually goes on undisturbed and, seemingly, unheard by other birds. I have heard, in March, both the Jay and Pied Wagtail uttering this sweet warbling ; neither bird seemed to be disturbed by my close proximity, nor apparently was the sub-song noticed by any other bird.

Great care must be taken when discussing sub-song, because our knowledge is very limited. It does happen, however, that birds which naturally have a harsh or a soft voice mostly sing a very discreet tune in the early Spring or in the Autumn. Provided the listener has a well-trained ear and is not more than 30 yards away (10 yards is the best distance) he may hear this performance from many different birds. It is a pleasant surprise, for instance, suddenly to hear a musical phrase from a Jay, so well-known for its harsh notes, mostly when none of its own species is visible. Even a Blackbird has a sub-song before or after the breeding season, and probably more of our *Oscines* (song-birds) have it. I have observed that our warblers, such as the Blackcap and Whitethroat, sometimes retire into a thicket to produce this quiet sound, and in the middle of the breeding season I have heard and recorded a sub-song which made the name warbler more understandable.

Great Britain has no month during the whole year without its bird song. A Bird Song Calendar, in which a great number of British birds are listed, is reproduced in the Plates *facing pages* 518 and 519. It is based on one produced many years ago, which appeared in *Songs of Wild Birds*, by E. M. Nicholson and Ludwig Koch (H. F. & G. Witherby), 1936, but it includes additional information. From it the song periods of 84 birds can be studied. The following comparative table of song birds has also been extracted from the same source, which should be consulted.

1. *Highly Developed Songs* : Blackbird, Blackcap, Garden-Warbler, Marsh-Warbler, Nightingale, Robin, Sedge-Warbler, Skylark, Song-Thrush, Wood-Lark.

2. *Finished Song-Pattern* : Black Redstart, Chaffinch, Chiffchaff, Cirl Bunting, Corn-Bunting, Dartford Warbler, Dipper, Goldcrest, Grasshopper-Warbler, H e d g e - S p a r r o w , Lesser Whitethroat, Meadow-Pipit, Mistle-Thrush, Nuthatch, Pied Flycatcher, Redstart, Reed-Bunting, Ring-Ouzel, Rock-Pipit, Snow-Bunting, Stonechat, Tree-Creeper, Tree-Pipit, Wheatear, Whinchat, Whitethroat, Willow-Warbler, Wood-Warbler, Wren, Yellow Hammer.

3. *More Primitive Types of Song* : Bullfinch, Crossbill, Goldfinch, Greenfinch, Grey Wagtail, Hawfinch, House-Sparrow, House-Martin, Jay, Kingfisher, Lesser Redpoll, Linnet, Marsh-Tit, Pied Wagtail, Reed-Warbler, Red-backed Shrike, Redwing, Sand-Martin, Siskin, Spotted Flycatcher, Starling, Swallow, Tree-Sparrow, Twite, Willow-Tit, Yellow Wagtail.

4. *Breeding Notes and Song Substitutes** : Bittern, Black Grouse, Black-throated Diver, Blue Tit, Capercaillie, Coal-Tit, Common Sandpiper, Common Snipe, Corncrake, Crested Tit, Cuckoo, Curlew, Dunlin, Golden Plover, Great Crested Grebe, Greater Spotted Woodpecker, Great Tit, Greenshank, Green Woodpecker, Kentish Plover, Kestrel, Lapwing, Leach's Petrel, Lesser Spotted Woodpecker, Little Grebe, Little Owl, Long-eared Owl, Manx Shearwater, Nightjar, Oystercatcher, Partridge, Ptarmigan, Quail, Red Grouse, Red-legged Partridge, Redshank, Red-throated Diver, Ringed Plover, Rock-Dove, Spotted Crake, Stock-Dove, Stone-Curlew, Storm-Petrel, Swift, Tawny Owl, Turtle-Dove, Whimbrel, Whooper-Swan, Woodcock, Wood-Pigeon, Wryneck.

   * *Breeding Notes :* Call notes to indicate alarm, feeding, warning. *Song substitute :* A prolonged combination of call notes.

The above classification of British bird-songs and breeding notes is an attempt—open to

Arthur Brook

SONG. *Few people can have failed to hear the beautiful song of the Blackbird—a bird that is with us throughout the year*

SONG-THRUSH. *Three notes, repeated several times, make it easy to identify this bird's song*

Arthur Brook

revision in the light of further studies—at assessing these songs according to their wealth of tunes, their command of a wide or smaller range of sound, their more or less distinctive character, and so on.

SONG-THRUSH—Turdus ericetorum. One of the best known of British songsters, the Song-Thrush or Throstle—called the Mavis in Scotland—is a familiar and common bird, seen nearly everywhere. It haunts woods, thickets, hedgerows and all cultivated areas, and has a decided liking for suburban gardens and city parks. It is less common in hilly country. In the Autumn many British song-thrushes cross the Channel, but as against this, large numbers arrive from the Continent in September and October ; some of these stay the Winter, others only pass through. Abroad, the Song-Thrush is found throughout Europe and temperate Asia, and winters in northern Africa.

Smaller than the Mistle-Thrush, the Song-Thrush is dressed in a warmer shade of olive brown. Its underparts are whitish, with a slight reddish tinge on the breast and flanks ; the breast is covered with dark brown spots. Its golden-brown underwing is very noticeable in flight, and its tail feathers lack the whitish tips of the Mistle-Thrush's tail. Its bill is brown, and its legs flesh-coloured. The sexes are alike ; the juvenile has buff streaks on the underparts. The length is 9 in., and the tarsus 1·2 in. ; the wing span is 10 in. or 11 in., and the weight 3 oz.

The Song-Thrush is not specially gregarious, except on migration, but will, on occasion, feed with other thrushes. In its direct and undulating flight it travels faster than the Mistle-Thrush.

Its carriage is upright ; the typical movement on the ground consists of short runs or hops, separated by a moment's pause. It listens with its head on one side for any movement of worm or insect. Snails are its choicest morsels of food ; they are carried to its special " anvil ", or to a rock or wall, and there prised open. The Song-Thrush roosts in shrubberies, bushes and hedgerows, sometimes in company with redwings, fieldfares and blackbirds.

The Song-Thrush has no elaborate spring display, the puffing-out of his breast feathers is the cock's chief method of attracting his mate.

The loud clear song of the Song-Thrush is unique through the repetition of three notes. I have recorded twelve repetitions, but this is extremely rare. Within the song are a multitude of variations, and it would take a lifetime of watching and listening to become acquainted with them all. On returning to England from the Continent, I received the impression that the song of the thrush in this country was more melodious, as well as more varied. It is usually delivered from a high tree, but also on the ground or from a building ; it is occasionally heard at night. The call note is the sweetest bird music imaginable, while the alarm note is reminiscent of the Blackbird's harsh call. The Song-Thrush is a good mimic, and frequently re-produces the songs and calls of other species nesting in its neighbourhood. The song is best heard from January to July. During the Autumn the Song-Thrush has a low musical sub-song before once more starting its true song at the beginning of another year.—EDITOR.

Hedgerows, bushes, trees, wall ivy, and sometimes buildings—but rarely the ground—are favourite breeding places of the Song-Thrush. The substantial nest, built by the hen, is made of grasses, roots, leaves and moss, and is solidified with mud ; it is lined with a mixture of bits of wood and horse dung. The number of eggs varies, but it is usually four or five ; they are bluish-green, spotted over in black. Two or three broods are reared in a season, the first eggs being laid in April ; the hen does most of the hatching, with a little assistance from her mate, for a fortnight. The nestlings are fed and reared for the same period.

Earthworms, molluscs (especially snails) and insects are the Song-Thrush's favourite food ; although it takes a certain amount of fruit it is, on the whole, beneficial to Man.

SOOTY SHEARWATER—Procellaria grisea. Like all shearwaters, the Sooty, outside its breeding season, is a happy wanderer over the wide oceans ; of all its nesting sites, those on the desolate islands between New Zealand and south Africa are the most remote from the British Isles. From time to time, however, it is seen off our coasts, usually in the Autumn.

Dressed in blackish-brown plumage, relieved only by greyish-white under-wing coverts, noticeable in flight, the Sooty Shearwater is a sombre-looking bird. Its slightly hooked bill has the typical tubular nostrils. Its legs are dark. Its length is 16 in., and its tarsus 2 in. ; its wing span is 2 ft. to 2½ ft., and its weight is approximately 1½ lb.

The behaviour and habits of the Sooty are identical with those of the Great Shearwater.

SOOTY TERN—Sterna fuscata. Recorded as having wandered to southern Britain about fifteen times, the Sooty Tern is a native of tropical ocean islands in the Caribbean Sea, and off the coasts of the Atlantic, Pacific and Indian Oceans, and Australia.

Its plumage is sooty-black above, with white underparts. Its forehead and cheeks are white, and through its eye runs a dark stripe. Its tail is deeply forked ; its bill and legs are black. The sexes are alike. The length is 14 or 15 in., the tarsus 0·9 in., the wing span about 20 in.

The Sooty is the most pelagic of the terns ; it wanders the wide oceans constantly outside the breeding season, coming to land only to breed. As far as is known, its habits and behaviour resemble the Common Tern's.

SORA RAIL — Porzana carolina. A rare visitor to Great Britain, this bird has been recorded at least half-a-dozen times, but not in recent years. It breeds in north America and winters in the south.

It can be distinguished from the Spotted Crake only at close quarters, when it is seen to be smaller and to have a black face and black stripe down its throat ; the white spots so evident in the Spotted Crake are absent. In the type of country it frequents, and in behaviour and nesting habits, it shows no difference from the Spotted Crake. Its length is 7 in., and its wing span is about 10 in. The Sora Rail is often called the Carolina Crake in this country.

SOUTHERN CORMORANT — Phalacrocorax carbo sinensis. The Southern Cormorant is the only other bird under the name of the Cormorant genus which occurs in Britain. It has many characteristics of the common Cormorant, and it is likely that many of the Southern birds may have bred here without being specifically recognized as such. It is, however, a bird which frequents wide areas of the Continent, where it breeds much more freely on inland lakes and rivers than its close relative. Its nests are often also built in trees, and sometimes even away from water.

SOUTHERN DUNLIN. *See* Dunlin.

SOUTH EUROPEAN GREAT GREY SHRIKE—Lanius excubitor meridionalis. A bird of the Mediterranean region and a subspecies of the Great Grey Shrike, this bird has made one recorded visit to Great Britain—to Sussex, in 1911. A darker mantle, underparts deeper tinged with pink, and a smaller white wing bar distinguish it. Its length is 9·8 in.

SPARROW. Most people in this country, and certainly all townsmen, when speaking of sparrows refer to the House-Sparrow (*Passer domesticus*), which though not the most common —an honour held at present by the Chaffinch— is certainly one of the most familiar birds, and too well-known to need description. But there are many other sparrows, of which two are on the British list : the Tree-Sparrow (*P. montanus*), which belongs to the same genus, and the Hedge-Sparrow also, and more correctly, called Hedge-Accentor or Dunnock, of which three subspecies are recorded, and which belongs to a different genus—*Prunella*.

The Tree-Sparrow, which is both a resident and a winter visitor from the Continent, is very similar to the House-Sparrow, but is smaller,

SOOTY TERN. This is the most sea-going of all terns and comes inland only to breed. It is a native of the tropical oceans, and has been seen here but 15 times

Lewis Wayne Walker

SPARROW. The three sparrows on the British list are (left to right) the House-Sparrow, Hedge-Sparrow—also called Hedge-Accentor or Dunnock—and Tree-Sparrow

John Markham; Eric Hosking

scarcer and more local. Moreover, the male has a rich chocolate-brown forehead and crown (instead of grey or greyish), and a black or blackish patch on whitish ear coverts that almost form a white collar.

The Dunnock has a sparrow-like appearance, but its bill is more slender and pointed, and it has a distinctive shuffling gait. Three sub-species appear on the British list. A close relative, only rarely seen in Britain, is the Alpine Accentor. *See also* under separate headings.

SPARROW-HAWK—Accipiter nisus. One of the most arboreal birds of prey—and, next to the Kestrel, the commonest—the Sparrow-Hawk is found throughout the British Isles, except in the treeless districts of the north. Abroad, it inhabits Europe, Asia, north-west Africa and the Atlantic islands.

So variable is the plumage of the Sparrow-Hawk that it is difficult to give an accurate description. Generally speaking, the male has dark grey upper parts, with more or less russet coloured underparts, barred in white and shaded lighter towards the neck. His long tail and broad, rounded wings are in a browner grey with darker bars. The female is much larger, with browner upper parts and whiter underparts; she has very little russet except at the flanks. There is a white stripe over her eye. Both sexes have some white patches on their heads, but these vary greatly. The hooked bill is grey, with a yellow cere; the legs and eye are yellow. The length of the male is 13 in., and his tarsus 2·1 in.; his wing span is about 1½ ft., and his weight 4—6 oz. The length of the female is 15 in., and her tarsus 2·4 in., her wing span about 2 ft., her weight 7—10 oz.

The Sparrow-Hawk can be most easily identified by its characteristic method of hunting. Keeping a silent watch from some hidden perch, it pounces before its prey has time to seek cover; and, flying low, and with amazing speed, it dashes through trees and hedgerows, down waterways and along streams, to seize its victim. It is the deadly enemy of every small bird; it is estimated that a Sparrow-Hawk may kill about 1,000 small birds in a season. Often the Sparrow-Hawk will pursue its quarry relentlessly in the open, even round human habitations, but it also soars at a great height, from which, on sighting its prey, it plunges like a Gannet, with wings folded.

The prey secured, the Sparrow-Hawk carries it to some concealed " plucking place " on the ground or in a branch of a tree, where, with both feet fastened on the victim and with its wings dropped to form a tent, it tears off the fur or feathers before devouring it or carrying it to its nest to feed its young. Sometimes it has a " prospecting flight ", when it glides and circles round, flapping its wings several times at intervals. The Sparrow-Hawk walks on the ground, and can also hop; in common with all its species, it ejects pellets.

Both male and female take part in the spring display, when they soar together, first one above, then the other, at a great height over their nesting site. Sometimes the female will soar and display on her own.

The voice of the Sparrow-Hawk is rarely heard outside the breeding season. At the nest it has a loud harsh call, together with various plaintive mewings and whistles. The young have a high-pitched note, also a plaintive call that continues for hours.

Trees are the favourite nesting places of sparrow-hawks, with some preference for conifers. A pair usually build the bulky nest for themselves, but they will often use the old nest of crows, magpies, or jays; the same nest may be used by the same pair year after year. The female builds alone, but the male brings the material—twigs of larch and other trees. Dry leaves are used as lining. Four or five bluish-white eggs, blotched and spotted in dark brown, are laid in May, and for 4½–6 weeks the female hatches them, starting at the laying of the second egg. The nestlings, at first clad in white down, later in grey, are fed by the female with food passed to her by the male either at the nest or in the air. One brood is reared in a season.

As well as small birds, the Sparrow-Hawk consumes bats, weasels, moles and rodents, and not infrequently raids poultry farms.

SPATULA. Genus of ducks of the family *Anatidae* of the order *Anseriformes*. It contains four species, only one of which, the Shoveler (*q.v.*), occurs in the Northern Hemisphere.

SPECIES. Group, or aggregate, of birds of the same kind, which are similar anatomically, have the same general appearance, and are capable of interbreeding with other members of the same group. The species is the fundamental unit of the modern scientific system of classification (*q.v.*) and the only one (with its sub-units) having a strictly biological basis. It is subordinate to genus (*q.v.*), which groups together similar species ; and superior to a subspecies (geographical race or variety) of which there may be several within the same species.

The term is difficult to define precisely, and even the so-called experts disagree on several points. The definition given above, although helpful in providing a general idea of what is meant by species, is an over-simplification and begs the question. The only thing that can be said unequivocally about a species is that its members must be capable of breeding together to produce fertile offspring. The converse is not, however, true. The old dictum " that if two animals can breed together and produce fertile offspring they must be of the same species " has had to be abandoned in the light of modern knowledge. There are many examples of fertile wild hybrids of what are known as " good species," and a lesser number of hybrids

between members of different genera and even families (*see* Hybrid).

The word species means look or appearance, and one of the considerations is that members of the same species should look alike, subject to the qualification that the individuals being compared should be of the same sex, and at the same stage of development—since, in many species, the males and females are distinctly different both from one another and at different seasons, and the juveniles may resemble either parent or neither. Even so, in most cases, no more than a general resemblance may be expected, because no two animals are alike, and, even in the physical dimensions of members of the same species, there is usually a variation of from 5 to 20 per cent from the average—sometimes sufficient to cause an appreciable difference in the silhouette.

There may also be a gradation, or cline (*q.v.*) in the average size with change of latitude. There is often a considerable variation in the colour of plumage of individual members of the same " good species ". In some there are two, or more, distinct phases — dark, white and intermediate. Thus, the Fulmar shows every gradation from white on the head and underparts, to deep, smoky grey all over. Even more striking is the male Ruff in summer dress, where the " ruffs " during courtship show the most wonderful range of coloration, no two birds being exactly alike (*see* page 409). Nevertheless, they are obviously members of the same species.

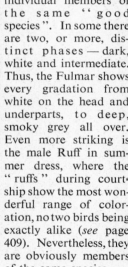

John Markham
SPARROW-HAWK. *Apart from the Kestrel (a falcon), this is our most common bird of prey*

To make matters still more difficult, at least superficially, some birds of different species are so alike that only an expert can tell them apart, for example, the Chiffchaff, Willow-Warbler, Reed- and Marsh-Warbler—yet they can be readily distinguished by their nests.

Enough has been shown to indicate the difficulty of the problem, and why classification (*q.v.*) is a matter for the expert. Species are sub-divided into subspecies, sometimes also called geographical races, which are derived from geographical isolation of a population of the original (or parent) species, from which they differ in form and often in behaviour and habit.

SPECULUM. Bar of bright colour, often with a metallic sheen, along the secondaries (*q.v.*) in surface-feeding ducks and, less prominently, in some diving ducks. *See also* Duck.

SPEED. Most birds have two flight speeds : a normal rate, and an emergency accelerated speed which may be nearly double the normal rate. Many migratory birds also have a comparatively fast speed which they can maintain for hours on their twice-yearly long-distance flights.

Occasionally special meteorological conditions cause birds to fly at high speed for much longer periods than normal. *British Birds* of June 1928 reported that in December 1927 some lapwings flew from Britain across the Atlantic, landing in Newfoundland and Labrador—a distance of some 2,200 miles—in about 24 hours of what was almost certainly non-stop flight. Although they were helped by a tail-wind averaging about 50 m.p.h. nearly all the way, their airspeed of some 40 m.p.h. for 24 hours non-stop was a remarkable feat.

It is necessary to stress the wind factor in bird flight because to ignore it results in highly inaccurate information. These lapwings, for instance, had a ground speed of over 90 m.p.h., but the tail-wind of 50 m.p.h. must be deducted from this to obtain the true air speed. Col. R. Meinertzhagen, who has done so much to increase our knowledge of bird flight, says that, when he was in the Outer Hebrides in a wind of a speed of about 60 m.p.h. he saw some eiders flying in the teeth of the gale, at about 15 m.p.h. One bird although flying with all its strength, was actually slowly travelling backwards over the ground, although its air-speed was nearly 60 m.p.h.

Rising currents of air (thermals) can also affect a bird's speed. The American ornithologists Broun and Goodwin give an interesting illustration of this. They timed an Osprey over a course of two-thirds of a mile at 80 m.p.h. During the whole time the bird hardly ever beat its wings—it was making use of a very strong thermal " so that the bird was in reality in steep diving flight without losing altitude ".

In view of these and other factors, accurate records for the air-speed of birds are very difficult to obtain. All figures given in this article should, therefore, be regarded as approximate. Moreover, all birds of the same species are not capable of equal speed. Age, state of plumage, and other factors modify a bird's powers of flight. One bird in a covey of partridges was seen to fly about 15 per cent faster than the others when the whole covey was in full panic flight before a bird of prey.

Speeds have been recorded in various ways ; by stop-watch over a known distance ; by observations from trains, cars and motorcycles ; by marking birds and noting time and distance travelled ; by aeroplanes ; and by special apparatus. In France, birds have been harnessed by silk thread to an indicator which recorded both the amount of line taken out as the bird flew, and the time occupied in flight.

Visual observations of flying birds, unless

SPEED, HEIGHT AND WING-BEAT				
The following abbreviations are used : M-C for motor-cycle, S-W for stop-watch, Pl for Aeroplane (*see* third column, entitled " How Timed ")				
Species	Speed in m.p.h.	How timed	Wing-beats per second	Height in ft.
Blue Tit	21	M-C		
Green Woodpecker	23	Car		
Sparrow-Hawk	25	Car		
Snow-Bunting	26			
Goldfinch	26	M-C		
Cuckoo	27	Car	4·8	
Common Tern	29	Car		
Blackbird	33	Car	5·6	
Chaffinch	35	Car		
Crow	35	Car	4·2	
House-Sparrow	35	S-W	13·0	14,000
Raven	35		3·6	
Skylark	35			
Magpie	35	Car	3·0	
Heron	35	Car	2·9	3,000
Mistle-Thrush	35	Car		
Herring-Gull	36	Car		
Manx Shearwater	40		5·4	
Swallow	40			
Woodcock	40			
Little Owl	40	M-C		
Shrike	40			
Kestrel	40			7,000
Whooper-Swan	44	S-W		
Cormorant	45		4·4	2,500
Rook	45		3·0	11,000
Tawny Owl	45			
House-Martin	45			
Gannet	48	Pl	4·3	
Jackdaw	50		4·2	800
Snow-Goose	50	Pl		
Lapwing	50	Pl	4·8	8,500
Curlew	50	Car	4·2	4,600
Starling	50	S-W	7·5	3,500
Common Snipe	50		5·8	
Partridge	50			
Pheasant	50		9 (*rising*)	
Red Grouse	50			
Sand-Grouse	50		6·0	
Wood-Pigeon	51	Car	5·2	
Racing Pigeon	58·7		8·0	
Stock-Dove	59	M-C		400
Whimbrel	60			
Canada Goose	60	Pl		
Mallard	60		5·1	6,300
Pintail	60			
Teal	60		10·0	
Golden Plover	60			6,600
Swift	60			6,700
Eider-Duck	70		4·9	
Albatross	100			
American Sand-piper	110	Pl		12,000
Golden Eagle	120	S-W		9,750
Peregrine Falcon	200+	Pl	4·4	
Needle-tailed Swift	219	S-W		

NOTE : All figures should be regarded as approximate. Generally the highest authentic figures have been given throughout this Table.

Arthur Brook

SPOONBILL. *Although flying in the slow, heavy manner of herons, the Spoonbill will often soar to great heights and delights in gliding in the air*

assistants, timed these birds on a number of occasions in the Cachar Hills, Assam.

It had previously been ascertained by them that the hill on which Baker's house stood was exactly 2 miles from a ridge. He says:

> In the evenings the spine-tails used to come over my house and fly straight to the opposite ridge and, on reaching it, at once dip down into the farther valley. With a stop watch, I could time them as they swished over my house until they dipped into the valley over the ridge . . . The actual times taken to traverse the two miles varied between 32·8 and 41·8 seconds.

Thus their fastest speed over the two-mile course was 219·5 m.p.h., and special air conditions may account for this. Baker says that the difference in speed between the British and the needle-tailed swifts is extraordinary : it is doubtful if any British swift can fly faster than 60 m.p.h. (*Country Life*, March 13, 1942).

Wing Beats. There is a great difference in the speed at which birds beat their wings. Unless the timing is done by instruments, preferably by high-speed cinematograph camera, exact figures for all but the slowest birds are almost impossible to obtain. But it is known that large-winged birds, such as herons, have a frequency of about two beats a second, and that a Humming-Bird sometimes beats its tiny wings 75 times a second.

The same bird does not maintain a constant frequency. When taking-off, accelerating, or in panic flight, many birds beat their wings faster than in ordinary flight. Charles H. Blake found that a Blue Jay beat its wings four times a second when taking-off, but only 2·6 times in steady flapping flight, and 2·2 times when descending.

How High Do Birds Fly ? In crossing mountain ranges on migration, some birds are forced to ascend to great altitudes ; choughs, for instance, reach some 28,000 ft.—almost the height of Mount Everest. But such statements as this are rather misleading, since " altitude of flight " should signify height above the ground and not height above sea-level.

Altitude records have been estimated in various ways : by theodolite, astronomical telescope, aeroplanes and scale models. Generally, birds do not fly as high as was once thought. Meinertzhagen says : ' Among the smaller

checked with instruments, are apt to give very misleading impressions. The smaller the bird the faster it appears to be flying, yet in fact some of the largest, such as geese, are among the swiftest of all British birds, sometimes attaining an air-speed of a mile a minute. This is about twice the speed of such small birds as sparrows, chaffinches and thrushes.

An air-speed in excess of a mile a minute is exceptional for any bird. Tests during the Second World War with R.A.F. pigeons showed that even these expert fliers did not reach 60 m.p.h. The fastest recorded speed in these tests was 58·7 m.p.h., although there is no doubt that some pigeons could fly over 60 m.p.h. for short distances. Racing pigeons have flown with a favourable wind at about 100 m.p.h. During a race in Northern Ireland in 1914, a pigeon flew at nearly 94 m.p.h. for 80 miles.

Other British birds which can reach 60 m.p.h. are Mallard, Eider-Duck, Teal and Pintail, Canada and Brent geese, and Red Grouse.

Dr. Fraser Darling has recorded timing a Golden Eagle at 120 m.p.h., when it was being pursued by two peregrine falcons. Darling took a careful note of the time and the distance the eagle flew, and found that it rose 1,000 ft. during its epic flight (*Nature*, September 1, 1934). A pilot observed that when he was nose-diving at over 170 m.p.h. a peregrine, stooping on some ducks, flashed past him " as though the plane was standing still ". Other observers have also testified to the speed of this bird, but it appears that it can reach its highest speed—200 m.p.h. or so—only when it is stooping from a height.

The highest reasonably authentic speed for any bird on the British list is probably that recorded for the Needle-tailed Swift (known as Spine-tailed Swift in India) by E. C. Stuart Baker, an authority on Indian birds, who, with several

Passerines, whether on land or sea, migration takes place almost always at under 200 feet, in rough weather usually much lower ". Yet there are records of aircraft occasionally meeting birds at several thousand feet above the earth. The highest altitude record for this country appears to be a flock of 60 to 70 rooks encountered by air pilots 11,000 ft. above Salisbury.

Consult ; " The Speed and Altitude of Bird Flight (with notes on other animals) ", Col. R. Meinertzhagen, *Ibis,* Jan. 1955 ; to which the author is indebted for some of his information.

SPOONBILL—Platalea leucorodia. That the beautiful and oriental-looking Spoonbill was once a dweller in the counties of Norfolk and Suffolk, and even in the vicinity of London— they are known to have bred in 1523 in the Bishop of London's park at Fulham—will come as a surprise to many people. To-day, like many other Fenland birds, the Spoonbill comes to Britain only as a winter visitor ; it is more or less regular in the southern and eastern counties of England, but elsewhere a very rare and unusual vagrant. Abroad, the Spoonbill breeds throughout Europe in suitable countries — especially Holland—also in Asia, and in north-west Africa, wintering in tropical Africa.

Its white plumage and remarkable spatulate bill, from which it gets its name, give the Spoonbill a unique appearance. In Summer, it has a bright orange patch on its breast contrasting with the snowy plumage, and a sweeping crest sometimes also tinged with yellow. The bill is black, the spoon-end being yellow ; the red eye is surrounded with yellow skin. The legs and feet are black. The sexes are alike. In the iuvenile the tips of the wings are blackish, and there is no crest. The Spoonbill's total length is 34 in., the body being 15 in. ; the tarsus is $5\frac{1}{2}$ in., the wing span approximately 3 ft., and the bird's weight is $3\frac{3}{4}$ lb.

In the air the Spoonbill has the slow heavy movement of the Heron, but it flies with neck, as well as legs, outstretched. Like the storks, it will fly at a great height, and delights in soaring and gliding. In the display flight the male raises his crest in the shape of a fan, rattles his bill, and is said to perform a " dance " in the same way as the storks. The Spoonbill stalks on the ground and, like the Heron, perches on trees. Occasionally it swims.

Spoonbills are, as a rule, found in small parties —occasionally in large flocks—and fly in single file. Estuaries, marshland and shallow lagoons near the sea are their favourite feeding grounds, where, usually at dusk, they like to wade, sweeping the shallow mud with their spoon-like bills for food. The Spoonbill is a silent bird ; even at its breeding site the only sound is a low, crooning grunt. The nestlings have a low, wheezing squeak.

These birds nest in colonies—some containing only a few pairs, others up to 200 or more pairs —but consort only with their own species. The nests in Europe are generally placed among the dense vegetation of reed-beds, but sometimes also among the tamarisk bushes of marshes. One eastern race always builds in trees. The nest is built of whatever material is close at hand. The breeding season is from April to May, according to the country frequented, and the white eggs usually number four. Both male and female incubate for about three weeks, and both feed the young also. Some nestlings are usually lost by becoming buried beneath the accumulated mass of filth round the nesting site. The young cannot fly freely until they are seven or eight weeks old. One brood is reared in a season.

In the Middle Ages the Spoonbill went by the name of " Shovelard " or " Shoveler ", while today the Shoveler *(q.v.)* duck, which has a rather similar spoon-like bill, is sometimes, though quite erroneously, called the " Spoonbill ".

Arthur Christiansen

SPOONBILL. *Once a common breeding bird—it even nested in a London park—this oriental-looking creature is now one of our winter visitors*

SPOTTED CRAKE—Porzana porzana.

These rare birds are known to breed in several counties in England, and may well breed in many more, and in larger numbers than we know, for they are so secretive in their habits and frequent such impenetrable marshy ground that observation is very difficult. They are also passage migrants, and some are known to remain during the Winter. Abroad, they breed all over Europe, and winter in Africa.

In appearance the Spotted Crake is rather like a small dark Corncrake, but it has very grey underparts and, as its name suggests, its plumage is spotted in white. It is larger than the Little Crake and Baillon's Crake. It is almost impossible to see it at close quarters, and in the distance it is often taken for a Moorhen. Its length is 9 in., and its tarsus 1 in.; its wing span is about 1 ft., and its weight is 4 oz.

It walks, runs, swims and dives. When flying it dangles its legs; its flight is weak, except on migration. One of its many different notes is a pronounced ticking call. A conspicuous summer note is a whistling, similar to that of the Nuthatch, but harsher and higher.

The Spotted Crake, which resembles the Water-Rail in behaviour and habits, breeds in swamps, fens and bogs. Its nest is made of weeds, grasses, and vegetable matter, and lined with finer grasses. The 8-12 eggs are laid in May; information regarding the hatching of the eggs and rearing of the young is scanty. Two broods are usual in a season. The Spotted Crake's food consists mostly of water insects.

SPOTTED EAGLE—Aquila clanga.

It is many years since a specimen of this very rare vagrant was seen in Great Britain. It breeds in Finland, the Baltic States and possibly Russia, and winters in Africa.

This is a large brown bird, but smaller than the Golden Eagle. Only the immature birds have the broad white spots on the plumage which give the species its English name; it is in this dress that the bird's infrequent visits to Great Britain have been made. The adult Spotted Eagle is a darker brown than the Golden Eagle, and its tail is not barred. Its length is 26-29 in.

The Spotted Eagle breeds and winters in the neighbourhood of marshes, lakes and rivers. Its eyrie resembles the Golden Eagle's nest in structure. Its flight is typical of its family. It has a high-pitched, barking call. Its breeding habits do not seem to differ from those of other eagles. One brood is reared.

SPOTTED FLYCATCHER — Muscicapa striata.

One of the shortest-staying of our summer visitors, the Spotted Flycatcher scarcely puts in an appearance before the end of April, and it is well into May before all have settled in to breed; it begins to depart for warmer

C. W. Teager

SPOTTED FLYCATCHER. Our shortest summer visitor, arriving in late April and going in July

climes as early as July, and by the beginning of September all have gone. The Spotted Flycatcher occurs throughout the British Isles except in the Outer Hebrides. Abroad, it breeds in Europe, temperate Asia and north Africa.

Inconspicuous in plumage, and not even so " spotted " as to warrant the name, the Spotted Flycatcher is dressed in greyish-brown, with some dark streaks on the head and breast, and has whitish underparts. Its legs are black, and its bill brown. Male and female are alike; the spotted young are more worthy of the name than their parents. The length is 5½ in., and the tarsus 0·55 in.; the wing span is between 7 and 8 in., and the weight just under ½ oz.

All flycatchers are adept at catching insects in the air, but the Spotted species outstrips them in skill and dash. To the watcher, this ability is its best identification, for no other small bird spends so much of its life in the pursuit of flying insects—its only form of food.

Clearings in woods, gardens, parklands, town parks and even suburban built-up areas all attract the Spotted Flycatcher. Choosing an observation post—sometimes it has two favourite spots—from which it can best see the passing insects, it sits motionless and watchful for hours, ready to dart in a flash to seize its prey.

On migration, and when of some duration, its flight is rapid and undulating. It hops on the ground, but rarely does so unless pursuing an elusive titbit.

The Spotted Flycatcher is not inclined to be sociable even where it is plentiful, and in its

John Markham

STARLING, *as a city dweller, a nuisance resisting eviction*

For text see page 530

winter quarters generally resides alone. In its spring display the constant flirting of the tail, and the action of the head and neck held stiffly with the bill raised, are very reminiscent of the Robin. The Spotted Flycatcher also has a chasing flight, performed by both sexes.

The call note is also Robin-like but less musical. The song varies with the individual bird, as in all species, but it is in the main made up of some half-dozen shrill squeaky notes, interspersed with an occasional musical warble. It is usually delivered from an inconspicuous perch, and is best heard at the end of May and the beginning of June ; but the Editor had heard the full song in August, both day and night, from a pair which chose to nest in a hotel dining-room.

Selection of breeding site and preparations for nest-building begin shortly after the birds' arrival. Human habitations and outhouses are often favourite spots, and the nest may be placed in a projecting beam or a hole in a wall, or among creepers ; but it is often built against a tree trunk or in an old nest of another species. It is slightly constructed of moss, wool and hair, woven together with cobwebs, and both birds take their share in making it. In late May or early June, four or five greenish-grey eggs, with brown spots, are laid. Both birds incubate for a fortnight, and feed and tend the chicks for the same period. One brood is usually raised in a season, but two are not unknown.

SPOTTED REDSHANK—Tringa erythropus. On its spring and autumn migration, the Spotted Redshank occasionally visits the British Isles, occurring both round the coasts and inland on marshy areas, reservoirs and so forth, chiefly in the southern part of England, but sometimes farther north. Abroad, the Spotted Redshank is found in northern Europe and Asia, wintering in the Mediterranean region and southern Asia.

In appearance the Spotted is much darker than the common Redshank—whence its other name, Dusky Redshank, which is especially applicable to the winter dress in which it is likely to be seen here. The two birds are not difficult to distinguish. The plumage of the Spotted is ashy-grey, and it lacks the conspicuous white on the wings of the common Redshank. It is also larger, and has longer legs and bill. Its summer dress of black, with its white spotted mantle, is distinctive and unlike that of any other wader. Its white rump and barred tail are similar at all seasons to its relative's. The sexes are alike. The length is 12 in., and the tarsus 2 in. ; the wing span is 12 in.-14 in., and the weight 6 oz.-7 oz.

In behaviour, habits, walk and flight the Spotted scarcely differs from the common Redshank. It is very shy, and keeps company only with its own family. Only its voice is characteristic, and to those who are familiar with the flight note it is easily identified. Its call note is described as having a less musical quality than the common Redshank's.

The Spotted Redshank breeds on open ground of coniferous and birch forests. A mere depression in the grass houses four greenish eggs, laid in May or early June. The hen is thought to incubate alone, but the period is unknown. At first both parents tend the young ; later they are cared for by one. Only a single brood is reared and brought out each season.

The Spotted Redshank lives entirely on animal matter.

SPOTTED SANDPIPER — Tringa macularia. This north American species, which breeds throughout Canada and the United States, is a very rare visitor on migration to the British Isles ; only about a dozen records have been accepted as authentic. It is so similar to the Common Sandpiper that identification, even by the expert, is not always easy. The bird's chief mark of distinction lies in its summer plumage, when its underparts are covered with round black spots. The length is 7½ in., the tarsus ¾ in., and the wing span 9 or 10 in. The adults of both sexes are alike.

The type of country frequented, behaviour,

Arthur Christiansen

SPOTTED REDSHANK. *Darker than the common Redshank, the Spotted is also often called the Dusky Redshank. It is seen here only on migration*

Arthur Brook

SQUACCO HERON. Breeding in southern Europe, this fawn-coloured heron
is a rare visitor, and it is mostly immature birds that are seen in Britain

habits and voice, are all similar to those of the Common Sandpiper. There is one authentic record of this bird, after it had been disturbed, carrying a chick between its thighs in flight.

SPOTTED WOODPECKER. *See* Greater Spotted Woodpecker (and its allied Northern race) ; *also* Lesser Spotted Woodpecker.

SPRING MOULT. Partial moult (*q.v.*), affecting only the covering feathers, which occurs in some species at the beginning of the breeding season. The timing is irregular, starting with some of the species affected in January, and with others not finishing until June.

SQUACCO HERON — Ardeola ralloides. An irregular and rare vagrant from its home in southern Europe, the Squacco Heron has been recorded in the British Isles, chiefly in the south and east. The majority of visits have been paid by young birds in immature plumage during the early Summer.

This is a fawn-coloured heron with short legs, white wings and tail, and with a long graceful sweep of white feathers edged with black falling back from its crown. It is unlikely to be confused with any other heron. The total length is 18 in., the body being 9 in. ; the tarsus is 2·6 in. The wing span is approximately 20 in., and the weight about 1 lb.

In habits and behaviour the Squacco Heron follows closely the pattern of its family. Except in the breeding season, when harsh calls are heard, usually in the late evening, it is a silent bird. It breeds in colonies in marshes and floodlands, on the banks of rivers and lagoons, as well as in woods, willow-thickets and so on, associating freely with the Little Egret, Glossy Ibis, Buff-backed and Night Heron. It is said to be more inclined than its companions,

to seek cover in reeds, and to be most active at night. It perches on on trees and bushes.

The site and construction of the nest depend on the surroundings, and it may be either a substantial or flimsy structure. Four to six greenish-blue eggs are usually laid in May, but the time varies with the type of country. Information regarding the incubation and the tending of the young is scanty, but the work seems to be shared by both parents. One brood is reared in a season. The chief food is insects, but a little vegetable matter is eaten.

STARE. Local name for the Starling.

STARLING — Sturnus vulgaris. A century ago the Starling was entirely a migratory bird. But its tameness and willingness to be fed on all kinds of table scraps and titbits resulted in its remaining in the British Isles during the Winter, and it has now become a common and resident bird all the year round in both town and country. The consequent continued growth in its numbers has created a difficult problem, which is increased by the arrival in Autumn of great droves from the Continent to winter here. The Starling's habit of roosting in vast buildings and trees in the centre of cities has produced a nuisance which local authorities have tried in vain to remove.

Nets have been placed on the tops of buildings, electrified wires have been run along ledges, and ingenious traps have been invented, but the wily birds have so far managed to elude all efforts to disperse them or to capture them in any appreciable numbers. The Starling has been blamed by some authorities for bringing foot-and-mouth disease into the country, but there is no evidence to substantiate this.

The Starling is increasing in Scotland where, until recently, it was only a local bird ; but it has always bred in the Orkneys. In Ireland, it is scarce in some parts. The House-Sparrow is its only possible rival as the most abundant land bird in the world.

The Starling's comical actions have caused it to be called the humorist of the bird world. It is also a very clever mimic and can reproduce equally well the sound of a railway engine and the Blackbird's song—the latter so perfectly that many people believe they have heard that bird singing in November.

Perhaps it is because so many of these birds are daily seen around us that the beauty of their dress is not appreciated. When seen in the sunshine, the Starling's variegated iridescent colourings of brown, purple, blue and green are most beautiful. Unlike many of our birds, the Starling seldom or never hops, but always runs. Male and female are alike, with variations in the plumage at different times of the year. The young are a smoky brown. The length of the Starling is 8½ in., and its tarsus 1 in. ; its wing span is 1 ft., and its weight 3½ oz.

The Starling's song, heard almost all the year round, is a series of rather musical whistles, especially pleasant in the early Spring. When angry or alarmed it utters a harsh scream. Assembled in their hundreds, or even thousands, at their roosting spots, starlings keep up a continuous twittering chorus for hours. Suddenly, as if at a word of command by their leader, the whole flock will rise with a loud swishing sound and perform the most impressive aerial evolutions *en masse* before settling again to resume its deafening chorus. Springtime sees the birds, often in flocks,

chasing and pursuing each other at their breeding sites. The Starling will build its nest almost anywhere—in a tree, on a building, in wall ivy, in a haystack, in a nesting box. The very untidy nest is made of straw and lined with hair and wool, or anything soft. The four to seven eggs, laid in April, are pale blue, sometimes even white. Both parents help in the hatching, which takes about 12 days, but the hen bird is said to sit alone at night. The young are fed by both parents for about 20 days. Most starlings have only one brood in a season, but it is not uncommon for them to lay a second time.

As soon as the nesting season is over, starlings become the most gregarious of birds and move in flocks about the countryside wherever they can find food. In the evening they make their way in vast numbers to their roosting places—the city streets and squares.

The feeding habits of the Starling have placed it on the gardener's " black list ", but it also eats an enormous amount of injurious insects. The farmer counts it his friend ; but the market gardener most decidedly disagrees, and there is no doubt that in Summer and Autumn starlings consume much fruit.

STATUS. This answers the question as to whether a species or subspecies occurs in a certain area as a resident, visitor, migrant, straggler or accidental, or as a combination of any two or more of these terms, which may also be further defined as follows :

Resident: Term applied to a species or race that remains in a particular geographical area throughout the year. The term may be qualified by such adjectives as scarce, local and common. The first two are self-explanatory, but common may mean widespread (the meaning attributed to it in this Encyclopedia), abundant or regularly seen by a particular observer.

Visitor: One that visits one area from another and *stays* in it for part of the year. Usually qualified by some such term as Summer (s.v.) or Winter (w.v.), often further qualified by the normal period of stay (e.g. September to April), Breeding (B.V.), Non-breeding (N.B.V.), or irregular (I.V.).

Migrant: This term has the same meaning as visitor unless qualified by passage (P.M.)—which means that the migrants are only passing through on their journey to somewhere else.

Straggler: A bird that has strayed a great distance from its normal habitat, carried, for example, by strong winds or by being " caught up " in the migratory movements of other species. Also called a *Vagrant*.

Accidental: A straggler which has been *recorded* less than 20 times in a given area.

Stationary: Term applied to species, races or individuals that normally remain in, or do not move far from, an area throughout the year.

Some works make a practice of defining the status of families, orders and even higher

Eric Hosking

STARLING. *Its comical actions have caused it to become known as the humorist of the bird world*

categories of classification (*q.v.*), such as classes and phyla. The *Encyclopedia of British Birds*, however, on the whole follows the British list in only describing the status of species and subspecies (races).

Certain species may be described by a combination of the above terms. Thus : " Resident, scarce, Scotland. Non-breeding visitor and passage migrant September to November and May to June ", which means that a few of this particular species are resident all the year round in Scotland ; that for part of the year their numbers are increased by visitors from elsewhere, who, though making a prolonged stay, do not breed in Scotland ; and that during the named months passage migrants " touch down " for a short time before proceeding on their journey.

Another common expression is " Resident, partially migratory ", meaning that some members of the species remain in residence throughout the year, while others migrate.

STELLER'S EIDER — Polysticta stelleri. This very rare visitor to Great Britain has been recorded only three times. It is a native of Arctic regions, breeding in Siberia and Alaska, and wintering on the coasts of the Pacific and northern Scandinavia.

A much smaller duck than the other two eiders, the drake has a rich chestnut breast and belly, shading to a darker tint on his flanks. His mantle is black and white, the white predominating, and his head and cheeks are also white. His nape has the greenish tinge common to all eiders. The duck is a small mottled brown bird. The length of both is about 18 in., the body being 12.

Very little information is available concerning the habits and behaviour of Steller's Eider, but it does not seem to differ greatly from its relatives. The male has a soft crooning note, not unlike that of the Eider-Duck, and the female a hoarse call comparable to that of the female Wigeon. The food is principally animal matter, such as fish, mussels, prawns and worms.

STEPPE BUZZARD — Buteo buteo vulpinis. This is a very rare visitor to Britain. The *Handbook of British Birds* says that the skin of one killed in 1864 is preserved in the British Museum, and that two others had been recorded earlier in Great Britain. It breeds in the woodlands of Sweden, Finland, the Baltic states and parts of Russia, and winters in Africa and Asia.

In appearance, habits, nest, and number of eggs the Steppe Buzzard resembles the common Buzzard. Its breeding season is from early April to the end of May in Finland, but varies in other countries. The eggs are hatched chiefly by the hen for about four weeks, and the young are on the wing in about 42 days. One brood is reared in a season.

STERCORARIIDAE. Family of sea-birds (the skuas) of the order *Charadriiformes*. Its members breed mostly in high northern or southern latitudes, but outside the breeding season they are distributed over all the oceans.

The skuas are contained in a single genus, *Stercorarius*. There are four species on the British list : the Arctic Skua, Great Skua, Long-tailed Skua, and Pomatorhine Skua. These are separately described under their own headings.

These birds have a strong, hooked bill, the horny covering of which consists of four parts—a horny cere, two lateral sections, and the " end section ", or tip, which is hooked. The wings are long. The tail is of medium length, and the central tail-feathers are slightly, or considerably, longer than the rest. The tarsus is fairly short, rougher than in gulls, with rather prominent scutes (horny scales). The front toes are webbed, and have sharp, hooked claws.

STERNA. Genus of medium-sized and small terns of the family *Laridae* of the order *Charadriiformes*. It contains more than thirty species, distributed over all parts of the globe. The seven species on the British list are the Common Tern, Arctic Tern, Roseate Tern, Sooty Tern, Bridled Tern, Little Tern, and the Sandwich Tern, all of which see.

Paul Popper

STERCORARIIDAE. All skuas are members of this family. They have some superficial resemblance to gulls, but are larger and very much more fierce

The members of this genus have a slender, slightly curved, laterally compressed, and pointed bill of medium length. The wings are long and pointed. The tail is deeply forked, with the outer tail-feathers elongated and forming the so-called " streamers ". The tarsus is short, and the three front toes are united by webs. There is a small hind toe.

STINT. Common name of a group of small wading birds belonging to the genus *Calidris* of the family *Scolopacidae*. They are closely related to the Knot, Dunlin and Sanderling, which birds they resemble in general appearance and habits. The name is probably connected with the verb " to stint " in its old sense of " to shorten ", as stints are the smallest members of their family, being only about 5½ in. long.

They have the spindly legs characteristic of waders, but the straight pointed bill, though longish, is relatively short for a wader (shorter than the head). Three stints appear on the British List : Little Stint ; Temminck's Stint ; American Stint. The first two are passage migrants, and the last a rare straggler. All are described under their own headings.

STOCK-DOVE—Columba oenas. Recent years have seen an increase in the range of the Stock-Dove, which at one time was very local in its distribution throughout the British Isles. Today it is common, if still inclined to be local, in the extreme north of England ; in Scotland, where it was first recorded as breeding in 1870, it has rapidly increased, and occurs everywhere except in the extreme north ; and in Ireland it has also increased its range. Abroad, the Stock-Dove breeds throughout Europe and temperate Asia.

The absence of any white in the grey-blue plumage of the Stock-Dove is its clearest distinguishing feature ; of our other doves, the Rock has white on the rump, the Wood-Pigeon on the wings and neck, and the Turtle-Dove on the outer tail feathers. The throat and breast of the Stock-Dove are tinged with wine colour, and on the side of the neck is a patch of iridescent green. The underparts are pale grey. Both the wings and tail have black tips, and across the wings there are two broken black bars. The bill is yellow, and the legs are pink. The sexes are alike, but the young are duller. The length is 13 in., and the tarsus 1·1 in. ; the wing span is about 18 in., and the weight 14 oz.

Except for its less restricted habitat—it frequents woodlands, open country and park-land with old trees, as well as maritime cliffs, rocks, sand dunes and so on—the Stock-Dove has much in common with the Wood-Pigeon, though its flight is faster and more dashing.

Like all doves, it is sociable and mingles with other members of its family, especially when feeding.

A remarkably graceful display-flight takes place in the Spring, both male and female flying round in circles and gliding now and again with raised wings. " Wing-clapping " also occurs, and there is a most engaging bowing ceremony before mating.

A double " coo ", the first accented, is the principal vocal production of the Stock-Dove. At least a dozen of the calls are uttered in succession from a tallish tree, each sequence

Arthur Brook

STOCK-DOVE. *Quitting its nest-hole in an old tree-trunk to forage for more food for its young*

lasting for some seven to eight seconds. The Stock-Dove's call will be readily recognized by those who are familiar with the calls of the other members of the genus.

Several pairs of stock-doves may nest in close proximity where suitable nesting holes are abundant ; holes in trees, rocks, sea-cliffs and sand dunes, and rabbit warrens, are all used. Little or no material is used for the nest, and as often as not the two creamy-white eggs are laid on the floor. Since there are always two, and sometimes three, clutches the breeding season extends from the end of March until July. Both male and female share the hatching for 18 days, and the young are fed with " pigeons' milk " for a varying period, usually lasting about 28 days.

Like other doves, the Stock-Dove consumes principally vegetable food—clover, swede and turnip leaves, beans, peas, and, particularly, grain, but occasionally takes snails and larvae.

Eric Hosking

STONECHAT. *This little songster likes a bush as a look-out post from which to guard its nest*

STONECHAT—Saxicola torquata. Although the Stonechat is a resident widely distributed throughout the British Isles, its appearance in any district is always uncertain, as it is extremely local in its choice of breeding sites ; moreover, it is said to be decreasing. A hard Winter takes a tremendous toll of such small birds, and during that of 1946-47 the numbers of stonechats were greatly diminished. Coastal heath or common land is where it is most likely to be seen. There is evidence that some British birds move south in the Autumn ; others remain where they have bred ; and some emigrate. The Stonechat is also a bird of passage in the Spring. Abroad, it is found throughout Europe, Asia and Africa.

The cock in his summer dress of black and chestnut is a beautiful little bird. His head, throat, mantle and tail are black ; his under-parts chestnut shading to buff. White patches are conspicuous on his neck, wings and rump. In Winter he becomes drab-looking. The hen and juvenile are brown, with darker streaks. The length is 5 in., and the tarsus 0.85 in. ; the wing span is 6-7 in., and the weight ½ oz.

The Stonechat and Whinchat, which frequent the same type of country, have much in common. The former, however, shows a special liking for gorse bushes, choosing the topmost branch as a point of vantage. There it sits, guarding the nest, constantly bobbing its plump body up and down and jerking its tail. If disturbed, it flits restlessly from bush to bush, uttering its curious and metallic alarm call, which sounds like little pebbles being sharply knocked together ; it is from this sound that the bird gets its name.

The Stonechat has an upright carriage, and hops rapidly on the ground. A late rooster, it does not seek cover among the dense vegetation

until darkness falls. It is not a sociable bird ; during Autumn it roams the countryside in small parties, but in Winter it is usually seen alone.

The song of the Stonechat varies, but is, in the main, a rapidly repeated series of sweet warbling notes. Some versions are not at all unlike the Whinchat's song, and one closely resembles the Hedge-Sparrow's. It is usually delivered from a perch, or in its dancing song-flight when it rises almost vertically from the perch to a height of 40-100 ft., sinks a few feet, and rises again, over and over. When delivered from a perch the song lasts 2 or 3 seconds, but it is longer in the song-flight. The Stonechat is best heard from mid-March until the beginning of July. Outside the breeding season it is usually silent.

Stonechats nest on heaths, commons, downs, hillsides, cliffs and wherever gorse and whin bushes grow, especially near the sea. The nest is placed carefully in a well-concealed nook, on or near the ground, at the foot of a gorse or other bush. It is built by the hen of moss, grass and roots, and lined with fine bents, hair and feathers. Five or six pale blue-green eggs, marked with reddish speckles, are laid from April to July, two broods being reared. For a fortnight the hen hatches them alone, and the nestlings are fed for another fortnight by both parents. They fly a few days later.

Insects are the Stonechat's chief diet, but some seeds are also eaten.

The subspecies known as the Hebridean Stonechat (*Saxicola torquata theresae*) is largely confined to the Outer Hebrides. There are some small differences in plumage, the Hebridean bird being darker, but in habits or behaviour the two birds are similar.

The Siberian Stonechat (*Saxicola torquata maura*) is a bird of north-east Russia and western Siberia. Two only are known to have wandered to the British Isles. This bird is paler in plumage than the mainland Stonechat, but is otherwise similar in habits and behaviour.

STONE-CURLEW—Burhinus oedicnemus. A bird of barren chalky downlands, open stony heaths and shingle shores, the Stone-Curlew is a summer visitor of restricted and local occurrence. At one time it was much more abundant than now ; it is, however, well established where it still breeds in south-west England and occasionally further north. Some birds remain all the Winter. In both Scotland and Ireland the Stone-Curlew is extremely rare. Outside the breeding season, it is a vagrant on migration. Abroad, it is found throughout Europe, Asia and north Africa, and winters in tropical Africa.

The Stone-Curlew is also known by the names of Great Plover, Norfolk Plover, and Thick-Knee—the last refers to its thick ankle-joint. Although in appearance it has something of the Curlew, it has the long legs of the plovers and resembles the latter bird in other ways. Its breeding haunts are more in keeping with those of the bustards.

The Stone-Curlew's most prominent features are its large yellow eyes which can be seen even when its body, excellently camouflaged, merges completely into the background. Its mantle is sandy-brown with darker streaks ; its black-and-white wing pattern is conspicuous in flight. Its chin and throat, and the line under the large eye, are white ; its breast and flanks streaked ; and its underparts white. Its tail is brown with black tips, white showing at the sides. Its legs are pale yellow, and its bill black at the tip, yellow at the base. The sexes are alike, and the juvenile does not differ greatly from the adult. The length is 16 in., and the tarsus 3 in. ; the wing span is between 18 and 20 in., and the weight 1 lb.

The Stone-Curlew is sociable at all times but especially in the Autumn, when flocks of 10 or 20 birds—sometimes many more—are to be seen. Its flight is low and straight in course, with regular, rather slow wing-beats ; its legs trail out behind. Evening flocks often fly higher, and perform aerial evolutions. The Stone-Curlew walks with a tripping step ; when necessary, it can run very fast, disappearing rapidly and stealthily. It is extremely shy, and during the day lies hidden, crouching close to the ground, motionless and unseen. The young Stone-Curlew adopts a characteristic " freezing " attitude, with its body flat on the ground and its head and neck extended ; the same attitude is adopted by the adult when alarmed, but the nestlings only crouch. The

Stone-Curlew never perches, but rests on its belly or sits with the whole length of the tarsus (*q.v.*) on the ground.

The spring display, which takes place on the ground and in which both male and female take part, includes many and varied attitudes and ceremonies, the birds bowing to each other, skipping, dancing, and leaping in the air. In the Autumn, stone-curlews indulge in some extraordinary communal displays. They also have a curious and unexplained habit of picking up small stones and throwing them about.

In the Stone-Curlew's breeding haunts its voice, heard as darkness falls, is one of the loveliest and strangest in Nature. Its call, wild and musical, resembles to some extent the Curlew's plaintive wail—a circumstance no doubt responsible for the bird's name. It is heard through the breeding season, both in the air and on the ground. As the flocks collect ready for departure in the Autumn, the clamour of their chorus has an unforgettable beauty.

The Stone-Curlew builds no real nest, but lays its two stone-coloured eggs with dark spots—very difficult to see—on the ground, in late April or early May. Both male and female share the incubation for $3\frac{1}{2}$ to 4 weeks. The chicks, clad in sandy-buff with black lines, leave the nest within a day or two, and are tended by both parents. They fly in six weeks. One brood is reared in a season.

Molluscs, worms, insects, small rodents and suchlike are the chief items in the bird's diet.

STONE-FALCON. Alternative name for Merlin (*q.v.*), smallest of our resident falcons.

STONEHATCH. Alternative name for the Ringed Plover (*q.v.*), a shore-nesting wader.

STONE-CURLEW. *An extremely shy bird which freezes to the ground at the first sign of danger. It is excellently camouflaged, except for its prominent yellow eyes*

Eric Hosking

STORK. Group of birds whose general appearance is too well-known to warrant description. Apart from the characteristic long, stout bill, these birds are noted for their method of sleeping—standing on one leg, with the neck folded and the head turned backward on the shoulder. In spite of their bulk, they fly very strongly and high in the air, with a slow and measured movement.

Storks are usually divided into " true " storks and American " wood ibises ". There are several genera, comprising about a dozen species, of which only two are represented on the British list ; the White Stork, which visits Britain irregularly between March and October, and the Black Stork, which is a straggler that has visited England at least twenty-two times, and Scotland once. Both are fully described.

STORMCOCK. Alternative name for Mistle-Thrush (*q.v.*), a common resident.

STORM-PETREL — **Hydrobates pelagicus.** Of the 22 species of petrel, only two—Leach's Petrel and the Storm-Petrel—are resident in the British Isles. The latter is the smaller ; it is, in fact, the smallest known sea-bird. Abundant on the islands off the Pembrokeshire coast (Skokholm and Skomer), where its habits have been extensively studied by well-known ornithologists, it also breeds on the Isles of Scilly, Orkney and Shetland, and on many islands off the west coasts of Scotland and Ireland, as well as on Muller Peninsula, in Co. Mayo.

The Storm-Petrel is dressed in very dark brown—almost black—only relieved by its white rump, conspicuous in flight. Some white, not always visible, appears on its long narrow wings and under tail-coverts ; a narrow but quite distinct white line forms a wing-bar. Its tail is square-shaped, in contrast to those of its near relatives. Its bill is slightly hooked, with tubular nostrils, and its long legs are black. The sexes are alike. The length is 6 in., and the tarsus 0·9 in. ; the wing span is approximately 12 in., and the weight less than $\frac{1}{2}$ oz.

An essentially marine bird like all petrels, the Storm-Petrel spends the greater part of its life far out at sea. Only as Spring approaches does it come within reach of its breeding place, and, except when storm-blown, is never seen inland.

The sailor's name for this gentle and charming little bird is " Mother Carey's Chicken ", for it habitually follows ships for many miles, as well as voyaging on its own. " Mother Carey " is probably a corruption of *Mater cara* (Beloved Mother) from a medieval prayer sent up by mariners caught in a sudden storm or disaster at sea. The French mariner calls the Storm-Petrel " Our Lady's Bird ". Its appearance in large numbers, mariners say, warns of a storm.

The Storm-Petrel skims with many turns and twists along the surface with a bat-like, fluttering and erratic flight ; occasionally it will settle to patter along the water as if attempting to walk, a habit which earned it the name of " Little Peter ". It swims bouyantly, and floats easily like a very small duck. It cannot walk on the land, but flutters along without great difficulty on the full length of its legs. During the breeding season, it is nocturnal in habit and rarely approaches its nest until nightfall. Like other birds of this genus, its presence is indicated by the curious musty odour that issues from the nesting burrow. When either disturbed or irritated, the Storm-Petrel shoots out oil with a similar musty smell from its mouth.

In their nocturnal spring display both male and female abandon their fluttering flight and dash round in circles at a great rate.

An island in the North of Scotland was where I first made a recording of the voice of the Storm-Petrel. The nest was in a wall close to the sea. Between the lapping of the waves the bird repeatedly uttered its excited alarm note, interspersed with its very typical call note. On that occasion there was only one bird on the nest. Some years later I was recording on one of the rough islands among the Scillies. I heard a very strange noise in the neighbourhood, and soon found that under the boulders and stones, about 50 yards away, there was a colony of storm-petrels. Meanwhile, the noise of the colony changed to strange wailing and raucous cries. During this performance, some birds flew up from the rocks and swooped round my head like so many bats, but without uttering a single sound while in the air.—EDITOR.

In the south, the birds arrive at their nesting sites at the end of April or beginning of May, but in the north they come some weeks later.

Eric Hosking

STORM-PETREL. *Smallest of all sea-birds and called Mother Carey's Chicken by sailors*

They nest in colonies of varying sizes, and all activities connected with breeding are conducted by night. The one white egg is laid at the end of May or early June, in a chamber at the end of a burrow, either natural or excavated by the birds themselves, in the peaty soil ; or in a crevice in a rock, wall or boulder ; or sometimes even in a ruined building. No nesting material is used. Male and female take turns in hatching the egg for 38 days, and the chick, covered in soft, dark, greyish down, is fed by night by both parents ; sometimes it is left without food for a day or two. After about 60 days the parents abandon it and return to the sea. Some days later, the chick makes its lonely and difficult way to the sea where, once it is safely launched and swimming, it will, first of all, take a drink. The young bird will not breed until the second year after that in which it is hatched. The breeding sites will now be deserted until the urge of Spring brings the birds back again.

The Storm-Petrel feeds on plankton—floating organic life—or oil floating on the sea.

STREPTOPELIA. Genus of the family *Columbidae* of the order *Columbiformes*. Its species are distributed over Europe, Asia, and Africa. There is one breeding British species, the Turtle-Dove (*q.v.*) ; and one other species, the Eastern Turtle-Dove (*q.v.*), which has been recorded here on two occasions.

The members of this genus are *somewhat* smaller than those of the genus *Columba* (Wood-Pigeon, Stock-Dove and Rock-Dove), and also have shorter wings, longer tails, and a completely bare tarsus.

STRIGIDAE (Latin, " screech-owl "). The only family of the owl order *Strigiformes* which is on the British list. Its numerous genera, distributed over all parts of the globe, include the following nine which are on the British list : *Tyto, Otus, Bubo, Nyctea, Surnia, Athene, Strix, Asio* and *Aegolius*.

The members of this family are nocturnal birds of prey, varying considerably in size. They have a relatively large head, with large eyes directed forward and surrounded by a well-marked disc formed by the facial feathers. The ears are large, and the hearing apparatus is very highly developed ; the right and left ears are often of different shapes. The tarsus is fairly short and generally feathered, and the feet are strong, the toes having sharp, curved claws. There are four toes, and the fourth, or outer, toe is reversible (i.e. it can be turned backward or forward). The plumage is long, very soft and downy, so that the flight is noiseless. The down-covered young are born blind.

STRIX. Genus of medium-sized and large owls of the family *Strigidae* of the order *Strigiformes*. It contains more than twenty species, distributed over Europe, America, northern and western Asia, north-west Africa, parts of China, and Formosa. The only species on the British list is the Tawny Owl (*q.v.*), a common resident

STRIX. Only British member of this genus is the Tawny Owl, seen here indulging in a tug-of-war with its young, the rope—and prize for the contest—being a worm

Arthur Brook

FACILITIES FOR STUDYING BIRDS

ERIC SIMMS, M.A., M.B.O.U

This article groups under a single heading the educational bodies, societies and various organizations for those interested in bird-life—amateurs and serious students alike— and gives a brief description of each (see separate entries), together with its aims

STUDY, Facilities for. This article describes the various societies, organizations and educational bodies offering opportunities for all those interested in birds to increase their knowledge— whether they be amateurs desiring to take up an interesting hobby or serious students of ornithology.

For ease of reference, all these various bodies have been grouped here under one heading, but larger organizations, such as, for example, the British Trust for Ornithology, are also described under their own heading in this Encyclopedia.

School Societies. One of the most encouraging features of present times is the growing interest in Natural History, and this nowhere shows itself more clearly than in the great increase in school Natural History Societies. The origin of some school societies goes back to the last century. Several produce scholarly annual reports. One school alone has ringed nearly 10 per cent of all the starlings so far recovered abroad. A few years ago an *Association of School Natural History Societies* was formed by a small group of Public Schools, and it is to be hoped that even more teachers will come to realize the importance of this work, and its great instructional value.

Other Facilities for the Young. Foremost in the encouragement of young people in the intelligent study of birds has been the *Royal Society for the Protection of Birds*, which seeks to attract children to a new and worth-while interest, to the saving and protection of birds,

and to the making of accurate observations. In pursuit of these aims the R.S.P.B. has established a *Junior Bird Recorders' Club* solely for boys and girls of from 11 to 18 years of age, and a *Bird and Tree Challenge Shield Competition* open to all schools in Great Britain and Northern Ireland for children of all ages up to 15. The Club has an annual conference, courses in ringing and field-work, and carries out educationally co-operative enquiries, such as the study of the song-periods of six common birds made in 1952 and 1953. The Society controls several important reserves, and possesses a film unit and film hire service.

The *Haslemere Educational Museum* also provides facilities for children ; it holds exhibitions, runs short courses, and is regularly visited by parties of school children. Once a year the Museum combines with the R.S.P.B. for a joint meeting. In the *London Natural History Museum* is a centre for children from 7 to 15 years of age which develops powers of observation, and also a *Junior Naturalists' Club* for members aged from 11 to 15½, recruited from the centre. Members of the Club must produce some original field-work. For children from 12 to 17 who live outside London, a *Country Club* gives advice and assistance.

International Organizations. After an international conference the *International Committee for Bird Preservation* was set up in 1922. The British section of the Committee in 1936 began an investigation into the status of wild ducks and geese, and this has been its primary task since. The enquiry covers western Europe, and the Wildfowl Enquiry Committee of the British section has been given the task of correlating the information thus obtained.

In 1948 an International Wildfowl Institute was formed, and amateur bird watchers take part in the periodic counts of wildfowl. Every four years an *International Ornithological Conference* is held.

John Clegg

STUDY. *Young visitors to the Haslemere Educational Museum looking at fir-cones that have been opened and discarded by hungry crossbills*

National Organizations. In Great Britain the senior society for the advancement of the science of ornithology is the *British Ornithologists' Union*, which arranges scientific meetings and publishes authoritative articles on classification and behaviour, and the list of British birds. Members of the Union are eligible to become members of the *British Ornithologists' Club*, which holds regular dinners at which lectures and scientific communications are delivered. The *Zoological Society of London* exists for the advancement of zoology and animal physiology

Eric Hosking

STUDY. *Havergate, the famous breeding ground of avocets, is now managed by tne Nature Conservancy and Royal Society for the Protection of Birds*

and, apart from its wide collection of birds, holds scientific meetings, has a large library, and publishes material on birds.

The *Nature Conservancy*, established in 1949 under Royal Charter, is concerned with the whole of Great Britain. Its main tasks are to provide scientific advice on the conservation and control of the natural flora and fauna of Britain, to set up reserves, and to develop research. Grants are made to Universities and other bodies for research, and a number of postgraduate studentships are awarded every year. The Conservancy has two research stations.

The *British Trust for Ornithology* was formed to promote, organize, and encourage study and research, and particularly field-work, for the advancement of knowledge in all branches of the science of ornithology, and the preservation and study of bird-life generally. Its headquarters are in Oxford ; its 1953 membership was 2,250 (the lower age limit is 17). The Trust organizes extensive co-operative enquiries and also supports certain individual investigations. Research activities include ringing, migration studies, censuses and other field investigations. Work is often done in conjunction with other bodies. Available to the Trust for research purposes are sets of the B.B.C.'s bird-recordings made by Ludwig Koch and Eric Simms.

Closely linked with the British Trust is the *Edward Grey Institute*, also in Oxford, which in the early stages of its history received funds from the Trust. The Institute, which is now part of the University of Oxford, consists of professional ornithologists carrying out individual research on field ornithology. It houses the *Alexander Library*, probably the most complete library of modern bird literature ; this is available for reference to all members of the University, the Trust, the British Ornithologists' Union and the Oxford Ornithological Society. A duplicate lending library, now the property of the Trust and available to all members, is without doubt one of the most useful services that the Trust offers.

Concerned especially with the study and conservation of geese, swans and ducks is the *Wildfowl Trust*, the headquarters of which are at Slimbridge, in Gloucestershire. Opportunities exist there for seeing the unrivalled collection of waterfowl, as well as wild geese in the Winter. Anyone may apply for membership and corporate membership is open to schools, universities, youth clubs and teachers' training colleges.

The *British Museum* (*Natural History*) possesses a Bird Room (*q.v.*), open daily to allow students to examine the collections and consult books in the library. Applications for students' tickets should be addressed to the Director. Many other museums in this country have bird rooms which offer great opportunities to the student and much expert advice.

The *Council for the Promotion of Field Studies* is a State-aided organization formed to encourage educational field-work and for the study of various aspects of natural science in the field. The Council runs four field-study centres at Dale Fort, Flatford Mill, Juniper Hall and Malham Tarn, at which individual research can be carried out, as well as work on organized courses. Some courses are specially reserved for schools and for university students.

Founded in 1905, the *British Naturalists' Association* (B.E.N.A.) is an organization of field naturalists devoted to the preservation of wild life and to the extension and popularisation of the study of Nature. It holds central and local meetings, field excursions and weeks, and has recently carried out an investigation over several years into the autumn movements of several passerine birds. It aims also to develop the study of Natural History in schools and youth organizations.

The *Association for the Study of Animal Behaviour* provides co-ordinated work on all aspects of behaviour and, like the *British Ecological Society* which fosters a study of ecology in its widest sense, includes in its reports much valuable ornithological information. The *Avicultural Society* exists for the study of British and foreign birds in freedom and captivity, and serves as a centre for the exchange of data on this aspect of bird study.

The *Bird Research Station* at Glanton, in Northumberland, deals with a special type of

W. Farnsworth
STURNIDAE. *Found alike in town and country, the Starling is the best-known bird of this group*

bird study, but is nevertheless dependent for much of its vital information on a large number of amateur bird watchers. It was founded in 1930 on the basis that " the clearest insight into the habits of wild birds is gained by a combination of field-study with more controlled observations on tame birds ". In 1933 the first synchronised dawn chorus study was made in Britain, and since that time the Station has organized many dawn and dusk studies, not only in the British Isles but throughout the world. Many hundreds of watchers have taken part in this exciting recording of the passage of

song across various land masses. The Station is open to visitors in the summer, and informal courses of study are available to those staying at the Hostel.

In Scotland all aspects of ornithology are dealt with by the *Scottish Ornithologists' Club*, The Club has five branches—in Aberdeen. Edinburgh, Glasgow, Perth and St. Andrews— and each has a full and separate programme. Reports on its enquiries are published in the *Scottish Naturalist*. A special committee is concerned with the protection of rare birds.

Regional Unions. Chief among the regional unions of natural history societies in England are the *Northern Naturalists' Union* with 15 societies, the *North-Western Naturalists' Union* with more than 20, the *South-Eastern Union of Scientific Societies* with 70, and the *South-Western Naturalists' Union* with about 20.

Regional Societies. There are very many county and local ornithological societies which undertake items of research and study, and also give reports devoted wholly to birds or including bird notes. All who are interested in birds should make the acquaintance of their local society. The " Directory of Natural History Societies," issued by the Amateur Entomologists' Society, should be consulted, and there is a useful reference list of ornithological organizations in the Nineteenth Annual Report (1952) of the British Trust for Ornithology.

STURNIDAE—(Latin, " Starling "). Family of the order *Passeriformes*, containing the starlings. Its members are distributed over Europe, Africa, Asia and the Pacific Islands. The one genus on the British list, *Sturnus*, includes the common Starling (*q.v.*), of which two forms are resident in the British Isles, and the Rose-coloured Starling (*q.v.*), which is an irregular visitor to these islands.

The members of this genus have a flattish, wide and straight bill. The nostrils, which lie at the base of the upper mandible, are bare of feathers, but are protected by an operculum (*q.v.*). The wings are long and pointed, with 10 primary feathers, of which the first is much reduced. The tail is comparatively short, and straight. The tarsus is of medium length, and at the back is covered with an unbroken lamina (*q.v.*). The plumage is glossy, and the feathers of the fore-part of the body are narrow and somewhat elongated. The sexes are alike.

SUBALPINE WARBLER—Sylvia cantillans. A native of the Mediterranean region, this warbler occasionally wanders to Britain ; four in Scotland and two in Ireland have been identified, all at lighthouses or on small islands.

Its appearance is not unlike that of the Dartford Warbler, but it is a paler-looking bird with a shorter tail. A conspicuous white moustachial stripe distinguishes the male. The female is a drab brown colour. The length is 4¾ in., and the tarsus ¾ in. ; the wing span is between 6 and 7 in., and the weight a fraction of an ounce.

This warbler rather resembles a small White-throat in form, movements, habits, song, and dancing song-flight. In Italy, the song is best heard during April, May and part of June.

SUB-SONG. Soft, often continuous, song uttered by some birds, which is completely at variance from their ordinary, loud song and their call notes. It is usually a sweet warbling or twittering, audible only at very close quarters, that goes on undisturbed, and seemingly unheard, by other birds. The Editor has often heard it, for instance, early in Spring from pied wagtails and jays. Whether the sub-song serves any special purpose and, if so, what, is as yet unknown. *See also* Song.

SULA. Genus (the only one) of the family *Sulidae* of the order *Pelecaniformes*. It contains about nine species, distributed over all the temperate and tropical seas of the world, except the North Pacific. The genus contains one British species, the Gannet (*q.v.*).

SUMMER PLUMAGE. Sometimes, perhaps more correctly, called breeding, or nuptial, plumage (or dress). It is a brighter plumage than the normal winter dress, generally acquired at the spring moult (*q.v.*), but may, as with most ducks, be assumed in the Autumn.

In many brightly coloured species, which have only a single, post-nuptial moult, the heightening of colour before the breeding season is produced not by moulting, but by shedding the tips to the feathers and outer surface of the barbs (*q.v.*) and barbules (*q.v.*), to expose brighter colours beneath (e.g. Linnet, Chaffinch, Brambling, House-Sparrow and Snow-Bunting).

As some species, typically coastal birds, commence their so-called autumn moult in July or even earlier, they are not in full plumage during the most popular British summer-holiday months. *See also* Breeding Dress ; Plumage.

SUMMER SNIPE. Local name for Common Sandpiper (*q.v.*), a breeding summer visitor.

SUMMER TEAL. Alternative name for Garganey (*q.v.*), another of our summer visitors.

SURF-SCOTER—Melanitta perspicillata. This species of scoter breeds only in Arctic America, but occasionally wanders on migration to the British Isles, most of the records coming from the Orkney and Shetland Islands and Fair Isle. Other scoters are usually its companions, and, as it is very like the Common Scoter, it is not very easily picked out. Close inspection reveals that the male Surf-Scoter has a very remarkable eider-like bill, boldly coloured in red and yellow (his best identification) ; his

Ronald Thompson

SWALLOW. *Braking hard, a Swallow comes in to land by its nest, carrying food for its nestlings*

head and nape have two white patches which contrast vividly with the glossy dark plumage. No white appears on the wings of either duck or drake of the Surf species. The duck and juvenile are almost indistinguishable from those of the Velvet Scoter, but at close range a white patch similar to that on the nape of the drake can be seen. The bill of the duck is dark. The legs of both male and female are red. The length is 21 in., the body being 14½ in. ; the tarsus is 1½ in., and the wing span 1½ ft.-2 ft.

The Surf-Scoter is very like the Velvet species in habits and behaviour, but more closely resembles the Common species in flight.

The main food consists of animal matter, chiefly molluscs and suchlike.

SURNIA. Genus of medium-sized owls of the family *Strigidae* of the order *Strigiformes*. Its members are mainly distributed over northern Europe, northern Asia, and northern north America. The only species on the British list is the Hawk-Owl (*q.v.*), two forms of which have been recorded in this country.

SWALLOW—Hirundo rustica. The Swallow is even more welcome as the harbinger of Summer than the vocal Cuckoo. It is also a much more attractive, graceful and friendly visitor, haunting homesteads in open country, especially if near water, within sight and sound of the countryman. It is not often seen in big towns and cities. The first batch of swallows arrives in the south about the middle of March, but it is well into April before they reach the north, and those making for Scotland do not arrive until May. Abroad, the Swallow is found throughout Europe, Asia, Africa and America.

The Swallow can be recognized from other aerial birds with long wings and forked tails—

Ronald Thompson

SWALLOW. Hungry offspring opening their bills as far as is possible, in their eagerness to be the first to be fed by one of their hard-working parents

house-martins and swifts—by its glossy blue-black upper parts and breast band, its chestnut throat and forehead, and the long outer feathers of its forked tail, which is patterned in white. Its underparts are whitish, tinged with pink. Its thin bill and legs are black. The sexes are alike, though the female is rather duller ; the juvenile is also duller, with shorter " streamers ". The Swallow's length is 7 in.-7½ in. according to the length of the elongated tail feathers ; the tarsus is ½ in. ; the wing span is about 11 in. and the weight is 1 oz.

Swallows are gregarious, especially when feeding, and keep company with martins and swifts. They roost together in hundreds in reed and osier beds, also in small parties in trees. Even after the young are fledged, they return for a time to roost in the nest.

The Swallow's song is a pleasant and constant twitter, occasionally intermingled with a short trill lasting for 3-5 sec. The bird usually sings on the wing, but will also do so on a perch. The song, which has little carrying power, is often heard before dawn. Its twitter is heard during the whole of its sojourn here, but is at its best from the end of April until June.

> During my life-long observation of numerous swallows in different parts of Europe, I have noticed the interesting fact that when, during the early morning hours, a number of swallows have their typical gossiping conversation on a telegraph wire, they do not utter their throaty trill. But I have followed swallows after 10 a.m., and at close quarters have heard their trill repeatedly.—EDITOR.

Constantly on the wing, the Swallow has an elegant and easy flight, sweeping first in one direction, then in another, always with its characteristic grace of movement. On the ground, where it seldom settles except to collect

mud for its nest, the Swallow has a clumsy and awkward waddle ; but it is quite at home perching on buildings, telegraph wires and so on, though less comfortable on trees.

The gathering of swallows on telegraph wires in preparation for their long journey south is a familiar phenomenon, and is most noticeable in September. The flocks soar and glide at varying heights—sometimes completely disappearing from sight. The speed on migration is put at about 100 m.p.h., but this, of course, depends on wind and weather. Against a gale the Swallow flies low, just skimming the surface of the sea.

The beams and rafters of outhouses, stables, and so on, are favourite nesting sites of swallows, but many choose a chimney stack, hence their local name of " Chimney-Swallow ". The saucer-shaped nest is cleverly put together with straw and feathers, both birds taking a share in the work. The eggs, usually from four to six, are white, speckled reddish-brown. Two broods—sometimes three—are reared in a season, which extends from May to September ; what happens to the late broods as their parents wing their way south is not known. For a fortnight the hen incubates practically alone, but the chicks are fed and tended by both parents for three weeks.

Insects taken on the wing, from the surface of water, and from plants, walls, buildings, and suchlike, form the food of the Swallow.

SWAN. Group of birds constituting a distinct genus of the Duck (*q.v.*), family *Anatidae*, of which they are the largest members. Their general appearance is too well-known to need a detailed description. The bill is about as long as the head, of equal length throughout, and more high than wide at the base, with a soft cere (*q.v.*), and the nostrils placed about the middle. The neck is longer than the body. The legs are short and placed far back on the body ; the front toes are fully webbed, and the hind toe is without a membrane.

There are three species on the British list. The Mute Swan (*q.v.*), which is a common resident about 5 ft. long and weighing about 30 lb. Adults of both sexes are pure white, with a reddish bill ; the young (cygnets) have a dark, bluish-grey plumage and lead-coloured bill. The bill is surmounted by a black knob, and has a black nail at the tip.

The Whooper-Swan, sometimes called the Whistling Swan or Elk Swan, is about the same size as the Mute Swan but is less heavily built and has a black, and more slender bill (without knob), with the base and lower border of the upper mandible yellow. The young are darker than those of the Mute Swan, and the back of the neck is greyish. It is chiefly a winter visitor to Scotland, particularly the Outer Hebrides, and northern England. In severe Winters it may be found farther south.

Bewick's Swan is about one-third smaller than the Whooper-Swan, compared with which it has similar bill colours, but with less prominent yellow, a relatively shorter neck, and it floats more buoyantly in the water. It is another native of Europe which does not breed in Britain, but is a fairly frequent winter visitor to England, Wales and Ireland, less often to Scotland and rarely to the Outer Hebrides, Orkneys and Shetlands.

SWANNERY. Term describing a sanctuary where, regularly, wild swans arrive and stay during the breeding season and beyond, and where special, expert care is taken of them. Although wild swans occasionally settle elsewhere, the only Swannery in the British Isles is at Abbotsbury (*q.v.*) in Dorset.

SWAN-UPPING. Every year at mid-July one of the most ancient and picturesque of the Thames pageants takes place, a custom which has been going on for 500 years. This is the marking, or " upping ", of the cygnets between London Bridge and Henley. At one time this annual observance was more widespread, but nowadays it is honoured only on the river Thames, the Wensum and the Yare.

Swans have always been closely associated with Royalty, and the Thames upping is arranged by the Lord Chamberlain's Office. There is a tradition that the present Thames swans are the descendants of a pair given to Richard I by Queen Beatrice of Cyprus when he visited that island 700 years ago. Swans were probably domesticated here before that date. It is believed,

from the character of the bird's feathers and down, which is 2 in. thick, that the Mute Swan must have originated in a colder climate than the Mediterranean. Possibly it was indigenous to East Anglia.

So far as is known swans have been regarded as Royal birds since Norman times, and the reigning Sovereign is still Seigneur of the Swans. The privilege of owning them and using a private swan mark was granted only by the Sovereign, and was highly valued by those subjects who enjoyed it. In the reign of Queen Elizabeth I, more than 900 corporations or private individuals had swan marks of their own ; but in the 18th century the marking of swans started to die out, and the birds began to go wild again. When marking was national, there were as many as thirty Swan Orders, which provided for the appointment of a Swan Master, fixed the " swan-upping daies ", stated what persons should " up no swans ", and referred to a Court now extinct, " the King's Majestie's Justices of Sessions of Swans ". These Swan-mootes met to settle arguments as to the ownership of cygnets.

To-day the ownership of the swans that grace the waters of the River Thames is shared between the Sovereign and two ancient City Companies, the Vintners and the Dyers. The Dyers' Company received permission to keep a game (that is, a flock) of swans as early as 1473 and the Vintners probably about the same period. The Sovereign's swans used to be marked with a diamond mark on their bills, but Queen Alexandra caused this custom to be discontinued, and they now go unmarked. Those of the Vintners' Company are distinguished by a nick made with a sharp penknife on each side

Erica

SWAN-UPPING. The Swan Master of the Dyers' Company, distinguished by the badge on his left sleeve, watches a swan being held down for marking

of the bill, and the Dyers' birds by a nick on the right side only. Where the parents belong to different owners, the young brood is divided equally between the two Companies, and any odd cygnet goes to the Sovereign.

The picturesque flotilla of the Swan Masters, usually six boats strong, sets out from a point behind the Vintners' Hall by Southwark Bridge. The honour of providing the Sovereign's Swan Keeper has long fallen to the famous Turk family of watermen. He and his assistants have two of the skiffs, one of which flies a white banner, with a red Royal monogram, surmounted by a gold crown, while a similar, though smaller, banner flies in the second. The other pair-oared skiffs carry the respective red-and-white and blue-and-white swan banners of the Vintners' and Dyers' Companies.

The Sovereign's Swan Keeper wears a blazer of royal scarlet, and his men scarlet jerseys and caps, with white slacks. The Swan Master to the Vintners wears a jacket of dark green and silver, and the Swan Master to the Dyers one of blue and gold. Their crews have white jerseys with stripes of light or dark blue, bearing the arms of the respective companies, and the words "Vintners' Royalty" or "Dyers' Royalty", in reference to the Royal privilege of keeping swans. Every man sports a swan's feather in his cap. As they move away up stream on their time-honoured excursion, the little flotilla makes a gay picture against the drab background of Thames-side.

The first day's work ends at Ditton, the second at Staines, the third at Maidenhead, and so on to Henley, where the end of their travels up-stream is reached. At Staines, if there are any "colts"—that is, young watermen newly appointed as swan-uppers—an age-old ceremony is carried out. The colt is taken ashore, bumped against the old boundary stone, frog-marched back to the river, and thrown in ! Until he has endured this ordeal he cannot claim to be a fully-fledged swan-upper ; but as the young watermen are entitled to put up a sturdy resistance, their elders do not always get things their own way. Another more formal engagement has to be carried through when the Courts, with the Swan Wardens of the two liveries, appear in motor-launches to make their annual inspection of the marking.

The first birds are usually picked up near Teddington. The first man to observe a family of swans raises the cry, "All up ! " and the skiffs are then manoeuvred to trap the brood. Separating the young "clear bills", as the un-marked cygnets are called, demands both ex-perience and much patience. It is also a formidable job, since a wild swan has been known to beat off the attacks even of an eagle

Eric Hosking

SWIFT. *The feet of this, the most aerial of our summer visitors, are adapted for clinging to walls*

by powerful buffets of its wings. The parents are on the alert immediately they sense danger to their brood, and the uppers have the not very enviable task of seizing them, pinioning their wings, and tying their legs together. From time to time some of the men take a ducking during the tussles, but such mishaps are endured in good part. The cygnets are then secured by catching them round the neck with a long pole to which a crook is attached, and, if they belong to the Companies, their bills are nicked.

Swan-upping provided the origin of that inn sign not uncommon along the Thames, "The Swan With Two Necks", referring not to some freak but to a bird marked with two nicks.

SWIFT—Apus apus. The most aerial and fastest flying of our summer visitors, the aptly named Swift announces its arrival in April by its loud screaming call as it wheels and turns in the air. It is generally distributed throughout the British Isles, except in the north-west of Scotland ; it is also a passage migrant. Abroad, the Swift breeds in Europe, in Asia and in Africa, wintering in south Africa.

The Swallow and the martins are the only birds with which the Swift is likely to be con-fused, but, except for their similar aerial habits, there is no real relationship between the species. A characteristic outline distinguishes the Swift. Its forked tail, for instance, is shorter than the Swallow's, and its long narrow wings are curved in the shape of a scythe blade—very different from those of either the swallows or martins. It is dressed wholly in dark brown, except for

SWALLOWS *frequently build nests in most odd places*

To face page 544

For text see page 541

some greenish-white on the throat. Its thin bill and short feathered legs are black. The structure of the toes of the Swift family is different from that of the Swallow ; in the former, all four point forward ; whereas in the latter, three point forward and one behind. The sexes of the Swift are alike. The length is 6½ in., and the tarsus 0·55 in. ; the wing span is 12–14 in., and the weight 1 oz.

It is difficult to give an adequate description of the Swift's amazing aerial performance. Virtually its whole life is spent in flight. The birds wheel and turn, dashing about in all directions, with rapid wing beats giving place to long glides with outstretched wings. On fine summer evenings, as the dusk deepens, numbers of swifts collect, rise to a great height, their screams echoing at their loudest, and then disappear from sight. This curious behaviour has attracted much attention. One theory is that they spend the night in the air, but according to the *Handbook of British Birds* this is improbable, since at least some birds have been seen returning to the nest.

The Editor has never witnessed this behaviour. He has spent a whole night watching about ten pairs of swifts nesting in barns, but not one bird has been seen to leave its nest.

With its short and unsuitable legs and feet, the Swift rarely if ever settles on the ground ; but, despite assertions to the contrary, it can rise quite easily from a level surface. Owing to the position of the toes it cannot perch on trees, but instead clings to the walls of houses and buildings. Swifts leave their summer quarters at the end of July or beginning of August for their long journey southwards ; by the end of August they have all gone.

The ordinary voice of the Swift is its familiar loud scream, but a different version, a higher-pitched screaming squeal, is uttered as it joins in the communal flight round the breeding site. The Swift is usually silent on migration. Its call is heard best from May to July.

Swifts nest in colonies under the eaves of houses and other buildings, in thatched roofs, and so on, but sometimes in crevices in cliffs, in the old nests of house-martins, and in nesting boxes. In Europe they make use of the old holes of woodpeckers. The cup-shaped nest is built of straw, feathers and other bits of material picked up in the air and glued together with saliva. At the end of May or in early June, three white eggs—sometimes only two—are laid. Both birds share the hatching for 18 or 19 days and the nestlings are fed by both parents for six weeks. One brood is reared.

Insects, always caught on the wing or, if near water, by the bird skimming over the surface, form the entire food of the Swift.

SYLVIA. Genus of the family *Sylviidae* of the order *Passeriformes*. It contains many species, mainly distributed over Europe, northern and western Asia, northern parts of Africa, and, outside the breeding season, tropical Africa and southern Asia. The following species belonging to this genus are on the British list : Blackcap, Garden-Warbler, Whitethroat, Lesser Whitethroat, Dartford Warbler, Barred Warbler, Orphean Warbler, Rüppell's Warbler, Sardinian Warbler, and Subalpine Warbler. These are separately described under their own headings.

SYLVIIDAE. Family of the order *Passeriformes*, containing the warblers. Its many genera are distributed over most parts of the eastern hemisphere ; the following eight are on the British list : *Cettia, Locustella, Lusciniola, Acrocephalus, Hippolais, Sylvia, Agrobates*, and *Phylloscopus*.

SYRINX. Voice, or song, organ of birds, serving a similar purpose to the larynx in Man, but differing in structure and position in the windpipe, or trachea. Birds have a larynx, but it has no vocal chords and is silent.

The syrinx is usually placed where the windpipe sub-divides into two branches (*bronchi*) to convey air to the lungs ; less commonly it

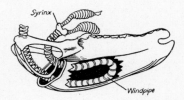

SYRINX. Fig. 1 : If the windpipe is very long, it may be stored in a special cavity of the breast bone

is in the lower part of the windpipe alone, or in the bronchi. It is really a modification of the bottom end of the windpipe and/or the bronchial tubes.

In the most usual form (*see* Fig. 2) the lower rings of the windpipe coalesce to form what is commonly regarded as a resonating chamber (or tympanum) to which the neighbouring bronchial rings are movably attached. It has a bony framework, surprisingly strong, within which are one or more tensely stretched membranes, over which air passes as it is expelled, causing them to vibrate and thus produce a variety of sounds.

The membranes are controlled by muscles which can alter their tension and also move the windpipe. The typical syrinx then resembles a set of bagpipes with the pipes cut off short.

There are, however, many departures from the typical form. In the cassowaries the wind-pipe is not apparently modified in any way to form a syrinx, yet these birds are capable of producing a great variety of sounds, and, when excited, they give vent to a great roar. Whereas, with the closely related emus, the tracheal rings fail to unite in the syrinx, leaving a long narrow aperture through which the lining membrane of the tube emerges to form a large sac which can be inflated at will, and which probably acts as a resonator to assist in the production of its characteristic booming note.

Some interesting examples are provided by the Duck family. The syrinx of the Mallard drake is a large, bony, thin-walled chamber at the bottom of the windpipe, immediately over one of the bronchial tubes—protruding only on the left side. If this is a resonating chamber, as is commonly supposed, it seems strange that the Mallard drake utters only a low note, but the call of the female, who has no such chamber, is quite loud.

All males of fresh-water, surface-swimming ducks have a similar chamber, differing from one another only in size. In diving ducks the chamber is much larger, and instead of being spherical, is shaped like a disc, consisting of a ring of bone, wider at the top than at the

SYRINX. Fig. 2: The various arrangements among different duck

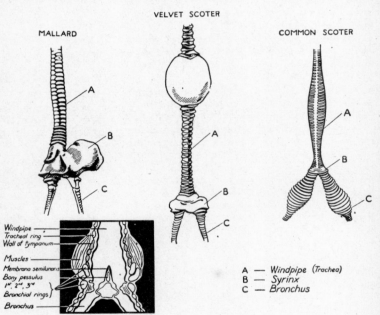

MALLARD

VELVET SCOTER

COMMON SCOTER

A — Windpipe (Trachea)
B — Syrinx
C — Bronchus

Windpipe
Tracheal ring
Wall of tympanum
Muscles
Membrana semilunaris
Bony pessulus
1st, 2nd, 3rd Bronchial rings
Bronchus

bottom, across which a thin membrane is stretched tautly. This structure reaches its maximum size in the mergansers, where it is supplemented by a smaller tympanum on the right side and bulbous swellings in the centre of the windpipe. The Velvet Scoter provides a more remarkable example. In this bird the bulb at the end of the trachea is wanting, but there is a spherical swelling in the windpipe (composed of tracheal rings fused together) about a third of the way up, and below the larynx is a second, and smaller, chamber. In the Common Scoter the upward ends of the two bronchi are enlarged to form the syrinx.

It is one of the many mysteries of Nature that there appears to be no relationship between the degree of complexity of a bird's syrinx and

the beauty of its song. Moreover, nobody has yet been able to explain why it is that species with apparently similar vocal structures produce totally different sounds. A very striking example of this is afforded by the Carrion-Crow and the Nightingale, whose syrinxes are identical.

The structure of the windpipe also frequently plays a part in the production of sound and in some species the windpipes are extra-ordinarily long, and in some species they are enormous, and have to be stowed away in coils (Fig. 2). This is done in one of three ways : between the breast muscles and the skin (Semi-palmated Goose, some passerines and some sandpipers) ; in a cavity in the keel of the breast bone (Whooper-, Trumpeter- and Berwick's swans, and some cranes) ; or beneath the lungs. Usually, only the male has an elongated windpipe, sometimes both sexes, and rarely the female alone. It is assumed that the object of the extra long windpipe is to increase the volume of sound, but some species so affected are practically silent. In one species of Spoonbill, and in the Tantalus Stork, the windpipe is coiled in a figure-of-eight loop, and in the storks the bronchi are also of great length—in the Black Stork taking an S-shaped twist before entering the lungs.

SYRRHAPTES. Genus of the family *Pteroclidae* of the order *Columbiformes*. It contains only two species, which are mainly distributed over central Asia.

One species, however, frequently, though irregularly, visits south-east Europe, and some-times penetrates to parts of western Europe also.

TIT (MICE)

TADORNA. Genus of ducks of the family *Anatidae* of the order *Anseriformes*. It contains only one species—the Sheld-Duck (*q.v.*)—which mainly occurs in Europe and northern and western Asia, and is a fairly common resident in the British Isles.

TAIL. Compared with the long, lizard-like tail of the fossil bird Archaeopteryx, tails of existing birds are very short. In flying birds about four of the terminal vertebrae are fused together to form the ploughshare bone, or "pygostyle", which carries the tail-feathers.

The long quill-feathers of the tail are called "rectrices", from their steering function. They grow in pairs, of which most birds have six, and, like the large wing-feathers, they are covered above and below by rows of smaller feathers called upper- and under-coverts.

The tail-feathers vary considerably in size, chiefly according to the bird's flight habits. In the Wren, which spends much of its time in thick undergrowth near the ground, they are conveniently small. In the Swallow, however, the outer feathers are very elongated, a characteristic accounted for by the bird's aerial habits.

Although the main function of the tail is to act as a rudder, it is also used for braking purposes, especially when landing. In a few birds the tail performs certain additional functions, e.g. the stiff spiny tail-feathers of the woodpeckers and tree-creepers are used as a support when these birds are clinging to a tree-trunk.

The shape and size of the tail are often useful aids to the identification (*q.v.*) of a species. *See* illustration in page 304. *See also* Feather.

John Markham

TARROCK. The young of the Kittiwake— the prettiest of gulls—is called by this name

TAIL-COVERTS. Series of small feathers covering the bases of the quills of the tail feathers to form an unbroken and unresisting surface, and divided into upper and under tail-coverts, according to whether they are above or below the main tail feathers. *See plate f.p.* 1.

TARROCK. Local name for young Kittiwake (*q.v.*), the most pelagic of gulls.

TARSIGER. Genus of the family *Turdidae* of the order *Passeriformes*. Its members are mainly distributed over Asia and eastern Europe, but some occasionally find their way to western Europe. The only species on the British list, the Red-flanked Bluetail, has been recorded in the British Isles only twice.

TARSUS. Popularly, and as used in most ornithological works, including this Encyclopedia, the "leg" or "shank" of a bird. Strictly anatomically, however, it is the part of the foot from the *base* of the toes to *near the top* of the ankle (tarsus being a shortened form for *metatarsus*, which itself is an abbreviation of *tarso-metatarsus*).

It will thus be seen from the diagram that tarsus is commonly taken to be that part of the leg which lies between what to the uninitiated, appears to be the bird's "ankle" and its "knee", i.e. the visible part which in many species is covered with scales. It is the length of this part that is quoted against tarsus under the various entries on birds.

A bird's feet and legs cannot be judged by human standards, for what appears to be its thigh is really its shin, i.e. the leg *below* the true knee. This, together with the toes, is in some species the only part of the leg appearing externally. The true thigh-bone, connected at one end to the hip girdle, is usually fairly short and runs in a slightly forward direction to the knee proper. The knee itself is often held close to the body — approximately under the centre of gravity. Running downwards and slightly backwards from the knee is the tibia or true shin bone (apparent thigh). In adult birds the tibia fuses at its lower end (at what appears to be the knee, but is, in fact, the ankle) with a single bone derived from the fusing together of originally separate bones forming part of the ankle and three of the toes.

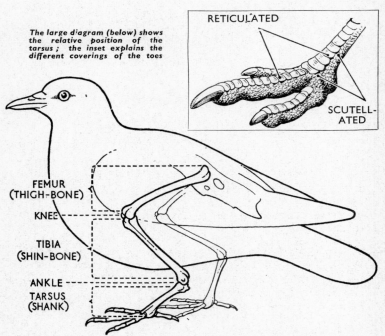

The large diagram (below) shows the relative position of the tarsus ; the inset explains the different coverings of the toes

RETICULATED

SCUTELLATED

FEMUR (THIGH-BONE)

KNEE

TIBIA (SHIN-BONE)

ANKLE
TARSUS (SHANK)

TARSUS. Usually, this is synonymous with the "visible" leg ; scientifically, it is the part from the base of the toes to near the top of the ankle

The net effect is that a bird literally walks on "tiptoe", thus enabling it to spring more easily into the air and to keep its balance on the most improbable of supports, and reducing the risk of sprain on landing and suchlike.

TASTE. All the available evidence suggests that the sense of taste is not strong in birds, although it may be more acute in some species than in others. Birds are much given to bolting their food, and it has been observed that repellent substances are often readily swallowed, but, on the other hand, herring-gulls will refuse any strongly salted fish.

The bird's tongue is a rather horny and insensitive structure. It is true that it appears to be rich in sensory organs of some sort, but they often lie so deep beneath the horny sheath, that they are unlikely to perform any taste function, though they may well act as organs of touch. Moreover, these same sensory organs are widely distributed over other parts of the body, as well as in the region of the bill. Probably the nerve terminations of the tongue discharge the function of taste to a very limited extent, as may also the soft patch of skin (the "cere") situated at the base of the bill in many birds. But flavours are detected by the sense of smell, and although in birds this sense is usually very weak, they would probably savour their food slightly while in the mouth if it were not for the fact that they usually bolt it.

TATTLER, WANDERING. *See* Wandering Tattler.

TAWNY OWL—Strix aluco. The Tawny Owl, also called the Brown Owl and Wood-Owl —which names are equally descriptive—is, in contrast to the Barn-Owl, a bird of the woodlands ; but it is also sometimes found in other types of country, and even in the suburbs of towns. A British resident, and confined to this country, it is well distributed in the south, but scarcer in the north of Scotland. It is almost unknown in Orkney, Shetland and Ireland.

The Tawny is one of the most strictly nocturnal owls. During the day it dozes the time away in some well-concealed nook. Its plumage is very variable, but the dominant colouring is a rich chestnut brown, mingled with many shades of grey, buff and brown. It has a round stout body, a head which seems almost too big for its size, and broad round wings, barred with dark and light brown. Its legs are feathered. The hen is similar but larger—a common characteristic of owls. Some tawny owls, especially the birds breeding in the north and on the Continent, are greyer than normal. The length is about 15 in., and the tarsus 2 in. ; the wing span is about 2 ft., and the weight about 1 lb. 6 oz.

The Tawny Owl has the typical slow, silent, flapping flight of its family. If it should appear during the day it will be immediately mobbed by a host of small birds. It is a formidable bird in defence of its young, and instances are recorded of a human intruder being attacked with its strong talons.

Although few may have actually seen the Tawny Owl at close quarters, most people will have heard its very characteristic voice. This is an eerie and not unmusical sound, uttered by night, nearly always from some tree or building and rarely on the wing. Often, especially in the Spring, two birds will be heard calling, one answering the other. The call is at its best from April to June, but is often heard both earlier and later in the year. A Sussex proverb runs : " When owls whoop much at night, expect a fair tomorrow."

No material is used for the nest, for which a hole in an old tree or the deserted nest of some other bird, such as a Rook, Magpie or hawk, is chosen ; occasionally an old rabbit hole or even a sheltered nook on the ground is used and a large nesting box was once occupied. Two to four (or more) white eggs are laid at intervals of a day or two in late March or early April, and the hatching, by the hen alone, begins as soon as the first egg is laid. It is about three weeks before the young birds appear. They are fed for another three weeks by both parents, the male bringing the food. One brood is reared in a season.

The Tawny Owl's food consists principally of small animals of many kinds, but it also unfortunately takes various small birds, and has even been known to seize fowls, pheasants and so on.

J. Marchant

TAWNY OWL. *The woodland owl spends the day dozing in a hidden nook and hunts only by night*

TAWNY PIPIT—Anthus campestris. Records show that the Tawny Pipit has bred at least once in the county of Sussex, but it is at best a very irregular autumn migrant, usually on the Kent-Sussex coast. It breeds throughout Europe— in France, Holland, Belgium and other countries —and also in temperate Asia and Africa.

The Tawny is a large, slim pipit, dressed in pale sandy-brown, much less streaked than is usual among pipits. Its long legs and tail, as well as many of its movements, resemble those of a wagtail rather than of a pipit. Above its eye is a very distinct light eye stripe. The sexes are alike. The juvenile is more boldly marked. The length is 6½ in., and the tarsus 1·1 in. ; the wing span is from 7 in. to 8 in., and the weight about 1½ oz.

The Tawny is speedy on the ground ; when suspicious, it moves its tail up and down in the wagtail manner, and it has the wagtail's undulating and dipping flight. It perches on rocks and walls, but rarely on trees.

The song is louder than other pipits', and has a clear and metallic timbre. It is mainly uttered during the fluttering song-flight, occasionally at a considerable height.

TEAL — Anas crecca. The smallest European duck, the Teal, as a British resident, breeds to a varying degree in many parts of England, Wales and Ireland, especially in the north ; in Scotland it is abundant in most counties. It is also a passage migrant and a plentiful winter visitor. Abroad, it is widespread throughout Europe, temperate Asia, north America, Greenland and Spitzbergen.

The drake is a very beautiful little bird. His most striking feature is his rich chestnut head, decorated with a lustrous green band bordered in buff and curving back from, and including, the eye to his nape. His back and flanks are finely vermiculated, and above his black and green speculum is a broad and conspicuous white line. His breast is speckled with small dark spots ; patches of buff contrast vividly with the dark under-tail coverts. The duck, the drake in his eclipse, and the juvenile are brown with darker streaks. The bill and legs are grey. The total length is 14 in., the body being 10 in. ; the tarsus is 1 in., the wing span between 16 in. and 18 in., and the weight 12 oz.

Teal show a decided preference for quiet fresh waters, but in the Winter large numbers resort to tidal estuaries and mudflats. They are very gregarious, and are usually in company with other surface-feeding ducks, especially the Mallard. The Teal's flight is swift and low, outstripping that of the Mallard. A flock flies in compact formation and performs aerial manoeuvres, turning and twisting much

Eric Hosking

TEAL. Smallest of European ducks, the male can be distinguished by his chestnut and green head

in the manner of the waders. When flushed, a "spring" of Teal shoots upwards vertically with amazing speed and agility.

On the ground, the bird has an awkward waddle. Adult Teal do not, as a rule, dive unless wounded or alarmed. The young, however, will disappear at once under the water if frightened ; on land, they hide among the long grass and are very difficult to see.

In common with the Mallard, the Teal, unless disturbed, spends most of the day resting in its sheltered nook ; at evening it becomes active and resorts to its feeding places. Occasionally it will be seen feeding by day.

In Winter the flocks carry on a chuckling conversation, and in the breeding season a clear musical whistling call is constantly heard. The duck has a harsh quack.

The Teal breeds among the vegetation of heaths, woods and marshes and may even nest some distance from water. The nest, a sheltered hollow among the heather, gorse, etc., is prepared by the duck and lined with dead leaves, bracken and down. Eight to ten eggs are usual (more have been recorded) they are pale greenish-buff in colour and are laid in April and May. The duck hatches them for a period of three weeks. In contrast to the majority of ducks, the drake takes some interest in the rearing of ducklings. They are soon independent, and fly in about three weeks. One brood is reared in a season.

Teal feed chiefly on vegetable matter, but some animal food is also taken.

The Green-winged Teal (*Anas crecca carolinensis*), the American species, is very similar in size and appearance to the European Teal. The chief difference in the plumage of the drake is a narrow white stripe at the side of the breast in front of the wing. This duck has wandered only seven times to the British Isles.

TEMMINCK'S GRASSHOPPER-WARBLER — Locustella lanceolata. This bird of north Russia and Siberia has visited the British Isles some six times. The ordinary observer might mistake it for the Grasshopper-Warbler, one of our summer residents, but it is, in fact, smaller and more boldly streaked on the upper parts, breasts and flanks. The length is $4\frac{1}{2}$ in., the tarsus 0.7 in., and the wing span is approximately 6 in.

As far as is known, the behaviour and habits of this warbler closely resemble those of the Grasshopper-Warbler. Its song is described, by those who have heard it in its home, as having the same trilling note. Insects are presumed to be its staple food.

TEMMINCK'S STINT — Calidris temminckii. One of the least frequent of British passage migrants and winter visitors, Temminck's Stint has twice, within comparatively recent years, attempted to nest—although unsuccessfully—in the Scottish Highlands. Its close relative, the Little Stint, a much more frequent visitor, has on the other hand never attempted to nest in this country. Abroad, Temminck's Stint is found in Scandinavia, Russia and Siberia.

One of the smallest of the waders, it resembles a minor edition of the Dunlin. At all seasons its plumage is greyer than that of the Little Stint; in Summer there is a less rufous tinge, and in Winter, although it has the same white underparts, grey takes the place of the pure white seen on the breast of the Little Stint. The outer tail feathers of Temminck's Stint are white. Its bill is very dark brown, and its legs are of variable shades of green or yellow. The sexes are alike. The length is $5\frac{1}{2}$ in., and the tarsus 0.6 in. ; the wing span is from 7 in. to 8 in., and the weight a fraction of an ounce.

Delivered during its fairy-like and charming display flight, its song is a musical, high-pitched, rather haunting trill, lasting for one or two minutes. When it is flushed on the breeding ground, its call note has a high-pitched twittering sound; there are also various other notes. Insects form the main food.

TENGMALM'S OWL — Aegolius funereus. A denizen of the pine forests of northern and the mountains of central Europe, this species of owl wanders occasionally to the British Isles, usually in Winter. The majority of the records are for the eastern counties of England, but there are a few for Scotland. A little larger than the Little Owl, Tengmalm's Owl is not unlike it in appearance, except that the brown in its mantle is of a warmer tone and its mottled underparts are almost pure white. Its head is round and large, and its facial disk more clearly defined than in the Little Owl. It has no ear tufts. Its legs and feet are decorated with long white feathers extending right to the toes. The length is 10 in. and the tarsus 0·95 in. ; the wing span is between 12 in. and 14 in., and the weight approximately 9 oz.

In Switzerland this owl is wholly nocturnal in habit, roosting by day in a well-concealed nook in a tree. Its song is a single liquid and musical hoot. It feeds on small mammals.

TEREK SANDPIPER — Xenus cinerea. A native of north Russia and Siberia, this species of sandpiper has paid seven visits to England — all to Kent and Sussex, and all in the month of May. On the ground it is not unlike a small edition of the Redshank, but its long, greenish-black and upturned bill and its yellow legs are distinctive. Its general coloration is grey, dark on the mantle with some lighter streaks on the head. The underparts are white, with some mottling on the breast and flanks. The sexes are alike. The length is 9 in., and the tarsus 1 in. ; the wing span 11 in.–12 in.

In carriage and behaviour the Terek shows some similarity to the Common Sandpiper, and it has the same habit of moving its body up and down. Tame and easily approached, it associates little with other waders.

Its ordinary call is a characteristic clear and musical trill, but during the breeding season there are many variations of the theme.

TERN. Name applied to a group of birds belonging to the same family (*Laridae*) as the gulls, to whom they are closely related. Terns are, however, smaller, and more slender in build than gulls, narrower of wing and more graceful in flight. Moreover, the bills, which are as long, or longer, than the head, taper to a sharp point, and are usually held downwards. The wings are also long and pointed, and the longish tail is usually forked. Most of the terns are whitish and possess black caps.

The majority of terns are coastal birds, seldom seen either far inland or, alternatively, out of sight of land—except when migrating. But a few species, known as marsh-terns, are normally to be found inhabiting freshwater marshes and inland lakes, and a few others are largely pelagic (oceanic birds), outside the breeding season.

Terns seldom alight on water, but are to be seen on rocks, posts, partly submerged bushes, and on the shore itself. Unlike some of their close relatives, the gulls, they never scavenge or follow ships, but obtain their food from the surface of the water.

Terns are very sociable birds, and usually fly and feed together in scattered groups. During the breeding season they form densely packed colonies, or terneries, in which it is not unusual to find several species nesting together.

Four genera appear on the British list (*Chlidonias, Gelochelidon, Hydroprogne,* and *Sterna*), and the following twelve species, all of which are fully described under their own headings : Black Tern; White-winged Black Tern; Whiskered Tern; Gull-billed Tern; Caspian Tern; Common Tern*; Arctic Tern*; Roseate Tern*; Sooty Tern; Bridled Tern; Little Tern*; Sandwich Tern*. Those starred are breeding visitors from April to October; some are also passage migrants. The rest are stragglers, with the exception of the Black Tern, which used to breed here, but, apart from a few pairs, has not done so since 1885, and is now only a passage migrant.

TERNERY. A breeding colony of terns. The Sandwich Tern breeds in crowded colonies of varying size on sandy or shingle beaches, sand-dunes and low-lying rocky or sandy islands, sometimes on shores of inland waters— mostly within the areas indicated in black in the map below ; to a lesser extent in the stippled areas.

The Common Tern has the same range of sites as the Sandwich, but it may nest further from the sea, often in very large colonies. The Arctic Tern also favours similar nesting sites, but is more maritime, and found more frequently on rocky off-shore islets (*see* map). The Roseate Tern is exclusively maritime, but nests socially with common or arctic terns on islands, occasionally on beaches (*see* map).

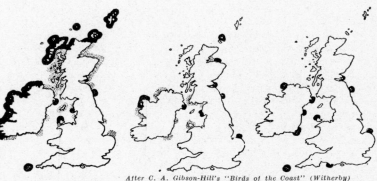

After C. A. Gibson-Hill's "Birds of the Coast" (Witherby)

TERNERY. From left to right, these maps show the breeding areas in the British Isles of the Arctic, Sandwich and the Roseate Tern respectively

TERRITORY-HOLDING AMONG BIRDS

DAVID LACK, M.A., Sc.D., F.R.S.

Many theories have attempted to account for this fact, known since pre-Christian times, that certain birds select and lay claim to a definite territory ; but the true reasons are only beginning to emerge now, after many years of patient field-work

TERRITORY. The meaning of territory has provoked more argument than almost any other problem connected with the life of birds. The idea that each pair of birds requires and defends its own feeding area goes back at least to Aristotle (in his *History of Animals*, 4th century B.C.) ; and Aristotle was presumably quoting from what was believed by others. His observations referred to eagles and ravens, and the solitary nature of one other bird, the Robin, was also recorded in classical times, by Zenodotus in the 3rd century B.C. Several of the early European naturalists made passing references to territory, and in the 18th century Gilbert White ascribed the spacing out of birds in Spring to rivalry among the males. But the territory theory as it is understood today is really due to one man, H. Eliot Howard, whose detailed observations on warblers and buntings were set out at length in *The British Warblers* (1907–14), and in shorter form, with various other species added, in *Territory in Bird Life* (1920). At this period, most of the research on birds was concerned with museum skins, and Howard's views did not really catch the imagination of ornithologists until the revival of interest in field-work in the late 'twenties, due particularly to a stimulating and provocative re-statement of them by E. M. Nicholson in *How Birds Live* (1927).

What Eliot Howard observed, and it has since been fully confirmed by others, is that in Spring, when the cock warblers return from the south, each settles in a limited area where it sings vigorously, and from which it drives out other cocks of its own species. Here, some days later, a hen bird arrives and forms a pair with it, and here the pair later raise their brood. This limited area is the territory. Warblers, of course, are summer visitors, but the story is essentially the same in resident birds. Thus in the early Spring the cock

Eric Hosking

TERRITORY. Yellow Hammer in aggressive display to frighten off a possible intruder

Yellow Hammer or Reed-Bunting leaves the flock to take up an isolated station in a hedgerow or on a marsh, where it sings. It does this at first only in the early morning, after which it returns to the flock to feed for the rest of the day. But gradually, as the weather improves, it spends longer in its territory, until finally it spends most of the day there. By this time the hen birds are also leaving the flocks, and they form pairs with the cocks in their territories and later, as among warblers, the pair nest in their territory.

The territory, then, is first claimed by the cock bird, the pair later breed there, and the territory is abandoned in Autumn. This is the usual pattern, but a few song-birds, such as the Robin in England and the Mocking-bird in America, also claim territories in the Autumn. This autumn territory is not used for breeding and it is held by one bird only, which may be a member of either sex.

Eliot Howard showed that the fighting so often seen between cock birds in Spring is not primarily for mates, as formerly supposed, but for ownership of territory. Each cock normally fights only in its own territory, except when one bird tries to dispossess another, as sometimes happens. But a casual intruder or trespasser puts up no resistance and flees before the territory-holding aggressor.

Fighting may be direct (or actual) but much more often a threatening display, with raised feathers and loud song, is enough to drive off an intruder. Eliot Howard also showed that song, which was formerly supposed to be used chiefly in courtship, is used primarily to announce ownership of a territory. The cock bird normally sings only in its own territory, and the easiest way to map the territories of birds is to mark where each is singing. The song announces occupation of the territory both to rival cocks and to hens in search of mates ; and the song is usually quieter once the bird has found a mate.

The description so far applies to song-birds, but many other kinds of birds are territorial. Lapwings, ringed plovers and other wading birds defend an area round the nest from which others of their kind are excluded. So, often at least, do great crested grebes. So, it is claimed, do various birds of prey, but these birds have not been studied in sufficient detail for discussion here. A form of territory is even found in some colonial and social species. For instance the male Heron takes up an isolated position on a branch in the heronry, it defends this station from neighbouring birds, it gives a peculiar call there which might be called its song, and it later attracts a female there to nest with it. Its territory is, of course, extremely small, and there is no suggestion of a group territory for the whole colony. Again, male blackcocks display in groups on communal display grounds termed " leks ", and here each cock has its own small bit of ground from which it drives out other cocks and to which it tries to attract passing females to mate with it. After mating, however, the hen goes off to nest by herself, so the territory is not used for nesting.

These observations are enough to show that territory takes different forms in different species. Eliot Howard claimed two main functions for territory, the first that it assists in pair-formation, the second that it ensures an adequate supply of food for the young. A method by which each cock stations itself in isolation and sings loudly, particularly when unmated, while the hens search for the cocks, seems likely to be efficient in bringing cocks and hens together into pairs, and this function of territory has never been questioned. (The birds which do not have territories usually form pairs when in flocks, each cock then having to keep in constant attendance on its selected hen ; this method has been little studied.)

It is the other function, or supposed function, of territory which has given rise to all the argument. It is an attractive idea to suppose that each pair of birds defends a definite area of such a size that it has enough food there for its young. It was a view that was certainly worth putting forward, but before it can be proven, we have to know whether birds in fact defend areas of fixed size, and whether this size corresponds with the correct amount of food, and these questions cannot yet be answered with certainty—which is why there has been so much dispute.

First, however, it should be made clear that only a few of the territorial species find their food in their own territories. Such birds as the Heron or Blackcock, with their extremely small territories, obviously feed outside them, but even birds such as plovers, grebes or harriers, which defend a fairly large area round the nest, find most of their food outside this area, and neighbouring birds often hunt over common ground. The same applies even to the Reed-Warbler and Yellow Hammer, two of the species on which Eliot Howard's original theories were based. In such birds, the size of the territory bears no fixed relation to the size of the available feeding grounds, so that any possible connection between territory and food seems ruled out. There are, however a few species which obtain

TERRITORY. *Although herons normally nest in colonies (heronries), each male will claim a special area as his own, to which he will try and attract a female*

W. Farnsworth

most, if not all, their food in their own territories, including the Robin, tits and various owls, and it is to these, if any, species that Howard's concept of the food-territory applies. The latter is at most but a secondary value of territory, evolved in only a few species.

To prove Howard's view, it is necessary to know, among other things, the amount of food needed by a bird to raise its young, the amount of this type of food that is present in the territory, and the ease or difficulty that the bird has in finding what is present. Extremely few measurements have been made of the first two points, and these suggest that much more food is present than the bird needs, but the essential point is what proportion of the food present can be found by the bird, and this has never been measured.

Fischer-Wahrenholz

THICK-BILLED NUTCRACKER. *This rare visitor from central Europe is a member of the Crow family. It has been seen here only six times*

There is also a more fundamental question that has not been answered. It is not yet known whether a territorial bird defends an area of fixed size, in other words whether territorial behaviour sets an upper limit to the number of breeding pairs, or whether it merely spaces out the number of pairs that are present, the density of which has been determined by other factors. It may seem surprising that a point so fundamental to the whole theory of territory has not been settled, but it is one which is very hard to settle by means of field observations.

In all the territorial species that have been studied, the size of individual territories has been found to vary considerably, and the largest may be five or even ten times the smallest. In addition to such individual variation, there is a strong tendency for territories to be smaller where food is more abundant. While this strongly suggests that each species does not defend a territory of fixed size, it might be considered as favouring the idea of territories having food value. On the other hand, the same situation is found in non-territorial birds. In the Heron, for instance, the nesting colonies are larger or closer together where food is more abundant, and though the individual Heron defends a small territory within the colony, there is no reason to think that territorial behaviour determines the size or spacing of the colonies. There is no " colonial territory ", so far as known.

Hence it is true to say that birds settle to breed more densely where food is more plentiful, but it is far from clear whether territorial behaviour plays any part in the matter.

Summing up, many birds of different kinds defend territories. In many species the territory probably assists in pair-formation, as it is claimed by the cock and the hen seeks him there. The idea that, in a small number of species, territory also ensures a food supply for the young is extremely interesting, but not enough is known to say whether it is true or not, or even whether it is more likely to be true or false.

TERTIARIES. Another name for wing coverts. These are small feathers that lie in several series on the top and beneath the wing, concealing the base of the primaries (*q.v.*) and forming an almost airtight surface in a region where this would otherwise be lacking, because the webs of the primaries do not extend thus far. *See also* Feather ; Wing ; *further Plate f.p.* 1.

TETRAONIDAE (Latin, " black cock "). Family of game-birds of the order *Galliformes*, containing the grouse. Its members are mainly distributed over the northern parts of the northern hemisphere. It contains three genera on the British list, *Lagopus*, *Lyrurus* and *Tetrao*.

The genus *Tetrao* contains two species, distributed over Europe and northern and western Asia ; the only species on the British list is the Capercaillie (*q.v.*).

THICK-BILLED NUTCRACKER—Nucifraga caryocatactes. This member of the Crow family is a very rare visitor to Britain. It has only been certainly identified six times, in the Autumn in the south of England. Its natural home is in the forests of central Europe and parts of Asia, but at intervals it wanders to other parts of the world in great numbers.

In appearance it has little resemblance to the crows as we know them, for its plumage is dark brown with white spots. Its wings are black with a white border, and it has a very pointed and powerful bill. It is worth while remembering that the Thick-billed Nutcracker is the only bird of this size which has white spots. Its length is about 13 in., its tarsus about 2 in., and its wing span 15 in.

THICK-KNEE. Local name for Stone-Curlew (*q.v.*), a breeding visitor.

THROSTLE. Alternative name for Song-Thrush (*q.v.*), a common resident.

THRUSH. Common name of a group of passerine birds belonging to the family *Turdidae*, and, in respect of those on the British List, with one exception, to the genus *Turdus*.

The name is derived from the Anglo-Saxon, *thrysce*, which is probably akin to the Greek *trizo*, " to twitter "—hardly flattering when used in connection with some of our most beautiful songsters. The species on the British list, all described in separate articles, are : Mistle-Thrush ; Fieldfare ; Song-Thrush ; Redwing ; Dusky Thrush ; Black-throated Thrush; Ring-Ouzel ; Blackbird ; Golden Mountain-Thrush (formerly White's Thrush) ; and the Rock-Thrush (*Monticola saxatilis*).

THRUSH-NIGHTINGALE—Luscinia luscinia. A very infrequent wanderer from its home in eastern Europe, Russia and Siberia, the Thrush-Nightingale has been recorded in Great Britain only twice : once in England and once in Scotland. It closely resembles the Nightingale in appearance, but at close range is seen to have a spotted breast and less rufous plumage. Its length is 6½ in., its tarsus 1·2 in., and its wing span about 7 in.

In habit and behaviour the Thrush-Nightingale shows little or no difference from the Nightingale, though it appears to have an even greater preference for rivers and marshland.

> Although varying in different regions, its calls and song, as the bird's name indicates, always resemble those of both the Thrush and the Nightingale. The call and alarm notes are similar to the Nightingale's. But the song has a different tune ; in it long notes similar to the Nightingale's are interspersed with the loud and typically repetitive notes of the Thrush. The incomparable crescendo of the Nightingale is missing.—EDITOR.

The Thrush-Nightingale nests on the ground in damp woodlands ; the construction of its nest and the number of its eggs are similar to the Nightingale's. One brood is reared in a season. The food consists of worms, insects and their larvae, and also of some berries.

TIBIA. Shortened form of *tibiotarsus*, that portion of a bird's anatomy which, together with the degenerate *fibula* (the second leg bone), forms what corresponds in the human leg to the part between the ankle and knee. At its lower end, the *tibia* fuses, in adult birds, with the three upper ankle bones, hence its double name —*tibiotarsus*. It is often mistaken for the thigh (*see* Tarsus). The tibial feathers are those covering the *tibia*.

TICHODROMA. Genus of the family *Sittidae* of the order *Passeriformes*. It contains only one species—the Wall-Creeper (*q.v.*).

TIT or TITMOUSE. A name given to members of several genera of passerine birds belonging to the family *Paridae*, widely distributed throughout the world. " Tit " comes from old Icelandic *titr*, meaning " something small " ; " mouse " is a corruption of *mase*, Anglo-Saxon for a " kind of bird ".

Typical tits are small sprightly birds with soft, fluffy and often gay plumage. The bill is small, short, somewhat conical, the base surrounded by hairs and the nostrils generally concealed by feathers. Tits are extremely active birds, flitting from branch to branch, running along in quest of insects, and often, clinging back-downwards to the underside of branches. Not only do they feed on insects, but also on grain and seeds.

The following tits are on the British list : Great Tit ; Blue Tit ; Coal-Tit ; Crested Tit ; Marsh-Tit ; Willow-Tit ; Long-tailed Tit ; Bearded Tit—all fully described separately.

Fischer-Wahrenholz

THRUSH. *One of the smallest thrushes to occur in Britain, the Redwing is a Continental visitor*

TITLARK. Name for Meadow-Pipit (*q.v.*).

TITTEREL. Alternative name for Whimbrel (*q.v.*), a member of the Sandpiper family.

TOE. Most birds possess four toes, never more. Some, however, have three toes, while the Ostrich has to make do with only two.

The " number ", or order, of the toes is determined by counting the number of joints ; in most cases these increase from two in the first (" big ") toe to three in the second, four in the third and five in the fourth toe. In the swifts, however, the second, third and fourth toes all have three joints, while in the nightjars and sand-grouse the fourth (outer) toe has only four joints instead of the more usual five.

The second, third and fourth toes are attached to the lower end of three fused instep bones, known as metatarsals, to the upper end of which are attached the ankle-bones, or tarsals. However, the first toe, or " hallux ", is often turned backwards to form the so-called " hind-toe ", and possesses a small separate metatarsal bone of its own. But in many birds the latter toe is undeveloped, particularly in those species which spend all or most of their time on the ground.

The number and arrangement of the toes varies according to habits and environment. The perching birds, for example, have three forward-pointing toes and a well-developed hind-toe.

The owls are able to reverse their outer toe at will, while the cuckoos, woodpeckers and parrots have a permanent arrangement of two forward-pointing and two backward-pointing toes. In the swifts and nightjars all four toes point forwards.

The swimming, or " webbed ", foot is exhibited by most aquatic species, the three front toes being joined by membranes. In the cormorants and gannets the " hind-toe " is brought forward and webbed along with the others. Coots and grebes have lobed toes, while the Moorhen's large feet and long toes enable it to run over the surface of the water and over aquatic plants. *See also* Web.

The toes of the birds of prey are very strong and are armed with deadly needle-sharp claws.

For a fuller description of these various toe arrangements *see also* Feet.

TOM-TIT. Name for Blue-Tit (*q.v.*).

TONGUE. A bird's tongue is not an organ of taste—or only to a very minor extent—nor is it of great importance as an organ of touch. Its primary function is as an organ of manipulation, or as an accessory to the bill in the capture of insects, or in conveying nectar or honey to the mouth.

Tongues exhibit many variations in birds. In the Green Woodpecker, for example, the

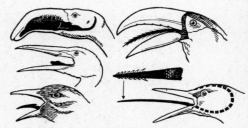

TONGUE. *Fig. I : The following are shown here : (top) Flamingo, Toucan ; (centre) Gannet ; (base) Blackbird, Green Woodpecker—note special barbs*

tongue is not only unusually long and sticky, but is armed at the tip with short backwardly-directed barbs. It is also protrusible, and can be thrust into ant-heaps or holes in the bark of trees, and drawn out with the insects adhering to it. The various barb-like projections on the woodpecker's tongue also serve to increase the thickness of the sticky salivary coating which is secreted by large glands on each side of the head. Another feature is the remarkable muscular arrangement which enables the bird to whip its tongue in and out with extreme rapidity. The muscles of the tongue are fixed to a pair of curved rods or bones. These rods start, one on either side of the windpipe, continue upwards over the top of he head, where they meet, and, continuing forwards in a deep groove in the skull, then turn to one side before entering the nasal cavity. The muscles attached to these rods enable them to be pulled backwards, downwards and forwards, and thus the tongue is thrust out, the saliva glands simultaneously pouring out the sticky secretion. Sap-sucking woodpeckers have a shorter tongue, with a brush-like instead of a " barbed " tip. Humming-birds also possess long and protrusible tongues. They are tubular at the base, but about half-way along they divide into two free brush-like tips. The humming-birds' tongues are suitable both for sipping nectar and for capturing small insects.

The tongues of members of the order *Anseriformes* (ducks, geese and swans) vary considerably in shape, but they are generally thick and

a - Two slender cartilages
b - Long muscle which follows cartilage

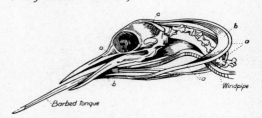

Fig. 2 : Head of Green Woodpecker, dissected to show muscle and cartilage that " shoot out " tongue

fleshy, and are lined along the sides with fine lamellae or horny " teeth ". In all Anserine birds the tip of the tongue is horny and somewhat scoop-shaped. The tongue of fish-eating ducks, such as the Red-breasted Merganser and the Goosander, are, however, rather less fleshy than those of other Anserines, and, in addition to bristle-like lamellae along the sides, they have conical, horny projections towards the back, which help these birds to hold their prey.

In some species the tongue is scarcely developed at all. This is particularly true of those birds which are in the habit of swallowing their food whole and in large bulk, so that a long, or even a medium-sized tongue would be an obstruction to feeding. Examples are the Gannet, Cormorant, Stork, Ibis and Spoonbill, in which the tongue is reduced to a mere nodule.

In most birds, the tongue is, in size, midway between the lengthy instrument of the Green Woodpecker and the tiny " stump " of the Cormorant.

In most species it is horny at the tip, while at the back it bears a number of small pointed projections directed towards the throat.

TRAPS AND NETS. The passing of the Protection of Birds Act, 1954 (*q.v.*), placed many restrictions on the taking of wild birds, and made it illegal to use certain types of traps, decoys, snares and bait. But the legitimate interests of ornithologists and bona fide bird watchers have not been interfered with, and it is still lawful to use a cage, trap or net to catch a wild bird solely for the purpose of ringing (*q.v.*) or marking it (provided it is immediately released), or for certain authorised experiments. Anyone wishing to be fully acquainted with the exact position should obtain a copy of the Act from Her Majesty's Stationery Office.

At one time birds were usually ringed when they were nestlings, but nowadays, owing to improved methods of live-trapping, about equal numbers of adult birds and nestlings are ringed.

There are many different kinds of live-traps, of which the most widely used are briefly described below ; for further details consult *Trapping Methods for Bird Ringers*, by P. A. D. Hollum, published by the British Trust for Ornithology as their Field Guide No. 1.

Sieve Trap. One of the simplest traps, this is merely a development of the old method, still sometimes used by small boys, of propping up a garden sieve on a small stick which can be jerked away by a draw-string. The modern version is a rectangular box, rather like a seed tray, with solid wooden sides and a top of wire—or, preferably, string—netting. In one of the sides, usually near a corner, is a small door against which can be placed a catch-up—a small box with netting at one end and a drop door at the other, into which a bird can be driven from the main trap.

Funnel Trap. Although this trap may take various forms and vary in size from the small

Arnold Benington

TRAPS AND NETS. Setting a clap-net at Copeland Bird Observatory, Belfast Lough, Ireland. In the foreground, the net is being pegged down

sparrow-trap to the much larger ones for rooks, the principle is the same in all cases. Entry into the baited trap is by one or more funnel-shaped openings, which present no difficulty to a bird on its way in but make it impossible for it to find its way out. The smaller traps usually have horizontal openings, but some rook-traps have vertical ones, which may be entered directly from flight.

Potter Trap. This small trap, suitable both for field and garden use, consists of a series of baited chambers. On entering one of these chambers, the bird treads on a small platform inside, and a trap-door immediately drops down, blocking the entrance.

House-Trap. This is a recent development, much larger than those previously described : it consists of a large wire cage, in which a man can stand upright, entered by double doors. To receive the bird these doors are left slightly ajar, and, as they open in opposite directions, the bird has difficulty in finding its way out.

Heligoland Trap. This type of trap, evolved at the Heligoland Migration Station, has proved so effective that it has been almost universally adopted by migration stations and bird observatories. It consists essentially of a large tapering tunnel built up of wire netting supported on wooden posts, terminating in a reception chamber into which birds may be baited or driven. The entrance, which in the larger versions may be as much as 30 ft. across, is usually heavily planted with shrubs and bushes to provide cover for the birds, from which they can be driven into the tunnel. The reception chamber is usually a glass or gauze box, with a door on one side, through which the birds can be extracted by hand or driven into a catch-up.

Clap-Net. This may be either single or double. The single form consists essentially of a net supported between two poles, pivoted at ground level and held in a vertical position by guy ropes. The net hangs loosely from the supports, and its free end is usually pegged to the ground. A pull-rope is attached to one of the posts, and when this is drawn the net is pulled over to the other side, falling on top of any birds that may be feeding at a line of bait. There are several variants of this trap.

One disadvantage of the clap-net is that birds caught by it tend to struggle and to be entangled in its meshes, and are, therefore, rather difficult to remove. The best method is to grasp the bird in such a way that the fingers can be used to open up the mesh as widely as possible.

Bat-Fowling Net. This is a long net fastened to bamboo-poles, hinged at the top so that they can be clapped together. Although primarily intended to catch birds in flight, this net is most successful when used against roosting

John Markham
TREE-CREEPER. *Apart from the Wryneck, this is the only bird to creep up and down tree-trunks*

birds at night. Those who have experience of these nets consider that they are of little use during the day.

Kingfisher Nets. These really consist of two nets, one of coarse and the other of much smaller mesh. If a bird flies into one of the nets in the correct direction, it pulls the fine-meshed net between one of the larger meshes, and is thus trapped in a little pocket from which it is unable to escape. Such nets were originally strung between the arches of bridges to catch kingfishers for the plumage trade, but they can be used for other smallish birds, and may equally well be stretched between trees or other supports.

Being caught in a net usually frightens a bird, but the cage-trap suffers from no such objection. Some birds even appear to enjoy being trapped and do not necessarily enter a trap for food. Lack reports the case of a Robin that returned to a trap as soon as it was released, and eventually proved such a nuisance that a trap set to catch other birds had to be shifted.

Carefully carried out, trapping does not hurt birds, but traps must be constantly visited so that birds are not imprisoned for long. Each evening the trap should be closed—or, in the case of smaller traps, turned over after the final visit at night. Birds should not be trapped during the nesting season, for even a short delay in returning with food to nestlings may be fatal. For resident birds, winter trapping is advisable in order that the birds can be marked before the breeding season commences. Hard Winters produce particularly favourable results. Migrants are trapped on or shortly after their arrival in this country. *See also* Ringing.

TREE-CREEPER—Certhia familiaris. The remarkable little Tree-Creeper is the only member of its family to reside in the British Isles. Although it is fairly plentiful wherever woods abound, its unobtrusive habits often cause its presence to be overlooked. Well-timbered parks and old gardens also attract it, and occasionally it visits hedgerows and trees in open country. The British Tree-Creeper is confined to these islands, but allied species and subspecies occur throughout Europe, Asia and north America.

The Tree-Creeper is an inconspicuous and sober-looking little bird, in its brown mantle with paler shadings, and silky-white underparts ; but it is distinguished by being the only small bird with a long, slender, curved beak. Its wings are barred in buff, its tail is graduated, and over its eye is a white stripe. Its legs are pale brown. The sexes are alike. The length is 4¼ in., and the tarsus 0·65 in. ; the wing span is from 5 in. and 6 in., the weight about ½ oz.

The Tree-Creeper looks more like a mouse than a bird as it creeps up the tree trunks and along the branches. (It is the only bird, except the Wryneck, which habitually does this.) Starting at the foot of a tree, it works its way with feet apart, aided by the stiff feathers of its tail, up the trunk or along a promising stout branch. One tree explored, it descends tail first —not head first like the Nuthatch—and renews its upward spiral journey on another. Its specially adapted beak fits into the narrow cracks to secure lurking insects.

The Tree-Creeper's short flight is tit-like in movement. It has a curious ethereal and bat-like display flight, seldom seen, in which the male excitedly chases his mate round and round a tree-trunk, uttering his call notes.

Not a highly gregarious bird, the Tree-Creeper is usually seen in small family parties ; but outside the breeding season it may roam the countryside in search of food in company with tits and goldcrests. It roosts in a small crevice in the bark of a tree.

Like the bird itself, the song of the Tree-Creeper is inconspicuous and goes unnoticed amid the spring chorus of bird song ; but it is sweet and melodious, a quieter version of the Goldcrest's high-pitched little song. It is usually delivered while the bird is climbing, or on its short flights. Although occasionally heard in almost every month of the year, it is at its height in late March, April and early May.

A crevice in the bark of a tree is the usual site of the Tree-Creeper's nest, but it may be placed in the hole of a building or stone wall, or behind the trunk of wall ivy. Said to be built by both male and female, it is composed of twigs, rootlets, moss, and so on, and lined with the finer bits of tree bark, wool and feathers. Five to eight—even more at times—white eggs with reddish-brown spots are laid in late May. The major part of the hatching, which takes a fortnight, is done by the hen, and for the same period both birds rear their nestlings. Two broods are raised in a season.

The Tree-Creeper's food consists of insects and their larvae, spiders, woodlice, and so on.

TREE-PIPIT—Anthus trivialis. As its name indicates, the Tree-Pipit is the arboreal member of its family, although a ground-nesting bird. It is a summer visitor generally distributed throughout the British Isles, but it does not breed in the extreme west of Cornwall or the north of Scotland. In some Scottish islands it is a passage migrant, and Ireland sees it only as a rare visitor. Abroad, the Tree-Pipit occurs throughout Europe and western and central Asia, wintering in tropical Africa.

All the small pipits are more or less similar in plumage. The Tree-Pipit has the common brown mantle with darker markings, and pale underparts with some streaks on the breast and

Eric Hosking

TREE-PIPIT. Distinguished from other pipits by its wonderful song, this is a summer visitor

flanks. To the casual observer it is very similar to the Meadow-Pipit, even to the white outer-tail feathers showing so conspicuously in flight. Nearer inspection, however, reveals that the Tree-Pipit is rather larger and more stoutly built. Its hind claw is shorter and curved, and better adapted to its more arboreal habits. It has a flitting and erratic flight, not quite so undulating as some other pipits', and on the ground it walks and runs. In Winter, the Tree-Pipit is usually seen alone ; it roosts in some sheltering bush or plant.

It is the distinctive song and charming song-flight which constitute the Tree-Pipit's best identification. In its song-flight the bird rises steeply from its song-post; the song, unlike the Meadow-Pipit's, beginning as it nears the summit of its flight and continuing as it parachutes perpendicularly down with its wings stiffly raised, to rest again very often on the same starting point. This may be a tall tree, a telegraph pole, or a bush, occasionally even the ground ; but, as a rule, its singing stances are higher than those of the Meadow-Pipit. Neither the latter nor the Tree-Pipit rises to a height approaching the larks, for 100 feet is about the pipit's highest altitude.

The song of the Tree-Pipit is the best and most finely delivered of pipit songs. It has extraordinary carrying power, for its loud and clear closing notes, with their canary-like quality, are audible at a distance of a quarter of a mile. The full song is uttered only in the song-flight, but the bird also sings from its post and occasionally on the ground. Its rather harsh and rasping call notes are distinct from those of the Meadow-Pipit ; its alarm note is a soft and metallic sound. The Tree-Pipit does not sing in its winter quarters. The song is best heard from late April until the end of June, and sometimes even into July.

The Tree-Pipit nests in a depression on the ground, and the well-built nest is composed of dry grasses and bents, lined with finer materials, including some hair. The eggs vary in colour, and can be pale blue, pinkish, greenish, brownish or grey. Four to six of them are laid in May and June. The hen hatches them for a fortnight, and both parents tend and feed the young for the same period. One brood is usually reared in a season, sometimes two. Insects form the Tree-Pipit's main food.

TREE-SPARROW — Passer montanus. A shy and retiring bird compared with the House-Sparrow, the Tree-Sparrow is a widely spread resident throughout the British Isles. It is much more prevalent in the eastern and Midland counties of Great Britain than elsewhere ; it is very local indeed in Ireland, although it has increased its status there within recent years. In October many tree-sparrows arrive from the Continent to augment the British residents. Abroad, this bird is found throughout Europe — except Iceland—and Asia.

Though often mistaken for the House-Sparrow, the Tree-Sparrow has in fact a more elegant and dapper appearance. Its crown and nape are a rich warm chestnut, its cheeks are white with a contrasting black patch on the ear coverts, and its chin and throat are black. Its mantle is brown streaked in black, and across the dark brown wings run two narrow white bars. Its underparts are whitish. The stout bill is black, and the legs pale brown. Unlike the House-Sparrow, the cock and hen are alike. The length is 6 in., and the tarsus 0·7 in. ; the wing span is between 6 in. and 7 in., and the weight less than 1 oz.

Tree-sparrows usually haunt areas with old pollarded trees, such as orchards and parklands, and, if encouraged, will occupy a nesting box. Very gregarious, they flock in Winter, roaming the countryside with chaffinches and other small birds.

Though its movements bear a close resemblance to those of the House-Sparrow, the

John Markham

TREE-SPARROW. *Against its noisy cousin, the House-Sparrow, it is a shy, retiring bird*

Tree-Sparrow is more agile both on the wing and on the ground ; it has the same bounding and direct flight. Its courtship resembles that of its relative, but both male and female run along the branches with tails erect and bills pointed straight out, one or other of the pair bowing frequently.

The song of the Tree-Sparrow, though simple, is an improvement on the House-Sparrow's ; it is a not unmusical repetition of chirping notes, and sometimes a number sing together in a pleasant chorus. The call notes are similar to its relative's familiar chirp, but more musical and higher pitched.

The favourite nesting sites of tree-sparrows are holes in trees, haystacks, thatched roofs or buildings, and also the old nests of other birds. Both cock and hen provide the material and build the nest in much the same manner as the House-Sparrow, but the four to six eggs, laid in May or later, are smaller and darker. Both parents share the hatching for a fortnight, and tend and feed the nestlings for much the same period. Two broods, and sometimes three, are reared in a season.

The seeds of weeds, other plants and bushes are the Tree-Sparrow's favourite food, but some insects and spiders are also taken.

TRINGA. Genus of wading birds of the family *Scolopacidae* of the order *Charadriiformes*. Its species are distributed over most parts of the globe. The following twelve on the British list are separately described under their own headings : Green Sandpiper, Wood-Sandpiper, Solitary Sandpiper, Common Sandpiper, Spotted Sandpiper, Redshank (which occurs here in three different forms), Spotted Redshank, Greater Yellow-Legs, Lesser Yellow-Legs, Greenshank, Marsh-Sandpiper and Grey-rumped Sandpiper.

The members of this genus have a long and slender bill, which is straight or slightly up-curved but has a slightly down-curved hard tip. The wings are long and pointed. The tail is squarish in shape, and of the tail-feathers the two middle ones are the longest. The tarsus is long, particularly in the Marsh-Sandpiper and species of similar size ; it is covered with scutes (horny scales) behind. The three front toes are webbed. There is a small hind toe.

TURDIDAE, *not popularly regarded as a Thrush—the Whinchat*

For text see pages 555 and 561

TROGLODYTES (Greek, " cave-dweller "). Genus of the large family *Troglodytidae* of the order *Passeriformes*. Its species are distributed over most parts of the globe. There is only one European species, the Wren (*q.v.*).

TRYNGITES. Genus of wading birds of the family *Scolopacidae* of the order *Charadriiformes*. It contains only one species—the Buffbreasted Sandpiper—which is mainly distributed over Arctic America, and parts of south America outside the breeding season, and occasionally wanders to Europe and Asia, having been recorded in the British Isles not much more than a dozen times.

TUFTED DUCK—Aythya fuligula. As a British breeding bird the Tufted Duck has shown a great increase during the past 50 years, both in numbers and in range of habitat. It now nests regularly in all suitable districts throughout the British Isles, but is less abundant on the west coasts of Great Britain and the south-east coast of Ireland. The Tufted Duck is also a widespread passage migrant and winter visitor. Abroad, it is found in most European countries, and in many parts of Asia.

One of the commonest ducks to be seen on the ponds and lakes of city and town parks, the drake is strikingly dressed in a boldly patterned dress—black above and pure white below—and is the only duck with a crest of graceful black feathers. He has also a broad white wing-bar, very conspicuous in flight. The drake in eclipse plumage, the duck and the juvenile are all more or less dark brown with whitish flanks, and all have the white wing-bar. The bill and legs are blue-grey, and the eye yellow. The total length is 17 in., the body being 11 in. ; the tarsus is 1 in., the wing span between 16 in. and 18 in., and the weight 2 lb.

The flight, walk and habits of the Tufted Duck conform to the general pattern of other diving ducks, but especially resemble the Pochard's. It is an active and expert diver, usually slipping unobtrusively down but sometimes kicking up a spray of water in the manner of the Pochard. In clear water it can easily be seen swimming at a depth of 10 ft. or more. Its greatest recorded depth is 16 ft., and its longest dive lasted about 40 seconds. On the surface it sails along like a small black-and-white boat driven by the wind.

The spring courtship is not at all spectacular ; some slight display takes place on the water, with the drakes bowing, throwing back their heads and chasing the ducks. In the breeding season the drake has a pleasant, low, whistling subsong, and the duck a growling croak.

Many pairs may nest together near water in a well-concealed place among the grass, bushes,

reeds or other vegetation. The hollow that serves for a nest is arranged by the duck and lined with grass, rushes and plenty of dark down. The greenish-grey eggs may number from six to 14, and even more ; they are laid daily during late May or early June. When the last egg is laid, the duck begins hatching ; this lasts for about three weeks or a little longer. The chicks, clad in brown and yellow down, are tended by the duck, but they soon learn to dive and are independent in six or seven weeks.

The Tufted Duck has a varied animal and vegetable diet—small fish, water insects, worms, frogs and many kinds of aquatic plants.

TURDIDAE (Latin, " thrush "). Family of the order *Passeriformes*, containing the thrushes and their allies. Its genera are to be found in most parts of the world, though they are most numerous in Europe and in northern and western Asia. There are nine genera on the British list : *Turdus, Monticola, Oenanthe, Saxicola, Tarsiger, Phoenicurus, Luscinia, Cyanosylvia* and *Erithacus*.

TURDUS (Latin, " thrush "). Genus of medium-sized birds of the family *Turdidae* of the order *Passeriformes*. Its species are to be found in most parts of the world. The following nine species are on the British list and are separately described : Mistle-Thrush, Song-Thrush, Fieldfare, Redwing, Blackbird, Ring-Ouzel, Dusky Thrush, Black-throated Thrush, and Golden Mountain-Thrush. The three last are very rare.

In members of this genus the bill is relatively short, with the culmen curved and the front part of the cutting edge of the upper mandible distinctly notched. The nostrils are roundish or oval in shape, and partially covered by a membrane and by feathers. The wings are of medium length or rather long, and are pointed.

G. K. Yeates

TUFTED DUCK. *The little drake is the only one of its kind to sport a crest of long feathers*

TURNSTONE—Arenaria interpres. Reports that the Turnstone has bred in the British Isles have been received from time to time, but proof has always been lacking. It is, however, a common and widespread winter visitor and passage migrant on all coasts. Many birds remain all the Winter, and some non-breeders are seen during the Summer, especially in the Orkneys and Shetlands and on North Rona. The Turnstone occurs inland only on passage, and rarely during the Winter. Abroad, it breeds in northern Europe and Asia, Greenland and north America.

In its summer dress the male Turnstone is boldly patterned in a variegated design of black, white and chestnut ; its winter plumage is very dark brown, with no chestnut. Its underparts at both seasons are white, with a black breast band. Its short, stout and slightly upturned bill is black, and its short legs are bright orange-yellow. The female resembles the male in winter dress, but is duller. The length is 9 in., and the tarsus 1 in. ; the wing span is about 12 in.–14 in., and the weight 4 oz.

The Turnstone keeps company with dunlins and other small waders. As its name indicates, it habitually turns up stones with its useful bill in its search for insects.

In flight its conspicuous pied appearance distinguishes the Turnstone from all other waders. For short distances its pace is slow and uncertain, but on migration the flight is swift and sure. The Turnstone is as a rule tame, and only rises at a near approach. Its voice is a short, metallic, clear twittering call ; more varied notes are heard in the breeding season.

" Stanepecker " and " Tanglepicker " are among the Turnstone's different local names.

Arthur Christiansen

TURNSTONE. Several birds may co-operate and turn over any object that one alone cannot shift

TURTLE-DOVE—Streptopelia turtur. This dove is not a resident, but only a summer visitor to the British Isles. The southern, eastern and Midland counties of England see it in abundance ; elsewhere it is inclined to be local, but is said to be increasing its status. In Scotland and Ireland it is best known as a scarce passage migrant, but it has bred in both countries. Abroad, the Turtle-Dove is found throughout Europe, temperate Asia and north Africa ; and, in the non-breeding season, in tropical Africa.

The smallest and most graceful of the pigeons and doves, the Turtle-Dove is readily recognized by its brown, rather than grey, mantle, and by the conspicuous black and white patches on the side of its neck ; its throat and neck are pinkish, shading into pale and whitish underparts. Its beautiful long, graduated, fan-shaped tail with a broad white band at the tip, is the Turtle-Dove's best identification mark. The bill is dark brown, and the legs pinkish ; the skin round the yellow eye is also pinkish. The sexes are alike ; the immature birds are browner, and have no black and white patches on the neck. The length is 10¾ in., and the tarsus 0·9 in. ; the wing span is approximately 18 in., and the weight 6 oz.

In his courtship display the cock rises steeply with rapidly beating wings and tail outspread, then glides down in circles often to the same perch, where he will resume his " song " ; the ceremony is usually performed in sight of his mate. There is also a bowing and bobbing display rapidly performed by the male, and accompanied with a special caressing note.

The purring " coo " of the Turtle-Dove, one of the pleasantest sounds to echo through the woods, is usually delivered from a tree or telegraph pole, and rarely at a lower level. The call is uttered three times in succession, followed by a short interval, then repeated over and over again ; a typical performance has 15 coos in groups of three. The Turtle-Dove is late in arriving, and its voice is seldom heard until well into May ; it lasts until July or August.

Every type of well-timbered country, open woodlands, and large gardens are the familiar nesting haunts of turtle-doves. Several pairs may decide to nest together. The nest, placed in a tall bush or high hedge, at no great distance from the ground, is a flimsy affair composed of twigs, with a scanty lining of roots, and so on. Two white eggs are laid in late May or June, and both birds share the incubation for two weeks. The young are fed with " pigeon's milk " (*q.v.*) for 18 days, and fly a few days later. Two broods are normally reared in a season.

The food of the Turtle-Dove is almost entirely vegetable, and includes seeds of many varieties, and corn picked from the stubble.

TWIST-TAILED SKUA. Local name for Pomatorhine Skua. (*q.v.*) ; known in north America as Pomarine Jaeger.

TWITE—Carduelis flavirostris. A bird of moorland and heather, and consequently a rarity in many parts of the British Isles, the Twite or " Mountain Linnet " is common in the west Highlands and islands of Scotland, but less so in the south ; England sees it only locally in the Pennines. In Wales there is only one instance of its nesting, but in Ireland it is found in all suitable districts. The Twite is a distinct geographical race, resident only in the British Isles. During the Autumn numbers of the Continental Twite (*Carduelis flavirostris flavirostris*), a subspecies breeding principally in Norway, appear on the south and east coasts of England ; this bird has very slight differences in plumage, evident only to the expert.

The Twite is a close relative of the Linnet, with which it might be confused. But the cock with his rosy-pink rump should be easily recognized ; he also lacks the red on the crown and breast of the cock Linnet. The hen is less easily identified, but the general plumage of both cock and hen is darker and has a warmer reddish twinge than that of the Linnet. The underparts shade to white, and the brown wings have a white wing-bar. The cleft tail is longer. The legs are dark brown ; the strong bill is grey in Summer, and (another good identification), yellow in Winter. The length is 5¼ in., and the tarsus 0·65 in. ; the wing span is between 7 in. and 8 in., and the weight is only a little over ½ oz.

The Twite is an interesting and sprightly little bird to watch. It is gregarious, and, when its domestic duties are over, it leaves its lonely uplands and descends to roam the stubble fields, marshes and shores. Its flight and movements are similar to the Linnet's ; fairy-like and erratic, it dances above the fields, and the flocks utter a twittering chorus as they fly. The Twite hops on the ground, and perches on bushes, walls and railings. During the spring courtship, the male makes much of his rosy rump, opening and depressing his wings so that it may show to the best advantage to his mate.

The Twite's chirping call note gives it its name. The twittering song and song-flight are linnet-like, but also have an individual nasal, twanging quality. The song is delivered from a rock, post, or bush, but is as often heard on the wing ; it is at its best from April to July.

A bird of the open country, the Twite nests among the heather of moors, rough pastures, and hillsides. The nest, placed on the ground and sheltered among heather and ling, is prepared entirely by the hen, with the cock in attendance. It is composed of grass and

Eric Hosking

TWITE. *Also called the " Mountain Linnet," this is an inhabitant of wild moorland and hillsides*

stalks, and lined with hair, wool and feathers. The eggs, very like those of the Linnet, but bluer, number five or six, and are laid in May and June. The hen incubates alone for 12 or 13 days, and both parents tend and feed the nestlings for about a month. Two broods are normally raised in a season.

The food consists mainly of seeds of various trees and plants, but some insects are eaten.

TWO-BARRED CROSSBILL — Loxia leucoptera. This bird, also called the White-winged Crossbill, is a very rare wanderer to the British Isles from its home in Northern Europe, where it is widely distributed. It can at all ages be distinguished from the common Crossbill by the double white wing-bars in both male and female ; but these may deceive the ordinary observer into confusing it with our Chaffinch, especially as its beak, although crossed, is smaller and therefore less noticeable than that of the common Crossbill. The Two-barred Crossbill is about the same size as a Chaffinch, its length being about 6 in.

This is a bird of the coniferous forests. From the details available it has much the same habits as others of its family regarding nesting, breeding and food. Its song, however, is described as being quite distinctive, and louder, clearer and superior to that of the common Crossbill.

TYSTIE. Name for Black Guillemot (*q.v.*).

TYTO. Genus of medium-sized owls of the family *Strigidae* of the order *Strigiformes*. It contains several species, distributed over many parts of the globe. Only a single species, the Barn-Owl (*q.v.*), occurs in the British Isles.

VULTURE

UPLAND PLOVER. American name for Bartram's Sandpiper (*q.v.*).

UPLAND SANDPIPER. Alternative name for Bartram's Sandpiper (*q.v.*).

UPUPA (Latin, " hoopoe "). The only genus in the family *Upupidae* of the order *Coraciiformes*. It contains only one species—the Hoopoe (*q.v.*) —which occurs in several different forms in Europe, Asia, and Africa.

URIA. Genus of marine birds of the family *Alcidae* of the order *Charadriiformes*. It contains four species, widely distributed over the seas of the Northern Hemisphere. Three are on the British list : the Guillemot (*q.v.*), Black Guillemot (*q.v.*), and Brünnich's Guillemot (*q.v.*).

The members of this genus are medium-sized birds, with a straight, pointed and slightly laterally compressed bill of medium length. The neck is short. The wings are short and narrow, and the tail, which is very short, is rounded. The legs are short and are placed far back, near the tail ; there are only three toes.

Maslowski & Goodpaster

UPLAND PLOVER. This American bird is known in this country from only thirteen recorded visits

VAGRANTS. Of the 600 or so kinds of birds which have been recorded in the British Isles from time to time, only about 200 can be counted as regular breeders, and not more than another hundred as regular visitors or passage migrants. That leaves the large total of some 300 as occasional visitors or vagrants.

There is scarcely any part of the world from the Arctic and Antarctic regions to the tropics from which wanderers have not reached the British Isles. Until recently it was not believed possible that many of these could have reached our shores unaided, and ornithologists had postulated that those which are natives of very distant countries must have had an assisted passage on board ship, or have been imported in captivity and deliberately or accidentally released. With increased modern knowledge of the possibilities of drift migration (*q.v.*), it has become necessary to accept the probability that most of these birds are natural migrants.

Most birds have such wide geographical distribution (*q.v.*) that it is not easy to say from exactly which part of the world an individual vagrant has come. North America, however, forms a very distinct geographical region, and it can be said with some confidence that at least 75 of our vagrant species came from there, and five more from the Caribbean area. From the south American area the sole vagrant species is a Cayenne Lapwing recorded in Lancashire in 1936. The Antarctic provides three wanderers—Wilson's Petrel, the Blackbrowed Albatross, and the Cape Sea-Pigeon. Not surprisingly there are no land birds from the Australasian region on the British list, but there are two petrels from the Pacific Ocean. A specimen of the Collared Petrel, which breeds in the New Hebrides and Fiji, was shot in Cardiganshire in 1889, and a Kermadec Petrel, from the sub-tropical zone of the South Pacific, was picked up dead in Cheshire in 1908. These records become a little less surprising when it is remembered that two regular passage migrants through British waters are the Great Shearwater, which breeds on Tristan da Cunha, and the Sooty Shearwater, which nests off the west coast of south America and on various islands of New Zealand.

A dozen African land-birds have wandered to the British Isles, as well as eight sea-birds which nest in various parts of the Atlantic Ocean. Many species nest on both the African and European shores of the Mediterranean, and Mediterranean species are numerous in the list of our wanderers ; among the total of 37 species are two buntings, three shrikes, six warblers, two wheatears, four birds of prey, four herons and two ducks. The Alps and Pyrenees are the presumed origin of a smaller group of mountain species, which includes the Alpine Chough, Citril Finch, Snow-Finch, Water-Pipit, Wall-Creeper, Alpine Ring-Ouzel, Alpine Accentor, and Alpine Swift.

Western Europe provides rather fewer vagrants, but only because there are comparatively few birds breeding in Western Europe that do not either breed in the British Isles or visit us regularly in Autumn and Winter. Even so, there are 23 vagrants from this area, including five species of warbler. Northern Europe provides a substantial number of vagrants, largely because its cold climate forces nearly all the breeding birds to move southwards in Winter. The list of 44 species from this area includes six finches, three buntings, three tits, two flycatchers, six warblers, four owls and four other birds of prey. Both the north European area and the Balkan area overlap with Russia and Asia as far as their breeding species are concerned. The Balkan area provides a score of vagrants, including such interesting species as the Red-footed Falcon, the Great White Heron, and the Black-winged Pratincole. Between European Russia and Siberia in the north and the deserts and steppes of central Asia in the south it is hard to draw a firm faunistic line ; from this vast area some 50 species have wandered to the British Isles, many of them having been recorded at Fair Isle in the Shetlands. Indeed, the majority of the rarities for which Fair Isle is famous seem to be of Siberian origin. Some of these, such as the Yellow-browed Warbler, which breeds from the northern Urals to the Sea of Okhotsk, occur almost every year ; others, like the Yellow-headed Wagtail, which was first seen here in 1954, have appeared only once.

An analysis of the 650 individual north American birds recorded in the British Isles over the past 150 years shows that the majority of them appear in Autumn, at the normal migration time, having been blown off course by adverse winds while migrating down the eastern side of north America. Out of 184 individual dated records of north American

waders, 146 appeared in the months from August to December, of which 43 were in September, 49 in October, and 25 in November. Of the total of 70 dated records of north American land-birds, 44 occurred from August to December (6 in September, 21 in October, and 9 in November).

Waders form the largest group of north American vagrants ; 19 different species have been recorded since October 1801, when a Dowitcher was obtained on the coast of Devon. The year 1954 was notable for the addition of two fresh American waders to the British list : a Stilt Sandpiper, which occurred in Yorkshire, and a Wilson's Phalarope in Fife.

The increase in the number of bird watchers since the Second World War has contributed

Lynwood M. Chace

VAGRANTS. *The Red-eyed Vireo was seen for the first time in the British Isles in the year 1951*

to the greatly enlarged number of records of American waders every year from 1946 onwards. Whereas in 1932–39 an average of only two American waders was seen each year, in 1946–53 there was an average of eight in each year. The increased vigilance of bird watchers also led to several other transatlantic bird species being recorded in the British Isles for the first time. These vagrants have included a Red-eyed Vireo in Co. Wexford in 1951 ; a Man o' War Bird in the Hebrides, and a Gray-cheeked Thrush on Fair Isle, both in 1953 ; a Black Duck in Co. Kerry in February 1954 ; and a Myrtle Warbler in 1955.—R. S. R. FITTER.

VANELLUS. Genus of the family *Charadriidae* of the order *Charadriiformes*. It contains only one species—the Lapwing (*q.v.*)—mainly distributed over Europe and northern Asia, and also over southern Asia and northern Africa outside the breeding season.

VASCULAR SYSTEM. *See* Anatomy.

VELVET SCOTER—Melanitta fusca. A regular winter visitor and passage migrant to the British Isles, the Velvet Scoter is seen chiefly off the east coasts of Great Britain and rarely goes inland. Some birds are known to spend the Summer here, and from time to time the Velvet Scoter has been suspected of breeding in Scotland, but definite proof has always been lacking. The Velvet Scoter is found in northern Europe, Asia, and north America.

In build the Velvet resembles the Common Scoter, but it is distinguished by a white wing patch contrasting vividly against its all-black plumage. This patch, however, is often invisible unless the bird is in flight or rising from the surface to flap its wings, and watchers must wait for one or other of these movements for the certain identification of the drake.

Closer inspection reveals other differences: his larger size, a small white patch just below his eye, and his black bill, yellow or orange at the sides, and with a small black knob at its base. His eyes are white, and his legs reddish. His eclipse change is slight: his glossy black becomes duller, and his flanks and underparts browner. The duck and juveniles are blackish-brown, with two white face patches, and both have the white wing patch. The duck's bill is black with no knob, her legs are duller than the drake's, and her eyes brown. The total length is 22 in., the body being 14 in.; the tarsus is 2 in., the wing span approximately 22 in.–24 in., and the weight varies from 2 lb. to 4 lb.

The habits and behaviour of the Velvet Scoter resemble those of the Common Scoter. The tamest of the family, it is usually seen in small parties—seldom in large flocks.

Its flight is fast and low over the water, but it has a difficult and pattering take-off. Its walk on the ground is slow and laboured, but it rarely comes to land unless to die, a victim of oil pollution. On the water velvet scoters move as a rule in single file; they are excellent divers, swimming beneath the surface with the aid of wings and feet. Dives of 3 min. and a depth of 66 ft. have been recorded, but a normal dive is for ¾ min. to about 24 ft. The Velvet Scoter is generally a silent bird;

the drake's voice is very similar to that of the Common Scoter, and the duck has the usual hoarse churring note.

The nesting sites are varied; the bird likes fresh-water lakes, ponds in wooded country, open tundra, moors and fells. The nest has a foundation of grasses, and is plentifully lined with down. The five to eight eggs, laid in May or June according to the country, are creamy or buff. The duck hatches during 28 days, and also tends the ducklings alone. One brood is reared in a season.

The Velvet Scoter feeds on mollusca and crustacea, but in the breeding season will take tubers, roots, and aquatic plants.

VULTURE. The only vultures in this country outside of zoos and aviaries are rare stragglers.

The Egyptian Vulture (*Neophron perenopterus*) has paid two recorded visits to England from its natural haunts in southern

Zoological Society of San Diego

VULTURE. The Griffon-Vulture, shown above, is by far the larger of the two vultures that have been seen in this country outside zoos and aviaries

Europe, southern Asia, and Africa. It is much smaller than other vultures, and has a distinctive flight silhouette with long, straight-edged, but pointed, black and white wings, and wedge-shaped white tail. The head and throat of adults exhibit bare yellow skin above a shaggy whitish ruff. The plumage is off-white, with contrasting black primaries.

The Griffon-Vulture (*Gyps fulvus*) has paid three recorded visits to England and one to Ireland. Its normal haunts are somewhat, but not exactly, the same as the Egyptian Vulture. It is a large bird, with very long, broad wings, with widely spaced groups of primaries forming rounded ends, and a very short, dark, wedge-shaped or squarish tail. Its small head is sunk well back into its whitish ruff, and its sandy plumage contrasts with its blackish wings and tail.

WREN

WAGTAIL. Name given to a family (*Motacillidae*) and a genus (*Motacilla*) of Passerine birds. The family includes the true wagtails and the pipits (*q.v.*). Three species of wagtail are on the 1952 British list : *Motacilla alba ; M. cinerea ; M. flava*—or the White, Grey, and Yellow Wagtail groups respectively. But the systematics of these various groups, particularly the Yellow, are very complex, and some authors classify some of the various forms as distinct species. Furthermore, there are many intermediate gradations where the ranges of different subspecies of Yellow Wagtail overlap, and mutants resembling other races breed with birds of normal appearance. Thus, in England, birds identical with Sykes's Wagtail (*M.f. beema*) breed with normal yellow wagtails, *M.f. flavissima*. As at 1955, the various races resident or visiting Britain are :

> **White Wagtail Group,** *Motacilla alba.* Distinguished by lack of yellow or olive in plumage. Pied Wagtail (*M. a. yarelli*) ; White Wagtail (*M. a. alba*).

> **Grey Wagtail Group,** *Motacilla cinerea.* Distinguished by grey back and yellow underparts. Grey Wagtail (*M. c. cinerea*).

> **Yellow Wagtail Group,** *Motacilla flava.* Distinguished by olive-green back and yellow underparts. Yellow (or Green-headed) Wagtail (*M.f flavissima*) ; Blue-headed Wagtail (*M.f. flava*) ; Ashy-headed Wagtail (*M.f. cinereocapilla*) ; Grey-headed Wagtail (*M.f. thunbergi*) ; Black-headed Wagtail (*M.f. feldegg*).

All these are described in detail under their own names, and the classification of the Yellow Wagtail is discussed under that heading.

WALES, Birds in. *See* Welsh Birds.

WALL-CREEPER—Tichodroma muraria. A bird of the mountains of central and southern Europe and temperate Asia, the Wall-Creeper occasionally visits England, and has several times been identified in the southern and eastern counties. It is a very striking and colourful bird ; its dress is of grey, and its beautifully patterned wings in dark-brown and crimson are decorated with some spots of white Some white also appears in the corners of the tail. The throat and breast are black in Summer, whitish in Winter. The slender curved bill is 1 in. long. The bird's length is 6½ in., the tarsus 0·9 in., and the wing span between 7 in. and 8 in.

The flight of the Wall-Creeper recalls the airy actions of the Hoopoe. Cliffs, precipices and rocks are its favourite haunts. Most of its time is spent clambering among stones and rocks—not using its tail for support like the Tree-Creeper, but making jerky hops and darts—and probing with its bill for insects in the crevices. The Wall-Creeper settles on the ground, rarely in a tree. It is usually seen singly outside the breeding season, and roosts in a hole in a rock or wall.

Its voice is rarely heard, but its call note is described as a pleasant clear pipe ; and its song as short, musical phrases uttered by both birds.

WANDERING TATTLER. American name for Grey-rumped Sandpiper (*q.v.*).

WARBLER. Name popularly applied to all birds belonging to the family *Sylviidae*, which was formerly larger even than it is now, and included such species as the Nightingale, Hedge-Sparrow, Robin and Redstart. Even

Ronald Thompson

WAGTAIL. *Despite the name, these birds do not " wag " their tails, but they jerk them up and down*

WATER-RAIL. One of our shyest birds, this is an adept at "freezing" on the approach of danger

so, there are still among the *Sylviidae* a number of species which do not bear the name warbler —Blackcap*, Whitethroat*, Lesser Whitethroat* and Chiffchaff*.

Among the large number of species on the British list which have warbler as part of their name are : Cetti's Warbler ; Grasshopper-Warbler* ; Temminck's Grasshopper-Warbler ; Savi's Warbler ; Pallas's Grasshopper-Warbler; Moustached Warbler ; Great Reed-Warbler ; Reed-Warbler* ; Marsh-Warbler* ; Blyth's Reed-Warbler ; Paddy-field Warbler ; Sedge-Warbler* ; Aquatic Warbler ; Melodious Warbler ; Icterine Warbler ; Olivaceous Warbler ; Booted Warbler ; Barred Warbler ; Orphean Warbler ; Garden-Warbler* ; Rüppell's Warbler ; Sardinian Warbler ; Subalpine Warbler ; Dartford Warbler† ; Rufous Warbler ; Willow-Warbler* ; Greenish Warbler ; Wood-Warbler* ; Bonelli's Warbler ; Arctic Warbler ; Yellow-browed Warbler ; Pallas's Warbler ; Dusky Warbler ; and Radde's Bush-Warbler. (* Breeding visitor ; † Resident, local.)

All of the above—which are often represented by more than one subspecies—are described under their own headings.

WARBLING GRASS-PARROT. Australian name for Budgerigar (*q.v.*).

WATER-HEN. Alternative name for Moorhen (*q.v.*). also sometimes called Merehen

WATER-OUZEL. Alternative name for Dipper (*q.v.*). of which three races appear here.

WATER-PIPIT—Anthus spinoletta. On its more or less regular winter visits from its home in the mountains of Europe, the Water-Pipit—also called the Alpine Pipit—is not easily distinguished from the British Rock-Pipit, whom it closely resembles in both size and coloration. Its chief points of difference are its broad whitish eye-stripe ; its unstreaked breast, which in

Summer is tinged with pink ; and its pure white outer tail feathers. In Winter the Water-Pipit is also a warmer brown than the Rock. The sexes are alike. The length is 6¼ in., and the tarsus 1 in. ; the wing span is about 8 in., and the weight less than ½ oz.

The habits, behaviour and movements of the Water- and the Rock-Pipit are very similar.

WATER-RAIL—Rallus aquaticus. This shy and secretive bird is a resident in the British Isles, except for the west of Scotland. It is also a winter visitor and passage migrant. Abroad, water-rails are found throughout Europe, in Asia and in north Africa.

The chief distinguishing feature of the Water-Rail is the long and curved red bill with a brown tip. The bird's upper parts are a rich brown streaked in black ; the under parts are buff, the flanks being boldly patterned in black and white. The tail coverts are white. The cheeks, neck and breast are tinged in soft lavender-grey. The legs are flesh-brown, and the eyes red. The sexes are alike, and the young are olive-brown, with their underparts softly barred and mottled. The length is 11 in., and the tarsus 1·7 in. ; the wing span is between 10 in. and 12 in., and the weight 4½ oz.

A bird of the marshes, reed beds, swamps, bogs and fens, the Water-Rail has the usual build of rails and crakes, but its body is even more compressed than that of other crakes. It seldom flies unless forced to do so, and in the air has a weak and heavy flight, with its long legs dangling behind it, and only for short distances. On migration, however, like all the rails and crakes, it is capable of long and sustained flight. On the ground it moves with ease and grace, sometimes flirting its tail.

If the Water-Rail is difficult to see, it is by no means difficult to hear ; its "sharming," as it is called in Norfolk, consists of an extraordinary medley of sounds. I have listened to this voice for many years, both in Britain and on the Continent. It is a frightening shriek, with a wide range of sounds. It is astonishing how many variations on this shrieking note the Water-Rail can produce ; I have heard fifteen different cries, but have recorded less than half of them. In contrast, soft purring and crooning notes are uttered by both male and female from the nest. The newly hatched chicks have a faint " cheep."—EDITOR.

The Water-Rail's nest is built of sedge, flags, reeds, and so on. From April to July two broods are usually reared. The eggs, numbering 6–11 in each clutch, are creamy-white spotted in reddish-brown ; they are laid on consecutive days. Both sexes share the hatching for 20 days, and the nestlings leave the nest almost as soon as they are hatched ; they are independent in seven or eight weeks The Water-Rail has a varied diet of both animal and vegetable matter

WATER-WAGTAIL. Local name for Pied (*q.v.*) and White (*q.v.*) Wagtail.

WAXEN CHATTERER. Alternative name for Waxwing (*q.v.*).

WAXWING—Bombycilla garrulus. In some years the Waxwing occurs in Great Britain in what can only be called "invasions". Every Winter brings a few, but in an "invasion" year there is scarcely a district which does not have its complement of visiting waxwings, although they are naturally more abundant in the eastern than the western counties, and are rarely seen in Ireland. The *Handbook of British Birds* gives a long list of "Waxwing years", beginning with 1686; the next date given is 1834–35, and after that only a few years separate the invasions. The very large invasion of 1946–47 brought hundreds of waxwings to Scotland and the north of England; a smaller one, 1948–49, affected the eastern and south-eastern counties of England. The Waxwing breeds in northern and middle Europe, in Asia and in north America.

The appearance of this beautiful and distinctive bird is unmistakable. With the build and size of the Starling, it is the only small bird likely to be seen here with a prominent and erect rich chestnut crest. Its general colour is a soft buffish brown, much darker on the mantle and much paler on the underparts. Its lower back and rump are grey, and its chin and throat black. The wax-red, yellow and white markings on the dark wings are responsible for its name; the dark tail has a conspicuous yellow tip, and from the forehead to behind the eye runs a dark stripe. The legs and bill are black. The sexes are alike; the young are duller, and have shorter crests and no black on the throat. The length is 7 in., and the tarsus 0·8 in.; the wing span is between 8 in. and 9 in., and the weight 2 oz.

The Waxwing is rather silent, and its alternative name of "Bohemian Chatterer" scarcely seems appropriate. The usual call note is a high and feeble trill; occasionally in the breeding season it is said to have a "chattering" note. The song is only a more elaborate version of the call note trill.

WEB. 1. Collectively the barbs on either side of the shaft of a contour feather; also known as the "vane" or "vexillum" (*see* Feather). 2. The membrane or fold of skin which, in certain species, mainly aquatic birds, forms a connecting link between the toes.

When *all* of the toes are *wholly* connected by webs, as with the Shag, the foot is described as totipalmate (Lat. *totus*, "entire"; *palma*, "palm"); when, as in the Guillemot and Merganser, only three of the toes are connected by webs, as palmate; and if less than three, or not wholly webbed (e.g. Avocet), as semi-palmate hence Semi-palmated Sandpiper (*q.v.*) and Semi-palmated Ringed Plover (*q.v.*).

Webbed feet are a powerful aid to swimming. In general, the web is folded up when the foot is being drawn forward, and expanded again as the foot moves backwards, so exerting a driving force against the resistance of the water. Web-footed birds usually swim with alternate strokes of the legs, although in moments of excitement or stress they may use both legs at once.

Not all swimming birds have webbed feet, and some birds with webbed feet are not notable swimmers. For example, coots and moorhens are expert swimmers and divers, yet their toes are free. The toes of the former are certainly provided with wide lobes on either side (i.e. they are lobate), but those of the latter have no such aid. On the other hand, gulls have webbed feet, although they are not great swimmers.

Finally, to add to the confusion, of the species that have *all* the toes enclosed in a web (i.e. are totipalmate), such as the cormorants, divers, frigate birds, gannets and pelicans, only the first two spend more time on water than gulls.

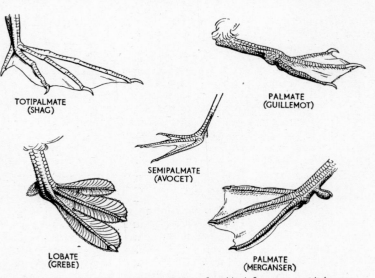

TOTIPALMATE (SHAG)

PALMATE (GUILLEMOT)

SEMIPALMATE (AVOCET)

LOBATE (GREBE)

PALMATE (MERGANSER)

WEB. There are three main varieties of webbed feet among birds, as shown above: but not all waterfowl have webbed feet, as witness the grebes

BIRD WATCHING IN WALES

H. MORREY SALMON, C.B.E., M.C.

Wales offers many attractions to bird watchers ; a wealth of sea-bird colonies, two famous observatories, a large Nature Reserve, and the opportunity to see species not found in England or only very scarce there—such as the Gannet, Kite, and Buzzard

WELSH BIRDS. Wales has much to offer to bird watchers, both organized and individual. For the scientific there are bird observatories on the islands of Skokholm and Bardsey, where recording of migration and studies of sea-birds are carried on under the aegis of the West Wales Field Society, and on the Pembrokeshire mainland the Dale Fort Field Centre of the Council for the Promotion of Field Studies. Wales also offers ample opportunities for individual studies : for example, the distribution of a species such as the Buzzard, which may well be drastically affected by the loss, through myxomatosis, of its staple food over a great part of the year, the rabbit. Those whose interest in birds is general rather than specialised will find something unusual or rare almost everywhere.

Wales is traditionally divided into north and south, but there is also a mid-Wales. This area is centred on that wild, bare expanse of the Cambrian mountains where the shires of Brecknock, Carmarthen, Radnor and Cardigan meet ; it might even be extended a little northwards, perhaps, over the borders of Montgomery and Merioneth.

In mid-Wales good bird watchers are expected to refrain from searching out the Kite, which is still only holding on precariously. But almost anywhere in this area it is quite possible that one may see a Kite from any public road, soaring or gliding overhead on angled pinions with its long, forked tail to confirm its identity. Broad-winged, short-tailed buzzards will be seen almost everywhere, perched on roadside trees and bushes, on telephone posts and fence-stakes, or soaring and wheeling overhead.

The Raven, too, is numerous in this central area, and its croak a familiar sound ; but here it has become mainly a tree-nesting species, having deserted most of its long occupied sites amongst the hill crags because of continuous disturbance, first by collectors and latterly by the

Arthur Brook

WALES. *Buzzards are found throughout the Cambrian mountains, and so is the rare Kite*

increased numbers of hikers and hill-walkers. The Peregrine Falcon has also suffered from these intrusions, and, being unadapted for arboreal breeding, has been driven away from many almost immemorial eyries.

Both species are to be found now on the sea-cliffs and perhaps more frequently in north Wales on inland crags. Snowdonia is apt to be somewhat disappointing from the bird watcher's point of view, since the larger birds have been driven from it by the great numbers of climbing and holiday folk. It does, however, hold one of the few inland breeding haunts of the Chough —small numbers of which are also to be seen at somewhat widely scattered places on the west coast, in Pembrokeshire and elsewhere.

Interest in mid-Wales is by no means confined to the larger birds. The river valleys and hill-woodlands abound in smaller species ; Dipper, Grey Wagtail, Redstart, Wood-Warbler, Tree-Pipit, tits and Nuthatch, to mention but a few. Throughout this area and in north Wales that attractive woodland bird, the Pied Flycatcher, is numerous and for some time has been increasing.

From rough fields in the valleys up to higher levels in the hills the bubbling call of the Curlew can be heard, and on the bare, bleak hill-tops a very few Golden Plover, and still fewer Dunlin, come to nest. A newcomer to this part of Wales since the beginning of this century is the Black-headed Gull, but now colonies varying from a few pairs up to several thousand are to be seen in every county. The Ring-Ouzel is to be found, albeit scarce in recent years, in the hill-dingles and ravines, with the Wheatear among the old walls and rocky outcrops, and Whinchat sharing the bracken-clad slopes with the ever-present Meadow-Pipit. Montagu's harriers come to the western coastal counties every Summer, and nest in most years, but the measure of their successful breeding is usually correlated with the amount of active protection that can be afforded them during the critical weeks of incubation.

In its wealth of sea-bird colonies Wales can vie with almost any part of the British coast. St. Margaret's Isle and the Eligug stacks on the Bristol Channel coast support guillemots, razorbills, kittiwakes and larger gulls, shags and cormorants. Skokholm and Skomer, off west Pembrokeshire, have all those species and, in addition, storm-petrels and vast numbers of Manx shearwaters and puffins. Ramsey adds a large colony of Atlantic Grey Seals to its many birds. Anglesey can show tern colonies, and Bardsey and Puffin Island many other birds.

It is an unforgettable experience to watch, on summer evenings from Skokholm, the daily assembly of the Manx shearwaters on the sea between that island and Skomer—a vast raft of birds up to a mile long and a quarter of a mile or more wide—and later, as the darkness falls, to hear their wild, eerie calls as they come in to land, to change places with their sitting mates or to feed their young during the brief dark hours of a summer night.

Even more spectacular is the great Gannet colony on the small islet of Grassholm, in St. George's Channel, just visible from the west Pembrokeshire coast. Access is not easy, but there is no other large colony of gannets where it is possible to observe these great white birds under such conditions of ease as on this small islet of just over 20 acres, on which now probably 10,000 pairs of gannets come to nest each year. Several acres of the birds can be watched at a few yards distance from the edge of the colony ; the clamour is deafening, and the whirling thousands provide a truly magnificent spectacle.

WESTERN BLACK-EARED WHEATEAR. This bird is almost identical to the Eastern Black-Eared Wheatear (*q.v.*).

WESTERN LARGE-BILLED REED-BUNTING—Emberiza schoeniclus compilator. Only two visits—and these no doubt accidental —are recorded of the appearance of this rare migrant in England ; one in Kent, and the other in Sussex. Its natural breeding home is in Italy and Sicily. *See also* Reed-Bunting.

WESTERN LITTLE BUSTARD. *See* Little Bustard, a rare visitor.

WESTERN MEDITERRANEAN SHEARWATER. *See* Balearic Shearwater.

WEST WALES FIELD SOCIETY. This Society sprang from the more specialised Pembrokeshire Bird Protection Society, founded in 1938, when a local committee took over the wardenship of the coasts of Pembrokeshire from the Royal Society for the Protection of Birds. The famous bird islands of Skokholm, Skomer, Grassholm and Bardsey, as well as the magnificent cliffs of the near-by mainland, have always attracted ornithologists—and collectors who illegally sought to take the eggs of rare birds. In 1945 the P.B.P.S. expanded into the present West Wales Field Society in order to cover all branches of natural history.

In 1946 an experimental field survey was made of Skomer Island, resulting in the book *Island of Skomer*. The Bird Observatory at Skokholm Island (the first island observatory in Britain, founded in 1933 by R. M. Lockley) was re-established in 1946. The remote island of Grassholm, famous for its colony of 16,000 gannets, is under the wardenship of the W.W.F.S., although owned by the Royal Society for the Protection of Birds.

The W.W.F.S. has (1955) about 750 members, many living far from west Wales, but visiting the area on holiday. The Society owns Dale Fort at the entrance to Milford Haven, and leases Skokholm Bird Observatory, and several small islands off the coast. It has a regular programme of lectures and field meetings.

Its chief publication is the quarterly, *Nature in Wales* (editorial address: Orielton, Pembroke).

R. P. Bagnall-Oakeley

WALES. *The coasts are famed for their sea-birds, ranging from Skokholm with its thousands of Manx shearwaters to Grassholm's huge Gannet colony*

WHAUP. Scottish name for Curlew (*q.v.*) and Whimbrel (*q.v.*).

WHEATEAR—Oenanthe oenanthe. One of the earliest—if not the earliest—of our summer visitors, the Wheatear arrives in early March. It is distributed throughout the British Isles. It is also a passage migrant, mingling in Spring and Autumn with the Greenland Wheatear, which passes through the British Isles on its journey north ; the two birds are so similar that the ordinary observer finds difficulty in distinguishing them. Abroad, the Wheatear is found in Europe, Asia, Africa and north America, and winters in tropical Africa.

The cock Wheatear in summer plumage is easily picked out, for his white rump, white tail coverts, and the white base of his tail contrasting with the black tip and central tail feathers,

G. K. Yeates

WHEATEAR. *The clear black and white markings make it an easy matter to identify the cock bird*

catch the eye at once. His upper parts are pearl-grey, his wings black, and his under parts in varied shades of buff. A black patch appears on the side of his face, and above his eye is a prominent white eye-stripe. In winter plumage he resembles the hen, which is much less colourful in a dress of sandy-brown above and light buff below ; but she also possesses the striking rump and tail. The bill and legs are black. The length is 5¾ in., and the tarsus 1 in. ; the wing span is between 7 in. and 8 in., and the weight is a little less than ½ oz.

A sprightly and restless bird, the Wheatear is constantly on the move. With its flitting flight it skips happily from stone to stone or from tussock to tussock, keeping near the ground. It settles only for a moment, bobbing and bowing with spreading tail ; then moves on again, ever retreating. The Wheatear hops on the ground, and perches on walls, fences and sometimes bushes, but rarely in trees, except in the far north. It roosts in a hole, among rocks or among sheltering vegetation. It is not habitually gregarious even on migration.

Hopping and chasing round his mate, and exposing his white rump and tail, are the male's chief courtship activities. The call note is hard and grating. The song, which is superior to those of other chats, is generally delivered with great vigour from a stone, fence or wall, from the ground, or on the wing in the dancing song-flight which recalls those of the Stonechat and Whitethroat. It is a medley of sweet and harsh notes producing a not unmusical warbling. The Wheatear has some imitative ability, and occasionally sings at night. The song commences soon after its arrival, and continues until mid-June and sometimes into July.

Wheatears nest in open and uncultivated country, choosing sheltered nooks of all kinds ; holes and crevices in walls, rocks or stones, drain-pipes, tins are used. The nest is built by both birds of grasses, moss, and so on, and lined with wool and hair. The six pale-blue eggs laid in April or early May are hatched by the hen during 14 days. The nestlings are fed by both parents, and leave the nest after about the same period. One brood is usual in a season, but two have been recorded.

Insects are the Wheatear's chief food, beetles making up a good part of its winter diet.

WHIMBREL—Numenius phaeopus. Although a few pairs still breed regularly in some remote Scottish islands, the Whimbrel is best known in the British Isles as a spring and autumn migrant. Occurring on all coasts as well as inland, it arrives about the end of April, starting to leave in July. Abroad, the Whimbrel nests in Scandinavia and Russia, wintering in Africa.

A smaller edition of the Curlew, the Whimbrel is very similar to that bird in appearance, except for the different head pattern of two broad dark stripes separated by a narrow pale stripe, and for its rather darker upper parts. The long down-curved bill is also shorter. The legs are greenish-grey. The juvenile is darker than the adult, with contrasting light markings. The sexes are alike. The length is about 15 in., the bill being little over 3 in. ; the tarsus is 2·3 in., the wing span 20 in.–22 in., and the weight 12 oz.

Tamer and more approachable than the Curlew, the Whimbrel otherwise differs from it very little in habits and behaviour, but its walk and flight are faster, the latter with more rapid wing-beats.

The communal cries of whimbrels on migration are heard high in the air. But this bird's call has nothing in common with the sounds heard on the breeding ground Outside the breeding season, it is a musical, repeated trill. On the breeding ground it can never be confused with the call of the Curlew.

After several successive days and nights of listening and watching, I found first of all that the Whimbrel's song has a very different timbre from the Curlew's—although it is difficult to say where the call ends and the song begins. On its song-flight the Whimbrel utters a succession of babbling notes as it mounts high into the air with quick wing strokes, descending again to the ground with spread wings. I have also heard the same song when the bird was flying low over the ground and when resting on a hillside. The female was always in the vicinity, sometimes calling the same tune, but in a voice of poorer quality. The male's note varies in duration from only four seconds to its usual 11 seconds. I managed to bring my microphone into such a position that the bird was almost bound to fly by it. Sometimes the long tune was interrupted by a short call, similar in rhythm to the Curlew's but with the Whimbrel's characteristic timbre. I only once heard the male and female calling to each other ; this was a sound very different from the " song ", but very musical.—EDITOR.

The unmistakable voice of the Whimbrel is responsible for its two alternative names, " Titteral " and " Seven Whistler " (referring to the bird's seven notes).

WHINCHAT—Saxicola rubetra. Although a summer visitor breeding—sometimes abundantly—throughout the British Isles, the Whinchat is inclined to be local in its distribution. It is to be seen on some moorlands of Wales and northern England, on Dartmoor, in Cornwall, on some Scottish islands and in Ireland. It arrives in late April and departs in September; occasionally some birds remain through the Winter. It is also a passage migrant. Abroad, it occurs in Europe and temperate Asia.

The white eye-stripe is the Whinchat's best identification. The mantle is brown, streaked darker ; the underparts are buff, shading deeper on the breast ; on the wings is a broad white patch ; the chin is white, and white appears at the base of the dark tail. The female is duller, with a less conspicuous eye-stripe and wing patch. The bills and legs are black. The length is 5 in., and the tarsus 0·7 in. ; the wing span is about 6 in., and the weight under ¼ oz.

The Whinchat is not gregarious. It haunts rough grass and waste-lands, and has a preference, as the name suggests, for districts where gorse and whin bushes abound. In habits and behaviour it much resembles the Stonechat. An active and spritely bird, it flits from perch to perch, darting out now and then to seize some passing insect, and bobs its tail and flicks its wings somewhat in the manner of the Robin. Upright in carriage, it hops rapidly.

As the male sings his love-song to his mate, his wings are drooped and quivering, and his breast and the white of his wings and tail are displayed. The brief warbling and variable song of the Whinchat has much in common with those of its relatives, the other chats and redstarts. Pleasant and melodious, it is based on some half-a-dozen notes hurriedly delivered from a low bush, telegraph wire or fence— occasionally from the ground or on the wing. It is best heard from late April until June. The Whinchat will sometimes mimic other birds in the area. The call-note is a hard short click.

The well-concealed nest is placed at the foot of a bush, among meadow grass, on the side of a railway cutting, or in some similar site. It is built by the hen, accompanied by her mate, with dry grass and moss as a foundation, and lined with grass. Five to six bluish-green eggs, speckled in rusty-brown, are laid late in May or early June. For 13 days the hen hatches alone, and for the same period both parents feed the chicks. One brood is usual, but two often occur. Insects and their larvae are the Whinchat's principal food.

WHISKERED TERN—Chlidonias hybrida. A native of southern Europe and Asia, and also of Africa and Australia, this tern has been recorded several times in England and once each in Scotland and Ireland, usually in early Autumn. A near relative of the Black Tern, it haunts much the same breeding sites and differs very little in behaviour and habits. Its chief distinguishing features are its black cap, the white sides of its head and neck, and its dark grey underparts. Its bill is blood-red. its length is 9¾ in., its tarsus 0·9 in., and its wing span approximately 2 ft.

Its ordinary call is a raucous note similar to that of the Black Tern, but its alarm note rather recalls the call note of the Corncrake.

G. K. Yeates

WHISKERED TERN. This, the palest of the so-called " black " or marsh-terns, is a rare vagrant

WHISTLER. Alternative name for Golden-Eye (*q.v.*), a non-breeding visitor.

WHITE - BILLED DIVER — Columbus adamsii. The White-billed Diver, which breeds in much the same northern countries as its near relative, the slightly smaller Great Northern Diver, has been recorded very few times in the British Isles. Only in its bill, which is deeper, more massive-looking and slightly uptilted at the end, does it differ from the Great Northern. It is 33 in. in length ; its tarsus is 3·4 in. and its wing span about 2½ ft. In north America this bird is known as Yellow-billed Loon.

WHITE - COLLARED FLYCATCHER — Muscicapa albicollis. Four male birds of this rare visitor have been recorded as having wandered to the British Isles. It breeds in many parts of Europe—France, Germany, Austria, south Russia—and winters in central Africa. Its appearance is similar to that of our Pied Flycatcher, except that the male has a very distinct white collar, and both sexes have a more prominent white wing bar. The female's upper parts are greyer.

WHITE-EYED POCHARD—Aytha nyroca. An occasional wanderer to this country, a few at a time or singly, this species has been recorded chiefly in east Anglia in the Autumn or Winter. There has been a recent increase in their numbers ; but some may have been escapes from estates where ornamental water fowl are kept. This diving duck has many of the characteristics common to the Scaup, Tufted Duck and Pochard ; its voice is more or less the same as that of the Pochard. It is often called Ferruginous Duck in this country.

Its all-over colouring is a rich chestnut brown, darker on the back ; the larger area of white on its underparts, and the white under its tail, should prevent confusion with the Tufted Duck. The White-eyed Pochard has also a white wing bar, but this is not easily seen, especially when it is swimming. Male and female are alike, except that the male has a distinctive white eye. The body is 10½ in. long, and the total length is 16 in. ; the weight is about 1¼ lb.

WHITE-FACED PETREL. American name for Frigate-Petrel (*q.v.*).

WHITE-FRONTED GOOSE—Anser albifrons. As a winter visitor arriving in October and departing in early March, the White-fronted Goose is the most widespread of the grey geese in the British Isles. Abroad, it is found in north-east Russia, Siberia and Arctic north America, wintering in the south.

The darkest of the grey geese, the White-fronted Goose is easily distinguished—except from the Lesser White-fronted Goose—by the prominent white band at the base of the bill and the large area of black bars on the breast.

The White-fronted Goose is smaller than the Grey Lag. Its bill, which is orange with a white nail, differs from that of both the Bean Goose and Pink-Foot. Its plumage is ashy-brown with the under-parts boldly barred in black, and its tail is white, with a dark band, as are the tail coverts. The legs are orange. The sexes are alike. The length is 26 in.–30 in., the body accounting for 17 in.–19 in. ; the tarsus is 2·6 in., the wing span nearly 3 ft., and the weight 5½ lb.

The habits and behaviour of the White-fronted Goose are similar to those of other grey geese, and it arrives and departs at about the same time of year. More apt to be seen in small family parties than is usual with grey geese, White-fronted are also often seen in hundreds together with Pink-footed geese. The flight of the White-fronted is swift and active, and it indulges in aerial manoeuvres. The call is a pleasant, somewhat musical sound.

In 1948 the Greenland race of the White fronted Goose (*Anser albifrons flavirostris*) was recognized as a separate species and added to the British list. It breeds in north-west and west Greenland (not in Iceland) and has a yellow or orange bill.

Arthur Christiansen

WHITE-FRONTED GOOSE. The most widespread of grey geese in Britain, the White-front is recognized by the white band at the base of its bill

WHITE OWL. Alternative name for Barn-Owl (*q.v.*) a common resident.

WHITE-RUMPED SANDPIPER. American name for Bonaparte's Sandpiper (*q.v.*).

WHITE-SPOTTED BLUETHROAT — Cyanosylvia svecica cyanecula. A passage-migrant to Great Britain, much less frequent than the Red-spotted Bluethroat, this bird has been recorded only nine or ten times, chiefly on the east coast. Except for the white spot on its throat, it is identical with the Red-spotted variety both in appearance and habits.

> I have recorded the song of the White-spotted Bluethroat in Germany. It shows a close relationship to that of the Nightingale, with the same gradually increasing volume of sound, but lacks the power and pitch of that bird. It is also an excellent mimic, and I have heard it give excellent imitations of both the Great Tit and the Song-Thrush.—EDITOR.

The White-spotted Bluethroat breeds in southern, western, and central Europe, and winters in north Africa.

WHITE'S THRUSH. Alternative name for Golden Mountain Thrush (*q.v.*).

WHITE STORK—Ciconia ciconia. Whether or not the White Stork could ever have been claimed as a British breeding bird is not known for certain ; but an existing record states that a pair nested on St. Giles Cathedral, Edinburgh, in 1412. Since then no record places it as anything but a rare vagrant from Holland, Germany and Scandinavia, where even under protection and encouragement its numbers are decreasing. Ralph Whitlock, in his *Rare and Extinct Birds of Britain*, mentions an interesting experiment believed to have taken place in Surrey and Sussex, in which the eggs and young of the White Stork were placed in herons' nests. Although the young eventually flew and migrated southwards, attracting some attention *en route*, they did not return the following year to any English heronry. Recent appearances of the White Stork have occurred chiefly in the southern and eastern counties of England, but it is probable that some at least of these were escapes from captivity.

No bird is more easily recognized than this. Its great size—larger than the heron's—and pure white plumage, with contrasting black on wings and mantle, at once attract attention. The bill, long legs and feet are red. The sexes are alike ; in the juvenile the black is browner, and the bill and legs less red. The length is 40 in., the body accounting for 21 in. ; the tarsus is 8·8 in., the wing span approximately 4 ft.–4½ ft., and the weight up to 9 lb.

The tall and elegant White Stork walks with dignity, and flies with slow wing beats, its legs,

F. Haverschmidt

WHITE STORK. *These birds do not seem to have bred in this country since the fifteenth century*

dropped slightly downwards, trailing out behind. It can reach a great height, soaring with rigid wings and gracefully gliding down to settle. In the non-breeding season, open grasslands and marshy country are the storks' favourite haunts. On migration they collect in large flocks, especially if locusts, one of their favourite foods, are present.

" Bill-clattering ", a rapid and regular clapping of both mandibles, which produce a loud trilling sound, together with some strange movements of its body, are the chief ceremonies of the courtship display. It is normally a silent bird, but when annoyed, it hisses.

White storks breed on buildings of all kinds, both high and low, in towns and villages, but mainly some miles away from a marsh which can be searched for the necessary food. Ruins of viaducts, and trees (which sometimes contain several nests close together) are other haunts.

WHITE-TAILED EAGLE—Haliaeetus albicilla. The White-tailed or Sea-Eagle must now be added to the sorry list of our birds of prey which have vanished for ever from the British scene. It was recognized as extinct here about the year 1918. Until 1908, one pair was still breeding in the Shetland Islands, but in that year the male bird was shot, and for the next ten years the widowed hen returned each year to the empty eyrie. Abroad it breeds in Europe, Greenland and Asia.

At one time the White-tailed Eagle bred in the Lake District, Isle of Man, Lundy Island and the Isle of Wight, but its principal home was always in the Hebrides and the Orkney and Shetland Islands. The bird was then feared and hated, and was ruthlessly persecuted.

The White-tailed Eagle has several points which distinguish it from the Golden Eagle.

It has the same immense body, but the breadth of its huge wings is even greater, and it has a distinctly shorter and more wedge-shaped tail. Its head is at all times lighter in colour, and the adult birds have a white tail ; but it is some years before this latter difference appears, and the immature birds have a brown tail. But at all ages the White-tailed Eagle lacks the distinctive feathered legs of its relative. It lacks, too, much of the Golden Eagle's alertness, and is a less graceful bird both in movement and flight. It has a powerful-looking hooked yellow beak, with yellow cere. Its length is about 3 ft., the female, as is usual among eagles, being larger. From what facts can be ascertained it is believed that the White-tailed Eagle pairs for life. It is a silent bird, but has a shrill chattering cry which seems quite out of keeping with its huge bulk.

WHITETHROAT — Sylvia communis.

Known as the common or greater Whitethroat, to distinguish it from its Lesser relative (which is also a summer visitor), the Whitethroat arrives in the British Isles in the middle of April and departs in October. It is generally distributed, except in the north of Scotland, where it is inclined to be very local. Abroad, it is found in Europe, Asia and north-west Africa.

At all seasons the white throats of these two birds distinguish them from all other warblers. The rufous back and wings of the larger bird, and the much darker ear-coverts of the smaller, are safe distinctions. The general colour of the male Whitethroat in Spring is grey-brown, greyer on crown and tail coverts. The outer tail-feathers are bordered in white, and the underparts are light buff tinged with pink on the breast and flanks. The female is browner, and has no pink tinge on the breast. The male in winter plumage and the juvenile are both like the hen. The bill is thin, and the legs pale-brown. The length is $5\frac{1}{2}$ in., and the tarsus $\frac{1}{2}$ in. ; the wing span is about 6 in., and the weight less than $\frac{1}{4}$ oz.

The Whitethroat is not gregarious. Less shy than other warblers, the Whitethroat is nevertheless, seldom on view for long. It moves restlessly, creeping hrough the dense hedges and bramble bushes—a habit which has earned it the name of " Nettlecreeper ". It rarely settles on the ground. Its flight is warbler-like, as it flits jerkily from bush to bush, appearing only for a moment as it darts after a passing insect.

In his spring song-flight the Whitethroat suddenly rises in the air, with crown feathers erect and tail spread, then descends again like some figure dancing on a suspended string ; time and again this ceremony is performed while he sings his love song. Both male and female show great excitement by raising the

Eric Hosking

WHITETHROAT. *Although a warbler, its song lacks the sweetness and power of other warblers'*

feathers of both crown and mantle, and moving their quivering wings up and down.

Although the Whitethroat belongs to the *Sylvia* genus, which includes such warblers as the Blackcap and Garden-Warbler, its song lacks their sweetness. Yet, when heard in some lonely spot on a sunny day, it is a pleasant and inspiring performance. I have watched and listened to the Whitethroat both in Britain and on the Continent, and have been interested to note that the song of the Continental bird is generally more extended than that of the British. I heard one singing for 15 seconds without pause, almost like a Garden-Warbler.

The quality of the Whitethroat's song varies with the individual bird. There are oddities in the song, which sometimes ends with three staccato notes. During early Spring and early Autumn, the Whitethroat has an inward warble, very similar to that of the Blackcap. The call note, including the alarm, is different from other British warblers', although on the same lines. The Whitethroat is best heard from the second half of April until early June, although some birds may continue till the end of that month.—EDITOR.

The nest of the Whitethroat, built by both cock and hen, is placed among low bushes or brambles, or in a thick hedge bottom. It is formed into a deep cup-shaped structure of grass and roots, and lined with hair, the hen adding some decoration of wool and down. The eggs, which vary greatly in colour from greenish to stone, speckled over with reddish or black spots, number four or five. They are laid from early May onwards. Both parents hatch them for 11 to 13 days, and tend and feed the chicks for much the same period. Two broods are normal.

Insects and larvae are the chief food, but in the Autumn some fruit and berries are eaten.

WHITETHROAT, *builds a deep cup-shaped nest for its young*

For text see pages 329, 375 and 576

WHITE WAGTAIL—Motacilla alba. A close relative of the Pied Wagtail, the White Wagtail is mainly a spring and autumn migrant, chiefly to the west coasts of the British Isles, but also inland to sewage farms and reservoirs. It is also an occasional summer visitor and has bred in districts as far apart as the Shetlands and the Isle of Wight. There are records of this Continental species interbreeding with the Pied Wagtail, a fact which sometimes makes identification very difficult indeed. Abroad, the White Wagtail is found throughout Europe.

As its name suggests, the White Wagtail is paler in appearance than the Pied. In breeding plumage its mantle and rump are distinctly light grey, in contrast to the black of the Pied Wagtail; this is, indeed, its safest identification mark. In winter plumage the female and juvenile white wagtails are recognized by the grey instead of black on the tops of their heads. Otherwise there is little difference between the white and pied wagtails; their habitats, habits and behaviour are said to be all similar. The length is 7 in., the tarsus 1 in., and the wing span about 8 in.

> The song, softer in timbre than its relative's, is frequently heard from the birds of passage. There is also a subsong-like twittering which can be heard until August, but only at very close quarters. Nearly every male has his own tune, and changes it frequently.—EDITOR.

WHITE-WINGED BLACK TERN—Chlidonias leucopterus. An occasional wanderer to the British Isles, this tern is a native of southeast Europe and temperate Asia. In summer, the White-winged Black Tern is distinguished from the Whiskered Tern by its white upper and under tail-coverts and white tail, both of which contrast vividly against the black plumage and are especially conspicuous in flight. Its bill and legs are red. In winter plumage both adults and juveniles are very like the Black Tern, but are then recognizable by the absence of that bird's dark patches at the side of the breast. The length is 9¼ in., the tarsus ½ in., and the wing span about 1¾ ft.

Its behaviour differs little from its close relative's, but it is said to be faster and more agile in the air. It breeds in colonies along with the Black Tern.

WHITE-WINGED CROSSBILL. American name for Two-Barred Crossbill (*q.v.*).

WHITE-WINGED LARK—Melanocorypha leucoptera. This lark from the central Asiatic steppes has been recorded in *England* only 15 times. In general form and habits the White-winged Lark resembles its relative, the Calandra Lark. Its distinguishing features are a chestnut-tinted cap, a prominent white wing-bar, and white under-wing coverts. The mantle is tawny-brown; the throat and breast are tinged buff, with some reddish spots on the throat and flanks. The length is 7 in., the tarsus 1 in., and the wing span 8 in.–9 in.

WHITE-WINGED PETREL—Bulweria leucoptera brevipes. This species of Petrel breeds in the Pacific Ocean, and is usually confined to the New Hebrides and Fiji Islands. The only specimen known to have ventured as far as the British Isles was shot many years ago in Wales, and is now exhibited in the British Museum.

This is a small petrel with grey upper parts shading to much lighter colouring on its forehead and throat; its underparts are pale grey, darker at the sides. Its length is about 10½ in.

WHOOPER-SWAN—Cygnus cygnus. The Whooper-Swan maintains its status as a breeding species in the British Isles only by reason of the nesting of a few pairs in the Highlands of Scotland. It is, however, a frequent winter visitor from October to April. Abroad it inhabits the northern waters of Europe and Asia.

The huge size and pure white plumage of this magnificent swan makes recognition simple. Its best distinction from the resident Mute Swan is the colouring of the bill, which in the Whooper

Arthur Christiansen

WHOOPER-SWAN. *The yellow, black-tipped bill makes it easy to distinguish this huge bird from the Mute Swan. It is also a less graceful swimmer*

is lemon-yellow at the base, with a black tip, and no knob (that of the Mute is orange with a prominent knob). The sexes are alike, but the female is rather smaller. The young are greyish brown with paler bills at the tip, but the basal yellow soon begins to show. The legs are blackish. The length is 5 ft., the body accounting for about half ; the tarsus is 4·3 in., the wing span approximately 5 ft., and the weight 16 lb.

Outside the breeding season, whooper-swans gather in considerable flocks, which fly in oblique lines or in V-formation. In its general characteristics the Whooper resembles the Mute Swan, but in its steady and direct flight, with extended neck, its wings do not make the metallic whistling sound of the Mute's, but merely produce the usual " swish " of a large bird's flight. The Whooper walks more gracefully than its relative, moving briskly over the ground, but on the water it is less attractive, swimming with a characteristic stiffness of neck that contrasts with the grace of the Mute's curving neck. When annoyed or angry, the Whooper does not arch its wings ; it is said not to sense the approach of an intruder although its eyesight is extraordinarily good. It feeds by day and night, and its sallies in quest of food depend, as with ducks, on tide and moon.

On the water the Whooper-Swan has many varied call-notes, some soft, some harsh, and many conversational in tone.

WIGEON—Anas penelope. It is more than 100 years since the Wigeon first bred in the north of Scotland. Many have since been introduced and Wigeon now nest regularly in nearly all the Highland counties of Scotland, and in the Outer Hebrides, as well as in Orkney and Shetland. More recently they have bred further

Eric Hosking

WIGEON. *As against other surface-feeding duck, the Wigeon has a very short neck and a round head*

south, and there are several nesting records for the more southerly counties of Scotland and a good many counties of England, notably Cumberland, Northumberland, Yorkshire, Lincolnshire, Norfolk, Essex and Kent. The Wigeon is also known to have bred in both Wales and Ireland. Otherwise, it is a common winter visitor and passage migrant. Abroad, it is found throughout northern Europe, Asia and Siberia ; it has also bred in Greenland.

The Wigeon's yellowish forehead and crown are distinctive. The mantle and flanks are vermiculated grey, the head chestnut, and the breast pinkish-brown, shading into the white of the underparts. The under tail-coverts are black, with a pure white patch in front. On the forewing is a prominent and large area of white, most conspicuous in flight. The speculum on the wings of both duck and drake is black, green and white. The bill is grey-blue, with a black tip, and the legs vary from brown to grey. The length is 18 in., the body accounting for 12 in. ; the tarsus is 1¾ in., the wing span 20 in.–24 in. and the weight 1 lb. 6 oz.

The Wigeon has no elaborate spring display. Several drakes " crowd " round a duck, raising their head feathers and stretching their necks and wings ; this performance is accompanied by the characteristic whistling call.

> The Wigeon is the master among whistling ducks. The drake has a loud and very pleasant whistle, uttered with an open bill. The duck, on the other hand, has a harsher purring growl. There are other varieties of call notes, one a rarer piercing shriek uttered by the female on the water.—EDITOR.

Inland waters or moorlands, sometimes coastal marshes, islands in lochs and rough pasture land are the favourite breeding places of Wigeon. The nest, placed on the ground among the heather, bracken or grass, and lined with down, is prepared by the duck. This late nester does not lay its seven or eight creamy-buff eggs of its single brood—in Scotland—until well into May, and in Iceland not until June. The duck incubates alone, beginning with the last egg laid, for about 25 days, but the drake keeps watch near by. The ducklings, clad in reddish-buff down, are soon led to the water by the duck. For six weeks the young are fed and looked after by both parents. They attain their adult plumage the first year after hatching, but the conspicuous white wing patch does not appear until the second year.

Wigeon feed almost wholly on vegetable matter, and are particularly fond of the sea plant, *Zostera marina*.

WILD BIRDS PROTECTION ACT. *See* Protection of Birds.

WILD DUCK. Local name of Mallard (*q.v.*).

THE WORK OF THE WILDFOWL TRUST

PETER SCOTT, C.B.E., D.S.C.

The Wildfowl Trust, founded by the author in 1946 to make a world-wide study of ducks, geese and swans, carries out intensive research at its grounds, has the world's most representative collection of wild waterfowl, and is visited by thousands of geese yearly

WILDFOWL TRUST. Formed in November 1946, on the Severn estuary, at Slimbridge, in Gloucestershire, to advance the study of the world's wildfowl—ducks, geese, and swans—many of which are in danger of extermination.

The New Grounds on the Severn Estuary consist of an area, some four miles long and one mile wide, of flat alluvial fields reclaimed from the river, and lie to the south of the Severn, between it and the Berkeley-Gloucester Canal. These fields are protected from the high spring tides by a sea wall, outside which lies an area of salting, known as the Dumbles, which is the principal winter feeding ground for between 2,000 and 5,000 wild geese. Along the sea wall four " pill-boxes " were built during the invasion danger of 1940, and these are so situated that they can be entered without disturbing the geese feeding on the Dumbles.

Erica

WILDFOWL TRUST. *Peter Scott feeding a few of his many bird " visitors " to Slimbridge*

Between the pillboxes a number of thatched observation huts have been built overlooking the salting, so that wherever the geese may be feeding it is possible to watch them.

The first geese, which arrive at the end of September, are usually pink-footed geese. They come in small bunches, and are followed in October by white-fronted geese. The Pink-feet usually leave in November, and there is a great influx of white-fronts in the second half of December or in early January, which may bring the total up to 4,000. Usually by March 10 the last of the geese have migrated north-eastward. Most of the white-fronts breed in the extreme north of Russia, and birds ringed at the New Grounds have been recovered on the Kanin Peninsula and on the island of Kolguev. In addition to the white-fronts all twelve of the British species and subspecies of geese have been seen, notably the very rare Lesser White-fronted Goose, which appears in most seasons.

Beyond the Dumbles lies the mile-wide expanse of estuary sand and mud on which the geese and countless other birds roost. Some thousands of ducks spend the Winter here, and large numbers of waders pass through on migration. The broad estuary lying in the heart of Gloucestershire provides a sort of oasis for cross-country migrants, such as the Spoonbill, Night Heron, Little Egret, Bewick's Swan, Scoter, Goosander, Blacktailed Godwit, Little Crake, Snowy Owl, and Peregrine.

The sea wall passes within 300 yards of a group of buildings which form the headquarters of the Trust. Between the cottages and the salting is a small spinney containing a decoy (*q.v.*) pool of about an acre. This decoy was originally completed in 1843, and had fallen into disrepair, but it has now been put into full working order again, and large numbers of ducks are ringed and released here.

A series of marshy enclosures round the headquarters of the Trust contains the largest comparative collection of live waterfowl in existence. Special efforts are made to maintain species in danger of extinction. For example, one of the rarest living birds, the Ne-ne, or Hawaiian Goose, is represented in the collection and breeds well ; in 1951 only 32 of these birds were known to exist. The enclosures, which contain over 1,000 birds of about 140 different kinds, are open to the public daily.

At the New Grounds extensive research is being carried out in the studies of evolution, breeding biology, population dynamics, diseases, parasites, and other subjects. But the Trust's activities are not confined to Slimbridge. Close liaison is maintained with foreign organizations working on wildfowl, notably in North America. Expeditions have been undertaken to Arctic Canada, the United States, Swedish Lapland, Iceland, Patagonia, Bolivia, and so forth, to study wildfowl. At a time when many species of wildfowl are declining in numbers, the close study which the Trust has undertaken is of first importance, if the stocks of these fine birds are to be maintained for the enjoyment of future generations.

In order to administer its projects successfully, the Trust needs the support of members and associates. Membership costs two guineas a year, and Associate Membership ten shillings. A special Corporate Membership is open to educational establishments.

WILLOCK. Local name for Guillemot (*q.v.*), Puffin (*q.v.*) and Razorbill (*q.v.*).

WILLOW-TIT—Parus atricapillus. So closely related are the Willow- and Marsh-Tit that it is only within comparatively recent decades that the two have been scheduled as separate species. Both birds tend to breed in the same type of country, a fact which greatly adds to the difficulty of identification ; it is therefore not surprising that the distribution and habits of the Willow-Tit are not yet completely defined. Abroad, the Willow-Tit is found through-out Europe and Asia ; in north America it is the well-known Chickadee.

Apart from their completely different songs, the only points of identification between the willow- and marsh-tits lie in the dull sooty crown of the Willow, which replaces the glossy black of the Marsh, and the pale buff patch on the secondaries of the Willow-Tit's wing.

The nasal call note of the Willow-Tit is very similar to that of the Marsh-Tit, but patient and careful listeners will not confuse the two. The song, which has no similarity whatever to that of any other species of the Tit family, is the Willow-Tit's most striking characteristic. It has been compared with the songs of the Canary and Wood-Wren, but the example which I recorded had a definite resemblance to that of the Nightingale, though including only short phrases from that bird's crescendo note, and having less carrying power. There is also a feeble, inward, warbling subsong. The song is best heard from February until May, with a revival from the end of July, through August, to the beginning of September.—EDITOR.

The nest of the Willow-Tit, excavated in the soft rotting wood of old timber, is cup-shaped.

The Northern Willow-Tit (*Parus atricapillus borealis*) has made one authentic visit to the British Isles from its home in Scandinavia. It is distinguishable by its generally paler appearance. Its behaviour and habits are similar to those of the British Willow-Tit.

WILLOW-WARBLER—Phylloscopus trochilus. One of the most familiar and abundant of summer visitors arriving in April, the Willow-Warbler, or Willow-Wren, is widely distributed throughout the British Isles, though inclined to be local in the north of Scotland and some of the Western Isles. It is also a common passage migrant to the south-west and east coasts of England and the east coast of Scotland.

Abroad, the Willow-Warbler is found through-out Europe and Asia.

In size, colour and plumage, the Willow-Warbler and Chiffchaff are more or less similar and, were it not for their totally different songs, would undoubtedly cross-breed.

The plaintive call and alarm notes of the Willow-Warbler resemble those of the Chiffchaff. The song, however, is entirely characteristic : delivered from a tree or bush and also on the wing, it is a wonderfully pleasing and liquid melody of short duration, repeated again and again. As with many song birds, individual renderings vary : one bird may produce a perfect song, another a song of poor quality. I have heard many variations on the Continent. In Germany, for instance, the song reminded me of the Robin's, and the sweetest and most musical Willow-Warbler I ever heard was in Belgium. The British bird's song is usually one second longer than the Continental bird's. The song of the small and retiring Willow-Warbler contributes greatly to the volume of spring bird melody from April until May. It continues into June and early July, falling off gradually until the bird's departure for warmer climes in August and September.—EDITOR.

The breeding season is from the end of April to early May, and six or seven white eggs,

G. K. Yeates

WILLOW-WARBLER. Almost identical with our Chiffchaff in appearance, except for lighter legs

marked in reddish-brown, are laid. The little hen incubates alone for 13 days.

WILSON'S PETREL—Oceanites oceanites. This petrel, which breeds on the barren cliffs and rocky islets of the Antarctic, has occasionally wandered to British waters.

In size Wilson's Petrel is midway between the Storm- and Leach's Petrel. Its appearance is very similar to that of the former, but it has longer legs, which project beyond its tail in flight, and its feet have yellow webs on the black toes. The band on the upper tail coverts is paler, and the under tail coverts darker.

WILSON'S SNIPE. See American Snipe.

WING—THE ORGAN OF FLIGHT

C. HORTON-SMITH, Ph.D.

This article should be read together with those on Feather and Flight. It compares the bone-structure of the wing with that of the arm, describes how its movements are controlled, and discusses the relationship between wing-shape and the bird's way of life

WING. The wing is the forelimb of the bird, the counterpart of the foreleg of the lizard, and of the arm, wrist and hand of Man. In its change from a walking, or grasping to a flying organ, the skeleton of the bird's forelimb has undergone considerable change. The human hand can be moved from side to side and up and down quite easily, and there is considerable freedom of movement at the wrist ; a large part of this freedom of movement is owed to a group of light little wrist bones which are almost entirely independent of one another. In the skeleton of the bird's wing the hand and wrist show the greatest differences. If the wrist were flexible, it is obvious that in flight the pressure of the air on the feathers of an extended wing would tend to rotate it about the wrist, and thus make it useless as a flying structure. Flight demands a rigid framework for the wing, and six of the small wrist bones are fused together with the palm bones of the hand. Little difference is noticeable in the upper arm (*humerus*), which is easily recognizable, or in the two forearm bones (*ulna* and *radius*), which retain their individuality. The larger ulna is recognized by its notches for the insertion of the strong secondary wing feathers.

There are fewer fingers in the bird hand than in the human hand. We can best picture the condition in birds by imagining that we have lost our fourth and fifth fingers, and that all but two of our wrist bones have fused with the long palm bones which extend to the bases of the thumb, index and middle fingers respectively. Although the bird-wing shows little superficial resemblance to the human arm and hand, the differences between them are really only small, and all are the outome of this fusion of bones and reduction in the number of fingers.

There are marked differences in the relative size of wing bones in birds of different habit. Each type of flight has its own characteristic skeletal wing structure. The length of the hand varies in proportion to the length of the upper and lower arms within each type of flight. Thus a long hand is associated with great speed and agility in flight, and the hand in the Swift's wing has the same length as the upper and lower arms added together. Awkward or slow flight is typical of the short-handed wing, and in flightless birds like the Ostrich the upper arm is considerably longer than the forearm and hand added together.

The shoulder skeleton or pectoral girdle is built up of the merry-thought or collar bones (*clavicles*), shoulder blades (*scapulae*), and two other bones (*coracoids*) which support the breastbone. The cup in which the upper arm moves is formed by the coracoid and scapula, and is sufficiently large to allow free movement of the wing. The collar bones give support to the working wing, and flight becomes impossible if they are broken.

There is a complicated arrangement of muscles controlling the movements of the wing. The source of power for wing movement lies in the great pectoral, or breast, muscles which are attached to the deep keel of the breastbone in flying birds. These muscles contribute as much as one-quarter to one-sixth of the total weight of a bird. The larger of these pectoral muscles, situated behind the shoulder, conceal the breast-bone ; they lie beneath the wing insertion, and make for stability in flight.

Muscles must be secured firmly to a rigid bone at one end, and to a moveable bone at the

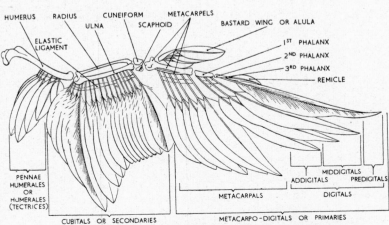

WING. Fig. 1 : Skeleton of the Mallard's wing, showing the relationship between the main flight feathers and the bones after which they are named

other. The great pectoral muscles are attached to the lower side of the keel of the breastbone, which is immovable, and at the other end by tendons to the lower side of the upper arm. These muscles pull the wing down. Above the great pectoral muscles are the elevator muscles, which pull the wing up. This movement is accomplished by a sort of pulley system, the pulley being represented by a hole at the inner side of the shoulder joint, over

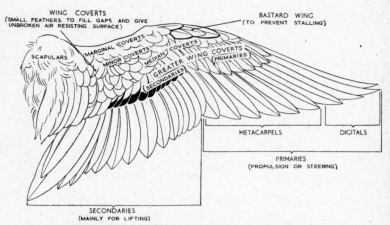

WING. Fig. 2 : Mallard's wing, showing the coverts forming an almost airtight web across the tops of the main flight feathers (see also Fig. 1)

which the muscle passes to pull downwards, thus lifting the wing in much the same way as one pulls down on a rope to raise a clothes-drier to the ceiling. Another muscle, which is attached to the coracoid and breast-bone at one end and to the upper side of the upper arm at the other, can pull the wing backwards. Other muscles bend or straighten the forearm in relation to the upper arm. Others extend the hand, causing the feathers to be spaced. The fingers are supplied with one to three muscles, and the thumb, which carries the alula (q.v.), with five. There are many other muscles, including thousands which serve to lower or raise the individual feathers.

That part of the wing near the bony framework to which the calami of the quill feathers are attached, would be far from airtight if there was no membrane to prevent leakage—and the efficiency of flight would be gravely impaired if leakage occurred. There are actually two membranes, one extending from the collar bone to the hand, and one joining the wing to the side of the body. When the wing is extended the membranes are stretched, and the supporting surface is thereby increased. The outstanding importance of feathers in providing a considerable surface area is obvious when one recalls the small surface that remains when a wing is stripped of its feathers.

The wing is arched, or cambered, and the extent to which the lower surface is hollowed varies at different points along its length, or even at the same point at different times. The whole surface is therefore flexible. Flexibility is a necessary feature in a structure that must rapidly readjust itself to meet the varying conditions met with in flight.

The outlines and contours of wings differ greatly between species. Wings in which the

length greatly exceeds the breadth are termed " high aspect ratio " wings ; rounded wings in which there is little difference between length and breadth are referred to as wings of " low aspect ratio ". The Swift, for example, has wings of high, and the eagle, wings of low, aspect ratio. Birds with short, blunt wings, like most of the Passerines, are typically birds of heavily vegetated country. True the Swift also lives in vegetated country, but it does not search the hedgerows for its food but captures insects in the air. On the whole, the long wing is associated with sea-birds, birds of open country, and birds which pursue fast-flying prey. Long, narrow wings are inconvenient to a bird which has to pass through tangled hedges and undergrowth.

The hawks illustrate the point quite well. The Peregrine, Merlin, and Kestrel are birds of open country, and have wings of high aspect ratio ; the Kite, Osprey and Sparrow Hawk have broad wings with rounded tips and are, typically birds of low-flying habit in vegetated country. An exception is the Hobby, which has sharp wings and yet is a woodland bird ; in hunting, however, it frequently glides and hovers over country of low scrub. These remarks must be regarded as broad generalisations which do not always cover individual cases.

The varying degree of camber in wings of different kinds of birds is seen if we section selected wings from leading edge to trailing edge. There are really two types of wing sections—a high velocity section, in which there is little camber ; and a high lift section, in which there is substantial camber. Swifts have wings of high velocity section ; but birds of prey, which often make use of up-currents of air and frequently carry comparatively heavy prey, have wings of high lift section. See also Flight.

WING-BAR. *See* Alar Bar.

WING-COVERTS. Series of small feathers overlying the bases of the flight feathers, to fill in the gaps between them, and so form an unbroken and air-resisting surface. They are found both above (upper wing-coverts) and below (under wing-coverts) the wing, and are further distinguished by names according to the respective positions. *See* Wing, *in particular* Fig. 2 in page 582. *See also Plate facing* page 1.

WINTER PLUMAGE. *See* Plumage.

WINTER RESIDENTS. *See* Residents.

WOODCHAT-SHRIKE—Lanius senator. A familiar bird in many parts of France and other countries of the Continent, as well as western Asia and north-west Africa, this beautiful shrike occasionally visits the British Isles. It is seen chiefly in the south of England, but sometimes as far north as Fair Isle ; Ireland has some records.

With his striking black and white dress and lovely chestnut crown and nape, the cock Woodchat at once attracts notice. His whole underparts, shoulders, rump, wing bar and tip of tail are white ; his mantle, forehead and cheeks, wings and longish tail are black. The slightly hooked bill is dark, and the legs are blackish-grey. The female is similar, but her colours are duller. The length is 6¾ in., and the tarsus 0·95 in. ; the wing span is 8 in.–9 in., and the weight about 2 oz.

In habits and behaviour — including the impaling of prey on thorns—the Woodchat is very similar to the Red-backed Shrike.

Like all shrikes, the Woodchat has a variety of harsh calls, with some chattering rather reminiscent of the Magpie. From the Continent it is reported that the song, rarely heard, is a kind of warble, interspersed with a vibrating rattle. It is delivered from a bush or tree, sometimes from under cover. The young have a high-pitched, squeaking note when feeding.

WOODCOCK—Scolopax rusticola. One of the large group of waders and a favourite game-bird, the Woodcock is a resident, a winter visitor and a passage migrant. It breeds regularly throughout the British Isles, except in Anglesey, some parts of western England, west Wales and the Midlands ; it breeds commonly in Scotland, except in some northern islands ; and Ireland has it in every county. Abroad, it is found in most parts of middle and northern Europe. It is gregarious only on migration.

The appearance of the Woodcock is unmistakable. A stoutly built and round-winged bird of medium size, it is dressed in brown, with the mantle beautifully marbled in tints of rich russet-brown, buff and black. The lighter brown underparts are delicately barred all over in dark brown, and across the crown and neck run some black lines. But the most noticeable features are the straight 3-inch-long bill, and the large eye, placed well back on the round head. The legs are flesh coloured. The sexes are alike, but the female is the larger. The young are marked more or less in the same way as the adult. The length is 13½ in., excluding the 3-in. bill ; the tarsus is 1½ in., the wing span between 16 in. and 18 in., and the weight 12 oz.

An observer cannot gain more than a fleeting glance of the Woodcock as it rises from its cover of dead leaves and bracken, and flies off with a twisting, wavering flight, its wings producing a swishing sound as it dodges in and out among the branches. The bird's whole appearance harmonises so perfectly with its surroundings that, when at rest, it is extremely difficult to see. On the ground it walks with its head drawn in and bill pointing downwards, but rarely for more than a short distance. It does not normally

W. Farnsworth

WOODCOCK. *Night after night the Woodcock will travel the same way—the "cock-road"—to feed*

perch on trees, although there are reliable instances of its doing so, in some cases among the higher branches. In common with some other waders, it has been seen to stamp on the ground to bring up worms.

Unless disturbed, the Woodcock remains under cover by day, but as evening falls it leaves its retreat, and on silent and steady wings seeks its feeding ground—usually some marshy place, often a considerable distance away. Night after night it journeys the same unvaried way through the glades of the wood, so aptly called the " cock-road ".

In its " roding " display flight, the male flies a circuit, about 100 ft. above the ground, at dusk and dawn, with a somewhat owlish movement and interrupted wing-beats, uttering two distinct notes—the "roding" call. (The word roding may have originated from the Earl of Roden, whose gamekeeper is said to have named the peculiar nuptial flight and call of the Woodcock in honour of his master.) Roding takes place with clockwork regularity, the evening one starting very soon after sunset (e.g. in early June at 9 p.m.), and ending about 10 p.m. On a bright and calm evening it is a very rapid flight, and in cold and windy weather it is faster.

I had to wait several days and nights, and to overcome many serious difficulties, before I finally got a recording of the full sound of the Woodcock's "roding." It might seem that such a regular event could be easily recorded by a microphone placed at the top of a tree. I put my microphone in a tree about 60 ft. high, at a spot recommended to me by people living in close vicinity. When, punctually at 9.15 p.m., the bird flew over the tree, everyone was astonished that my microphone failed to pick up any sound, while the whole performance was clearly heard by human ears near the tree.
This was due to the nature of the sound. The "roding" is a short croaking, accompanied by a high-pitched call, and its duration is about 2 seconds. The frequencies of the croak are from 60 to 80, while those of the high-pitched whistle range through a full octave from 5,000 to 10,000 cycles and more. The human ear is more selective than the microphone. If the bird is approaching a watching post at an altitude of 100 ft., one can see it coming, even half a mile away, and one can hear both calls, even if the sound is faint after the bird has passed. But a microphone, which "hears" directionally, will not pick up the sound clearly after the bird has passed. My first position was wrong from a recording point of view, as the bird always called after he had passed my microphone. Even if the microphone had picked up the sound faintly, it would have been impossible to amplify it without also amplifying the background noises. Therefore I had to find a tree where the bird would not only pass but also perform about 10 ft. to 20 ft. over the tiny microphone.—EDITOR.

Open parklands, plantations and coverts—especially those containing oak, birch, larch, spruce and Scots pine—moorland and rough ground affording some cover ; these are the favourite haunts of the Woodcock. The nest is a mere hollow in the ground, often close to a tree, and is lined with autumn leaves. The eggs usually number four, the colour ranging in various shades from buff to brown ; both the eggs and the female, which hatches them alone, merge so completely into the background as to be almost invisible. The incubation begins on the completion of the clutch, and takes about three weeks. The young are tended by the female alone for an unknown period, and two broods are usually reared in a season.

Since the nest of the Woodcock is often some distance from its feeding grounds, the feeding of the chicks presents a problem, which the Woodcock solves by simply carrying the chicks one by one to the food. The chick is usually held between the thighs, and pressed against the breast, but sometimes it is apparently held by the feet. Some observers have thought that the chick is gripped by the claws, but this is still doubtful. Transport on the parent's back has also been observed, and there are several authentic instances of the parent's making one, two, three and even four journeys to and fro to fetch the nestlings to their food.

The Woodcock's food consists chiefly of earthworms, but it also eats some varieties of insects and their larvae, spiders, molluscs crustaceans, and seeds.

WOOD GROUSE. Alternative name for Capercaillie (*q.v.*).

WOOD-LARK—Lullula arborea. A British resident, the Wood-Lark is by no means as abundant as the Skylark, although there are still many areas of open uncultivated country where it might be expected to nest. It is commonest in the south and south-eastern counties of England ; plentiful but very local in some parts of Wales ; scarce in the north; and in Scotland only a rare, if regular, autumn visitor to Fair Isle. At one time the Wood-Lark bred in some counties of Ireland, but it has not been seen there for many years. Abroad, it is found in most parts of Europe, Asia and north-west Africa.

Although they belong to different families and their songs have nothing in common, at a distance the Wood-Lark and Skylark are not dissimilar in appearance. Closer inspection, however, reveals the smaller size of the Wood-Lark and its shorter tail, seen conspicuously in flight. The plumage, streaked on mantle and

G. K. Yeates

WOODLARK. Its song is probably the sweetest of all birds'. It is uttered both day and night

Eric Hosking

YOUNG, *Cock Linnet busily feeding its nestlings*

For text see pages 332 and 591

breast, is also a warmer and richer brown than the Skylark's, and it has a distinct buffish-white eye-stripe running back to the nape. The underparts are whitish, and the tail dark with whitish tips. There is a well-developed crest, but this is not always apparent except at close quarters. The thin bill is brown, and the legs flesh-brown. The sexes are alike, but the juvenile has a more spotted plumage. The length is 6 in., and the tarsus 0·8 in. ; the wing span is from 7 in. to 8 in., the weight 1½ oz.

Less gregarious than the Skylark, the Wood-Lark roams the countryside in small family parties. Its flight is undulating ; a ground-loving bird, it walks and runs with ease, and is fond of taking dust baths.

In the spring display both cock and hen take part, bobbing, exhibiting their raised crests, and expanding and closing their wings. The Wood-Lark's song-flight, although resembling that of the Skylark in some degree, ranges over a wider area. The bird mounts with wide circling movements ; then plunges earthward.

The Wood-Lark ranks among the finest songsters, and to human ears its song is the sweetest and most appealing of all British birds' songs. It is an unforgettable experience to hear the Wood-Lark on a moonlight night as it circles overhead. The song, which is also uttered from a tree or perch, and even on the ground, has no great variety, being made up of short phrases ; but its lovely melody has no equal. It is best heard from late February until mid-July.

The Wood-Lark nests on the ground. The strong and well-built nest is made by both cock and hen on a foundation of moss and bents, lined with hair and wool. The breeding season begins at the end of March, and, since two broods are normal and three not unusual, extends sometimes into August. The eggs, three or four in each clutch, are greyish-white speckled over in reddish or olive-brown spots. They are apparently hatched by the hen alone for a fortnight. The chicks leave the nest before they can fly, and are looked after by both parents for a further fortnight.

WOOD-OWL. Alternative name for Tawny Owl (*q.v.*)—also sometimes called Brown Owl.

WOODPECKER. Common name of a group of wood-boring birds belonging to the family *Picidae*. Woodpeckers are remarkable not only for their chisel-like bills, and modifications to the skull, which make wood-boring possible, but also for their remarkably long, flexible tongues (*see* Fig. 2 in page 556), which they use for extracting insects from holes and crevices in trees. They have short, stiff tails, which act as props when climbing trees, and powerful feet, usually with two toes pointing to the front, and two to the rear. Many of the species are very colourful, and the males of most have some red on the head.

There are at least 250 species and subspecies combined, distributed throughout the world ; the majority in the south American and oriental regions, fewer in Europe, Africa, and north America, and none in Australia. Three species, all described in this work under their own names, are included in the British List : Green Woodpecker ; Greater Spotted Woodpecker ; and Lesser Spotted Woodpecker. The Wryneck (*q.v.*) is a member of the same family ; its feet are like those of the woodpeckers, but its markings are similar to the Nightjar's, and in its general habits and attitudes it closely resembles the Passerines. In general appearance, all of the British woodpeckers show a close family likeness, but they differ markedly in size and plumage.

Heinz Sielmann
WOODPECKER. The tree-front has been removed to show the inside of the nest with the 20-day-old young

WOOD-PIGEON—Columba palumbus. The muffled cooing of the Wood-Pigeon is a familiar sound on a summer afternoon, but the countryman is perhaps reminded that, for all its soothing tones and gentle appearance, this bird can cause great damage to crops and gardens.

The Wood-Pigeon is the largest of our native pigeons. The mature bird is distinguished from other British species not only by its size but by a broad white band across the wing (conspicuous in flight) and small white patches on the sides of the neck. In both the male and female adult, the head, ear-coverts, chin and throat are greyish-blue, and the sides and upper neck have a greenish-metallic lustre with purplish lights. The lower neck has a zone of metallic purple separated from the green on the sides of the neck by a patch of white. The mantle, wings and scapulars are brownish-grey, and the back, rump, and upper tail feathers greyish-blue. The breast is a purplish-brown (at first tinged with grey after moult), merging into the ashy blue-grey of the belly and under tail-coverts. The tail feathers are broadly tipped brownish-black, with a broad central band of pale-grey. The juvenile lacks the neck markings, and is otherwise duller than the adult. The length is 16 in., the tarsus 2·3 in., and the wing span 1½ ft.

The Wood-Pigeon is a resident and winter visitor. It is widely distributed throughout the British Isles, but is scarce in the extreme north of Scotland, and only a passage migrant in Shetland—though it breeds in the Orkneys, Lewis, and the Outer Hebrides. It is generally more abundant in the Winter. Abroad, it occurs throughout Europe (except the north of Scandinavia and Iceland) palaearctic Asia and north-west Africa. British-bred birds are mostly sedentary, seldom taking long journeys from

Eric Hosking

WOOD-PIGEON. *The largest of our native pigeons, this bird is the farmer's and fruit-grower's inveterate enemy, for grain and fruit are its diet*

home, though some individuals have been known to make flights of 100-200 miles.

Nesting sites vary considerably. Occasionally nests, consisting of a mere lattice of small twigs, are built on or close to the ground, on ledges of rocks, or on buildings, but more frequently are to be found in tall hedgerows and trees, in old nests of members of the Crow family, and squirrels' dreys. The elliptical white-shelled eggs, normally two, but occasionally one, and exceptionally three, are laid from April to September. Incubation, which takes about 17 days, begins with the first egg, both parents sharing in the hatching ; the male by day, the female by night. Three broods are reared annually. The young are fed on pigeon's milk (*q.v.*) produced in the crop of both sexes.

The food includes cereals, roots, potatoes, peas and beans, fruit, leaves of plants, seeds, and earthworms, slugs, snails, larvae and insects.

WOOD-SANDPIPER—Tringa glareola. It is known that this sandpiper bred in Northumberland in 1853, but whether this was a rare occurrence, or at that time the Wood-Sandpiper bred habitually in the British Isles, is not certain. Now a more or less regular passage migrant in the Autumn—occasionally in the Spring—it is likely to be seen on inland marshes, sewage farms, reservoirs, etc., either singly or in small parties, in the south-eastern counties of England. Scotland and Ireland rarely see it. Abroad, the Wood-Sandpiper is abundant on the marshes and swamps of northern Europe and Asia.

The smallest amongst the sandpipers, the Wood-Sandpiper, is not unlike the larger Green Sandpiper, especially in its winter plumage, but it lacks the black and white so conspicuous in that bird. Its mantle is grey-brown, and in Summer copiously covered with dark and light markings. Its underparts and upper tail-coverts are white, as are its rump and darkly barred tail, and there is a whitish eye-stripe. Its legs are yellowish-green, and its bill is dark brown. The sexes are alike. The length is 8 in., the tarsus 1½ in., and the wing span varies from 11 in. to 12 in.

The habits and behaviour of the Wood-Sandpiper follow the pattern of its species. Its flight is described as less zig-zag, and it appears less inclined to tower on rising, but otherwise its movements are the same as other sandpipers'. The characteristic voice of the Wood-Sandpiper is perhaps the best identification. Its ordinary call, also heard when it is flushed, is a shrill, excited note, repeated three to seven times, different from the Green Sandpiper's call. This call is repeated when the bird is approaching its nest and on other occasions. Early in the morning and in the evening the male Wood-Sandpiper performs a series of slow and flute-like trills. A quick crescendo metallic trill can be rarely heard in flight during display.

WOOD-WARBLER—Phylloscopus sibilatrix. As the most woodland of the warblers, the Wood-Warbler, or Wood-Wren, is naturally somewhat restricted in its distribution in the British Isles. As a summer resident arriving rather later in April than its close relative the Chiffchaff, it haunts open woodlands and parks, but is also found in the wooded valleys of more hilly country. It is fairly common in Scotland, although scarce, or absent altogether, from some of the islands ; in Ireland it is very scarce and extremely local. Abroad, the Wood-Warbler is found throughout Europe ; in the non-breeding season it migrates to Atlantic islands, south-west Asia and tropical Africa.

As well as by its characteristic voice, the Wood-Warbler is distinguished from other leaf-warblers by its larger size, rather longer wings and shorter tail. The yellow-brown mantle is in a brighter shade ; the throat and breast are sulphur-yellow, in contrast to the pure white of the underparts, and there is a conspicuous yellow eye-stripe. Some of the darker wing feathers are edged with yellow. The thin bill is brown, and the legs are yellowish. The colouring is duller in Autumn, and in-the young birds. The length is 5 in., and the tarsus 0·7 in. ; the wing span is between 7 in. and 8 in., and the weight a fraction of an ounce.

Although the Wood-Warbler is the most arboreal of the leaf-warblers, its habits and behaviour are much the same as the others'. It has the same restless, flitting flight, but does not flick its tail like the Willow-Warbler and the Chiffchaff. Frequent aerial excursions are made after some passing insect, or the bird may hover for a moment to pick a delicate morsel from under the leaves.

In his display flight before his mate, the male performs a beautiful dragonfly-like movement with a spiral descent, his wings rapidly vibrating. An occasional flight recalling the song-flight of the Tree-Pipit is also described.

> The Wood-Warbler has two songs. The one most frequently heard usually starts with 4–10 staccato notes and ends in a buzzing trill. It is uttered on the wing, from a perch, or while the bird is flitting from branch to branch. The second song is a series of pleasantly plaintive sounds. I have heard 20 or more repetitions, and there are reports from the Continent of 30, but the usual performance comprises from 5 to 15 repetitions. The call and alarm notes are as plaintive as this second song, but there are many variations to be heard when a special study of the bird is made.—EDITOR.

The Wood-Warbler nests in woods among the undergrowth of bracken and brambles, but will often make use of a natural hole in the ground. Built by the hen alone, the nest is composed of dead bracken, leaves and grass, and lined with bents and hair, but no feathers. The latter part of May and early June are the breeding season, and six or seven white eggs, spotted dark reddish-brown, are laid. The hen hatches alone for 13 days, leaving the nest to feed. The chicks are fed by both parents for 11 or 12 days. One brood is reared in a season.

Small insects, cleverly caught on the wing, are the Wood-Warbler's food. Wild berries may also occasionally be taken in the Autumn.

John Markham

WREN. *One of our best-loved birds, the little Wren is found everywhere—except in large towns*

WREN — Troglodytes troglodytes. The familiar bird whose figure adorns the reverse of the farthing, the tiny and charming Jenny Wren is almost as well known as the Robin Redbreast. A British resident, universally distributed, it is found in almost every type of country except that it is rarely seen in large cities.

Everybody knows this tiny brown bird, with its round body and stumpy cocked tail. The warm russet-brown mantle is slightly barred, the wings, tail and flanks distinctly so, and the underparts are buffish. The thin bill is brown, and the legs are flesh-coloured. The sexes are alike ; the juveniles are similar, but less distinctly barred. The length is 3¾ in., and the tarsus ¾ in. ; the wing span is about 5 in., and the weight is less than ¼ oz.

The display, which consists of the song, accompanied by much showing off of wings and tail, occurs in Autumn as well as in Spring. The song, disproportionately loud for such a small, body, consists of high-pitched notes and trills, partially soft and lyrical, but with interspersed harsher sounds. The vehemence and energy of its performance are astonishing ; but since its frequencies vary between 3,000 and 5,100 cycles per second, the listener may miss much of it. The song is usually delivered from a bush, post or tree, but frequently also on the wing, and is occasionally heard at night. Like so many other songs it is at its height from early March until early June, but can be heard more or less all the year round. At midsummer there is a feeble warbling subsong, rather reminiscent of the Whitethroat's after and before the " rattle ". The call note is a hard clicking, and a churring note can also be heard.

The Wren's choice of a nesting site is varied. It may be a hedge, a tree hole, a bush, a thatched

Eric Hosking

WRYNECK. *Strangely enough, this queer-looking creature belongs to the same family as woodpeckers*

roof—in fact, any place which will accommodate the domed dwelling with its side entrance. For some reason the Wren has a passion for nest-building. The cock selects sites, and is architect, designer and builder of his many " cock's nests ", which are by no means all completed. One after another—as many as a dozen have been begun—they are fashioned of grass, moss, leaves and bracken. Of these the hen takes her choice, and lines it with feathers. Five or six—often more—white eggs, spotted in brownish-red, are laid in late April, and for a fortnight she hatches them alone. The large family is fed by both parents for a fortnight. Two broods are normally reared in a season.

Insects and their larvae are the chief food, but spiders and some varieties of seeds are taken. The young are fed largely on moth larvae.

WRYNECK—Jynx torquilla. For some unexplained reason the Wryneck has decreased as a British summer visitor ; it has disappeared altogether, or entered the category of rarities, in many of the former haunts where once it was well known. The south-eastern counties of England are now its chief nesting centre, but even there, it is by no means plentiful. The northern counties have lost it altogether, and in the north Midlands, where it still appears to nest, it is extremely local. Elsewhere throughout the British Isles the Wryneck is a more or less scarce passage migrant. Abroad, it breeds much more abundantly on the Continent, where the Editor has seen more than 50 together ; also in Asia and north-west Africa.

" Cuckoo's Mate " and " Leader " are two other names given to the Wryneck. The former refers to its April arrival which coincides with that of the Cuckoo, the latter to the curious and unique twisting movements of its neck, from which it also gets its usual name. A relative of the woodpeckers, the Wryneck has a slim and elongated body, and is dressed in greyish-brown beautifully streaked and vermiculated in darker shadings. The underparts are paler, and barred rather than speckled. The bill and legs are brownish. The sexes are alike, and the young are very similar to their parents. The length is $6\frac{1}{2}$ in., and the tarsus 0·7 in. ; the wing span is between 8 in. and 9 in., and the weight $1\frac{1}{4}$ oz.

During the Summer the Wryneck is seldom seen other than in pairs, but in Winter and on passage small parties meet together. Were it not for its voice, the presence of the Wryneck might well go unnoticed, for it is extremely shy and also possesses excellent camouflage.

Both male and female take part in the display, which occurs in, but is not confined to, the Spring. In the simple form, the two perch opposite each other, throw back their heads and shake them up and down, with open bills.

The long, high-pitched spring call of the Wryneck—one can hardly call it a " song "—carries for more than a quarter of a mile. It can be heard in April and May, but fades out in mid-June. In the south of England I was fortunate once in having a pair of wrynecks nesting in a box outside my bedroom window. I spent a whole night endeavouring to hear the " song " amid many competing noises from the surrounding houses, and eventually in the morning of May 1, about 5 a.m., I managed to record the loud call of the Wryneck ; it continued for 20 minutes, and drowned other noises.

Two months later I found in Surrey a Wryneck's nest, where the young were being hatched. My equipment was placed about 80 yards away, hidden from the tree where the young were in a nesting box. When I approached the tree, the adults, especially the female, uttered a terrific alarm note which lasted so long that I was able to get back to my recording gear and record it before it finished. I saw the female feeding her chicks, and recorded the noise of the young, which sounds like jingling silver coins. Finally, I heard the female's short call, and an abbreviation of the male's long spring call.—EDITOR.

Open parklands, heaths, hedge-rows, woodlands with old timber, and also orchards and gardens, are the favourite haunts of the Wryneck. The nest is a natural hole in a tree, bank, thatch or wall, and often a nesting box will attract it. No nesting material is used, seven to ten white eggs are merely laid on the floor of the hole from May onwards. According to the *Handbook of British Birds*, if the eggs are removed as they are laid, the Wryneck has been known to lay a further 40 or more eggs. Both sexes more or less share the hatching for a fortnight, and for three weeks the chicks are fed and tended. One brood is the rule, but two occasionally occur.

Insects of many varieties, procured by its useful tongue, are the chief food of the Wryneck; also wood-lice and spiders. Like the woodpeckers, its relatives, it is very fond of ants.

YELLOW HAMMER

XANTHOCHROISM. From the Greek *xanthos*, yellow. An abnormal yellowness of feathers. It is a rare condition, quite distinct from albinism (*q.v.*), which, when found in wild birds, is usually associated with those normally having green, red, or orange plumage. It is especially noted in parrots, but in 1954 a pair of wood-warblers with this abnormality was discovered in the upper Wye Valley in Wales and photographed by Eric Hosking.

According to an article by Stuart Smith in *The Times*, the head and back of the variant female bird were a beautiful primrose yellow, and the shoulders and lower back near the tail coverts carried splashes of darker yellow. The underparts were pure white, and the two outer tail feathers were also white. The darker yellow on the shoulders, by contrast with the paler yellow, gave the appearance of a collar running round the neck. A very distinct black mark ran down the base of one of the primary feathers, on either side, but more extensive and accentuated on the right than on the left. The bill and legs were described as being of the colour of dead bracken. The male bird had the normal coloration of the Wood-Warbler (*q.v.*), except for his head. This had a pale straw-coloured cap, running backwards to the nape, with several dark brownish marks on it.

XEMA. Genus of sea-birds of the family *Laridae* of the order *Charadriiformes*. It contains two species, found in many parts of the globe, but rare in Europe. One species, Sabine's Gull (*q.v.*), is on the British list.

XENUS. Genus of wading birds of the family *Scolopacidae* of the order *Charadriiformes*. It contains only one species, the Terek Sandpiper (*q.v.*), which has been recorded about half a dozen times in the British Isles.

YAFFLE. Local name for Green Woodpecker (*q.v.*), common in England and Wales.

YARWHELP. Local name for Bar-tailed Godwit (*q.v.*), a non-breeding visitor.

YELLOW-BILLED CUCKOO — Coccyzus americanus. This cuckoo is an extremely rare visitor to the British Isles from its home in north and south America. Both it and the Black-billed Cuckoo, which is the other cuckoo of America, differ from their family by building their own nests and rearing their young themselves. Otherwise the Yellow-billed Cuckoo resembles our bird in many ways.

Its appearance is not unlike that of a dove, and its nest resembles a dove's. A graceful bird, it is coloured brown above, with much lighter underparts ; and it has the long tail of its relatives with some reddish-brown and black tail feathers showing conspicuously white at the tips. Its yellow bill, of course, gives it its name. It is about 11 in. in length, and is a smaller bird than the British Cuckoo. Its song is a succession of deep calls.

The Yellow-billed Cuckoo's nest of twigs lined with grass is found in thickets, bushy roadsides and orchards.

Eric Hosking

XANTHOCHROISM. *Yellow variant of Wood-Warbler, found in Wales in 1954. Unfortunately, it is unknown whether this colouring is hereditary*

Eric Hosking

YELLOW HAMMER. Differing from the Serins in its white tail-feathers and its chestnut back

YELLOW-BREASTED BUNTING — Emberiza aureola. A very rare visitor to Britain (it has been recorded in England only three times), this bird breeds in northern Russia and Asia, and winters in the south. It is often imported as a cage-bird.

In appearance the male Yellow-breasted Bunting is distinct from all other buntings. About the size of a Linnet, it is completely yellow underneath, with a dark chestnut band across its breast, and a dark chestnut mantle. In Summer its face and throat are black, and it has a white wing patch, very noticeable in flight. The female is much like the Yellow Bunting, except that the yellow underneath is not streaked and her crown is darker.

YELLOW-BROWED WARBLER — Phylloscopus inornatus. This warbler is a regular bird of passage along the east coast of Great Britain, and to Fair Isle during its autumn migration. Its home is in northern Siberia.

Rather smaller than the Willow-Warbler, it is not difficult to recognize. Its mantle is pale-green, its underparts are whitish, and it has a pale yellowish streak above the eye. It has also a double wing-bar. The sexes are alike. The length is 4 in., the tarsus 0·7 in., and the wing span between 5 in. and 6 in.

YELLOW BUNTING. Name for Yellow Hammer (*q.v.*) ; also called Scribbler Clerk.

YELLOW HAMMER—Emberiza citrinella. The Yellow Hammer or Yellow Bunting is one of the most popular, as well as useful, of our resident birds. It is widely distributed throughout the British Isles, and is common everywhere except in Orkney and Shetland. Abroad, it is found in Europe and Asia.

The Yellow Bunting can be recognized at a glance. Yellow is the predominating colour of its head, breast and under parts ; it is a warm chestnut above, and has a stout grey bill. The female resembles her mate, but the yellow is less prominent in her. There is reason for believing that Yellow Buntings mate for life ; in any case, they pair very early in the year. The length is 6 in., and the tarsus 0·7 in., the wing span is about 8 in., and the weight 1 oz.

The song of the " Canary of the North," as the Yellow Hammer is sometimes called, is by no means the most musical, but is one of the most familiar of our country sounds. It is a continuous repetition of several notes, with variations, ending usually with a more emphatic drawling note, but this is sometimes omitted. The whole is popularly rendered in the phrase " A little bit of bread and *no* cheese " ; in Scotland they render it as " De'il de'il, de'il de'il, tak' ye ! " It is usually delivered from a telegraph wire, bush or hedge, and continues from the end of January to well into August.

The breeding season lasts from May until August. The nest is placed on the ground, commonly at the foot of a bush or young tree, or on a road side, and is made of stalks, bents and moss, lined with horsehair. Its three to five eggs are beautifully marked and lined ; in some districts the bird is called the " Writing Lark " or " Scribbling Lark," from the marks on the eggs. The hatching, which is usually done by the hen, takes about a fortnight. Both parents feed the young for the same period. Two or three broods are reared in a season.

The diet consists mainly of insects, many of which are injurious to agriculture.

YELLOW-LEGS. *See* Greater Yellow-Legs *and* Lesser Yellow-Legs.

YELLOWSHANK. Alternative name for Greater and/or Lesser Yellow-legs (*q.v.*).

YELLOW WAGTAIL—Motacilla flava. At present there are five distinct geographical variants of this species on the British list ; all have yellow underparts, but have different head coloration. So marked are these differences that the revision of the whole Yellow Wagtail group is under consideration, and it may well be that some members of the present group will be classified as distinct species.

When the term Yellow Wagtail is used in this country, without qualification, it is the Green-headed (Yellow) Wagtail (*M. f. flavissima*) that is inferred ; this is the only member of the group to breed freely in the British Isles, being a common breeding visitor from March to October. It is sometimes referred to as the British Yellow Wagtail, and where, below, Yellow Wagtail is mentioned, without further qualification, it is this subspecies that is intended. The so-called *Continental* Wagtail is the Blue-headed (Yellow) Wagtail (*M.f. flava*), which has bred in England, but is, in the main, the Yellow Wagtail of central Europe, being supplanted by the Grey-headed (Yellow) Wagtail (*M.f. thunbergi*) in north Scandinavia, the Ashy-headed (Yellow) Wagtail (*M.f. cinereocapilla*), in Italy, Corsica, Sardinia, and Albania, and the Black-headed (Yellow) Wagtail (*M.f. feldegg*), in the Balkans. The Green-headed variant is described here; the others are separately described under their own names.

The British Yellow Wagtail is very local in its distribution, and is also a passage migrant. Abroad, it breeds in various parts of Europe, wintering in tropical west Africa.

On arrival in this country the cock makes a brilliant splash of colour. The top of his head and ear-coverts are greenish-yellow, but his chin, throat, sides of neck, eye-stripe, and underparts are all a vivid yellow. The mantle is greenish-yellow, the wings are blackish-brown with two whitish wing bars, and the long dark tail has white outer feathers. The thin bill is greyish-black, and the legs black. The female is much duller, and in Autumn the male resembles her. The throat of the young is bordered by a kind of black bib. The length is 6½ in., and the tarsus 0·9 in.; the wing span is from 7 in. to 8 in., and the weight ¼ oz.

The undulating flight and ground actions of this Yellow Wagtail do not differ from those of other wagtails; it has the common rapid walk or run and the constant motion of both tail and head. It perches freely on fences, bushes and trees, and delights to follow the plough and mingle with the cattle in the fields.

The display of the Green-headed Wagtail is similar to the Blue-headed Wagtail's. Both birds have a nuptial flight, with feathers puffed out, bills pointing upwards, tails spread and hanging down, and wings shivering.

In the Spring the characteristic call note of the Yellow Wagtail rings out over the meadows near rivers; it is composed of one or two syllables—occasionally a high-pitched phrase—uttered from a fence or bush, and often repeated fifty times on end. The rarely heard song is only a repetition of the call notes, but softer and pleasanter to the ear; it is best heard from the end of May until mid-July.

Yellow wagtails usually breed in lowland pastures, water meadows, marshes and cultivated fields, often—but not always—near water. Its six eggs are laid in the latter part of May or early June. The hen hatches alone for a fortnight, and the nestlings are fed by both parents for much the same period. Two broods are normally reared in a season.

YELPER. Local name for two of our waders—the Avocet (*q.v.*) and Redshank (*q.v.*).

YOUNG, CARE OF. Among birds the duties of parenthood may be considered to begin at a stage earlier than among mammals, inasmuch as they start with the laying and, usually, brooding of the eggs—or, even earlier, with the building of more or less elaborate structures to house the eggs during the process of hatching (*see* Nest).

. *Eggs and Nests.* Although birds reputedly take great care to safeguard their eggs, there is considerable evidence to suggest that, while they recognize their own particular nest and its contents, they do not know eggs as such, since they frequently confuse them with similarly shaped objects. Domestic hens are easily deceived by china eggs, and a Black-headed Gull will roll back not only any of the eggs that have been moved from the nest, but also any other roundish objects—provided they are not more than a foot away from the nest; if this distance is exceeded, the bird will sit on an empty nest rather than make any effort to retrieve the eggs, although it can see them quite clearly.

Many ways have been evolved for protecting the nest and its contents. Ground-birds can shut off their body scent during the incubation period, and gun-dogs can approach quite closely without detecting them. The Snipe puts earth on its back, partly to conceal its scent and partly as a precaution against being seen. The Chaffinch's nest is very beautifully camouflaged to blend with its surroundings.

When the nest has to be left, some species set all danger at defiance and rely on the protective colouring, if any, of the eggs. Others, for example the grebes, carefully cover their eggs with earth or decaying vegetable matter. Ducks usually pluck down from their breasts to cover their eggs during an enforced absence. The Eider-Duck, if *suddenly alarmed* when

G. K. Yeates

YELLOW WAGTAIL. *Britain's breeding member of this wagtail group is the Green-headed Wagtail*

sitting, discharges offensively smelling excrement over its eggs to deter any potential thief.

Incubation. The share taken by the parents in incubating the eggs varies with the species (*see* Table in page 381).

Incubation does not usually begin until the full complement of eggs has been laid, but in some species of diurnal birds of prey, and owls, incubation starts with the first egg laid, so that the later eggs are partly incubated by the earlier hatched nestlings. The duration of the incubation period varies both with the species and the individual (*see* Breeding Tables in pages 96 and 97). If the eggs have not hatched by the end of the normal incubation period, most birds usually brood them for a few days or even up to a week longer ; but they do not continue brooding indefinitely.

Feeding. Usually the feeding of the helpless infants requires incessant toil from early morning to late at night, and most of this work falls to the cock bird. At first he may attempt to attack the nestlings, but after being foiled a few times by the hen, he soon accepts the inevitable and settles down to his onerous duties. It is not uncommon for him to have to make hundreds of forages each day, or, with fewer trips, to cover several miles each journey.

Because of the number of journeys the parents have to make with small beakfuls, they cannot waste time in waiting for young beaks to open ; if it is not already agape, at one touch of the parent's bill, a mouth is opened instinctively. As a guide to the parents, particularly in dim light, many nestlings have a bright gape—sometimes with contrasting spots (*see* Plate f.p. 544 *and* Research ; *also* Food).

Finches feed their young on insects at first, and then on regurgitated seeds. The Green Woodpecker also regurgitates, while the Greater and Lesser Spotted species retain the more primitive method of rearing their young on undigested insects. With some species, the regurgitated food is unchanged ; with others, it undergoes considerable alteration. Thus, petrels feed their young on oil derived from the fish and crustaceans on which they live, and pigeons are fed on "Pigeon's Milk" (*q.v.*). The method of conveying regurgitated food varies ; the young pigeon thrusts its beak down the throat of the parent bird, but with the martin's the operation is reversed.

Education. It is commonly believed that birds are taught to fly, but those who have made a close study of the subject hold that this is not true, stating that no one has seen an adult bird actually *teaching* its young to fly.

But many adult birds certainly encourage their young to fly—sometimes forcibly. Young guillemots have been seen to take their first trip to the sea by being pushed off a high ledge by the parents, who broke their fall by continuously darting underneath them until the water was reached. Similarly, ducklings have to be encouraged to take to the water. It is a moot point whether young grebes are taught, or merely encouraged, to dive. *See also* Educating Young Birds ; *and* Shell Disposal.

Arthur Brook

YOUNG, CARE OF. "*Eyes left*" *seems to be the order of the day for the seven young kingfishers who are eagerly awaiting the return of their parents with some food*